PEARSON   ALWAYS LEARNING

Elaine N. Marieb • Katja Hoehn

Human Anatomy & Physiology
Volume 1

Second Custom Edition for Quinsigamond Community College

Taken from:
Human Anatomy & Physiology, Ninth Edition
by Elaine N. Marieb and Katja Hoehn

Cover Art: Courtesy of Christopher Morris/Corbis Images.

Taken from:

Human Anatomy & Physiology, Ninth Edition
by Elaine N. Marieb and Katja Hoehn
Copyright © 2013, 2010, 2007 by Pearson Education, Inc.
Upper Saddle River, New Jersey 07458

This special edition published in cooperation with Pearson Learning Solutions.

Pearson Learning Solutions, 501 Boylston Street, Suite 900, Boston, MA 02116
A Pearson Education Company
www.pearsoned.com

Printed in the United States of America

5 6 7 8 9 10 V0CR 17 16 15 14 13

0002000102716 79251

RH/CK

ISBN 10: 1-256-79318-3
ISBN 13: 978-1-256-79318-2

About the Authors

*We dedicate this work to our students both present and past,
who always inspire us to "push the envelope."*

Elaine N. Marieb

For Elaine N. Marieb, taking the student's perspective into account has always been an integral part of her teaching style. Dr. Marieb began her teaching career at Springfield College, where she taught anatomy and physiology to physical education majors. She then joined the faculty of the Biological Science Division of Holyoke Community College in 1969 after receiving her Ph.D. in zoology from the University of Massachusetts at Amherst. While teaching at Holyoke Community College, where many of her students were pursuing nursing degrees, she developed a desire to better understand the relationship between the scientific study of the human body and the clinical aspects of the nursing practice. To that end, while continuing to teach full time, Dr. Marieb pursued her nursing education, which culminated in a Master of Science degree with a clinical specialization in gerontology from the University of Massachusetts. It is this experience that has informed the development of the unique perspective and accessibility for which her publications are known.

Dr. Marieb has partnered with Benjamin Cummings for over 30 years. Her first work was *Human Anatomy & Physiology Laboratory Manual (Cat Version)*, which came out in 1981. In the years since, several other lab manual versions and study guides, as well as the softcover *Essentials of Human Anatomy & Physiology* textbook, have hit the campus bookstores. This textbook, now in its 9th edition, made its appearance in 1989 and is the latest expression of her commitment to the needs of students studying human anatomy and physiology.

Dr. Marieb has given generously to provide opportunities for students to further their education. She contributes to the New Directions, New Careers Program at Holyoke Community College by funding a staffed drop-in center and by providing several full-tuition scholarships each year for women who are returning to college after a hiatus or attending college for the first time and who would be unable to continue their studies without financial support. She funds the E. N. Marieb Science Research Awards at Mount Holyoke College, which promotes research by undergraduate science majors, and has underwritten renovation and updating of one of the biology labs in Clapp Laboratory at that college. Dr. Marieb also contributes to the University of Massachusetts at Amherst where she generously provided funding for reconstruction and instrumentation of a cutting-edge cytology research laboratory. Recognizing the severe national shortage of nursing faculty, she underwrites the Nursing Scholars of the Future Grant Program at the university.

In 1994, Dr. Marieb received the Benefactor Award from the National Council for Resource Development, American Association of Community Colleges, which recognizes her ongoing sponsorship of student scholarships, faculty teaching awards, and other academic contributions to Holyoke Community College. In May 2000, the science building at Holyoke Community College was named in her honor.

Dr. Marieb is an active member of the Human Anatomy and Physiology Society (HAPS) and the American Association for the Advancement of Science (AAAS). Additionally, while actively engaged as an author, Dr. Marieb serves as a consultant for the Benjamin Cummings *Interactive Physiology*® CD-ROM series.

When not involved in academic pursuits, Dr. Marieb is a world traveler and has vowed to visit every country on this planet. Shorter term, she serves on the scholarship committee of the Women's Resources Center and on the board of directors of several charitable institutions in Sarasota County. She is an enthusiastic supporter of the local arts and enjoys a competitive match of doubles tennis.

Katja Hoehn

Dr. Katja Hoehn is an associate professor in the Department of Chemical and Biological Sciences at Mount Royal University in Calgary, Canada. Dr. Hoehn's first love is teaching. Her teaching excellence has been recognized by several awards during her 17 years at Mount Royal University. These include a PanCanadian Educational Technology Faculty Award (1999), a Teaching Excellence Award from the Students' Association of Mount Royal (2001), and the Mount Royal Distinguished Faculty Teaching Award (2004).

Dr. Hoehn received her M.D. (with Distinction) from the University of Saskatchewan, and her Ph.D. in Pharmacology from Dalhousie University. In 1991, the Dalhousie Medical Research Foundation presented her with the Max Forman (Jr.) Prize for excellence in medical research. During her Ph.D. and postdoctoral studies, she also pursued her passion for teaching by presenting guest lectures to first- and second-year medical students at Dalhousie University and at the University of Calgary.

Dr. Hoehn has been a contributor to several books and has written numerous research papers in Neuroscience and Pharmacology. She oversaw a recent revision of the Benjamin Cummings *Interactive Physiology®* CD-ROM series modules, and coauthored the newest module, *The Immune System*.

Following Dr. Marieb's example, Dr. Hoehn provides financial support for students in the form of a scholarship that she established in 2006 for nursing students at Mount Royal University.

Dr. Hoehn is also actively involved in the Human Anatomy and Physiology Society (HAPS) and is a member of the American Association of Anatomists. When not teaching, she likes to spend time outdoors with her husband and two sons, compete in triathlons, and play Irish flute.

Introduce yourself to the chapter

Improved readability and navigability makes the
text more accessible and easier to study.

Chapter Outlines

Chapter outlines provide
a preview of the chapter
and help you locate
information easily.

Learning Objectives

Learning objectives
are integrated into the
chapter and give you a preview
of what content is to come
and what you are expected
to learn.

Bulleted Narrative

The narrative has been
bulleted wherever possible
to make the text easier to
read and navigate.

Check Your Understanding

Concept check
questions are tied to
the sections' Learning
Objectives and ask you
to stop, think, and check
your understanding
before moving on.

MasteringA&P®

Reading Questions
keep you on track.

14

The Autonomic Nervous System

The human body is exquisitely sensitive to changes in its internal
environment, and engages in a lifelong struggle to balance competing demands
for resources under ever-changing conditions. Although all body systems contribute, the stability of our internal environment depends largely on the **autonomic nervous system (ANS)**, the system of motor neurons that innervates smooth and cardiac muscle and glands (Figure 14.1).

At every moment, signals stream from visceral organs into the CNS, and autonomic nerves make adjustments as necessary to ensure optimal support for body activities. In response to changing conditions, the ANS shunts blood to "needy" areas, speeds or slows heart rate, adjusts blood pressure and body temperature, and increases or decreases stomach secretions.

Most of this fine-tuning occurs without our awareness or attention. Can you tell when your arteries are constricting or your pupils are dilating? Probably not—but if you've ever been stuck in a checkout line, and your full bladder was contracting as if it had a mind of its own, you've been very aware of visceral activity. The ANS controls all these functions, both those we're aware of and those we're not. Indeed, as the term *autonomic* (*auto* = self; *nom* = govern) implies, this motor subdivision of the peripheral nervous system has a certain amount of functional independence. The ANS is also called the **involuntary nervous system**, which reflects its subconscious control, or the **general visceral motor system**, which indicates the location of most of its effectors.

Overview

✓ Define autonomic nervous system and explain its relationship to the peripheral nervous system.

✓ Compare the somatic and autonomic nervous systems relative to effectors, efferent pathways, and neurotransmitters released.

✓ Compare and contrast the functions of the parasympathetic and sympathetic divisions.

ANS Anatomy

✓ For the parasympathetic and sympathetic divisions, describe the site of CNS origin, locations of ganglia, and general fiber pathways.

Anatomically, the sympathetic and parasympathetic divisions differ in

■ **Sites of origin.** Parasympathetic fibers are craniosacral—they originate in the brain (cranium) and sacral spinal cord. Sympathetic fibers are thoracolumbar—they originate in the thoracic and lumbar regions of the spinal cord.

■ **Relative lengths of their fibers.** The parasympathetic division has long preganglionic and short postganglionic fibers. The sympathetic division has the opposite condition—the preganglionic fibers are short and the postganglionic fibers are long.

☑ **Check Your Understanding**

1. Name the three types of effectors of the autonomic nervous system.
2. Which relays instructions from the CNS to muscles more quickly, the somatic nervous system or the ANS? Explain why.
3. Which branch of the ANS would predominate if you were lying on the beach enjoying the sun and the sound of the waves? Which branch would predominate if you were on a surfboard and a shark appeared within a few feet of you?

_____ *For answers, see Appendix H.*

Chapter 14 Chapter Test Question 5   Resources ▼ Help | Close ✕

Item Type: Reading Questions | Difficulty: 2 | Time: 2m | Learning Outcomes ▼ | Contact the Publisher   Manage this Item: Standard View ▼

Chapter Test - Chapter 14 Question 5

Part A

Once a preganglionic axon reaches a trunk ganglion, one of three things can happen to the axon. Which of the following is *not* one of these three things?

○ The axon can ascend or descend the sympathetic trunk to synapse in another trunk ganglion.
○ The axon can pass through the trunk ganglion and emerge from the sympathetic trunk without synapsing.
○ The axon can synapse with a ganglionic neuron in the same trunk ganglion.
○ The axon can emerge from the sympathetic trunk to synapse in another axon.

submit   my answers   show answer   review part

Follow complex processes step by step

Focus Figures help you grasp tough topics in A&P by walking you through carefully developed step-by-step illustrations that use a big-picture layout and dramatic art to provide a context for understanding the process.

Overview

Each Overview quicky summarizes the key idea of the figure.

Big Picture Orientation

The big picture provides you with a concrete starting point for the process.

Blue Text

This text acts as the instructor's voice and explains difficult concepts. In some figures the text is broken into numbered steps to help you more easily understand difficult processes.

FOCUS — **Bulk Flow Across Capillary Walls**

Figure 19.17 Bulk fluid flow across capillary walls causes continuous mixing of fluid between the plasma and the interstitial fluid compartments, and maintains the interstitial environment.

The big picture
Fluid filters from capillaries at their arteriolar end and flows through the interstitial space. Most is reabsorbed at the venous end.

Arteriole

For all capillary beds, 20 L of fluid is filtered out per day—almost 7 times the total plasma volume!

Fluid moves through the interstitial space.

Net filtration pressure (NFP) determines the direction of fluid movement. Two kinds of pressure drive fluid flow:

Hydrostatic pressure (HP)	Osmotic pressure (OP)
• Due to fluid pressing against a boundary • HP "pushes" fluid across the boundary • In blood vessels, is due to blood pressure	• Due to nondiffusible solutes that cannot cross the boundary • OP "pulls" fluid across the boundary • In blood vessels, is due to plasma proteins

Piston

Boundary

"Pushes"

Solute molecules (proteins)

Boundary

"Pulls"

17 L of fluid per day is reabsorbed into the capillaries at the venous end.

About 3 L per day of fluid (and any leaked proteins) are removed by the lymphatic system (see Chapter 20).

Venule

Lymphatic capillary

Focus Figure
Tutorials

All Focus Figures have related tutorials in MasteringA&P that your instructor can assign and that will guide you through the figures step by step.

How do the pressures drive fluid flow across a capillary?

Net filtration occurs at the arteriolar end of a capillary.

To determine the pressure driving the fluid out of the capillary at any given point, we calculate the **net filtration pressure (NFP)**—the outward pressures (HP_c and OP_{if}) minus the inward pressures (HP_{if} and OP_c). So,

$$NFP = (HP_c + OP_{if}) - (HP_{if} + OP_c)$$
$$= (35 + 1) - (0 + 26)$$
$$= 10 \text{ mm Hg (net outward pressure)}$$

As a result, fluid moves from the capillary into the interstitial space.

Net reabsorption occurs at the venous end of a capillary.

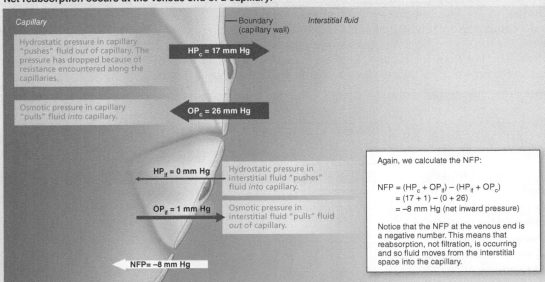

Again, we calculate the NFP:

$$NFP = (HP_c + OP_{if}) - (HP_{if} + OP_c)$$
$$= (17 + 1) - (0 + 26)$$
$$= -8 \text{ mm Hg (net inward pressure)}$$

Notice that the NFP at the venous end is a negative number. This means that reabsorption, not filtration, is occurring and so fluid moves from the interstitial space into the capillary.

Study figures as you read the text

Select pieces of art provide more visual content and often have step-by-step text that helps you better understand structure, functions, and processes.

▼ 3-D anatomy art

Stunning 3-D anatomy art is rendered in a dramatically more dynamic, realistic style that uses vibrant, saturated colors to help you visualize key anatomical structures.

Figure 9.5 Relationship of the sarcoplasmic reticulum and T tubules to myofibrils of skeletal muscle. The tubules of the SR (blue) encircle each myofibril like a "holey" sleeve. These tubules fuse to form a net of communicating channels at the level of the H zone and saclike elements called terminal cisterns abutting the A-I junctions. The T tubules (gray) are inward invaginations of the sarcolemma that run deep into the cell between the terminal cisterns. (See detailed view in Figure 9.11, pp.290-291) Sites of close contact of these three elements (terminal cistern, T tubule, and terminal cistern) are called triads.

MasteringA&P

NEW! **Art Labeling** and **Ranking/Sorting Questions** are drag and drop activities that allow you to assess your knowledge of terms and structures as well as the order of steps and elements involved in physiological processes.

Prepare for your future career

Clinical coverage and case studies have been expanded throughout.

 Homeostatic Imbalance 6.1

Minute changes from the homeostatic range for blood calcium can lead to severe neuromuscular problems ranging from hyper-excitability (when blood Ca^{2+} levels are too low) to nonresponsiveness and inability to function (with high blood Ca^{2+} levels). In addition, sustained high blood levels of Ca^{2+}, a condition known as *hypercalcemia* (hi″per-kal-se′me-ah), can lead to undesirable deposits of calcium salts in the blood vessels, kidneys, and other soft organs, which may hamper their function. ✚

◀ Homeostatic Imbalance

Homeostatic Imbalance sections are integrated within the text and alert you to the consequences of body systems not functioning optimally. These pathological conditions are integrated with the text to clarify and illuminate normal functioning.

MasteringA&P®

NEW! **Homeostatic Imbalance Clinical Questions** can be assigned to you by your instructor on MasteringA&P. They help strengthen your understanding of how the body works to stay in balance and what happens when it falls out of balance.

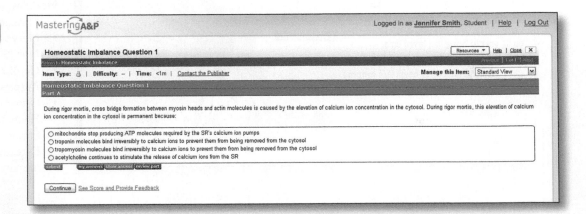

AT THE CLINIC

Case Study Muscular System

Let's continue our tale of Mrs. DeStephano's medical problems, this time looking at the notes made detailing observations of her skeletal musculature.

- Severe lacerations of the muscles of the right leg and knee
- Damage to the blood vessels serving the right leg and knee
- Transection of the sciatic nerve (the large nerve serving most of the lower limb), just above the right knee

Her physician orders daily passive range-of-motion (ROM) exercise and electrical stimulation for her right leg and a diet high in protein, carbohydrates, and vitamin C.

1. Describe the step-by-step process of wound healing that will occur in her fleshy (muscle) wounds, and note the consequences of the specific restorative process that occurs.

2. What complications in healing can be anticipated owing to vascular (blood vessel) damage in the right leg?

3. What complications in muscle structure and function result from transection of the sciatic nerve? Why are passive ROM and electrical stimulation of her right leg muscles ordered?

4. Explain the reasoning behind the dietary recommendations.

(Answers in Appendix H)

▲ NEW! At the Clinic

End-of-chapter sections now contain an At the Clinic feature, which help you apply what you've learned. By learning related clinical terms and reading short Case Studies and answering questions, you will begin to prepare for your future career.

MasteringA&P®

NEW! **Case Study Coaching Activities** increase your problem-solving skills and prepare you for your future career.

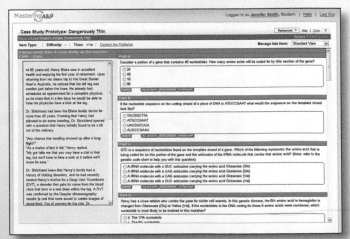

Practice what you don't understand with MasteringA&P®

MasteringA&P includes a Study Area that has many tools to help you succeed, including:

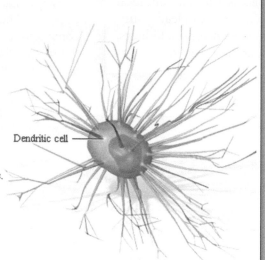

Only a few kinds of cells have class II MHC proteins. These are the antigen-presenting cells: dendritic cells, macrophages, and B cells. These cells communicate with CD4 cells, which are destined to become, or have already become, helper T cells. The antigens that are presented on class II MHC proteins are exogenous antigens—they originate from outside the cell.

Let's follow an exogenous antigen on its way to being displayed on a class II MHC protein.

Click the dendritic cell to begin this process.

Dendritic cell

◄ Interactive Physiology® iP 10-System Suite

IP helps you understand the hardest part of A&P: physiology. Fun, interactive tutorials, games, and quizzes give you additional explanations to help you grasp difficult concepts.

Modules:
- Muscular System
- Nervous System I
- Nervous System II
- Cardiovascular System
- Respiratory System
- Urinary System
- Fluids & Electrolytes
- Endocrine System
- Digestive System
- Immune System

Troponin

◄ A&P Flix

A&P Flix™ are 3-D movie-quality animations with self-paced tutorials and gradable quizzes that help you master the toughest topics in A&P:

Cell Physiology
- Membrane Transport
- DNA Replication
- Mitosis
- Protein Synthesis

Muscle Physiology
- Events at the Neuromuscular Junction
- Excitation-Contraction Coupling
- Cross-Bridge Cycle

Neurophysiology
- Resting Membrane Potential
- Generation of an Action Potential
- Propagation of an Action Potential

Origins, Insertions, Actions, Innervations
- 63 animations on this topic

Group Muscle Actions & Joints
- 54 animations on this topic

◄PAL | practice anatomy lab™

Practice Anatomy Lab™ (PAL™) 3.0 is a virtual anatomy study and practice tool that gives you 24/7 access to the most widely used lab specimens, including the human cadaver, anatomical models, histology, cat, and fetal pig. PAL 3.0 retains all of the key advantages of version 2.0, including ease of use, built-in audio pronunciations, rotatable bones, and simulated fill-in-the-blank lab practical exams.

Annotation Function
Allows you to take notes.

Google®-based
search function.

Highlight Function
Lets you highlight what you want to remember.

Zoom
Lets you zoom in and out for better viewing.

Pearson eText ▶

Pearson eText gives you access to the text whenever and wherever you can access the Internet. The eText pages look exactly like the printed text, plus you get powerful interactive and customization features.

Interactive Glossary
Provides pop-up definitions and terms.

Instructor Notes
Your instructor might also share his or her notes and highlights with the class.

Hyperlinks
Links to quizzes, tests, activities, and animations.

Get 24/7 lab practice

NEW! PAL | practice anatomy lab

PAL 3.0 is an indispensable virtual anatomy study and practice tool that gives you 24/7 access to the most widely used lab specimens, including the human cadaver, anatomical models, histology, cat, and fetal pig. PAL 3.0 retains all of the key advantages of version 2.0, including ease of use, built-in audio pronunciations, rotatable bones, and simulated fill-in-the-blank lab practical exams.

NEW! Carefully prepared dissections show nerves, blood vessels, and arteries across body systems.

SHOW LABELS

Spinal cord, cervical region

LAYERS

Vertebral artery

◀ 8 of 34 ▶

HIDE GALLERY

SPINAL CORD   BRAIN

NEW! Layering slider allows you to peel back layers of the human cadaver and view and explore hundreds of brand-new dissections especially commissioned for 3.0.

NEW! Photo gallery allows you to quickly see thumbnails of images for a particular region or sub region.

PAL 3.0 is available in the Study Area of MasteringA&P (www.masteringaandp.com). The PAL 3.0 DVD can be packaged with the book for no extra charge.

◄ **NEW!** Interactive Histology

Interactive Histology module allows you to view the same tissue slide at varying magnifications, thereby helping you identify structures and their characteristics.

Lateral Left

◄ 3-D Anatomy Animations

3-D Anatomy Animations of origins, insertions, actions, and innervations of over 65 muscles are now viewable in both Cadaver and Anatomical Models and modules. A new closed-captioning option provides textual presentation of narration to help you retain information and supports ADA compliance.

PAL | practice anatomy lab™

PAL 3.0 also includes:

- **NEW!** Question randomization feature gives you more opportunities for practice and self-assessment. Each time you retake a quiz or lab practical, a new set of questions is generated.
- **NEW!** Hundreds of new images and views are included, especially of the human cadaver, anatomical models, and histology.
- **NEW!** Turn-off highlight feature in quizzes and lab practicals gives you the option to see a structure without the highlight overlay.

physioEX™
VERSION 9

NEW! PhysioEx 9.0

PhysioEx 9.0: Laboratory Simulations in Physiology is easy-to-use laboratory simulation software with an accompanying lab manual that consists of 12 exercises containing 63 physiology lab activities. It can be used to supplement or substitute for wet labs. PhysioEx allows you to repeat labs as often as you like, perform experiments without harming live animals, and conduct experiments that are difficult to perform in a wet lab environment because of time, cost, or safety concerns.

To the Instructor: Everything from the Book is now Integrated with MasteringA&P®

All text features of *Human Anatomy & Physiology* are now assignable in MasteringA&P, providing students with unlimited opportunities to study.

NEW! Focus Figure Tutorials ▶

Focus Figure Tutorials guide students through key parts of each Focus Figure, assessing their understanding of the major concepts through a variety of assessment tools—multiple choice questions with hints and specific wrong-answer feedback, interactive ranking and sorting exercises, and labeling activities.

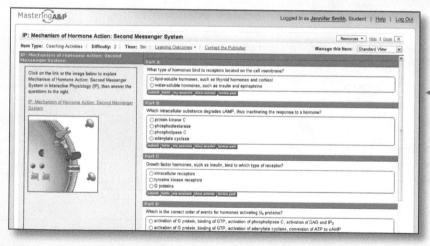

◀ *Interactive Physiology®* Coaching Activities

20 new *Interactive Physiology* Coaching Activities have been added to the Item Library.

NEW! Homeostatic ▶ Imbalance Clinical Questions

Homeostatic Imbalance Clinical Questions are higher-order thinking questions that assess students on their comprehension of the Homeostatic Imbalance content in each chapter, making one of the text's hallmark features now assignable.

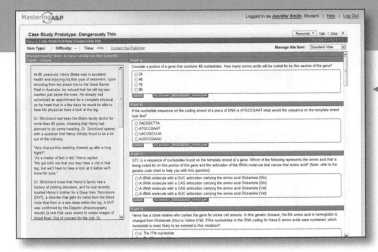

◄ NEW! Case Study Coaching Activities

Case Study Coaching Activities increase problem-solving skills and prepare students for future careers in allied health. Corresponding Teaching Notes give instructors valuable tips on when and how to use case studies in the classroom.

◄ Video Tutor Coaching Activities

Video Tutors instruct and coach students on key A&P concepts using art from the book and are accompanied by questions with video hints and feedback specific to their misconceptions.

Other Text Features Now Assignable in MasteringA&P:

- **A&P Flix™ Coaching Activities** offer stunning 3-D visuals of core concepts and tough physiological concepts with in-depth assessments to test student understanding. Seven new topics have been added to the Ninth Edition.

- **Art-Based Questions** are conceptual questions related to art and instruct students with wrong-answer feedback.

- **Art Labeling and Ranking/Sorting Questions** are drag and drop activities that allow students to assess their knowledge of terms and structures as well as the order of steps and elements involved in physiological processes.

- **PAL™ 3.0** and assessments

- **PhysioEx™ 9.0** and assessments

- **Clinical Application questions** (under Test Bank) give students the opportunity to apply their knowledge to clinical scenarios.

- **Reading Questions** keep students on track and are pre-built for easy set-up and delivery.

- **Test Bank questions** have been heavily revised with up to 600 new questions to help better assess your students.

All the Tools to Help Instructors Succeed

Instructor Resource DVD for Human Anatomy & Physiology
by Elaine N. Marieb and Katja Hoehn
978-0-321-80289-7 • 0-321-80289-6

Instructor Guide to Text and Media for Human Anatomy & Physiology
by Elaine N. Marieb, Katja Hoehn, and Laura Steele
978-0-321-79440-6 • 0-321-79440-0

Printed Test Bank for Human Anatomy & Physiology
by Elaine N. Marieb, Katja Hoehn, and Jerri Lindsey
978-0-321-80290-3 • 0-321-80290-X

Blackboard Instant Access for Human Anatomy & Physiology
by Elaine N. Marieb and Katja Hoehn
978-0-321-79603-5 • 0-321-79603-9

Human Anatomy & Physiology Laboratory Manual Update versions with MasteringA&P and PhysioEx 9.0
by Elaine N. Marieb and Susan Mitchell

MAIN: (student edition) 978-0-321-73526-3 • 0-321-73526-9
(p-copy) 978-0-321-75022-8 • 0-321-75022-5

CAT: (student edition) 978-0-321-73528-7 • 0-321-73528-5
(p-copy) 978-0-321-75021-1 • 0-321-75021-7

PIG: (student edition) 978-0-321-73527-0 • 0-321-73527-7
(p-copy) 978-0-321-73324-5 • 0-321-73324-X

RAT: (student edition) 978-0-321-73567-6 • 0-321-75367-6
(p-copy) 978-0-321-65136-5 • 0-321-65136-7

For more supplements and information, go to:
www.pearsonhighered.com/educator.

All the Tools to Help Students Succeed

Interactive Physiology® 10-System Suite
by Pearson Benjamin Cummings
978-0-8053-6117-9 • 0-8053-6117-0

Practice Anatomy Lab™ (PAL™)
by Ruth Heisler, Nora Hebert, Jett Chinn,
Karen Krabbenhoft, and Olga Malakhova,
978-0-321-68211-6 • 0-321-68211-4

physioEX VERSION 9
PhysioEx™ 9.0: Laboratory Simulations in Physiology
by Peter Zao, Timothy Stabler, Lori Smith,
Andrew Lokuta, and Edwin Griff
978-0-321-69217-7 • 0-321-69217-9

NEW! *Get Ready for A&P,* **Third Edition**
by Lori K. Garrett
978-0-321-81336-7 • 0-321-81336-7

Study Guide for Human Anatomy & Physiology
by Elaine N. Marieb
978-0-321-79439-0 • 0-321-79439-7

A Brief Atlas of the Human Body, **Second Editon**
by Elaine N. Marieb, Patricia Brady Wilhelm,
Jon B. Mallatt, and Matt Hutchinson
978-0-321-66261-3 • 0-321-66261-X

Anatomy & Physiology Coloring Workbook: A Complete Study Guide
by Elaine N. Marieb
978-0-321-74305-3 • 0-321-74305-9

Preface

As educators, clinically trained individuals, and perennial students, we are continually challenged by the learning mind. What works best to help students apply new information to the world they personally understand? Our clinical backgrounds have served our teaching and writing purposes well. Perhaps even more important, our clinical experience has allowed us to see our presentations through our students' eyes and from the vantage points of their career interests.

For this edition, as for those preceding it, feedback from student and instructor reviews indicated areas of the text that needed to be revised for clarity, timeliness, and just plain reduction of verbal meatiness. Overall, feedback was positive, verifying that our approach is effective: Explaining fundamental principles and unifying themes first creates a strong base for what comes later. Backing these explanations up with comfortable analogies and familiar examples enhances students' understanding of the workings of the human body.

Unifying Themes

Three integrating themes that organized, unified, and set the tone of the first edition of this text continue to be valid and are retained in this edition. These themes are:

Interrelationships of body organ systems. The fact that nearly all regulatory mechanisms require interaction of several organ systems is continually emphasized. For example, Chapter 25, which deals with the structure and function of the urinary system, discusses the vital importance of the kidneys not only in maintaining adequate blood volume to ensure normal blood circulation, but also in continually adjusting the chemical composition of blood so that all body cells remain healthy. The unique *System Connections* feature is the culmination of this approach and should help students think of the body as a dynamic community of interdependent parts rather than as a number of isolated structural units.

Homeostasis. The normal and most desirable condition of body functioning is homeostasis. Its loss or destruction always leads to some type of pathology—temporary or permanent. Pathological conditions are integrated with the text to clarify and illuminate normal functioning, not as an end in and of themselves. For example, Chapter 19, which deals with the structure and function of blood vessels, explains how the ability of healthy arteries to expand and recoil ensures continuous blood flow and proper circulation. The chapter goes on to discuss the effects on homeostasis when arteries lose their elasticity: high blood pressure and all of its attendant problems. These homeostatic imbalances are indicated visually by a pink symbol with a fulcrum:

Whenever students see the imbalance symbol in text, the concept of disease as a loss of homeostasis is reinforced. Every Homeostatic Imbalance section has a new, related clinical question that is assignable in MasteringA&P. These new clinical questions help strengthen students' understanding of how the body works to stay in balance.

Complementarity of structure and function. Students are encouraged to understand the structure of an organ, a tissue, or a cell as a prerequisite to comprehending its function. Concepts of physiology are explained and related to structural characteristics that promote or allow the various functions to occur. For example, the lungs can act as a gas exchange site because the walls of their air sacs present an incredibly thin barrier between blood and air.

NEW TO THE NINTH EDITION

With every edition, our goal is powerful but simple—to make anatomy and physiology as engaging, accurate, and relevant as possible for both instructors and students. The Ninth Edition represents a monumental revision, with changes to the text and art presentation that build upon the hallmark strengths of the previous eight editions. The changes to the Ninth Edition are all driven by the needs of today's students, as we seek to make the learning of key concepts in A&P as easy as possible for them. Key concepts are important because of the overwhelming amount of material in this course. Mastering this material gives students structure for organizing this wealth of information. Below are the ways in which we've revised the Ninth Edition to make this book the one where learning happens most effectively, followed by a detailed list of specific chapter-by-chapter content changes.

An expanded art program. The drive for this revision began as a simple list. We sat down together and created a chapter-by-chapter list of the key concepts in A&P where students struggle the most. This list became the basis for our art revision plans for both the Eighth and Ninth editions. We first boiled it down to some of the toughest topics to get our list of Focus figures. These Focus figures are illustrations that use a "big picture" layout and dramatic art to walk the student through difficult physiological processes in a step-by-step way. These have been wildly popular with both instructors and students. In response to repeated requests for more, we are pleased to present 12 new Focus figures. We hope you'll be as pleased with the results of the added Focus figures in the Ninth Edition as you were in the Eighth.

All of the art in the Eighth Edition was carefully examined and reviewed by both instructors and students. Many of their suggested changes have been incorporated into this edition. As always, we have updated many figures to reflect the latest scientific findings and to improve their ability to teach important concepts. Finally, many new photos—histology, cadaver, and others—were painstakingly chosen for this edition to enhance the learning process.

Flipping through the Ninth Edition, you can see that we have built upon the dynamic, three-dimensional, and realistic art style, utilizing dramatic views and perspectives and vibrant, saturated colors.

Improved text presentation. New text features initiated in the Eighth Edition that focus students on key concepts have been retained and expanded in the Ninth Edition. In the current edition, student objectives still appear by topic throughout the chapter and some new *Check Your Understanding* questions have been added at the end of sections. These changes along with a brand-new design make the book easier than ever to study from and navigate. Our hallmark analogies and accessible, friendly style while using simpler, more concise language and shorter paragraphs make the information easier for students to manage.

Factual updates and accuracy. As authors we pride ourselves on keeping our book as up-to-date and as accurate as possible in all areas—a monumental task that requires painstaking selectivity. Although information changes even as a textbook goes to press, be assured that our intent and responsibility to update has been carried out to the best of our ability. We have incorporated current research in the field as much as possible; many of these updates are included in the chapter-by-chapter changes. A more complete list is available from your Pearson sales representative and in the *Instructor Guide to Text and Media.*

Terminology changes. For this edition we've substantially updated the terminology to be in accordance with *Terminologia Anatomica* and *Terminologia Histologica.* Professors can find a complete list of terminology changes detailed in the *Instructor Guide to Text and Media.*

Chapter-by-Chapter Changes

Chapter 1 The Human Body: An Orientation
- Updated information on diagnostic uses of MRI scans (*A Closer Look*).
- New MRI photo of frontal section through the torso (Figure 1.8a).
- Enhanced art showing layers of the pericardium (Figure 1.10).

Chapter 2 Chemistry Comes Alive
- Updated information on stress and aging.
- Improved art showing structure of an atom (Figure 2.1).
- New photos of blood (Figure 2.4).
- New photo of a water strider (Figure 2.10).
- Updated art for levels of protein structure (Figure 2.19).

Chapter 3 Cells: The Living Units
- New information on RNA in translation, rRNA, and tRNA.
- Revised Focus Figure 3.10: Primary Active Transport: The Na^+-K^+ Pump.
- Revised art for three types of endocytosis (Figure 3.13).
- Improved Focus Figure 3.16: G Proteins.
- New photo of smooth and rough endoplasmic reticulum (Figure 3.18).
- New TEM of lysosomes (Figure 3.21).
- Revised art and new TEM for centrioles (Figure 3.25).
- Revised Focus Figure 3.33: Mitosis.
- New Focus Figure 3.37: Translation.

Chapter 4 Tissue: The Living Fabric
- New photomicrographs of epithelium (Figure 4.3).
- New photomicrographs of connective tissues (Figure 4.8).
- New photomicrographs of muscle (Figure 4.10).
- Simplified explanation of polarity.
- Improved rendering of goblet cell (Figure 4.4), with more realistic details.
- Improved teaching effectiveness of Figure 4.11 (classes of membranes).
- Improved layout of Figure 4.12 (tissue repair).
- Added explanation to art for embryonic germ layers (Figure 4.13).

Chapter 5 The Integumentary System
- Updated information on the skin's epithelial cells and stratum corneum.
- New information on tinea versicolor ("sunspots") and friction ridges.
- Updated information on importance of the stratum corneum as a physical barrier.
- Added new term scleroderma, an autoimmune disorder characterized by hardened skin, in *At the Clinic: Related Clinical Terms.*
- New research on the role of friction ridges in the sense of touch.

Chapter 6 Bones and Skeletal Tissues
- Updated information on bone resorption and remodeling.
- New bone-related information on serotonin, glucose intolerance, and diabetes mellitus.
- Updated information on osteogenic cells and microscopic anatomy of bone cells.
- New information on osteoporosis in prostate cancer patients who receive androgen-suppressing therapy.
- New information on osteocalcin, a hormone which helps regulate bone formation and also protects against obesity, glucose intolerance, and diabetes mellitus.
- New information on the monoclonal antibody drug denosumab as a treatment for osteoporosis.

Chapter 7 The Skeleton
- New Clinical Case Study.
- New photos of the skull, temporal bone, sphenoid and ethmoid bones, mandible, and orbits (Figures 7.5–7.12).
- New photos of defects in spinal curvature (Figure 7.17).
- New photos of proximal tibia (Figure 7.33).

Chapter 8 Joints
- New Clinical Case Study.
- New Focus Figure 8.7: Types of Synovial Joints.
- Added information on meniscal transplant surgery.
- Updated information on treatment of sprains.
- Updated statistics on arthritis; updated treatment of rheumatoid arthritis.
- Updated description of sinovitis.
- Updated statistics on joint replacements in the U.S.
- Updated research aimed at future treatments of joint problems.

Chapter 9 Muscles and Muscle Tissue
- New discussion of EPOC (excess postexercise oxygen consumption).
- New photomicrograph of skeletal muscle (Figure 9.1).
- New Figure 9.9 (skeletal muscle action potentials).
- Added information of myosin head orientation in smooth muscle.
- Updated information on treatments for Duchenne muscular dystrophy.
- Streamlined discussion of muscle fatigue.
- Added skeletal muscle fibers to Figure 9.17 for better teaching effectiveness.

Chapter 10 The Muscular System
- New Focus Figure 10.1: Muscle Action.
- New Clinical Case Study.
- New photo of hip and thigh muscles (Figure 10.21).

Chapter 11 Fundamentals of the Nervous System and Nervous Tissue
- Update on multiple sclerosis risk factors and treatment.
- New information on addiction treatment and prescription drug abuse (*A Closer Look*).
- New Clinical Case Study.
- Updated discussion on neuronal transport.
- New information on gasotransmitters.
- Update on shingles and vaccination available for its prevention.

- Discuss direct and indirect neurotransmitter receptor mechanisms in two figures (Figures 11.20 and 11.21). Added relay-runner motif to G-protein linked receptor figure (Figure 11.21) to tie it to previous G-protein figure in Chapter 3.

Chapter 12 The Central Nervous System
- New Clinical Case Study.
- Updated information on premotor cortex and the role of the basal nuclei.
- New information on Alzheimer's disease and Parkinson's disease.
- Update on amyotrophic lateral sclerosis.
- Updated information on genetic causes of autism.
- New photos of brain sections (Figures 12.9, 12.10, and 12.12).
- New photo of spinal cord (Figure 12.26).

Chapter 13 The Peripheral Nervous System and Reflex Activity
- New information on vanilloid receptors, pain tolerance, and Bell's palsy.
- New SEM of nerve cross-section (Figure 13.4).
- New photos of brachial and sacral plexuses (Figures 13.10 and 13.12).
- New Clinical Case Study.

Chapter 14 The Autonomic Nervous System
- Updated information on aging and blood pressure receptors.
- Streamlined discussion of sympathetic trunks and pathways.
- More explicit statement about the "background" firing rate of neurons along sympathetic and parasympathetic axons in ANS.

Chapter 15 The Special Senses
- New Clinical Case Study.
- New information on link between vitamin C and cataract formation.
- New photos of retina (Figure 15.7), cataract (Figure 15.9), and refraction (Figure 15.11).
- New summary Table 15.1—differences between rods and cones.
- Updated discussion of olfactory processing.
- New summary Table 15.2—structures of internal ear and their functions.

Chapter 16 The Endocrine System
- New research on ghrelin and growth hormone release.
- New photo showing effects of growth hormone excess and deficiency (Figure 16.7).
- Updated information on type 1 diabetes.
- New Focus Figure 16.5: Hypothalamus and Pituitary Interactions.
- New photomicrographs of thyroid (Figure 16.8), parathyroid (Figure 16.12), adrenal gland (Figure 16.14), and pancreas (Figure 16.18).
- New flowchart of parathyroid hormone effects (Figure 16.13).

Chapter 17 Blood
- New Clinical Case Study.
- New SEMs of normal and sickled RBCs (Figure 17.8).

- New photomicrographs of leukocytes (Figure 17.10).
- Updated Figure 17.11 (leukocyte formation).
- Updated statistics on sickle cell anemia and malaria.
- Improved teaching effectiveness of Figure 17.14 (pathways of coagulation).

Chapter 18 The Cardiovascular System: The Heart

- New Clinical Case Study.
- New Focus Figure 18.9: Blood Flow Through the Heart.
- Updated information on ischemic cell death in myocardial infarction.
- New photos of the heart (Figures 18.4 and 18.6).
- Expanded overview of systemic and pulmonary circuits (in response to focus group feedback).
- Reorganized presentation of heart anatomy.
- Updated the effects of hyperkalemia and hypercalcemia on the heart.

Chapter 19 The Cardiovascular System: Blood Vessels

- Update on obesity-linked hypertension.
- New Focus Figure 19.17: Bulk Flow Across Capillary Walls.
- New photomicrograph of artery and vein (Figure 19.1).
- Added information on C-reactive protein as a marker of systemic inflammation and a predictor of future heart attacks and strokes.
- Reorganized Figure 19.15 for better teaching effectiveness.
- Reorganized section on venous return.
- Reorganized discussion of baroreceptor reflex.
- Consolidated discussion of renal regulation of blood pressure by adding material previously in Chapter 25. Moved details of renin-angiotensin-aldosterone mechanism from Figure 25.10 to Figure 19.10.
- Reorganized presentation on homeostatic imbalances of blood pressure.

Chapter 20 The Lymphatic System and Lymphoid Organs and Tissues

- New information on the spleen as a monocyte reservoir.
- New photomicrographs of thymus (Figure 20.7) and tonsil (Figure 20.8).
- Improved discussion of lymphoid cells and lymphoid tissues.
- Reorganized section on mucosa-associated lymphoid tissue (MALT).
- Updated statistics for non-Hodgkin's lymphoma.

Chapter 21 The Immune System: Innate and Adaptive Body Defenses

- Major revision of chapter to streamline presentation.
- New Clinical Case Study.
- Added coverage of lectin pathway (Figure 21.6).
- New SEM of macrophage engaged in phagocytosis (Figure 21.2).
- Two new summary tables (Tables 21.3 and 21.5).

Chapter 22 The Respiratory System

- Update on early detection of lung cancer.
- Updated discussion of cystic fibrosis.
- New Focus Figure 22.20: Oxygen-Hemoglobin Dissociation Curve.
- New photomicrograph of lung tissue (Figure 22.8).
- New SEM of pulmonary capillary casts (Figure 22.9).

Chapter 23 The Digestive System

- New photomicrograph of esophagus-stomach junction (Figure 23.12).
- New photograph of gastric ulcer (Figure 23.16).
- New photomicrograph of pancreas (Figure 23.26).
- New art on the absorption of monosaccharides (Figure 23.35).

Chapter 24 Nutrition, Metabolism, and Body Temperature Regulation

- Coverage of the USDA's new MyPlate logo (Figure 24.1) and dietary recommendations.
- New Focus Figure 24.8: Oxidative Phosphorylation.
- New Clinical Case Study.
- Updated information on obesity (*A Closer Look*).

Chapter 25 The Urinary System

- Major revision of chapter to streamline presentation.
- New Focus Figure 25.16: Medullary Osmotic Gradient.
- New information on symptoms and manifestations of renal failure.
- New Clinical Case Study.
- New SEM of nephron blood vessel casts (Figure 25.7).
- New illustration of net filtration forces (Figure 25.11).
- New illustration on tubular reabsorption and secretion (Figure 25.15).
- New photo of kidney (Figure 25.3).

Chapter 26 Fluid, Electrolyte, and Acid-Base Balance

- Updated discussion of regulation of sodium and water balance, and dehydration.
- New text and summary table (Table 26.2) contrasting extracellular fluid sodium concentration and body sodium content.

Chapter 27 The Reproductive System

- New photo of testis (Figure 27.3).
- New illustration of male perineum (Figure 27.4).
- New SEM of seminiferous tubules (Figure 27.8).
- New graph of plasma testosterone versus age (Figure 27.11).
- New photomicrograph of ovary (Figure 27.13).
- Update on circumcision and statistics on reduction in risk of HIV and other infections.

Chapter 28 Pregnancy and Human Development

- New Focus Figure 28.2: Sperm Penetration and the Cortical Reaction.
- Updated contraception methods (*A Closer Look*).
- New Clinical Case Study.
- Updated information on role of hCG.
- Updated information on assisted reproductive technologies.
- Simplified Figure 28.10 to improve teaching effectiveness.
- New photo of nursing mother (Figure 28.19).

Chapter 29 Heredity

- New Clinical Case Study.
- New photos of karyotyping (Figure 29.1).

Acknowledgments

Each new edition of this textbook holds out a promise to its authors. "You're done—the book is perfect!" Not! Although it would appear that this would be so after all the work bestowed upon it over eight editions, it still takes the better part of two years, demands our participation in many focus groups, mobilizes our library research skills, and tests our creativity once again before we finally put the last page of the new edition to rest. It never really gets easier as we grind away—the grist finer with each edition.

In all fairness, we don't work alone. Many people shared the work of this edition and deserve their proper due. Once the first draft of each chapter was complete in our estimations, it was sent off to Alice Fugate, the text developmental editor, who wielded her pen to ensure readability and consistency—factors very important to student success. Backing up Alice's work was the director of development Barbara Yien, well known for her ability to see the whole picture. After we perused and processed Alice's suggestions, the manuscript went to Shannon Cutt. Shannon, our cheery associate project editor, checked every aspect of the newly modified text before sending it on to production. Nobody escapes Shannon's ministrations—especially her amazing ability to chase down things that threaten to fall through the cracks. If we failed to meet her deadlines, a barrage of emails rained down, all asking us in the sweetest way to get the missing item in. After Shannon had assured herself that all was well, the manuscript went to Anita Wagner, our skilled copyeditor for the last several editions. Anita knows our text as well or better than we do. She checks grammar, spelling of new drugs or procedures, and verifies statistics; much of the superb accuracy of this text is to her credit as a copyeditor par excellence.

Whew! But that's not all, folks. Once the writing and editing part of the revision is complete, the manuscript goes to the production department, where the text and art come together. This business-like domain is headed by Michele Mangelli, our production manager once again. Always knowledgeable, Michele guides the production process with great skill and works seamlessly with the members of her excellent staff. She makes sure the artists are on schedule producing art with the appropriate look and accuracy, directs the industrious photo researcher Kristin Piljay, and oversees the work of David Novak (the conscientious production supervisor) and that hard-working art coordinator Jean Lake.

The last edition of this text touched every figure—making each piece of art more timely, more colorful, more accurate, or better pedagogically. The really big success in the art arena was the fabulous one- to two-page Focus figures introduced in the Eighth Edition. These new figures selected physiological concepts that students have the most difficulty with and "unpacked them." They say you never really have too much of a good thing, so this edition has 12 new Focus Figures. We hope you will like these as much as you did the last offerings. Helping to ensure that you will is Laura Southworth, the art developmental manager who worked tirelessly on these figures. She is not only the art manager but also a skilled professional artist who can illustrate just about any concept we ask for. This capability ensures that the art manuscript delivered to the talented artists of Imagineering and Electronic Publishing Services, who drew the final art, had all the information they needed to produce a quality product. Laura is truly amazing. Important in a different art arena was Lisa Lee, who supplied several of our histology photos and served as a consultant on images from other sources. Tom Fink (East Carolina University), William Karkow (Dubuque University), and Olga Malakhova and Charles Poulton (both from University of Florida College of Medicine, Gainesville) provided histology and cadaver images on an incredibly tight schedule. Thanks so much!

We also thank two people who contributed significantly to this edition: James Hewlett and William Karkow. Working on a tight schedule, James Hewlett contributed 13 new case studies, which were expertly reviewed for clinical accuracy by thoracic surgeon William Karkow.

Thanks also to Yvo Riezebos, cover designer, and tani hasegawa, text designer. Their creativity helped to produce a truly beautiful book. We are very happy that our cover photo, taken by renowned photographer Annie Leibovitz, is of the best known female goalkeeper in the world — Hope Solo. Hope won an Olympic gold medal in 2008, was named Women's Professional Soccer's Goalkeeper of the Year in 2009, and was awarded the Golden Glove at the 2011 World Cup. Sustaining the effort to produce a beautiful book all the way to press were our excellent proofreader, Martha Ghent, and S4Carlisle Publishing Services, the proficient compositor who assembled the final pages with their customary expertise.

The sponsoring editor for the last edition, Serina Beauparlant, has a jazzy new title, "Editor-in-Chief." Even with a slew of new duties, she is resolute about producing the best educational product possible—both in textbook and media. Her replacement for this edition, who took over a large number of Serina's duties, is Gretchen Puttkamer, a real go-getter. We haven't seen too much of Gretchen because she spends most of her time in the field talking to professors, students, and anyone else that will listen to her. Also contributing were several others that we rarely get to talk to, including: editorial assistants Lisa Damerel and John Maas, managing editor Debbie Cogan, Stacey Weinberger, who has been our expert manufacturing buyer for years, and our crackerjack marketing manager, Derek Perrigo, who goes the extra mile to make sure professors are enlightened about special features of the text. Kudos also to our media staff—Lauren Fogel, director of media development, Aimee Pavy, media producer, and the entire media team for PAL 3.0 and PhysioEx 9.0.

Benjamin Cummings spares no effort in its drive to publish an accurate and instructive book. Over 400 reviews were commissioned, enlisting comments and suggestions from both generalist academicians and specialists in various niches of anatomy and physiology. These reviewers' contributions have been of inestimable value in the continuing development of this text. We also want to thank the many students and colleagues who were generous with their time and comments. They did not always tell us what we wanted to hear, but assured of the sincerity of their criticism, we always listened. Input from the following reviewers resulted in the continued excellence and accuracy of this text.

Kim Aaronson, *Columbia College Chicago*
Beth Altschafl, *University of Wisconsin, Madison*
Lynne Anderson, *Meridian Community College*
Marcia Anglin, *Miami Dade College*
Peggy Arnos, *University of Toledo*
Terry Austin, *Temple College*
David Babb, *West Hills Community College*
Stephanie Baiyasi, *Delta College*
Jamal Bittar, *University of Toledo*
William Brewer, *Rochester Institute of Technology*
David Brown, *Brady School of Medicine, East Carolina University*
Bruce Butler, *Canadian University College*
Linda Canobbio, *Ocean County College*
Bob Carter, *Volunteer State Community College*
Jana Causey, *Pearl River Community College*
David Champlin, *University of Southern Maine*
Roger Choate, *Oklahoma City Community College*
Linda Costanzo, *Virginia Commonwealth University*
John Cummings, *Clemson University*
Tina Davis, *Florida State College at Jacksonville, North Campus*
Trevor Day, *Mount Royal University*
Jason Dechant, *University of Pittsburgh*

Mary Dettman, *Seminole State College of Florida*
John Druin, *Lock Haven University*
Jeff Eichold, *Oakland Community College*
Michael Ferrari, *University of Missouri, Kansas City*
Dani Frederick-Duus, *Midlands Technical College*
Sarah Gaffen, *University of Pittsburgh*
Lynn Gargan, *Tarrant County College–Northeast*
Ron Gerrits, *Milwaukee School of Engineering*
Mike Gilbert, *Fresno City College*
Lauren Gollahon, *Texas Tech University*
Cara Hampton-Sandholt, *Cosumnes River College*
William Hanna, *Massasoit Community College*
Pamela Harrison, *Mesa Community College*
Chris Harvey, *Brevard Community College–Palm Bay*
Nora Hebert, *Red Rocks Community College*
Gary Heiserman, *Salem State College*
Deb Heitzman, *Mesa Community College*
DJ Hennager, *Kirkwood Community College*
Mark Hollier, *Georgia Perimeter College*
Rodney Holmes, *Waubonsee Community College*
Mark Hubley, *Prince George's Community College*
William Karkow, *University of Dubuque*
Greg Kelly, *University of Western Ontario*
Michael Kielb, *Eastern Michigan University*
John Lepri, *University of North Carolina–Greensboro*
M. Locke, *University of Western Ontario*
Jodi Long, *Santa Fe College*
Jerri Lindsey, *Tarrant County College–Northeast Campus*
Abigail Mabe, *Walters State College*
Susan Macleod, *Fulton-Montgomery Community College*
Jane Marone, *University of Illinois at Chicago*
Laura Mastrangeo, *Hudson Valley Community College*
Alice McAfee, *University of Toledo*
Rebecca McCane, *Bluegrass Community & Technical College*
Marc McKee, *McGill University*
Marvin Merrit, *Keiser University*
Susan Mitchell, *SUNY Onondaga Community College*
Justin Moore, *American River College*
Syeda Muniam, *SUNY–Schenectady County Community College*
Mary Jane Niles, *University of San Francisco*
Lourdes Norman, *Florida State College–Jacksonville*
Justicia Opoku-Edusei, *University of Maryland*
David Osborne, *Paul L. Foster School of Medicine, Texas Tech University*
Deborah Palatinus, *Roane State Community College*
Izak Paul, *Mount Royal University*
Fred Pavalko, *Indiana University School of Medicine*
Karen Payne, *Chattanooga State Technical College*
Rafaella Pernice, *Hudson County Community College*

Sarah Pugh, *Shelton State*
Wanda Ragland, *Macomb Community College*
Terry Ravine, *University of South Alabama*
Jean Revie, *South Mountain Community College*
Mattie Roig-Watnik, *Palm Beach State College*
Sharon Schapel, *Mott Community College*
Steve Schenk, *Truckee Meadows Community College*
Michelle Stettner, *Meridian Community College*
Richard Symmons, *Cal State University–East Bay*
Bonnie Tarricone, *Ivy Tech Community College*
Carol Veil, *Anne Arundel Community College*
Delon Washo-Krupps, *Arizona State University*
Janice Webster, *Ivy Tech Community College*
Ruby White, *Eastern Michigan University*
Ruth Williams, *Oakton University*
Janice Yoder-Smith, *Tarrant County Community College*

We also want to acknowledge Katja's colleagues at Mount Royal University (Trevor Day, Janice Meeking, Izak Paul, Michael Pollock, Ruth Pickett-Seltner, Sarah Hewitt, and Kartika Tjandra) for stimulating discussions of the text; Associate Dean Tom MacAlister and Chair Tracy O'Connor for supporting Katja's involvement in this project; and Mount Royal University for providing an Internal Research Grant. We are also grateful to Katja's focus group students at Mount Royal University for their valuable and detailed feedback on the Eighth Edition's art program:

Rebecca Aje
Sarah Ankerman
Nikolina Arbutina
Sara Bird
Krizia Carlos
Darrah Crocker
Justine Hamill
Donalea Muir
Jessica Mulli
Sandra Okilj
Melissa Rowson

Robyn Shields
Sengchou Vilay-Wong
Fiona Villamar

Additionally, we would like to thank the following students at Ivy Tech Community College and Massasoit Community College, who each completed a useful and informative survey: Amanda Blevins, Jane Botelho, Paul Bowler, Erica Dupree, Elvia Garza-Sandoval, John Golbranson, Meagan Home, Joseph Madden, George Mager, Joe McManus, Ann Pavia, and Wendy Treesh.

Once again, Dr. Marieb's husband, Harvey Howell, served as a sounding board for some of her ideas, manned the copy machine, and ran the manuscript to the FedEx box daily with nary a complaint during the unbelievably busy days. Thanks also to Katja's husband, Dr. Lawrence W. Haynes, who as a fellow physiologist has provided invaluable assistance to her during the course of the revision. She also thanks her sons, Eric and Stefan Haynes, who are an inspiration and a joy.

Well, our tenure on this edition is over, but there will be another edition three years hence. We would really appreciate hearing from you concerning your opinion—suggestions and constructive criticisms—of this text. It is this type of feedback that provides the basis of each revision, and underwrites its improvement.

Elaine N. Marieb

Katja Hoehn

Elaine N. Marieb and Katja Hoehn
Anatomy and Physiology
Benjamin Cummings
1301 Sansome Street
San Francisco, CA 94111

Brief Contents

Contents

9 Muscles and Muscle Tissue 276

10 The Muscular System 319

UNIT 3 **Regulation and Integration
of the Body**

11 Fundamentals of the Nervous System and Nervous Tissue 386

Appendices

1

The Human Body: An Orientation

Welcome to the study of one of the most fascinating subjects possible—your own body. Such a study is not only highly personal, but timely as well. We get news of some medical advance almost daily. To appreciate emerging discoveries in genetic engineering, to understand new techniques for detecting and treating disease, and to make use of published facts on how to stay healthy, you'll find it helpful to learn about the workings of your body. If you are preparing for a career in the health sciences, the study of anatomy and physiology has added rewards because it provides the foundation needed to support your clinical experiences.

In this chapter we define and contrast anatomy and physiology and discuss how the human body is organized. Then we review needs and functional processes common to all living organisms. Three essential concepts—*the complementarity of structure and function, the hierarchy of structural organization,* and *homeostasis*—will unify and form the bedrock for your study of the human body. The final section of the chapter deals with the language of anatomy—terminology that anatomists use to describe the body or its parts.

An Overview of Anatomy and Physiology

✓ Define anatomy and physiology and describe their subdivisions.

✓ Explain the principle of complementarity.

Two complementary branches of science—anatomy and physiology—provide the concepts that help us to understand the human body. **Anatomy** studies the *structure* of body parts and their relationships to one another. Anatomy has a certain appeal because it is concrete. Body structures can be seen, felt, and examined closely. You don't need to imagine what they look like.

Physiology concerns the *function* of the body, in other words, how the body parts work and carry out their life-sustaining activities. When all is said and done, physiology is explainable only in terms of the underlying anatomy.

To simplify the study of the body, when we refer to body structures and/or physiological values (body temperature, heart rate, and the like), we will assume that we are talking about a healthy young (22-year-old) male weighing about 155 lb (the *reference man*) or a healthy young female weighing about 125 lb (the *reference woman*).

Topics of Anatomy

Anatomy is a broad field with many subdivisions, each providing enough information to be a course in itself. **Gross**, or **macroscopic, anatomy** is the study of large body structures visible to the naked eye, such as the heart, lungs, and kidneys. Indeed, the term *anatomy* (derived from the Greek words meaning "to cut apart") relates most closely to gross anatomy because in such studies preserved animals or their organs are dissected (cut up) to be examined.

Gross anatomy can be approached in different ways. In **regional anatomy**, all the structures (muscles, bones, blood vessels, nerves, etc.) in a particular region of the body, such as the abdomen or leg, are examined at the same time.

In **systemic anatomy** (sis-tem′ik),* body structure is studied system by system. For example, when studying the cardiovascular system, you would examine the heart and the blood vessels of the entire body.

Another subdivision of gross anatomy is **surface anatomy**, the study of internal structures as they relate to the overlying skin surface. You use surface anatomy when you identify the

---

*For the pronunciation guide rules, see the first page of the glossary in the back of the book.

bulging muscles beneath a bodybuilder's skin, and clinicians use it to locate appropriate blood vessels in which to feel pulses and draw blood.

Microscopic anatomy deals with structures too small to be seen with the naked eye. For most such studies, exceedingly thin slices of body tissues are stained and mounted on glass slides to be examined under the microscope. Subdivisions of microscopic anatomy include **cytology** (si-tol′o-je), which considers the cells of the body, and **histology** (his-tol′o-je), the study of tissues.

Developmental anatomy traces structural changes that occur in the body throughout the life span. **Embryology** (em″bre-ol′o-je), a subdivision of developmental anatomy, concerns developmental changes that occur before birth.

Some highly specialized branches of anatomy are used primarily for medical diagnosis and scientific research. For example, *pathological anatomy* studies structural changes caused by disease. *Radiographic anatomy* studies internal structures as visualized by X-ray images or specialized scanning procedures.

Subjects of interest to anatomists range from easily seen structures down to the smallest molecule. In *molecular biology*, for example, the structure of biological molecules (chemical substances) is investigated. Molecular biology is actually a separate branch of biology, but it falls under the anatomy umbrella when we push anatomical studies to the subcellular level.

One essential tool for studying anatomy is a mastery of anatomical terminology. Others are observation, manipulation, and, in a living person, *palpation* (feeling organs with your hands) and *auscultation* (listening to organ sounds with a stethoscope). A simple example illustrates how some of these tools work together in an anatomical study.

Let's assume that your topic is freely movable joints of the body. In the laboratory, you will be able to *observe* an animal joint, noting how its parts fit together. You can work the joint (*manipulate* it) to determine its range of motion. Using *anatomical terminology*, you can name its parts and describe how they are related so that other students (and your instructor) will have no trouble understanding you. The list of word roots (at the back of the book) and the glossary will help you with this special vocabulary.

Although you will make most of your observations with the naked eye or with the help of a microscope, medical technology has developed a number of sophisticated tools that can peer into the body without disrupting it. Read about these exciting medical imaging techniques in *A Closer Look* on pp. 16–17.

Topics of Physiology

Like anatomy, physiology has many subdivisions. Most of them consider the operation of specific organ systems. For example, **renal physiology** concerns kidney function and urine production. **Neurophysiology** explains the workings of the nervous system. **Cardiovascular physiology** examines the operation of the heart and blood vessels. While anatomy provides us with a static image of the body's architecture, physiology reveals the body's dynamic and animated workings.

Physiology often focuses on events at the cellular or molecular level. This is because the body's abilities depend on those of its individual cells, and cells' abilities ultimately depend on the chemical reactions that go on within them. Physiology also rests on principles of physics, which help to explain electrical currents, blood pressure, and the way muscles use bones to cause body movements, among other things. We present basic chemical and physical principles in Chapter 2 and throughout the book as needed to explain physiological topics.

Complementarity of Structure and Function

Although it is possible to study anatomy and physiology individually, they are really inseparable because function always reflects structure. That is, what a structure can do depends on its specific form. This key concept is called the **principle of complementarity of structure and function**.

For example, bones can support and protect body organs because they contain hard mineral deposits. Blood flows in one direction through the heart because the heart has valves that prevent backflow. Throughout this book, we accompany a description of a structure's anatomy with an explanation of its function, and we emphasize structural characteristics contributing to that function.

☑ **Check Your Understanding**

1. In what way does physiology depend on anatomy?
2. Would you be studying anatomy or physiology if you investigated how muscles shorten? If you explored the location of the lungs in the body?

For answers, see Appendix H.

Levels of Structural Organization

✓ Name the different levels of structural organization that make up the human body, and explain their relationships.

✓ List the 11 organ systems of the body, identify their components, and briefly explain the major function(s) of each system.

The human body has many levels of structural organization (Figure 1.1). The simplest level of the structural hierarchy is the **chemical level**, which we study in Chapter 2. At this level, *atoms*, tiny building blocks of matter, combine to form *molecules* such as water and proteins. Molecules, in turn, associate in specific ways to form *organelles*, basic components of the microscopic cells. *Cells* are the smallest units of living things. We examine the **cellular level** in Chapter 3. All

cells have some common functions, but individual cells vary widely in size and shape, reflecting their unique functions in the body.

The simplest living creatures are single cells, but in complex organisms such as human beings, the hierarchy continues on to the **tissue level**. *Tissues* are groups of similar cells that have a common function. The four basic tissue types in the human body are epithelium, muscle, connective tissue, and nervous tissue.

Each tissue type has a characteristic role in the body, which we explore in Chapter 4. Briefly, epithelium covers the body surface and lines its cavities. Muscle provides movement. Connective tissue supports and protects body organs. Nervous tissue provides a means of rapid internal communication by transmitting electrical impulses.

An *organ* is a discrete structure composed of at least two tissue types (four is more common) that performs a specific function for the body. The liver, the brain, and a blood vessel are very different from the stomach, but each is an organ. You can think of each organ of the body as a specialized functional center responsible for a necessary activity that no other organ can perform.

At the **organ level**, extremely complex functions become possible. Let's take the stomach for an example. Its lining is an epithelium that produces digestive juices. The bulk of its wall is muscle, which churns and mixes stomach contents (food). Its connective tissue reinforces the soft muscular walls. Its nerve fibers increase digestive activity by stimulating the muscle to contract more vigorously and the glands to secrete more digestive juices.

The next level of organization is the **organ system level**. Organs that work together to accomplish a common purpose make up an *organ system*. For example, the heart and blood vessels of the cardiovascular system circulate blood continuously to carry oxygen and nutrients to all body cells. Besides the cardiovascular system, the other organ systems of the body are the integumentary, skeletal, muscular, nervous, endocrine, lymphatic, respiratory, digestive, urinary, and reproductive systems. (Note that the immune system is closely associated with the lymphatic system.) Look ahead to Figure 1.3 on pp. 6 and 7 for an overview of the 11 organ systems, which we discuss in the next section and study in more detail in Units 2–5.

The highest level of organization is the *organism*, the living human being. The **organismal level** represents the sum total of all structural levels working together to keep us alive.

☑ **Check Your Understanding**

3. What level of structural organization is typical of a cytologist's field of study?
4. What is the correct structural order for the following terms: tissue, organism, organ, cell?
5. Which organ system includes the bones and cartilages? Which includes the nasal cavity, lungs, and trachea?

For answers, see Appendix H.

Atoms

Molecule

Chemical level
Atoms combine to form molecules.

Organelle

Smooth muscle cell

Cellular level
Cells are made up of molecules.

Smooth muscle tissue

Tissue level
Tissues consist of similar types of cells.

Cardiovascular system

Heart

Blood vessels

Blood vessel (organ)

Smooth muscle tissue

Connective tissue

Epithelial tissue

Organ level
Organs are made up of different types of tissues.

Organismal level
The human organism is made up of many organ systems.

Organ system level
Organ systems consist of different organs that work together closely.

Figure 1.1 Levels of structural organization. Components of the cardiovascular system are used to illustrate the levels of structural organization in a human being.

Maintaining Life

✓ List the functional characteristics necessary to maintain life in humans.

✓ List the survival needs of the body.

Necessary Life Functions

Now that you know the structural levels of the human body, the question that naturally follows is: What does this highly organized human body do?

Like all complex animals, humans maintain their boundaries, move, respond to environmental changes, take in and digest nutrients, carry out metabolism, dispose of wastes, reproduce themselves, and grow. We will introduce these necessary life functions here and discuss them in more detail in later chapters.

We cannot emphasize too strongly that all body cells are interdependent. This interdependence is due to the fact that humans are multicellular organisms and our vital body functions are parceled out among different organ systems. Organ systems, in turn, work cooperatively to promote the well-being of the entire body. This theme is repeated throughout the book. Figure 1.2 identifies some of the organ systems making major contributions to necessary life functions. Also, as you read this section, check Figure 1.3 for more detailed descriptions of the body's organ systems.

Maintaining Boundaries

Every living organism must **maintain its boundaries** so that its internal environment (its inside) remains distinct from the external environment surrounding it (its outside). In single-celled organisms, the external boundary is a limiting membrane that encloses its contents and lets in needed substances while restricting entry of potentially damaging or unnecessary substances. Similarly, all the cells of our body are surrounded by a selectively permeable membrane.

Additionally, the body as a whole is enclosed and protected by the integumentary system, or skin (Figure 1.3a). This system protects our internal organs from drying out (a fatal change), bacteria, and the damaging effects of heat, sunlight, and an unbelievable number of chemicals in the external environment.

Movement

Movement includes the activities promoted by the muscular system, such as propelling ourselves from one place to another by running or swimming, and manipulating the external environment with our nimble fingers (Figure 1.3c). The skeletal system provides the bony framework that the muscles pull on as they work (Figure 1.3b). Movement also occurs when substances such as blood, foodstuffs, and urine are propelled through internal organs of the cardiovascular, digestive, and urinary systems, respectively. On the cellular level, the muscle cell's ability to move by shortening is more precisely called **contractility**.

Responsiveness

Responsiveness, or **excitability**, is the ability to sense changes (which serve as stimuli) in the environment and then respond to them. For example, if you cut your hand on broken glass, a withdrawal reflex occurs—you involuntarily pull your hand away from the painful stimulus (the broken glass). You don't have to think about it—it just happens! Likewise, when carbon dioxide in your blood rises to dangerously high levels, chemical sensors respond by sending messages to brain centers controlling respiration, and you breathe more rapidly.

Because nerve cells are highly excitable and communicate rapidly with each other via electrical impulses, the nervous system is most involved with responsiveness (Figure 1.3d). However, all body cells are excitable to some extent.

Digestion

Digestion is the breaking down of ingested foodstuffs to simple molecules that can be absorbed into the blood. The nutrient-rich blood is then distributed to all body cells by the cardiovascular system. In a simple, one-celled organism such as an amoeba,

Digestive system
Takes in nutrients, breaks them down, and eliminates unabsorbed matter (feces)

Respiratory system
Takes in oxygen and eliminates carbon dioxide

Cardiovascular system
Via the blood, distributes oxygen and nutrients to all body cells and delivers wastes and carbon dioxide to disposal organs

Urinary system
Eliminates nitrogenous wastes and excess ions

Integumentary system
Protects the body as a whole from the external environment

Nutrients and wastes pass between blood and cells via the interstitial fluid

Figure 1.2 Examples of interrelationships among body organ systems.

the cell itself is the "digestion factory," but in the multicellular human body, the digestive system performs this function for the entire body (Figure 1.3i).

Metabolism

Metabolism (mĕ-tab′o-lizm; "a state of change") is a broad term that includes all chemical reactions that occur within body cells. It includes breaking down substances into their simpler building blocks (more specifically, the process of *catabolism*), synthesizing more complex cellular structures from simpler substances (*anabolism*), and using nutrients and oxygen to produce (via *cellular respiration*) ATP, the energy-rich molecules that power cellular activities. Metabolism depends on the digestive and respiratory systems to make nutrients and oxygen available to the blood and on the cardiovascular system to distribute them throughout the body (Figure 1.3i, h, and f, respectively). Metabolism is regulated largely by hormones secreted by endocrine system glands (Figure 1.3e).

1

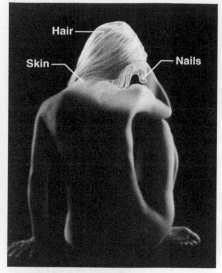

(a) Integumentary System
Forms the external body covering, and protects deeper tissues from injury. Synthesizes vitamin D, and houses cutaneous (pain, pressure, etc.) receptors and sweat and oil glands.

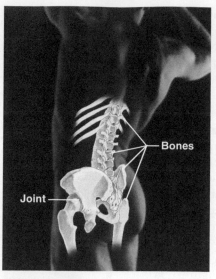

(b) Skeletal System
Protects and supports body organs, and provides a framework the muscles use to cause movement. Blood cells are formed within bones. Bones store minerals.

(c) Muscular System
Allows manipulation of the environment, locomotion, and facial expression. Maintains posture, and produces heat.

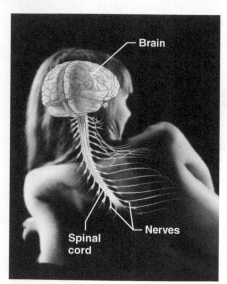

(d) Nervous System
As the fast-acting control system of the body, it responds to internal and external changes by activating appropriate muscles and glands.

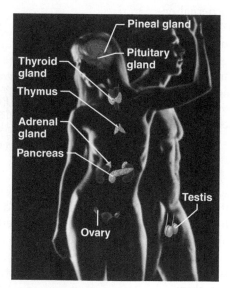

(e) Endocrine System
Glands secrete hormones that regulate processes such as growth, reproduction, and nutrient use (metabolism) by body cells.

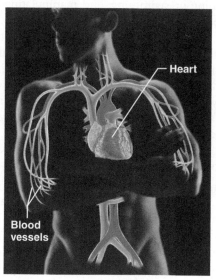

(f) Cardiovascular System
Blood vessels transport blood, which carries oxygen, carbon dioxide, nutrients, wastes, etc. The heart pumps blood.

Figure 1.3 The body's organ systems and their major functions.

Excretion

Excretion is the process of removing wastes, or *excreta* (ek-skre′tah), from the body. If the body is to operate as we expect it to, it must get rid of nonuseful substances produced during digestion and metabolism.

Several organ systems participate in excretion. For example, the digestive system rids the body of indigestible food residues in feces, and the urinary system disposes of nitrogen-containing metabolic wastes, such as urea, in urine (Figure 1.3i and j). Carbon dioxide, a by-product of cellular respiration, is carried in

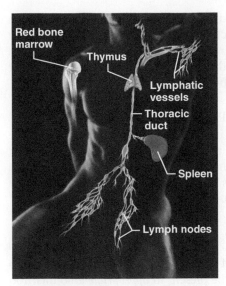

(g) Lymphatic System/Immunity
Picks up fluid leaked from blood vessels and returns it to blood. Disposes of debris in the lymphatic stream. Houses white blood cells (lymphocytes) involved in immunity. The immune response mounts the attack against foreign substances within the body.

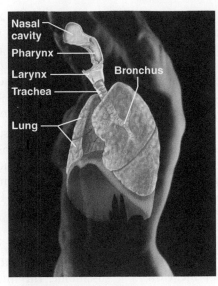

(h) Respiratory System
Keeps blood constantly supplied with oxygen and removes carbon dioxide. The gaseous exchanges occur through the walls of the air sacs of the lungs.

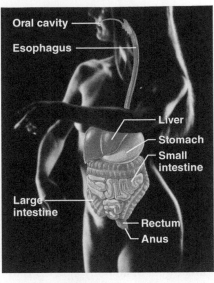

(i) Digestive System
Breaks down food into absorbable units that enter the blood for distribution to body cells. Indigestible foodstuffs are eliminated as feces.

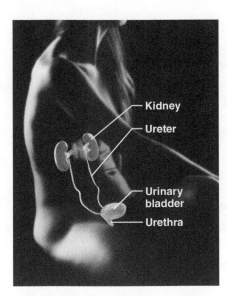

(j) Urinary System
Eliminates nitrogenous wastes from the body. Regulates water, electrolyte and acid-base balance of the blood.

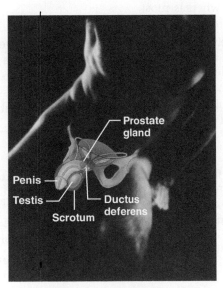

(k) Male Reproductive System
Overall function is production of offspring. Testes produce sperm and male sex hormone, and male ducts and glands aid in delivery of sperm to the female reproductive tract. Ovaries produce eggs and female sex hormones. The remaining female structures serve as sites for fertilization and development of the fetus. Mammary glands of female breasts produce milk to nourish the newborn.

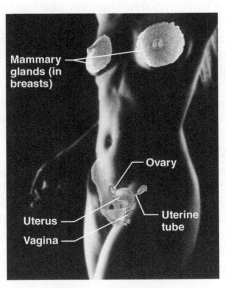

(l) Female Reproductive System

the blood to the lungs, where it leaves the body in exhaled air (Figure 1.3h).

Reproduction

Reproduction occurs at the cellular and the organismal level. In cellular reproduction, the original cell divides, producing two identical daughter cells that may then be used for body growth or repair. Reproduction of the human organism, or making a whole new person, is the major task of the reproductive system. When a sperm unites with an egg, a fertilized egg forms and develops into a baby within the mother's body. The reproductive system is directly responsible for producing offspring, but its function is exquisitely regulated by hormones of the endocrine system (Figure 1.3e).

Because males produce sperm and females produce eggs (ova), there is a division of labor in reproduction, and the reproductive organs of males and females are different (Figure 1.3k, l). Additionally, the female's reproductive structures provide the site for fertilization of eggs by sperm, and then protect and nurture the developing fetus until birth.

Growth

Growth is an increase in size of a body part or the organism as a whole. It is usually accomplished by increasing the number of cells. However, individual cells also increase in size when not dividing. For true growth to occur, constructive activities must occur at a faster rate than destructive ones.

Survival Needs

The ultimate goal of all body systems is to maintain life. However, life is extraordinarily fragile and requires several factors. These factors, which we will call *survival needs*, include nutrients (food), oxygen, water, and appropriate temperature and atmospheric pressure.

Nutrients

Nutrients, taken in via the diet, contain the chemical substances used for energy and cell building. Most plant-derived foods are rich in carbohydrates, vitamins, and minerals, whereas most animal foods are richer in proteins and fats.

Carbohydrates are the major energy fuel for body cells. Proteins, and to a lesser extent fats, are essential for building cell structures. Fats also provide a reserve of energy-rich fuel. Selected minerals and vitamins are required for the chemical reactions that go on in cells and for oxygen transport in the blood. The mineral calcium helps to make bones hard and is required for blood clotting.

Oxygen

All the nutrients in the world are useless unless **oxygen** is also available. Because the chemical reactions that release energy from foods are *oxidative* reactions that require oxygen, human cells can survive for only a few minutes without oxygen. Approximately 20% of the air we breathe is oxygen. The cooperative efforts of the respiratory and cardiovascular systems make oxygen available to the blood and body cells.

Water

Water accounts for 60–80% of our body weight and is the single most abundant chemical substance in the body. It provides the watery environment necessary for chemical reactions and the fluid base for body secretions and excretions. We obtain water chiefly from ingested foods or liquids. We lose it from the body by evaporation from the lungs and skin and in body excretions.

Normal Body Temperature

If chemical reactions are to continue at life-sustaining rates, **normal body temperature** must be maintained. As body temperature drops below 37°C (98.6°F), metabolic reactions become slower and slower, and finally stop. When body temperature is too high, chemical reactions occur at a frantic pace and body proteins lose their characteristic shape and stop functioning. At either extreme, death occurs. The activity of the muscular system generates most body heat.

Appropriate Atmospheric Pressure

Atmospheric pressure is the force that air exerts on the surface of the body. Breathing and gas exchange in the lungs depend on *appropriate* atmospheric pressure. At high altitudes, where atmospheric pressure is lower and the air is thin, gas exchange may be inadequate to support cellular metabolism.

■ ■ ■

The mere presence of these survival factors is not sufficient to sustain life. They must be present in *appropriate* amounts. Too much and too little may be equally harmful. For example, oxygen is essential, but excessive amounts are toxic to body cells. Similarly, the food we eat must be of high quality and in proper amounts. Otherwise, nutritional disease, obesity, or starvation is likely. Also, while the needs listed above are the most crucial, they do not even begin to encompass all of the body's needs. For example, we can live without gravity if we must, but the quality of life suffers.

☑ Check Your Understanding

6. What separates living beings from nonliving objects?
7. What name is given to all chemical reactions that occur within body cells?
8. Why is it necessary to be in a pressurized cabin when flying at 30,000 feet?

For answers, see Appendix H.

Homeostasis

✓ Define homeostasis and explain its significance.

✓ Describe how negative and positive feedback maintain body homeostasis.

✓ Describe the relationship between homeostatic imbalance and disease.

When you think about the fact that your body contains trillions of cells in nearly constant activity, and that remarkably little usually goes wrong with it, you begin to appreciate what a marvelous machine your body is. Walter Cannon, an American physiologist of the early twentieth century, spoke of the "wisdom of the body," and he coined the word **homeostasis** (ho″me-o-sta′sis) to describe its ability to maintain relatively stable internal conditions even though the outside world changes continuously.

Although the literal translation of homeostasis is "unchanging," the term does not really mean a static, or unchanging, state. Rather, it indicates a *dynamic* state of equilibrium, or a balance, in which internal conditions vary, but always within relatively

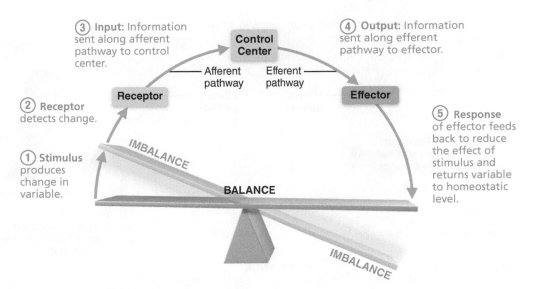

Figure 1.4 Interactions among the elements of a homeostatic control system maintain stable internal conditions.

narrow limits. In general, the body is in homeostasis when its needs are adequately met and it is functioning smoothly.

Maintaining homeostasis is more complicated than it appears at first glance. Virtually every organ system plays a role in maintaining the constancy of the internal environment. Adequate blood levels of vital nutrients must be continuously present, and heart activity and blood pressure must be constantly monitored and adjusted so that the blood is propelled to all body tissues. Also, wastes must not be allowed to accumulate, and body temperature must be precisely controlled. A wide variety of chemical, thermal, and neural factors act and interact in complex ways—sometimes helping and sometimes hindering the body as it works to maintain its "steady rudder."

Homeostatic Control

Communication within the body is essential for homeostasis. Communication is accomplished chiefly by the nervous and endocrine systems, which use neural electrical impulses or blood-borne hormones, respectively, as information carriers. We cover the details of how these two great regulating systems operate in later chapters, but here we explain the basic characteristics of control systems that promote homeostasis.

Regardless of the factor or event being regulated—the **variable**—all homeostatic control mechanisms are processes involving at least three components that work together **(Figure 1.4)**. The first component, the **receptor**, is some type of sensor that monitors the environment and responds to changes, called *stimuli*, by sending information (input) to the second component, the *control center*. Input flows from the receptor to the control center along the so-called *afferent pathway*.

The **control center** determines the *set point*, which is the level or range at which a variable is to be maintained. It also analyzes the input it receives and determines the appropriate response or course of action. Information (output) then flows from the control center to the third component, the *effector*, along the *efferent*

pathway. (To help you remember the difference between "afferent" and "efferent," you might note that information traveling along the afferent pathway *approaches* the control center and efferent information *exits* from the control center.)

The **effector** provides the means for the control center's response (output) to the stimulus. The results of the response then *feed back* to influence the effect of the stimulus, either reducing it (in negative feedback) so that the whole control process is shut off, or enhancing it (in positive feedback) so that the whole process continues at an even faster rate.

Negative Feedback Mechanisms

Most homeostatic control mechanisms are **negative feedback mechanisms**. In these systems, the output shuts off the original effect of the stimulus or reduces its intensity. These mechanisms cause the variable to change in a direction *opposite* to that of the initial change, returning it to its "ideal" value; thus the name "negative" feedback mechanisms.

Let's start with an example of a nonbiological negative feedback system: a home heating system connected to a temperature-sensing thermostat. The thermostat houses both the receptor (thermometer) and the control center. If the thermostat is set at 20°C (68°F), the heating system (effector) is triggered ON when the house temperature drops below that setting. As the furnace produces heat and warms the air, the temperature rises, and when it reaches 20°C or slightly higher, the thermostat triggers the furnace OFF. This process results in a cycling of "furnace-ON" and "furnace-OFF" so that the temperature in the house stays very near the desired temperature of 20°C. Your body "thermostat," located in a part of your brain called the hypothalamus, operates in a similar fashion **(Figure 1.5)**.

Regulation of body temperature is only one of the many ways the nervous system maintains the constancy of the internal environment. Another type of neural control mechanism is seen in the *withdrawal reflex* mentioned earlier, in which the hand is jerked away from a painful stimulus such as broken glass.

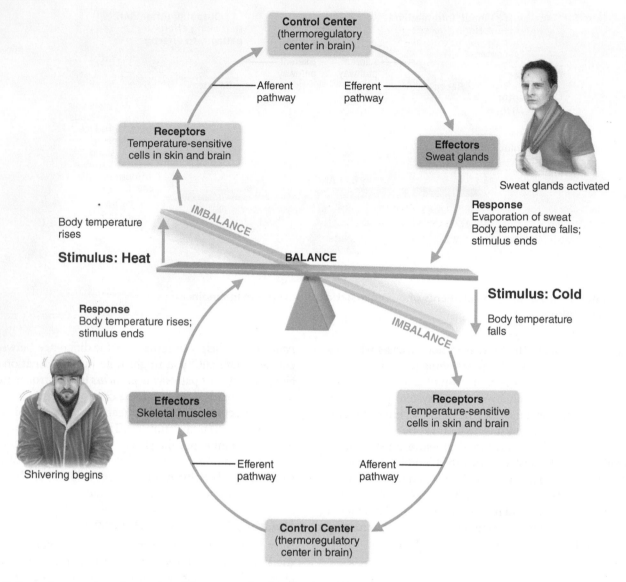

Figure 1.5 Body temperature is regulated by a negative feedback mechanism.

The endocrine system is equally important in maintaining homeostasis. A good example of a hormonal negative feedback mechanism is the control of blood sugar (glucose) by insulin. As blood sugar rises, receptors in the body sense this change, and the pancreas (the control center) secretes insulin into the blood. This change in turn prompts body cells to absorb more glucose, removing it from the bloodstream. As blood sugar falls, the stimulus for insulin release ends. The body's ability to regulate its internal environment is fundamental. All negative feedback mechanisms have the same goal: preventing sudden severe changes within the body. Body temperature and blood volume are only two of the variables that need to be regulated. There are hundreds! Other negative feedback mechanisms regulate heart rate, blood pressure, the rate and depth of breathing, and blood levels of oxygen, carbon dioxide, and minerals. Now, let's take a look at the other type of feedback control mechanism—positive feedback.

Positive Feedback Mechanisms

In **positive feedback mechanisms**, the result or response enhances the original stimulus so that the response is accelerated. This feedback mechanism is "positive" because the change that results proceeds in the *same* direction as the initial change, causing the variable to deviate further and further from its original value or range.

In contrast to negative feedback controls, which maintain some physiological function or keep blood chemicals within narrow ranges, positive feedback mechanisms usually control infrequent events that do not require continuous adjustments. Typically, they set off a series of events that may be self-perpetuating and that, once initiated, have an amplifying or waterfall effect. Because of these characteristics, positive feedback mechanisms are often referred to as *cascades* (from the Italian word meaning "to fall"). Two familiar examples of their use as homeostatic mechanisms are the enhancement of labor contractions during birth and blood clotting.

Chapter 28 describes the positive feedback mechanism in which oxytocin, a hypothalamic hormone, intensifies labor contractions during the birth of a baby (see Figure 28.17). Oxytocin causes the contractions to become both more frequent and more powerful. The increased contractions cause more oxytocin to be released, which causes more contractions, and so on until the baby is finally born. The birth ends the stimulus for oxytocin release and shuts off the positive feedback mechanism.

Blood clotting is a normal response to a break in the wall of a blood vessel and is an excellent example of an important body function controlled by positive feedback. Basically, once a vessel has been damaged, blood elements called platelets immediately begin to cling to the injured site and release chemicals that attract more platelets. This rapidly growing pileup of platelets temporarily "plugs" the tear and initiates the sequence of events that finally forms a clot **(Figure 1.6)**. Positive feedback mechanisms are likely to race out of control, so they are rarely used to promote the moment-to-moment well-being of the body. However, some positive feedback mechanisms, including this one, may have only local reach. For example, blood clotting is accelerated in injured vessels, but does not normally spread to the entire circulation.

Homeostatic Imbalance

Homeostasis is so important that most disease can be regarded as a result of its disturbance, a condition called **homeostatic imbalance**. As we age, our body's control systems become less efficient, and our internal environment becomes less and less stable. These events increase our risk for illness and produce the changes we associate with aging.

Another important source of homeostatic imbalance occurs when the usual negative feedback mechanisms are overwhelmed and destructive positive feedback mechanisms take over. Some instances of heart failure reflect this phenomenon.

Examples of homeostatic imbalance appear throughout this book to enhance your understanding of normal physiological mechanisms. This symbol ⚖ introduces the homeostatic imbalance sections and alerts you to the fact that we are describing an abnormal condition. Each Homeostatic Imbalance section is numbered to correspond with critical thinking questions available in the Study Area of MasteringA&P—visit www.masteringaandp.com to find Homeostatic Imbalance questions and other helpful study tools. (MAP)

☑ Check Your Understanding

9. What process allows us to adjust to either extreme heat or extreme cold?
10. When we begin to get dehydrated, we usually get thirsty, which causes us to drink fluids. Is thirst part of a negative or a positive feedback control system? Defend your choice.
11. Why is the control mechanism shown in Figure 1.6 called a positive feedback system? What event ends it?

For answers, see Appendix H.

① Break or tear occurs in blood vessel wall.

Positive feedback cycle is initiated.

③ Released chemicals attract more platelets.

Positive feedback loop

② Platelets adhere to site and release chemicals.

Feedback cycle ends when plug is formed.

④ Platelet plug is fully formed.

Figure 1.6 A positive feedback mechanism regulates formation of a platelet plug.

The Language of Anatomy

✓ Describe the anatomical position.

✓ Use correct anatomical terms to describe body directions, regions, and body planes or sections.

Most of us are naturally curious about our bodies, but our interest sometimes dwindles when we are confronted with the terminology of anatomy and physiology. Let's face it—you can't just pick up an anatomy and physiology book and read it as though it were a novel.

Unfortunately, confusion is likely without precise, specialized terminology. To prevent misunderstanding, anatomists use universally accepted terms to identify body structures precisely and with a minimum of words. We present and explain the language of anatomy next.

Anatomical Position and Directional Terms

To describe body parts and position accurately, we need an initial reference point, and we must indicate direction. The anatomical reference point is a standard body position called the **anatomical position**. In the anatomical position, the body is erect with feet slightly apart. This position is easy to remember because it resembles "standing at attention," except that the palms face

Table 1.1   Orientation and Directional Terms

TERM	DEFINITION	EXAMPLE	
Superior (cranial)	Toward the head end or upper part of a structure or the body; above		The head is superior to the abdomen.
Inferior (caudal)	Away from the head end or toward the lower part of a structure or the body; below		The navel is inferior to the chin.
Ventral (anterior)*	Toward or at the front of the body; in front of		The breastbone is anterior to the spine.
Dorsal (posterior)*	Toward or at the back of the body; behind		The heart is posterior to the breastbone.
Medial	Toward or at the midline of the body; on the inner side of		The heart is medial to the arm.
Lateral	Away from the midline of the body; on the outer side of		The arms are lateral to the chest.
Intermediate	Between a more medial and a more lateral structure		The collarbone is intermediate between the breastbone and shoulder.
Proximal	Closer to the origin of the body part or the point of attachment of a limb to the body trunk		The elbow is proximal to the wrist.
Distal	Farther from the origin of a body part or the point of attachment of a limb to the body trunk		The knee is distal to the thigh.
Superficial (external)	Toward or at the body surface		The skin is superficial to the skeletal muscles.
Deep (internal)	Away from the body surface; more internal		The lungs are deep to the skin.

*The terms *ventral* and *anterior* are synonymous in humans, but this is not the case in four-legged animals. *Anterior* refers to the leading portion of the body (abdominal surface in humans, head in a cat), but *ventral* specifically refers to the "belly" of a vertebrate animal, so it is the inferior surface of four-legged animals. Likewise, although the dorsal and posterior surfaces are the same in humans, the term *dorsal* specifically refers to an animal's back. Thus, the dorsal surface of four-legged animals is their superior surface.

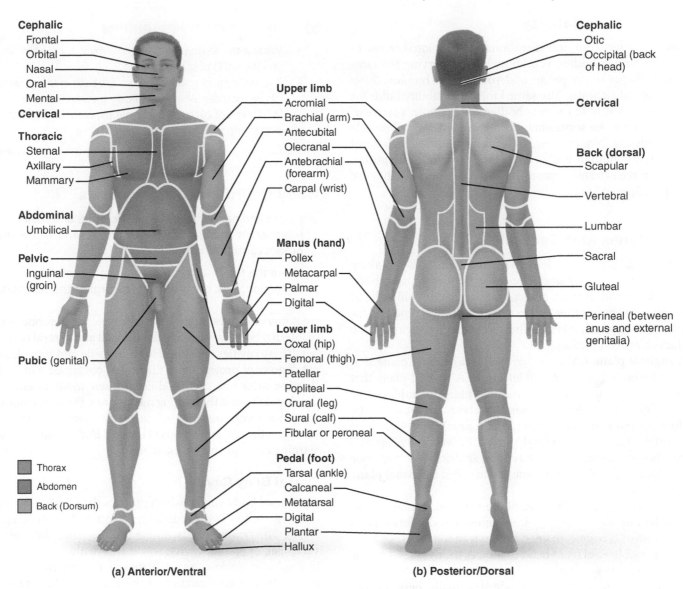

Figure 1.7 Regional terms used to designate specific body areas. (a) The anatomical position. **(b)** The heels are raised to show the plantar surface of the foot, which is actually on the inferior surface of the body.

forward and the thumbs point away from the body. You can see the anatomical position in **Table 1.1** (top) and **Figure 1.7a**.

It is essential to understand the anatomical position because most of the directional terms used in this book refer to the body *as if it were in this position, regardless of its actual position*. Another point to remember is that the terms "right" and "left" refer to those sides of the person or the cadaver (body of a deceased person) being viewed—not those of the observer.

Directional terms allow us to explain where one body structure is in relation to another. For example, we could describe the relationship between the ears and the nose informally by stating, "The ears are located on each side of the head to the right and left of the nose." Using anatomical terminology, we can condense this to "The ears are lateral to the nose." Using anatomical terms saves words and is less ambiguous.

Commonly used orientation and directional terms are defined and illustrated in Table 1.1. Many of these terms are also used in everyday conversation, but keep in mind as you study them that their anatomical meanings are very precise.

Regional Terms

The two fundamental divisions of our body are its *axial* and *appendicular* (ap″en-dik′u-lar) parts. The **axial part**, which makes up the main *axis* of our body, includes the head, neck, and trunk. The **appendicular part** consists of the *appendages*, or *limbs*, which are attached to the body's axis. **Regional terms** used to designate specific areas within these major body divisions are indicated in Figure 1.7. The common terms for a few of these body regions are given in parentheses.

Anatomical Variability

Although we use common directional and regional terms to refer to all human bodies, you know from observing the faces and body shapes of people around you that we humans differ in our external anatomy. The same kind of variability holds for internal organs as well. In some bodies, for example, a nerve or blood vessel may be somewhat out of place, or a small muscle may be missing. Nonetheless, well over 90% of all structures present in any human body match the textbook descriptions. We seldom see extreme anatomical variations because they are incompatible with life.

Body Planes and Sections

For anatomical studies, the body is often cut, or *sectioned*, along a flat surface called a *plane*. The most frequently used body planes are *sagittal*, *frontal*, and *transverse* planes, which lie at right angles to one another (**Figure 1.8**). A section is named for the plane along which it is cut. Thus, a cut along a sagittal plane produces a sagittal section.

A **sagittal plane** (saj′ĭ-tal; "arrow") is a vertical plane that divides the body into right and left parts. A sagittal plane that lies exactly in the midline is the **median plane**, or **midsagittal plane** (Figure 1.8c). All other sagittal planes, offset from the midline, are **parasagittal planes** (*para* = near).

Frontal planes, like sagittal planes, lie vertically. Frontal planes, however, divide the body into anterior and posterior parts (Figure 1.8a). A frontal plane is also called a **coronal plane** (kŏ-ro′nal; "crown").

A **transverse**, or **horizontal**, **plane** runs horizontally from right to left, dividing the body into superior and inferior parts (Figure 1.8b). Of course, many different transverse planes exist, at every possible level from head to foot. A transverse section is also called a **cross section**.

Oblique sections are cuts made diagonally between the horizontal and the vertical planes. Because oblique sections are often confusing and difficult to interpret, they are seldom used.

At the bottom of Figure 1.8, you can see examples of magnetic resonance imaging (MRI) scans that correspond to the three different sections shown in the figure. Clinically, the ability to interpret sections made through the body, especially transverse sections, is important. Additionally, the new medical imaging devices (*A Closer Look*, pp. 16–17) produce sectional images rather than three-dimensional images.

It takes practice to determine or figure out an object's overall shape from sectioned material. A cross section of a banana, for example, looks like a circle and gives no indication of the whole banana's crescent shape. Likewise, sectioning the body or an organ along different planes often results in very different views. For example, a transverse section of the body trunk at the level of the kidneys would show kidney structure in cross section very nicely. A frontal section of the body trunk would show a different view of kidney anatomy, and a midsagittal section would miss the kidneys completely. With experience, you will gradually learn to relate two-dimensional sections to three-dimensional shapes.

☑ **Check Your Understanding**

12. What is the anatomical position? Why is it important that *you* learn this position?
13. The axillary and acromial regions are both in the general area of the shoulder. Where specifically is each located?
14. What type of cut would separate the brain into anterior and posterior parts?

For answers, see Appendix H.

Body Cavities and Membranes

✓ Locate and name the major body cavities and their subdivisions and associated membranes, and list the major organs contained within them.

✓ Name the four quadrants or nine regions of the abdominopelvic cavity and list the organs they contain.

Anatomy and physiology textbooks typically describe two sets of internal body cavities called the dorsal and ventral body cavities. These cavities are closed to the outside and provide different degrees of protection to the organs contained within them. Because these two cavities differ in their mode of embryonic development, and their lining membranes, the dorsal body cavity is not recognized as such in many anatomical references. However, the idea of two sets of internal body cavities is a useful learning concept and we use it here.

Dorsal Body Cavity

The **dorsal body cavity**, which protects the fragile nervous system organs, has two subdivisions (**Figure 1.9**, on p. 18, gold areas). The **cranial cavity**, in the skull, encases the brain. The **vertebral**, or **spinal**, **cavity**, which runs within the bony vertebral column, encloses the delicate spinal cord. The spinal cord is essentially a continuation of the brain, and the cranial and spinal cavities are continuous with one another.

Ventral Body Cavity

The more anterior and larger of the closed body cavities is the **ventral body cavity** (Figure 1.9, deep-red areas). Like the dorsal cavity, it has two major subdivisions, the *thoracic cavity* and the *abdominopelvic cavity*. The ventral body cavity houses internal organs collectively called the **viscera** (vis′er-ah; *viscus* = an organ in a body cavity), or visceral organs.

The superior subdivision, the **thoracic cavity** (tho-ras′ik), is surrounded by the ribs and muscles of the chest. The thoracic cavity is further subdivided into lateral **pleural cavities** (ploo′ral), each enveloping a lung, and the medial **mediastinum** (me″de-ah-sti′num). The mediastinum contains the **pericardial cavity** (per″ĭ-kar′de-al), which encloses the heart, and it also surrounds the remaining thoracic organs (esophagus, trachea, and others).

The thoracic cavity is separated from the more inferior **abdominopelvic cavity** (ab-dom′ĭ-no-pel′vic) by the diaphragm, a dome-shaped muscle important in breathing. The abdominopelvic cavity, as its name suggests, has two parts. However,

(Text continues on p. 18.)

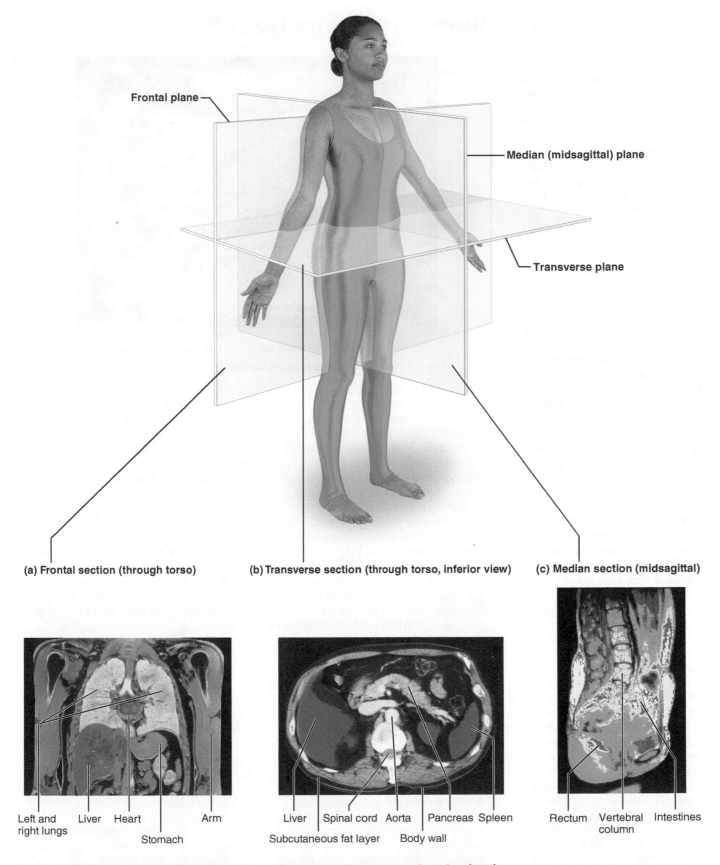

Frontal plane

Median (midsagittal) plane

Transverse plane

(a) Frontal section (through torso)

(b) Transverse section (through torso, inferior view)

(c) Median section (midsagittal)

Left and right lungs Liver Heart Stomach Arm

Liver Spinal cord Aorta Pancreas Spleen Subcutaneous fat layer Body wall

Rectum Vertebral column Intestines

Figure 1.8 Planes of the body with corresponding magnetic resonance imaging (MRI) scans.

Medical Imaging: Illuminating the Body

Until 50 years ago, the magical but murky X ray was the only nonsurgical means to extract information from within a living body. Produced by directing X rays, electromagnetic waves of very short wavelength, at the body, an **X ray** or **radiograph** is essentially a shadowy negative image of internal structures. Dense structures absorb the X rays most and so appear as light areas. Hollow air-containing organs and fat, which absorb the X rays less, show up as dark areas. What X rays do best is visualize hard, bony structures and locate abnormally dense structures (tumors, tuberculosis nodules) in the lungs.

The 1950s saw the advent of ultrasound and of nuclear medicine, which uses radioisotopes to scan the body to not only reveal the structure of our "insides" but also wring out information about the hidden workings of their molecules.

Computed tomography (**CT**, formerly called **computerized axial tomography**, **CAT**) uses a refined version of X-ray equipment. As the patient is slowly moved through the doughnut-shaped CT machine, its X-ray tube rotates around the body and sends beams from all directions to a specific level of the patient's body. Because at any moment its beam is confined to a "slice" of the body about as thick as a dime, CT ends the confusion resulting from overlapping structures seen in conventional X rays. The device's computer translates this information into a detailed, cross-sectional picture of each body region scanned. CT scans are at the forefront for evaluating most problems that affect the brain and abdomen. Their clarity, illustrated in photo (a), has all but eliminated exploratory surgery.

Xenon CT is a CT brain scan enhanced with radioactive xenon gas to quickly trace blood flow. Inhaled xenon rapidly enters the bloodstream and distributes to different body tissues in proportion to their blood flow. Absence of xenon from part of the brain indicates that a stroke is occurring there, information that aids treatment.

Dynamic spatial reconstruction (DSR) uses ultrafast CT scanners to provide three-dimensional images of body organs from any angle, and scrutinize their movements and changes in their internal volumes at normal speed, in slow motion, and at a specific moment. DSR's greatest value has been to visualize the heart beating and blood flowing through blood vessels. This information

(a) A CT scan through the superior abdomen.

Liver Vertebra Pancreas Left kidney Spleen

allows clinicians to evaluate heart defects, constricted or blocked blood vessels, and the status of coronary bypass grafts.

Another computer-assisted X-ray technique, **digital subtraction angiography (DSA)** (*angiography* = vessel pictures), provides an unobstructed view of small arteries. Conventional radiographs are taken before and after a contrast medium is injected into an artery. The computer subtracts the "before" image from the "after" image, eliminating all traces of body structures that obscure the vessel. DSA is often used to identify blockages in the arteries that supply the heart wall, as in photo (b), and in the brain.

Just as the X ray spawned related technologies, so too did nuclear medicine in the form of **positron emission tomography (PET)**. PET excels in observing *metabolic processes*. The patient is given an injection of radioisotopes tagged to biological molecules (such as glucose) and is then positioned in the PET scanner. As the radioisotopes are absorbed by the most active brain cells, high-energy gamma rays are produced. The computer analyzes the gamma-ray emission and produces a live-action picture of the brain's biochemical activity in vivid colors. PET's greatest value has been its ability to provide insights into brain activity in people affected by mental illness, stroke, Alzheimer's disease, and epilepsy. One of its most exciting uses has been to determine which areas of the healthy brain

are most active during certain tasks (e.g., speaking, listening to music, or figuring out a mathematical problem), providing direct evidence of the functions of specific brain regions. Currently PET can reveal signs of trouble in those with undiagnosed Alzheimer's disease (AD) because regions of beta-amyloid accumulation (a defining characteristic of AD) show up in brilliant red and yellow, as in photo (c). PET scans can also help to predict who may develop AD in the future by identifying areas of decreased metabolism in crucial memory areas of the brain.

Sonography, or **ultrasound imaging**, has some distinct advantages over the approaches examined so far. The equipment is inexpensive, and the ultrasound used as its energy source seems to be safer than the ionizing forms of radiation used in nuclear medicine. The body is probed with pulses of sound waves that cause echoes when reflected and scattered by body tissues. A computer analyzes these echoes to construct somewhat blurry outlines of body organs. A single easy-to-use handheld device emits the sound and picks up the echoes, so sections can be scanned from many different body planes.

Because of its safety, ultrasound is the imaging technique of choice in obstetrics for determining fetal age and position and locating the placenta. However, sound waves have low penetrating power and rapidly dissipate in air, so sonography

(b) A DSA image of the arteries that supply the heart.

Narrowing of artery

Artery supplying heart

Max

Min

(c) In a PET scan, regions of beta-amyloid accumulation "light up" (red-yellow) in an Alzheimer's patient (*left*) but not in a healthy person (*right*).

is of little value for looking at air-filled structures (the lungs) or those surrounded by bone (the brain and spinal cord).

Magnetic resonance imaging (MRI) produces high-contrast images of our soft tissues, an area in which X rays and CT scans are weak. As initially developed, MRI primarily maps the body's content of hydrogen, most of which is in water. The technique subjects the body to magnetic fields up to 60,000 times stronger than that of the earth to pry information from the body's molecules. The patient lies in a chamber within a huge magnet. Hydrogen molecules act like tiny magnets, spinning like tops in the magnetic field. Their energy is further enhanced by radio waves, and when the radio waves are turned off, the energy released is translated into a visual image.

MRI distinguishes body tissues based on their water content, so it can differentiate between the fatty white matter and the more watery gray matter of the brain. Because dense structures do not show up at all in MRI, it peers easily into the skull and vertebral column, enabling the delicate nerve fibers of the spinal cord to be seen. MRI is also particularly good at detecting tumors and degenerative disease. Multiple sclerosis plaques do not show up well in CT scans, but are dazzlingly clear in MRI scans. MRI can also tune in on metabolic reactions, such as processes that generate energy-rich ATP molecules.

Until recently, trying to diagnose asthma and other lung problems has been off limits to MRI scans because the lungs have a low water content. However, an alternate tack—filling the lungs with a gas that can be magnetized (hyperpolarized helium-3 or xenon-129)—has yielded spectacular pictures

of the lungs in just the few seconds it takes the patient to inhale, hold the breath briefly, and then exhale. This technique offers a distinct improvement over the hours required for conventional MRI and it has the additional advantage of using a magnetic field as little as one-tenth that of the conventional MRI. Lately, MRI scans have become the "diagnostic darling" in emergency rooms for their ability to accurately diagnose heart attacks or ischemic strokes—conditions that require rapid treatment to prevent fatal consequences. Also exciting are the so-called **bloodless MRIs** currently being tested in animals, which measure water flow instead of blood flow.

Newer variations of MRI include **magnetic resonance spectroscopy (MRS)**, which maps the distribution of elements other than hydrogen to reveal more about how disease changes body chemistry. Other advances in computer techniques display MRI scans in three dimensions to guide laser surgery.

The **functional MRI** tracks blood flow into the brain in real time. Prior to the 1990s, matching thoughts, deeds, and disease to brain activity was the sole domain of PET. Because functional MRI does not require injections of tracers and can pinpoint much smaller brain areas than PET, it may provide a desirable alternative and has transformed neuroscience. Clinical studies are also using functional MRI to determine if a patient in the vegetative state has conscious thought. However, some researchers worry that the brightly colored images explain little about the mechanisms of human thought—that is, it is not possible to assume a particular mental state from the activation of a particular brain region.

Despite its advantages, the powerful magnets of the clanging, claustrophobia-inducing MRI present some thorny problems. For example, they can "suck" metal objects, such as implanted pacemakers and loose tooth fillings, through the body. Moreover, although such strong magnetic fields are currently considered safe, there is no convincing evidence that they are risk free.

Although stunning, medical images other than straight X rays are abstractions assembled within the "mind" of a computer. They are artificially enhanced for sharpness and artificially colored to increase contrast (all their colors are "phony"). The images are several steps removed from direct observation.

As you can see, medical science offers remarkable diagnostic tools. Consider the **M2A Swallowable Imaging Capsule**, a tiny camera that a patient swallows like a pill, and then excretes normally 8–72 hours later. As the M2A travels through the digestive tract, it photographs the small intestine and beams the color images to a small video data recorder worn on a belt or harness. A study found the device to be 60% effective at detecting intestinal problems, compared to a 35% success rate with other imaging techniques. At present the M2A can provide images only of the small intestine because the battery gives out before it enters the large intestine.

New imaging technologies also make long-distance surgery possible. Visual images of a diseased organ travel via fiber-optic cable to surgeons at another location (even a different country), who manipulate delicate robotic instruments to remove the organ.

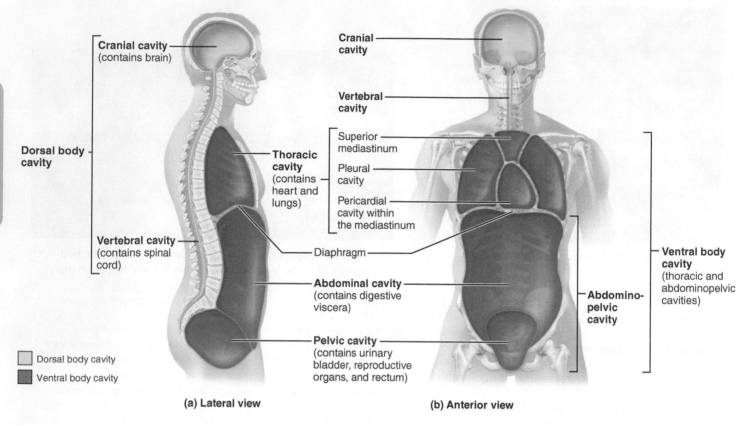

(a) Lateral view

(b) Anterior view

Figure 1.9 Dorsal and ventral body cavities and their subdivisions.

these regions are not physically separated by a muscular or membrane wall. Its superior portion, the **abdominal cavity**, contains the stomach, intestines, spleen, liver, and other organs. The inferior part, the **pelvic cavity**, lies in the bony pelvis and contains the urinary bladder, some reproductive organs, and the rectum. The abdominal and pelvic cavities are not aligned with each other. Instead, the bowl-shaped pelvis tips away from the perpendicular as shown in Figure 1.9a.

Homeostatic Imbalance 1.1

When the body is subjected to physical trauma (as in an automobile accident), the abdominopelvic organs are most vulnerable. Why? This is because the walls of the abdominal cavity are formed only by trunk muscles and are not reinforced by bone. The pelvic organs receive a somewhat greater degree of protection from the bony pelvis. ✚

Membranes in the Ventral Body Cavity   The walls of the ventral body cavity and the outer surfaces of the organs it contains are covered by a thin, double-layered membrane, the **serosa** (se-ro'sah), or **serous membrane**. The part of the membrane lining the cavity walls is called the **parietal serosa** (pah-ri'ĕ-tal; *parie* = wall). It folds in on itself to form the **visceral serosa**, covering the organs in the cavity.

You can visualize the relationship between the serosal layers by pushing your fist into a limp balloon **(Figure 1.10a)**. The

part of the balloon that clings to your fist can be compared to the visceral serosa clinging to an organ's external surface. The outer wall of the balloon then represents the parietal serosa that lines the walls of the cavity. (However, unlike the balloon, the parietal serosa is never exposed but is always fused to the cavity wall.) In the body, the serous membranes are separated not by air but by a thin layer of lubricating fluid, called **serous fluid**, which is secreted by both membranes. Although there is a potential space between the two membranes, the barely present, slitlike cavity is filled with serous fluid.

The slippery serous fluid allows the organs to slide without friction across the cavity walls and one another as they carry out their routine functions. This freedom of movement is especially important for mobile organs such as the pumping heart and the churning stomach.

The serous membranes are named for the specific cavity and organs with which they are associated. For example, as shown in Figure 1.10b, the *parietal pericardium* lines the pericardial cavity and folds back as the *visceral pericardium*, which covers the heart. Likewise, the *parietal pleurae* (ploo're) line the walls of the thoracic cavity, and the *visceral pleurae* cover the lungs. The *parietal peritoneum* (per"ĭ-to-ne'um) is associated with the walls of the abdominopelvic cavity, while the *visceral peritoneum* covers most of the organs within that cavity. (The pleural and peritoneal serosae are illustrated in Figure 4.11c on p. 141.)

(a) **A fist thrust into a flaccid balloon demonstrates the relationship between the parietal and visceral serous membrane layers.**

- Outer balloon wall (comparable to parietal serosa)
- Air (comparable to serous cavity)
- Inner balloon wall (comparable to visceral serosa)

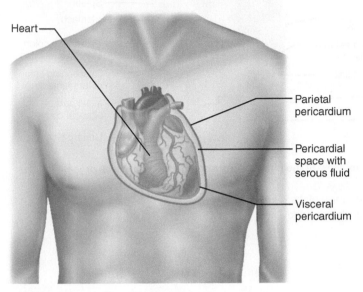

Heart

- Parietal pericardium
- Pericardial space with serous fluid
- Visceral pericardium

(b) **The serosae associated with the heart.**

Figure 1.10 Serous membrane relationships.

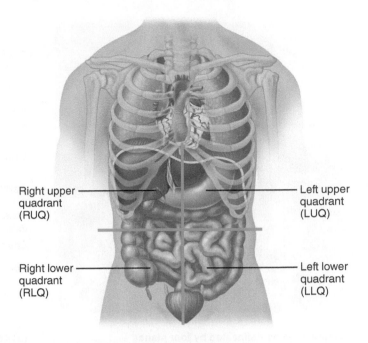

Figure 1.11 The four abdominopelvic quadrants. In this scheme, the abdominopelvic cavity is divided into four quadrants by two planes.

- Right upper quadrant (RUQ)
- Left upper quadrant (LUQ)
- Right lower quadrant (RLQ)
- Left lower quadrant (LLQ)

Homeostatic Imbalance 1.2

When serous membranes are inflamed, their normally smooth surfaces become roughened. This roughness causes the organs to stick together and drag across one another, leading to excruciating pain, as anyone who has experienced *pleurisy* (inflammation of the pleurae) or *peritonitis* (inflammation of the peritoneums) knows. ✚

Abdominopelvic Regions and Quadrants Because the abdominopelvic cavity is large and contains several organs, it helps to divide it into smaller areas for study. Medical personnel usually use a simple scheme to locate the abdominopelvic cavity organs **(Figure 1.11)**. In this scheme, a transverse and a median plane pass through the umbilicus at right angles. The four resulting quadrants are named according to their positions from the subject's point of view: the **right upper quadrant (RUQ)**, **left upper quadrant (LUQ)**, **right lower quadrant (RLQ)**, and **left lower quadrant (LLQ)**.

Another division method, used primarily by anatomists, uses two transverse and two parasagittal planes. These planes, positioned like a tic-tac-toe grid on the abdomen, divide the cavity into nine regions **(Figure 1.12)**:

- The **umbilical region** is the centermost region deep to and surrounding the umbilicus (navel).
- The **epigastric region** is located superior to the umbilical region (*epi* = upon, above; *gastri* = belly).
- The **hypogastric (pubic) region** is located inferior to the umbilical region (*hypo* = below).
- The **right** and **left iliac**, or **inguinal**, **regions** (ing′gwĭ-nal) are located lateral to the hypogastric region (*iliac* = superior part of the hip bone).
- The **right** and **left lumbar regions** lie lateral to the umbilical region (*lumbus* = loin).
- The **right** and **left hypochondriac regions** lie lateral to the epigastric region and deep to the ribs (*chondro* = cartilage).

Other Body Cavities

In addition to the large closed body cavities, there are several smaller body cavities. Most of these are in the head and most open to the body exterior. Figure 1.7 provides the terms that will help you locate all but the last two cavities mentioned here.

- **Oral and digestive cavities.** The oral cavity, commonly called the mouth, contains the teeth and tongue. This cavity is part of and continuous with the cavity of the digestive organs, which opens to the body exterior at the anus.
- **Nasal cavity.** Located within and posterior to the nose, the nasal cavity is part of the respiratory system passageways.
- **Orbital cavities.** The orbital cavities (orbits) in the skull house the eyes and present them in an anterior position.

(a) Nine regions delineated by four planes

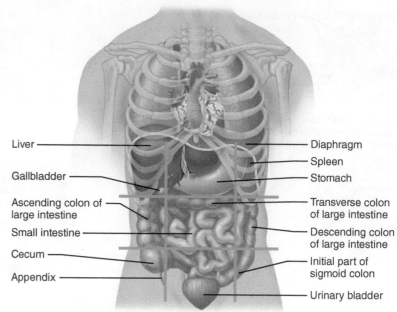

Liver
Gallbladder
Ascending colon of large intestine
Small intestine
Cecum
Appendix

Diaphragm
Spleen
Stomach
Transverse colon of large intestine
Descending colon of large intestine
Initial part of sigmoid colon
Urinary bladder

(b) Anterior view of the nine regions showing the superficial organs

Figure 1.12 The nine abdominopelvic regions. In **(a)** the superior transverse plane is just inferior to the ribs; the inferior transverse plane is just superior to the hip bones; and the parasagittal planes lie just medial to the nipples.

- **Middle ear cavities.** The middle ear cavities in the skull lie just medial to the eardrums. These cavities contain tiny bones that transmit sound vibrations to the hearing receptors in the inner ears.

- **Synovial cavities.** Synovial (sĭ-no′ve-al) cavities are joint cavities. They are enclosed within fibrous capsules that surround freely movable joints of the body (such as the elbow and knee joints). Like the serous membranes, membranes lining synovial cavities secrete a lubricating fluid that reduces friction as the bones move across one another.

☑ **Check Your Understanding**

15. Joe went to the emergency room where he complained of severe pains in the lower right quadrant of his abdomen. What might be his problem?
16. Of the uterus, small intestine, spinal cord, and heart, which is/are in the dorsal body cavity?
17. When you rub your cold hands together, the friction between them results in heat that warms your hands. Why doesn't warming friction result during movements of the heart, lungs, and digestive organs?

For answers, see Appendix H.

Chapter Summary

 For more chapter study tools, go to the Study Area of MasteringA&P at **www.masteringaandp.com**.
There you will find:
- Interactive Physiology **iP**
- A&PFlix **A&PFlix**
- Practice Anatomy Lab PAL
- PhysioEx **PEx**
- Videos, Practice Quizzes and Tests, MP3 Tutor Sessions, Case Studies, and much more!

An Overview of Anatomy and Physiology (pp. 2–3)

1. Anatomy is the study of body structures and their relationships. Physiology is the science of how body parts function.

Topics of Anatomy (p. 2)

2. Major subdivisions of anatomy include gross anatomy, microscopic anatomy, and developmental anatomy.

Topics of Physiology (pp. 2–3)

3. Typically, physiology concerns the functioning of specific organs or organ systems. Examples include cardiac physiology, renal physiology, and muscle physiology.

4. Physiology is explained by chemical and physical principles.

Complementarity of Structure and Function (p. 3)

5. Anatomy and physiology are inseparable: What a body can do depends on the unique architecture of its parts. This principle is called the complementarity of structure and function.

Levels of Structural Organization (pp. 3–4)

1. The levels of structural organization of the body, from simplest to most complex, are: chemical, cellular, tissue, organ, organ system, and organismal.
2. The 11 organ systems of the body are the integumentary, skeletal, muscular, nervous, endocrine, cardiovascular, lymphatic, respiratory, digestive, urinary, and reproductive systems. The immune system is a functional system closely associated with the lymphatic system. (For functions of these systems see pp. 6–7.)

Maintaining Life (pp. 4–8)

Necessary Life Functions (pp. 4–8)

1. All living organisms carry out certain vital functional activities necessary for life, including maintenance of boundaries, movement, responsiveness, digestion, metabolism, excretion, reproduction, and growth.

Survival Needs (p. 8)

2. Survival needs include nutrients, water, oxygen, and appropriate temperature and atmospheric pressure.

Homeostasis (pp. 8–11)

1. Homeostasis is a dynamic equilibrium of the internal environment. All body systems contribute to homeostasis, but the nervous and endocrine systems are most important. Homeostasis is necessary for health.

Homeostatic Control (pp. 9–11)

2. Control mechanisms of the body contain at least three elements that work together: receptor(s), control center, and effector(s).
3. Negative feedback mechanisms reduce the effect of the original stimulus, and are essential for maintaining homeostasis. Body temperature, heart rate, breathing rate and depth, and blood levels of glucose and certain ions are regulated by negative feedback mechanisms.
4. Positive feedback mechanisms intensify the initial stimulus, leading to an enhancement of the response. They rarely contribute to homeostasis, but blood clotting and labor contractions are regulated by such mechanisms.

Homeostatic Imbalance (p. 11)

5. With age, the efficiency of negative feedback mechanisms declines, and positive feedback mechanisms occur more frequently. These changes underlie certain disease conditions.

The Language of Anatomy (pp. 11–20)

Anatomical Position and Directional Terms (pp. 11–13)

1. In the anatomical position, the body is erect, facing forward, feet slightly apart, arms at sides with palms forward.
2. Directional terms allow body parts to be located precisely. Terms that describe body directions and orientation include: superior/inferior; anterior/posterior; ventral/dorsal; medial/lateral; intermediate; proximal/distal; and superficial/deep.

Regional Terms (p. 13)

3. Regional terms are used to designate specific areas of the body (see Figure 1.7).

Anatomical Variability (p. 14)

4. People vary internally as well as externally, but extreme variations are rare.

Body Planes and Sections (p. 14)

5. The body or its organs may be cut along planes, or imaginary lines, to produce different types of sections. Frequently used planes are sagittal, frontal, and transverse.

Body Cavities and Membranes (pp. 14–20)

6. The body contains two major closed cavities. The dorsal cavity, subdivided into the cranial and spinal cavities, contains the brain and spinal cord. The ventral cavity is subdivided into the thoracic cavity, which houses the heart and lungs, and the abdominopelvic cavity, which contains the liver, digestive organs, and reproductive structures.
7. The walls of the ventral cavity and the surfaces of the organs it contains are covered with thin membranes, the parietal and visceral serosae, respectively. The serosae produce a thin fluid that decreases friction during organ functioning.
8. The abdominopelvic cavity may be divided by four planes into nine abdominopelvic regions (epigastric, umbilical, hypogastric, right and left iliac, right and left lumbar, and right and left hypochondriac), or by two planes into four quadrants. (For boundaries and organs contained, see Figures 1.11 and 1.12.)
9. There are several smaller body cavities. Most of these are in the head and open to the exterior.

Review Questions

Multiple Choice/Matching

(Some questions have more than one correct answer. Select the best answer or answers from the choices given.)

1. The correct sequence of levels forming the structural hierarchy is **(a)** organ, organ system, cellular, chemical, tissue, organismal; **(b)** chemical, cellular, tissue, organismal, organ, organ system; **(c)** chemical, cellular, tissue, organ, organ system, organismal; **(d)** organismal, organ system, organ, tissue, cellular, chemical.
2. The structural and functional unit of life is **(a)** a cell, **(b)** an organ, **(c)** the organism, **(d)** a molecule.
3. Which of the following is a *major* functional characteristic of all organisms? **(a)** movement, **(b)** growth, **(c)** metabolism, **(d)** responsiveness, **(e)** all of these.
4. Two of these organ systems bear the *major* responsibility for ensuring homeostasis of the internal environment. Which two? **(a)** nervous system, **(b)** digestive system, **(c)** cardiovascular system, **(d)** endocrine system, **(e)** reproductive system.
5. In (a)–(e), a directional term [e.g., distal in (a)] is followed by terms indicating different body structures or locations (e.g., the

elbow/the wrist). In each case, choose the structure or organ that matches the given directional term.

(a) distal: the elbow/the wrist
(b) lateral: the hip bone/the umbilicus
(c) superior: the nose/the chin
(d) anterior: the toes/the heel
(e) superficial: the scalp/the skull

6. Assume that the body has been sectioned along three planes: (1) a median plane, (2) a frontal plane, and (3) a transverse plane made at the level of each of the organs listed below. Which organs would be visible in only one or two of these three cases? (a) urinary bladder, (b) brain, (c) lungs, (d) kidneys, (e) small intestine, (f) heart.

7. Relate each of the following conditions or statements to either the dorsal body cavity or the ventral body cavity.
(a) surrounded by the bony skull and the vertebral column
(b) includes the thoracic and abdominopelvic cavities
(c) contains the brain and spinal cord
(d) contains the heart, lungs, and digestive organs

8. Which of the following relationships is *incorrect*?
(a) visceral peritoneum/outer surface of small intestine
(b) parietal pericardium/outer surface of heart
(c) parietal pleura/wall of thoracic cavity

9. Which ventral cavity subdivision has no bony protection? (a) thoracic cavity, (b) abdominal cavity, (c) pelvic cavity.

10. Terms that apply to the backside of the body in the anatomical position include:
(a) ventral; anterior
(b) back; rear
(c) posterior; dorsal
(d) medial; lateral

Short Answer Essay Questions

11. According to the principle of complementarity, how does anatomy relate to physiology?

12. Construct a table that lists the 11 systems of the body, names two organs of each system (if appropriate), and describes the overall or major function of each system.

13. List and describe briefly five external factors that must be present or provided to sustain life.

14. Define homeostasis.

15. Compare and contrast the operation of negative and positive feedback mechanisms in maintaining homeostasis. Provide two examples of variables controlled by negative feedback

mechanisms and one example of a process regulated by a positive feedback mechanism.

16. Why is an understanding of the anatomical position important?

17. Define plane and section.

18. Provide the anatomical term that correctly names each of the following body regions: (a) arm, (b) thigh, (c) chest, (d) fingers and toes, (e) anterior aspect of the knee.

19. Use as many directional terms as you can to describe the relationship between the elbow's olecranal region and your palm.

20. (a) Make a diagram showing the nine abdominopelvic regions, and name each region. Name two organs (or parts of organs) that could be located in each of the named regions. (b) Make a similar sketch illustrating how the abdominopelvic cavity may be divided into quadrants, and name each quadrant.

Critical Thinking and Clinical Application Questions

1. John has been suffering agonizing pain with each breath and has been informed by the physician that he has pleurisy. (a) Specifically, what membranes are involved in this condition? (b) What is their usual role in the body? (c) Explain why John's condition is so painful.

2. At the clinic, Harry was told that blood would be drawn from his antecubital region. What body part was Harry asked to hold out? Later, the nurse came in and gave Harry a shot of penicillin in the area just distal to his acromial region. Did Harry take off his shirt or drop his pants to receive the injection? Before Harry left, the nurse noticed that Harry had a nasty bruise on his gluteal region. What part of his body was black and blue?

3. A man is behaving abnormally, and his physician suspects that he has a brain tumor. Which of the following medical imaging techniques would best localize the tumor in the man's brain (and why)? Conventional X ray, DSA, PET, sonography, MRI.

4. Calcium levels in Mr. Gallariani's blood are dropping to dangerously low levels. The hormone PTH is released and soon blood calcium levels begin to rise. Shortly after, PTH release slows. Is this an example of a positive or negative feedback mechanism? What is the initial stimulus? What is the result?

5. Mr. Harvey, a computer programmer, has been complaining of numbness and pain in his right hand. The nurse practitioner diagnosed his problem as carpal tunnel syndrome and prescribed use of a splint. Where will Mr. Harvey apply the splint?

2

Chemistry Comes Alive

Why study chemistry in an anatomy and physiology course? The answer is simple. Your entire body is made up of chemicals, thousands of them, continuously interacting with one another at an incredible pace. Although it is possible to study anatomy without much reference to chemistry, chemical reactions underlie all physiological processes—movement, digestion, the pumping of your heart, and even your thoughts. This chapter presents the basic chemistry and biochemistry (the chemistry of living material) you need to understand body functions.

PART 1
Basic Chemistry

Definition of Concepts: Matter and Energy

✓ Differentiate between matter and energy and between potential energy and kinetic energy.

✓ Describe the major energy forms.

Matter

Matter is the "stuff" of the universe. More precisely, **matter** is anything that occupies space and has mass. With some exceptions, it can be seen, smelled, and felt.

For all practical purposes, we can consider mass to be the same as weight. However, this statement is not quite accurate. The *mass* of an object is equal to the actual amount of matter in the object, and it remains constant wherever the object is. In contrast, weight varies with gravity. So while your mass is the same at sea level and on a mountaintop, you weigh just slightly less on that mountaintop. The science of chemistry studies the nature of matter, especially how its building blocks are put together and interact.

States of Matter

Matter exists in *solid*, *liquid*, and *gaseous states*. Examples of each state are found in the human body. Solids, like bones and teeth, have a definite shape and volume. Liquids such as blood plasma have a definite volume, but they conform to the shape of their container. Gases have neither a definite shape nor a definite volume. The air we breathe is a gas.

Energy

Compared with matter, energy is less tangible. It has no mass, does not take up space, and we can measure it only by its effects on matter. **Energy** is defined as the capacity to do work, or to put matter into motion. The greater the work done, the more energy is used doing it. A baseball player who has just hit the ball over the fence uses much more energy than a batter who bunts the ball back to the pitcher.

Kinetic Versus Potential Energy

Energy exists in two forms, or work capacities, and each can be transformed to the other. **Kinetic energy** (ki-net′ik) is energy in action. We see evidence of kinetic energy in the constant movement of the tiniest particles of matter (atoms) as well as in larger objects (a bouncing ball). Kinetic energy does work by moving objects, which in turn can do work by moving or pushing on other objects. For example, a push on a swinging door sets it into motion.

Potential energy is stored energy, that is, inactive energy that has the *potential*, or capability, to do work but is not presently doing so. The batteries in an unused toy have potential energy, as does water confined behind a dam. Your leg muscles have potential energy when you sit still on the couch. When potential energy is released, it becomes kinetic energy and so is capable of doing work. For example, dammed water becomes a rushing torrent when the dam is opened, and that rushing torrent can move a turbine at a hydroelectric plant, or charge a battery.

Actually, energy is a topic of physics, but matter and energy are inseparable. Matter is the substance, and energy is the mover of the substance. All living things are composed of matter and they all require energy to grow and function. The release and use of energy by living systems gives us the elusive quality we call life. Now let's consider the forms of energy used by the body as it does its work.

Forms of Energy

- **Chemical energy** is the form stored in the bonds of chemical substances. When chemical reactions occur that rearrange the atoms of the chemicals in a certain way, the potential energy is unleashed and becomes kinetic energy, or energy in action.

  For example, some of the energy in the foods you eat is eventually converted into the kinetic energy of your moving arm. However, food fuels cannot be used to energize body activities directly. Instead, some of the food energy is captured temporarily in the bonds of a chemical called *adenosine triphosphate* (ATP) (ah-den′o-sēn tri″fos′fāt). Later, ATP's bonds are broken and the stored energy is released as needed to do cellular work. Chemical energy in the form of ATP is the most useful form of energy in living systems because it is used to run almost all functional processes.

- **Electrical energy** results from the movement of charged particles. In your home, electrical energy is found in the flow of electrons along the household wiring. In your body, electrical currents are generated when charged particles called *ions* move along or across cell membranes. The nervous system uses electrical currents, called *nerve impulses*, to transmit messages from one part of the body to another. Electrical currents traveling across the heart stimulate it to contract (beat) and pump blood. (This is why a strong electrical shock, which interferes with such currents, can cause death.)

- **Mechanical energy** is energy *directly* involved in moving matter. When you ride a bicycle, your legs provide the mechanical energy that moves the pedals.

- **Radiant energy**, or **electromagnetic energy** (e-lek″tro-mag-net′ik), is energy that travels in waves. These waves, which vary in length, are collectively called the *electromagnetic spectrum*. They include visible light, infrared waves, radio waves, ultraviolet waves, and X rays. Light energy, which stimulates the retinas of our eyes, is important in vision. Ultraviolet waves cause sunburn, but they also stimulate your body to make vitamin D.

Energy Form Conversions

With few exceptions, energy is easily converted from one form to another. For example, the chemical energy (in gasoline) that powers the motor of a speedboat is converted into the mechanical energy of the whirling propeller that makes the boat skim across the water.

Energy conversions are quite inefficient. Some of the initial energy supply is always "lost" to the environment as heat. (It is not really lost because energy cannot be created or destroyed, but that portion given off as heat is at least partly *unusable*.) It is easy to demonstrate this principle. Electrical energy is converted into light energy in a lightbulb. But if you touch a lit bulb, you will soon discover that some of the electrical energy is producing heat instead.

Likewise, all energy conversions in the body liberate heat. This heat helps to maintain our relatively high body temperature, which influences body functioning. For example, when matter is heated, the kinetic energy of its particles increases and they begin to move more quickly. The higher the temperature, the faster the body's chemical reactions occur. We will learn more about this later.

☑ Check Your Understanding

1. What form of energy is found in the food we eat?
2. What form of energy is used to transmit messages from one part of the body to another?
3. What type of energy is available when we are still? When we are exercising?

For answers, see Appendix H.

Composition of Matter: Atoms and Elements

✓ Define chemical element and list the four elements that form the bulk of body matter.

✓ Define atom. List the subatomic particles, and describe their relative masses, charges, and positions in the atom.

✓ Define atomic number, atomic mass, atomic weight, isotope, and radioisotope.

All matter is composed of **elements**, unique substances that cannot be broken down into simpler substances by ordinary chemical methods. Among the well-known elements are oxygen, carbon, gold, silver, copper, and iron.

At present, 118 elements are recognized. Of these, 92 occur in nature. The rest are made artificially in particle accelerator devices.

Four elements—carbon, oxygen, hydrogen, and nitrogen—make up about 96% of body weight, and 20 others are present in the body, some in trace amounts. **Table 2.1** on p. 26 lists the elements contributing to body mass and gives their importance. In Appendix E, an oddly shaped checkerboard called the **periodic table** provides a more complete listing of the known elements and helps to explain the properties of each element that make it react as it does with other elements.

Each element is composed of more or less identical particles or building blocks, called **atoms**. The smallest atoms are less than 0.1 nanometer (nm) in diameter, and the largest are only about five times as large. [1 nm = 0.0000001 (or 10^{-7}) centimeter (cm), or 40 billionths of an inch!]

Every element's atoms differ from those of all other elements and give the element its unique physical and chemical properties. *Physical properties* are those we can detect with our senses (such as color and texture) or measure (such as boiling point and freezing point). *Chemical properties* pertain to the way atoms interact with other atoms (bonding behavior) and account for the facts that iron rusts, animals can digest their food, and so on.

We designate each element by a one- or two-letter chemical shorthand called an **atomic symbol**, usually the first letter(s) of the element's name. For example, C stands for carbon, O for oxygen, and Ca for calcium. In a few cases, the atomic symbol

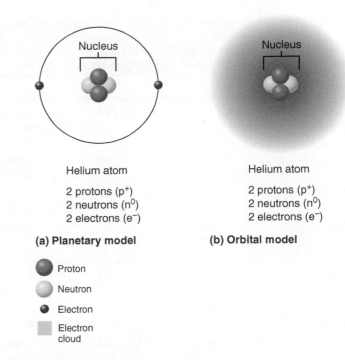

Helium atom

2 protons (p^+)
2 neutrons (n^0)
2 electrons (e^-)

(a) Planetary model

Helium atom

2 protons (p^+)
2 neutrons (n^0)
2 electrons (e^-)

(b) Orbital model

● Proton
○ Neutron
● Electron
▨ Electron cloud

Figure 2.1 Two models of the structure of an atom.

is taken from the Latin name for the element. For example, sodium is indicated by Na, from the Latin word *natrium*.

Atomic Structure

The word *atom* comes from the Greek word meaning "indivisible." However, we now know that atoms are clusters of even smaller particles called protons, neutrons, and electrons and that even those subatomic particles can be subdivided with high-technology tools. Still, the old idea of atomic indivisibility is useful because an atom loses the unique properties of its element when it is split into its subatomic particles.

An atom's subatomic particles differ in mass, electrical charge, and position in the atom. An atom has a central **nucleus** containing protons and neutrons tightly bound together. The nucleus, in turn, is surrounded by orbiting electrons **(Figure 2.1)**. **Protons** (p^+) bear a positive electrical charge, and **neutrons** (n^0) are neutral, so the nucleus is positively charged overall. Protons and neutrons are heavy particles and have approximately the same mass, arbitrarily designated as 1 **atomic mass unit** (1 amu). Since all of the heavy subatomic particles are concentrated in the nucleus, the nucleus is fantastically dense. It accounts for nearly the entire mass (99.9%) of the atom.

The tiny **electrons** (e^-) bear a negative charge equal in strength to the positive charge of the proton. However, an electron has only about 1/2000 the mass of a proton, and the mass of an electron is usually designated as 0 amu.

All atoms are electrically neutral because the number of protons in an atom is precisely balanced by its number of electrons (the + and − charges will then cancel the effect of each other). For example, hydrogen has one proton and one electron, and iron has 26 protons and 26 electrons. For any atom, the number of protons and electrons is always equal.

Table 2.1	Common Elements Composing the Human Body*		
ELEMENT	**ATOMIC SYMBOL**	**APPROX. % BODY MASS†**	**FUNCTIONS**
Major (96.1%)			
Oxygen	O	65.0	A major component of both organic (carbon-containing) and inorganic (non-carbon-containing) molecules. As a gas, it is needed for the production of cellular energy (ATP).
Carbon	C	18.5	A primary component of all organic molecules, which include carbohydrates, lipids (fats), proteins, and nucleic acids.
Hydrogen	H	9.5	A component of all organic molecules. As an ion (proton), it influences the pH of body fluids.
Nitrogen	N	3.2	A component of proteins and nucleic acids (genetic material).
Lesser (3.9%)			
Calcium	Ca	1.5	Found as a salt in bones and teeth. Its ionic (Ca^{2+}) form is required for muscle contraction, conduction of nerve impulses, and blood clotting.
Phosphorus	P	1.0	Part of calcium phosphate salts in bones and teeth. Also present in nucleic acids, and part of ATP.
Potassium	K	0.4	Its ion (K^+) is the major positive ion (cation) in cells. Necessary for conduction of nerve impulses and muscle contraction.
Sulfur	S	0.3	Component of proteins, particularly muscle proteins.
Sodium	Na	0.2	As an ion (Na^+), sodium is the major positive ion found in extracellular fluids (fluids outside of cells). Important for water balance, conduction of nerve impulses, and muscle contraction.
Chlorine	Cl	0.2	Its ion (chloride, Cl^-) is the most abundant negative ion (anion) in extracellular fluids.
Magnesium	Mg	0.1	Present in bone. Also an important cofactor in a number of metabolic reactions.
Iodine	I	0.1	Needed to make functional thyroid hormones.
Iron	Fe	0.1	Component of hemoglobin (which transports oxygen within red blood cells) and some enzymes.
Trace (less than 0.01%)			

Chromium (Cr); cobalt (Co); copper (Cu); fluorine (F); manganese (Mn); molybdenum (Mo); selenium (Se); silicon (Si); tin (Sn); vanadium (V); zinc (Zn)

These elements are referred to as *trace elements* because they are required in very minute amounts; many are found as part of enzymes or are required for enzyme activation.

*A listing of the elements by ascending order of atomic number appears in the periodic table, Appendix E.

†Percentage of "wet" body mass; includes water.

The **planetary model** of the atom, illustrated in Figure 2.1a, is a simplified (and now outdated) model of atomic structure. As you can see, it depicts electrons moving around the nucleus in fixed, generally circular orbits. But we can never determine the exact location of electrons at a particular time because they jump around following unknown trajectories. So, instead of speaking of specific orbits, chemists talk about **orbitals**—regions around the nucleus in which a given electron or electron pair is likely to be found most of the time. This more modern model of atomic structure, called the **orbital model**, is more useful for predicting the chemical behavior of atoms. As illustrated in Figure 2.1b, the orbital model depicts *probable* regions of greatest electron density by denser shading (this haze is called

the *electron cloud*). However, the planetary model is simpler to depict, so we will use that model in most illustrations of atomic structure in this text.

Hydrogen, with just one proton and one electron, is the simplest atom. You can visualize the spatial relationships in the hydrogen atom by imagining it as a sphere enlarged until its diameter equals the length of a football field. In that case, the nucleus could be represented by a lead ball the size of a gumdrop in the exact center of the sphere. Its lone electron could be pictured as a fly buzzing about unpredictably within the sphere. Though not completely accurate, this mental image demonstrates that most of the volume of an atom is empty space, and nearly all of its mass is concentrated in the central nucleus.

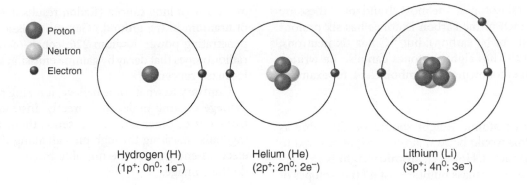

Figure 2.2 Atomic structure of the three smallest atoms.

Identifying Elements

All protons are alike, regardless of the atom considered. The same is true of all neutrons and all electrons. So what determines the unique properties of each element? The answer is that atoms of different elements are composed of *different numbers* of protons, neutrons, and electrons.

The simplest and smallest atom, hydrogen, has one proton, one electron, and no neutrons (**Figure 2.2**). Next in size is the helium atom, with two protons, two neutrons, and two orbiting electrons. Lithium follows with three protons, four neutrons, and three electrons. If we continued this step-by-step progression, we would get a graded series of atoms containing from 1 to 112 protons, an equal number of electrons, and a slightly larger number of neutrons at each step.

All we really need to know to identify a particular element, however, are its atomic number, mass number, and atomic weight. Taken together, these provide a fairly complete picture of each element.

Atomic Number

The **atomic number** of any atom is equal to the number of protons in its nucleus and is written as a subscript to the left of its atomic symbol. Hydrogen, with one proton, has an atomic number of 1 ($_1$H). Helium, with two protons, has an atomic number of 2 ($_2$He), and so on. The number of protons is always equal to the number of electrons in an atom, so the atomic number *indirectly* tells us the number of electrons in the atom as well. As we will see shortly, this information is important indeed, because electrons determine the chemical behavior of atoms.

Mass Number and Isotopes

The **mass number** of an atom is the sum of the masses of its protons and neutrons. The mass of the electrons is so small that it is ignored. Recall that protons and neutrons have a mass of 1 amu. Hydrogen has only one proton in its nucleus, so its atomic and mass numbers are the same: 1. Helium, with two protons and two neutrons, has a mass number of 4.

The mass number is usually indicated by a superscript to the left of the atomic symbol. For example, helium is $_2^4$He. This simple notation allows us to deduce the total number and kinds of subatomic particles in any atom because it indicates the number of protons (the atomic number), the number of electrons (equal to the atomic number), and the number of neutrons (mass number minus atomic number). In our example, we can do the subtraction to find that $_2^4$He has two neutrons.

From what we have said so far, it may appear as if each element has one, and only one, type of atom representing it. This is not the case. Nearly all known elements have two or more structural variations called **isotopes** (iso-tōps), which have the same number of protons (and electrons), but differ in the number of neutrons they contain. Earlier, when we said that hydrogen has a mass number of 1, we were speaking of ^{1}H, its most abundant isotope. Some hydrogen atoms have a mass of 2 or 3 amu (atomic mass units), which means that they have one proton and, respectively, one or two neutrons (**Figure 2.3**).

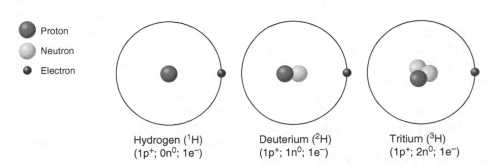

Figure 2.3 Isotopes of hydrogen.

Carbon has several isotopes. The most abundant of these are ^{12}C, ^{13}C, and ^{14}C. Each of the carbon isotopes has six protons (otherwise it would not be carbon), but ^{12}C has six neutrons, ^{13}C has seven, and ^{14}C has eight. Isotopes can also be written with the mass number following the symbol: C-14, for example.

Atomic Weight

You might think that atomic weight should be the same as atomic mass, and this would be so if atomic weight referred to the weight of a single atom. However, **atomic weight** is an average of the relative weights (mass numbers) of *all* the isotopes of an element, taking into account their relative abundance in nature. As a rule, the atomic weight of an element is approximately equal to the mass number of its most abundant isotope. For example, the atomic weight of hydrogen is 1.008, which reveals that its lightest isotope (^{1}H) is present in much greater amounts in our world than its ^{2}H or ^{3}H forms.

Radioisotopes

The heavier isotopes of many elements are unstable, and their atoms decompose spontaneously into more stable forms. This process of atomic decay is called *radioactivity*, and isotopes that exhibit this behavior are called **radioisotopes** (ra″de-o-i′so-tōps). The disintegration of a radioactive nucleus may be compared to a tiny explosion. It occurs when subatomic *alpha* (α) *particles* (packets of 2p + 2n), *beta* (β) *particles* (electron-like negative particles), or *gamma* (γ) *rays* (electromagnetic energy) are ejected from the atomic nucleus.

Why does this happen? The answer is complex, but for our purposes, the important point to know is that the dense nuclear particles are composed of even smaller particles called *quarks* that associate in one way to form protons and in another way to form neutrons. Apparently, the "glue" that holds these nuclear particles together is weaker in the heavier isotopes. When radioisotopes disintegrate, the element may transform to a different element.

Because we can detect radioactivity with scanners, and radioactive isotopes share the same chemistry as their more stable isotopes, radioisotopes are valuable tools for biological research and medicine. Most radioisotopes used in the clinical setting are used for diagnosis, that is, to localize and illuminate damaged or cancerous tissues. For example, iodine-131 is used to determine the size and activity of the thyroid gland and to detect thyroid cancer. The sophisticated PET scans described in *A Closer Look* in Chapter 1 use radioisotopes to probe the workings of molecules deep within our bodies. All radioisotopes, regardless of the purpose for which they are used, damage living tissue, and all radioisotopes gradually lose their radioactive behavior. The time required for a radioisotope to lose one-half of its activity is called its *half-life*. The half-lives of radioisotopes vary dramatically from hours to thousands of years.

Alpha emission is easily blocked outside the body but if absorbed causes considerable damage. For this reason, inhaled alpha particles from decaying radon are second only to smoking as a cause of lung cancer. (Radon results naturally from decay of uranium in the ground.) Gamma emission has the greatest penetrating power. Radium-226, cobalt-60, and certain other radioisotopes that decay by gamma emission are used to destroy localized cancers.

Contrary to what some believe, ionizing radiation does not damage organic molecules directly. Instead, it knocks electrons out of other atoms and sends them flying, like bowling balls smashing through pins all along their path. It is the electron energy and the unstable molecules left behind that do the damage.

☑ Check Your Understanding

4. What two elements besides H and N make up the bulk of living matter?
5. An element has a mass of 207 and has 125 neutrons in its nucleus. How many protons and electrons does it have and where are they located?
6. How do the terms atomic mass and atomic weight differ?

For answers, see Appendix H.

How Matter Is Combined: Molecules and Mixtures

✓ Define molecule, and distinguish between a compound and a mixture.

✓ Compare solutions, colloids, and suspensions.

Molecules and Compounds

Most atoms do not exist in the free state, but instead are chemically combined with other atoms. Such a combination of two or more atoms held together by chemical bonds is called a **molecule**.

If two or more atoms of the *same* element combine, the resulting substance is called a *molecule of that element*. When two hydrogen atoms bond, the product is a molecule of hydrogen gas and is written as H_2. Similarly, when two oxygen atoms combine, a molecule of oxygen gas (O_2) is formed. Sulfur atoms commonly combine to form sulfur molecules containing eight sulfur atoms (S_8).

When two or more *different* kinds of atoms bind, they form molecules of a **compound**. Two hydrogen atoms combine with one oxygen atom to form the compound water (H_2O). Four hydrogen atoms combine with one carbon atom to form the compound methane (CH_4). Notice again that molecules of methane and water are compounds, but molecules of hydrogen gas are not, because compounds always contain atoms of at least two different elements.

Compounds are chemically pure, and all of their molecules are identical. So, just as an atom is the smallest particle of an element that still has the properties of the element, a molecule is the smallest particle of a compound that still has the specific

Solution	Colloid	Suspension
Solute particles are very tiny, do not settle out or scatter light.	Solute particles are larger than in a solution and scatter light; do not settle out.	Solute particles are very large, settle out, and may scatter light.

Figure 2.4 The three basic types of mixtures.

characteristics of the compound. This concept is important because the properties of compounds are usually very different from those of the atoms they contain. Water, for example, is very different from the elements hydrogen and oxygen. Indeed, it is next to impossible to tell what atoms are in a compound without analyzing it chemically.

Mixtures

Mixtures are substances composed of two or more components *physically intermixed*. Most matter in nature exists in the form of mixtures, but there are only three basic types: *solutions*, *colloids*, and *suspensions* (Figure 2.4).

Solutions

Solutions are homogeneous mixtures of components that may be gases, liquids, or solids. *Homogeneous* means that the mixture has exactly the same composition or makeup throughout—a sample taken from any part of the mixture has the same composition (in terms of the atoms or molecules it contains) as a sample taken from any other part of the mixture. Examples include the air we breathe (a mixture of gases) and seawater (a mixture of salts, which are solids, and water). The substance present in the greatest amount is called the **solvent** (or dissolving medium). Solvents are usually liquids. Substances present in smaller amounts are called **solutes**.

Water is the body's chief solvent. Most solutions in the body are *true solutions* containing gases, liquids, or solids dissolved in water. True solutions are usually transparent. Examples are saline solution [table salt (NaCl) and water], a mixture of glucose and water, and mineral water. The solutes of true solutions are minute, usually in the form of individual atoms and molecules. Consequently, they are not visible to the naked eye, do not settle out, and do not scatter light. In other words, if a beam of light is passed through a true solution, you will not see the path of light.

Concentration of Solutions We describe true solutions in terms of their *concentration*, which may be indicated in various ways. Solutions used in a college laboratory or a hospital are often described in terms of the **percent** (parts per 100 parts) of the solute in the total solution. This designation always refers to the solute percentage, and unless otherwise noted, water is assumed to be the solvent.

Milligrams per deciliter (*mg/dl*) is another common concentration measurement. (A deciliter is 100 milliliters or 0.1 liter.)

Still another way to express the concentration of a solution is in terms of its **molarity** (mo-lar'ĭ-te), or moles per liter, indicated by *M*. This method is more complicated but much more useful. To understand molarity, you must understand what a mole is. A **mole** of any element or compound is equal to its atomic weight or **molecular weight** (sum of the atomic weights) weighed out in grams. This concept is easier than it seems, as illustrated by the following example.

Glucose is $C_6H_{12}O_6$, which indicates that it has 6 carbon atoms, 12 hydrogen atoms, and 6 oxygen atoms. To compute the molecular weight of glucose, you would look up the atomic weight of each of its atoms in the periodic table (see Appendix E) and compute its molecular weight as follows:

Atom	Number of Atoms		Atomic Weight		Total Atomic Weight
C	6	×	12.011	=	72.066
H	12	×	1.008	=	12.096
O	6	×	15.999	=	95.994
					180.156

Then, to make a *one-molar* solution of glucose, you would weigh out 180.156 grams (g), called a *gram molecular weight*, of glucose and add enough water to make 1 liter (L) of solution. In short, a one-molar solution (abbreviated 1.0 *M*) of a chemical substance is one gram molecular weight of the substance (or one gram atomic weight in the case of elemental substances) in 1 L (1000 milliliters) of solution.

The beauty of using the mole as the basis of preparing solutions is its precision. One mole of any substance always contains exactly the same number of solute particles, that is, 6.02×10^{23}. This number is called **Avogadro's number** (av"o-gad'rōz). So whether you weigh out 1 mole of glucose (180 g) or 1 mole of water (18 g) or 1 mole of methane (16 g), in each case you will have 6.02×10^{23} molecules of that substance.* This allows almost mind-boggling precision to be achieved.

Because solute concentrations in body fluids tend to be quite low, those values are usually reported in terms of millimoles (m*M*; 1/1000 mole).

Colloids

Colloids (kol'oidz), also called *emulsions*, are *heterogeneous* mixtures, which means that their composition is dissimilar in different areas of the mixture. Colloids often appear translucent or milky and although the solute particles are larger than those in true solutions, they still do not settle out. However, they do scatter light, so the path of a light beam shining through a colloidal mixture is visible.

Colloids have many unique properties, including the ability of some to undergo **sol-gel transformations**, that is, to change reversibly from a fluid (sol) state to a more solid (gel) state. Jell-O, or any gelatin product (Figure 2.4), is a familiar example of a nonliving colloid that changes from a sol to a gel when refrigerated (and that gel will liquefy again if placed in the sun). Cytosol, the semifluid material in living cells, is also a colloid,

largely because of its dispersed proteins. Its sol-gel transformations underlie many important cell activities, such as cell division and changes in cell shape.

Suspensions

Suspensions are *heterogeneous* mixtures with large, often visible solutes that tend to settle out. An example of a suspension is a mixture of sand and water. So is blood, in which the living blood cells are suspended in the fluid portion of blood (blood plasma). If left to stand, the suspended cells will settle out unless some means—mixing, shaking, or circulation in the body—keeps them in suspension.

As you can see, all three types of mixtures are found in both living and nonliving systems. In fact, living material is the most complex mixture of all, since it contains all three kinds of mixtures interacting with one another.

Distinguishing Mixtures from Compounds

Now let's zero in on how to distinguish mixtures and compounds from one another. Mixtures differ from compounds in several important ways:

- The chief difference between mixtures and compounds is that no chemical bonding occurs between the components of a mixture. The properties of atoms and molecules are not changed when they become part of a mixture. Remember they are only physically intermixed.

- Depending on the mixture, its components can be separated by physical means—straining, filtering, evaporation, and so on. Compounds, by contrast, can be separated into their constituent atoms only by chemical means (breaking bonds).

- Some mixtures are homogeneous, whereas others are heterogeneous. A bar of 100% pure (elemental) iron is homogeneous, as are all compounds. As already mentioned, heterogeneous substances vary in their makeup from place to place. For example, iron ore is a heterogeneous mixture that contains iron and many other elements.

☑ Check Your Understanding

7. What is the meaning of the term "molecule"?
8. Why is sodium chloride (NaCl) considered a compound, but oxygen gas is not?
9. Blood contains a liquid component and living cells. Would it be classified as a compound or a mixture? Why?

For answers, see Appendix H.

Chemical Bonds

✓ Explain the role of electrons in chemical bonding and in relation to the octet rule.

✓ Differentiate among ionic, covalent, and hydrogen bonds.

✓ Compare and contrast polar and nonpolar compounds.

---

*The important exception to this rule concerns molecules that ionize and break up into charged particles (ions) in water, such as salts, acids, and bases (see p. 39). For example, simple table salt (sodium chloride) breaks up into two types of charged particles. Therefore, in a 1.0 *M* solution of sodium chloride, 2 *moles* of solute particles are actually in solution.

As noted earlier, when atoms combine with other atoms, they are held together by **chemical bonds**. A chemical bond is not a physical structure like a pair of handcuffs linking two people together. Instead, it is an energy relationship between the electrons of the reacting atoms, and it is made or broken in less than a trillionth of a second.

The Role of Electrons in Chemical Bonding

Electrons forming the electron cloud around the nucleus of an atom occupy regions of space called **electron shells** that consecutively surround the atomic nucleus. The atoms known so far can have electrons in seven shells (numbered 1 to 7 from the nucleus outward), but the actual number of electron shells occupied in a given atom depends on the number of electrons that atom has. Each electron shell contains one or more orbitals. (Recall from our earlier discussion that *orbitals* are regions around the nucleus in which a given electron is likely to be found most of the time.)

It is important to understand that each electron shell represents a different **energy level**, because this prompts you to think of electrons as particles with a certain amount of potential energy. In general, the terms *electron shell* and *energy level* are used interchangeably.

How much potential energy does an electron have? The answer depends on the energy level that it occupies. The attraction between the positively charged nucleus and negatively charged electrons is greatest when electrons are closest to the nucleus and falls off with increasing distance. This statement explains why electrons farthest from the nucleus (1) have the greatest potential energy (it takes more energy for them to overcome the nuclear attraction and reach the more distant energy levels) and (2) are most likely to interact chemically with other atoms. (They are the least tightly held by their own atomic nucleus and the most easily influenced by other atoms and molecules.)

Each electron shell can hold a specific number of electrons. Shell 1, the shell immediately surrounding the nucleus, accommodates only 2 electrons. Shell 2 holds a maximum of 8, and shell 3 has room for 18. Subsequent shells hold larger and larger numbers of electrons, and the shells tend to be filled with electrons consecutively. For example, shell 1 fills completely before any electrons appear in shell 2.

Which electrons are involved in chemical bonding? When we consider bonding behavior, the only electrons that are important are those in the atom's outermost energy level. Inner electrons usually do not take part in bonding because they are more tightly held by the atomic nucleus.

When the outermost energy level of an atom is filled to capacity or contains eight electrons, the atom is stable. Such atoms are *chemically inert*, that is, unreactive. A group of elements called the *noble gases*, which include helium and neon, typify this condition **(Figure 2.5a)**. On the other hand, atoms in which the outermost energy level contains fewer than eight electrons tend to gain, lose, or share electrons with other atoms to achieve stability (Figure 2.5b).

What about atoms that have more than 20 electrons, in which the energy levels beyond shell 2 can contain *more* than

(a) Chemically inert elements

Outermost energy level (valence shell) complete

Helium (He)
($2p^+$; $2n^0$; $2e^-$)

Neon (Ne)
($10p^+$; $10n^0$; $10e^-$)

(b) Chemically reactive elements

Outermost energy level (valence shell) incomplete

Hydrogen (H)
($1p^+$; $0n^0$; $1e^-$)

Carbon (C)
($6p^+$; $6n^0$; $6e^-$)

Oxygen (O)
($8p^+$; $8n^0$; $8e^-$)

Sodium (Na)
($11p^+$; $12n^0$; $11e^-$)

Figure 2.5 Chemically inert and reactive elements. (*Note*: For simplicity, each atomic nucleus is shown as a sphere with the atom's symbol; individual protons and neutrons are not shown.)

eight electrons? The number of electrons that can participate in bonding is still limited to a total of eight. The term **valence shell** (va'lens) specifically indicates an atom's outermost energy level *or that portion of it* containing the electrons that are chemically reactive. Hence, the key to chemical reactivity is the **octet rule** (ok-tet'), or **rule of eights**. Except for shell 1, which is full when it has two electrons, atoms tend to interact in such a way that they have eight electrons in their valence shell.

Types of Chemical Bonds

Three major types of chemical bonds—*ionic, covalent,* and *hydrogen bonds*—result from attractive forces between atoms.

Sodium atom (Na)
(11p$^+$; 12n^0; 11e$^-$)

Chlorine atom (Cl)
(17p$^+$; 18n^0; 17e$^-$)

Sodium ion (Na$^+$)

Chloride ion (Cl$^-$)

Sodium chloride (NaCl)

(a) Sodium gains stability by losing one electron, and chlorine becomes stable by gaining one electron.

(b) After electron transfer, the oppositely charged ions formed attract each other.

Cl$^-$

Na$^+$

(c) Large numbers of Na$^+$ and Cl$^-$ ions associate to form salt (NaCl) crystals.

Figure 2.6 Formation of an ionic bond.

Ionic Bonds

Recall that atoms are electrically neutral. However, electrons can be transferred from one atom to another, and when this happens, the precise balance of + and − charges is lost so that charged particles called **ions** are formed. An **ionic bond** (i-on′ik) is a chemical bond between atoms formed by the transfer of one or more electrons from one atom to the other. The atom that gains one or more electrons is the *electron acceptor*. It acquires a net negative charge and is called an **anion** (an′i-on). The atom that loses electrons is the *electron donor*. It acquires a net positive charge and is called a **cation** (kat′i-on). (To remember this term, think of the "t" in "cation" as a + sign.) Both anions and cations are formed whenever electron transfer between atoms occurs. Because opposite charges attract, these ions tend to stay close together, resulting in an ionic bond.

One example of ionic bonding is the formation of table salt, or sodium chloride (NaCl), by interaction of sodium and chlorine atoms (**Figure 2.6**). Sodium, with an atomic number of 11, has only one electron in its valence shell. It would be very difficult to attempt to fill this shell by adding seven more. However, if this single electron is lost, shell 2 with eight electrons becomes the valence shell (outermost energy level containing electrons) and is full. Thus, by losing the lone electron in its third energy

level, sodium achieves stability and becomes a cation (Na$^+$). On the other hand, chlorine, atomic number 17, needs only one electron to fill its valence shell. By accepting an electron, chlorine achieves stability and becomes an anion.

When sodium and chlorine atoms interact, this is exactly what happens. Sodium donates an electron to chlorine (Figure 2.6a), and the oppositely charged ions created in this exchange attract each other, forming sodium chloride (Figure 2.6b). Ionic bonds are commonly formed between atoms with one or two valence shell electrons (the metallic elements, such as sodium, calcium, and potassium) and atoms with seven valence shell electrons (such as chlorine, fluorine, and iodine).

Most ionic compounds fall in the chemical category called *salts*. In the dry state, salts such as sodium chloride do not exist as individual molecules. Instead, they form **crystals**, large arrays of cations and anions held together by ionic bonds (Figure 2.6c).

Sodium chloride is an excellent example of the difference in properties between a compound and its constituent atoms. Sodium is a silvery white metal, and chlorine in its molecular state is a poisonous green gas used to make bleach. However, sodium chloride is a white crystalline solid that we sprinkle on our food.

Covalent Bonds

Electrons do not have to be completely transferred for atoms to achieve stability. Instead, they may be *shared* so that each atom is able to fill its outer electron shell at least part of the time. Electron sharing produces molecules in which the shared electrons occupy a single orbital common to both atoms, which constitutes a **covalent bond** (ko-va′lent).

Hydrogen with its single electron can fill its only shell (shell 1) by sharing a pair of electrons with another atom. When it shares with another hydrogen atom, a molecule of hydrogen gas is formed. The shared electron pair orbits around the molecule as a whole, satisfying the stability needs of each atom.

Hydrogen can also share an electron pair with different kinds of atoms to form a compound (**Figure 2.7a**). Carbon has four electrons in its outermost shell, but needs eight to achieve stability. Hydrogen has one electron, but needs two. When a methane

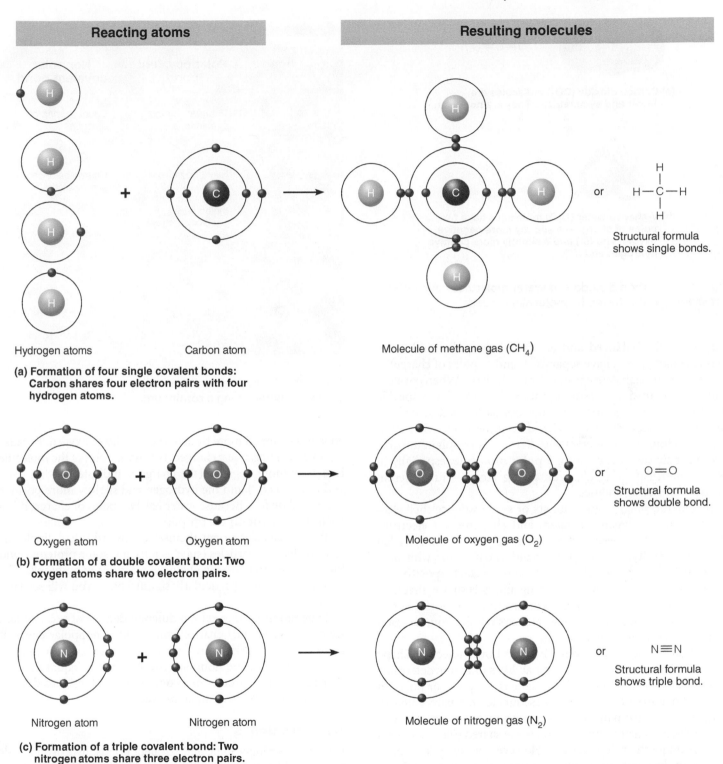

| Reacting atoms | Resulting molecules |

Hydrogen atoms   Carbon atom

(a) Formation of four single covalent bonds: Carbon shares four electron pairs with four hydrogen atoms.

Molecule of methane gas (CH_4)

Structural formula shows single bonds.

Oxygen atom   Oxygen atom

(b) Formation of a double covalent bond: Two oxygen atoms share two electron pairs.

Molecule of oxygen gas (O_2)

Structural formula shows double bond.

Nitrogen atom   Nitrogen atom

(c) Formation of a triple covalent bond: Two nitrogen atoms share three electron pairs.

Molecule of nitrogen gas (N_2)

Structural formula shows triple bond.

Figure 2.7 Formation of covalent bonds.

molecule (CH_4) is formed, carbon shares four pairs of electrons with four hydrogen atoms (one pair with each hydrogen). Again, the shared electrons orbit and "belong to" the whole molecule, ensuring the stability of each atom.

When two atoms share one pair of electrons, a single covalent bond is formed (indicated by a single line connecting the atoms, such as H—H). In some cases, atoms share two or three electron pairs, resulting in *double* or *triple covalent bonds* (Figure 2.7b and c). (These bonds are indicated by double or triple connecting lines such as O=O or N≡N.)

Polar and Nonpolar Molecules In the covalent bonds we have discussed, the shared electrons are shared equally between the atoms of the molecule for the most part. The molecules formed

(a) Carbon dioxide (CO_2) molecules are linear and symmetrical. They are nonpolar.

(b) V-shaped water (H_2O) molecules have two poles of charge—a slightly more negative oxygen end (δ^-) and a slightly more positive hydrogen end (δ^+).

Figure 2.8 **Carbon dioxide and water molecules have different shapes, as illustrated by molecular models.**

Ionic bond	Polar covalent bond	Nonpolar covalent bond
Complete transfer of electrons	Unequal sharing of of electrons	Equal sharing of electrons
Separate ions (charged particles) form	Slight negative charge (δ^-) at one end of molecule, slight positive charge (δ^+) at other end	Charge balanced among atoms
Na^+ Cl^-	Water	$O=C=O$
Sodium chloride	Water	Carbon dioxide

Figure 2.9 **Ionic, polar covalent, and nonpolar covalent bonds compared along a continuum.**

are electrically balanced and are called **nonpolar molecules** (because they do not have separate + and − poles of charge).

Such electrical balance is not always the case. When covalent bonds are formed, the resulting molecule always has a specific three-dimensional shape, with the bonds formed at definite angles. A molecule's shape helps determine what other molecules or atoms it can interact with. It may also result in unequal electron pair sharing, creating a **polar molecule**, especially in nonsymmetrical molecules containing atoms with different electron-attracting abilities.

In general, *small* atoms with six or seven valence shell electrons, such as oxygen, nitrogen, and chlorine, are electron-hungry and attract electrons very strongly, a capability called **electronegativity**. On the other hand, most atoms with only one or two valence shell electrons tend to be **electropositive**. In other words, their electron-attracting ability is so low that they usually lose *their* valence shell electrons to other atoms. Potassium and sodium, each with one valence shell electron, are good examples of electropositive atoms.

Carbon dioxide and water illustrate how molecular shape and the relative electron-attracting abilities of atoms determine whether a covalently bonded molecule is nonpolar or polar. In carbon dioxide (CO_2), carbon shares four electron pairs with two oxygen atoms (two pairs are shared with each oxygen). Oxygen is very electronegative and so attracts the shared electrons much more strongly than does carbon. However, because the carbon dioxide molecule is linear and symmetrical **(Figure 2.8a)**, the electron-pulling ability of one oxygen atom offsets that of the other, like a standoff between equally strong teams in a game of tug-of-war. As a result, the shared electrons orbit the entire molecule and carbon dioxide is a nonpolar compound.

In contrast, a water molecule (H_2O) is bent, or V shaped (Figure 2.8b). The two electropositive hydrogen atoms are located at the same end of the molecule, and the very electronegative oxygen is at the opposite end. This arrangement allows oxygen to pull the shared electrons toward itself and away from the two hydrogen atoms. In this case, the electron pairs are *not* shared

equally, but spend more time in the vicinity of oxygen. Because electrons are negatively charged, the oxygen end of the molecule is slightly more negative (the charge is indicated with a delta and minus as δ^-) and the hydrogen end slightly more positive (indicated by δ^+). Because water has two poles of charge, it is a *polar molecule*, or **dipole** (di′pōl).

Polar molecules orient themselves toward other dipoles or toward charged particles (such as ions and some proteins), and they play essential roles in chemical reactions in body cells. The polarity of water is particularly significant, as you will see later in this chapter.

Different molecules exhibit different degrees of polarity, and we can see a gradual change from ionic to nonpolar covalent bonding as summarized in **Figure 2.9**. Ionic bonds (complete electron transfer) and nonpolar covalent bonds (equal electron sharing) are the extremes of a continuum, with various degrees of unequal electron sharing in between.

Hydrogen Bonds

Unlike the stronger ionic and covalent bonds, hydrogen bonds are more like attractions than true bonds. Hydrogen bonds form when a hydrogen atom, already covalently linked to one electronegative atom (usually nitrogen or oxygen), is attracted by another electron-hungry atom, so that a "bridge" forms between them.

Hydrogen bonding is common between dipoles such as water molecules, because the slightly negative oxygen atoms of one molecule attract the slightly positive hydrogen atoms of other molecules **(Figure 2.10a)**. Hydrogen bonding is responsible for the tendency of water molecules to cling together and form films, referred to as *surface tension*. This tendency helps explain why water beads up into spheres when it sits on a hard surface and why water striders can walk on a pond's surface (Figure 2.10b).

Although hydrogen bonds are too weak to bind atoms together to form molecules, they are important *intramolecular bonds* (literally, bonds within molecules), which hold different parts of a single large molecule in a specific three-dimensional shape. Some large biological molecules, such as proteins and DNA, have numerous hydrogen bonds that help maintain and stabilize their structures.

☑ **Check Your Understanding**

10. What kinds of bonds form between water molecules?
11. Oxygen ($_8$O) and argon ($_{18}$A) are both gases. Oxygen combines readily with other elements, but argon does not. What accounts for this difference?
12. Assume imaginary compound XY has a polar covalent bond. How does its charge distribution differ from that of XX molecules?

For answers, see Appendix H.

Chemical Reactions

✓ Define the three major types of chemical reactions: synthesis, decomposition, and exchange. Comment on the nature of oxidation-reduction reactions and their importance.

✓ Explain why chemical reactions in the body are often irreversible.

✓ Describe factors that affect chemical reaction rates.

As we noted earlier, all particles of matter are in constant motion because of their kinetic energy. Movement of atoms or molecules in a solid is usually limited to vibration because the particles are united by fairly rigid bonds. But in liquids or gases, particles dart about randomly, sometimes colliding with one another and interacting to undergo chemical reactions. A **chemical reaction** occurs whenever chemical bonds are formed, rearranged, or broken.

Chemical Equations

We can write chemical reactions in symbolic form as chemical equations. For example, we indicate the joining of two hydrogen atoms to form hydrogen gas as

$$H + H \rightarrow H_2 \text{ (hydrogen gas)}$$

reactants → product

and the combining of four hydrogen atoms and one carbon atom to form methane as

$$4H + C \rightarrow CH_4 \text{ (methane)}$$

reactants → product

Notice that in equations, a number written as a *subscript* indicates that the atoms are joined by chemical bonds. But a number written as a *prefix* denotes the number of *unjoined* atoms or molecules. For example, CH_4 reveals that four hydrogen

(a) The slightly positive ends (δ^+) of the water molecules become aligned with the slightly negative ends (δ^-) of other water molecules.

— Hydrogen bond (indicated by dotted line)

(b) A water strider can walk on a pond because of the high surface tension of water, a result of the combined strength of its hydrogen bonds.

Figure 2.10 Hydrogen bonding between polar water molecules.

atoms are bonded together with carbon to form the methane molecule, but 4H signifies four unjoined hydrogen atoms.

A chemical equation is like a sentence describing what happens in a reaction. It contains the following information: the number and kinds of reacting substances, or **reactants**; the chemical composition of the **product(s)**; and in balanced equations, the relative proportion of each reactant and product.

In the equations above, the reactants are atoms, as indicated by their atomic symbols (H, C). The product in each case is a

(a) **Synthesis reactions**	(b) **Decomposition reactions**	(c) **Exchange reactions**
Smaller particles are bonded together to form larger, more complex molecules.	Bonds are broken in larger molecules, resulting in smaller, less complex molecules.	Bonds are both made and broken (also called displacement reactions).

Figure 2.11 Patterns of chemical reactions.

molecule, as represented by its **molecular formula** (H_2, CH_4). The equation for the formation of methane may be read in terms of molecules or moles—as *either* "four hydrogen atoms plus one carbon atom yield one molecule of methane" *or* "four moles of hydrogen atoms plus one mole of carbon yield one mole of methane." Using moles is more practical because it is impossible to measure out one atom or one molecule of anything!

Patterns of Chemical Reactions

Most chemical reactions exhibit one of three recognizable patterns: They are either *synthesis*, *decomposition*, or *exchange reactions*.

When atoms or molecules combine to form a larger, more complex molecule, the process is a **synthesis**, or **combination**, **reaction**. A synthesis reaction always involves bond formation. It can be represented (using arbitrary letters) as

$$A + B \rightarrow AB$$

Synthesis reactions are the basis of constructive, or **anabolic**, activities in body cells, such as joining small molecules called amino acids into large protein molecules (**Figure 2.11a**). Synthesis reactions are conspicuous in rapidly growing tissues.

A **decomposition reaction** occurs when a molecule is broken down into smaller molecules or its constituent atoms:

$$AB \rightarrow A + B$$

Essentially, decomposition reactions are reverse synthesis reactions: Bonds are broken. Decomposition reactions underlie all degradative, or **catabolic**, processes in body cells. For example,

the bonds of glycogen molecules are broken to release simpler molecules of glucose sugar (Figure 2.11b).

Exchange, or **displacement**, **reactions** involve both synthesis and decomposition. Bonds are both made and broken. In an exchange reaction, parts of the reactant molecules change partners, so to speak, producing different product molecules:

$$AB + C \rightarrow AC + B \quad \text{and} \quad AB + CD \rightarrow AD + CB$$

An exchange reaction occurs when ATP reacts with glucose and transfers its end phosphate group (indicated by a circled P in Figure 2.11c) to glucose, forming glucose-phosphate. At the same time, the ATP becomes ADP. This important reaction occurs whenever glucose enters a body cell, and it effectively traps the glucose fuel molecule inside the cell.

Another group of important chemical reactions in living systems is **oxidation-reduction reactions**, called **redox reactions** for short. Oxidation-reduction reactions are decomposition reactions in that they are the basis of all reactions in which food fuels are broken down for energy (that is, in which ATP is produced). They are also a special type of exchange reaction because electrons are exchanged between the reactants. The reactant losing the electrons is referred to as the *electron donor* and is said to be **oxidized**. The reactant taking up the transferred electrons is called the *electron acceptor* and is said to become **reduced**.

Redox reactions also occur when ionic compounds are formed. Recall that in the formation of NaCl (see Figure 2.6), sodium loses an electron to chlorine. Consequently, sodium is oxidized and becomes a sodium ion, and chlorine is reduced and becomes a chloride ion. However, not all oxidation-reduction reactions involve *complete transfer* of electrons—some simply change the pattern of electron sharing in covalent bonds. For example, a substance is oxidized both by losing hydrogen atoms and by combining with oxygen. The common factor in these events is that electrons that formerly "belonged" to the reactant molecule are lost. The electrons are lost either entirely (as when hydrogen is removed and takes its electron with it) or relatively (as the shared electrons spend more time in the vicinity of the very electronegative oxygen atom).

To understand the importance of oxidation-reduction reactions in living systems, take a look at the overall equation for *cellular respiration*, which represents the major pathway by which glucose is broken down for energy in body cells:

$$C_6H_{12}O_6 + 6O_2 \rightarrow 6CO_2 + 6H_2O + ATP$$

glucose oxygen carbon   water cellular
                 dioxide   energy

As you can see, it is an oxidation-reduction reaction. Consider what happens to the hydrogen atoms (and their electrons). Glucose is oxidized to carbon dioxide as it loses hydrogen atoms, and oxygen is reduced to water as it accepts the hydrogen atoms. This reaction is described in detail in Chapter 24, along with other topics of cellular metabolism.

Energy Flow in Chemical Reactions

Because all chemical bonds represent stored chemical energy, all chemical reactions ultimately result in net absorption or release of energy. Reactions that release energy are called **exergonic reactions**. These reactions yield products with less energy than the initial reactants, along with energy that can be harvested for other uses. With a few exceptions, catabolic and oxidative reactions are exergonic.

In contrast, the products of energy-absorbing, or **endergonic**, reactions contain more potential energy in their chemical bonds than did the reactants. Anabolic reactions are typically energy-absorbing endergonic reactions. Essentially this is a case of "one hand washing the other"—the energy released when fuel molecules are broken down (oxidized) is captured in ATP molecules and then used to synthesize the complex biological molecules the body needs to sustain life.

Reversibility of Chemical Reactions

All chemical reactions are theoretically reversible. If chemical bonds can be made, they can be broken, and vice versa. Reversibility is indicated by a double arrow. When the arrows differ in length, the longer arrow indicates the major direction in which the reaction proceeds:

$$A + B \rightleftharpoons AB$$

In this example, the forward reaction (reaction going to the right) predominates. Over time, the product (AB) accumulates and the reactants (A and B) decrease in amount.

When the arrows are of equal length, as in

$$A + B \rightleftharpoons AB$$

neither the forward reaction nor the reverse reaction is dominant. In other words, for each molecule of product (AB) formed, one product molecule breaks down, releasing the reactants A and B. Such a chemical reaction is said to be in a state of **chemical equilibrium**.

Once chemical equilibrium is reached, there is no further *net change* in the amounts of reactants and products unless more of either are added to the mix. Product molecules are still formed and broken down, but the balance established when equilibrium was reached (such as greater numbers of product molecules) remains unchanged.

Chemical equilibrium is analogous to the admission scheme used by many large museums in which tickets are sold according to time of entry. If 300 tickets are issued for the 9 AM admission, 300 people will be admitted when the doors open. Thereafter, when 6 people leave, 6 are admitted, and when another 15 people leave, 15 more are allowed in. There is a continual turnover, but the museum contains about 300 art lovers throughout the day.

All chemical reactions are reversible, but many biological reactions show so little tendency to go in the reverse direction that they are irreversible for all practical purposes. Chemical reactions that release energy will not go in the opposite direction unless energy is put back into the system. For example, when our cells break down glucose via the reactions of cellular respiration to yield carbon dioxide and water, some of the energy released is trapped in the bonds of ATP. Because the cells then use ATP's energy for various functions (and more glucose will be along with the next meal), this particular reaction is never reversed in our cells. Furthermore, if a product of a reaction is continuously removed from the reaction site, it is unavailable to take part in the reverse reaction. This situation occurs when the carbon dioxide that is released during glucose breakdown leaves the cell, enters the blood, and is eventually removed from the body by the lungs.

Factors Influencing the Rate of Chemical Reactions

What influences how quickly chemical reactions go? For atoms and molecules to react chemically in the first place, they must *collide* with enough force to overcome the repulsion between their electrons. Interactions between valence shell electrons—the basis of bond making and breaking—cannot occur long distance. The force of collisions depends on how fast the particles are moving. Solid, forceful collisions between rapidly moving particles in which valence shells overlap are much more likely to cause reactions than are collisions in which the particles graze each other lightly.

Temperature   Increasing the temperature of a substance increases the kinetic energy of its particles and the force of their collisions. For this reason, chemical reactions proceed more quickly at higher temperatures.

Concentration   Chemical reactions progress most rapidly when the reacting particles are present in high numbers, because the chance of successful collisions is greater. As the concentration of the reactants declines, the reaction slows. Chemical equilibrium eventually occurs unless additional reactants are added or products are removed from the reaction site.

Particle Size Smaller particles move faster than larger ones (at the same temperature) and tend to collide more frequently and more forcefully. Hence, the smaller the reacting particles, the faster a chemical reaction goes at a given temperature and concentration.

Catalysts Many chemical reactions in nonliving systems can be speeded up simply by heating, but drastic increases in body temperature are life threatening because important biological molecules are destroyed. Still, at normal body temperatures, most chemical reactions would proceed far too slowly to maintain life were it not for the presence of catalysts. **Catalysts** (kat′ah-lists) are substances that increase the rate of chemical reactions without themselves becoming chemically changed or part of the product. Biological catalysts are called *enzymes* (en′zīmz). Later in this chapter we describe how enzymes work.

☑ **Check Your Understanding**

13. Which reaction type—synthesis, decomposition, or exchange—occurs when fats are digested in your small intestine?
14. Why are many reactions that occur in living systems irreversible for all intents and purposes?
15. What specific name is given to decomposition reactions in which food fuels are broken down for energy?

For answers, see Appendix H.

PART 2
Biochemistry

Biochemistry is the study of the chemical composition and reactions of living matter. All chemicals in the body fall into one of two major classes: organic or inorganic compounds. **Organic compounds** contain carbon. All organic compounds are covalently bonded molecules, and many are large.

All other chemicals in the body are considered **inorganic compounds**. These include water, salts, and many acids and bases. Organic and inorganic compounds are equally essential for life. Trying to decide which is more valuable is like trying to decide whether the ignition system or the engine is more essential to run your car!

Inorganic Compounds

✓ Explain the importance of water and salts to body homeostasis.

✓ Define acid and base, and explain the concept of pH.

Water

Water is the most abundant and important inorganic compound in living material. It makes up 60–80% of the volume of most living cells. What makes water so vital to life? The answer lies in several properties:

- **High heat capacity.** Water has a high heat capacity. In other words, it absorbs and releases large amounts of heat before changing appreciably in temperature itself. This property of water prevents sudden changes in temperature caused by external factors, such as sun or wind exposure, or by internal conditions that release heat rapidly, such as vigorous muscle activity. As part of blood, water redistributes heat among body tissues, ensuring temperature homeostasis.

- **High heat of vaporization.** When water evaporates, or vaporizes, it changes from a liquid to a gas (water vapor). This transformation requires that large amounts of heat be absorbed to break the hydrogen bonds that hold water molecules together. This property is extremely beneficial when we sweat. As perspiration (mostly water) evaporates from our skin, large amounts of heat are removed from the body, providing efficient cooling.

- **Polar solvent properties.** Water is an unparalleled solvent. Indeed, it is often called the **universal solvent**. Biochemistry is "wet chemistry." Biological molecules do not react chemically unless they are in solution, and virtually all chemical reactions occurring in the body depend on water's solvent properties.

    Because water molecules are polar, they orient themselves with their slightly negative ends toward the positive ends of the solutes, and vice versa, first attracting the solute molecules, and then surrounding them. This polarity of water explains why ionic compounds and other small reactive molecules (such as acids and bases) *dissociate* in water, their ions separating from each other and becoming evenly scattered in the water, forming true solutions (Figure 2.12).

    Water also forms layers of water molecules, called **hydration layers**, around large charged molecules such as proteins, shielding them from the effects of other charged substances in the vicinity and preventing them from settling out of solution. Such protein-water mixtures are *biological colloids*. Blood plasma and cerebrospinal fluid (which surrounds the brain and spinal cord) are examples of colloids.

    Water is the body's major transport medium because it is such an excellent solvent. Nutrients, respiratory gases, and metabolic wastes carried throughout the body are dissolved in blood plasma, and many metabolic wastes are excreted from the body in urine, another watery fluid. Specialized molecules that lubricate the body (e.g., mucus) also use water as their dissolving medium.

- **Reactivity.** Water is an important *reactant* in many chemical reactions. For example, foods are digested to their building blocks by adding a water molecule to each bond to be broken. Such decomposition reactions are more specifically called **hydrolysis reactions** (hi-drol′ĭ-sis; "water splitting"). Conversely, when large carbohydrate or protein molecules are synthesized from smaller molecules, a water molecule is removed for every bond formed, a reaction called **dehydration synthesis**.

- **Cushioning.** By forming a resilient cushion around certain body organs, water helps protect them from physical trauma.

The cerebrospinal fluid surrounding the brain exemplifies water's cushioning role.

Salts

A **salt** is an ionic compound containing cations other than H^+ and anions other than the hydroxyl ion (OH^-). As already noted, when salts are dissolved in water, they dissociate into their component ions (Figure 2.12). For example, sodium sulfate (Na_2SO_4) dissociates into two Na^+ ions and one SO_4^{2-} ion. It dissociates easily because the ions are already formed. All that remains is for water to overcome the attraction between the oppositely charged ions.

All ions are **electrolytes** (e-lek'tro-līts), substances that conduct an electrical current in solution. (Note that groups of atoms that bear an overall charge, such as sulfate, are called *polyatomic ions.*)

Salts commonly found in the body include NaCl, $CaCO_3$ (calcium carbonate), and KCl (potassium chloride). However, the most plentiful salts are the calcium phosphates that make bones and teeth hard. In their ionized form, salts play vital roles in body function. For instance, the electrolyte properties of sodium and potassium ions are essential for nerve impulse transmission and muscle contraction. Ionic iron forms part of the hemoglobin molecules that transport oxygen within red blood cells, and zinc and copper ions are important to the activity of some enzymes. Other important functions of the elements found in body salts are summarized in Table 2.1 on p. 26.

⚖ Homeostatic Imbalance 2.1

Maintaining proper ionic balance in our body fluids is one of the most crucial homeostatic roles of the kidneys. When this balance is severely disturbed, virtually nothing in the body works. All the physiological activities listed above and thousands of others are disrupted and grind to a stop. ✦

Acids and Bases

Like salts, acids and bases are electrolytes. They ionize and dissociate in water and can then conduct an electrical current.

Acids

Acids have a sour taste, can react with (dissolve) many metals, and "burn" a hole in your rug. But for our purposes the most useful definition of an acid is a substance that releases **hydrogen ions** (H^+) in detectable amounts. Because a hydrogen ion is just a hydrogen nucleus, or "naked" proton, acids are also defined as **proton donors**.

When acids dissolve in water, they release hydrogen ions (protons) and anions. It is the concentration of protons that determines the acidity of a solution. The anions have little or no effect on acidity. For example, hydrochloric acid (HCl), an acid produced by stomach cells that aids digestion, dissociates into a proton and a chloride ion:

$$HCl \rightarrow H^+ + Cl^-$$
proton   anion

Figure 2.12 Dissociation of salt in water.

Other acids found or produced in the body include acetic acid ($HC_2H_3O_2$, commonly abbreviated as HAc), which is the acidic portion of vinegar; and carbonic acid (H_2CO_3). The molecular formula for an acid is easy to recognize because the hydrogen is written first.

Bases

Bases have a bitter taste, feel slippery, and are **proton acceptors**— that is, they take up hydrogen ions (H^+) in detectable amounts. Common inorganic bases include the *hydroxides* (hi-drok'sīds), such as magnesium hydroxide (milk of magnesia) and sodium hydroxide (lye). Like acids, hydroxides dissociate when dissolved in water, but in this case **hydroxyl ions (OH^-)** (hi-drok'sil) and cations are liberated. For example, ionization of sodium hydroxide (NaOH) produces a hydroxyl ion and a sodium ion, and the hydroxyl ion then binds to (accepts) a proton present in the solution. This reaction produces water and simultaneously reduces the acidity (hydrogen ion concentration) of the solution:

$$NaOH \rightarrow Na^+ + OH^-$$
cation   hydroxyl
ion

and then

$$OH^- + H^+ \rightarrow H_2O$$
water

Concentration
(moles/liter)

Figure 2.13 The pH scale and pH values of representative substances. The pH scale is based on the number of hydrogen ions in solution. The actual concentrations of hydrogen ions, [H$^+$], and hydroxyl ions, [OH$^-$], in moles per liter are indicated for each pH value noted. At a pH of 7, [H$^+$] = [OH$^-$] and the solution is neutral.

Bicarbonate ion (HCO$_3^-$), an important base in the body, is particularly abundant in blood. **Ammonia (NH$_3$)**, a common waste product of protein breakdown in the body, is also a base. It has one pair of unshared electrons that strongly attracts protons. By accepting a proton, ammonia becomes an ammonium ion:

$$NH_3 + H^+ \rightarrow NH_4^+$$
$$\text{ammonium}$$
$$\text{ion}$$

pH: Acid-Base Concentration

The more hydrogen ions in a solution, the more acidic the solution is. Conversely, the greater the concentration of hydroxyl ions (the lower the concentration of H$^+$), the more basic, or *alkaline* (al'kuh-līn), the solution becomes. The relative concentration of hydrogen ions in various body fluids is measured in concentration units called **pH units** (pe-āch').

The idea for a pH scale was devised by a Danish biochemist and part-time beer brewer named Sören Sörensen in 1909. He was searching for a convenient means of checking the acidity of his alcoholic product to prevent its spoilage by bacterial action. (Acidic conditions inhibit many bacteria.) The pH scale that resulted is based on the concentration of hydrogen ions in a solution, expressed in terms of moles per liter, or molarity. The pH scale runs from 0 to 14 and is *logarithmic*. In other words, each successive change of one pH unit represents a tenfold change in hydrogen ion concentration **(Figure 2.13)**. The pH of a solution is thus defined as the negative logarithm of the hydrogen ion concentration [H$^+$] in moles per liter, or $-$log[H$^+$]. (Note that brackets [ ] indicate concentration of a substance.)

At a pH of 7 (at which [H$^+$] is 10^{-7} *M*), the solution is *neutral*—neither acidic nor basic. The number of hydrogen ions exactly equals the number of hydroxyl ions (pH = pOH). Absolutely pure (distilled) water has a pH of 7.

Solutions with a pH below 7 are acidic—the hydrogen ions outnumber the hydroxyl ions. The lower the pH, the more acidic the solution. A solution with a pH of 6 has ten times as many hydrogen ions as a solution with a pH of 7.

Solutions with a pH higher than 7 are alkaline, and the relative concentration of hydrogen ions decreases by a factor of 10 with each higher pH unit. Thus, solutions with pH values of 8 and 12 have, respectively, 1/10 and 1/100,000 (1/10 × 1/10 × 1/10 × 1/10 × 1/10) as many hydrogen ions as a solution of pH 7.

The approximate pH of several body fluids and of a number of common substances appears in Figure 2.13. Notice that as the hydrogen ion concentration decreases, the hydroxyl ion concentration rises, and vice versa.

Neutralization

What happens when acids and bases are mixed? They react with each other in displacement reactions to form water and a salt. For example, when hydrochloric acid and sodium hydroxide interact, sodium chloride (a salt) and water are formed.

$$HCl + NaOH \rightarrow NaCl + H_2O$$
$$\text{acid} \quad \text{base} \quad \text{salt} \quad \text{water}$$

This type of reaction is called a **neutralization reaction**, because the joining of H$^+$ and OH$^-$ to form water neutralizes the solution. Although the salt produced is written in molecular form (NaCl), remember that it actually exists as dissociated sodium and chloride ions when dissolved in water.

Buffers

Living cells are extraordinarily sensitive to even slight changes in the pH of the environment. In high concentrations, acids and bases are extremely damaging to living tissue. Imagine what would happen to all those hydrogen bonds in biological molecules with large numbers of free H$^+$ running around. (Can't you just hear those molecules saying "Why share hydrogen when I can have my own?")

Homeostasis of acid-base balance is carefully regulated by the kidneys and lungs and by chemical systems (proteins and other types of molecules) called **buffers**. Buffers resist abrupt and large swings in the pH of body fluids by releasing hydrogen ions (acting as acids) when the pH begins to rise and by binding hydrogen ions (acting as bases) when the pH drops. Because blood comes into close contact with nearly every body cell, regulating its pH is particularly critical. Normally, blood pH varies within a very narrow range (7.35 to 7.45). If blood pH varies from these limits by more than a few tenths of a unit, it may be fatal.

To comprehend how chemical buffer systems operate, you must thoroughly understand strong and weak acids and bases. The first important concept is that the acidity of a solution reflects *only* the free hydrogen ions, not those still bound to anions. Consequently, acids that dissociate completely and irreversibly in water are called **strong acids**, because they can dramatically change the pH of a solution. Examples are hydrochloric acid and sulfuric acid. If we could count out 100 hydrochloric acid molecules and place them in 1 milliliter (ml) of water, we could expect to end up with 100 H$^+$, 100 Cl$^-$, and no undissociated hydrochloric acid molecules in that solution.

Acids that do not dissociate completely, like carbonic acid (H$_2$CO$_3$) and acetic acid (HAc), are **weak acids**. If we were to place 100 acetic acid molecules in 1 ml of water, the reaction would be something like this:

$$100 \text{ HAc} \rightarrow 90 \text{ HAc} + 10 \text{ H}^+ + 10 \text{ Ac}^-$$

Because undissociated acids do not affect pH, the acetic acid solution is much less acidic than the HCl solution. Weak acids dissociate in a predictable way, and molecules of the intact acid are in dynamic equilibrium with the dissociated ions. Consequently, the dissociation of acetic acid may also be written as

$$\text{HAc} \rightleftharpoons \text{H}^+ + \text{Ac}^-$$

This viewpoint allows us to see that if H$^+$ (released by a strong acid) is added to the acetic acid solution, the equilibrium will shift to the left and some H$^+$ and Ac$^-$ will recombine to form HAc. On the other hand, if a strong base is added and the pH begins to rise, the equilibrium shifts to the right and more HAc molecules dissociate to release H$^+$. This characteristic of weak acids allows them to play important roles in the chemical buffer systems of the body.

The concept of strong and weak bases is more easily explained. Remember that bases are proton acceptors. Thus, **strong bases** are those, like hydroxides, that dissociate easily in water and quickly tie up H$^+$. On the other hand, sodium bicarbonate (commonly known as baking soda) ionizes incompletely and reversibly. Because it accepts relatively few protons, its released bicarbonate ion is considered a **weak base**.

Now let's examine how one buffer system helps to maintain pH homeostasis of the blood. Although there are other chemical blood buffers, the **carbonic acid–bicarbonate system** is a major one. Carbonic acid (H$_2$CO$_3$) dissociates reversibly, releasing bicarbonate ions (HCO$_3^-$) and protons (H$^+$):

Response to rise in pH

$$\text{H}_2\text{CO}_3 \rightleftharpoons \text{HCO}_3^- + \text{H}^+$$

H$^+$ donor   Response to drop in pH   H$^+$ acceptor   proton
(weak acid)   (weak base)

The chemical equilibrium between carbonic acid (a weak acid) and bicarbonate ion (a weak base) resists changes in blood pH by shifting to the right or left as H$^+$ ions are added to or removed from the blood. As blood pH rises (becomes more alkaline due to the addition of a strong base), the equilibrium shifts to the right, forcing more carbonic acid to dissociate. Similarly, as blood pH begins to drop (becomes more acidic due to the addition of a strong acid), the equilibrium shifts to the left as more bicarbonate ions begin to bind with protons. As you can see, strong bases are replaced by a weak base (bicarbonate ion) and protons released by strong acids are tied up in a weak one (carbonic acid). In either case, the blood pH changes much less than it would in the absence of the buffering system. We discuss acid-base balance and buffers in more detail in Chapter 26.

☑ Check Your Understanding

16. Water makes up 60–80% of living matter. What property makes it an excellent solvent?
17. Salts are electrolytes. What does that mean?
18. Which ion is responsible for increased acidity?
19. To minimize the sharp pH shift that occurs when a strong acid is added to a solution, is it better to add a weak base or a strong base? Why?

For answers, see Appendix H.

Organic Compounds

✓ Describe and compare the building blocks, general structures, and biological functions of carbohydrates and lipids.

✓ Explain the role of dehydration synthesis and hydrolysis in forming and breaking down organic molecules.

Molecules unique to living systems—carbohydrates, lipids (fats), proteins, and nucleic acids—all contain carbon and hence are organic compounds. Organic compounds are generally distinguished by the fact that they contain carbon, and inorganic

(a) Dehydration synthesis

Monomers are joined by removal of OH from one monomer
and removal of H from the other at the site of bond formation.

Monomers linked by covalent bond

(b) Hydrolysis

Monomers are released by the addition of a water molecule, adding OH to one monomer and H to the other.

Monomers linked by covalent bond

(c) Example reactions

Dehydration synthesis of sucrose and its breakdown by hydrolysis

Figure 2.14 Dehydration synthesis and hydrolysis. Biological molecules are formed
from their monomers, or units, by dehydration synthesis and broken down to the monomers
by hydrolysis reactions.

compounds are defined as compounds that lack carbon. You
should be aware of a few irrational exceptions to this generalization: Carbon dioxide and carbon monoxide, for example, contain carbon but are considered inorganic compounds.

For the most part, organic molecules are very large molecules, but their interactions with other molecules typically
involve only small, reactive parts of their structure called *functional groups* (acid groups, amines, and others). The most important functional groups involved in biochemical reactions are
illustrated in Appendix B.

What makes carbon so special that "living" chemistry depends on its presence? To begin with, no other *small* atom is
so precisely **electroneutral**. The consequence of its electro-
neutrality is that carbon never loses or gains electrons. Instead, it always shares them. Furthermore, with four valence
shell electrons, carbon forms four covalent bonds with other

elements, as well as with other carbon atoms. As a result, carbon can help form long, chainlike molecules (common in
fats), ring structures (typical of carbohydrates and steroids),
and many other structures that are uniquely suited for specific roles in the body.

As you will see shortly, many biological molecules (carbohydrates and proteins for example) are polymers. **Polymers**
are chainlike molecules made of many similar or repeating
units (**monomers**), which are joined together by dehydration synthesis (**Figure 2.14**). During dehydration synthesis, a hydrogen atom is removed from one monomer and
a hydroxyl group is removed from the monomer it is to be
joined with. As a covalent bond unites the monomers, a water molecule is released. This removal of a water molecule at
the bond site occurs each time a monomer is added to the
growing polymer chain.

Carbohydrates

Carbohydrates, a group of molecules that includes sugars and starches, represent 1–2% of cell mass. Carbohydrates contain carbon, hydrogen, and oxygen, and generally the hydrogen and oxygen atoms occur in the same 2:1 ratio as in water. This ratio is reflected in the word *carbohydrate* ("hydrated carbon").

A carbohydrate can be classified according to size and solubility as a monosaccharide ("one sugar"), disaccharide ("two sugars"), or polysaccharide ("many sugars"). Monosaccharides are the monomers, or building blocks, of the other carbohydrates. In general, the larger the carbohydrate molecule, the less soluble it is in water.

Monosaccharides

Monosaccharides (mon″o-sak′ah-rīdz), or *simple sugars*, are single-chain or single-ring structures containing from three to seven carbon atoms (**Figure 2.15a**). Usually the carbon, hydrogen, and oxygen atoms occur in the ratio 1:2:1, so a general formula for a monosaccharide is $(CH_2O)_n$, where *n* is the number of carbons in the sugar. Glucose, for example, has six carbon atoms, and its molecular formula is $C_6H_{12}O_6$. Ribose, with five carbons, is $C_5H_{10}O_5$.

Monosaccharides are named generically according to the number of carbon atoms they contain. Most important in the body are the pentose (five-carbon) and hexose (six-carbon) sugars. For example, the pentose *deoxyribose* (de-ok″sĭ-ri′bōs) is part of DNA, and *glucose*, a hexose, is blood sugar.

Two other hexoses, *galactose* and *fructose*, are **isomers** (ī′so-mers) of glucose. That is, they have the same molecular formula ($C_6H_{12}O_6$), but as you can see in Figure 2.15a, their atoms are arranged differently, giving them different chemical properties.

Disaccharides

A **disaccharide** (di-sak′ah-rīd), or *double sugar*, is formed when two monosaccharides are joined by *dehydration synthesis* (Figure 2.14a, c). In this synthesis reaction, a water molecule is lost as the bond is made, as illustrated by the synthesis of sucrose (soo′krōs):

$$2C_6H_{12}O_6 \rightarrow C_{12}H_{22}O_{11} + H_2O$$
glucose + fructose   sucrose   water

Notice that the molecular formula for sucrose contains two hydrogen atoms and one oxygen atom less than the total number of hydrogen and oxygen atoms in glucose and fructose, because a water molecule is released during bond formation.

Important disaccharides in the diet are *sucrose* (glucose + fructose), which is cane or table sugar; *lactose* (glucose + galactose), found in milk; and *maltose* (glucose + glucose), also called malt sugar (Figure 2.15b). Disaccharides are too large to pass through cell membranes, so they must be digested to their simple sugar units to be absorbed from the digestive tract into the blood. This decomposition process is *hydrolysis*, essentially the reverse of dehydration synthesis (Figure 2.14a, b). A water molecule is added to each bond, breaking the bonds and releasing the simple sugar units.

Polysaccharides

Polysaccharides (pol″e-sak′ah-rīdz) are polymers of simple sugars linked together by dehydration synthesis. Because polysaccharides are large, fairly insoluble molecules, they are ideal storage products. Another consequence of their large size is that they lack the sweetness of the simple and double sugars.

Only two polysaccharides are of major importance to the body: starch and glycogen. Both are polymers of glucose. Only their degree of branching differs.

Starch is the storage carbohydrate formed by plants. The number of glucose units composing a starch molecule is high and variable. When we eat starchy foods such as grain products and potatoes, the starch must be digested for its glucose units to be absorbed. We are unable to digest *cellulose*, another polysaccharide found in all plant products. However, it is important in providing the *bulk* (one form of fiber) that helps move feces through the colon.

Glycogen (gli′ko-jen), the storage carbohydrate of animal tissues, is stored primarily in skeletal muscle and liver cells. Like starch, it is highly branched and is a very large molecule (Figure 2.15c). When blood sugar levels drop sharply, liver cells break down glycogen and release its glucose units to the blood. Since there are many branch endings from which glucose can be released simultaneously, body cells have almost instant access to glucose fuel.

Carbohydrate Functions

The major function of carbohydrates in the body is to provide a ready, easily used source of cellular fuel. Most cells can use only a few types of simple sugars, and glucose is at the top of the "cellular menu." As described in our earlier discussion of oxidation-reduction reactions (pp. 36–37), glucose is broken down and oxidized within cells. During these chemical reactions, electrons are transferred. This relocation of electrons releases the bond energy stored in glucose, and this energy is used to synthesize ATP. When ATP supplies are sufficient, dietary carbohydrates are converted to glycogen or fat and stored. Those of us who have gained weight from eating too many carbohydrate-rich snacks have personal experience with this conversion process!

Only small amounts of carbohydrates are used for structural purposes. For example, some sugars are found in our genes. Others are attached to the external surfaces of cells where they act as "road signs" to guide cellular interactions.

Lipids

Lipids are insoluble in water but dissolve readily in other lipids and in organic solvents such as alcohol and ether. Like carbohydrates, all lipids contain carbon, hydrogen, and oxygen, but the proportion of oxygen in lipids is much lower. In addition, phosphorus is found in some of the more complex lipids. Lipids include *triglycerides*, *phospholipids* (fos″fo-lip′idz), *steroids* (stĕ′roidz), and a number of other lipoid substances. **Table 2.2** on p. 46 gives the locations and functions of some lipids found in the body.

2

(a) Monosaccharides

Monomers of carbohydrates

Example
Hexose sugars (the hexoses shown here are isomers)

Glucose

Fructose

Galactose

Example
Pentose sugars

Deoxyribose

Ribose

(b) Disaccharides

Consist of two linked monosaccharides

Example
Sucrose, maltose, and lactose
(these disaccharides are isomers)

Glucose   Fructose

Sucrose

Glucose   Glucose

Maltose

Galactose   Glucose

Lactose

(c) Polysaccharides

Long chains (polymers) of linked monosaccharides

Example
This polysaccharide is a simplified representation of
glycogen, a polysaccharide formed from glucose units.

Glycogen

Figure 2.15 Carbohydrate molecules important to the body.*

*Notice that in Figure 2.15 the carbon (C) atoms present at the angles of the carbohydrate ring structures are not illustrated and in Figure 2.15c only the oxygen atoms and one CH_2 group are shown. The illustrations at right give an example of this shorthand style: The full structure of glucose is on the left and the shorthand structure on the right. This style is used for nearly all organic ringlike structures illustrated in this chapter.

(a) Triglyceride formation

Three fatty acid chains are bound to glycerol by dehydration synthesis.

| Glycerol | 3 fatty acid chains | Triglyceride, or neutral fat | 3 water molecules |

(b) "Typical" structure of a phospholipid molecule

Two fatty acid chains and a phosphorus-containing group are attached to the glycerol backbone.

Example
Phosphatidylcholine

Polar "head"

Nonpolar "tail"
(schematic phospholipid)

| Phosphorus-containing group (polar "head") | Glycerol backbone | 2 fatty acid chains (nonpolar "tail") |

(c) Simplified structure of a steroid

Four interlocking hydrocarbon rings form a steroid.

Example
Cholesterol (cholesterol is the
basis for all steroids formed in the body)

Figure 2.16 Lipids. The general structure of **(a)** triglycerides, or neutral fats, **(b)** phospholipids, and **(c)** cholesterol.

and **glycerol** (glis'er-ol), in a 3:1 ratio of fatty acids to glycerol **(Figure 2.16a)**. Fatty acids are linear chains of carbon and hydrogen atoms (hydrocarbon chains) with an organic acid group (—COOH) at one end. Glycerol is a modified simple sugar (a sugar alcohol).

Fat synthesis involves attaching three fatty acid chains to a single glycerol molecule by dehydration synthesis. The result is an E-shaped molecule. The glycerol backbone is the same in all triglycerides, but the fatty acid chains vary, resulting in different kinds of fats and oils.

These are large molecules, often consisting of hundreds of atoms, and ingested fats and oils must be broken down to their building blocks before they can be absorbed. Their hydrocarbon chains make the triglycerides nonpolar molecules. Because polar and nonpolar molecules do not interact, oil (or fats) and water do not mix. Consequently, triglycerides provide the body's

Triglycerides (Neutral Fats)

Triglycerides (tri-glis'er-īdz), also called **neutral fats**, are commonly known as *fats* when solid or *oils* when liquid. A triglyceride is composed of two types of building blocks, **fatty acids**

Table 2.2	Representative Lipids Found in the Body
LIPID TYPE	**LOCATION/FUNCTION**
Triglycerides (Neutral Fats)	
	Fat deposits (in subcutaneous tissue and around organs) protect and insulate body organs, and are the major source of *stored* energy in the body.
Phospholipids (phosphatidylcholine; cephalin; others)	
	Chief components of cell membranes. Participate in the transport of lipids in plasma. Prevalent in nervous tissue.
Steroids	
Cholesterol	The structural basis for manufacture of all body steroids. A component of cell membranes.
Bile salts	These breakdown products of cholesterol are released by the liver into the digestive tract, where they aid fat digestion and absorption.
Vitamin D	A fat-soluble vitamin produced in the skin on exposure to UV radiation. Necessary for normal bone growth and function.
Sex hormones	Estrogen and progesterone (female hormones) and testosterone (a male hormone) are produced in the gonads. Necessary for normal reproductive function.
Adrenocortical hormones	Cortisol, a glucocorticoid, is a metabolic hormone necessary for maintaining normal blood glucose levels. Aldosterone helps to regulate salt and water balance of the body by targeting the kidneys.
Other Lipoid Substances	
Fat-soluble vitamins:	
A	Ingested in orange-pigmented vegetables and fruits. Converted in the retina to retinal, a part of the photoreceptor pigment involved in vision.
E	Ingested in plant products such as wheat germ and green leafy vegetables. Claims have been made (but not proved in humans) that it promotes wound healing, contributes to fertility, and may help to neutralize highly reactive particles called free radicals believed to be involved in triggering some types of cancer.
K	Made available to humans largely by the action of intestinal bacteria. Also prevalent in a wide variety of foods. Necessary for proper clotting of blood.
Eicosanoids (prostaglandins; leukotrienes; thromboxanes)	Group of molecules derived from fatty acids found in all cell membranes. The potent prostaglandins have diverse effects, including stimulation of uterine contractions, regulation of blood pressure, control of gastrointestinal tract motility, and secretory activity. Both prostaglandins and leukotrienes are involved in inflammation. Thromboxanes are powerful vasoconstrictors.
Lipoproteins	Lipid and protein-based substances that transport fatty acids and cholesterol in the bloodstream. Major varieties are high-density lipoproteins (HDLs) and low-density lipoproteins (LDLs).

most efficient and compact form of stored energy, and when they are oxidized, they yield large amounts of energy.

Triglycerides are found mainly beneath the skin, where they insulate the deeper body tissues from heat loss and protect them from mechanical trauma. For example, women are usually more successful English Channel swimmers than men. Their success is due partly to their thicker subcutaneous fatty layer, which helps insulate them from the bitterly cold water of the Channel.

The length of a triglyceride's fatty acid chains and their degree of *saturation* with H atoms determine how solid the molecule is at a given temperature. Fatty acid chains with only single covalent bonds between carbon atoms are referred to as **saturated**. Their fatty acid chains are straight and, at room temperature, the molecules of a saturated fat are packed closely together, forming a solid. Fatty acids that contain one or more double bonds between carbon atoms are said to be **unsaturated** (**monounsaturated** and **polyunsaturated**, respectively). The double bonds cause the fatty acid chains to kink so that they cannot be packed closely enough to solidify. Hence, triglycerides with short fatty acid chains or unsaturated fatty acids are oils (liquid at room temperature) and are typical of plant lipids. Examples include olive and peanut oils (rich in monounsaturated fats) and corn, soybean, and safflower oils, which contain a high percentage of polyunsaturated fatty acids. Longer fatty acid chains and more saturated fatty acids are common in animal fats such as butterfat and the fat of meats, which are solid at room temperature. Of the two types of fatty acids, the unsaturated variety, especially olive oil, is said to be more "heart healthy."

Trans fats, common in many margarines and baked products, are oils that have been solidified by addition of H atoms at sites of carbon double bonds. They have recently been branded as increasing the risk of heart disease even more than the solid animal fats. Conversely, the **omega-3 fatty acids**, found naturally in cold-water fish, appear to decrease the risk of heart disease and some inflammatory diseases.

Phospholipids

Phospholipids are modified triglycerides. Specifically, they are diglycerides with a phosphorus-containing group and two, rather than three, fatty acid chains (Figure 2.16b). The phosphorus-containing group gives phospholipids their distinctive chemical properties. Although the hydrocarbon portion (the "tail") of the molecule is nonpolar and interacts only with nonpolar molecules, the phosphorus-containing part (the "head") is polar and attracts other polar or charged particles, such as water or ions. This unique characteristic of phospholipids allows them to be used as the chief material for building cellular membranes. Some biologically important phospholipids and their functions are listed in Table 2.2.

Steroids

Structurally, steroids differ quite a bit from fats and oils. **Steroids** are basically flat molecules made of four interlocking hydrocarbon rings. Like triglycerides, steroids are fat soluble and contain little oxygen. The single most important molecule in our steroid chemistry is *cholesterol* (ko-les′ter-ol) (Figure 2.16c). We ingest cholesterol in animal products such as eggs, meat, and cheese, and our liver produces some.

Cholesterol has earned bad press because of its role in atherosclerosis, but it is essential for human life. Cholesterol is found in cell membranes and is the raw material for synthesis of vitamin D, steroid hormones, and bile salts. Although steroid hormones are present in the body in only small quantities, they are vital to homeostasis. Without sex hormones, reproduction would be impossible, and a total lack of the corticosteroids produced by the adrenal glands is fatal.

Eicosanoids

The **eicosanoids** (i-ko′sah-noyds) are diverse lipids chiefly derived from a 20-carbon fatty acid (arachidonic acid) found in all cell membranes. Most important of these are the *prostaglandins* and their relatives, which play roles in various body processes including blood clotting, regulation of blood pressure, inflammation, and labor contractions (Table 2.2). Their synthesis and inflammatory actions are blocked by NSAIDs (nonsteroidal anti-inflammatory drugs) and the newer COX inhibitors.

☑ Check Your Understanding

20. What are the monomers of carbohydrates called? Which monomer is blood sugar?
21. What is the animal form of stored carbohydrate called?
22. How do triglycerides differ from phospholipids in body function and location?
23. What is the result of hydrolysis reactions and how are these reactions accomplished in the body?

For answers, see Appendix H.

Proteins

✓ Describe the four levels of protein structure.
✓ Indicate the function of molecular chaperones.
✓ Describe enzyme action.

The full set of proteins made by the body, called the *proteome*, and the way those proteins network in the body or change with disease, is a matter of intense biotech research.

Protein composes 10–30% of cell mass and is the basic structural material of the body. However, not all proteins are construction materials. Many play vital roles in cell function. Proteins, which include enzymes (biological catalysts), hemoglobin of the blood, and contractile proteins of muscle, have the most varied functions of any molecules in the body. All proteins contain carbon, oxygen, hydrogen, and nitrogen, and many contain sulfur as well.

Amino Acids and Peptide Bonds

The building blocks of proteins are molecules called **amino acids**, of which there are 20 common types (see Appendix C). All amino acids have two important functional groups: a basic group called an *amine* (ah′mēn) *group* ($-NH_2$), and an organic *acid group* ($-COOH$). An amino acid may therefore act either as a base (proton acceptor) or an acid (proton donor). All amino acids are identical except for a single group of atoms called their *R group*. Hence, it is differences in the R group that make each amino acid chemically unique, as the examples in **Figure 2.17** show.

Proteins are long chains of amino acids joined together by dehydration synthesis, with the amine end of one amino acid linked to the acid end of the next. The resulting bond produces a characteristic arrangement of linked atoms called a **peptide bond** (Figure 2.18). Two united amino acids form a *dipeptide*, three a *tripeptide*, and ten or more a *polypeptide*. Although polypeptides containing more than 50 amino acids are called proteins, most proteins are **macromolecules**, large, complex molecules containing from 100 to over 10,000 amino acids.

Because each type of amino acid has distinct properties, the sequence in which they are bound together produces proteins that vary widely in both structure and function. We can think of the 20 amino acids as a 20-letter "alphabet" used in specific combinations to form "words" (proteins). Just as a change in one letter can produce a word with an entirely different meaning (flour → floor) or that is nonsensical (flour → flocr), changes in the kinds or positions of amino acids can yield proteins with different functions or proteins that are nonfunctional. Nevertheless, there are thousands of different proteins in the body, each with distinct functional properties, and all constructed from different combinations of the 20 common amino acids.

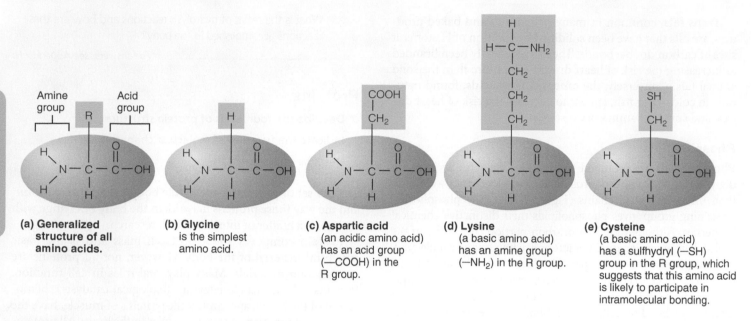

Figure 2.17 Amino acid structures. All amino acids have both an amine group (—NH₂) and an acid group (—COOH). They differ only in their R groups (green). Differences in their R groups allow them to function differently in the body.

Structural Levels of Proteins

Proteins can be described in terms of four structural levels. The linear sequence of amino acids composing the polypeptide chain is called the *primary structure* of a protein. This structure, which resembles a strand of amino acid "beads," is the backbone of the protein molecule **(Figure 2.19a)**.

Proteins do not normally exist as simple, linear chains of amino acids. Instead, they twist or bend upon themselves to form a more complex *secondary structure*. The most common type of secondary structure is the **alpha (α)-helix**, which resembles a Slinky toy or the coils of a telephone cord (Figure 2.19b). The α-helix is formed by coiling of the primary chain and is stabilized by hydrogen bonds formed between NH and CO groups in amino acids in the primary chain which are approximately

four amino acids apart. Hydrogen bonds in α-helices always link different parts of the *same* chain together.

In another type of secondary structure, the **beta (β)-pleated sheet**, the primary polypeptide chains do not coil, but are linked side by side by hydrogen bonds to form a pleated, ribbonlike structure that resembles an accordion's bellows (Figure 2.19b). Notice that in this type of secondary structure, the hydrogen bonds may link together *different polypeptide chains* as well as *different parts* of the same chain that has folded back on itself. A single polypeptide chain may exhibit both types of secondary structure at various places along its length.

Many proteins have *tertiary structure* (ter′she-a″re), the next higher level of complexity, which is superimposed on secondary structure. Tertiary structure is achieved when α-helical or

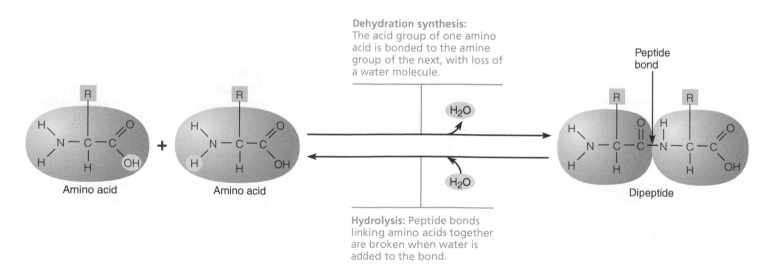

Dehydration synthesis: The acid group of one amino acid is bonded to the amine group of the next, with loss of a water molecule.

Hydrolysis: Peptide bonds linking amino acids together are broken when water is added to the bond.

Figure 2.18 Amino acids are linked together by peptide bonds. Peptide bonds are formed by dehydration synthesis and broken by hydrolysis reactions.

2

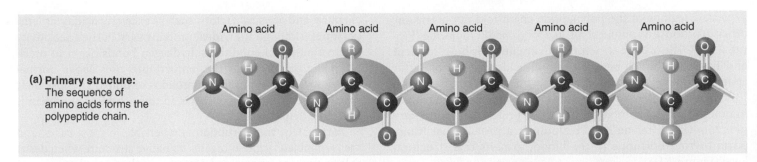

(a) Primary structure:
The sequence of amino acids forms the polypeptide chain.

(b) Secondary structure:
The primary chain forms spirals (α-helices) and sheets (β-sheets).

α-Helix: The primary chain is coiled to form a spiral structure, which is stabilized by hydrogen bonds.

β-Sheet: The primary chain "zig-zags" back and forth forming a "pleated" sheet. Adjacent strands are held together by hydrogen bonds.

(c) Tertiary structure:
Superimposed on secondary structure. α-Helices and/or β-sheets are folded up to form a compact globular molecule held together by intramolecular bonds.

Tertiary structure of prealbumin (transthyretin), a protein that transports the thyroid hormone thyroxine in blood and cerebro-spinal fluid.

(d) Quaternary structure:
Two or more polypeptide chains, each with its own tertiary structure, combine to form a functional protein.

Quaternary structure of a functional prealbumin molecule. Two identical prealbumin subunits join head to tail to form the dimer.

Figure 2.19 Levels of protein structure.

β-pleated regions of the polypeptide chain fold upon one another to produce a compact ball-like, or *globular*, molecule (Figure 2.19c). The unique structure is maintained by both covalent and hydrogen bonds between amino acids that are often far apart in the primary chain.

When two or more polypeptide chains aggregate in a regular manner to form a complex protein, the protein has *quaternary structure* (kwah'ter-na"re). Prealbumin, a protein that transports thyroid hormone in the blood, exhibits this structural level (Figure 2.19d).

How do these different levels of structure arise? Although a protein with tertiary or quaternary structure looks a bit like a clump of congealed pasta, the ultimate overall structure of any protein is very specific and is dictated by its primary structure. In other words, the types and relative positions of amino acids in the protein backbone determine where bonds can form to produce the complex coiled or folded structures that keep water-loving amino acids near the surface and water-fleeing amino acids buried in the protein's core. In addition, cells decorate many proteins by attaching sugars or fatty acids to them in ways that are difficult to imagine or predict.

Fibrous and Globular Proteins

The overall structure of a protein determines its biological function. In general, proteins are classified according to their overall appearance and shape as either fibrous or globular.

Fibrous proteins are extended and strandlike. Some exhibit only secondary structure, but most have tertiary or even quaternary structure as well. For example, *collagen* (kol'ah-jen) is a composite of the helical tropocollagen molecules packed together side by side to form a strong ropelike structure. Fibrous proteins are insoluble in water, and very stable—qualities ideal for providing mechanical support and tensile strength to the body's tissues. Besides collagen, which is the single most abundant protein in the body, the fibrous proteins include keratin, elastin, and certain contractile proteins of muscle **(Table 2.3)**. Because fibrous proteins are the chief building materials of the body, they are also known as **structural proteins**.

Globular proteins are compact, spherical proteins that have at least tertiary structure. Some also exhibit quaternary structure. The globular proteins are water-soluble, chemically active molecules, and they play crucial roles in virtually all biological processes. Consequently, this group is also called **functional proteins**. Some (antibodies) help to provide immunity, others (protein-based hormones) regulate growth and development, and still others (enzymes) are catalysts that oversee just about every chemical reaction in the body. The roles of these and selected other proteins found in the body are summarized in Table 2.3.

Protein Denaturation

Fibrous proteins are stable, but globular proteins are quite the opposite. The activity of a protein depends on its specific three-dimensional structure, and intramolecular bonds, particularly hydrogen bonds, are important in maintaining that structure. However, hydrogen bonds are fragile and easily broken by many chemical and physical factors, such as excessive acidity or temperature. Although individual proteins vary in their sensitivity to environmental conditions, hydrogen bonds begin to break when the pH drops or the temperature rises above normal (physiological) levels, causing proteins to unfold and lose their specific three-dimensional shape. In this condition, a protein is said to be **denatured**.

Fortunately, the disruption is reversible in most cases, and the "scrambled" protein regains its native structure when desirable conditions are restored. However, if the temperature or pH change is so extreme that protein structure is damaged beyond repair, the protein is *irreversibly denatured*. The coagulation of egg white (primarily albumin protein) that occurs when you boil or fry an egg is an example of irreversible protein denaturation. There is no way to restore the white, rubbery protein to its original translucent form.

When globular proteins are denatured, they can no longer perform their physiological roles because their function depends on the presence of specific arrangements of atoms, called **active sites**, on their surfaces. The active sites are regions that fit and interact chemically with other molecules of complementary shape and charge. Because atoms contributing to an active site may actually be far apart in the primary chain, disruption of intramolecular bonds separates them and destroys the active site. For example, hemoglobin becomes totally unable to bind and transport oxygen when blood pH is too acidic, because the structure needed for its function has been destroyed.

We will describe most types of body proteins in conjunction with the organ systems or functional processes to which they are closely related. However, two groups of proteins—*molecular chaperones* and *enzymes*—are intimately involved in the normal functioning of all cells, so we will consider these incredibly complex molecules here.

☑ Check Your Understanding

24. What does the name "amino acid" tell you about the structure of this molecule?
25. What is the primary structure of proteins?
26. What are the two types of secondary structure in proteins?

For answers, see Appendix H.

Molecular Chaperones

In addition to enzymes, all cells contain a class of unrelated globular proteins called **molecular chaperones** which, among other things, help proteins to achieve their functional three-dimensional structure. Although its amino acid sequence determines the precise way a protein folds, the folding process also requires the help of molecular chaperones to ensure that the folding is quick and accurate. Molecular chaperones can associate with a broad range of "client" proteins, allowing them to perform a dizzying array of jobs. For example, specific molecular chaperones

- Prevent accidental, premature, or incorrect folding of polypeptide chains or their association with other polypeptides
- Aid the desired folding and association process

Table 2.3 Representative Types of Proteins in the Body

CLASSIFICATION ACCORDING TO

OVERALL STRUCTURE	GENERAL FUNCTION	EXAMPLES FROM THE BODY
Fibrous		
	Structural framework/ mechanical support	*Collagen*, found in all connective tissues, is the single most abundant protein in the body. It is responsible for the tensile strength of bones, tendons, and ligaments.
		Keratin is the structural protein of hair and nails and a water-resistant material of skin.
		Elastin is found, along with collagen, where durability and flexibility are needed, such as in the ligaments that bind bones together.
		Spectrin internally reinforces and stabilizes the surface membrane of some cells, particularly red blood cells. *Dystrophin* reinforces and stabilizes the surface membrane of muscle cells. *Titin* helps organize the intracellular structure of muscle cells and accounts for the elasticity of skeletal muscles.
	Movement	*Actin* and *myosin*, contractile proteins, are found in substantial amounts in muscle cells, where they cause muscle cell shortening (contraction); they also function in cell division in all cell types. Actin is important in intracellular transport, particularly in nerve cells.
Globular		
	Catalysis	Protein enzymes are essential to virtually every biochemical reaction in the body; they increase the rates of chemical reactions by at least a millionfold. Examples include *salivary amylase* (in saliva), which catalyzes the breakdown of starch, and *oxidase enzymes*, which act to oxidize food fuels.
	Transport	*Hemoglobin* transports oxygen in blood, and *lipoproteins* transport lipids and cholesterol. Other transport proteins in the blood carry iron, hormones, or other substances. Some globular proteins in plasma membranes are involved in membrane transport (as carriers or channels).
	Regulation of pH	Many plasma proteins, such as *albumin*, function reversibly as acids or bases, thus acting as buffers to prevent wide swings in blood pH.
	Regulation of metabolism	*Peptide* and *protein hormones* help to regulate metabolic activity, growth, and development. For example, *growth hormone* is an anabolic hormone necessary for optimal growth; *insulin* helps regulate blood sugar levels.
	Body defense	*Antibodies* (immunoglobulins) are specialized proteins released by immune cells that recognize and inactivate foreign substances (bacteria, toxins, some viruses).
		Complement proteins, which circulate in blood, enhance both immune and inflammatory responses.
	Protein management	*Molecular chaperones* aid folding of new proteins in both healthy and damaged cells and transport of metal ions into and within the cell. They also promote breakdown of damaged proteins.

- Help to translocate proteins and certain metal ions (copper, iron, zinc) across cell membranes
- Promote the breakdown of damaged or denatured proteins
- Interact with immune cells to trigger the immune response to diseased cells in the body

The first such proteins discovered were called *heat shock proteins* (*hsp*) because they seemed to protect cells from the destructive effects of heat. It was later found that these proteins are produced in response to a variety of traumatizing stimuli—for example, in the oxygen-deprived cells of a heart attack patient—and the name *stress proteins* replaced hsp for that particular group of molecular chaperones. It is now clear that these proteins are vitally important to cell function in all types of stressful circumstances. Although a lot of environmental stress can turn your hair gray or cause cardiac problems, it seems that a little stress can delay aging. As part of the heat shock response, special protein repair molecules patch up damaged proteins and refold them correctly, helping to hold off the grim reaper and prolong life.

Enzymes and Enzyme Activity

Enzymes are globular proteins that act as biological catalysts. *Catalysts* are substances that regulate and accelerate the rate of biochemical reactions but are not used up or changed in those

Figure 2.20 Enzymes lower the activation energy required for a reaction.

reactions. More specifically, enzymes can be thought of as chemical traffic cops that keep our metabolic pathways flowing. Enzymes cannot force chemical reactions to occur between molecules that would not otherwise react. They can only increase the speed of reaction, and they do so by staggering amounts—from 100,000 to over 1 billion times the rate of an uncatalyzed reaction. Without enzymes, biochemical reactions proceed so slowly that for practical purposes they do not occur at all.

Characteristics of Enzymes Some enzymes are purely protein. In other cases, the functional enzyme consists of two parts, collectively called a **holoenzyme**: an **apoenzyme** (the protein portion) and a **cofactor**. Depending on the enzyme, the cofactor may be an ion of a metal element such as copper or iron, or an organic molecule needed to assist the reaction in some particular way. Most organic cofactors are derived from vitamins (especially the B complex vitamins). This type of cofactor is more precisely called a **coenzyme**.

Each enzyme is chemically specific. Some enzymes control only a single chemical reaction. Others exhibit a broader specificity in that they can bind with molecules that differ slightly and thus regulate a small group of related reactions. The substance on which an enzyme acts is called a **substrate**.

The presence of specific enzymes determines not only which reactions will be speeded up, but also which reactions will occur—no enzyme, no reaction. This also means that unwanted or unnecessary chemical reactions do not occur.

Most enzymes are named for the type of reaction they catalyze. *Hydrolases* (hi′druh-lās-es) add water during hydrolysis reactions, *oxidases* (ok′sĭ-dās-es) oxidize reactants by adding oxygen or removing hydrogen, and so on. You can recognize most enzyme names by the suffix *-ase*.

In many cases, enzymes are part of cellular membranes in a bucket-brigade type of arrangement. The product of one enzyme-catalyzed reaction becomes the substrate of the neighboring enzyme, and so on. Some enzymes are produced in an inactive form and must be activated in some way before they can function, often by a change in the pH of their surroundings. For example,

digestive enzymes produced in the pancreas are activated in the small intestine, where they actually do their work. If they were produced in active form, the pancreas would digest itself.

Sometimes, enzymes are inactivated immediately after they have performed their catalytic function. This is true of enzymes that promote blood clot formation when the wall of a blood vessel is damaged. Once clotting is triggered, those enzymes are inactivated. Otherwise, you would have blood vessels full of solid blood instead of one protective clot. (Eek!)

Enzyme Action How do enzymes perform their catalytic role? Every chemical reaction requires that a certain amount of energy, called **activation energy**, be absorbed to prime the reaction. The activation energy is the amount of energy needed to break the bonds of the reactants so that they can rearrange themselves and become the product. It is present when kinetic energy pushes the reactants to an energy level where their random collisions are forceful enough to ensure interaction. Activation energy is needed regardless of whether the overall reaction is ultimately energy absorbing or energy releasing.

One way to increase kinetic energy is to increase the temperature, but higher temperatures denature proteins. (This is why a high fever can be a serious event.) Enzymes allow reactions to occur at normal body temperature by decreasing the amount of activation energy required **(Figure 2.20)**.

Exactly how do enzymes accomplish this remarkable feat? The answer is not fully understood. However, we know that, due to structural and electrostatic factors, they decrease the randomness of reactions by binding to the reacting molecules temporarily and presenting them to each other in the proper position for chemical interaction (bond making or breaking) to occur.

Three basic steps appear to be involved in enzyme action **(Figure 2.21)**.

① **Substrate(s) bind to the enzyme's active site, temporarily forming an enzyme-substrate complex.** Substrate binding causes the active site to change shape so that the substrate and the active site fit together precisely, and in an orientation that favors reaction. Whether the shape of the substrate

Substrates (S)
e.g., amino acids

Active site

Enzyme (E)

Enzyme-substrate complex (E-S)

① Substrates bind at active site, temporarily forming an enzyme-substrate complex.

Energy is absorbed; bond is formed.

Water is released.

H_2O

② The E-S complex undergoes internal rearrangements that form the product.

Product (P)
e.g., dipeptide

Peptide bond

Enzyme (E)

③ The enzyme releases the product of the reaction.

Figure 2.21 Mechanism of enzyme action. In this example, the enzyme catalyzes the formation of a dipeptide from specific amino acids. *Summary:* E + S → E-S → P + E

forces the enzyme to wiggle into a complementary shape or whether the enzyme wiggles around trying several different conformations until one finally fits the substrate is still a question. Although enzymes are specific for particular substrates, other (nonsubstrate) molecules may act as *enzyme inhibitors* if their structure is similar enough to occupy or block the enzyme's active site.

② **The enzyme-substrate complex undergoes internal rearrangements that form the product(s).** This step shows the catalytic role of an enzyme.

③ **The enzyme releases the product(s) of the reaction.** If the enzyme became part of the product, it would be a reactant and not a catalyst. The enzyme is not changed and returns to its original shape, available to catalyze another reaction.

Because enzymes are unchanged by their catalytic role and can act again and again, cells need only small amounts of each enzyme. Catalysis occurs with incredible speed. Most enzymes can catalyze millions of reactions per minute.

☑ **Check Your Understanding**

27. What is the main event that molecular chaperones prevent?
28. How do enzymes reduce the amount of activation energy needed to make a chemical reaction go?

——————————————— *For answers, see Appendix H.*

Nucleic Acids (DNA and RNA)

✓ Compare and contrast DNA and RNA.

The **nucleic acids** (nu-kle′ic), composed of carbon, oxygen, hydrogen, nitrogen, and phosphorus, are the largest molecules in the body. The nucleic acids include two major classes of molecules, **deoxyribonucleic acid (DNA)** (de-ok″sĭ-ri″bo-nu-kle′ik) and **ribonucleic acid (RNA)**.

The structural units of nucleic acids, called **nucleotides**, are quite complex. Each nucleotide consists of three components: a nitrogen-containing base, a pentose sugar, and a phosphate group **(Figure 2.22a)**. Five major varieties of nitrogen-containing bases can contribute to nucleotide structure: **adenine**, abbreviated **A** (ad′ĕ-nēn); **guanine**, **G** (gwan′ēn); **cytosine**, **C** (si′to-sēn); **thymine**, **T** (thi′mēn); and **uracil**, **U** (u′rah-sil). Adenine and guanine are large, two-ring bases (called purines), whereas cytosine, thymine, and uracil are smaller, single-ring bases (called pyrimidines).

The stepwise synthesis of a nucleotide involves the attachment of a base to the pentose sugar to form first a *nucleoside*, named for the nitrogenous base it contains. The nucleotide is formed when a phosphate group is bonded to the sugar of the nucleoside.

Although DNA and RNA are both composed of nucleotides, they differ in many respects, as summarized in **Table 2.4** on p. 55. Typically, DNA is found in the nucleus (control center) of the cell, where it constitutes the *genetic material*, also called the *genes*, or more recently the *genome*. DNA has two fundamental roles: It replicates (reproduces) itself before a cell divides, ensuring that the genetic information in the descendant cells is identical, and it provides the basic instructions for building every protein in the body. Although we have said that enzymes govern all chemical reactions, remember that enzymes, too, are proteins formed at the direction of DNA.

By providing the information for protein synthesis, DNA determines what type of organism you will be—frog, human, oak tree—and directs your growth and development. It also accounts for your uniqueness. A technique called DNA fingerprinting can help solve forensic mysteries (for example, verify one's presence at a crime scene), identify badly burned or mangled bodies at a disaster scene, and establish or disprove paternity. DNA fingerprinting analyzes tiny samples of DNA taken from blood, semen, or other body tissues and shows the results as a "genetic barcode" that distinguishes each of us from all others.

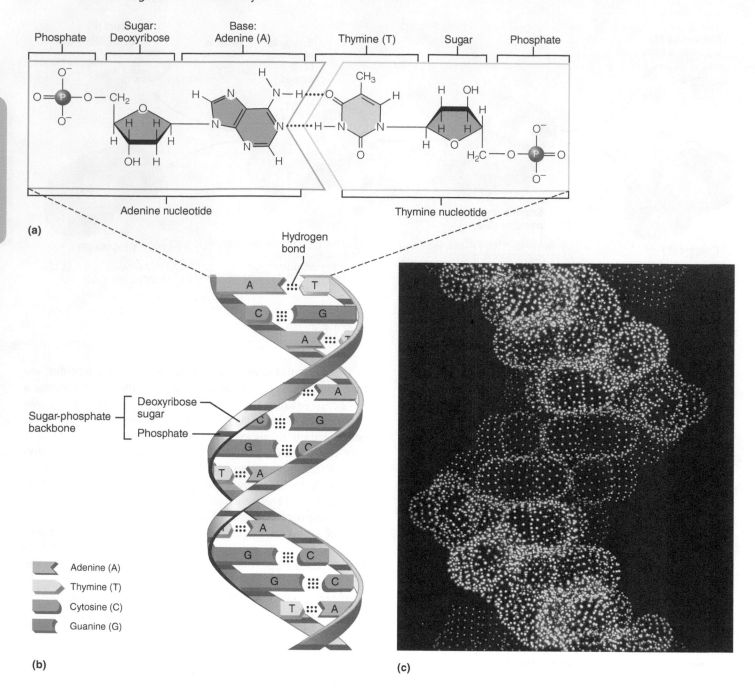

(a)

(b)

(c)

Figure 2.22 Structure of DNA. (a) The unit of DNA is the nucleotide, which is composed of a deoxyribose sugar molecule linked to a phosphate group, with a base attached to the sugar. Two nucleotides, linked by hydrogen bonds between their complementary bases, are illustrated. **(b)** DNA is a coiled double polymer of nucleotides (a double helix). The backbones of the ladderlike molecule are formed by alternating sugar and phosphate units. The rungs are formed by the binding together of complementary bases (A-T and G-C) by hydrogen bonds (shown by dotted lines). **(c)** Computer-generated image of a DNA molecule.

DNA is a long, double-stranded polymer—a double chain of nucleotides (Figure 2.22b and c). The bases in DNA are A, G, C, and T, and its pentose sugar is *deoxyribose* (as reflected in its name). Its two nucleotide chains are held together by hydrogen bonds between the bases, so that a ladderlike molecule is formed. Alternating sugar and phosphate components of each chain form the *backbones* or "uprights" of the "ladder," and the joined bases form the "rungs." The whole molecule is coiled into a spiral staircase–like structure called a **double helix**.

Bonding of the bases is very specific: A always bonds to T, and G always bonds to C. A and T are therefore called **complementary bases**, as are C and G. According to these base-pairing rules, ATGA on one DNA nucleotide strand would necessarily be bonded to TACT (a complementary base sequence) on the other strand.

Table 2.4	Comparison of DNA and RNA	
CHARACTERISTIC	**DNA**	**RNA**
Major cellular site	Nucleus	Cytoplasm (cell area outside the nucleus)
Major functions	Is the genetic material; directs protein synthesis; replicates itself before cell division	Carries out the genetic instructions for protein synthesis
Sugar	Deoxyribose	Ribose
Bases	Adenine, guanine, cytosine, thymine	Adenine, guanine, cytosine, uracil
Structure	Double strand coiled into a double helix	Single strand, straight or folded

RNA is located chiefly outside the nucleus and can be considered a "molecular slave" of DNA. That is, RNA carries out the orders for protein synthesis issued by DNA. [Viruses in which RNA (rather than DNA) is the genetic material are an exception to this generalization.]

RNA molecules are single strands of nucleotides. RNA bases include A, G, C, and U (U replaces the T found in DNA), and its sugar is *ribose* instead of deoxyribose. The three major varieties of RNA (messenger RNA, ribosomal RNA, and transfer RNA) are distinguished by their relative size and shape, and each has a specific role to play in carrying out DNA's instructions for protein synthesis. In addition to these three RNAs, small RNA molecules called *microRNAs* (*miRNAs*) appear to control genetic expression by shutting down genes or altering their expression. We discuss DNA replication and the relative roles of DNA and RNA in protein synthesis in Chapter 3.

☑ **Check Your Understanding**

29. How do DNA and RNA differ in the bases and sugars they contain?
30. What are two important roles of DNA?

For answers, see Appendix H.

Adenosine Triphosphate (ATP)

✓ Explain the role of ATP in cell metabolism.

Glucose is the most important cellular fuel, but none of the chemical energy contained in its bonds is used directly to power cellular work. Instead, energy released during glucose catabolism is coupled to the synthesis of **adenosine triphosphate** (**ATP**). In other words, some of this energy is captured and stored as small packets of energy in the bonds of ATP. ATP is the primary energy-transferring molecule in cells and it provides a form of energy that is immediately usable by all body cells.

Structurally, ATP is an adenine-containing RNA nucleotide to which two additional phosphate groups have been added **(Figure 2.23)**. Chemically, the triphosphate tail of ATP can be compared to a tightly coiled spring ready to uncoil with tremendous energy when the catch is released. Actually, ATP is a very unstable energy-storing molecule because its three negatively charged phosphate groups are closely packed and repel

each other. When its terminal high-energy phosphate bonds are broken (hydrolyzed), the chemical "spring" relaxes and the molecule as a whole becomes more stable.

Cells tap ATP's bond energy during coupled reactions by using enzymes to transfer the terminal phosphate groups from ATP to other compounds. These newly *phosphorylated* molecules are said to be "primed" and temporarily become more energetic and capable of performing some type of cellular work. In the process of doing their work, they lose the phosphate group. The amount of energy released and transferred during ATP hydrolysis corresponds closely to that needed to drive most biochemical reactions. As a result, cells are protected from excessive energy release that might be damaging, and energy squandering is kept to a minimum.

Cleaving the terminal phosphate bond of ATP yields a molecule with two phosphate groups—*adenosine diphosphate*

Figure 2.23 Structure of ATP (adenosine triphosphate). ATP is an adenine nucleotide to which two additional phosphate groups have been attached during breakdown of food fuels. When the terminal phosphate group is cleaved off, energy is released to do useful work and ADP (adenosine diphosphate) is formed. When the terminal phosphate group is cleaved off ADP, a similar amount of energy is released and AMP (adenosine monophosphate) is formed.

2

(a) **Transport work:** ATP phosphorylates transport proteins, activating them to transport solutes (ions, for example) across cell membranes.

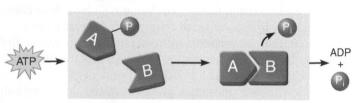

(b) **Mechanical work:** ATP phosphorylates contractile proteins in muscle cells so the cells can shorten.

(c) **Chemical work:** ATP phosphorylates key reactants, providing energy to drive energy-absorbing chemical reactions.

Figure 2.24 Three examples of cellular work driven by energy from ATP.

(*ADP*)—and an inorganic phosphate group, indicated by P_i, accompanied by a transfer of energy:

$$ATP \rightleftharpoons ADP + P_i + energy$$

As ATP is hydrolyzed to provide energy for cellular needs, ADP accumulates. Cleavage of the terminal phosphate bond of ADP liberates a similar amount of energy and produces adenosine monophosphate (AMP).

The cell's ATP supplies are replenished as glucose and other fuel molecules are oxidized and their bond energy is released. The same amount of energy that is liberated when ATP's terminal phosphates are cleaved off must be captured and used to reverse the reaction to reattach phosphates and re-form the energy-transferring phosphate bonds. Without ATP, molecules cannot be made or degraded, cells cannot transport substances across their membrane boundaries, muscles cannot shorten to tug on other structures, and life processes cease **(Figure 2.24).**

☑ **Check Your Understanding**

31. Glucose is an energy-rich molecule. So why do body cells need ATP?
32. What change occurs in ATP when it releases energy?

_____ *For answers, see Appendix H.*

Chapter Summary

 For more chapter study tools, go to the Study Area of MasteringA&P at **www.masteringaandp.com**
There you will find:

- Interactive Physiology **iP**
- A&PFlix ***A&PFlix***
- Practice Anatomy Lab PAL
- PhysioEx **PEx**
- Videos, Practice Quizzes and Tests, MP3 Tutor Sessions, Case Studies, and much more!

PART 1 **Basic Chemistry**

Definition of Concepts: Matter and Energy   (pp. 23–25)

Matter   (p. 24)

1. Matter is anything that takes up space and has mass.

Energy   (pp. 24–25)

2. Energy is the capacity to do work or put matter into motion.
3. Energy exists as potential energy (stored energy or energy of position) and kinetic energy (active or working energy).
4. Forms of energy involved in body functioning are chemical, electrical, radiant, and mechanical. Of these, chemical (bond) energy is most important.
5. Energy may be converted from one form to another, but some energy is always unusable (lost as heat) in such transformations.

Composition of Matter: Atoms and Elements (pp. 25–28)

1. Elements are unique substances that cannot be decomposed into simpler substances by ordinary chemical methods. Four elements (carbon, hydrogen, oxygen, and nitrogen) make up 96% of body weight.

Atomic Structure (pp. 25–26)

2. The building blocks of elements are atoms.

3. Atoms are composed of positively charged protons, negatively charged electrons, and uncharged neutrons. Protons and neutrons are located in the atomic nucleus, constituting essentially the atom's total mass. Electrons are outside the nucleus in the electron shells. In any atom, the number of electrons equals the number of protons.

Identifying Elements (pp. 27–28)

4. Atoms may be identified by their atomic number (p^+) and mass number ($p^+ + n^0$). The notation ^4_2He means that helium (He) has an atomic number of 2 and a mass number of 4.

5. Isotopes of an element differ in the number of neutrons they contain. The atomic weight of any element is approximately equal to the mass number of its most abundant isotope.

Radioisotopes (p. 28)

6. Many heavy isotopes are unstable (radioactive). These so-called radioisotopes decompose to more stable forms by emitting alpha or beta particles or gamma rays. Radioisotopes are useful in medical diagnosis and treatment and in biochemical research.

How Matter Is Combined: Molecules and Mixtures (pp. 28–30)

Molecules and Compounds (pp. 28–29)

1. A molecule is the smallest unit resulting from the chemical bonding of two or more atoms. If the atoms are different, they form a molecule of a compound.

Mixtures (pp. 29–30)

2. Mixtures are physical combinations of solutes in a solvent. Mixture components retain their individual properties.

3. The types of mixtures, in order of increasing solute size, are solutions, colloids, and suspensions.

4. Solution concentrations are typically designated in terms of percent or molarity.

Distinguishing Mixtures from Compounds (p. 30)

5. Compounds are homogeneous; their elements are chemically bonded. Mixtures may be homogeneous or heterogeneous; their components are physically combined and separable.

Chemical Bonds (pp. 30–35)

The Role of Electrons in Chemical Bonding (p. 31)

1. Electrons of an atom occupy areas of space called electron shells or energy levels. Electrons in the shell farthest from the nucleus (valence shell) are most energetic.

2. Chemical bonds are energy relationships between valence shell electrons of the reacting atoms. Atoms with a full valence shell or eight valence shell electrons are chemically unreactive (inert). Those with an incomplete valence shell interact with other atoms to achieve stability.

Types of Chemical Bonds (pp. 31–35)

3. Ionic bonds are formed when valence shell electrons are completely transferred from one atom to another.

4. Covalent bonds are formed when atoms share electron pairs. If the electron pairs are shared equally, the molecule is nonpolar. If they are shared unequally, it is polar (a dipole).

5. Hydrogen bonds are weak bonds formed between one hydrogen atom, already covalently linked to an electronegative atom, and another electronegative atom (such as nitrogen or oxygen). They bind together different molecules (e.g., water molecules) or different parts of the same molecule (as in protein molecules).

Chemical Reactions (pp. 35–38)

Chemical Equations (pp. 35–36)

1. Chemical reactions involve the formation, breaking, or rearrangement of chemical bonds.

Patterns of Chemical Reactions (pp. 36–37)

2. Chemical reactions are either anabolic (constructive) or catabolic (destructive). They include synthesis, decomposition, and exchange reactions. Oxidation-reduction reactions may be considered a special type of exchange (or decomposition) reaction.

Energy Flow in Chemical Reactions (p. 37)

3. Bonds are energy relationships and there is a net loss or gain of energy in every chemical reaction.

4. In exergonic reactions, energy is liberated. In endergonic reactions, energy is absorbed.

Reversibility of Chemical Reactions (p. 37)

5. If reaction conditions remain unchanged, all chemical reactions eventually reach a state of chemical equilibrium in which the reaction proceeds in both directions at the same rate.

6. All chemical reactions are theoretically reversible, but many biological reactions go in only one direction because of energy requirements or the removal of reaction products.

Factors Influencing the Rate of Chemical Reactions (pp. 37–38)

7. Chemical reactions occur only when particles collide and valence shell electrons interact.

8. The smaller the reacting particles, the greater their kinetic energy and the faster the reaction rate. Higher temperature or reactant concentration, as well as the presence of catalysts, increases chemical reaction rates.

PART 2 Biochemistry

Inorganic Compounds (pp. 38–41)

1. Most inorganic compounds do not contain carbon. Those found in the body include water, salts, and inorganic acids and bases.

Water (pp. 38–39)

2. Water is the single most abundant compound in the body. It absorbs and releases heat slowly, acts as a universal solvent, participates in chemical reactions, and cushions body organs.

Salts (p. 39)

3. Salts are ionic compounds that dissolve in water and act as electrolytes. Calcium and phosphorus salts contribute to the hardness of bones and teeth. Ions of salts are involved in many physiological processes.

Acids and Bases (pp. 39–41)

4. Acids are proton donors; in water, they ionize and dissociate, releasing hydrogen ions (which account for their properties) and anions.

iP **Fluid, Electrolyte and Acid/Base Balance; Topic: Acid Base Homeostasis, pp. 1–12, 16, 17.**

5. Bases are proton acceptors. The most common inorganic bases are the hydroxides; bicarbonate ion and ammonia are important bases in the body.

6. pH is a measure of hydrogen ion concentration of a solution (in moles per liter). A pH of 7 is neutral; a higher pH is alkaline, and a lower pH is acidic. Normal blood pH is 7.35–7.45. Buffers help to prevent excessive changes in the pH of body fluids.

iP **Fluid, Electrolyte and Acid/Base Balance; Topic: Introduction to Body Fluids, pp. 1–8.**

Organic Compounds (pp. 41–56)

1. Organic compounds contain carbon. Those found in the body include carbohydrates, lipids, proteins, and nucleic acids, all of which are synthesized by dehydration synthesis and digested by hydrolysis. All of these biological molecules contain C, H, and O. Proteins and nucleic acids also contain N.

Carbohydrates (p. 43)

2. Carbohydrate building blocks are monosaccharides, the most important of which are hexoses (glucose, fructose, galactose) and pentoses (ribose, deoxyribose).

3. Disaccharides (sucrose, lactose, maltose) and polysaccharides (starch, glycogen) are composed of linked monosaccharide units.

4. Carbohydrates, particularly glucose, are the major energy fuel for forming ATP. Excess carbohydrates are stored as glycogen or converted to fat for storage.

Lipids (pp. 43–47)

5. Lipids dissolve in fats or organic solvents, but not in water.

6. Triglycerides are composed of fatty acid chains and glycerol. They are found chiefly in fatty tissue where they provide insulation and reserve body fuel. Unsaturated fatty acid chains produce oils. Saturated fatty acids produce solid fats typical of animal fats.

7. Phospholipids are modified phosphorus-containing triglycerides that have polar and nonpolar portions. They are found in all plasma membranes.

8. The steroid cholesterol is found in cell membranes and is the basis of steroid hormones, bile salts, and vitamin D.

Proteins (pp. 47–53)

9. The unit of proteins is the amino acid, and 20 common amino acids are found in the body.

10. Many amino acids joined by peptide bonds form a polypeptide. A protein (one or more polypeptides) is distinguished by the number and sequence of amino acids in its chain(s) and by the complexity of its three-dimensional structure.

11. Fibrous proteins, such as keratin and collagen, have secondary (α-helix or β-pleated sheet) and perhaps tertiary and quaternary structure. Fibrous proteins are used as structural materials.

12. Globular proteins achieve tertiary and sometimes quaternary structure and are generally spherical, soluble molecules. Globular proteins (e.g., enzymes, some hormones, antibodies, hemoglobin) perform special functional roles for the cell (e.g., catalysis, molecule transport).

13. Proteins are denatured by extremes of temperature or pH. Denatured globular proteins are unable to perform their usual function.

14. Molecular chaperones assist in folding proteins into their functional 3-D shape. They are synthesized in greater amounts when cells are stressed by environmental factors.

15. Enzymes are biological catalysts. They increase the rate of chemical reactions by decreasing the amount of activation energy needed. They do this by combining with the reactants and holding them in the proper position to interact. Many enzymes require cofactors to function.

Nucleic Acids (DNA and RNA) (pp. 53–55)

16. Nucleic acids include deoxyribonucleic acid (DNA) and ribonucleic acid (RNA). The structural unit of nucleic acids is the nucleotide, which consists of a nitrogenous base (adenine, guanine, cytosine, thymine, or uracil), a sugar (ribose or deoxyribose), and a phosphate group.

17. DNA is a double-stranded helix. It contains deoxyribose and the bases A, G, C, and T. DNA specifies protein structure and replicates itself exactly before cell division.

18. RNA is single stranded. It contains ribose and the bases A, G, C, and U. RNAs involved in carrying out DNA's instructions for protein synthesis include messenger, ribosomal, and transfer RNA.

Adenosine Triphosphate (ATP) (pp. 55–56)

19. ATP is the universal energy compound of body cells. Some of the energy liberated by the breakdown of glucose and other food fuels is captured in the bonds of ATP molecules and transferred via coupled reactions to energy-consuming reactions.

Review Questions

Multiple Choice/Matching

(Some questions have more than one correct answer. Select the best answer or answers from the choices given.)

1. Which of the following forms of energy is the stimulus for vision? (a) chemical, (b) electrical, (c) mechanical, (d) radiant.

2. All of the following are examples of the four major elements contributing to body mass except (a) hydrogen, (b) carbon, (c) nitrogen, (d) sodium, (e) oxygen.

3. The mass number of an atom is (a) equal to the number of protons it contains, (b) the sum of its protons and neutrons, (c) the sum of all of its subatomic particles, (d) the average of the mass numbers of all of its isotopes.

4. A deficiency in this element can be expected to reduce the hemoglobin content of blood: (a) Fe, (b) I, (c) F, (d) Ca, (e) K.

5. Which set of terms best describes a proton? (a) negative charge, massless, in the orbital; (b) positive charge, 1 amu, in the nucleus; (c) uncharged, 1 amu, in the nucleus.

6. The subatomic particles responsible for the chemical behavior of atoms are (a) electrons, (b) ions, (c) neutrons, (d) protons.

7. In the body, carbohydrates are stored in the form of (a) glycogen, (b) starch, (c) cholesterol, (d) polypeptides.

8. Which of the following does *not* describe a mixture?
(a) properties of its components are retained, (b) chemical
bonds are formed, (c) components can be separated physically,
(d) includes both heterogeneous and homogeneous examples.

9. In a beaker of water, the water-water bonds can properly be called
(a) ionic bonds, (b) polar covalent bonds, (c) nonpolar covalent
bonds, (d) hydrogen bonds.

10. When a pair of electrons is shared between two atoms, the bond
formed is called (a) a single covalent bond, (b) a double covalent
bond, (c) a triple covalent bond, (d) an ionic bond.

11. Molecules formed when electrons are shared unequally are
(a) salts, (b) polar molecules, (c) nonpolar molecules.

12. Which of the following covalently bonded molecules are polar?

(a)　　　　(b)　　　　(c)　　　　(d)

13. Identify each reaction as one of the following: (a) a synthesis
reaction, (b) a decomposition reaction, (c) an exchange reaction.
_____ (1) $2Hg + O_2 \rightarrow 2HgO$
_____ (2) $HCl + NaOH \rightarrow NaCl + H_2O$

14. Factors that accelerate the rate of chemical reactions include all
but (a) the presence of catalysts, (b) increasing the temperature,
(c) increasing the particle size, (d) increasing the concentration of
the reactants.

15. Which of the following molecules is an inorganic molecule?
(a) sucrose, (b) cholesterol, (c) collagen, (d) sodium chloride.

16. Water's importance to living systems reflects (a) its polarity
and solvent properties, (b) its high heat capacity, (c) its high
heat of vaporization, (d) its chemical reactivity, (e) all of
these.

17. Acids (a) release hydroxyl ions when dissolved in water, (b) are
proton acceptors, (c) cause the pH of a solution to rise, (d) release
protons when dissolved in water.

18. A chemist, during the course of an analysis, runs across a
chemical composed of carbon, hydrogen, and oxygen in the
proportion 1:2:1 and having a six-sided molecular shape. It is
probably (a) a pentose, (b) an amino acid, (c) a fatty acid,
(d) a monosaccharide, (e) a nucleic acid.

19. A triglyceride consists of (a) glycerol plus three fatty acids,
(b) a sugar-phosphate backbone to which two amino groups are
attached, (c) two to several hexoses, (d) amino acids that have
been thoroughly saturated with hydrogen.

20. A chemical has an amine group and an organic acid group.
It does not, however, have any peptide bonds. It is (a) a
monosaccharide, (b) an amino acid, (c) a protein, (d) a fat.

21. The lipid(s) used as the basis of vitamin D, sex hormones, and
bile salts is/are (a) triglycerides, (b) cholesterol, (c) phospholipids,
(d) prostaglandin.

22. Enzymes are organic catalysts that (a) alter the direction in
which a chemical reaction proceeds, (b) determine the nature of
the products of a reaction, (c) increase the speed of a chemical
reaction, (d) are essential raw materials for a chemical reaction
that are converted into some of its products.

Short Answer Essay Questions

23. Define or describe energy, and explain the relationship between
potential and kinetic energy.

24. Some energy is lost in every energy conversion. Explain the
meaning of this statement. (Direct your response to answering
the question: Is it really lost? If not, what then?)

25. Provide the atomic symbol for each of the following elements:
(a) calcium, (b) carbon, (c) hydrogen, (d) iron, (e) nitrogen,
(f) oxygen, (g) potassium, (h) sodium.

26. Consider the following information about three atoms:
$$^{12}_{6}C \quad ^{13}_{6}C \quad ^{14}_{6}C$$
(a) How are they similar to one another? (b) How do they differ
from one another? (c) What are the members of such a group of
atoms called? (d) Using the planetary model, draw the atomic
configuration of $^{12}_{6}C$ showing the relative position and numbers of
its subatomic particles.

27. How many moles of aspirin, $C_9H_8O_4$, are in a bottle containing
450 g by weight? (*Note*: The approximate atomic weights of its
atoms are C = 12, H = 1, and O = 16.)

28. Given the following types of atoms, decide which type of
bonding, ionic or covalent, is most likely to occur: (a) two oxygen
atoms; (b) four hydrogen atoms and one carbon atom; (c) a
potassium atom ($^{39}_{19}K$) and a fluorine atom ($^{19}_{9}F$).

29. What are hydrogen bonds and how are they important in the body?

30. The following equation, which represents the oxidative
breakdown of glucose by body cells, is a reversible reaction.
Glucose + oxygen → carbon dioxide + water + ATP
(a) How can you indicate that the reaction is reversible? (b) How
can you indicate that the reaction is in chemical equilibrium?
(c) Define chemical equilibrium.

31. Differentiate clearly between primary, secondary, and tertiary
protein structure.

32. Dehydration and hydrolysis reactions are essentially opposite
reactions. How are they related to the synthesis and degradation
(breakdown) of biological molecules?

33. Describe the mechanism of enzyme action.

34. Explain the importance of molecular chaperones.

35. Explain why, if you pour water into a glass very carefully, you can
"stack" the water slightly above the rim of the glass.

Critical Thinking and Clinical Application Questions

1. As Ben jumped on his bike and headed for the freshwater lake,
his mother called after him, "Don't swim if we have an electrical
storm—it looks threatening." This was a valid request. Why?

2. Some antibiotics act by binding to certain essential enzymes in the
target bacteria. (a) How might these antibiotics influence the chemical
reactions controlled by the enzymes? (b) What is the anticipated effect
on the bacteria? On the person taking the antibiotic prescription?

3. Mrs. Roberts, in a diabetic coma, has just been admitted to Noble
Hospital. Her blood pH indicates that she is in severe acidosis,
and measures are quickly instituted to bring her blood pH back
within normal limits. (a) Define pH and note the normal pH of
blood. (b) Why is severe acidosis a problem?

4. Jimmy, a 12-year-old boy, was awakened suddenly by a loud
crash. As he sat up in bed, straining to listen, his fright was
revealed by his rapid breathing (hyperventilation), a breathing
pattern effective in ridding the blood of CO_2. At this point, was
his blood pH rising or falling?

5. After you eat a protein bar, which chemical reactions introduced
in this chapter must occur for the amino acids in the protein bar
to be converted into proteins in your body cells?

AT THE CLINIC

Related Clinical Terms

Acidosis (as"ĭ-do'sis; *acid* = sour, sharp) A condition of acidity or low pH (below 7.35) of the blood; high hydrogen ion concentration.

Alkalosis (al"kah-lo'sis) A condition of basicity or high pH (above 7.45) of the blood; low hydrogen ion concentration.

Heavy metals Metals with toxic effects on the body, including arsenic, mercury, and lead. Iron, also included in this group, is toxic in high concentrations.

Ionizing radiation Radiation that causes atoms to ionize; for example, radioisotope emissions and X rays.

Ketosis (ke-to'sis) A condition resulting from excessive ketones (breakdown products of fats) in the blood; common during starvation and acute attacks of diabetes mellitus.

Radiation sickness Disease resulting from exposure of the body to radioactivity; digestive system organs are most affected.

3

Cells: The Living Units

J ust as bricks and timbers are the structural units of a house, **cells** are
the structural units of all living things, from one-celled "generalists" like amoebas to
complex multicellular organisms such as humans, dogs, and trees. The human body
has 50 to 100 trillion of these tiny building blocks.

This chapter focuses on structures and functions shared by all cells. We address specialized cells and their unique functions in later chapters.

The Cellular Basis of Life

✓ Define cell.

✓ List the three major regions of a generalized cell and their functions.

The English scientist Robert Hooke first observed plant cells with a crude microscope in the late 1600s. Then, in the 1830s two German scientists, Matthias Schleiden and Theodor Schwann, proposed that all living things are composed of cells. German pathologist Rudolf Virchow extended this idea by contending that cells arise only from other cells.

Since the late 1800s, cell research has been exceptionally fruitful and provided us with four concepts collectively known as the **cell theory**:

- A *cell* is the basic structural and functional unit of living organisms. When you define cell properties, you define the properties of life.

- The activity of an organism depends on both the individual and the collective activities of its cells.

- According to the *principle of complementarity of structure and function*, the biochemical activities of cells are dictated by their shapes or forms, and by the relative number of their specific subcellular structures.

- Continuity of life from one generation to another has a cellular basis.

We will expand on all of these concepts as we progress. Let us begin with the idea that the cell is the smallest living unit. Whatever its form, however it behaves, the cell is the microscopic package that contains all the parts necessary to survive in an ever-changing world. It follows then that loss of cellular homeostasis underlies virtually every disease.

The trillions of cells in the human body include over 200 different cell types that vary greatly in shape, size, and function (**Figure 3.1**). The disc-shaped red blood cells, branching nerve cells, and cubelike cells of kidney tubules are just a few examples of the shapes cells take. Cells also vary in length—ranging from 2 micrometers (1/12,000 of an inch) in the smallest cells to over a meter in the nerve cells that cause you to wiggle your toes. A cell's shape reflects its function. For example, the flat, tilelike epithelial cells that line the inside of your cheek fit closely together, forming a living barrier that protects underlying tissues from bacterial invasion.

Regardless of type, all cells are composed chiefly of carbon, hydrogen, nitrogen, oxygen, and trace amounts of several other elements. In addition, all cells have the same basic parts and some common functions. For this reason, it is possible to speak of a **generalized**, or **composite**, **cell** (**Figure 3.2**).

A human cell has three main parts:

- The *plasma membrane*: the outer boundary of the cell.

- The *cytoplasm* (si′to-plazm): the intracellular fluid packed with *organelles*, small structures that perform specific cell functions.

- The *nucleus* (nu′kle-us): an organelle that controls cellular activities. Typically the nucleus lies near the cell's center.

(a) Cells that connect body parts, form linings, or transport gases

Fibroblasts

Erythrocytes

Epithelial cells

Skeletal muscle cell

Smooth muscle cells

(b) Cells that move organs and body parts

Fat cell

Macrophage

(c) Cell that stores nutrients   **(d) Cell that fights disease**

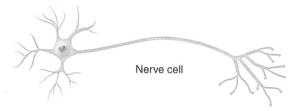

Nerve cell

(e) Cell that gathers information and controls body functions

Sperm

(f) Cell of reproduction

Figure 3.1 Cell diversity. (Note that cells are not drawn to the same scale.)

☑ **Check Your Understanding**

1. Summarize the four key points of the cell theory.
2. How would you explain the meaning of a "generalized cell" to a classmate?

For answers, see Appendix H.

Next, let's examine the three main parts of the cell in greater detail.

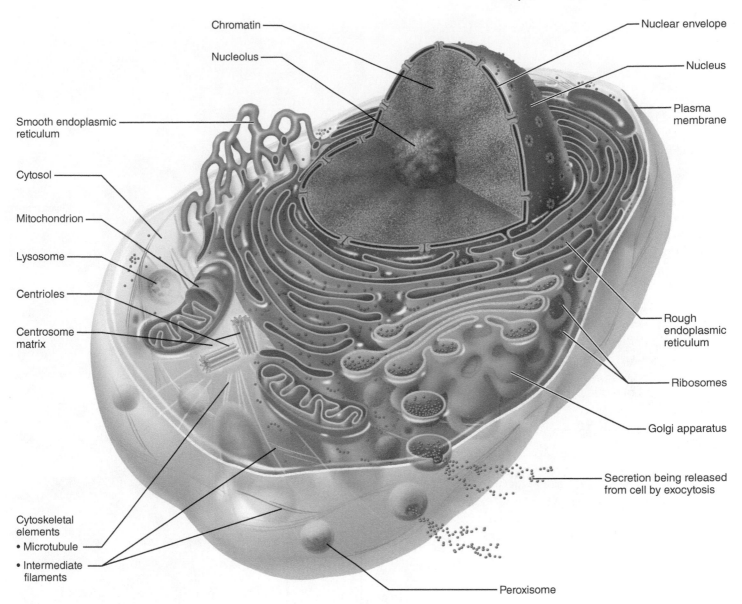

Figure 3.2 **Structure of the generalized cell.** No cell is exactly like this one, but this composite illustrates features common to many human cells. Note that not all of the organelles are drawn to the same scale in this illustration.

The Plasma Membrane: Structure

✓ Describe the chemical composition of the plasma membrane and relate it to membrane functions.

✓ Compare the structure and function of tight junctions, desmosomes, and gap junctions.

The flexible **plasma membrane** defines the extent of a cell, thereby separating two of the body's major fluid compartments—the *intracellular* fluid within cells and the *extracellular* fluid (ECF) outside cells. The term *cell membrane* is commonly used as a synonym for plasma membrane, but because nearly all cellular organelles are enclosed in a membrane, in this book we will always refer to the cell's surface, or outer limiting membrane, as the plasma membrane. The plasma membrane is much more than a passive envelope. As you will see, its unique structure allows it to play a dynamic role in cellular activities.

The Fluid Mosaic Model

The **fluid mosaic model** of membrane structure depicts the plasma membrane as an exceedingly thin (7–10 nm) structure composed of a double layer, or bilayer, of lipid molecules with protein molecules "plugged into" or dispersed in it **(Figure 3.3)**. The proteins, many of which float in the fluid *lipid bilayer*, form a constantly changing mosaic pattern. The model is named for this characteristic.

Membrane Lipids

The lipid bilayer forms the basic "fabric" of the membrane. It is constructed largely of *phospholipids*, with smaller amounts of *glycolipids*, *cholesterol*, and areas called *lipid rafts*.

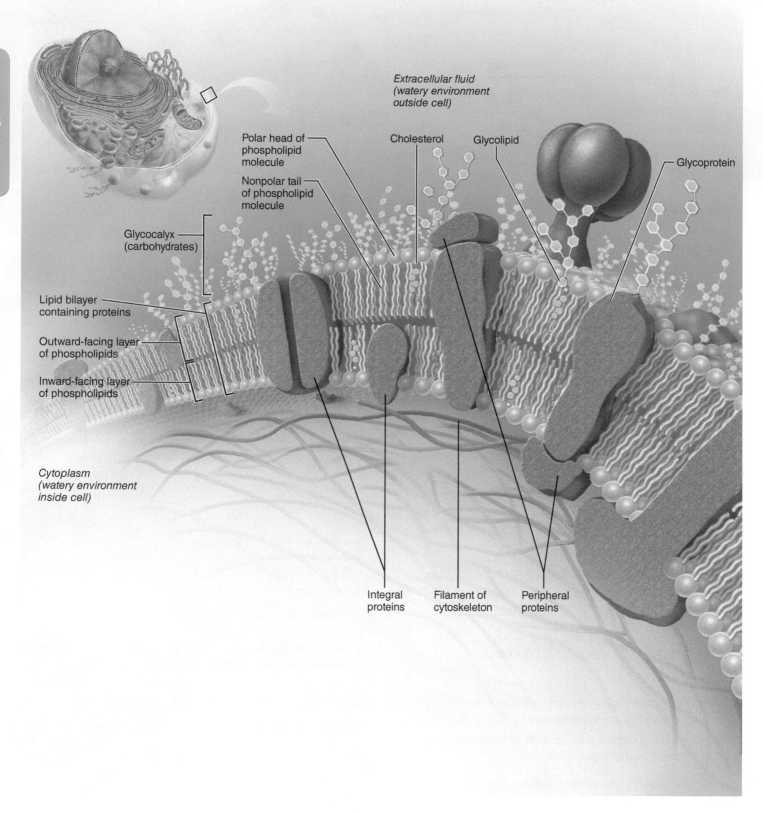

Figure 3.3 The plasma membrane. The lipid bilayer forms the basic structure of the membrane. The associated proteins are involved in membrane functions such as membrane transport, catalysis, and cell-to-cell recognition.

Phospholipids Each lollipop-shaped phospholipid molecule has a polar "head" that is charged and is **hydrophilic** (*hydro* = water, *philic* = loving), and an uncharged, nonpolar "tail" that is made of two fatty acid chains and is **hydrophobic** (*phobia* = fear). The polar heads are attracted to water—the main constituent of both the intracellular and extracellular fluids—and so they lie on both the inner and outer surfaces of the membrane. The nonpolar tails, being hydrophobic, avoid water and line up in the center of the membrane.

The result is that all plasma membranes, indeed all biological membranes, share a sandwich-like structure: They are composed of two parallel sheets of phospholipid molecules lying tail to tail, with their polar heads exposed to water on either side of the membrane or organelle. This self-orienting property of phospholipids encourages biological membranes to self-assemble into closed, generally spherical, structures and to reseal themselves when torn.

With a consistency similar to olive oil, the plasma membrane is a dynamic fluid structure in constant flux. Its lipid molecules move freely from side to side, parallel to the membrane surface, but their polar-nonpolar interactions prevent them from flip-flopping or moving from one half of the bilayer to the other half. The inward-facing and outward-facing surfaces of the plasma membrane differ in the kinds and amounts of lipids they contain, and these variations are important in determining local membrane structure and function. Most membrane phospholipids are unsaturated, a condition which kinks their tails (increasing the space between them) and increases membrane fluidity. (See the illustration of phosphatidylcholine in Figure 2.16b, p. 45.)

Glycolipids Glycolipids (gli″ko-lip′idz) are lipids with attached sugar groups. Found only on the outer plasma membrane surface, glycolipids account for about 5% of total membrane lipids. Their sugar groups, like the phosphate-containing groups of phospholipids, make that end of the glycolipid molecule polar, whereas the fatty acid tails are nonpolar.

Cholesterol Some 20% of membrane lipid is cholesterol. Like phospholipids, cholesterol has a polar region (its hydroxyl group) and a nonpolar region (its fused ring system). It wedges its platelike hydrocarbon rings between the phospholipid tails, stabilizing the membrane, while decreasing the mobility of the phospholipids and the fluidity of the membrane.

Membrane Proteins

A cell's plasma membrane bristles with proteins that allow it to communicate with its environment. Proteins make up about half of the plasma membrane by mass and are responsible for most of the specialized membrane functions. Some membrane proteins float freely. Others are "tethered" to intracellular structures that make up the *cytoskeleton* and are restricted in their movement.

There are two distinct populations of membrane proteins, integral and peripheral (Figure 3.3).

Integral Proteins **Integral proteins** are firmly inserted into the lipid bilayer. Some protrude from one membrane face only, but most are *transmembrane proteins* that span the entire membrane and protrude on both sides. Whether transmembrane or not, all integral proteins have both hydrophobic and hydrophilic regions. This structural feature allows them to interact with both the nonpolar lipid tails buried in the membrane and the water inside and outside the cell.

Some transmembrane proteins are involved in transport, and cluster together to form *channels*, or pores, through which small, water-soluble molecules or ions can move, thus bypassing the lipid part of the membrane. Others act as *carriers* that bind to a substance and then move it through the membrane **(Figure 3.4a)**. Some transmembrane proteins are enzymes (Figure 3.4d). Still others are receptors for hormones or other chemical messengers and relay messages to the cell interior—a process called *signal transduction* (Figure 3.4b).

Peripheral Proteins Unlike integral proteins, **peripheral proteins** (Figure 3.3) are not embedded in the lipid bilayer. Instead, they attach loosely to integral proteins and are easily removed without disrupting the membrane. Peripheral proteins include a network of filaments that helps support the membrane from its cytoplasmic side (Figure 3.4c). Some peripheral proteins are enzymes. Others are motor proteins involved in mechanical functions, such as changing cell shape during cell division and muscle cell contraction. Still others link cells together.

Lipid Rafts

About 20% of the outer membrane surface contains **lipid rafts**, dynamic assemblies of saturated phospholipids (which pack together tightly) associated with unique lipids called sphingolipids and lots of cholesterol. The quiltlike lipid rafts are more stable and less fluid than the rest of the membrane, and they can include or exclude specific proteins to various extents. Because of these qualities, lipid rafts are assumed to be concentrating platforms for certain receptor molecules or for protein molecules needed for cell signaling (discussed on p. 81), membrane invagination (see endocytosis, p. 77), or other functions.

The Glycocalyx

Many of the proteins that abut the extracellular fluid are glycoproteins with branching sugar groups. The term **glycocalyx** (gli″ko-kal′iks; "sugar covering") describes the fuzzy, sticky, carbohydrate-rich area at the cell surface. Quite honestly, you can think of your cells as sugar-coated. The glycocalyx on each cell's surface is enriched both by glycolipids and by glycoproteins secreted by the cell.

Because every cell type has a different pattern of sugars in its glycocalyx, the glycocalyx provides highly specific biological markers by which approaching cells recognize each other (Figure 3.4f). For example, a sperm recognizes an ovum (egg cell) by the ovum's unique glycocalyx. Cells of the immune system identify a bacterium by binding to certain membrane glycoproteins in the bacterial glycocalyx.

(a) Transport

- A protein (left) that spans the membrane may provide a hydrophilic channel across the membrane that is selective for a particular solute.
- Some transport proteins (right) hydrolyze ATP as an energy source to actively pump substances across the membrane.

(b) Receptors for signal transduction

- A membrane protein exposed to the outside of the cell may have a binding site that fits the shape of a specific chemical messenger, such as a hormone.
- When bound, the chemical messenger may cause a change in shape in the protein that initiates a chain of chemical reactions in the cell.

(c) Attachment to the cytoskeleton and extracellular matrix

- Elements of the cytoskeleton (cell's internal supports) and the extracellular matrix (fibers and other substances outside the cell) may anchor to membrane proteins, which helps maintain cell shape and fix the location of certain membrane proteins.
- Others play a role in cell movement or bind adjacent cells together.

(d) Enzymatic activity

- A membrane protein may be an enzyme with its active site exposed to substances in the adjacent solution.
- A team of several enzymes in a membrane may catalyze sequential steps of a metabolic pathway as indicated (left to right) here.

(e) Intercellular joining

- Membrane proteins of adjacent cells may be hooked together in various kinds of intercellular junctions.
- Some membrane proteins (cell adhesion molecules or CAMs) of this group provide temporary binding sites that guide cell migration and other cell-to-cell interactions.

(f) Cell-cell recognition

- Some glycoproteins (proteins bonded to short chains of sugars) serve as identification tags that are specifically recognized by other cells.

Figure 3.4 Membrane proteins perform many tasks. A single protein may perform a combination of these functions.

 Homeostatic Imbalance 3.1

Definite changes occur in the glycocalyx of a cell that is becoming cancerous. In fact, a cancer cell's glycocalyx may change almost continuously, allowing it to keep ahead of immune system recognition mechanisms and avoid destruction. (Cancer is discussed on pp. 145–146.) ✚

☑ **Check Your Understanding**

3. What basic structure do all cellular membranes share?
4. Why do phospholipids, which form the greater part of membranes, organize into a bilayer—tail-to-tail—in a watery environment?
5. What is the importance of the glycocalyx in cell interactions?

For answers, see Appendix H.

Cell Junctions

Although certain cell types—blood cells, sperm cells, and some immune system cells—are "footloose" in the body, many other types are knit into tight communities. Typically, three factors act to bind cells together:

- Glycoproteins in the glycocalyx act as an adhesive.
- Wavy contours of the membranes of adjacent cells fit together in a tongue-and-groove fashion.
- Special cell junctions form **(Figure 3.5)**.

Because junctions are the most important factor securing cells together, let's look more closely at the various types.

Tight Junctions

In a **tight junction**, a series of integral protein molecules in the plasma membranes of adjacent cells fuse together, forming an *impermeable junction* that encircles the cell (Figure 3.5a). Tight junctions help prevent molecules from passing through the extracellular space between adjacent cells. For example, tight junctions between epithelial cells lining the digestive tract keep digestive enzymes and microorganisms in the intestine from seeping into the bloodstream. (Although called "impermeable" junctions, some tight junctions are leaky and may allow certain ions to pass.)

Desmosomes

Desmosomes (des'muh-sōmz; "binding bodies") are *anchoring junctions*—mechanical couplings scattered like rivets along the sides of abutting cells to prevent their separation (Figure 3.5b). On the cytoplasmic face of each plasma membrane is a buttonlike thickening called a *plaque*. Adjacent cells are held together by thin linker protein filaments (cadherins) that extend from the plaques and fit together like the teeth of a zipper in the intercellular space. Thicker keratin filaments (intermediate filaments, which form part of the cytoskeleton) extend from the cytoplasmic side of the plaque across the width of the cell to anchor to the plaque on the cell's opposite side. In this way, desmosomes bind neighboring cells together and also contribute to a continuous internal network of strong "guy-wires."

This arrangement distributes tension throughout a cellular sheet and reduces the chance of tearing when it is subjected to

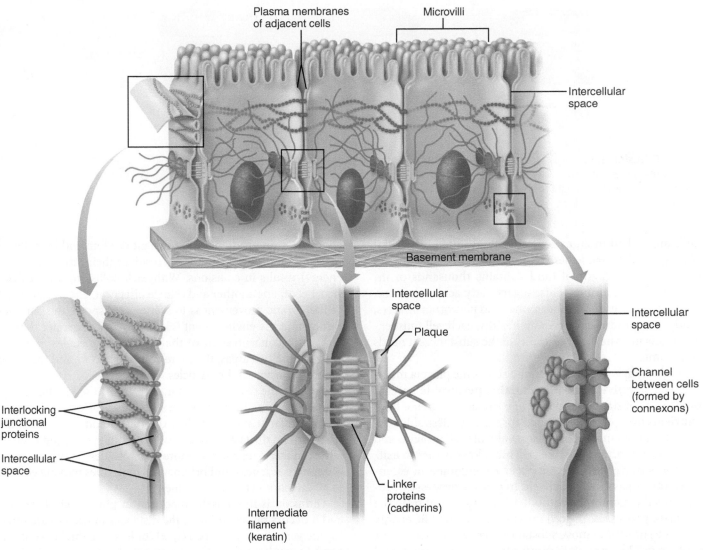

(a) **Tight junctions:** Impermeable junctions prevent molecules from passing through the intercellular space.

(b) **Desmosomes:** Anchoring junctions bind adjacent cells together like a molecular "Velcro" and help form an internal tension-reducing network of fibers.

(c) **Gap junctions:** Communicating junctions allow ions and small molecules to pass for intercellular communication.

Figure 3.5 Cell junctions. An epithelial cell is shown joined to adjacent cells by three common types of cell junctions. (Note: Except for epithelia, it is unlikely that a single cell will have all three junction types.)

pulling forces. Desmosomes are abundant in tissues subjected to great mechanical stress, such as skin and heart muscle.

Gap Junctions

A **gap junction**, or *nexus* (nek'sus; "bond"), is a communicating junction between adjacent cells. At gap junctions the adjacent plasma membranes are very close, and the cells are connected by hollow cylinders called *connexons* (kŏ-nek'sonz), composed of transmembrane proteins. The many different types of connexon proteins vary the selectivity of the gap junction channels. Ions, simple sugars, and other small molecules pass through these water-filled channels from one cell to the next (Figure 3.5c).

Gap junctions are present in electrically excitable tissues, such as the heart and smooth muscle, where ion passage from cell to cell helps synchronize their electrical activity and contraction.

☑ **Check Your Understanding**

6. Which two types of cell junctions would you expect to find between muscle cells of the heart?

For answer, see Appendix H.

The Plasma Membrane: Membrane Transport

✓ Relate plasma membrane structure to active and passive transport processes.

✓ Compare and contrast simple diffusion, facilitated diffusion, and osmosis relative to substances transported, direction, and mechanism.

Figure 3.6 Diffusion. Molecules in solution move continuously and collide constantly with other molecules, causing them to move away from areas of their highest concentration and become evenly distributed. From left to right, molecules from a dye pellet diffuse into the surrounding water down their concentration gradient.

Our cells are bathed in an extracellular fluid called **interstitial fluid** (in″ter-stish′al) that is derived from the blood. Like a rich, nutritious "soup," interstitial fluid contains thousands of ingredients, including amino acids, sugars, fatty acids, vitamins, regulatory substances such as hormones and neurotransmitters, salts, and waste products. To remain healthy, each cell must extract from this mix the exact amounts of the substances it needs at specific times.

Although there is continuous traffic across the plasma membrane, it is a **selectively**, or **differentially, permeable** barrier: It allows some substances to pass while excluding others. It allows nutrients to enter the cell, but keeps many undesirable substances out. At the same time, it keeps valuable cell proteins and other necessary substances in the cell, but allows wastes to exit.

Substances move through the plasma membrane in essentially two ways—passively or actively. In **passive processes**, substances cross the membrane without any energy input from the cell. In **active processes**, the cell provides the metabolic energy (usually ATP) needed to move substances across the membrane. Table 3.1 on p. 72 summarizes passive transport processes, and Table 3.2 on p. 78 summarizes active transport.

Homeostatic Imbalance 3.2

Selective permeability is a characteristic of healthy, intact cells. When a cell (or its plasma membrane) is severely damaged, the membrane becomes permeable to virtually everything, and substances flow into and out of the cell freely. This phenomenon is evident when someone has been severely burned. Precious fluids, proteins, and ions "weep" from the damaged cells. ✚

Passive Processes

The two main types of passive transport are *diffusion* (dĭ-fu′zhun) and *filtration*. Diffusion is an important means of passive membrane transport for every cell of the body. Because filtration generally occurs only across capillary walls, we will discuss it later in conjunction with capillary transport.

Diffusion

Diffusion is the tendency of molecules or ions to move from an area where they are in higher concentration to an area where they are in lower concentration, that is, down or along their **concentration gradient**. The constant random and high-speed motion of molecules and ions (a result of their intrinsic kinetic energy) results in collisions. With each collision, the particles ricochet off one another and change direction. The overall effect of this erratic movement is to scatter or disperse the particles throughout the environment **(Figure 3.6)**. The greater the difference in concentration of the diffusing molecules and ions between the two areas, the more collisions occur and the faster the net diffusion of the particles.

Because the driving force for diffusion is the kinetic energy of the molecules themselves, the speed of diffusion is influenced by molecular *size* (the smaller, the faster) and by *temperature* (the warmer, the faster). In a closed container, diffusion eventually produces a uniform mixture of molecules. In other words, the system reaches equilibrium, with molecules moving equally in all directions (no *net* movement).

Diffusion is immensely important in physiological systems and it occurs rapidly because the distances molecules are moving are very short, perhaps 1/1000 (or less) the thickness of this page! Examples include the movement of ions across cell membranes and the movement of neurotransmitters between two nerve cells.

The plasma membrane is a physical barrier to free diffusion because of its hydrophobic core. However, a molecule or ion *will* diffuse through the membrane if the molecule is (1) lipid soluble, (2) small enough to pass through membrane channels, or (3) assisted by a carrier molecule.

The unassisted diffusion of lipid-soluble or very small particles is called *simple diffusion*. Assisted diffusion is known as *facilitated diffusion*. A special name, *osmosis*, is given to the diffusion of a solvent (usually water) through a membrane.

Simple Diffusion   In **simple diffusion**, nonpolar and lipid-soluble substances diffuse directly through the lipid bilayer **(Figure 3.7a)**. Such substances include oxygen, carbon dioxide, and fat-soluble vitamins. Because oxygen concentration is always higher in the blood than in tissue cells, oxygen continuously diffuses from the blood into the cells. Carbon dioxide, on the other hand, is in higher concentration within the cells, so it diffuses from tissue cells into the blood.

Facilitated Diffusion   Certain molecules, notably glucose and other sugars, some amino acids, and ions are transported

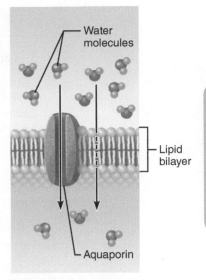

Extracellular fluid

Lipid-soluble solutes

Cytoplasm

(a) Simple diffusion of fat-soluble molecules directly through the phospholipid bilayer

Lipid-insoluble solutes (such as sugars or amino acids)

(b) Carrier-mediated facilitated diffusion via protein carrier specific for one chemical; binding of substrate causes transport protein to change shape

Small lipid-insoluble solutes

(c) Channel-mediated facilitated diffusion through a channel protein; mostly ions selected on basis of size and charge

Water molecules

Lipid bilayer

Aquaporin

(d) Osmosis, diffusion of a solvent such as water through a specific channel protein (aquaporin) or through the lipid bilayer

Figure 3.7 Diffusion through the plasma membrane.

passively even though they are unable to pass through the lipid bilayer. Instead they move through the membrane by a passive transport process called **facilitated diffusion** in which the transported substance either (1) binds to protein carriers in the membrane and is ferried across or (2) moves through water-filled protein channels.

■ **Carrier-mediated facilitated diffusion. Carriers** are transmembrane integral proteins that are specific for transporting certain polar molecules or classes of molecules, such as sugars and amino acids, that are too large to pass through membrane channels. Alterations in the shape of the carrier allow it to first envelop and then release the transported substance, shielding it en route from the nonpolar regions of the membrane. Essentially, changes in the conformation of the carrier protein move the binding site from one face of the membrane to the other (Figure 3.7b and Table 3.1).

Note that a substance transported by carrier-mediated facilitated diffusion, such as glucose, moves down its concentration gradient, just as in simple diffusion. Glucose is normally in higher concentrations in the blood than in the cells, where it is rapidly used for ATP synthesis. So, glucose transport within the body is *typically* unidirectional—into the cells. However, carrier-mediated transport is limited by the number of protein carriers present. For example, when all the glucose carriers are "engaged," they are said to be *saturated*, and glucose transport is occurring at its maximum rate.

■ **Channel-mediated facilitated diffusion. Channels** are transmembrane proteins that transport substances, usually ions or water, through aqueous channels from one side of the membrane to the other (Figure 3.7c and d). Channels are selective due to pore size and the charges of the amino acids lining the channel. *Leakage channels* are always open and simply allow ions or water to move according to concentration gradients. *Gated channels* are controlled (opened or closed) by chemical or electrical signals.

Like carriers, many channels can be inhibited by certain molecules, show saturation, and tend to be specific. Substances moving through them also follow the concentration gradient (always moving down the gradient). When a substance crosses the membrane by simple diffusion, the rate of diffusion is not controllable because the lipid solubility of the membrane is not immediately changeable. By contrast, the rate of facilitated diffusion *is* controllable because the permeability of the membrane can be altered by regulating the activity or number of individual carriers or channels.

Oxygen, water, glucose, and various ions are vitally important to cellular homeostasis. Their passive transport by diffusion (either simple or facilitated) represents a tremendous saving of cellular energy. Indeed, if these substances had to be transported actively, cell expenditures of ATP would increase exponentially!

Osmosis The diffusion of a solvent, such as water, through a selectively permeable membrane is **osmosis** (oz-mo´sis; *osmos* = pushing). Even though water is highly polar, it passes via osmosis through the lipid bilayer (Figure 3.7d). This is surprising because you'd expect water to be repelled by the hydrophobic lipid tails. One hypothesis is that random movements of the membrane lipids open small gaps between their wiggling tails, allowing water to slip and slide its way through the membrane by moving from gap to gap.

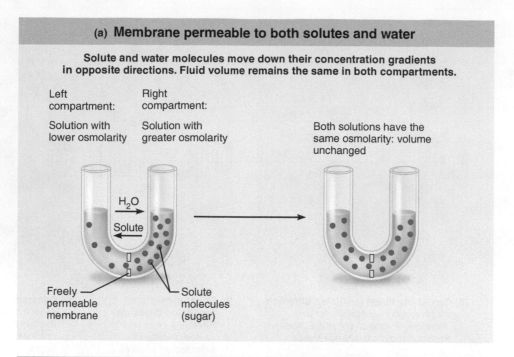

(a) Membrane permeable to both solutes and water

Solute and water molecules move down their concentration gradients in opposite directions. Fluid volume remains the same in both compartments.

Left compartment:

Right compartment:

Solution with lower osmolarity

Solution with greater osmolarity

Both solutions have the same osmolarity: volume unchanged

H_2O

Solute

Freely permeable membrane

Solute molecules (sugar)

(b) Membrane permeable to water, impermeable to solutes

Solute molecules are prevented from moving but water moves by osmosis. Volume increases in the compartment with the higher osmolarity.

Left compartment

Right compartment

Both solutions have identical osmolarity, but volume of the solution on the right is greater because only water is free to move

H_2O

Selectively permeable membrane

Solute molecules (sugar)

Figure 3.8 Influence of membrane permeability on diffusion and osmosis.

Water also moves freely and reversibly through water-specific channels constructed by transmembrane proteins called **aquaporins (AQPs)**, which allow single-file diffusion of water molecules. Although water-filled aquaporin channels are believed to be present in all cell types, they are particularly abundant in red blood cells and in cells involved in water balance such as kidney tubule cells.

Osmosis occurs whenever the water concentration differs on the two sides of a membrane. If distilled water is present on both sides of a selectively permeable membrane, no *net* osmosis occurs, even though water molecules move in both directions through

the membrane. If the solute concentration on the two sides of the membrane differs, water concentration differs as well (as solute concentration increases, water concentration decreases).

The extent to which solutes decrease water's concentration depends on the *number*—not the *type*—of solute particles, because one molecule or one ion of solute (theoretically) displaces one water molecule. The total concentration of all solute particles in a solution is referred to as the solution's **osmolarity** (oz″mo-lar′ĭ-te). When equal volumes of aqueous solutions of different osmolarity are separated by a membrane that is *permeable to all molecules* in the system, net diffusion of both solute

Figure 3.9 The effect of solutions of varying tonicities on living red blood cells.

and water occurs, each moving down its own concentration gradient. Equilibrium is reached when the water (and solute) concentration on both sides of the membrane is the same **(Figure 3.8a)**.

If we consider the same system, but make the membrane *impermeable to solute particles*, we see quite a different result (Figure 3.8b). Water quickly diffuses from the left to the right compartment and continues to do so until its concentration is the same on the two sides of the membrane. Notice that in this case equilibrium results from the movement of water alone (the solutes are prevented from moving). Notice also that the movement of water leads to dramatic changes in the volumes of the two compartments.

The last situation mimics osmosis across plasma membranes of living cells, with one major difference. In our examples, the volumes of the compartments are infinitely expandable and the effect of pressure exerted by the added weight of the higher fluid column is not considered. In living plant cells, which have rigid cell walls external to their plasma membranes, this is not the case. As water diffuses into the cell, the point is finally reached where the **hydrostatic pressure** (the back pressure exerted by water against the membrane) within the cell is equal to its **osmotic pressure** (the tendency of water to move into the cell by osmosis). At this point, there is no further (net) water entry. As a rule, the higher the amount of nondiffusible, or *nonpenetrating*, solutes in a cell, the higher the osmotic pressure and the greater the hydrostatic pressure must be to resist further net water entry. In our plant cell, hydrostatic pressure is pushing water out, and osmotic pressure is pulling water in; therefore, you could think of the osmotic pressure as an osmotic "suck."

However, such major changes in hydrostatic (and osmotic) pressures do not occur in living animal cells, which lack rigid cell walls. Osmotic imbalances cause animal cells to swell or shrink (due to net water gain or loss) until either (1) the solute concentration is the same on both sides of the plasma membrane, or (2) the membrane stretches to its breaking point.

Tonicity Such changes in animal cells lead us to the important concept of *tonicity* (to-nis´ĭ-te). As noted, many solutes, particularly intracellular proteins and selected ions, cannot diffuse through the plasma membrane. Consequently, any change in their concentration alters the water concentration on the two sides of the membrane and results in a net loss or gain of water by the cell.

Tonicity refers to the ability of a solution to change the shape or tone of cells by altering the cells' internal water volume (*tono* = tension).

- **Isotonic** ("the same tonicity") **solutions** have the same concentrations of nonpenetrating solutes as those found in cells (0.9% saline or 5% glucose). Cells exposed to isotonic solutions retain their normal shape, and exhibit no net loss or gain of water **(Figure 3.9a)**. As you might expect, the body's extracellular fluids and most intravenous solutions (solutions infused into the body via a vein) are isotonic.

- **Hypertonic solutions** have a higher concentration of nonpenetrating solutes than seen in the cell (for example, a strong saline solution). Cells immersed in hypertonic solutions lose water and shrink, or *crenate* (kre´nat) (Figure 3.9b).

Table 3.1 Passive Membrane Transport Processes

PROCESS	ENERGY SOURCE	DESCRIPTION	EXAMPLES
Diffusion			
Simple diffusion	Kinetic energy	Net movement of molecules from an area of their higher concentration to an area of their lower concentration, that is, along their concentration gradient	Fats, oxygen, carbon dioxide move through the lipid bilayer of the membrane
Facilitated diffusion	Kinetic energy	Same as simple diffusion, but the diffusing substance is attached to a lipid-soluble membrane carrier protein (carrier-mediated facilitated diffusion) or moves through a membrane channel (channel-mediated facilitated diffusion)	Glucose and some ions move into cells
Osmosis	Kinetic energy	Diffusion of water through a selectively permeable membrane	Movement of water into and out of cells directly through the lipid bilayer of the membrane or via membrane channels (aquaporins)

- **Hypotonic solutions** are more dilute (contain a lower concentration of nonpenetrating solutes) than cells. Cells placed in a hypotonic solution plump up rapidly as water rushes into them (Figure 3.9c). Distilled water represents the most extreme example of hypotonicity. Because it contains *no* solutes, water continues to enter cells until they finally burst, or *lyse*.

Notice that osmolarity and tonicity are not the same. A solution's osmolarity is based solely on its total solute concentration. In contrast, its tonicity is based on how the solution affects cell volume, which depends on (1) solute concentration and (2) solute permeability of the plasma membrane. Osmolarity is expressed as osmoles per liter (osmol/L) where 1 osmol is equal to 1 mole of nonionizing molecules.* A 0.3 osmol/L solution of NaCl is isotonic because sodium ions are usually prevented from diffusing through the plasma membrane. But if the cell is immersed in a 0.3 osmol/L solution of a penetrating solute, the solute will enter the cell and water will follow. The cell will swell and burst, just as if it had been placed in pure water.

Osmosis is extremely important in determining distribution of water in the various fluid-containing compartments of the body (cells, blood, and so on). In general, osmosis continues until osmotic and hydrostatic pressures acting at the membrane are equal. For example, the hydrostatic pressure of blood against the capillary wall forces water out of capillary blood, but the solutes in blood that are too large to cross the capillary membrane draw water back into the bloodstream. As a result, very little net loss of plasma fluid occurs.

Simple diffusion and osmosis occurring directly through the plasma membrane are not selective processes. In those processes, whether a molecule can pass through the membrane depends chiefly on its size or its solubility in lipid, not on its structure. Facilitated diffusion, on the other hand, is often highly selective. The carrier for glucose, for example, combines specifically with glucose, in much the same way an enzyme binds to its specific substrate and ion channels allow only selected ions to pass.

Homeostatic Imbalance 3.3

Hypertonic solutions are sometimes infused intravenously into the bloodstream of patients who are edematous (swollen because their tissues retain water). This is done to draw excess water out of the extracellular space and move it into the bloodstream so the kidneys can eliminate it. Hypotonic solutions may be used (with care) to rehydrate the tissues of extremely dehydrated patients. In mild cases of dehydration, drinking hypotonic fluids (such as apple juice and sports drinks) usually does the trick. ✚

Table 3.1 summarizes passive membrane transport processes.

☑ Check Your Understanding

7. What is the energy source for all types of diffusion?
8. What determines the direction of any diffusion process?
9. What are the two types of facilitated diffusion and how do they differ?

For answers, see Appendix H.

---

*Osmolarity (Osm) is determined by multiplying molarity (moles per liter, or M) by the number of particles resulting from ionization. For example, since NaCl ionizes to $Na^+ + Cl^-$, a $1\ M$ solution of NaCl is a 2 Osm solution. For substances that do not ionize (e.g., glucose), molarity and osmolarity are the same. More precisely, the term *osmolality* is used, which is equal to the number of particles mixed into a kilogram of water.

Active Processes

✓ Differentiate between primary and secondary active transport.

✓ Compare and contrast endocytosis and exocytosis in terms of function and direction.

✓ Compare and contrast pinocytosis, phagocytosis, and receptor-mediated endocytosis.

Whenever a cell uses energy to move solutes across the membrane, the process is referred to as *active*. Substances moved actively across the plasma membrane are usually unable to pass in the necessary direction by passive transport processes. The substance may be too large to pass through the channels, incapable of dissolving in the lipid bilayer, or unable to move down its concentration gradient.

There are two major means of active membrane transport: active transport and vesicular transport.

Active Transport

Like carrier-mediated facilitated diffusion, **active transport** requires carrier proteins that combine *specifically* and *reversibly* with the transported substances. However, facilitated diffusion always follows concentration gradients because its driving force is kinetic energy. In contrast, active transporters or **solute pumps** move solutes, most importantly ions, "uphill" *against* a concentration gradient. To do this work, cells must expend energy.

Active transport processes are distinguished according to their source of energy:

- In *primary active transport*, the energy to do work comes *directly from hydrolysis of ATP*.
- In *secondary active transport*, transport is driven indirectly *by energy stored in ionic gradients* created by primary active transport pumps. Secondary active transport systems are all *coupled systems*; that is, they move more than one substance at a time.

   In a **symport system,** the two transported substances move in the same direction (*sym* = same). In an **antiport system** (*anti* = opposite, against), the transported substances "wave to each other" as they cross the membrane in opposite directions.

Primary Active Transport
In **primary active transport**, hydrolysis of ATP results in the phosphorylation of the transport protein. This step causes the protein to change its shape in such a manner that it "pumps" the bound solute across the membrane.

Primary active transport systems include calcium and hydrogen pumps, but the most investigated example of a primary active transport system is the **sodium-potassium pump**, for which the carrier, or "pump," is an enzyme called **Na^+-K^+ ATPase**. In the body, the concentration of K^+ inside the cell is some 10 times higher than that outside, and the reverse is true of Na^+. These ionic concentration differences are essential for excitable cells like muscle and nerve cells to function normally and for all body cells to maintain their normal fluid volume. Because Na^+ and K^+ leak slowly but continuously through leakage channels in the plasma membrane along their concentration gradient (and cross more rapidly in stimulated muscle and nerve cells), the Na^+-K^+ pump operates almost continuously as an antiporter. It simultaneously drives Na^+ out of the cell against a steep concentration gradient and pumps K^+ back in.

Earlier we said that solutes diffuse down their concentration gradients. This is true for uncharged solutes, but only partially true for ions. The negatively and positively charged faces of the plasma membrane can help or hinder diffusion of ions driven by a concentration gradient. It is more correct to say that ions diffuse according to **electrochemical gradients**, thereby recognizing the effect of both electrical and concentration (chemical) forces. Hence, the electrochemical gradients maintained by the Na^+-K^+ pump underlie most secondary active transport of nutrients and ions, and are crucial for cardiac, skeletal muscle, and neuron function.

Figure 3.10 on p. 74, *Focus on Primary Active Transport: The Na^+-K^+ Pump*, describes the operation of the Na^+-K^+ pump. Make sure you understand this process thoroughly before moving on to the topic of secondary active transport.

Secondary Active Transport
A single ATP-powered pump, such as the Na^+-K^+ pump, can indirectly drive the **secondary active transport** of several other solutes. By moving sodium across the plasma membrane against its concentration gradient, the pump stores energy (in the ion gradient). Then, just as water pumped uphill can do work as it flows back down (to turn a water wheel, for instance), a substance pumped across a membrane can do work as it leaks back, propelled "downhill" along its concentration gradient. In this way, as sodium moves back into the cell with the help of a carrier protein, other substances are "dragged along," or cotransported, by the same carrier protein **(Figure 3.11)**. This is a symport system.

For example, some sugars, amino acids, and many ions are cotransported via secondary active transport into cells lining the small intestine. Because the energy for this type of transport is the concentration gradient of the ion (in this case Na^+), Na^+ has to be pumped back out of the cell to maintain its diffusion gradient. Ion gradients can also drive antiport systems such as those that help regulate intracellular pH by using the sodium gradient to expel hydrogen ions.

Regardless of whether the energy is provided directly (primary active transport) or indirectly (secondary active transport), each membrane pump or cotransporter transports only specific substances. Active transport systems provide a way for the cell to be very selective in cases where substances cannot pass by diffusion. No pump—no transport.

Vesicular Transport

In **vesicular transport**, fluids containing large particles and macromolecules are transported across cellular membranes inside membranous sacs called *vesicles*. Like active transport, vesicular transport moves substances into the cell (endocytosis) and out of the cell (exocytosis). It is also used for combination processes such as *transcytosis*, moving substances into, across, and then out of the cell, and *vesicular trafficking*, moving substances from one area (or membranous organelle) in the cell to another. Vesicular transport processes are energized by ATP (or in some cases another energy-rich compound, *GTP*—guanosine triphosphate).

Endocytosis, Transcytosis, and Vesicular Trafficking
Virtually all forms of vesicular transport involve an assortment of protein-coated vesicles of three types and, with some exceptions, all are mediated by membrane receptors. Before we get specific about each type of coated vesicular transport, let's look at the general scheme of endocytosis.

Figure 3.10 Primary active transport is the process in which solutes are moved across cell membranes against electrochemical gradients using energy supplied directly by ATP. The action of the Na⁺–K⁺ pump is an important example of primary active transport. *A&P Flix* Available at www.masteringaandp.com

Extracellular fluid — Na⁺

Na⁺–K⁺ pump

ATP
ATP-binding site

Cytoplasm — K⁺

① Three cytoplasmic Na⁺ bind to pump protein.

Na⁺ bound

P

ADP

② Na⁺ binding promotes hydrolysis of ATP. The energy released during this reaction phosphorylates the pump.

K⁺ released

ATP

⑥ Pump protein binds ATP; releases K⁺ to the inside, and Na⁺ sites are ready to bind Na⁺ again. The cycle repeats.

Na⁺ released

P

③ Phosphorylation causes the pump to change shape, expelling Na⁺ to the outside.

K⁺ bound

Pᵢ

⑤ K⁺ binding triggers release of the phosphate. The dephosphorylated pump resumes its original conformation.

K⁺

P

④ Two extracellular K⁺ bind to pump.

① Primary active transport
The ATP-driven Na⁺-K⁺ pump stores energy by creating a steep concentration gradient for Na⁺ entry into the cell.

② Secondary active transport
As Na⁺ diffuses back across the membrane through a membrane cotransporter protein, it drives glucose against its concentration gradient into the cell.

Figure 3.11 Secondary active transport is driven by the concentration gradient created by primary active transport.

Protein-coated vesicles provide the main route for endocytosis and transcytosis of bulk solids, most macromolecules, and fluids. On occasion, these vesicles are also hijacked by pathogens seeking entry into a cell.

Figure 3.12 shows the basic steps in endocytosis and transcytosis. ① An infolding portion of the plasma membrane, called a *coated pit*, progressively encloses the substance to be taken into the cell. The coating found on the cytoplasmic face of the pit is most often the bristlelike protein **clathrin** (klă′thrin; "lattice clad"). The clathrin coat (clathrin and some accessory proteins) acts in both selecting the cargo and deforming the membrane to produce the vesicle. ② The vesicle detaches, and ③ the coat proteins are recycled back to the plasma membrane. ④ The uncoated vesicle then typically fuses with a sorting vesicle called an *endosome*. ⑤ Some membrane components and receptors of the fused vesicle may be recycled back to the plasma membrane in a transport vesicle. ⑥ The remaining contents of the vesicle may (a) combine with a *lysosome* (li′so-sōm), a specialized cell structure containing digestive enzymes, where the ingested substance is degraded or released (if iron or cholesterol), or (b) be transported completely across the cell and released by exocytosis on the opposite side (*transcytosis*). Transcytosis is common in the endothelial cells lining blood vessels because it provides a quick means to get substances from the blood to the interstitial fluid.

Based on the nature and quantity of material taken up and the means of uptake, three types of endocytosis that use clathrin-coated vesicles are recognized: phagocytosis, pinocytosis, and receptor-mediated endocytosis.

■ **Phagocytosis.** In **phagocytosis** (fag″o-si-to′sis; "cell eating"), the cell engulfs some relatively large or solid material, such as a clump of bacteria, cell debris, or inanimate particles (asbestos fibers or glass, for example) **(Figure 3.13a)**. When a particle binds to receptors on the cell's surface, cytoplasmic extensions called pseudopods (soo′do-pahdz; *pseudo* = false, *pod* = foot) form and flow around the particle. This forms an endocytotic vesicle called a **phagosome** (fag′o-sōm; "eaten body"). In most cases, the phagosome then fuses with a lysosome and its contents are digested. Any indigestible contents are ejected from the cell by exocytosis.

In the human body, only macrophages and certain white blood cells are "experts" at phagocytosis. Commonly referred to as *phagocytes*, these cells help protect the body by ingesting and disposing of bacteria, other foreign substances, and dead tissue cells. The disposal of dying cells is crucial, because dead cell remnants trigger inflammation in the surrounding area or may stimulate an undesirable immune response. Most phagocytes move about by **amoeboid motion** (ah-me′boyd; "changing shape"); that is, the flowing of their cytoplasm into temporary extensions allows them to creep along.

■ **Pinocytosis.** In **pinocytosis** ("cell drinking"), also called **fluid-phase endocytosis**, a bit of infolding plasma membrane (which begins as a protein-coated pit) surrounds a very small volume of extracellular fluid containing dissolved molecules (Figure 3.13b). This droplet enters the cell and fuses with an endosome. Unlike phagocytosis, pinocytosis is a routine activity of most cells, affording them a nonselective way of sampling the extracellular fluid. It is particularly important in cells that absorb nutrients, such as cells that line the intestines.

As mentioned, bits of the plasma membrane are removed when the membranous sacs are internalized. However, these membranes are recycled back to the plasma membrane by exocytosis as described shortly, so the surface area of the plasma membrane remains remarkably constant.

3

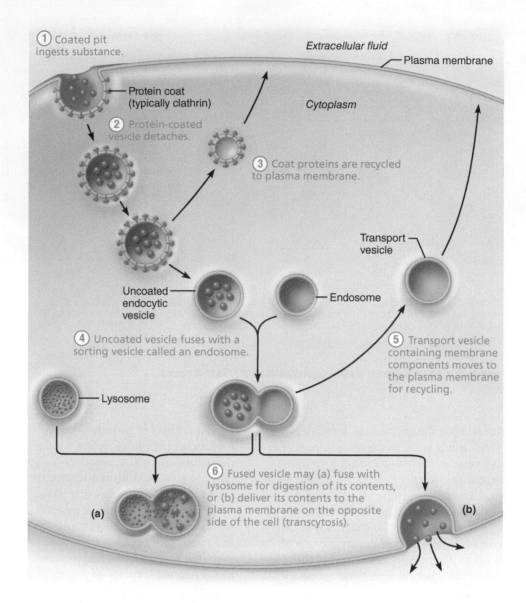

① Coated pit
ingests substance.

Extracellular fluid

Plasma membrane

Protein coat
(typically clathrin)

Cytoplasm

② Protein-coated
vesicle detaches.

③ Coat proteins are recycled
to plasma membrane.

Transport
vesicle

Uncoated
endocytic
vesicle

Endosome

④ Uncoated vesicle fuses with a
sorting vesicle called an endosome.

⑤ Transport vesicle
containing membrane
components moves to
the plasma membrane
for recycling.

Lysosome

⑥ Fused vesicle may (a) fuse with
lysosome for digestion of its contents,
or (b) deliver its contents to the
plasma membrane on the opposite
side of the cell (transcytosis).

(a)

(b)

Figure 3.12 Events of endocytosis mediated by protein-coated pits. Note the three possible
fates for a vesicle and its contents, shown in ⑤ and ⑥.

- **Receptor-mediated endocytosis.** The main mechanism for the *specific* endocytosis and transcytosis of most macromolecules by body cells is **receptor-mediated endocytosis** (Figure 3.13c). This exquisitely selective mechanism allows cells to concentrate material that is present only in small amounts in the extracellular fluid. The receptors for this process are plasma membrane proteins that bind only certain substances. Both the receptors and attached molecules are internalized in a clathrin-coated pit and then dealt with in one of the ways discussed above. Substances taken up by receptor-mediated endocytosis include enzymes, insulin (and some other hormones), low-density lipoproteins (such as cholesterol attached to a transport protein), and iron. Unfortunately, flu viruses, diphtheria, and cholera toxins also use this route to enter our cells.

Different coat proteins are used for certain other types of vesicular transport. For example, **caveolae** (ka″ve-o′le; "little

caves"), tubular or flask-shaped inpocketings of the plasma membrane seen in many cell types, are involved in a unique kind of receptor-mediated endocytosis. Like clathrin-coated pits, caveolae capture specific molecules (folic acid, tetanus toxin) from the extracellular fluid in coated vesicles and participate in some forms of transcytosis. However, caveolae are smaller than clathrin-coated vesicles. Additionally, their cage-like protein coat is thinner.

Caveolae are closely associated with lipid rafts that are platforms for G proteins, receptors for hormones (for example, insulin), and enzymes involved in cell regulation. These vesicles appear to provide sites for cell signaling and cross talk between signaling pathways. Their precise role in the cell is still being worked out.

Vesicles coated with still another coat protein (coatomer) function in most types of intracellular vesicular trafficking. Perhaps the most important thing to remember about the coat

(a) Phagocytosis
The cell engulfs a large particle by forming projecting pseudopods ("false feet") around it and enclosing it within a membrane sac called a phagosome. The phagosome is combined with a lysosome. Undigested contents remain in the vesicle (now called a residual body) or are ejected by exocytosis. Vesicle may or may not be protein-coated but has receptors capable of binding to microorganisms or solid particles.

(b) Pinocytosis
The cell "gulps" a drop of extracellular fluid containing solutes into tiny vesicles. No receptors are used, so the process is nonspecific. Most vesicles are protein-coated.

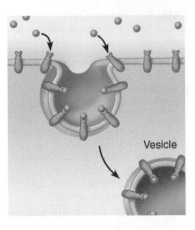

(c) Receptor-mediated endocytosis
Extracellular substances bind to specific receptor proteins, enabling the cell to ingest and concentrate specific substances (ligands) in protein-coated vesicles. Ligands may simply be released inside the cell, or combined with a lysosome to digest contents. Receptors are recycled to the plasma membrane in vesicles.

Figure 3.13 Comparison of three types of endocytosis.

(a) The process of exocytosis

① The membrane-bound vesicle migrates to the plasma membrane.

② There, proteins at the vesicle surface (v-SNAREs) bind with t-SNAREs (plasma membrane proteins).

③ The vesicle and plasma membrane fuse and a pore opens up.

④ Vesicle contents are released to the cell exterior.

(b) Photomicrograph of a secretory vesicle releasing its contents by exocytosis (100,000×)

Figure 3.14 Exocytosis.

proteins in general is that they play a significant role in all forms of endocytosis.

Exocytosis Vesicular transport processes that eject substances from the cell interior into the extracellular fluid are called **exocytosis** (ek″so-si-to′sis; "out of the cell"). Typically stimulated by a cell-surface signal such as binding of a hormone to a membrane receptor or a change in membrane voltage, exocytosis accounts for hormone secretion, neurotransmitter release, mucus secretion, and in some cases, ejection of wastes. The substance to be removed from the cell is first enclosed in a protein-coated membranous sac called a *secretory vesicle*. In most cases, the vesicle migrates to the plasma membrane, fuses with it, and then ruptures, spilling the sac contents out of the cell (**Figure 3.14**).

Table 3.2	Active Membrane Transport Processes		
PROCESS	**ENERGY SOURCE**	**DESCRIPTION**	**EXAMPLES**
Active Transport			
Primary active transport	ATP	Transport of substances against a concentration (or electrochemical) gradient. Performed across the plasma membrane by a solute pump, directly using energy of ATP hydrolysis.	Ions (Na^+, K^+, H^+, Ca^{2+}, and others)
Secondary active transport	Ion concentration gradient maintained with ATP	Cotransport (coupled transport) of two solutes across the membrane. Energy is supplied indirectly by the ion gradient created by primary active transport. Symporters move the transported substances in the same direction; antiporters move transported substances in opposite directions across the membrane.	Movement of polar or charged solutes, e.g., amino acids (into cell by symporters); Ca^{2+}, H^+ (out of cells via antiporters)
Vesicular Transport			
Endocytosis			
▪ Via clathrin-coated vesicles			
Phagocytosis	ATP	"Cell eating": A large external particle (proteins, bacteria, dead cell debris) is surrounded by a "seizing foot" and becomes enclosed in a vesicle (phagosome).	In the human body, occurs primarily in protective phagocytes (some white blood cells and macrophages)
Pinocytosis (fluid-phase endocytosis)	ATP	Plasma membrane sinks beneath an external fluid droplet containing small solutes. Membrane edges fuse, forming a fluid-filled vesicle.	Occurs in most cells; important for taking in dissolved solutes by absorptive cells of the kidney and intestine
Receptor-mediated endocytosis	ATP	Selective endocytosis and transcytosis. External substance binds to membrane receptors.	Means of intake of some hormones, cholesterol, iron, and most macromolecules
▪ Via caveolin-coated vesicles (caveolae)	ATP	Selective endocytosis (and transcytosis). External substance binds to membrane receptors (often associated with lipid rafts).	Roles not fully known; proposed roles include cholesterol regulation and trafficking, and platforms for signal transduction
Vesicular trafficking			
▪ Via coatomer-coated vesicles	ATP	Vesicles pinch off from organelles and travel to other organelles to deliver their cargo.	Accounts for nearly all intracellular trafficking between certain organelles (endoplasmic reticulum and Golgi apparatus). Exceptions include vesicles budding from the trans face of the Golgi apparatus, which are clathrin-coated.
Exocytosis	ATP	Secretion or ejection of substances from a cell. The substance is enclosed in a membranous vesicle, which fuses with the plasma membrane and ruptures, releasing the substance to the exterior.	Secretion of neurotransmitters, hormones, mucus, etc.; ejection of cell wastes

Exocytosis, like other mechanisms in which vesicles are targeted to their destinations, involves a "docking" process in which transmembrane proteins on the vesicles, fancifully called v-SNAREs (*v* for vesicle), recognize certain plasma membrane proteins, called t-SNAREs (*t* for target), and bind with them.

This binding causes the membranes to "corkscrew" together and fuse, rearranging the lipid monolayers without mixing them (Figure 3.14a). As described, membrane material added by exocytosis is removed by endocytosis—the reverse process.

Table 3.2 summarizes active membrane transport processes.

① K⁺ diffuse down their steep concentration gradient (out of the cell) via leakage channels. Loss of K⁺ results in a negative charge on the inner plasma membrane face.

② K⁺ also move into the cell because they are attracted to the negative charge established on the inner plasma membrane face.

③ A negative membrane potential (–90 mV) is established when the movement of K⁺ out of the cell equals K⁺ movement into the cell. At this point, the concentration gradient promoting K⁺ exit exactly opposes the electrical gradient for K⁺ entry.

Figure 3.15 The key role of K⁺ in generating the resting membrane potential. The resting membrane potential is largely determined by K⁺ because at rest, the membrane is much more permeable to K⁺ than Na⁺. The active transport of sodium and potassium ions (in a ratio of 3:2) by the Na⁺-K⁺ pump maintains these conditions.

✓ Check Your Understanding

10. What happens when the Na⁺-K⁺ pump is phosphorylated? When K⁺ binds to the pump protein?
11. As a cell grows, its plasma membrane expands. Does this membrane expansion involve endocytosis or exocytosis?
12. Phagocytic cells gather in the lungs, particularly in the lungs of smokers. What is the connection?
13. Which vesicular transport process allows a cell to take in cholesterol from the extracellular fluid?

For answers, see Appendix H.

The Plasma Membrane: Generation of a Resting Membrane Potential

✓ Define membrane potential and explain how the resting membrane potential is established and maintained.

As you're now aware, the selective permeability of the plasma membrane can lead to dramatic osmotic flows, but that is not its only consequence. An equally important result is the generation of a **membrane potential**, or voltage, across the membrane. A *voltage* is electrical potential energy resulting from the separation of oppositely charged particles. In cells, the oppositely charged particles are ions, and the barrier that keeps them apart is the plasma membrane.

In their resting state, all body plasma membranes exhibit a **resting membrane potential** that typically ranges from −50 to −100 millivolts (mV), depending on cell type. For this reason, all cells are said to be **polarized**. The minus sign before the voltage indicates that the *inside* of the cell is negative compared to its outside. This voltage (or charge separation) exists *only at the membrane*. If we added up all the negative and positive charges in the cytoplasm, we would find that the cell interior is electrically neutral. Likewise, the positive and negative charges in the extracellular fluid balance each other exactly.

So how does the resting membrane potential come about, and how is it maintained? The short answer is that diffusion causes ionic imbalances that polarize the membrane, and active transport processes *maintain* that membrane potential. First, let's look at how diffusion polarizes the membrane.

Selective Diffusion Establishes Membrane Potential

Many kinds of ions are found both inside cells and in the extracellular fluid, but the resting membrane potential is determined mainly by the concentration gradient of potassium (K⁺) and by the differential permeability of the plasma membrane to K⁺ and other ions **(Figure 3.15)**. Recall that K⁺ and protein anions predominate inside body cells, and the extracellular fluid contains relatively more Na⁺, which is largely balanced by Cl⁻. The unstimulated plasma membrane is somewhat permeable to K⁺ because of leakage channels, but impermeable to the protein anions. Consequently, K⁺ diffuses out of the cell along its concentration gradient but the protein anions are unable to follow, and this loss of positive charges makes the membrane interior more negative (Figure 3.15 ①).

As more and more K$^+$ leaves the cell, the negativity of the inner membrane face becomes great enough to attract K$^+$ back toward and even into the cell (Figure 3.15 ②). At a membrane voltage of -90 mV, potassium's concentration gradient is exactly balanced by the electrical gradient (membrane potential), and one K$^+$ enters the cell as one leaves (Figure 3.15 ③).

In many cells, sodium (Na$^+$) also contributes to the resting membrane potential. Sodium is strongly attracted to the cell interior by its concentration gradient, bringing the resting membrane potential to -70 mV. However, potassium still largely determines the resting membrane potential because the membrane is much more permeable to K$^+$ than to Na$^+$. Even though the membrane is permeable to Cl$^-$, in most cells Cl$^-$ does not contribute to the resting membrane potential, because its concentration and electrical gradients exactly balance each other.

We may be tempted to believe that massive flows of K$^+$ ions are needed to generate the resting potential, but this is not the case. Surprisingly, the number of ions producing the membrane potential is so small that it does not change ion concentrations in any significant way.

In a cell at rest, very few ions cross its plasma membrane. However, Na$^+$ and K$^+$ are not at equilibrium and there is some net movement of K$^+$ out of the cell and of Na$^+$ into the cell. Na$^+$ is strongly pulled into the cell by both its concentration gradient and the interior negative charge. If only passive forces were at work, these ion concentrations would eventually become equal inside and outside the cell.

Active Transport Maintains Electrochemical Gradients

Now let's look at how active transport processes maintain the membrane potential that diffusion has established, with the result that the cell exhibits a *steady state*. The rate of active transport is equal to, and depends on, the rate of Na$^+$ diffusion into the cell. If more Na$^+$ enters, more is pumped out. (This is like being in a leaky boat. The more water that comes in, the faster you bail!) The Na$^+$-K$^+$ pump couples sodium and potassium transport and, on average, each "turn" of the pump ejects 3Na$^+$ out of the cell and carries 2K$^+$ back in (see Figure 3.10). Because the membrane is always 50 to 100 times more permeable to K$^+$, the ATP-dependent Na$^+$-K$^+$ pump maintains both the membrane potential (the charge separation) and the osmotic balance. Indeed, if Na$^+$ was not continuously removed from cells, so much would accumulate intracellularly that the osmotic gradient would draw water into the cells, causing them to burst.

As we described on p. 73, diffusion of charged particles across the membrane is affected not only by concentration gradients, but by the electrical charge on the inner and outer faces of the membrane. Together these gradients make up the *electrochemical gradient*. The diffusion of K$^+$ across the plasma membrane is aided by the membrane's greater permeability to it and by the ion's concentration gradient, but the negative charges on the cell interior resist K$^+$ diffusion. In contrast, a steep electrochemical gradient draws Na$^+$ into the cell, but the membrane's relative impermeability to it limits Na$^+$ diffusion.

The transient opening of gated Na$^+$ and K$^+$ channels in the plasma membrane "upsets" the resting membrane potential. As we describe in later chapters, this is a normal means of activating neurons and muscle cells.

☑ Check Your Understanding

14. What process establishes the resting membrane potential?
15. Is the inside of the plasma membrane negative or positive relative to its outside in a polarized membrane?

For answers, see Appendix H.

The Plasma Membrane: Cell-Environment Interactions

✓ Describe the role of the glycocalyx when cells interact with their environment.

✓ List several roles of membrane receptors and that of voltage-gated membrane channel proteins.

Cells are biological minifactories and, like other factories, they receive and send orders from and to the outside community. But *how* does a cell interact with its environment, and *what* activates it to carry out its homeostatic functions?

Sometimes cells interact directly with other cells. However, in many cases cells respond to extracellular chemicals, such as hormones and neurotransmitters distributed in body fluids. Cells also interact with extracellular molecules that act as signposts to guide cell migration during development and repair.

Whether cells interact directly or indirectly, however, the glycocalyx is always involved. The best-understood glycocalyx molecules fall into two large families—cell adhesion molecules and plasma membrane receptors (see Figure 3.4, p. 66). Another group of membrane proteins, voltage-gated channel proteins, are important in cells that respond to electrical signals.

Roles of Cell Adhesion Molecules (CAMs)

Thousands of **cell adhesion molecules (CAMs)** are found on almost every cell in the body. CAMs play key roles in embryonic development and wound repair (situations where cell mobility is important) and in immunity. These sticky glycoproteins (*cadherins* and *integrins*) act as

- The molecular "Velcro" that cells use to anchor themselves to molecules in the extracellular space and to each other (see desmosome discussion on pp. 66–67)
- The "arms" that migrating cells use to haul themselves past one another
- SOS signals sticking out from the blood vessel lining that rally protective white blood cells to a nearby infected or injured area
- Mechanical sensors that respond to changes in local tension or fluid movement at the cell surface by stimulating synthesis or degradation of adhesive membrane (tight) junctions
- Transmitters of intracellular signals that direct cell migration, proliferation, and specialization

Roles of Plasma Membrane Receptors

A huge and diverse group of integral proteins and glycoproteins that serve as binding sites are collectively known as **membrane receptors**. Some function in contact signaling, and others in chemical signaling. Let's take a look.

Contact Signaling

Contact signaling, in which cells come together and touch, is the means by which cells recognize one another. It is particularly important for normal development and immunity. Some bacteria and other infectious agents use contact signaling to identify their "preferred" target tissues.

Chemical Signaling

Most plasma membrane receptors are involved in *chemical signaling*. **Ligands** are chemicals that bind specifically to plasma membrane receptors. Ligands include most *neurotransmitters* (nervous system signals), *hormones* (endocrine system signals), and *paracrines* (chemicals that act locally and are rapidly destroyed).

Different cells respond in different ways to the same ligand. Acetylcholine, for instance, stimulates skeletal muscle cells to contract, but inhibits heart muscle. Why do different cells respond so differently? The reason is that a target cell's response depends on the internal machinery that the receptor is linked to, not the specific ligand that binds to it.

Though cell responses to receptor binding vary widely, there is a fundamental similarity: When a ligand binds to a membrane receptor, the receptor's structure changes, and cell proteins are altered in some way. For example:

- *Catalytic receptor proteins* are membrane proteins that respond to ligands by becoming activated enzymes.

- *Chemically gated channel-linked receptors*, common in muscle and nerve cells, respond by transiently opening or closing ion gates, which in turn changes the excitability of the cell.

- **G protein–linked receptors** exert their effect indirectly through a **G protein**, a regulatory molecule that acts as a middleman or relay to activate (or inactivate) a membrane-bound enzyme or ion channel. This in turn generates one or more intracellular chemical signals, commonly called **second messengers**, which connect plasma membrane events to the internal metabolic machinery of the cell. Two important second messengers are **cyclic AMP** and ionic calcium, both of which typically activate *protein kinase enzymes*, which transfer phosphate groups from ATP to other proteins. In this way, the protein kinases can activate a whole series of enzymes that bring about the desired cellular activity. Because a single enzyme can catalyze hundreds of reactions, the amplification effect of such a chain of events is tremendous, much like that stirred up by a chain letter. *Focus on G Proteins* (**Figure 3.16**) on p. 82 describes a G protein signaling system. Take a moment to study this carefully because this key signaling pathway is involved in neurotransmission, smell, vision, and hormone action (Chapters 11, 15, and 16).

Nitric oxide (NO) is an important signaling molecule even though it doesn't act in any of the ways we have already described. One of nature's simplest molecules, NO is made of a single atom of nitrogen and one of oxygen. It is also an environmental pollutant and the first gas known to act as a biological messenger. Because of its tiny size, it slips into and out of cells easily. Its unpaired electron makes it highly reactive and it reacts with head-spinning speed with other key molecules to spur cells into a broad array of activities. You will hear more about NO in the neural, cardiovascular, and immune system chapters.

Role of Voltage-Gated Membrane Channel Proteins: Electrical Signaling

In *electrical signaling*, certain plasma membrane proteins are channel proteins that respond to changes in membrane potential by opening or closing the channel. Such voltage-gated channels are common in excitable tissues like neural and muscle tissues, and are crucial to their normal function.

☑ **Check Your Understanding**

16. What term is used to indicate signaling chemicals that bind to membrane receptors? Which type of membrane receptor is most important in directing intracellular events by promoting formation of second messengers?

For answer, see Appendix H.

The Cytoplasm

✓ Describe the composition of the cytosol.

✓ Discuss the structure and function of mitochondria.

✓ Discuss the structure and function of ribosomes, the endoplasmic reticulum, and the Golgi apparatus, including functional interrelationships among these organelles.

✓ Compare the functions of lysosomes and peroxisomes.

Cytoplasm ("cell-forming material"), the cellular material between the plasma membrane and the nucleus, is the site of most cellular activities. Although early microscopists thought that the cytoplasm was a structureless gel, the electron microscope reveals that it consists of three major elements: the cytosol, organelles, and inclusions.

The **cytosol** (si′to-sol) is the viscous, semitransparent fluid in which the other cytoplasmic elements are suspended. It is a complex mixture with properties of both a colloid and a true solution. Dissolved in the cytosol, which is largely water, are proteins, salts, sugars, and a variety of other solutes.

The **organelles** are the metabolic machinery of the cell. Each type of organelle carries out a specific function for the cell—some synthesize proteins, others package those proteins, and so on.

Inclusions are chemical substances that may or may not be present, depending on cell type. Examples include stored nutrients, such as the glycogen granules in liver and muscle cells; lipid droplets in fat cells; pigment (melanin) granules in certain skin and hair cells; and crystals of various types.

Figure 3.16 G proteins act as middlemen or relays between extracellular first messengers and intracellular second messengers that cause responses within the cell.

The sequence described here is like a molecular relay race. Instead of a baton passed from runner to runner, the message (a shape change) is passed from molecule to molecule as it makes its way across the cell membrane from outside to inside the cell.

Ligand (1st messenger)   Receptor   G protein   Enzyme   2nd messenger

① **Ligand* (1st messenger) binds to the receptor.** The receptor changes shape and activates.

② **The activated receptor binds to a G protein and activates it.** The G protein changes shape (turns "on"), causing it to release GDP and bind GTP (an energy source).

③ **Activated G protein activates (or inactivates) an effector protein by causing its shape to change.**

Extracellular fluid

Effector protein (e.g., an enzyme)

Ligand

Receptor

G protein

GDP   GTP

GTP

GTP

Inactive 2nd messenger

Active 2nd messenger

④ **Activated effector enzymes catalyze reactions that produce 2nd messengers in the cell.** (Common 2nd messengers include cyclic AMP and Ca^{2+}.)

⑤ **Second messengers activate other enzymes or ion channels.** Cyclic AMP typically activates protein kinase enzymes.

Activated kinase enzymes

⑥ **Kinase enzymes activate other enzymes.** Kinase enzymes transfer phosphate groups from ATP to specific proteins and activate a series of other enzymes that trigger various metabolic and structural changes in the cell.

Cascade of cellular responses (The amplification effect is tremendous. Each enzyme catalyzes hundreds of reactions.)

* Ligands include hormones and neurotransmitters.

Intracellular fluid

Cytoplasmic Organelles

The organelles ("little organs") are specialized cellular compartments or structures, each performing its own job to maintain the life of the cell. Some organelles, the *nonmembranous organelles*, lack membranes. Examples are the cytoskeleton, centrioles, and ribosomes.

Most organelles, however, are bounded by a membrane similar in composition to the plasma membrane. This membrane enables the *membranous organelles* (such as peroxisomes, lysosomes, endoplasmic reticulum, and Golgi apparatus) to maintain an internal environment different from that of the surrounding cytosol. This compartmentalization is crucial to cell functioning. Without it, thousands of enzymes would be randomly mixed and biochemical activity would be chaotic. Besides providing splendid isolation for an organelle, its membrane often unites it with the rest of an interactive intracellular system called the *endomembrane system* (see p. 87), and the lipid and protein makeup of the membrane allows it to recognize and interact with other organelles. Now let's consider what goes on in each of the workshops of our cellular factory.

Mitochondria

Mitochondria (mi″to-kon′dre-ah) are threadlike (*mitos* = thread) or lozenge-shaped membranous organelles. In living cells they squirm, elongate, and change shape almost continuously. They are the power plants of a cell, providing most of its ATP supply. The density of mitochondria in a particular cell reflects that cell's energy requirements, and mitochondria generally cluster where the action is. Busy cells like kidney and liver cells have hundreds of mitochondria, whereas relatively inactive cells (such as unchallenged lymphocytes) have just a few.

A mitochondrion is enclosed by *two* membranes, each with the general structure of the plasma membrane (**Figure 3.17**). The *outer membrane* is smooth and featureless, but the *inner membrane* folds inward, forming shelflike **cristae** (krĭ′ste; "crests") that protrude into the *matrix*, the gel-like substance within the mitochondrion. Intermediate products of food fuels (glucose and others) are broken down to water and carbon dioxide by teams of enzymes, some dissolved in the mitochondrial matrix and others forming part of the crista membrane.

As the metabolites are broken down and oxidized, some of the energy released is captured and used to attach phosphate groups to ADP molecules to form ATP. This multistep mitochondrial process (described in Chapter 24) is called *aerobic cellular respiration* (a-er-o′bik) because it requires oxygen.

Mitochondria are complex organelles: They contain their own DNA, RNA, and ribosomes and are able to reproduce themselves. Mitochondrial genes (some 37 of them) direct the synthesis of 1% of the proteins required for mitochondrial function, and the DNA of the cell's nucleus encodes the remaining proteins needed to carry out cellular respiration. When cellular requirements for ATP increase, the mitochondria synthesize more cristae or simply pinch in half (a process called *fission*) to increase their number, then grow to their former size.

Intriguingly, mitochondria are similar to bacteria in the purple bacteria phylum, and mitochondrial DNA is bacteria-like.

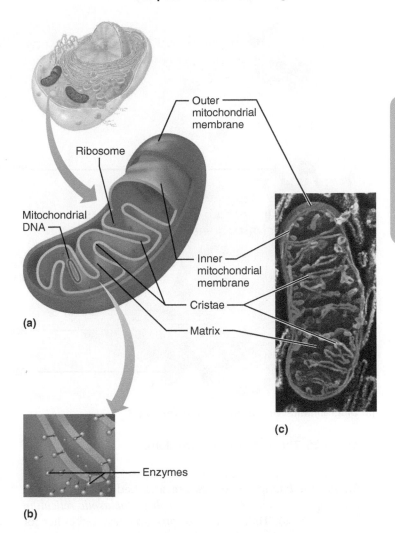

(a)

(b)

(c)

Figure 3.17 Mitochondrion. (a) Diagram of a longitudinally sectioned mitochondrion. **(b)** Close-up of a crista showing enzymes (stalked particles). **(c)** Electron micrograph of a mitochondrion (50,000×).

It is widely believed that mitochondria arose from bacteria that invaded the ancient ancestors of plant and animal cells, and that this unique merger gave rise to all complex cells.

Ribosomes

Ribosomes (ri′bo-sōmz) are small, dark-staining granules composed of proteins and a variety of RNAs called *ribosomal RNAs*. Each ribosome has two globular subunits that fit together like the body and cap of an acorn. Ribosomes are sites of protein synthesis, a function we discuss in detail later in this chapter.

Some ribosomes float freely in the cytoplasm. Others are attached to membranes, forming a complex called the *rough endoplasmic reticulum* (see p. 84). These two ribosomal populations appear to divide the chore of protein synthesis.

- *Free ribosomes* float freely in the cytoplasm. They make soluble proteins that function in the cytosol, as well as those imported into mitochondria and some other organelles.

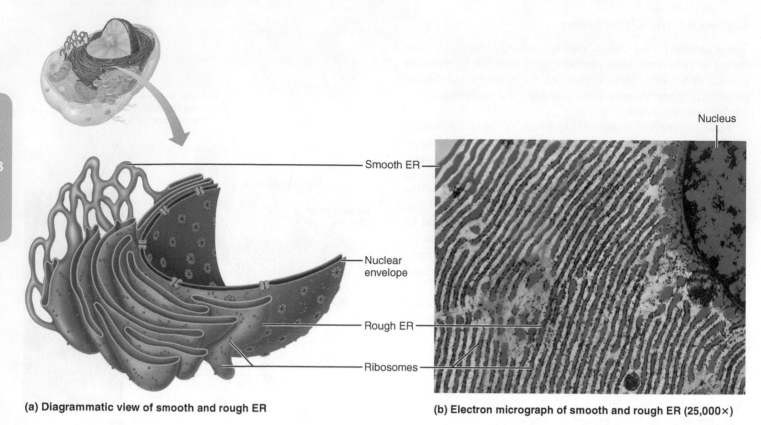

(a) Diagrammatic view of smooth and rough ER

(b) Electron micrograph of smooth and rough ER (25,000×)

Figure 3.18 The endoplasmic reticulum.

- *Membrane-bound ribosomes* are attached to membranes, forming a complex called the *rough endoplasmic reticulum* (Figure 3.18). They synthesize proteins destined either for incorporation into cell membranes or lysosomes, or for export from the cell.

Ribosome subunits can switch back and forth between these two functions, attaching to and detaching from the membranes of the endoplasmic reticulum, according to the type of protein they are making at a given time.

Endoplasmic Reticulum (ER)

The **endoplasmic reticulum** (**ER**) (en″do-plaz′mik rĕ-tik′u-lum; "network within the cytoplasm") is an extensive system of interconnected tubes and parallel membranes enclosing fluid-filled cavities, or **cisterns** (sis-ternz) as shown in Figure 3.18. Coiling and twisting through the cytosol, the ER is continuous with the outer nuclear membrane and accounts for about half of the cell's membranes. There are two distinct varieties: rough ER and smooth ER.

Rough Endoplasmic Reticulum   The external surface of the **rough ER** is studded with ribosomes, hence the name "rough" (see Figures 3.2 and 3.18a, b). Proteins assembled on these ribosomes thread their way into the fluid-filled interior of the ER cisterns (as described on pp. 105 and 108). When complete, the newly made proteins are enclosed in vesicles for their journey to the Golgi apparatus where they undergo further processing.

The rough ER has several functions. Its ribosomes manufacture all proteins secreted from cells. For this reason, the rough ER is particularly abundant and well developed in most secretory cells, antibody-producing plasma cells, and liver cells, which produce most blood proteins. It is also the cell's "membrane factory" where integral proteins and phospholipids that form part of all cellular membranes are manufactured. The enzymes needed to catalyze lipid synthesis have their active sites on the external (cytosolic) face of the ER membrane, where the needed substrates are readily available.

Smooth Endoplasmic Reticulum   The **smooth ER** (see Figures 3.2 and 3.18) is continuous with the rough ER and consists of tubules arranged in a looping network. Its enzymes (all integral proteins forming part of its membranes) play no role in protein synthesis. Instead, the enzymes catalyze reactions involved with the following tasks:

- Metabolize lipids, synthesize cholesterol, and synthesize the lipid components of lipoproteins (in liver cells)
- Synthesize steroid-based hormones such as sex hormones (testosterone-synthesizing cells of the testes are full of smooth ER)
- Absorb, synthesize, and transport fats (in intestinal cells)
- Detoxify drugs, certain pesticides, and cancer-causing chemicals (in liver and kidneys)
- Break down stored glycogen to form free glucose (in liver cells especially)

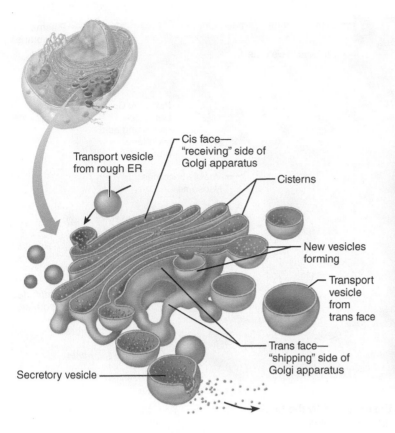

Cis face—
"receiving" side of
Golgi apparatus

Transport vesicle
from rough ER

Cisterns

New vesicles
forming

Transport
vesicle
from
trans face

Secretory vesicle

Trans face—
"shipping" side of
Golgi apparatus

(a) Many vesicles in the process of pinching off from the Golgi apparatus.

New vesicles forming

Golgi apparatus

Transport vesicle at
the trans face

(b) Electron micrograph of the Golgi apparatus (90,000×)

Figure 3.19 Golgi apparatus. Note: In (a), the vesicles shown in the process of pinching off from the membranous Golgi apparatus would have a protein coating on their external surfaces. The diagram omits these proteins for simplicity.

Additionally, skeletal and cardiac muscle cells have an elaborate smooth ER (called the sarcoplasmic reticulum) that plays an important role in storing and releasing calcium ions during muscle contraction. Except for the examples given above, most body cells contain relatively little, if any, smooth ER.

Golgi Apparatus

The **Golgi apparatus** (gol′je) consists of stacked and flattened membranous sacs, shaped like hollow dinner plates, associated with swarms of tiny membranous vesicles (**Figure 3.19**). The Golgi apparatus is the principal "traffic director" for cellular proteins. Its major function is to modify, concentrate, and package the proteins and lipids made at the rough ER and destined for export from the cell.

The Golgi's odd shape is a side effect of its job. A protein complex pulls membranous sacs containing newly synthesized proteins off the Golgi and in the process, the membranes are flattened like rubber bands. Transport vesicles that bud off from the rough ER move to and fuse with the membranes at the convex *cis face*, the "receiving" side, of the Golgi apparatus. Inside the apparatus, the proteins are modified: Some sugar groups are trimmed while others are added, and in some cases, phosphate groups are added.

The various proteins are "tagged" for delivery to a specific address, sorted, and packaged in at least three types of vesicles

that bud from the concave *trans face* (the "shipping" side) of the Golgi stack:

- Vesicles containing proteins destined for export pinch off from the trans face as **secretory vesicles, or granules**, which migrate to the plasma membrane and discharge their contents from the cell by exocytosis (**Figure 3.20**, pathway A). Specialized secretory cells, such as the enzyme-producing cells of the pancreas, have a prominent Golgi apparatus.

- The Golgi apparatus pinches off other vesicles containing lipids and transmembrane proteins destined for the plasma membrane (Figure 3.20, pathway B) or for other membranous organelles.

- The Golgi apparatus also packages digestive enzymes into membranous lysosomes that remain in the cell (Figure 3.20, pathway C), as discussed shortly.

Peroxisomes

Peroxisomes (pĕ-roks′ĭ-sōmz; "peroxide bodies") are spherical membranous sacs containing a variety of powerful enzymes, the most important of which are oxidases and catalases.

Oxidases use molecular oxygen (O_2) to detoxify harmful substances, including alcohol and formaldehyde. Their most important function is to neutralize **free radicals**, highly reactive

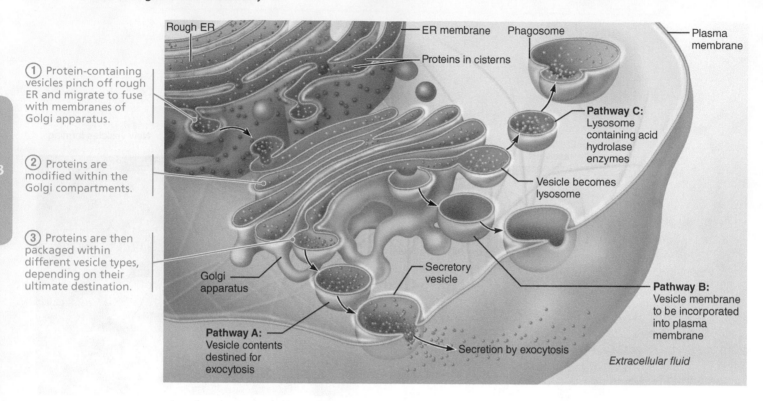

Rough ER

ER membrane   Phagosome

Plasma membrane

Proteins in cisterns

(1) Protein-containing vesicles pinch off rough ER and migrate to fuse with membranes of Golgi apparatus.

Pathway C:
Lysosome containing acid hydrolase enzymes

(2) Proteins are modified within the Golgi compartments.

Vesicle becomes lysosome

(3) Proteins are then packaged within different vesicle types, depending on their ultimate destination.

Golgi apparatus

Secretory vesicle

Pathway B:
Vesicle membrane to be incorporated into plasma membrane

Pathway A:
Vesicle contents destined for exocytosis

Secretion by exocytosis

Extracellular fluid

Figure 3.20 The sequence of events from protein synthesis on the rough ER to the final distribution of those proteins. The protein coats on the transport vesicles are not illustrated.

Lysosomes

Light green areas are regions where materials are being digested.

Figure 3.21 Electron micrograph of lysosomes (20,000×).

chemicals with unpaired electrons that can scramble the structure of biological molecules. Oxidases convert free radicals to hydrogen peroxide, which is also reactive and dangerous but which the catalases quickly convert to water. Free radicals and hydrogen peroxide are normal by-products of cellular metabolism, but they have devastating effects on cells if allowed to accumulate.

Peroxisomes are especially numerous in liver and kidney cells, which are very active in detoxification. They also play a role in energy metabolism by breaking down and synthesizing fatty acids. Peroxisomes look like small lysosomes (see Figure 3.2), and for many years it was thought that they were self-replicating organelles formed when existing peroxisomes simply pinch in half. Recent evidence, however, suggests that most new peroxisomes form by budding off of the endoplasmic reticulum via a special ER machinery that differs from that used for vesicles destined for modification in the Golgi apparatus.

Lysosomes

Born as endosomes which contain inactive enzymes, **lysosomes** ("disintegrator bodies") are spherical membranous organelles containing activated digestive enzymes **(Figure 3.21)**. As you might guess, lysosomes are large and abundant in phagocytes, the cells that dispose of invading bacteria and cell debris. Lysosomal enzymes can digest almost all kinds of biological molecules. They work best in acidic conditions and so are called *acid hydrolases.*

The lysosomal membrane is adapted to serve lysosomal functions in two important ways. First, it contains H^+ (proton) "pumps," which are ATPases that gather hydrogen ions from the surrounding cytosol to maintain the organelle's acidic pH. Second, it retains the dangerous acid hydrolases while permitting the final products of digestion to escape so that they can be used by the cell or excreted. In this way, lysosomes provide sites where digestion can proceed *safely* within a cell.

Lysosomes function as a cell's "demolition crew" by

- Digesting particles taken in by endocytosis, particularly ingested bacteria, viruses, and toxins

- Degrading worn-out or nonfunctional organelles

- Performing metabolic functions, such as glycogen breakdown and release

- Breaking down nonuseful tissues, such as the webs between the fingers and toes of a developing fetus and the uterine lining during menstruation

- Breaking down bone to release calcium ions into the blood

The lysosomal membrane is ordinarily quite stable, but it becomes fragile when the cell is injured or deprived of oxygen and when excessive amounts of vitamin A are present. When lysosomes rupture, the cell digests itself, a process called **autolysis** (aw″tol′ĭ-sis). Autolysis is the basis for desirable destruction of cells, as in the fourth list item above.

Homeostatic Imbalance 3.4

Lysosomes degrade glycogen and certain lipids in the brain at a relatively constant rate. In *Tay-Sachs disease*, an inherited condition seen mostly in Jews from Central Europe, the lysosomes lack an enzyme needed to break down a glycolipid abundant in nerve cell membranes. As a result, the nerve cell lysosomes swell with undigested lipids, which interfere with nervous system functioning. Affected infants typically have doll-like features and pink translucent skin. At 3 to 6 months of age, the first signs of disease appear (listlessness, motor weakness). These symptoms progress to mental retardation, seizures, blindness, and ultimately death within 18 months. ✚

The Endomembrane System

The **endomembrane system** is a system of organelles (most described above) that work together mainly to (1) produce, degrade, store, and export biological molecules, and (2) degrade potentially harmful substances. It includes the ER, Golgi apparatus, secretory vesicles, and lysosomes, as well as the nuclear membrane—that is, all of the membranous organelles or elements that are either structurally continuous or arise via forming or fusing transport vesicles (Figure 3.22). There are continuities between the nuclear envelope (itself an extension of the rough ER) and the rough and smooth ER (Figure 3.18). The plasma membrane, though not actually an *endo*membrane, is also functionally part of this system.

Besides these direct structural relationships, a wide variety of indirect interactions (indicated by arrows in Figure 3.22) occur among the members of the system. Some of the vesicles "born" in the ER migrate to and fuse with the Golgi apparatus or the plasma membrane, and vesicles arising from the Golgi

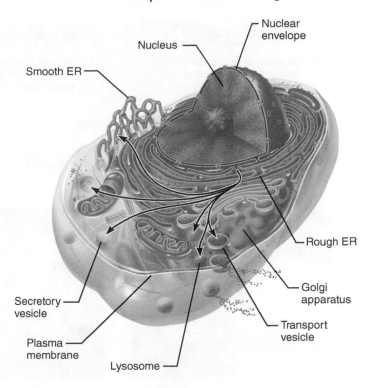

Figure 3.22 The endomembrane system.

apparatus can become part of the plasma membrane, secretory vesicles, or lysosomes.

☑ Check Your Understanding

17. Which organelle is the major site of ATP synthesis?
18. What are three organelles involved in protein synthesis and how do these organelles interact in that process?
19. Compare the functions of lysosomes and peroxisomes.

For answers, see Appendix H.

Cytoskeleton

✓ Name and describe the structure and function of cytoskeletal elements.

The **cytoskeleton**, literally, "cell skeleton," is an elaborate network of rods running through the cytosol and hundreds of accessory proteins that link these rods to other cell structures. It acts as a cell's "bones," "muscles," and "ligaments" by supporting cellular structures and providing the machinery to generate various cell movements. The three types of rods in the cytoskeleton are *microfilaments*, *intermediate filaments*, and *microtubules*. None of these is membrane covered.

Microfilaments   The thinnest elements of the cytoskeleton, **microfilaments** (mi″kro-fil′ah-ments), are semiflexible strands of the protein *actin* ("ray") (Figure 3.23a). Each cell has its own unique arrangement of microfilaments, so no two cells are alike. However, nearly all cells have a fairly dense cross-linked network of microfilaments, called the *terminal web*, attached to

(a) Microfilaments	(b) Intermediate filaments	(c) Microtubules
Strands made of spherical protein subunits called actins	Tough, insoluble protein fibers constructed like woven ropes composed of tetramer (4) fibrils	Hollow tubes of spherical protein subunits called tubulins

Actin subunit — 7 nm

Tetramer subunits — 10 nm

Tubulin subunits — 25 nm

Microfilaments form the blue network surrounding the pink nucleus in this photo.

Intermediate filaments form the purple batlike network in this photo.

Microtubules appear as gold networks surrounding the cells' pink nuclei in this photo.

Figure 3.23 Cytoskeletal elements support the cell and help to generate movement. Diagrams (above) and photos (below). The photos are of fibroblasts treated to fluorescently tag the structure of interest.

the cytoplasmic side of their plasma membrane (see Figure 3.28 on p. 91). The web strengthens the cell surface, resists compression, and transmits force during cellular movements and shape changes.

Most microfilaments are involved in cell motility (movement) or changes in cell shape. You could say that cells move "when they get their act(in) together." For example, actin filaments interact with another protein, *unconventional myosin* (mi′o-sin), to generate contractile forces in a cell **(Figure 3.24b)**. This interaction also forms the cleavage furrow that pinches one cell into two during cell division. Microfilaments attached to cell adhesion molecules (see Figure 3.4e) are responsible for the crawling movements of amoeboid motion, and for the membrane changes that accompany endocytosis and exocytosis. Except in muscle cells, where they are highly developed, stable, and long-lived, actin filaments are constantly breaking down and re-forming from smaller subunits whenever and wherever their services are needed.

Intermediate Filaments Intermediate filaments are tough, insoluble protein fibers that resemble woven ropes. Made of twisted units of *tetramer* (4) *fibrils*, they have a diameter between those of microfilaments and microtubules (Figure 3.23b). Intermediate filaments are the most stable and permanent of the cytoskeletal elements and have high tensile strength. They

attach to desmosomes, and their main job is to act as internal guy-wires to resist pulling forces exerted on the cell. Because the protein composition of intermediate filaments varies in different cell types, there are numerous names for these cytoskeletal elements—for example, they are called neurofilaments in nerve cells and keratin filaments in epithelial cells.

Microtubules The elements with the largest diameter, **microtubules** (mi″kro-tu′bŭlz), are hollow tubes made of spherical protein subunits called *tubulins* (Figure 3.23c). Most microtubules radiate from a small region of cytoplasm near the nucleus called the *centrosome* or *cell center* (see Figures 3.2, 3.25). Microtubules are remarkably dynamic organelles, constantly growing out from the centrosome, disassembling, and then reassembling at the same or different sites. The stiff but bendable microtubules determine the overall shape of the cell, as well as the distribution of cellular organelles.

Mitochondria, lysosomes, and secretory vesicles attach to the microtubules like ornaments hanging from tree branches. Tiny protein machines called **motor proteins** (*kinesins, dyneins,* and others) continually move and reposition the organelles along the microtubules.

Motor proteins work by changing their shapes. Powered by ATP, some motor proteins appear to act like train engines moving substances along on the microtubular "railroad tracks."

(a) **Motor molecules can attach to receptors on vesicles or organelles, and carry the organelles along the microtubule "tracks" of the cytoskeleton.**

(b) **In some types of cell motility, motor molecules attached to one element of the cytoskeleton can cause it to slide over another element, which the motor molecules grip, release, and grip at a new site. Muscle contraction and cilia movement work this way.**

Figure 3.24 Microtubules and microfilaments function in cell motility by interacting with motor molecules powered by ATP.

Others move "hand over hand" somewhat like an orangutan—gripping, releasing, and then gripping again at a new site further along the microtubule (Figure 3.24).

Centrosome and Centrioles

✓ Describe the roles of centrioles in cell division and in formation of cilia and flagella.

As mentioned, microtubules are anchored at one end in an inconspicuous region near the nucleus called the **centrosome** or *cell center*. The centrosome acts as a *microtubule organizing center*. It has few distinguishing marks other than a granular-looking *matrix* that contains paired **centrioles**, small, barrel-shaped organelles oriented at right angles to each other **(Figure 3.25)**. The centrosome matrix is best known for generating microtubules and organizing the mitotic spindle in cell division (see Figure 3.33). Each centriole consists of

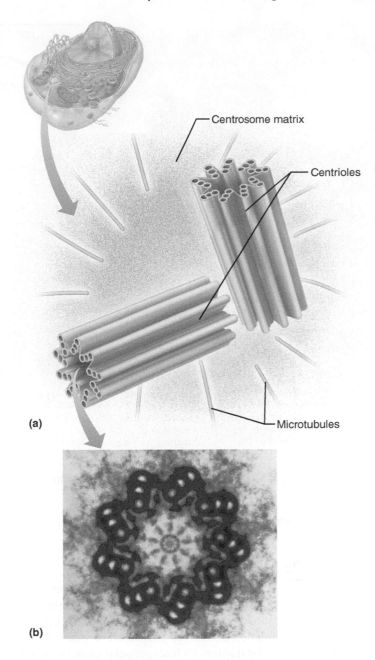

Figure 3.25 Centrioles. (a) Three-dimensional view of a centriole pair oriented at right angles, as they are usually seen in the cell. The centrioles are located in an inconspicuous region to one side of the nucleus called the centrosome, or cell center. **(b)** An electron micrograph showing a cross section of a centriole (190,000×). Notice that it is composed of nine microtubule triplets.

a pinwheel array of nine *triplets* of microtubules, each connected to the next by nontubulin proteins and arranged to form a hollow tube. Centrioles also form the bases of cilia and flagella, our next topics.

Cellular Extensions

✓ Describe how the two main types of cell extensions, cilia and microvilli, differ in structure and function.

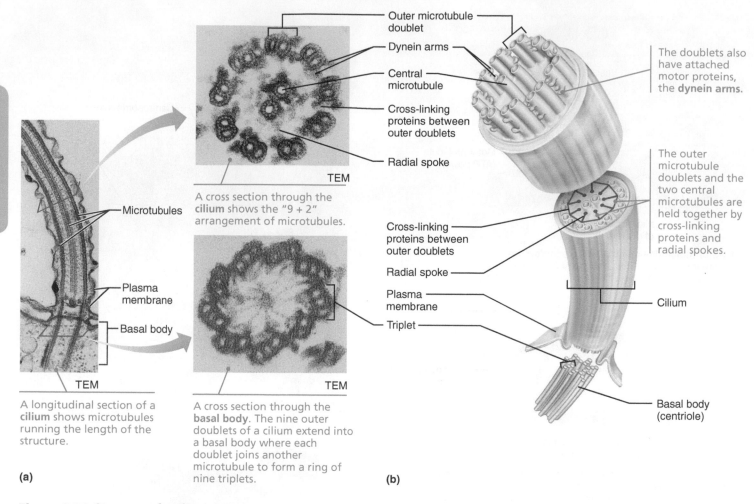

Microtubules

Plasma membrane

Basal body

TEM

A longitudinal section of a **cilium** shows microtubules running the length of the structure.

(a)

A cross section through the **cilium** shows the "9 + 2" arrangement of microtubules.

Outer microtubule doublet

Dynein arms

Central microtubule

Cross-linking proteins between outer doublets

Radial spoke

TEM

A cross section through the **basal body**. The nine outer doublets of a cilium extend into a basal body where each doublet joins another microtubule to form a ring of nine triplets.

The doublets also have attached motor proteins, the **dynein arms**.

The outer microtubule doublets and the two central microtubules are held together by cross-linking proteins and radial spokes.

Cross-linking proteins between outer doublets

Radial spoke

Plasma membrane

Triplet

Cilium

Basal body (centriole)

(b)

Figure 3.26 Structure of a cilium. (TEM = transmission electron micrograph.)

Cilia and Flagella

Cilia (sil′e-ah; "eyelashes") are whiplike, motile cellular extensions **(Figure 3.26)** that occur, typically in large numbers, on the exposed surfaces of certain cells. Ciliary action moves substances in one direction across cell surfaces. For example, ciliated cells that line the respiratory tract propel mucus laden with dust particles and bacteria upward away from the lungs.

When a cell is about to form cilia, the centrioles multiply and line up beneath the plasma membrane at the cell's free (exposed) surface. Microtubules then "sprout" from each centriole, forming the ciliary projections by exerting pressure on the plasma membrane.

Flagella (flah-jel′ah) are also projections formed by centrioles, but are substantially longer than cilia. The only flagellated cell in the human body is a sperm, which has one propulsive flagellum, commonly called a tail. Notice that cilia *propel other substances* across a cell's surface, whereas a flagellum *propels the cell itself.*

Centrioles forming the bases of cilia and flagella are commonly referred to as **basal bodies** (ba′sal) (Figure 3.26a). The "9 + 2" pattern of microtubules in the cilium or flagellum itself (nine *doublets*, or pairs, of microtubules encircling one central pair) differs slightly from that of a centriole (nine microtubule

triplets). Additionally, the cilium has flexible "wagon wheels" of cross-linking proteins (purple in Figure 3.26b), and motor proteins (green dynein arms in Figure 3.26b) that promote movement of the cilium or flagellum.

Just how ciliary activity is coordinated is not fully understood, but microtubules are definitely involved. Extending from the microtubule doublets are arms composed of the motor protein dynein (Figure 3.26). The dynein side arms of one doublet grip the adjacent doublet, and powered by ATP, push it up, release, and then grip again. Because the doublets are physically restricted by other proteins, they cannot slide far and instead are forced to bend. The collective bending action of all the doublets causes the cilium to bend.

As a cilium moves, it alternates rhythmically between a propulsive *power stroke*, when it is nearly straight and moves in an arc, and a *recovery stroke*, when it bends and returns to its initial position **(Figure 3.27a)**. With these two strokes, the cilium produces a pushing motion in a single direction that repeats some 10 to 20 times per second. The bending of one cilium is quickly followed by the bending of the next and then the next, creating a current at the cell surface that brings to mind the traveling waves that pass across a field of grass on a windy day (Figure 3.27b).

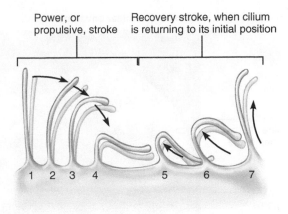

Power, or propulsive, stroke   Recovery stroke, when cilium is returning to its initial position

1 2 3 4   5   6   7

(a) Phases of ciliary motion.

Layer of mucus

Cell surface

(b) Traveling wave created by the activity of many cilia acting together propels mucus across cell surfaces.

Figure 3.27 Ciliary function.

The motile cilia just discussed are familiar to most biology students, but many have not heard of *primary cilia*, their non-motile cousins. Present as a single cilium on the surface of most body cells, primary cilia function as antennae that probe the external environment for molecules their receptors can recognize. Because of this ability, primary cilia can coordinate several intracellular pathways that regulate embryonic development and maintain healthy tissues later in life.

Microvilli

Microvilli (mi″kro-vil′i; "little shaggy hairs") are minute, fingerlike extensions of the plasma membrane that project from an exposed cell surface (Figure 3.5 top and **Figure 3.28**). They increase the plasma membrane surface area tremendously and are most often found on the surface of absorptive cells such as intestinal and kidney tubule cells. Microvilli have a core of bundled actin filaments that extend into the so-called *terminal web* of the cytoskeleton of the cell. Actin is sometimes a contractile protein, but in microvilli it appears to function as a mechanical "stiffener."

☑ Check Your Understanding

20. How are microtubules and microfilaments related functionally?

Microvillus

Actin filaments

Terminal web

Figure 3.28 Microvilli.

21. Of microfilaments, microtubules, or intermediate filaments, which is most important in maintaining cell shape?
22. The major function of cilia is to move substances across the free cell surface. What is the major role of microvilli?

For answers, see Appendix H.

The Nucleus

✓ Outline the structure and function of the nuclear envelope, nucleolus, and chromatin.

Anything that works, works best when it is controlled. For cells, the control center is the gene-containing **nucleus** (*nucle* = pit, kernel). The nucleus can be compared to a computer, design department, construction boss, and board of directors—all rolled into one. As the genetic library, it contains the instructions needed to build nearly all the body's proteins. Additionally, it dictates the kinds and amounts of proteins to be synthesized at any one time in response to signals acting on the cell.

Most cells have only one nucleus, but some, including skeletal muscle cells, bone destruction cells, and some liver cells, are **multinucleate** (mul″tĭ-nu′kle-āt), that is, they have many nuclei. The presence of more than one nucleus usually signifies that a larger-than-usual cytoplasmic mass must be regulated.

Except for mature red blood cells, whose nuclei are ejected before the cells enter the bloodstream, all of our body cells are nucleated. **Anucleate** (a-nu′kle-āt; *a* = without) cells cannot reproduce and therefore live in the bloodstream for only three to four months before they deteriorate. Without a nucleus, a cell cannot produce mRNA to make proteins, and when its enzymes and cell structures start to break down (as all eventually do), they cannot be replaced.

The nucleus, averaging 5 µm in diameter, is larger than any of the cytoplasmic organelles. Although most often spherical or oval, its shape usually conforms to the shape of the cell. The nucleus has three recognizable regions or structures: the *nuclear envelope* (*membrane*), *nucleoli*, and *chromatin* **(Figure 3.29a)**.

Surface of nuclear envelope.

Fracture line of outer membrane

Nuclear pores

Nucleus

Nuclear envelope

Chromatin (condensed)

Nucleolus

Cisterns of rough ER

Nuclear pore complexes. Each pore is ringed by protein particles.

Nuclear lamina. The netlike lamina composed of intermediate filaments formed by lamins lines the inner surface of the nuclear envelope.

(a)

(b)

Figure 3.29 The nucleus. (a) Three-dimensional diagram of the nucleus, showing the continuity of its double membrane with the ER. **(b)** Freeze-fracture transmission electron micrographs (TEMs).

The Nuclear Envelope

The nucleus is bounded by the **nuclear envelope**, a *double* membrane barrier separated by a fluid-filled space (similar to the mitochondrial membrane). The outer nuclear membrane is continuous with the rough ER of the cytoplasm and is studded with ribosomes on its external face. The inner nuclear membrane is lined by the *nuclear lamina*, a network of *lamins* (rod-shaped proteins that assemble to form intermediate filaments) that maintains the shape of the nucleus and acts as a scaffold to organize DNA in the nucleus (Figure 3.29b, bottom).

At various points, the nuclear envelope is punctuated by **nuclear pores**. An intricate complex of proteins, called a *nuclear pore complex*, lines each pore, forming an aqueous transport channel and regulating entry and exit of molecules (e.g., mRNAs) and large particles into and out of the nucleus (Figure 3.29b, middle).

Like other cell membranes, the nuclear envelope is selectively permeable, but here substances pass much more freely than elsewhere. Small molecules pass through the relatively large nuclear pore complexes unhindered. Protein molecules imported from the cytoplasm and RNA molecules exported from the nucleus are transported through the central channel of the pores in an energy-dependent process by soluble transport proteins (importins and others). Such large molecules must display specific signals to enter or exit the nucleus.

The nuclear envelope encloses a jellylike fluid called *nucleoplasm* (nu'kle-o-plazm) in which other nuclear elements are suspended. Like the cytosol, the nucleoplasm contains dissolved salts, nutrients, and other essential solutes.

Nucleoli

Nucleoli (nu-kle'o-li; "little nuclei") are the dark-staining spherical bodies found within the nucleus where ribosomal subunits are assembled. They are not membrane bounded. Typically, there are one or two nucleoli per nucleus, but there may be more. Nucleoli are usually large in growing cells that are making large amounts of tissue proteins.

Nucleoli are associated with *nucleolar organizer regions*, which contain the DNA that issues genetic instructions for synthesizing ribosomal RNA (rRNA). As molecules of rRNA are synthesized, they are combined with proteins to form the two kinds of ribosomal subunits. (The proteins are manufactured on ribosomes in the cytoplasm and "imported" into the nucleus.) Most of these subunits leave the nucleus through the nuclear pores and enter the cytoplasm, where they join to form functional ribosomes.

Chromatin

Seen through a light microscope, **chromatin** (kro'mah-tin) appears as a fine, unevenly stained network, but special techniques reveal it as a system of bumpy threads weaving through the nucleoplasm. Chromatin is composed of approximately

- 30% **DNA**, our genetic material
- 60% globular **histone proteins** (his'tōn), which package and regulate the DNA
- 10% RNA chains, newly formed or forming

The fundamental units of chromatin are **nucleosomes** (nu'kle-o-sōmz; "nuclear bodies"), which consist of flattened disc-shaped cores or clusters of eight histone proteins connected like beads on a string by a DNA molecule. The DNA winds (like a ribbon of Velcro) twice around each nucleosome and continues on to the next cluster via *linker* DNA segments (**Figure 3.30** ① and ②).

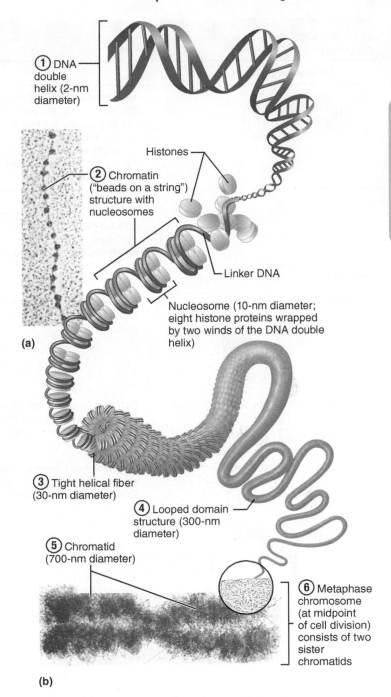

(a)

① DNA double helix (2-nm diameter)

Histones

② Chromatin ("beads on a string") structure with nucleosomes

Linker DNA

Nucleosome (10-nm diameter; eight histone proteins wrapped by two winds of the DNA double helix)

③ Tight helical fiber (30-nm diameter)

④ Looped domain structure (300-nm diameter)

⑤ Chromatid (700-nm diameter)

⑥ Metaphase chromosome (at midpoint of cell division) consists of two sister chromatids

(b)

Figure 3.30 Chromatin and chromosome structure.
(a) Electron micrograph of chromatin fiber (125,000×).
(b) DNA packed in a chromosome. The levels of increasing structural complexity (coiling) from the DNA helix to the metaphase chromosome are indicated in order from the smallest (① DNA double helix) to the largest and most complex (⑥ chromosome).

Histones provide a physical means for packing the very long DNA molecules (some 2 meters' worth per cell) in a compact, orderly way, but they also play an important role in gene regulation. In a nondividing cell, for example, the presence of methyl groups on histone proteins shuts down the nearby DNA, and attachment of a phosphate group to a particular histone protein

(Text continues on p. 96)

Table 3.3	Parts of the Cell: Structure and Function	
CELL PART*	**STRUCTURE**	**FUNCTIONS**
Plasma Membrane (Figure 3.3)		
	Membrane made of a double layer of lipids (phospholipids, cholesterol, and so on) within which proteins are embedded. Proteins may extend entirely through the lipid bilayer or protrude on only one face. Most externally facing proteins and some lipids have attached sugar groups.	Serves as an external cell barrier, and acts in transport of substances into or out of the cell. Maintains a resting potential that is essential for functioning of excitable cells. Externally facing proteins act as receptors (for hormones, neurotransmitters, and so on), transport proteins, and in cell-to-cell recognition.
Cytoplasm		
	Cellular region between the nuclear and plasma membranes. Consists of fluid **cytosol** containing dissolved solutes, **organelles** (the metabolic machinery of the cytoplasm), and **inclusions** (stored nutrients, secretory products, pigment granules).	
Organelles		
▪ Mitochondria (Figure 3.17)	Rodlike, double-membrane structures; inner membrane folded into projections called cristae.	Site of ATP synthesis; powerhouse of the cell.
▪ Ribosomes (Figures 3.18, 3.37–3.39)	Dense particles consisting of two subunits, each composed of ribosomal RNA and protein. Free or attached to rough endoplasmic reticulum.	The sites of protein synthesis.
▪ Rough endoplasmic reticulum (Figures 3.18, 3.39)	Membranous system enclosing a cavity, the cistern, and coiling through the cytoplasm. Externally studded with ribosomes.	Sugar groups are attached to proteins within the cisterns. Proteins are bound in vesicles for transport to the Golgi apparatus and other sites. External face synthesizes phospholipids.
▪ Smooth endoplasmic reticulum (Figure 3.18)	Membranous system of sacs and tubules; free of ribosomes.	Site of lipid and steroid (cholesterol) synthesis, lipid metabolism, and drug detoxification.
▪ Golgi apparatus (Figures 3.19, 3.20)	A stack of flattened membranes and associated vesicles close to the nucleus.	Packages, modifies, and segregates proteins for secretion from the cell, inclusion in lysosomes, and incorporation into the plasma membrane.
▪ Peroxisomes (Figure 3.2)	Membranous sacs of catalase and oxidase enzymes.	The enzymes detoxify a number of toxic substances. The most important enzyme, catalase, breaks down hydrogen peroxide.

* Individual cellular structures are not drawn to scale.

Table 3.3 (continued)		
CELL PART*	**STRUCTURE**	**FUNCTIONS**
Cytoplasm		
■ Lysosomes (Figure 3.21)	Membranous sacs containing acid hydrolases.	Sites of intracellular digestion.
■ Microtubules (Figures 3.23–3.25)	Cylindrical structures made of tubulin proteins.	Support the cell and give it shape. Involved in intracellular and cellular movements. Form centrioles and cilia and flagella, if present.
■ Microfilaments (Figures 3.23, 3.24)	Fine filaments composed of the protein actin.	Involved in muscle contraction and other types of intracellular movement, help form the cell's cytoskeleton.
■ Intermediate filaments (Figure 3.23)	Protein fibers; composition varies.	The stable cytoskeletal elements; resist mechanical forces acting on the cell.
■ Centrioles (Figure 3.25)	Paired cylindrical bodies, each composed of nine triplets of microtubules.	Organize a microtubule network during mitosis (cell division) to form the spindle and asters. Form the bases of cilia and flagella.
Inclusions	Varied; includes stored nutrients such as lipid droplets and glycogen granules, protein crystals, pigment granules.	Storage for nutrients, wastes, and cell products.
Cellular Extensions		
■ Cilia (Figures 3.26, 3.27)	Short cell-surface projections; each cilium composed of nine pairs of microtubules surrounding a central pair.	Coordinated movement creates a unidirectional current that propels substances across cell surfaces.
■ Flagellum	Like a cilium, but longer; only example in humans is the sperm tail.	Propels the cell.
■ Microvilli (Figure 3.28)	Tubular extensions of the plasma membrane; contain a bundle of actin filaments.	Increase surface area for absorption.
Nucleus (Figures 3.2, 3.29)		
	Largest organelle. Surrounded by the nuclear envelope; contains fluid nucleoplasm, nucleoli, and chromatin.	Control center of the cell; responsible for transmitting genetic information and providing the instructions for protein synthesis.

Table 3.3 Parts of the Cell: Structure and Function (continued)		
CELL PART*	**STRUCTURE**	**FUNCTIONS**
Nucleus (Figures 3.2, 3.29)		
▪ Nuclear envelope (Figure 3.29)	Double-membrane structure pierced by pores. Outer membrane continuous with the endoplasmic reticulum.	Separates the nucleoplasm from the cytoplasm and regulates passage of substances to and from the nucleus.
▪ Nucleolus (Figure 3.29)	Dense spherical (non-membrane-bounded) bodies, composed of ribosomal RNA and proteins.	Site of ribosome subunit manufacture.
▪ Chromatin (Figure 3.30)	Granular, threadlike material composed of DNA and histone proteins.	DNA constitutes the genes.

may indicate that the cell is about to commit suicide. On the other hand, addition of acetyl groups to histone exposes different DNA segments, or genes, so that they can dictate the specifications for synthesizing proteins or various RNA species. Such active chromatin segments, referred to as *extended chromatin*, are not usually visible under the light microscope. The generally inactive *condensed chromatin* segments are darker staining and more easily detected. Understandably, the most active body cells have much larger amounts of extended chromatin.

Interestingly, particular chromatin strands occupy discrete regions in the nucleus called *chromosome territories*. Depending on the specific genes contained, and the cell and tissue type, the chromosome territory patterns change during development. At the simplest level, active and inactive genetic regions can be separated from each other, which in turn would enhance or repress genetic expression.

When a cell is preparing to divide, the chromatin threads coil and condense enormously to form short, barlike bodies called **chromosomes** ("colored bodies") (Figure 3.30 ⑤ and ⑥). Chromosome compactness prevents the delicate chromatin strands from tangling and breaking during the movements that occur during cell division. Next, we describe the functions of DNA and the events of cell division.

Table 3.3 summarizes the parts of the cell beginning on p. 94.

Check Your Understanding

23. If a cell ejects or loses its nucleus, what is its fate and why?
24. What is the role of nucleoli?
25. What is the importance of the histone proteins present in the nucleus?

For answers, see Appendix H.

Cell Growth and Reproduction

The Cell Cycle

✓ List the phases of the cell cycle and describe the key events of each phase.

✓ Describe the process of DNA replication.

The **cell cycle** is the series of changes a cell goes through from the time it is formed until it reproduces. The outer ring of Figure 3.31 shows the two major periods of the cell cycle:

- *Interphase* (in green), in which the cell grows and carries on its usual activities
- *Cell division* or the *mitotic phase* (in yellow), during which it divides into two cells

Interphase

Interphase is the period from cell formation to cell division. Early cytologists, unaware of the constant molecular activity in cells and impressed by the obvious movements of cell division, called interphase the resting phase of the cell cycle. (The term *interphase* reflects this idea of a stage *between* cell divisions.) However, this image is misleading because during interphase a cell is carrying out all its routine activities and is "resting" only from dividing. Perhaps a more accurate name for this phase would be *metabolic phase* or *growth phase*.

Subphases   In addition to carrying on its life-sustaining reactions, an interphase cell prepares for the next cell division. Interphase is divided into G_1, S, and G_2 subphases (the Gs stand for *gaps* before and after the S phase, and S is for *synthetic*). In all three subphases, the cell grows by producing proteins and organelles, but chromatin is reproduced only during the S subphase.

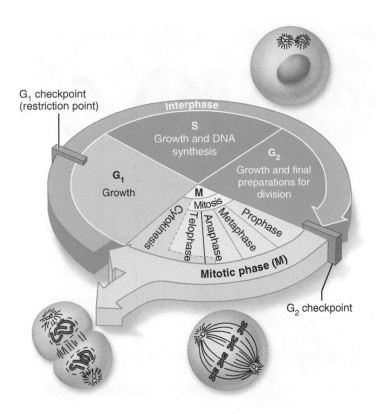

Figure 3.31 The cell cycle. During G₁, cells grow rapidly and carry out their routine functions. The S phase is the period of DNA synthesis. In G₂, materials needed for cell division are synthesized and growth continues. During the M phase (cell division), mitosis and cytokinesis occur, producing two daughter cells. Important checkpoints at which mitosis may be prevented from occurring are found throughout interphase; the diagram shows two.

- **G₁ (gap 1 subphase):** The cell is metabolically active, synthesizing proteins rapidly and growing vigorously (Figure 3.31, light green area). This is the most variable phase in terms of length. In cells that divide rapidly, G₁ typically lasts several minutes to hours, but in those that divide slowly, G₁ may last for days or even years. Cells that permanently cease dividing are said to be in the **G₀ phase**. For most of G₁, virtually no activities directly related to cell division occur. However, as G₁ ends, the centrioles start to replicate in preparation for cell division.

- **S phase:** DNA is replicated, ensuring that the two future cells being created will receive identical copies of the genetic material (Figure 3.31, blue area). New histones are made and assembled into chromatin. One thing is sure, without a proper S phase, there can be no correct mitotic phase. (We will describe DNA replication next.)

- **G₂ (gap 2 subphase):** The final phase of interphase is brief (Figure 3.31, dark green area). Enzymes and other proteins needed for division are synthesized and moved to their proper sites. By the end of G₂, centriole replication (begun in G₁) is complete. The cell is now ready to divide. Throughout S and G₂, the cell continues to grow and carries on with business as usual.

DNA Replication   Before a cell can divide, its DNA must be replicated exactly, so that identical copies of the cell's genes can be passed to each of its offspring. During the S phase, replication begins simultaneously on several chromatin threads and continues until all the DNA has been replicated.

Human DNA molecules are very long. Replication of a DNA molecule begins at several *origins of replication* along its length that have a specific nucleotide sequence, a strategy that greatly increases the speed of replication.

Replication is still being studied but appears to involve several events:

1. Enzymes attach to origins of replication and separate the DNA strands so that *replication bubbles* form. At each end of a replication bubble is a Y-shaped area, a *replication fork*, where the helical parental DNA strands are being unwound (Figure 3.32).

2. Once the bubbles are formed, the parental DNA strands are ready to serve as templates for making complementary DNA strands from free DNA precursors dissolved in the nucleoplasm (Figure 3.32). However, there is a problem here because the *polymerase enzymes* that synthesize DNA cannot start a new DNA strand from scratch. They can only add new nucleotides to a strand that already exists. This problem is solved by formation of a short, complementary **RNA primer**, about 10 bases long, by a *primase enzyme*.

3. Continuing from the primer, the enzyme **DNA polymerase** positions complementary nucleotides along the template strand and then covalently links them together. DNA polymerase works only in one direction. Consequently, one strand, the **leading strand**, is synthesized continuously once primed, following the movement of the replication fork. The other strand, called the **lagging strand**, is constructed in segments in the opposite direction and requires that a primer initiate replication of each segment.

4. Ligase enzymes splice the short segments of DNA together. Eventually DNA polymerases replace the primers with DNA nucleotides.

The end result is that two DNA molecules are formed from the original DNA helix (the template strands) and are identical to it. Because each new molecule consists of one old and one new nucleotide strand, this mechanism of DNA replication is called **semiconservative replication** (Figure 3.32).

As soon as replication ends, histones (synthesized in the cytoplasm and imported into the nucleus) associate with the DNA, completing the formation of two new chromatin strands. The chromatin strands, united by a buttonlike centromere (a stretch of repetitive DNA), remain held together by the centromere and a protein complex called *cohesin*, until the cell enters the anaphase stage of mitotic cell division (see p. 101). They are then distributed to the daughter cells as described next, ensuring that each cell has identical genetic information.

The progression from DNA replication into cell division presumes that the newly synthesized DNA is not damaged in any way. If damage occurs, the cell cycle stops until the DNA repair mechanism has fixed the problem.

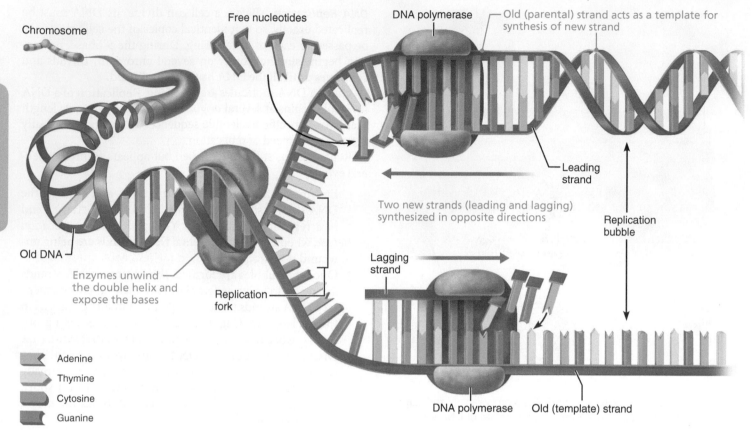

Chromosome

Free nucleotides

DNA polymerase

Old (parental) strand acts as a template for synthesis of new strand

Leading strand

Two new strands (leading and lagging) synthesized in opposite directions

Replication bubble

Old DNA

Enzymes unwind the double helix and expose the bases

Replication fork

Lagging strand

DNA polymerase

Old (template) strand

Adenine
Thymine
Cytosine
Guanine

Figure 3.32 Replication of DNA: summary. Once the DNA helix is uncoiled, and the hydrogen bonds between its base pairs are broken, each nucleotide strand of the DNA acts as a template for constructing a complementary strand, as illustrated on the right-hand side of the diagram. (The step in which RNA primers are formed to start the process at replication bubbles is not shown.) DNA polymerases work in one direction only, so the two new strands (leading and lagging) are synthesized in opposite directions. (The DNA ligase enzymes that join the DNA fragments on the lagging strand are not illustrated.) Each DNA molecule formed consists of one old (template) strand and one newly assembled strand and constitutes a chromatid of a chromosome.

Cell Division

Cell division is essential for body growth and tissue repair. Cells that continually wear away, such as cells of the skin and intestinal lining, reproduce themselves almost continuously. Others, such as liver cells, divide more slowly (to maintain the size of the organ they compose) but retain the ability to reproduce quickly if the organ is damaged. Most cells of nervous tissue, skeletal muscle, and heart muscle lose their ability to divide when they are fully mature, and repairs are made with scar tissue (a fibrous type of connective tissue).

Events of Cell Division In most body cells, cell division, which is called the **M (mitotic) phase** of the cell cycle, involves two distinct events (Figure 3.31, yellow area):

■ **Mitosis** (mi-to′sis; *mit* = thread; *osis* = process), the division of the nucleus

■ **Cytokinesis** (si-to-kǐ-ne′sis; *kines* = movement), the division of the cytoplasm

A different process of nuclear division called *meiosis* (mi-o′sis) produces sex cells (ova and sperm) with only half the number of genes found in other body cells. We discuss the

details of meiosis in Chapter 27. Here we concentrate on mitotic cell division.

Mitosis Mitosis is the series of events that parcels out the replicated DNA of the mother cell to two daughter cells. Described as four phases—**prophase**, **metaphase**, **anaphase**, and **telophase**—mitosis is actually a continuous process, with one phase merging smoothly into the next. Its duration varies according to cell type, but in human cells it typically lasts about an hour or less. *Focus on Mitosis* **(Figure 3.33)**, pp. 100–101, describes the phases of mitosis in detail.

Cytokinesis Cytokinesis, or the division of the cytoplasm, begins during late anaphase and is completed after mitosis ends. A *contractile ring* made of actin filaments (Figure 3.33) draws the plasma membrane inward to form a **cleavage furrow** over the center of the cell. The furrow deepens until it pinches the cytoplasmic mass into two parts, yielding two daughter cells. Each is smaller and has less cytoplasm than the mother cell, but is genetically identical to it. The daughter cells then enter the interphase portion of the life cycle until it is their turn to divide.

Control of Cell Division The signals that prod cells to divide are incompletely understood, but we know that the ratio of cell surface area to cell volume is important. The amount of nutrients a growing cell requires is directly related to its volume. Volume increases with the cube of cell radius, whereas surface area increases more slowly with the square of the radius.

For example, a 64-fold (4^3) increase in cell volume is accompanied by only a 16-fold (4^2) increase in surface area. Consequently, the surface area of the plasma membrane becomes inadequate for nutrient and waste exchange when a cell reaches a certain critical size. Cell division solves this problem because the smaller daughter cells have a favorable ratio of surface area to volume. These surface-volume relationships help explain why most cells are microscopic in size.

Two other factors that influence when cells divide are chemical signals (growth factors, hormones, and others) released by other cells and the availability of space. Normal cells stop proliferating when they begin touching, a phenomenon called *contact inhibition*. The system that controls the cell cycle has been compared to the timer on a washing machine. Like that timer, the control system for the cell cycle is driven by a built-in clock. However, just as the washer's cycle is subject to adjustments (by regulating the flow from the faucet, say, or by an internal water-level sensor), the cell cycle is regulated by both internal and external factors.

Two groups of proteins are crucial to the ability of a cell to accomplish the S phase and enter mitosis:

- **Cyclins**, regulatory proteins whose levels rise and fall during each cell cycle
- **Cdks (cyclin-dependent kinases)**, which are present in a constant concentration in the cell and are activated by binding to particular cyclins

A new batch of cyclins accumulates during each interphase. Subsequent joining of specific Cdk and cyclin proteins initiates enzymatic cascades that phosphorylate histones and other proteins needed for cell division. At the end of mitosis, enzymes destroy the cyclins.

A number of "switches" and crucial checkpoints for cell division occur throughout interphase. These built-in stop signals halt the cell cycle until overridden by internal or external go-ahead signals. In many cells, a G_1 checkpoint, called the *restriction point*, seems to be most important (see Figure 3.31). If the cell is prevented from progressing past this checkpoint, it enters the nondividing state (G_0). Another important checkpoint, and the first to be understood, occurs late in G_2, when a threshold amount of a protein complex called **MPF (M-phase promoting factor)** is required to give the okay signal to pass the G_2 checkpoint and enter M phase. Later in M phase, MPF is inactivated.

Besides these "go" signals, there are a number of so-called repressor genes that inhibit cell division. One example is the *p53* gene that initiates a series of enzymatic events that produce growth-inhibiting factors. Roughly half of all cancers have abnormal *p53* genes. Contact with other cells does not inhibit these cancerous cells and they divide wildly, making them dangerous to their host.

☑ **Check Your Understanding**

26. If one of the DNA strands being replicated "reads" CGAATG, what will be the base sequence of the corresponding DNA strand?
27. During what phase of the cell cycle is DNA synthesized?
28. What are three events occurring in prophase that are undone in telophase?

For answers, see Appendix H.

Protein Synthesis

✓ Define gene and genetic code and explain the function of genes.

✓ Name the two phases of protein synthesis and describe the roles of DNA, mRNA, tRNA, and rRNA in each phase.

✓ Contrast triplets, codons, and anticodons.

In addition to directing its own replication, DNA serves as the master blueprint for protein synthesis. Although cells also make lipids and carbohydrates, DNA does not dictate their structure. Historically, DNA is said to specify *only* the structure of protein molecules, including the enzymes that catalyze the synthesis of all classes of biological molecules.

Much of the metabolic machinery of the cell is concerned in some way with protein synthesis. This is not surprising, seeing as structural proteins constitute most of the dry cell material, and functional proteins direct almost all cellular activities. Essentially, cells are miniature protein factories that synthesize the huge variety of proteins that determine the chemical and physical nature of cells—and therefore of the whole body.

Recall from Chapter 2 that proteins are composed of polypeptide chains, which in turn are made up of amino acids. For purposes of this discussion, we define a **gene** as a segment of a DNA molecule that carries instructions for creating one polypeptide chain. Supposedly we humans have an estimated 25,000 protein coding genes. (Note, however, that some genes specify the structure of certain varieties of RNA as their final product.)

The four nucleotide bases (A, G, T, and C) are the "letters" used in the genetic alphabet, and the information of DNA is found in the sequence of these bases. Each sequence of three bases, called a **triplet**, can be thought of as a "word" that specifies a particular amino acid. For example, the triplet AAA calls for the amino acid phenylalanine, and CCT calls for glycine. The sequence of triplets in each gene forms a "sentence" that tells exactly how a particular polypeptide is to be made: It specifies the number, kinds, and order of amino acids needed to build a particular polypeptide.

Variations in the arrangement of A, T, C, and G allow our cells to make all the different kinds of proteins needed. Even a "small" gene has an estimated 210 base pairs in sequence. The ratio between DNA bases in the gene and amino acids in the polypeptide is 3:1 (because each triplet stands for one amino acid), so we would expect the polypeptide specified by such a gene to contain 70 amino acids.

(Text continues on p. 102.)

Figure 3.33 Mitosis is the process of nuclear division in which the chromosomes are distributed to two daughter nuclei. Together with cytokinesis, it produces two identical daughter cells. *A&PFlix* Available at www.masteringaandp.com

| Interphase | Early Prophase | Late Prophase |

Interphase — Centrosomes (each has 2 centrioles), Plasma membrane, Nucleolus, Nuclear envelope, Chromatin

Early Prophase — Early mitotic spindle, Aster, Chromosome consisting of two sister chromatids, Centromere

Late Prophase — Spindle pole, Polar microtubule, Fragments of nuclear envelope, Kinetochore, Kinetochore microtubule

| Interphase | Prophase—first phase of mitosis |

Interphase

Interphase is the period of a cell's life when it carries out its normal metabolic activities and grows. Interphase is not part of mitosis.

• During interphase, the DNA-containing material is in the form of chromatin. The nuclear envelope and one or more nucleoli are intact and visible.

• There are three distinct periods of interphase:
G₁: The centrioles begin replicating.
S: DNA is replicated.
G₂: Final preparations for mitosis are completed and centrioles finish replicating.

The light micrographs show dividing lung cells from a newt. The chromosomes appear blue and the microtubules green. (The red fibers are intermediate filaments.) The schematic drawings show details not visible in the micrographs. For simplicity, only four chromosomes are drawn.

Early Prophase
• The chromatin condenses, forming barlike *chromosomes*.

• Each duplicated chromosome consists of two identical threads, called *sister chromatids*, held together at the *centromere*. (Later when the chromatids separate, each will be a new chromosome.)

• As the chromosomes appear, the nucleoli disappear, and the two centrosomes separate from one another.

• The centrosomes act as focal points for growth of a microtubule assembly called the *mitotic spindle*. As the microtubules lengthen, they propel the centrosomes toward opposite ends (poles) of the cell.

• Microtubule arrays called *asters* ("stars") extend from the centrosome matrix.

Late Prophase
• The nuclear envelope breaks up, allowing the spindle to interact with the chromosomes.

• Some of the growing spindle microtubules attach to *kinetochores* (ki-ne′ to-korz), special protein structures at each chromosome's centromere. Such microtubules are called *kinetochore microtubules*.

• The remaining spindle microtubules (not attached to any chromosomes) are called *polar microtubules*. The microtubules slide past each other, forcing the poles apart.

• The kinetochore microtubules pull on each chromosome from both poles in a tug-of-war that ultimately draws the chromosomes to the center, or equator, of the cell.

Metaphase

Anaphase

Telophase   Cytokinesis

Spindle

Metaphase
plate

Daughter
chromosomes

Nuclear
envelope
forming

Nucleolus forming

Contractile
ring at
cleavage
furrow

Metaphase—second phase of mitosis

- The two centrosomes are at opposite poles of the cell.

- The chromosomes cluster at the midline of the cell, with their centromeres precisely aligned at the *equator* of the spindle. This imaginary plane midway between the poles is called the *metaphase plate*.

- Enzymes act to separate the chromatids from each other.

Anaphase—third phase of mitosis

The shortest phase of mitosis, anaphase begins abruptly as the centromeres of the chromosomes split simultaneously. Each chromatid now becomes a chromosome in its own right.

- The kinetochore microtubules, moved along by motor proteins in the kinetochores, gradually pull each chromosome toward the pole it faces.

- At the same time, the polar microtubules slide past each other, lengthen, and push the two poles of the cell apart.

- The moving chromosomes look V shaped. The centromeres lead the way, and the chromosomal "arms" dangle behind them.

- Moving and separating the chromosomes is helped by the fact that the chromosomes are short, compact bodies. Diffuse threads of chromatin would trail, tangle, and break, resulting in imprecise "parceling out" to the daughter cells.

Telophase—final phase of mitosis

Telophase
Telophase begins as soon as chromosomal movement stops. This final phase is like prophase in reverse.

- The identical sets of chromosomes at the opposite poles of the cell uncoil and resume their threadlike chromatin form.

- A new nuclear envelope forms around each chromatin mass, nucleoli reappear within the nuclei, and the spindle breaks down and disappears.

- Mitosis is now ended. The cell, for just a brief period, is binucleate (has two nuclei) and each new nucleus is identical to the original mother nucleus.

Cytokinesis—division of cytoplasm

Cytokinesis begins during late anaphase and continues through and beyond telophase. A contractile ring of actin microfilaments forms the *cleavage furrow* and pinches the cell apart.

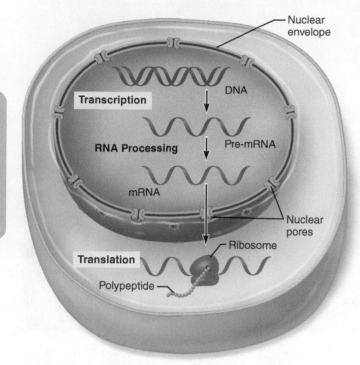

Figure 3.34 Simplified scheme of information flow from the DNA gene to mRNA to protein structure during transcription and translation. (Note that mRNA is first synthesized as pre-mRNA, which is processed by enzymes before leaving the nucleus.)

Most genes of higher organisms contain **exons**, which are amino acid–specifying informational sequences. Exons are often separated by **introns**, which are noncoding, often repetitive, segments that range from 60 to 100,000 nucleotides. Once considered a type of "junk DNA," intron DNA is believed to serve as a reservoir or scrapyard of ready-to-use DNA segments for genome evolution, as well as a rich source of small RNA molecules. The rest of the DNA (indeed, most of it) is essentially "dark matter" whose function is still a mystery. It is in these regions that *pseudogenes* (false genes) are found. Pseudogenes are genetic fossils that are the remains of damaged genes. They "look like" real genes but have deficits that render them functionless.

The Role of RNA

By itself, DNA is like a CD recording: The information it contains cannot be used without a decoding mechanism (a CD player). Furthermore, most polypeptides are manufactured at ribosomes in the cytoplasm, but in interphase cells, DNA never leaves the nucleus. So, DNA requires not only a decoder, but a messenger as well. The decoding and messenger functions are carried out by RNA, the second type of nucleic acid.

As you learned in Chapter 2, RNA differs from DNA: RNA is single stranded, and it has the sugar ribose instead of deoxyribose, and the base uracil (U) instead of thymine (T). Three forms of RNA typically act together to carry out DNA's instructions for polypeptide synthesis:

- **Messenger RNA (mRNA)**, relatively long nucleotide strands resembling "half-DNA" molecules (one of the two strands of a DNA molecule coding for protein structure). mRNA carries a transcript of the code to the cytoplasm, where protein synthesis occurs.
- **Ribosomal RNA (rRNA)**, along with proteins, forms the ribosomes, which consist of two subunits—one large and one small. The two subunit types combine to form functional ribosomes, which are the sites of protein synthesis.
- **Transfer RNA (tRNA)**, small, roughly L-shaped molecules that ferry amino acids to the ribosomes. There they decode mRNA's message for amino acid sequence in the polypeptide to be built.

All types of RNA are formed on the DNA in the nucleus in much the same way as DNA replicates itself: The DNA helix separates and one of its strands serves as a template for synthesizing a complementary RNA strand. Once formed, the RNA molecule is released from the DNA template and migrates into the cytoplasm. Its job done, the DNA recoils into its helical, inactive form.

Approximately 2% of the nuclear DNA codes for the synthesis of short-lived mRNA. DNA in the nucleolar organizer regions (mentioned previously) codes for the synthesis of rRNA, which is long-lived and stable, as is tRNA coded by other DNA sequences. Because rRNA and tRNA do not transport codes for synthesizing other molecules, they are the final products of the genes that code for them. Ribosomal RNA and tRNA act together to "translate" the message carried by mRNA.

Essentially, polypeptide synthesis involves two major steps:

1. *Transcription*, in which DNA's information is encoded in mRNA
2. *Translation*, in which the information carried by mRNA is decoded and used to assemble polypeptides

Figure 3.34 summarizes the information flow in these two major steps. The figure also indicates the "RNA processing" that removes introns from mRNA before this molecule leaves the nucleus and moves into the cytoplasm.

Transcription

A transcriptionist converts a message from a recording or shorthand notes into a written copy. In other words, information is transferred from one form or format to another.

In cells, **transcription** transfers information from a DNA base sequence to the complementary base sequence of an mRNA molecule. The form is different, but the same information is being conveyed. Once the mRNA molecule is made, it detaches and leaves the nucleus via a nuclear pore, and heads for the protein synthesis machinery, the ribosome.

Transcription cannot begin until gene-activating chemicals called *transcription factors* stimulate histones at the site-to-be of gene transcription to loosen. The transcription factors then bind to the promoter. The **promoter** is a special DNA sequence that contains the *start point* (beginning of the gene to be transcribed). It specifies where mRNA synthesis starts and which DNA strand is going to serve as the *template strand* (Figure 3.35,

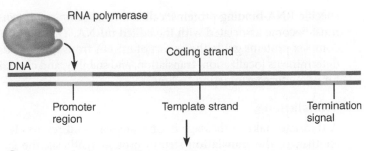

① **Initiation:** With the help of transcription factors, RNA polymerase binds to the promoter, pries apart the two DNA strands, and initiates mRNA synthesis at the start point on the template strand.

② **Elongation:** As the RNA polymerase moves along the template strand, elongating the mRNA transcript one base at a time, it unwinds the DNA double helix before it and rewinds the double helix behind it.

③ **Termination:** mRNA synthesis ends when the termination signal is reached. RNA polymerase and the completed mRNA transcript are released.

Figure 3.35 Overview of stages of transcription.

The DNA-RNA hybrid: At any given moment, 16–18 base pairs of DNA are unwound and the most recently made RNA is still bound to DNA. This small region is called the DNA-RNA hybrid.

top). The uncoiled DNA strand not used as a template is called the *coding strand* because it has the same (coded) sequence as the mRNA to be built (except for the U in mRNA in place of T in DNA). The transcription factors also help position **RNA polymerase**, the enzyme that oversees the synthesis of mRNA, correctly at the promoter. Once these preparations are made, RNA polymerase can initiate transcription.

Transcription involves three basic phases: initiation, elongation, and termination **(Figure 3.35)**.

① **Initiation.** Once properly positioned, RNA polymerase pulls apart the strands of the DNA double helix so transcription can begin at the start point in the promoter.

② **Elongation.** Using incoming RNA nucleotides as substrates, the RNA polymerase aligns them with complementary DNA bases on the template strand and then links them together. As RNA polymerase elongates the mRNA strand

one base at a time, it unwinds the DNA helix in front of it, and rewinds the helix behind it. At any given moment, 16 to 18 base pairs of DNA are unwound and the most recently made mRNA is still hydrogen-bonded (H-bonded) to the template DNA. This small region—called the **DNA-RNA hybrid**—is up to 12 base pairs long.

③ **Termination.** When the polymerase reaches a special base sequence called a **termination signal**, transcription ends and the newly formed mRNA separates from the DNA template.

Processing of mRNA Before translation can begin, editing and further processing are needed to clean up the mRNA transcript. Recall that mammalian DNA like ours has coding regions (exons) separated by non-protein-coding regions (introns). Because the DNA is transcribed sequentially, the mRNA initially made, called *pre-mRNA* or *primary transcript*, is still

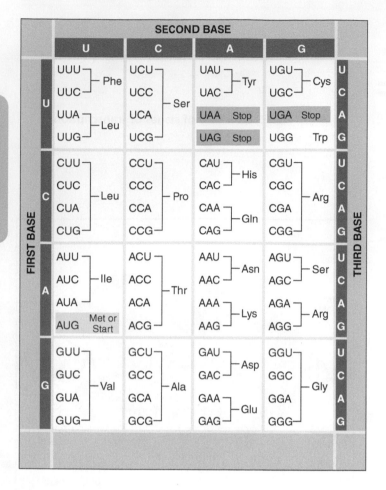

Figure 3.36 The genetic code. The three bases in an mRNA codon are designated as the first, second, and third. Each set of three specifies a particular amino acid, represented here by an abbreviation (see list below). The codon AUG (which specifies the amino acid methionine) is the usual start signal for protein synthesis. The word *stop* indicates the codons that serve as signals to terminate protein synthesis.

Abb.*	Amino acid	Abb.*	Amino acid
Ala	alanine	Leu	leucine
Arg	arginine	Lys	lysine
Asn	asparagine	Met	methionine
Asp	aspartic acid	Phe	phenylalanine
Cys	cysteine	Pro	proline
Glu	glutamic acid	Ser	serine
Gln	glutamine	Thr	threonine
Gly	glycine	Trp	tryptophan
His	histidine	Tyr	tyrosine
Ile	isoleucine	Val	valine

*Abbreviation for the amino acid

littered with introns. Before the newly formed RNA can be used as a messenger, it must be processed, or edited—that is, sections corresponding to introns must be removed. Large RNA-protein complexes called *spliceosomes* snip out the introns and splice together the remaining exon-coded sections in the order in which they occurred in the DNA, producing functional mRNA.

Although many introns degrade naturally, some contain active segments (such as microRNAs) that can function to control, interfere with, or silence other genes. Additionally, a number of

specific RNA-binding proteins, called *mRNA complex proteins*, must become associated with the edited mRNA. These mRNA complex proteins guide the export of mRNA from the nucleus, determine its localization, translation, and stability, and check it for premature termination codons.

Translation

A translator takes a message in one language and restates it in another. In the **translation** step of protein synthesis, the language of nucleic acids (base sequence) is translated into the language of proteins (amino acid sequence).

Genetic Code   The rules by which the base sequence of a gene is translated into an amino acid sequence are called the **genetic code**. For each triplet, or three-base sequence on DNA, the corresponding three-base sequence on mRNA is called a **codon**. Since there are four kinds of RNA (or DNA) nucleotides, there are 4^3, or 64, possible codons. Three of these 64 codons are "stop signs" that call for termination of polypeptide synthesis. All the rest code for amino acids.

Because there are only about 20 amino acids, some are specified by more than one codon. This redundancy in the genetic code helps protect against problems due to transcription (and translation) errors. **Figure 3.36** shows the genetic code and a complete codon list.

Role of tRNA   Translation involves the mRNAs, tRNAs, and rRNAs mentioned above. Before we get into the actual details of the translation process, let's look at how the tRNAs are so well suited for their roles in translation.

Shaped like a handheld drill, tRNA is well suited to its dual function of binding to both an amino acid and an mRNA codon. The amino acid (picked up from the cytoplasmic pool) is bound to one end of tRNA, at a region called the stem. At the other end, the head, is its **anticodon** (an″ti-ko′don), a three-base sequence complementary to the mRNA codon calling for the amino acid carried by that particular tRNA. Because anticodons form hydrogen bonds with complementary codons, tRNA is the link between the language of nucleic acids and the language of proteins. For example, if the mRNA codon is AUA, which specifies isoleucine, the tRNAs carrying isoleucine will have the anticodon UAU, which can bind to the AUA codons.

There are approximately 45 types of tRNA, each capable of binding with a specific amino acid. The attachment process is controlled by an aminoacyl-tRNA synthetase enzyme and is activated by ATP. Once its amino acid is loaded, the tRNA (now called an *aminoacyl-tRNA* because of its amino acid cargo) migrates to the ribosome, where its amino acid is maneuvered into the proper position, as specified by the mRNA codons and described below. The ribosome is more than just a passive attachment site for mRNA and tRNA. Like a vise, the ribosome holds the tRNA and mRNA close together to coordinate the coupling of codons and anticodons, and positions the next (incoming) amino acid for addition to the growing polypeptide chain. To do its job, the ribosome has a binding site for mRNA and three binding sites for tRNA: an A (aminoacyl) site for an incoming aminoacyl-tRNA, a P (peptidyl) site for the tRNA holding the growing polypeptide chain, and an E (exit) site for an outgoing tRNA, as illustrated in *Focus on Translation* (**Figure 3.37**, on pp. 106–107). Now we are ready to put the parts together—so let's go!

Sequence of Events in Translation Translation entails a now familiar sequence of named events—*initiation*, *elongation*, and *termination*—which occur in the cytoplasm. Each of these phases requires energy in the form of ATP and a specific set of protein factors and enzymes. Figure 3.37 summarizes these events.

① **Initiation.** A small ribosomal subunit binds to a special methionine-carrying **initiator tRNA**, and then to the "new" mRNA to be decoded. With the initiator tRNA still in tow, the small ribosomal subunit scans along the mRNA until it encounters the *start codon*—the first AUG triplet it meets. When the initiator tRNA's UAC anticodon "recognizes" and binds to the start codon, a large ribosomal subunit unites with the small one, forming a functional ribosome.

At the end of this phase the mRNA is firmly positioned in the groove between the ribosomal subunits, the initiator tRNA is sitting in the P site, and the A site is vacant, ready for the next aminoacyl tRNA to deliver its cargo. The next phase, elongation of the polypeptide, now begins.

② **Elongation.** During the three-step cycle of elongation, the mRNA is moved through the ribosome in one direction and one amino acid at a time is added to the growing polypeptide (Figure 3.37).

⓶ⓐ **Codon recognition.** The incoming aminoacyl-tRNA binds to a complementary codon in the A site of a ribosome.

⓶ⓑ **Peptide bond formation.** Once the accuracy of the codon-anticodon binding is checked, an enzymatic component in the large ribosomal subunit catalyzes peptide bond formation between the amino acid of the tRNA in the P site to that of the tRNA in the A site.

⓶ⓒ **Translocation.** This step translocates, or moves, the tRNA in the A site to the P site. The unloaded (vacant) tRNA is transferred to the E site, from which it is released and ready to be recharged with an amino acid from the cytoplasmic pool.

This orderly "musical chairs" process continues: the peptidyl-tRNAs transfer their polypeptide cargo to the aminoacyl-tRNAs, and then the P-site-to-E-site and A-site-to-P-site movements of the tRNAs occur (Figure 3.37). As the ribosome "chugs" along the mRNA track and the mRNA is progressively read, its initial portion passes through the ribosome and may become attached successively to several other ribosomes, all reading the same message simultaneously and sequentially. This multiple ribosome–mRNA complex, a *polyribosome*, efficiently produces multiple copies of the same protein (**Figure 3.38**, on p. 108).

③ **Termination.** The mRNA strand continues to be read sequentially until its last codon, the *stop codon* (one UGA, UAA, or UAG) enters the A site. The stop codon is the "period" at the end of the mRNA sentence—it tells the ribosome that translation of that mRNA is finished. As a result,

a *protein release factor* binds to the stop codon at the A site and directs the addition of water (instead of an amino acid) to the polypeptide chain. This hydrolyzes (breaks) the bond between the polypeptide and the tRNA in the P site. The completed polypeptide chain is then released from the ribosome, and the ribosome separates into its two subunits (Figure 3.38a). The released protein may undergo processing before it folds into its complex 3-D structure and floats off, ready to work. When the message of the mRNA that directed its formation is no longer needed, it is degraded.

Processing in the Rough ER As noted earlier in the chapter, ribosomes attach to and detach from the rough ER. When a short "leader" peptide called an ER **signal sequence** is present in a protein being synthesized, the associated ribosome attaches to the membrane of the rough ER. This signal sequence, with its attached cargo of a ribosome and mRNA, is guided to appropriate receptor sites on the ER membrane by a signal recognition particle (SRP), a protein chaperone that cycles between the ER and the cytosol. **Figure 3.39** on p.108 details the subsequent events occurring at the ER.

Summary: From DNA to Proteins The genetic information of a cell is translated into the production of proteins via a sequence of information transfer that is completely directed by complementary base pairing. The transfer of information goes from DNA base sequence (triplets) to the complementary base sequence of mRNA (codons) and then to the tRNA base sequence (anticodons), which is identical to the template DNA sequence except for the substitution of uracil (U) for thymine (T) (**Figure 3.40**, on p. 109).

Other Roles of DNA

The story of DNA doesn't end with the production of proteins encoded by exons. Scientists are finding that intron DNA actually codes for a surprising variety of active RNA species, including the following:

- **Antisense RNAs**, made on the DNA strand complementary to the template strand for mRNA, can intercept and bind to the protein-coding mRNA strand and prevent it from being translated into protein.

- **MicroRNAs** are small RNAs that can use RNA interference machinery to interfere with and suppress mRNAs made by certain exons, thus effectively silencing them.

- **Riboswitches** are folded RNAs that code, like mRNA, for a particular protein. What sets them apart from other mRNAs is a region that acts as a switch to turn protein synthesis on or off in response to metabolic changes in their immediate environment, such as shifting concentrations of amino acids or other small molecules in the cell. When it senses these changes, the riboswitch changes shape, thereby stopping or starting production of the protein it specifies.

Beyond the discussion here and in Chapter 29, we still have much to learn about these versatile RNA species that arise from intron DNA and appear to play a role in heredity. Another area of research focuses on the multitasking of DNA segments.

(Text continues on p. 109)

Figure 3.37 Translation is the process in which genetic information carried by an mRNA is decoded in the ribosome to form a particular polypeptide. The "translators" are tRNA molecules that can recognize and bind specifically both to a codon and an amino acid. *A&PFlix* Available at www.masteringaandp.com

Template strand of DNA

Pre-mRNA

mRNA

Nucleus (site of transcription)

Newly made (and edited) mRNA leaves nucleus and travels to a free or attached ribosome for decoding.

Cytosol (site of translation)

Amino acid corresponding to anticodon

Met

tRNA

U A C

The correct amino acid is attached to each species of tRNA by a synthetase enzyme.

Aminoacyl-tRNA synthetase

Methionine (amino acid)

Met

U A C

Initiator tRNA bearing anticodon

1 Initiation. Initiation occurs when four components combine:
• A small ribosomal subunit
• An initiator tRNA that carries the amino acid methionine
• The mRNA
• A large ribosomal subunit
Once this is accomplished, the next phase, elongation, begins.

Met

A site

P site

E site

Large ribosomal subunit

Start codon

Small ribosomal subunit

② Elongation. Amino acids are added one at a time to the growing peptide chain via a process that has three repeating steps.

Amino acid corresponding to anticodon

Leu

Ile
Pro

G A U — tRNA anticodon

E   P   A

G G C   C U A
A U A C C G C U A

②a Codon recognition. The anticodon of an incoming tRNA binds with the complementary mRNA codon (A to U and C to G) in the A site of the ribosome.

Complementary mRNA codon

Polypeptide

Ile
Pro — New peptide bond

Leu

E   P   A

G G C   G A U
A U A C C G C U A

②b Peptide bond formation. The growing polypeptide bound to the tRNA at the P site is transferred to the amino acid carried by the tRNA in the A site, and a new peptide bond is formed.

Released tRNA

Ile
Pro
Leu

G G C

E   P   A

G A U
C C G C U A C U C

Direction of ribosome movement

②c Translocation. As the entire ribosome translocates, it shifts by one codon along the mRNA:
• The unloaded tRNA in the P site is moved to the E site and then released.
• The tRNA in the A site moves to the P site.
• The next codon to be translated is now in the empty A site ready for step 2a again.

G A C

E   P

C C U
C U G G G A U G A

Release factor

Stop codon

Polypeptide

③ Termination. When a stop codon (UGA, UAA, or UAG) arrives at the A site, elongation ends. Release of the newly made polypeptide is triggered by a release factor and the ribosomal subunits separate, releasing the mRNA.

Growing polypeptides

Completed polypeptide

Incoming ribosomal subunits

Start of mRNA

Polyribosome

End of mRNA

(a) Each polyribosome consists of one strand of mRNA being read by several ribosomes simultaneously. In this diagram, the mRNA is moving to the left and the "oldest" functional ribosome is farthest to the right.

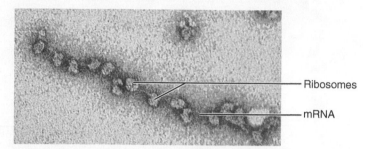

Ribosomes

mRNA

(b) This transmission electron micrograph shows a large polyribosome (400,000×).

Figure 3.38 Polyribosome arrays. Polyribosome arrays allow a single strand of mRNA to be translated into hundreds of the same polypeptide molecules in a short time.

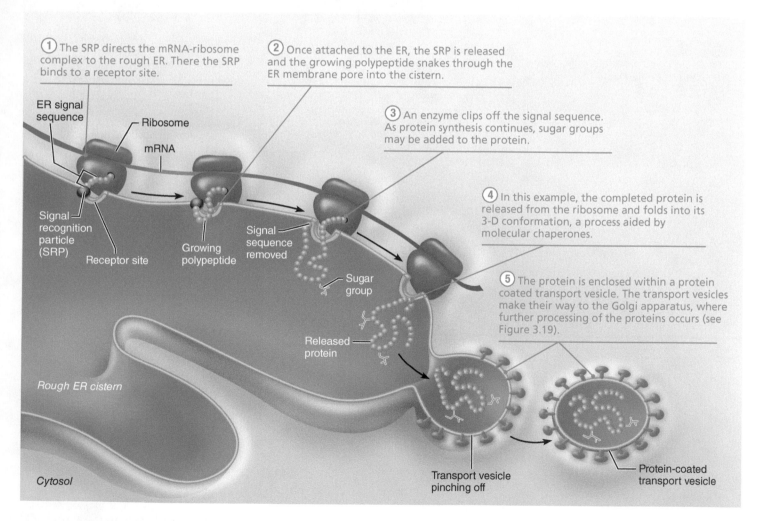

① The SRP directs the mRNA-ribosome complex to the rough ER. There the SRP binds to a receptor site.

② Once attached to the ER, the SRP is released and the growing polypeptide snakes through the ER membrane pore into the cistern.

③ An enzyme clips off the signal sequence. As protein synthesis continues, sugar groups may be added to the protein.

④ In this example, the completed protein is released from the ribosome and folds into its 3-D conformation, a process aided by molecular chaperones.

⑤ The protein is enclosed within a protein coated transport vesicle. The transport vesicles make their way to the Golgi apparatus, where further processing of the proteins occurs (see Figure 3.19).

ER signal sequence

Ribosome

mRNA

Signal recognition particle (SRP)

Receptor site

Growing polypeptide

Signal sequence removed

Sugar group

Released protein

Rough ER cistern

Cytosol

Transport vesicle pinching off

Protein-coated transport vesicle

Figure 3.39 Rough ER processing of proteins. An endoplasmic reticulum (ER) signal sequence in a newly forming protein causes the signal recognition particle (SRP) to direct the mRNA-ribosome complex to the rough ER.

Figure 3.40 Information transfer from DNA to RNA to polypeptide. Information is transferred from the DNA of the gene to the complementary messenger RNA molecule, whose codons are then "read" (translated) by transfer RNA anticodons. Notice that the "reading" of the mRNA by tRNA anticodons reestablishes the base (triplet) sequence of the DNA genetic code (except that T is replaced by U).

☑ **Check Your Understanding**

29. Codons and anticodons are both three-base sequences. How do they differ?
30. How do the A, P, and E ribosomal sites differ functionally during protein synthesis?
31. What is the role of DNA in transcription?

For answers, see Appendix H.

Degradation of Organelles and Cytosolic Proteins

✓ Define autophagy and indicate its major cellular function.

✓ Describe the importance of ubiquitin-dependent degradation of soluble proteins.

The workings of the cytoplasm are complex and seemingly unending. Without some system to get rid of malfunctioning or obsolete organelles, cells would soon become gummed up with debris.

Not to worry. The process called *autophagy* ("self-eating") sweeps up bits of cytoplasm and excess organelles into double-membrane vesicles called *autophagosomes*. They are then delivered to lysosomes for digestion of the contents to amino acids, fatty acids, and the like, which the cell reuses.

Autophagy may have evolved as a response to cell starvation and it speeds up in response to several kinds of stress, such as low oxygen, high temperature, or lack of growth factors. However, autophagosomes are busy continuously. Although autophagy can lead to programmed cell death (see apoptosis, p. 110), it makes a greater contribution to cell survival and provides a fail-safe system against complete self-destruction when such a dire response is not necessary.

Autophagy is exactly what the doctor ordered for disposal of large cytoplasmic structures and protein aggregates. But lysosomal enzymes do not have access to soluble proteins that are misfolded, damaged, or unneeded and need to be disposed of. Examples of unneeded proteins include some that are used only in cell division and must be degraded at precise points in the cell cycle, and short-lived transcription factors.

So how does the cell prevent such proteins from accumulating while stopping the cytosolic enzymes from destroying virtually all soluble proteins? It seems that the cell has a different strategy for destroying such proteins.

Proteins called **ubiquitins** (u-bǐ′kwǐ-tinz) mark doomed proteins for attack (proteolysis) by attaching to them in an ATP-dependent reaction. The tagged proteins are then hydrolyzed to small peptides by soluble enzymes or by **proteasomes**, giant "waste disposal" complexes composed of protein-digesting enzymes, and the ubiquitin is recycled. Proteasome activity is critical during starvation when these complexes degrade preexisting proteins to provide amino acids for synthesis of new and needed proteins.

Extracellular Materials

✓ Name and describe the composition of extracellular materials.

Extracellular materials are any substances contributing to body mass that are found outside the cells. Classes of extracellular materials include

- *Body fluids*, mainly interstitial fluid, blood plasma, and cerebrospinal fluid. These fluids are important transport and dissolving media.

- *Cellular secretions*, such as substances that aid in digestion (intestinal and gastric fluids) and some that act as lubricants (saliva, mucus, and serous fluids).

- The *extracellular matrix*, the most abundant extracellular material. Most body cells are in contact with a jellylike substance composed of proteins and polysaccharides. Secreted by the cells, these molecules self-assemble into an organized mesh in the extracellular space, where they serve as a universal "cell glue" that helps to hold body cells together. As described in Chapter 4, the extracellular matrix is particularly abundant in connective tissues—in some cases so abundant that it (rather than living cells) accounts for the bulk of that tissue type. Depending on the structure to be formed, the extracellular matrix in connective tissue ranges from soft to rock-hard.

☑ **Check Your Understanding**

32. What is the importance of ubiquitin in the life of a cell?
33. What are two body fluids that inhabit the extracellular space and what role does each play in the body?

For answers, see Appendix H.

Developmental Aspects of Cells

✓ Discuss some theories of cell differentiation and aging.

✓ Indicate the value of apoptosis to the body.

We all begin life as a single cell, the fertilized egg, and all the cells of our body arise from it. Very early in development, cells begin to specialize, some becoming liver cells, some nerve cells, and so on. All our cells carry the same genes, so how can one cell become so different from another? This is a fascinating question.

Apparently, cells in various regions of the embryo are exposed to different chemical signals that channel them into specific pathways of development. When the embryo consists of just a few cells, the major signals may be nothing more than slight differences in oxygen and carbon dioxide concentrations between the more superficial and the deeper cells. But as development continues, cells release chemicals that influence development of neighboring cells by triggering processes that switch some genes "off" and others "on." Some genes are active in all cells. For example, genes for rRNA and ATP synthesis are "on" in all cells, but genes for synthesizing the enzymes needed to produce thyroxine are "on" only in cells that are going to be part of the thyroid gland. Hence, the story of cell specialization lies in the kinds of proteins made and reflects the activation of different genes in different cell types.

Cell specialization leads to *structural* variation—different organelles come to predominate in different cells. For example, muscle cells make large amounts of actin and myosin, and their cytoplasm fills with microfilaments. Liver and phagocytic cells produce more lysosomes. The development of specific and distinctive features in cells is called **cell differentiation**.

Apoptosis and Modified Rates of Cell Division

During early development, cell death and destruction are normal events. Nature takes few chances. More cells than needed are produced, and excesses are eliminated later in a type of programmed cell death called **apoptosis** (ap″o-to′sis; "falling away"). Apoptosis is particularly common in the developing nervous system. It is also responsible for "carving out" fingers and toes from their embryonic webbed precursors. This process of controlled cellular suicide also eliminates cells that are stressed, no longer needed, injured, or aged.

How does apoptosis work? In response to internal cellular damage or to some extracellular signal, mitochondrial membranes become permeable, allowing cytochrome c and other factors to leak into the cytosol. These chemicals trigger apoptosis by activating intracellular enzymes called *caspases*. The activated caspases unleash a torrent of digestive activity within the cell, destroying the cell's DNA, cytoskeleton, and so on, producing a quick, neat death. The apoptotic cell shrinks without leaking its contents into the surrounding tissue, detaches from other cells, and rounds up. Because the dying cell releases a chemical that attracts macrophages, and sprouts "eat me" signals, it is immediately phagocytized.

Most organs are well formed and functional long before birth, but the body continues to grow and enlarge by forming new cells throughout childhood and adolescence. Once we reach adult size, cell division is important mainly to replace short-lived cells and repair wounds.

During young adulthood, cell numbers remain fairly constant. However, local changes in the rate of cell division are common. For example, when a person is anemic, his or her bone marrow undergoes **hyperplasia** (hi″per-pla′ze-ah), or accelerated growth (*hyper* = over; *plas* = grow), to produce red blood cells at a faster rate. If the anemia is remedied, the excessive marrow activity ceases. **Atrophy** (at′ro-fe), a decrease in size of an organ or body tissue, can result from loss of normal stimulation or from diseases like muscular dystrophy. Muscles that lose their nerve supply atrophy and waste away, and lack of exercise leads to thinned, brittle bones.

Cell Aging

Cell aging is a complicated process with many causes, but to be perfectly frank, the precise reason an otherwise healthy person grows old and dies is still a mystery.

The *wear-and-tear theory* attributes aging to little chemical insults and formation of free radicals, both of which have cumulative effects. For example, environmental toxins such as pesticides, alcohol, and bacterial toxins may damage cell membranes, poison enzyme systems, or cause "mistakes" in DNA replication. Temporary lack of oxygen, which occurs increasingly with age as our blood vessels clog with fatty materials, accelerates rates of cell death throughout the body.

According to the *mitochondrial theory of aging*, free radicals deserve most of the blame. Most free radicals are produced in the mitochondria, because these organelles have the highest metabolic rate. This finding implies that diminished energy production by radical-damaged mitochondria, due perhaps to an increasing burden of mutations in mitochondrial DNA, weakens (and ages) cells. X rays and other types of radiation, and some chemicals, also generate huge numbers of free radicals, which can overwhelm the peroxisomal enzymes. Vitamins C and E act as antioxidants in the body and may help to absorb or defuse free radicals. With age, glucose (blood sugar) becomes party to cross-linking proteins together, a condition that severely disrupts protein function and accelerates the course of atherosclerosis.

Another theory attributes cell aging to progressive disorders in the immune system. According to this theory, cell damage results from (1) autoimmune responses, which means the immune system turns against one's own tissues, and (2) a progressive weakening of the immune response, so that the body is less able to get rid of cell-damaging pathogens.

The idea that cell aging and chronic illnesses result from inflammation (and an overactive immune system) has been kicking around since the 1800s. In the 1990s evidence did in fact emerge to link inflammation to aging. C-reactive protein, a protein that indicates acute inflammation, is elevated in heart disease and is an amazingly accurate predictor of future heart attacks. It seems that as we age, acute episodes of inflammation tend to become chronic.

Perhaps the most widely accepted theory of cell aging is the *genetic theory*, which suggests that cessation of mitosis and cell aging are "programmed into our genes." One interesting notion here is that a *telomere clock* determines the number of times a cell can divide. **Telomeres** (*telo* = end; *mer* = piece) are nonsensical strings of nucleotides that cap the ends of chromosomes and provide protection from fraying, fusing with other chromosomes, inappropriate repair, and losing important genetic information, much like plastic caps preserve the ends of shoelaces. In human telomeres, the base sequence TTAGGG is repeated a thousand times or more (like a DNA stutter). Though telomeres carry no genes, they appear to be vital for chromosomal survival, because each time DNA is replicated, 100 to 200 of the end nucleotides are lost and the telomeres get a bit shorter. When telomeres reach a certain minimum length, it is thought that the stop-division signal is given.

The idea that cell longevity depends on telomere integrity was supported by the discovery of *telomerase*, an enzyme that lengthens the previously shortened telomeres. Pegged as the "immortality enzyme," telomerase is found in germ line cells (cells that give rise to sperm and ova), but it is absent or barely detectable in other adult cell types.

☑ Check Your Understanding

34. What is apoptosis and what is its importance in the body?
35. What is the wear-and-tear theory of aging?

For answers, see Appendix H.

In this chapter we have described the structure and function of the generalized cell. One of the wonders of the cell is the disparity between its minute size and its extraordinary activity, which reflects the diversity of its organelles. The evidence for division of labor and functional specialization among organelles is inescapable. Only ribosomes synthesize proteins, while protein packaging is the bailiwick of the Golgi apparatus. Membranes compartmentalize most organelles, allowing them to work without hindering or being hindered by other cell activities, and the plasma membrane regulates molecular traffic across the cell's boundary. Now that you know what cells have in common, you are ready to explore how they differ in the various body tissues, the topic of Chapter 4.

Chapter Summary

 For more chapter study tools, go to the Study Area of MasteringA&P at **www.masteringaandp.com**. There you will find:

- Interactive Physiology **iP**
- A&PFlix **A&PFlix**
- Practice Anatomy Lab PAL
- PhysioEx **PEx**
- Videos, Practice Quizzes and Tests, MP3 Tutor Sessions, Case Studies, and much more!

The Cellular Basis of Life (p. 62)

1. All living organisms are composed of cells—the basic structural and functional units of life. Cells vary widely in both shape and size.
2. The principle of complementarity states that the biochemical activity of cells reflects the operation of their organelles.
3. The generalized cell is a concept that typifies all cells. The generalized cell has three major regions—the nucleus, cytoplasm, and plasma membrane.

The Plasma Membrane: Structure   (pp. 63–67)

1. The plasma membrane encloses cell contents, mediates exchanges with the extracellular environment, and plays a role in cellular communication.

The Fluid Mosaic Model   (pp. 63–65)

2. The plasma membrane is a fluid bilayer of lipids (phospholipids, cholesterol, and glycolipids) within which proteins are inserted.

3. The lipids have both hydrophilic and hydrophobic regions that organize their aggregation and self-repair. The lipids form the structural part of the plasma membrane.

4. Most proteins are integral transmembrane proteins that extend entirely through the membrane. Some, appended to the integral proteins, are peripheral proteins.

5. Proteins are responsible for most specialized membrane functions: Some are enzymes, some are receptors, and others mediate membrane transport functions.

The Glycocalyx   (pp. 65–66)

6. Externally facing glycoproteins contribute to the glycocalyx.

Cell Junctions   (pp. 66–67)

7. Cell junctions join cells together and may aid or inhibit movement of molecules between or past cells.

8. Tight junctions are impermeable junctions. Desmosomes mechanically couple cells into a functional community. Gap junctions allow joined cells to communicate.

The Plasma Membrane: Membrane Transport   (pp. 67–69)

1. The plasma membrane acts as a selectively permeable barrier. Substances move across the plasma membrane by passive processes, which depend on the kinetic energy of molecules, and by active processes, which depend on the use of cellular energy (ATP).

Passive Processes   (pp. 68–72)

2. Diffusion is the movement of molecules (driven by kinetic energy) down a concentration gradient. Fat-soluble solutes can diffuse directly through the membrane by dissolving in the lipid.

3. Facilitated diffusion is the passive movement of certain solutes across the membrane either by their binding with a membrane carrier protein or by their moving through a membrane channel. As with other diffusion processes, it is driven by kinetic energy, but the carriers and channels are selective.

4. Osmosis is the diffusion of a solvent, such as water, through a selectively permeable membrane. Water diffuses through membrane channels (aquaporins) or directly through the lipid portion of the membrane from a solution of lesser osmolarity (total concentration of all solute particles) to a solution of greater osmolarity.

5. The presence of solutes unable to permeate the plasma membrane leads to changes in cell tone that may cause the cell to swell or shrink. Net osmosis ceases when the solute concentration on both sides of the plasma membrane reaches equilibrium.

6. Solutions that cause a net loss of water from cells are hypertonic. Those causing net water gain are hypotonic. Those causing neither gain nor loss of water are isotonic.

Active Processes   (pp. 72–79)

7. Active transport (solute pumping) depends on a carrier protein and energy. Substances transported move against concentration or electrical gradients. In primary active transport, such as that provided by the Na^+-K^+ pump, ATP directly provides the energy.

8. In secondary active transport, the energy of an ion gradient (produced by a primary active transport process) is used to transport a substance passively. Many active transport systems are coupled, and cotransported substances move in either the same (symport) or opposite (antiport) directions across the membrane.

9. Vesicular transport also requires that energy be provided. Endocytosis brings substances into the cell, typically in protein-coated vesicles. If the substance is relatively large particles, the process is called phagocytosis. If the substance is dissolved molecules, the process is pinocytosis. Receptor-mediated endocytosis is selective: Engulfed molecules attach to receptors on the membrane before endocytosis occurs. Exocytosis, which uses SNAREs to anchor the vesicles to the plasma membrane, ejects substances (hormones, wastes, secretions) from the cell.

10. Most endocytosis (and transcytosis) is mediated by clathrin-coated vesicles. Other types of protein coating are found in caveolae and vesicles involved in vesicular trafficking. Caveolae appear to be important as sites that accumulate receptors involved in cell signaling.

The Plasma Membrane: Generation of a Resting Membrane Potential   (pp. 79–80)

1. All cells in the resting stage exhibit a voltage across their membrane, called the resting membrane potential. Because of the membrane potential, both concentration and electrical gradients determine the ease of an ion's diffusion.

Selective Diffusion Establishes Membrane Potential   (pp. 79–80)

2. The resting membrane potential is generated by concentration gradients of ions and the differential permeability of the plasma membrane to ions, particularly potassium ions. Sodium is in high extracellular concentration and low intracellular concentration, and the membrane is poorly permeable to it. Potassium is in high concentration in the cell and low concentration in the extracellular fluid. The membrane is more permeable to potassium than to sodium. Protein anions in the cell are too large to cross the membrane and Cl^-, the main anion in extracellular fluid, is repelled by the negative charge on the inner membrane face.

Active Transport Maintains Electrochemical Gradients   (p. 80)

3. Essentially, a negative membrane potential is established when the movement of K^+ out of the cell equals K^+ movement into the cell. Na^+ movements across the membrane contribute minimally to establishing the membrane potential. The greater outward diffusion of potassium (than inward diffusion of sodium) leads to a charge separation at the membrane (inside negative). This charge separation is maintained by the operation of the sodium-potassium pump.

iP Nervous System I; Topics: Ion Channels, pp. 3, 8, 9; The Membrane Potential, pp. 1–17.

The Plasma Membrane: Cell-Environment Interactions   (pp. 80–81)

1. Cells interact directly and indirectly with other cells. Indirect interactions involve extracellular chemicals carried in body fluids or forming part of the extracellular matrix.

2. Molecules of the glycocalyx are intimately involved in cell-environment interactions. Most are cell adhesion molecules or membrane receptors.

3. Activated membrane receptors act as catalysts, regulate channels, or, like G protein–linked receptors, act through second messengers such as cyclic AMP and Ca^{2+}. Ligand

binding results in changes in protein structure or function within the targeted cell.

The Cytoplasm (pp. 81–91)

1. The cytoplasm, the cellular region between the nuclear and plasma membranes, consists of the cytosol (fluid cytoplasmic environment), inclusions (nonliving nutrient stores, pigment granules, crystals, etc.), and cytoplasmic organelles.

Cytoplasmic Organelles (pp. 83–89)

2. The cytoplasm is the major functional area of the cell. These functions are mediated by organelles.
3. Mitochondria, organelles limited by a double membrane, are sites of ATP formation. Their internal enzymes carry out the oxidative reactions of cellular respiration.
4. Ribosomes, composed of two subunits containing ribosomal RNA and proteins, are the sites of protein synthesis. They may be free or attached to membranes.
5. The rough endoplasmic reticulum is a ribosome-studded membrane system. Its cisterns act as sites for protein modification. Its external face acts in phospholipid synthesis. Vesicles pinched off from the ER transport the proteins to other cell sites.
6. The smooth endoplasmic reticulum synthesizes lipid and steroid molecules. It also acts in fat metabolism and in drug detoxification. In muscle cells, it is a calcium ion depot.
7. The Golgi apparatus is a membranous system close to the nucleus that packages protein secretions for export, packages enzymes into lysosomes for cellular use, and modifies proteins destined to become part of cellular membranes.
8. Lysosomes are membranous sacs of acid hydrolases packaged by the Golgi apparatus. Sites of intracellular digestion, they degrade worn-out organelles and tissues that are no longer useful, and they release ionic calcium from bone.
9. Peroxisomes are membranous sacs containing oxidase enzymes that protect the cell from the destructive effects of free radicals and other toxic substances by converting them first to hydrogen peroxide and then water.
10. The cytoskeleton includes microtubules, intermediate filaments, and microfilaments. Microtubules organize the cytoskeleton and are important in intracellular transport. Microfilaments are important in cell motility or movement of cell parts. Motility functions involve motor proteins. Intermediate filaments help cells resist mechanical stress and connect other elements.

Cellular Extensions (pp. 89–91)

11. Centrioles organize the mitotic spindle and are the bases of cilia and flagella.
12. Microvilli are extensions of the plasma membrane that increase its surface area for absorption.

The Nucleus (pp. 91–96)

1. The nucleus is the control center of the cell. Most cells have a single nucleus. Without a nucleus, a cell cannot divide or synthesize more proteins, and is destined to die.
2. The nucleus is surrounded by the nuclear envelope, a double membrane penetrated by fairly large pores.
3. Nucleoli are nuclear sites of ribosome subunit synthesis.
4. Chromatin is a complex network of slender threads containing histone proteins and DNA. The chromatin units are called nucleosomes. When a cell begins to divide, the chromatin coils and condenses, forming chromosomes.

Cell Growth and Reproduction (pp. 96–110)

The Cell Cycle (pp. 96–99)

1. The cell cycle is the series of changes that a cell goes through from the time it is formed until it divides.
2. Interphase is the nondividing phase of the cell cycle. Interphase consists of G_1, S, and G_2 subphases. During G_1, the cell grows and centriole replication begins. During the S phase, DNA replicates. During G_2, the final preparations for division are made. Many checkpoints occur during interphase at which the cell gets the go-ahead signal to go through mitosis or is prevented from continuing to mitosis.
3. DNA replication occurs before cell division, ensuring that both daughter cells have identical genes. The DNA helix uncoils, and each DNA nucleotide strand acts as a template for the formation of a complementary strand. Base pairing provides the guide for the proper positioning of nucleotides.
4. The semiconservative replication of a DNA molecule produces two DNA molecules identical to the parent molecule, each formed of one "old" and one "new" strand.
5. Cell division, essential for body growth and repair, occurs during the M phase. Cell division consists of two distinct phases: mitosis (nuclear division) and cytokinesis (division of the cytoplasm).
6. Mitosis, consisting of prophase, metaphase, anaphase, and telophase, parcels out the replicated chromosomes to two daughter nuclei, each genetically identical to the mother nucleus. Cytokinesis, which begins late in mitosis, divides the cytoplasmic mass into two parts.
7. Cell division is stimulated by certain chemicals (including growth factors and some hormones) and increasing cell size. Lack of space and inhibitory chemicals deter cell division. Cyclin-Cdk complexes regulate cell division.

Protein Synthesis (pp. 99–105)

8. A gene is defined as a DNA segment that provides the instructions to synthesize one polypeptide chain. Since the major structural materials of the body are proteins, and all enzymes are proteins, this amply covers the synthesis of all biological molecules.
9. The base sequence of exon DNA provides the information for protein structure. Each three-base sequence (triplet) calls for a particular amino acid to be built into a polypeptide chain.
10. The RNA molecules acting in protein synthesis are synthesized on single strands of the DNA template. RNA nucleotides are joined according to base-pairing rules.
11. Instructions for making a polypeptide chain are carried from the DNA to the ribosomes via messenger RNA. Ribosomal RNA forms part of the protein synthesis sites. A transfer RNA ferries each amino acid to the ribosome and binds to a codon on the mRNA strand specifying its amino acid.
12. Protein synthesis involves (a) transcription, synthesis of a complementary mRNA, and (b) translation, "reading" of the mRNA by tRNA and peptide bonding of the amino acids into the polypeptide chain. Ribosomes coordinate translation.

Other Roles of DNA (pp. 105–109)

13. Introns and other DNA sequences encode many RNA species that may interfere with or promote the function of specific genes.

Degradation of Organelles and Cytosolic Proteins (pp. 109–110)

14. Organelles and large protein aggregates are picked up by autosomes and delivered to lysosomes for digestion. This process, autophagy, is very important for keeping the cytoplasm free of deteriorating organelles and other debris.

15. Soluble proteins that are damaged or no longer needed are targeted for destruction by attachment of ubiquitin. Cytosolic enzymes or proteasomes then degrade these proteins.

Extracellular Materials   (p. 110)

1. Extracellular materials are substances found outside the cells. They include body fluids, cellular secretions, and extracellular matrix. Extracellular matrix is particularly abundant in connective tissues.

Developmental Aspects of Cells   (pp. 110–111)

1. The first cell of an organism is the fertilized egg. Early in development, cell specialization begins and reflects differential gene activation.

Apoptosis and Modified Rates of Cell Division   (p. 110)

2. Apoptosis is programmed cell death. Its function is to dispose of damaged or unnecessary cells.

3. During adulthood, cell numbers remain fairly constant. Cell division occurs primarily to replace lost cells.

Cell Aging   (p. 111)

4. Cellular aging may reflect chemical insults, progressive disorders of immunity, or a genetically programmed decline in the rate of cell division with age.

Review Questions

Multiple Choice/Matching

(Some questions have more than one correct answer. Select the best answer or answers from the choices given.)

1. The smallest unit capable of life by itself is (a) the organ, (b) the organelle, (c) the tissue, (d) the cell, (e) the nucleus.
2. The major types of lipid found in the plasma membranes are (choose two) (a) cholesterol, (b) triglycerides, (c) phospholipids, (d) fat-soluble vitamins.
3. Membrane junctions that allow nutrients or ions to flow from cell to cell are (a) desmosomes, (b) gap junctions, (c) tight junctions, (d) all of these.
4. The term used to describe the type of solution in which cells will lose water to their environment is (a) isotonic, (b) hypertonic, (c) hypotonic, (d) catatonic.
5. Osmosis always involves (a) a selectively permeable membrane, (b) a difference in solvent concentration, (c) diffusion, (d) active transport, (e) a, b, and c.
6. A physiologist observes that the concentration of sodium inside a cell is decidedly lower than that outside the cell. Sodium diffuses easily across the plasma membrane of such cells when they are dead, but *not* when they are alive. What cellular function that is lacking in dead cells explains the difference? (a) osmosis, (b) diffusion, (c) active transport (solute pumping), (d) dialysis.
7. The solute-pumping type of active transport is accomplished by (a) exocytosis, (b) phagocytosis, (c) electrical forces in the cell membrane, (d) changes in shape and position of carrier molecules in the plasma membrane.
8. The endocytotic process in which a sampling of particulate matter is engulfed and brought into the cell is called (a) phagocytosis, (b) pinocytosis, (c) exocytosis.
9. Which is *not* true of centrioles? (a) They start to duplicate in G_1, (b) they lie in the centrosome, (c) they are made of microtubules, (d) they are membrane-walled barrels lying parallel to each other.
10. The nuclear substance composed of histone proteins and DNA is (a) chromatin, (b) the nucleolus, (c) nuclear sap, or nucleoplasm, (d) nuclear pores.
11. The information sequence that determines the nature of a protein is the (a) nucleotide, (b) gene, (c) triplet, (d) codon.
12. Mutations may be caused by (a) X rays, (b) certain chemicals, (c) radiation from ionizing radioisotopes, (d) all of these.
13. The phase of mitosis during which centrioles reach the poles and chromosomes attach to the spindle is (a) anaphase, (b) metaphase, (c) prophase, (d) telophase.
14. Final preparations for cell division are made during the life cycle subphase called (a) G_1, (b) G_2, (c) M, (d) S.
15. The RNA synthesized on one of the DNA strands is (a) mRNA, (b) tRNA, (c) rRNA, (d) all of these.
16. The RNA species that travels from the nucleus to the cytoplasm carrying the coded message specifying the sequence of amino acids in the protein to be made is (a) mRNA, (b) tRNA, (c) rRNA, (d) all of these.
17. If DNA has a sequence of AAA, then a segment of mRNA synthesized on it will have a sequence of (a) TTT, (b) UUU, (c) GGG, (d) CCC.
18. A nerve cell and a lymphocyte are presumed to differ in their (a) specialized structure, (b) suppressed genes and embryonic history, (c) genetic information, (d) a and b, (e) a and c.
19. A pancreas cell makes proteins (enzymes) that it releases to the small intestine. Which of the following best describes the path of these proteins from synthesis to exocytosis at the pancreatic cell's plasma membrane (PM)? (a) Golgi → rough ER → PM, (b) smooth ER → Golgi → lysosome → PM, (c) rough ER → Golgi → PM, (d) nucleus → Golgi → PM.

Short Answer Essay Questions

20. Which organelle is responsible for a newborn having distinctive toes and fingers instead of webbed digits?
21. Explain why mitosis can be thought of as cellular immortality.
22. Contrast the roles of ER-bound ribosomes with those free in the cytosol.
23. Cells lining the trachea have whiplike motile extensions on their free surfaces. What are these extensions, what is their source, and what is their function?
24. Name the three phases of interphase and describe an activity unique to each phase.
25. Comment on the role of the sodium-potassium pump in maintaining a cell's resting membrane potential.
26. Differentiate between primary and secondary active transport processes.
27. Cell division typically yields two daughter cells, each with one nucleus. How is the occasional binucleate condition of liver cells explained?

Critical Thinking and Clinical Application Questions

1. Explain why limp celery becomes crisp and the skin of your fingertips wrinkles when placed in tap water. (The principle is exactly the same.)

2. A "red-hot" bacterial infection of the intestinal tract irritates the intestinal cells and interferes with digestion. Such a condition is often accompanied by diarrhea, which causes loss of body water. On the basis of what you have learned about osmotic water flows, explain why diarrhea may occur.

3. Two examples of chemotherapeutic drugs (drugs used to treat cancer) and their cellular actions are listed below. Explain why each drug could be fatal to a cell.
   - Vincristine (brand name Oncovin): damages the mitotic spindle
   - Doxorubicin (Adriamycin): binds to DNA and blocks mRNA synthesis

4. The normal function of one tumor suppressor gene is to prevent cells with damaged chromosomes and DNA from "progressing from G_1 to S," whereas another tumor suppressor gene prevents "passage from G_2 to M." When these tumor suppressor genes fail to work, cancer can result. Explain what the phrases in quotations mean.

5. In their anatomy lab, many students are exposed to the chemical preservatives phenol, formaldehyde, and alcohol. Our cells break down these toxins very effectively. What cellular organelle is responsible for this?

6. Dynein is missing from the cilia and flagella of individuals with a specific inherited disorder. These individuals have severe respiratory problems and, if males, are sterile. What is the structural connection between these two symptoms?

7. Explain why alcoholics are likely to have much more smooth ER than teetotalers.

8. Fresh water is a precious natural resource in Florida and it is said that supplies are dwindling. Desalinizing (removing salt from) ocean water has been recommended as a solution to the problem. Why shouldn't we drink salt water?

AT THE CLINIC

Related Clinical Terms

Anaplasia (an′ah-pla′ze-ah; *an* = without, not; *plas* = to grow) Abnormalities in cell structure and loss of differentiation; for example, cancer cells typically lose the appearance of the parent cells and come to resemble undifferentiated or embryonic cells.

Dysplasia (dis-pla′ze-ah; *dys* = abnormal) A change in cell size, shape, or arrangement due to chronic irritation or inflammation (infections, etc.).

Hypertrophy (hi-per′tro-fe) Growth of an organ or tissue due to an increase in the size of its cells. Hypertrophy is a normal response of skeletal muscle cells when they are challenged to lift excessive weight; differs from hyperplasia, which is an increase in size due to an increase in cell number.

Liposomes (lip′o-sōmz) Hollow microscopic sacs formed of phospholipids that can be filled with a variety of drugs. Serve as multipurpose vehicles for drugs, genetic material, and cosmetics.

Mutation A change in DNA base sequence that may lead to incorporation of incorrect amino acids in particular positions in the resulting protein; the affected protein may remain unimpaired or may function abnormally or not at all, leading to disease.

Necrosis (ně-kro′sis; *necros* = death; *osis* = process) Death of a cell or group of cells due to injury or disease. Acute injury causes the cells to swell and burst, and induces the inflammatory response. (This is uncontrolled cell death, in contrast to apoptosis described in the text.)

Tissue: The Living Fabric

nicellular (one-cell) organisms are rugged individualists. Each cell alone obtains and digests its food, ejects its wastes, and carries out all the other activities necessary to keep itself alive and "buzzin' around on all cylinders." But in the multicellular human body, cells do not operate independently. Instead, they form tight cell communities that live and work together.

Individual body cells are specialized, with each type performing specific functions that help maintain homeostasis and benefit the body as a whole. Cell specialization is obvious: Muscle cells look and act differently from skin cells, which in turn are easy to distinguish from brain cells. Cell specialization allows the body to function in sophisticated ways, but division of labor has certain hazards. When a particular group of cells is indispensable, its injury or loss can disable or even destroy the body.

Tissues (*tissu* = woven) are groups of cells that are similar in structure and perform a common or related function. Four primary tissue types interweave to form

Nervous tissue: Internal communication
- Brain
- Spinal cord
- Nerves

Muscle tissue: Contracts to cause movement
- Muscles attached to bones (skeletal)
- Muscles of heart (cardiac)
- Muscles of walls of hollow organs (smooth)

Epithelial tissue: Forms boundaries between different environments, protects, secretes, absorbs, filters
- Lining of digestive tract organs and other hollow organs
- Skin surface (epidermis)

Connective tissue: Supports, protects, binds other tissues together
- Bones
- Tendons
- Fat and other soft padding tissue

Figure 4.1 Overview of four basic tissue types: epithelial, connective, muscle, and nervous tissues.

the "fabric" of the body. These basic tissues are epithelial, connective, nervous, and muscle tissue.

If we summarized the role of each primary tissue in a single word, we could say that epithelial tissue *covers*, connective tissue *supports*, nervous tissue *controls*, and muscle tissue *produces movement*. However, these words reveal only a fraction of what each tissue does (Figure 4.1).

As we explained in Chapter 1, tissues are organized into organs such as the kidneys and heart. Most organs contain all four tissue types, and their arrangement determines the organ's structure and capabilities. The study of tissues, or **histology**, complements the study of gross anatomy. Together they provide the structural basis for understanding organ physiology.

Preparing Human Tissue for Microscopy

✓ List the steps involved in preparing animal tissue for microscopic viewing.

Microscopy allows us to study tissue structure. Before a specimen can be viewed through a microscope, it must be **fixed** (preserved) and then cut into **sections** (slices) thin enough to transmit light or electrons. Finally, the specimen must be **stained** to enhance contrast.

The stains used in light microscopy are beautifully colored organic dyes, most of which were originally developed by clothing manufacturers in the mid-1800s. Many dyes consist of negatively charged molecules (acidic stains) or positively charged molecules (basic stains) that bind within the tissue to macromolecules of the opposite charge. Different parts of cells and tissues take up different dyes, distinguishing different anatomical structures.

For transmission electron microscopy (TEM), tissue sections are "stained" with heavy metal salts. These metals deflect electrons in the beam to different extents, providing contrast. Electron-microscope images are in shades of gray because color is a property of light, not of electron waves, but the image may be artificially colored to enhance contrast. Another kind of electron microscopy, scanning electron microscopy (SEM), provides three-dimensional pictures of an unsectioned tissue surface.

Preserved tissue we see under the microscope has been exposed to many procedures that alter its original condition and introduce minor distortions called **artifacts**. For this reason, most microscopic structures we view are not exactly like those in living tissue.

☑ Check Your Understanding

1. What is the purpose of fixing tissue for microscopic viewing?
2. What types of stains are used to stain tissues to be viewed with an electron microscope?

For answers, see Appendix H.

Epithelial Tissue

✓ List several structural and functional characteristics of epithelial tissue.

✓ Name, classify, and describe the various types of epithelia, and indicate their chief function(s) and location(s).

Epithelial tissue (ep″ĭ-the′le-ul), or an **epithelium** (plural: epithelia), is a sheet of cells that covers a body surface or lines a body cavity (*epithe* = laid on, covering). Two forms occur in the body:

- *Covering and lining epithelium*, which forms the outer layer of the skin; dips into and lines the open cavities of the urogenital, digestive, and respiratory systems; and covers the walls and organs of the closed ventral body cavity
- *Glandular epithelium*, which fashions the glands of the body

Epithelia form boundaries between different environments, and nearly all substances received or given off by the body must pass through an epithelium. For example, the epidermis of the skin lies between the inside and the outside of the body. Epithelium lining the urinary bladder separates underlying cells of the bladder wall from urine.

In its role as an interface tissue, epithelium accomplishes many functions, including (1) protection, (2) absorption, (3) filtration, (4) excretion, (5) secretion, and (6) sensory reception, all of which will be touched upon later in this chapter.

Special Characteristics of Epithelium

Epithelial tissues have five distinguishing characteristics: polarity, specialized contacts, supported by connective tissues, being avascular but innervated, and having the ability to regenerate.

Polarity

All epithelia have an **apical surface**, an upper free surface exposed to the body exterior or the cavity of an internal organ, and a lower attached **basal surface**. The two surfaces differ in both structure and function. For this reason, we say that epithelia exhibit *apical-basal polarity*.

Although some apical surfaces are smooth and slick, most have **microvilli**, fingerlike extensions of the plasma membrane. Microvilli tremendously increase the exposed surface area. In epithelia that absorb or secrete (export) substances (those lining the intestine or kidney tubules, for instance), the microvilli are often so dense that the cell apices have a fuzzy appearance called a *brush border*. Some epithelia, such as that lining the trachea (windpipe), have motile **cilia** (tiny hairlike projections) that propel substances along their free surface.

Adjacent to the basal surface of an epithelium is a thin supporting sheet called the **basal lamina** (lam′ĭ-nah; "sheet"). This noncellular, adhesive sheet consists largely of glycoproteins secreted by the epithelial cells plus some fine collagen fibers. The basal lamina acts as a selective filter that determines which molecules diffusing from the underlying connective tissue are allowed to enter the epithelium. The basal lamina also acts as scaffolding along which epithelial cells can migrate to repair a wound.

Specialized Contacts

Except for glandular epithelia (discussed on pp. 124–125), epithelial cells fit closely together to form continuous sheets. Lateral contacts, including *tight junctions* and *desmosomes*, bind adjacent cells together at many points (these junctions are described in Chapter 3). The tight junctions help keep proteins in the apical region of the plasma membrane from diffusing into the basal region, and thus help to maintain epithelial polarity.

Supported by Connective Tissue

All epithelial sheets rest upon and are supported by connective tissue. Just deep to the basal lamina is the **reticular lamina**, a layer of extracellular material containing a fine network of collagen protein fibers that "belongs to" the underlying connective tissue. The two laminae form the **basement membrane**, which reinforces the epithelial sheet, helps it resist stretching and tearing, and defines the epithelial boundary.

◢ Homeostatic Imbalance 4.1

An important characteristic of cancerous epithelial cells is their failure to respect the basement membrane boundary, which they penetrate to invade the tissues beneath. ✚

Avascular but Innervated

Although epithelium is *avascular* (contains no blood vessels), it is *innervated* (supplied by nerve fibers). Epithelial cells are nourished by substances diffusing from blood vessels in the underlying connective tissue.

Regeneration

Epithelium has a high regenerative capacity. Some epithelia are exposed to friction and their surface cells rub off. Others are damaged by hostile substances in the external environment (bacteria, acids, smoke). If and when their apical-basal polarity and lateral contacts are destroyed, epithelial cells begin to reproduce themselves rapidly. As long as epithelial cells receive adequate nutrition, they can replace lost cells by cell division.

☑ **Check Your Understanding**

3. Epithelial tissue is the only tissue type that has polarity, that is, an apical and a basal surface. Why is this important?
4. Which of the following properties apply to epithelial tissue? Has blood vessels, can repair itself (regenerate), cells joined by lateral contacts.

For answers, see Appendix H.

Classification of Epithelia

Each epithelium has two names. The first name indicates the number of cell layers present, and the second describes the shape of its cells. Based on the number of cell layers, there are simple and stratified epithelia **(Figure 4.2a)**.

■ **Simple epithelia** consist of a single cell layer. They are typically found where absorption, secretion, and filtration occur and a thin epithelial barrier is desirable.

■ **Stratified epithelia**, composed of two or more cell layers stacked on top of each other, are common in high-abrasion areas where protection is important, such as the skin surface and the lining of the mouth.

In cross section, all epithelial cells have six (somewhat irregular) sides, and an apical surface view of an epithelial sheet looks like a honeycomb. This polyhedral shape allows the cells to be closely packed. However, epithelial cells vary in height, and on that basis, there are three common shapes of epithelial cells (Figure 4.2b):

■ **Squamous cells** (skwa′mus) are flattened and scalelike (*squam* = scale).

■ **Cuboidal cells** (ku-boi′dahl) are boxlike, approximately as tall as they are wide.

■ **Columnar cells** (kŏ-lum′nar) are tall and column shaped.

In each case, the shape of the nucleus conforms to that of the cell. The nucleus of a squamous cell is a flattened disc; that of a cuboidal cell is spherical; and a columnar cell nucleus is elongated from top to bottom and usually located closer to the cell base. Keep nuclear shape in mind when you attempt to identify epithelial types.

Simple epithelia are easy to classify by cell shape because the cells usually have the same shape. In stratified epithelia, however, cell shape differs in the different layers. To avoid ambiguity, stratified epithelia are named according to the shape of the cells in the *apical* layer. This naming system will become clearer as we explore the specific epithelial types.

As you read about the epithelial classes, study **Figure 4.3**. Try to pick out the individual cells within each epithelium. This is

(a) Classification based on number of cell layers.

(b) Classification based on cell shape.

Figure 4.2 Classification of epithelia. Note that cell shape influences the shape of the nucleus.

not always easy, because the boundaries between epithelial cells often are indistinct. Furthermore, the nucleus of a particular cell may or may not be visible, depending on the plane of the cut made to prepare the tissue slides.

Simple Epithelia

The simple epithelia are most concerned with absorption, secretion, and filtration. Because they consist of a single cell layer and are usually very thin, protection is not one of their specialties.

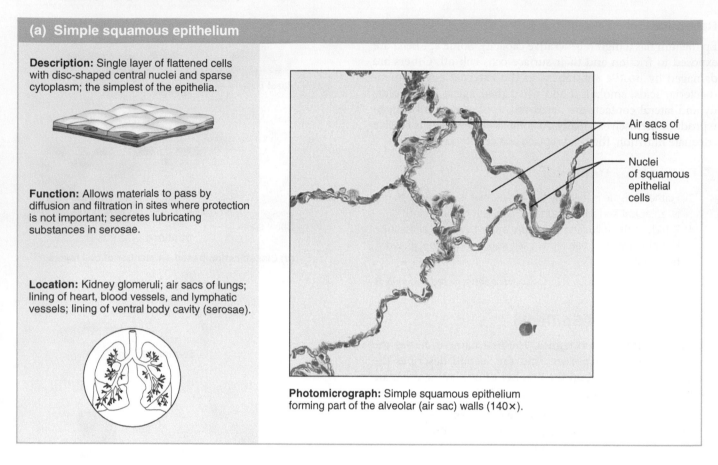

(a) Simple squamous epithelium

Description: Single layer of flattened cells with disc-shaped central nuclei and sparse cytoplasm; the simplest of the epithelia.

Function: Allows materials to pass by diffusion and filtration in sites where protection is not important; secretes lubricating substances in serosae.

Location: Kidney glomeruli; air sacs of lungs; lining of heart, blood vessels, and lymphatic vessels; lining of ventral body cavity (serosae).

Air sacs of lung tissue

Nuclei of squamous epithelial cells

Photomicrograph: Simple squamous epithelium forming part of the alveolar (air sac) walls (140×).

Figure 4.3 Epithelial tissues. (a) Simple epithelium. (For related images, see *A Brief Atlas of the Human Body*, Plates 1 and 2.)

Simple Squamous Epithelium The cells of a **simple squamous epithelium** are flattened laterally, and their cytoplasm is sparse (Figure 4.3a). In a surface view, the close-fitting cells resemble a tiled floor. When the cells are cut perpendicular to their free surface, they resemble fried eggs seen from the side, with their cytoplasm wisping out from the slightly bulging nucleus.

Thin and often permeable, simple squamous epithelium is found where filtration or the exchange of substances by rapid diffusion is a priority. In the kidneys, it forms part of the filtration membrane. In the lungs, it forms the walls of the air sacs across which gas exchange occurs (Figure 4.3a).

Two simple squamous epithelia in the body have special names that reflect their location.

- **Endothelium** (en″do-the′le-um; "inner covering") provides a slick, friction-reducing lining in lymphatic vessels and in all hollow organs of the cardiovascular system—blood vessels and the heart. Capillaries consist exclusively of endothelium, and its exceptional thinness encourages the efficient exchange of nutrients and wastes between the bloodstream and surrounding tissue cells.

- **Mesothelium** (mez″o-the′le-um; "middle covering") is the epithelium found in serous membranes, the membranes lining the ventral body cavity and covering its organs.

Simple Cuboidal Epithelium **Simple cuboidal epithelium** consists of a single layer of cells as tall as they are wide (Figure 4.3b).

The spherical nuclei stain darkly, causing the cell layer to look like a string of beads when viewed microscopically. Important functions of simple cuboidal epithelium are secretion and absorption. This epithelium forms the walls of the smallest ducts of glands and of many kidney tubules.

Simple Columnar Epithelium **Simple columnar epithelium** is a single layer of tall, closely packed cells, aligned like soldiers in a row (Figure 4.3c). It lines the digestive tract from the stomach through the rectum. Columnar cells are mostly associated with absorption and secretion, and the digestive tract lining has two distinct modifications that make it ideal for that dual function:

- Dense microvilli on the apical surface of absorptive cells
- Tubular glands made primarily of cells that secrete mucus-containing intestinal juice

Additionally, some simple columnar epithelia display cilia on their free surfaces, which help move substances or cells through an internal passageway.

Pseudostratified Columnar Epithelium The cells of **pseudostratified columnar epithelium** (soo″do-strā′tĭ-fĭd) vary in height (Figure 4.3d). All of its cells rest on the basement membrane, but only the tallest reach the free surface of the epithelium. Because the cell nuclei lie at different levels above the basement membrane, the tissue gives the false (pseudo) impression that

(b) Simple cuboidal epithelium

Description: Single layer of cubelike cells with large, spherical central nuclei.

Function: Secretion and absorption.

Location: Kidney tubules; ducts and secretory portions of small glands; ovary surface.

Simple cuboidal epithelial cells

Nucleus

Basement membrane

Connective tissue

Photomicrograph: Simple cuboidal epithelium in kidney tubules (430×).

(c) Simple columnar epithelium

Description: Single layer of tall cells with *round* to *oval* nuclei; some cells bear cilia; layer may contain mucus-secreting unicellular glands (goblet cells).

Function: Absorption; secretion of mucus, enzymes, and other substances; ciliated type propels mucus (or reproductive cells) by ciliary action.

Location: Nonciliated type lines most of the digestive tract (stomach to rectum), gallbladder, and excretory ducts of some glands; ciliated variety lines small bronchi, uterine tubes, and some regions of the uterus.

Microvilli

Simple columnar epithelial cell

Mucus of goblet cell

Basement membrane

Photomicrograph: Simple columnar epithelium of the small intestine mucosa (660×).

Figure 4.3 *(continued)* **(b)** and **(c)** Simple epithelium. (For related images, see *A Brief Atlas of the Human Body*, Plates 3, 4, and 5.)

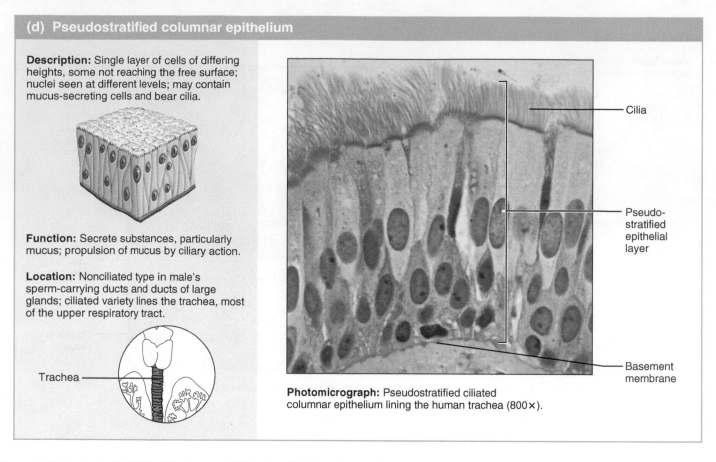

(d) Pseudostratified columnar epithelium

Description: Single layer of cells of differing heights, some not reaching the free surface; nuclei seen at different levels; may contain mucus-secreting cells and bear cilia.

Function: Secrete substances, particularly mucus; propulsion of mucus by ciliary action.

Location: Nonciliated type in male's sperm-carrying ducts and ducts of large glands; ciliated variety lines the trachea, most of the upper respiratory tract.

Trachea

Cilia

Pseudo-stratified epithelial layer

Basement membrane

Photomicrograph: Pseudostratified ciliated columnar epithelium lining the human trachea (800×).

Figure 4.3 *(continued)* **Epithelial tissues. (d)** Simple epithelium. (For a related image, see *A Brief Atlas of the Human Body*, Plate 6.)

several cell layers are present; hence "pseudostratified." The short cells are relatively unspecialized and give rise to the taller cells. This epithelium, like the simple columnar variety, secretes or absorbs substances. A ciliated version containing mucus-secreting cells lines most of the respiratory tract. Here the motile cilia propel sheets of dust-trapping mucus superiorly away from the lungs.

Stratified Epithelia

Stratified epithelia contain two or more cell layers. They regenerate from below; that is, the basal cells divide and push apically to replace the older surface cells. Stratified epithelia are considerably more durable than simple epithelia, and protection is their major (but not their only) role.

Stratified Squamous Epithelium **Stratified squamous epithelium** is the most widespread of the stratified epithelia (Figure 4.3e). Composed of several layers, it is thick and well suited for its protective role in the body. Its free surface cells are squamous, and cells of the deeper layers are cuboidal or columnar. This epithelium is found in areas subjected to wear and tear, and its surface cells are constantly being rubbed away and replaced by division of its basal cells. Because epithelium depends on nutrients diffusing from deeper connective tissue, the epithelial cells farther from the basement membrane are less viable and those at the apical surface are often flattened and atrophied.

To avoid memorizing all its locations, simply remember that this epithelium forms the external part of the skin and extends a short distance into every body opening that is directly continuous with the skin. The outer layer, or epidermis, of the skin is *keratinized* (ker'ah-tin"ĭzd), meaning its surface cells contain *keratin*, a tough protective protein. (We discuss the epidermis in Chapter 5.) The other stratified squamous epithelia of the body are *nonkeratinized*.

Stratified Cuboidal and Columnar Epithelia **Stratified cuboidal epithelium** is quite rare in the body, mostly found in the ducts of some of the larger glands (sweat glands, mammary glands). It typically has two layers of cuboidal cells.

Stratified columnar epithelium also has a limited distribution in the body. Small amounts are found in the pharynx, the male urethra, and lining some glandular ducts. This epithelium also occurs at transition areas or junctions between two other types of epithelia. Only its apical layer of cells is columnar. Because of their relative scarcity in the body, Figure 4.3 does not illustrate these two stratified epithelia (but see *A Brief Atlas of the Human Body*, Plates 8 and 9).

Transitional Epithelium **Transitional epithelium** forms the lining of hollow urinary organs, which stretch as they fill with urine (Figure 4.3f). Cells of its basal layer are cuboidal or columnar. The apical cells vary in appearance, depending on the degree of distension (stretching) of the organ. When the organ is distended with urine, the transitional epithelium thins from about six cell layers to three, and its domelike apical cells flatten

(e) Stratified squamous epithelium

Description: Thick membrane composed of several cell layers; basal cells are cuboidal or columnar and metabolically active; surface cells are flattened (squamous); in the keratinized type, the surface cells are full of keratin and dead; basal cells are active in mitosis and produce the cells of the more superficial layers.

Function: Protects underlying tissues in areas subjected to abrasion.

Location: Nonkeratinized type forms the moist linings of the esophagus, mouth, and vagina; keratinized variety forms the epidermis of the skin, a dry membrane.

Stratified squamous epithelium

Nuclei

Basement membrane

Connective tissue

Photomicrograph: Stratified squamous epithelium lining the esophagus (285×).

(f) Transitional epithelium

Description: Resembles both stratified squamous and stratified cuboidal; basal cells cuboidal or columnar; surface cells dome shaped or squamouslike, depending on degree of organ stretch.

Function: Stretches readily, permits stored urine to distend urinary organ.

Location: Lines the ureters, bladder, and part of the urethra.

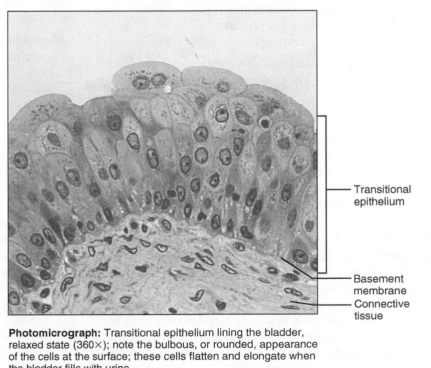

Transitional epithelium

Basement membrane

Connective tissue

Photomicrograph: Transitional epithelium lining the bladder, relaxed state (360×); note the bulbous, or rounded, appearance of the cells at the surface; these cells flatten and elongate when the bladder fills with urine.

Figure 4.3 *(continued)* **(e)** and **(f)** Stratified epithelium. (For related images, see *A Brief Atlas of the Human Body*, Plates 7 and 10.)

and become squamouslike. The ability of transitional cells to change their shape (undergo "transitions") allows a greater volume of urine to flow through a tubelike organ. In the bladder, it allows more urine to be stored.

☑ **Check Your Understanding**

5. Stratified epithelia are "built" for protection or to resist abrasion. What are the simple epithelia better at?
6. Some epithelia are pseudostratified. What does this mean?
7. Where is transitional epithelium found and what is its importance at those sites?

For answers, see Appendix H.

Glandular Epithelia

✓ Define gland.

✓ Differentiate between exocrine and endocrine glands, and between multicellular and unicellular glands.

✓ Describe how multicellular exocrine glands are classified structurally and functionally.

A **gland** consists of one or more cells that make and secrete a particular product. This product, called a **secretion**, is an aqueous (water-based) fluid that usually contains proteins, but there is variation. For example, some glands release a lipid- or steroid-rich secretion.

Secretion is an active process. Glandular cells obtain needed substances from the blood and transform them chemically into a product that is then discharged from the cell. Notice that the term *secretion* can refer to both the gland's *product* and the *process* of making and releasing that product.

Glands are classified according to two sets of traits:

- Where they release their product—glands may be *endocrine* ("internally secreting") or *exocrine* ("externally secreting")
- Relative cell number—glands may be *unicellular* ("one-celled") or *multicellular* ("many-celled")

Unicellular glands are scattered within epithelial sheets. By contrast, most multicellular epithelial glands form by invagination (inward growth) of an epithelial sheet into the underlying connective tissue. At least initially, most have *ducts*, tubelike connections to the epithelial sheets.

Endocrine Glands

Because **endocrine glands** eventually lose their ducts, they are often called *ductless glands*. They produce **hormones**, messenger chemicals that they secrete by exocytosis directly into the extracellular space. From there the hormones enter the blood or lymphatic fluid and travel to specific target organs. Each hormone prompts its target organ(s) to respond in some characteristic way. For example, hormones produced by certain intestinal cells cause the pancreas to release enzymes that help digest food in the digestive tract.

Endocrine glands are structurally diverse, so one description does not fit all. Most are compact multicellular organs, but some individual hormone-producing cells are scattered in the digestive tract lining (mucosa) and in the brain, giving rise to their collective description as the *diffuse endocrine system*. Endocrine secretions are also varied, ranging from modified amino acids to peptides, glycoproteins, and steroids. Since not all endocrine glands are epithelial derivatives, we defer consideration of their structure and function to Chapter 16.

Exocrine Glands

All **exocrine glands** secrete their products onto body surfaces (skin) or into body cavities. The unicellular glands do so directly (by exocytosis), whereas the multicellular glands do so via an epithelium-walled duct that transports the secretion to the epithelial surface. Exocrine glands are a diverse lot and many of their products are familiar. They include mucous, sweat, oil, and salivary glands, the liver (which secretes bile), the pancreas (which synthesizes digestive enzymes), and many others.

Unicellular Exocrine Glands The only important examples of **unicellular** (or one-celled) glands are *mucous cells* and *goblet cells*. Unicellular glands are sprinkled in the epithelial linings of the intestinal and respiratory tracts amid columnar cells with other functions (see Figure 4.3c).

In humans, all such glands produce **mucin** (mu'sin), a complex glycoprotein that dissolves in water when secreted. Once dissolved, mucin forms mucus, a slimy coating that protects and lubricates surfaces. In **goblet cells** the cuplike accumulation of mucin distends the top of the cell, making the cells look like a glass with a stem (thus "goblet" cell, **Figure 4.4**). This distortion does not occur in **mucous cells**.

Multicellular Exocrine Glands Compared to the unicellular glands, **multicellular exocrine glands** are structurally more complex. They have two basic parts: an epithelium-derived *duct* and a *secretory unit* (acinus) consisting of secretory cells. In all but the simplest glands, *supportive connective tissue* surrounds the secretory unit and supplies it with blood vessels and nerve fibers, and forms a *fibrous capsule* that extends into the gland and divides it into *lobes*.

Multicellular exocrine glands can be classified by structure and by type of secretion.

- **Structural classification.** On the basis of their duct structures, multicellular exocrine glands are either simple or compound **(Figure 4.5)**. **Simple glands** have an unbranched duct, whereas **compound glands** have a branched duct. The glands are further categorized by their secretory units as (1) **tubular** if the secretory cells form tubes; (2) **alveolar** (alve'o-lar) if the secretory cells form small, flasklike sacs (*alveolus* = "small hollow cavity"); or (3) **tubuloalveolar** if they have both types of secretory units. Note that the term **acinar** (as'ĭ-nar; "berrylike") is used interchangeably with alveolar.

- **Modes of secretion.** Multicellular exocrine glands secrete their products in different ways, so they can also be

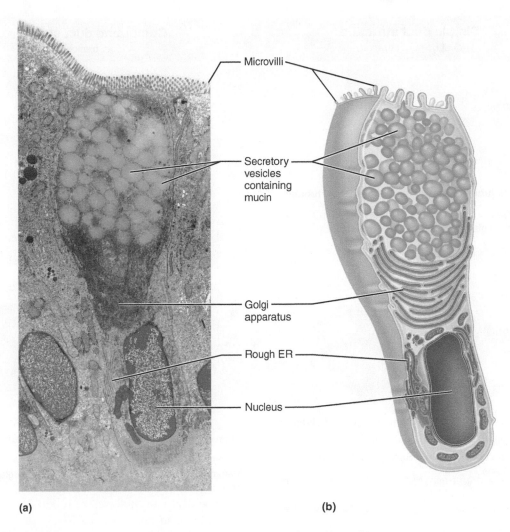

Microvilli

Secretory vesicles containing mucin

Golgi apparatus

Rough ER

Nucleus

(a)   (b)

Figure 4.4 Goblet cell (unicellular exocrine gland). (a) Photomicrograph of a goblet cell in the simple columnar epithelium lining the small intestine (1640×). **(b)** Corresponding diagram. Notice the secretory vesicles and well-developed rough ER and Golgi apparatus.

described functionally as *merocrine, holocrine,* or *apocrine* glands. Most are **merocrine glands** (mer'o-krin), which secrete their products by exocytosis as they are produced. The secretory cells are not altered in any way (so think "merely secrete" to remember their mode of secretion). The pancreas, most sweat glands, and salivary glands belong to this class **(Figure 4.6a)**.

Secretory cells of **holocrine glands** (hol'o-krin) accumulate their products within them until they rupture. (They are replaced by the division of underlying cells.) Because holocrine gland secretions include the synthesized product plus dead cell fragments (*holo* = whole, all), you could say that their cells "die for their cause." Sebaceous (oil) glands of the skin are the only true example of holocrine glands (Figure 4.6b).

Although *apocrine glands* (ap'o-krin) are present in other animals, there is some controversy over whether humans have this third gland type. Like holocrine glands, apocrine glands accumulate their products, but in this case only just

beneath the free surface. Eventually, the apex of the cell pinches off (*apo* = from, off), releasing the secretory granules and a small amount of cytoplasm. The cell repairs its damage and the process repeats again and again. The best possibility in humans is the release of lipid droplets by lactating mammary glands, but most histologists classify mammary glands as merocrine glands because this is the means by which milk proteins are secreted.

☑ **Check Your Understanding**

8. What common secretion do all unicellular exocrine glands produce?

9. How are multicellular exocrine glands classified?

10. Which gland type—merocrine or holocrine—would you expect to have the highest rate of cell division? Why?

For answers, see Appendix H.

4

Simple duct structure (duct does not branch)		Compound duct structure (duct branches)
Tubular secretory structure	**Simple tubular** *Example* Intestinal glands **Simple branched tubular** *Example* Stomach (gastric) glands	**Compound tubular** *Example* Duodenal glands of small intestine
Alveolar secretory structure	**Simple alveolar** *Example* No important example in humans **Simple branched alveolar** *Example* Sebaceous (oil) glands	**Compound alveolar** *Example* Mammary glands **Compound tubuloalveolar** *Example* Salivary glands

☐ Surface epithelium   ☐ Duct   ■ Secretory epithelium

Figure 4.5 **Types of multicellular exocrine glands.** Multicellular glands are classified according to duct type (simple or compound) and the structure of their secretory units (tubular, alveolar, or tubuloalveolar).

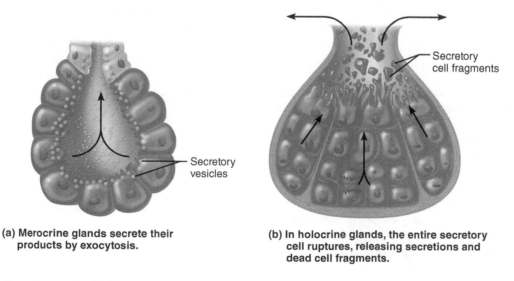

(a) Merocrine glands secrete their products by exocytosis.

Secretory vesicles

Secretory cell fragments

(b) In holocrine glands, the entire secretory cell ruptures, releasing secretions and dead cell fragments.

Figure 4.6 **Chief modes of secretion in human exocrine glands.**

Connective Tissue

✓ Indicate common characteristics of connective tissue, and list and describe its structural elements.

Connective tissue is the most abundant and widely distributed of the primary tissues, but its amount in particular organs varies. For example, skin consists primarily of connective tissue, while the brain contains very little.

There are four main classes of connective tissue and several subclasses (Table 4.1 on p. 129). The main classes are (1) *connective tissue proper* (which includes fat and the fibrous tissue of ligaments), (2) *cartilage*, (3) *bone*, and (4) *blood*.

Connective tissue does much more than just *connect* body parts. Its major functions include (1) *binding and supporting*, (2) *protecting*, (3) *insulating*, (4) *storing* reserve fuel, and (5) *transporting* substances within the body. For example, bone and cartilage support and protect body organs by providing the hard underpinnings of the skeleton. Fat insulates and protects body organs and provides a fuel reserve. Blood transports substances inside the body.

Common Characteristics of Connective Tissue

Connective tissues share three characteristics that set them apart from other primary tissues:

- **Common origin.** All connective tissues arise from *mesenchyme* (an embryonic tissue).

- **Degrees of vascularity.** Connective tissues run the gamut of vascularity. Cartilage is avascular. Dense connective tissue is poorly vascularized, and the other types of connective tissue have a rich supply of blood vessels.

- **Extracellular matrix.** All other primary tissues are composed mainly of cells, but connective tissues are largely nonliving **extracellular matrix** (ma′triks; "womb"), which separates, often widely, the living cells of the tissue. Because of its matrix, connective tissue can bear weight, withstand great tension, and endure abuses, such as physical trauma and abrasion that no other tissue can tolerate.

Structural Elements of Connective Tissue

Connective tissues have three main elements: *ground substance*, *fibers*, and *cells* (Table 4.1). Together ground substance and fibers make up the extracellular matrix. (Note that some authors use the term *matrix* to indicate the ground substance only.)

The composition and arrangement of these three elements vary tremendously. The result is an amazing diversity of connective tissues, each adapted to perform a specific function in the body. For example, the matrix can be delicate and fragile to form a soft "packing" around an organ, or it can form "ropes" (tendons and ligaments) of incredible strength. Nonetheless, connective tissues have a common structural plan, and we use *areolar connective tissue* (ah-re′o-lar) as our *prototype*, or model (Figure 4.7 and Figure 4.8a). All other subclasses are simply variants of this plan.

Ground Substance

Ground substance is the unstructured material that fills the space between the cells and contains the fibers. It is composed of *interstitial* (*tissue*) *fluid, cell adhesion proteins*, and *proteoglycans* (pro″te-o-gli′kanz). Cell adhesion proteins (*fibronectin, laminin*, and others) serve mainly as a connective tissue glue that allows connective tissue cells to attach to matrix elements. The proteoglycans consist of a protein core to which *glycosaminoglycans* (GAGs) (gli″kos-ah-me″no-gli′kanz) are attached. The strand-like GAGs, most importantly *chondroitin sulfate* and *hyaluronic acid* (hi″ah-lu-ron′ik), are large, negatively charged polysaccharides that stick out from the core protein like the fibers of a bottle brush. The proteoglycans tend to form huge aggregates in which the GAGs intertwine and trap water, forming a substance that varies from a fluid to a viscous gel. The higher the GAG content, the more viscous the ground substance.

The ground substance consists of large amounts of fluid and functions as a molecular sieve, or medium, through which nutrients and other dissolved substances can diffuse between the blood capillaries and the cells. The fibers embedded in the ground substance make it less pliable and hinder diffusion somewhat.

Connective Tissue Fibers

The fibers of connective tissue provide support. Three types of fibers are found in connective tissue matrix: collagen, elastic, and reticular fibers. Of these, collagen fibers are by far the strongest and most abundant.

Collagen fibers are constructed primarily of the fibrous protein *collagen*. Collagen molecules are secreted into the extracellular space, where they assemble spontaneously into cross-linked fibrils, which in turn are bundled together into the thick collagen fibers seen with a microscope. Because their fibrils cross-link, collagen fibers are extremely tough and provide high tensile strength (that is, the ability to resist being pulled apart) to the matrix. Indeed, stress tests show that collagen fibers are stronger than steel fibers of the same size!

Elastic fibers are long, thin fibers that form branching networks in the extracellular matrix. These fibers contain a rubber-like protein, *elastin*, that allows them to stretch and recoil like rubber bands. Connective tissue can stretch only so much before its thick, ropelike collagen fibers become taut. Then, when the tension lets up, elastic fibers snap the connective tissue back to its normal length and shape. Elastic fibers are found where greater elasticity is needed, for example, in the skin, lungs, and blood vessel walls.

Reticular fibers are short, fine, collagenous fibers with a slightly different chemistry and form. They are continuous with collagen fibers, and they branch extensively, forming delicate networks (*reticul* = network) that surround small blood vessels and support the soft tissue of organs. They are particularly abundant where connective tissue abuts other tissue types, for example, in the basement membrane of epithelial tissues, and around capillaries, where they form fuzzy "nets" that allow more "give" than the larger collagen fibers.

Cell types

Extracellular matrix

Macrophage

Fibroblast

Lymphocyte

Fat cell

Mast cell

Neutrophil

Capillary

Ground substance

Fibers
- Collagen fiber
- Elastic fiber
- Reticular fiber

Figure 4.7 Areolar connective tissue: A prototype (model) connective tissue. This tissue underlies epithelia and surrounds capillaries. Notice the various cell types and three classes of fibers (collagen, reticular, elastic) embedded in the ground substance. (See Figure 4.8a for a less idealized version.)

Connective Tissue Cells

Each major class of connective tissue has a resident cell type that exists in immature and mature forms (see Table 4.1). The immature (undifferentiated) cells, indicated by the suffix *blast* (literally, "bud" or "sprout," but the suffix means "forming"), are actively mitotic cells that secrete the ground substance and the fibers characteristic of their particular matrix. As listed in the third column of Table 4.1, the primary blast cell types by connective tissue class are (1) connective tissue proper: **fibroblast**; (2) cartilage: **chondroblast** (kon′dro-blast″); and (3) bone: **osteoblast** (os′te-o-blast″). The **hematopoietic stem cell** (hem″ah-to-poy-et′ik), which is the undifferentiated blast cell that produces blood cells, is not included in Table 4.1 because it is not located in "its" tissue (blood) and does not make the fluid matrix (plasma) of that tissue. Blood formation is considered in Chapter 17.

Once they synthesize the matrix, the blast cells assume their mature, less active mode, indicated by the suffix *cyte* (Table 4.1, third column). The mature cells maintain the health of the matrix. However, if the matrix is injured, they can easily revert to their more active state to repair and regenerate the matrix. (The blood-forming stem cells are always actively mitotic.)

Additionally, connective tissue is home to an assortment of other cell types, such as

- **Fat cells,** which store nutrients.

- **White blood cells** (neutrophils, eosinophils, lymphocytes), and other cell types that are concerned with tissue response to injury.

- **Mast cells,** which typically cluster along blood vessels. These oval cells detect foreign microorganisms (e.g., bacteria, fungi) and initiate local inflammatory responses against them. In mast cell cytoplasm are secretory granules (*mast* = stuffed full of granules) containing chemicals that mediate inflammation, especially in severe allergies. These chemicals include

  - *Heparin* (hep′ah-rin), an anticoagulant chemical that prevents blood clotting when free in the bloodstream (but in human mast cells it appears to regulate the action of other mast cell chemicals)
  - *Histamine* (his′tah-mēn), a substance that makes capillaries leaky
  - *Proteases* (protein-degrading enzymes)
  - Various other enzymes

- **Macrophages** (mak′ro-fāj″-es; *macro* = large; *phago* = eat), large, irregularly shaped cells that avidly phagocytize a broad variety of foreign materials, ranging from foreign molecules to entire bacteria to dust particles. These "big eaters" also dispose of dead tissue cells, and they are central actors in the immune system. Macrophages, which are peppered throughout loose connective tissue, bone marrow, and lymphatic tissue, may be attached to connective tissue fibers (fixed) or may migrate freely through the matrix. Some macrophages have

Table 4.1	Comparison of Classes of Connective Tissues			
		COMPONENTS		
TISSUE CLASS AND EXAMPLE	**SUBCLASSES**	**CELLS**	**MATRIX**	**GENERAL FEATURES**
Connective Tissue Proper *Dense regular connective tissue*	1. Loose connective tissue ▪ Areolar ▪ Adipose ▪ Reticular 2. Dense connective tissue ▪ Regular ▪ Irregular ▪ Elastic	Fibroblasts Fibrocytes Defense cells Adipocytes	Gel-like ground substance All three fiber types: collagen, reticular, elastic	Six different types; vary in density and types of fibers Functions as a binding tissue Resists mechanical stress, particulary tension Provides reservoir for water and salts Nutrient (fat) storage
Cartilage *Hyaline cartilage*	1. Hyaline cartilage 2. Elastic cartilage 3. Fibrocartilage	Chondroblasts found in growing cartilage Chondrocytes	Gel-like ground substance Fibers: collagen, elastic fibers in some	Resists compression because of the large amounts of water held in the matrix Functions to cushion and support body structures
Bone Tissue *Compact bone*	1. Compact bone 2. Spongy bone	Osteoblasts Osteocytes	Gel-like ground substance calcified with inorganic salts Fibers: collagen	Hard tissue that resists both compression and tension Functions in support
Blood	See Chapter 17 for details on blood cell formation and differentiation.	Erythrocytes (RBC) Leukocytes (WBC) Platelets	Plasma No fibers	A fluid tissue Functions to carry O_2, CO_2, nutrients, wastes, and other substances (hormones, for example)

selective appetites. For example, those of the spleen primarily dispose of aging red blood cells, but they will not turn down other "delicacies" that come their way.

☑ Check Your Understanding

11. What are four functions of connective tissue?
12. What are the three types of fibers found in connective tissues?

For answers, see Appendix H.

Types of Connective Tissue

✓ Describe the types of connective tissue found in the body, and indicate their characteristic functions.

As noted, all classes of connective tissue consist of living cells surrounded by a matrix. Their major differences reflect cell type, and types and relative amounts of fibers, as summarized in Table 4.1.

As mentioned earlier, mature connective tissues arise from a common embryonic tissue, called **mesenchyme** (meh′zin-kīm). Mesenchyme has a fluid ground substance containing fine sparse fibers and star-shaped *mesenchymal cells*. It arises during the early weeks of embryonic development and eventually differentiates (specializes) into all other connective tissue cells. However, some mesenchymal cells remain and provide a source of new cells in mature connective tissues.

Figure 4.8 illustrates the connective tissues that we describe in the next sections. Study this figure as you read along.

Connective Tissue Proper—Loose Connective Tissues

Connective tissue proper has two subclasses: **loose connective tissues** (areolar, adipose, and reticular) and **dense connective tissues** (dense regular, dense irregular, and elastic). Except for bone, cartilage, and blood, all mature connective tissues are connective tissue proper.

Areolar Connective Tissue   The functions of **areolar connective tissue** (Figure 4.8a) include:

- Supporting and binding other tissues (the job of the fibers)
- Holding body fluids (the ground substance's role)
- Defending against infection (via the activity of white blood cells and macrophages)
- Storing nutrients as fat (in fat cells)

Fibroblasts, flat branching cells that appear spindle shaped in profile, predominate, but numerous macrophages are also seen and present a formidable barrier to invading microorganisms. Fat cells appear singly or in clusters, and occasional mast cells are identified easily by the large, darkly stained cytoplasmic granules that often obscure their nuclei. Other cell types are scattered throughout.

The most obvious structural feature of this tissue is the loose arrangement of its fibers. The rest of the matrix, occupied by ground substance, appears to be empty space when viewed through the microscope, and in fact, the Latin term *areola* means "a small open space." Because of its loose nature, areolar connective tissue provides a reservoir of water and salts for surrounding body tissues, always holding approximately as much fluid as there is in the entire bloodstream. Essentially all body cells obtain their nutrients from and release their wastes into this "tissue fluid."

The high content of hyaluronic acid makes its ground substance viscous, like molasses, which may hinder the movement of cells through it. Some white blood cells, which protect the body from disease-causing microorganisms, secrete the enzyme hyaluronidase to liquefy the ground substance and ease their passage. (Unhappily, some harmful bacteria have the same ability.) When a body region is inflamed, the areolar tissue in the area soaks up excess fluids like a sponge, and the affected area swells and becomes puffy, a condition called **edema** (ĕ-de′mah).

Areolar connective tissue is the most widely distributed connective tissue in the body, and it serves as a universal packing material between other tissues. It binds body parts together while allowing them to move freely over one another; wraps small blood vessels and nerves; surrounds glands; and forms the subcutaneous tissue, which cushions and attaches the skin to underlying structures. It is the connective tissue that most epithelia rest on and is present in all mucous membranes as the *lamina propria*. (Mucous membranes line body cavities open to the exterior.)

Adipose (Fat) Tissue   **Adipose tissue** (ad′ĭ-pōs) is similar to areolar tissue in structure and function, but its nutrient-storing ability is much greater. Consequently, **adipocytes** (ad′ĭ-po-sītz), commonly called *adipose* or *fat cells*, account for 90% of this tissue's mass. The matrix is scanty and the cells are packed closely together, giving a chicken-wire appearance

to the tissue. A glistening oil droplet (almost pure triglyceride) occupies most of a fat cell's volume and displaces the nucleus to one side (Figure 4.8b). Mature adipocytes are among the largest cells in the body. As they take up or release fat, they become plumper or more wrinkled, respectively.

Adipose tissue is richly vascularized, indicating its high metabolic activity. Without the fat stores in our adipose tissue, we could not live for more than a few days without eating. Adipose tissue is certainly abundant: It constitutes 18% of an average person's body weight, and a chubby person's body can be 50% fat without being considered morbidly obese.

Adipose tissue may develop almost anywhere areolar tissue is plentiful, but it usually accumulates in subcutaneous tissue, where it acts as a shock absorber, as insulation, and as an energy storage site. Because fat is a poor conductor of heat, it helps prevent heat loss from the body. Other sites where fat accumulates include surrounding the kidneys, behind the eyeballs, and at genetically determined fat depots such as the abdomen and hips.

The abundant fat beneath the skin serves the general nutrient needs of the entire body, and smaller depots of fat serve the local nutrient needs of highly active organs. Such depots occur around the hard-working heart and around lymph nodes (where cells of the immune system are furiously fighting infection), within some muscles, and as individual fat cells in the bone marrow, where new blood cells are produced at a rapid rate. Many of these local depots are highly enriched in special lipids.

The adipose tissue just described is sometimes called *white fat*, or *white adipose tissue*, to distinguish it from **brown fat**, or **brown adipose tissue**. White fat stores nutrients (mainly for other cells), but brown fat contains abundant mitochondria, which use the lipid fuels to heat the bloodstream to warm the body (rather than to produce ATP molecules). The richly vascular brown fat occurs mainly on the back of babies who (as yet) lack the ability to produce body heat by shivering. Scant deposits occur in adults, mostly above the collar bones, on the neck and abdomen, and around the spine.

Reticular Connective Tissue   **Reticular connective tissue** resembles areolar connective tissue, but the only fibers in its matrix are reticular fibers, which form a delicate network along which fibroblasts called **reticular cells** (Figure 4.8c) are scattered. Although reticular *fibers* are widely distributed in the body, reticular tissue is limited to certain sites. It forms a labyrinth-like **stroma** (literally, "bed" or "mattress"), or internal framework, that can support many free blood cells (mostly lymphocytes) in lymph nodes, the spleen, and bone marrow.

Connective Tissue Proper—Dense Connective Tissues

The three varieties of dense connective tissue are dense regular, dense irregular, and elastic. Since all three have fibers as their prominent element, dense connective tissues are often called **fibrous connective tissues**.

Dense Regular Connective Tissue   **Dense regular connective tissue** contains closely packed bundles of collagen fibers running in the same direction, parallel to the direction of pull (Figure 4.8d). This arrangement results in white, flexible structures

(a) Connective tissue proper: loose connective tissue, areolar

Description: Gel-like matrix with all three fiber types; cells: fibroblasts, macrophages, mast cells, and some white blood cells.

Function: Wraps and cushions organs; its macrophages phagocytize bacteria; plays important role in inflammation; holds and conveys tissue fluid.

Location: Widely distributed under epithelia of body, e.g., forms lamina propria of mucous membranes; packages organs; surrounds capillaries.

Epithelium

Lamina propria

Elastic fibers

Ground substance

Fibroblast nuclei

Collagen fibers

Photomicrograph: Areolar connective tissue, a soft packaging tissue of the body (340×).

(b) Connective tissue proper: loose connective tissue, adipose

Description: Matrix as in areolar, but very sparse; closely packed adipocytes, or fat cells, have nucleus pushed to the side by large fat droplet.

Function: Provides reserve food fuel; insulates against heat loss; supports and protects organs.

Location: Under skin in subcutaneous tissue; around kidneys and eyeballs; within abdomen; in breasts.

Adipose tissue

Mammary glands

Nucleus of adipose (fat) cell

Fat droplet

Photomicrograph: Adipose tissue from the subcutaneous layer under the skin (350×).

Figure 4.8 Connective tissues. (a) and **(b)** Connective tissue proper. (For related images, see *A Brief Atlas of the Human Body*, Plates 11 and 12.)

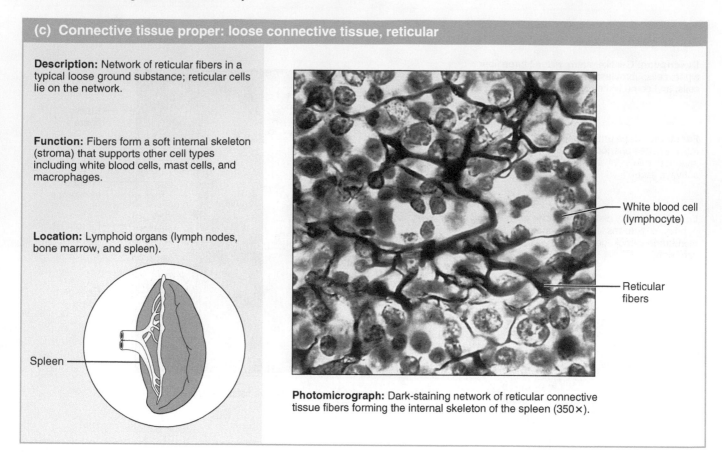

(c) Connective tissue proper: loose connective tissue, reticular

Description: Network of reticular fibers in a typical loose ground substance; reticular cells lie on the network.

Function: Fibers form a soft internal skeleton (stroma) that supports other cell types including white blood cells, mast cells, and macrophages.

Location: Lymphoid organs (lymph nodes, bone marrow, and spleen).

Spleen

White blood cell (lymphocyte)

Reticular fibers

Photomicrograph: Dark-staining network of reticular connective tissue fibers forming the internal skeleton of the spleen (350×).

Figure 4.8 *(continued)* **Connective tissues. (c)** Connective tissue proper. (For a related image, see *A Brief Atlas of the Human Body*, Plate 13.)

with great resistance to tension (pulling forces) where the tension is exerted in a single direction. Crowded between the collagen fibers are rows of fibroblasts that continuously manufacture the fibers and scant ground substance.

Collagen fibers are slightly wavy (see Figure 4.8d). This allows the tissue to stretch a little, but once the fibers straighten out, there is no further "give" to this tissue. Unlike our model (areolar) connective tissue, this tissue has few cells other than fibroblasts and is poorly vascularized.

With its enormous tensile strength, dense regular connective tissue forms *tendons*, which are cords that attach muscles to bones; flat, sheetlike tendons called *aponeuroses* (ap″o-nu-ro′sēz) that attach muscles to other muscles or to bones; and the *ligaments* that bind bones together at joints. Ligaments contain more elastic fibers than tendons and are slightly more stretchy. Dense regular connective tissue also forms fascia (fash′e-ah; "a bond"), a fibrous membrane that wraps around muscles, groups of muscles, blood vessels, and nerves, binding them together like plastic sandwich wrap.

Dense Irregular Connective Tissue **Dense irregular connective tissue** has the same structural elements as the regular variety. However, the bundles of collagen fibers are much thicker and they are arranged irregularly; that is, they run in more than one plane (Figure 4.8e). This type of tissue forms sheets in body areas where tension is exerted from many different directions. It

is found in the skin as the leathery *dermis*, and it forms fibrous joint capsules and the fibrous coverings that surround some organs (kidneys, bones, cartilages, muscles, and nerves).

Elastic Connective Tissue A few ligaments, such as those connecting adjacent vertebrae, are very elastic. The dense regular connective tissue in those structures is called **elastic connective tissue** (Figure 4.8f). Additionally, many of the larger arteries have stretchy sheets of elastic connective tissue in their walls.

Cartilage

Cartilage (kar′tĭ-lij), which stands up to both tension *and* compression, has qualities intermediate between dense connective tissue and bone. It is tough but flexible, providing a resilient rigidity to the structures it supports.

Cartilage lacks nerve fibers and is avascular. It receives its nutrients by diffusion from blood vessels located in the connective tissue membrane (perichondrium) surrounding it. Its ground substance contains large amounts of the GAGs chondroitin sulfate and hyaluronic acid, firmly bound collagen fibers (and in some cases elastic fibers), and is quite firm. Cartilage matrix also contains an exceptional amount of tissue fluid. In fact, cartilage is up to 80% water! The movement of tissue fluid in its matrix enables cartilage to rebound after being compressed and also helps to nourish the cartilage cells.

(d) Connective tissue proper: dense connective tissue, dense regular

Description: Primarily parallel collagen fibers; a few elastic fibers; major cell type is the fibroblast.

Function: Attaches muscles to bones or to muscles; attaches bones to bones; withstands great tensile stress when pulling force is applied in one direction.

Location: Tendons, most ligaments, aponeuroses.

Shoulder joint

Ligament

Tendon

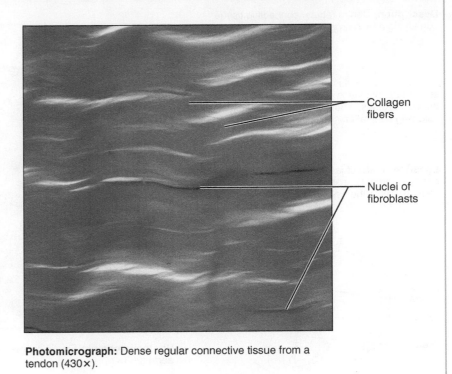

Collagen fibers

Nuclei of fibroblasts

Photomicrograph: Dense regular connective tissue from a tendon (430×).

(e) Connective tissue proper: dense connective tissue, dense irregular

Description: Primarily irregularly arranged collagen fibers; some elastic fibers; fibroblast is the major cell type.

Function: Withstands tension exerted in many directions; provides structural strength.

Location: Fibrous capsules of organs and of joints; dermis of the skin; submucosa of digestive tract.

Shoulder joint

Fibrous joint capsule

Nuclei of fibroblasts

Collagen fibers

Photomicrograph: Dense irregular connective tissue from the fibrous capsule of a joint (430×).

Figure 4.8 *(continued)* **(d)** and **(e)** Connective tissue proper. (For related images, see *A Brief Atlas of the Human Body*, Plates 14 and 15.)

(f) Connective tissue proper: dense connective tissue, elastic

Description: Dense regular connective tissue containing a high proportion of elastic fibers.

Function: Allows tissue to recoil after stretching; maintains pulsatile flow of blood through arteries; aids passive recoil of lungs following inspiration.

Location: Walls of large arteries; within certain ligaments associated with the vertebral column; within the walls of the bronchial tubes.

Elastic fibers

Aorta

Heart

Photomicrograph: Elastic connective tissue in the wall of the aorta (250×).

Figure 4.8 *(continued)* **Connective tissues. (f)** Connective tissue proper. (For a related image, see *A Brief Atlas of the Human Body*, Plate 16.)

Chondroblasts, the predominant cell type in growing cartilage, produce new matrix until the skeleton stops growing at the end of adolescence. The firmness of the cartilage matrix prevents the cells from becoming widely separated, so **chondrocytes**, or mature cartilage cells, are typically found in small groups within cavities called *lacunae* (lah-ku′ne; "pits").

Homeostatic Imbalance 4.2

Because cartilage is avascular and aging cartilage cells lose their ability to divide, injured cartilages heal slowly. This phenomenon is excruciatingly familiar to those who have experienced sports injuries. During later life, cartilages tend to calcify or even ossify (become bony). In such cases, the chondrocytes are poorly nourished and die. ✚

There are three varieties of cartilage: *hyaline cartilage, elastic cartilage*, and *fibrocartilage*, each dominated by a particular fiber type.

Hyaline Cartilage   **Hyaline cartilage** (hi′ah-lĭn), or *gristle*, is the most abundant cartilage in the body. Although it contains large numbers of collagen fibers, they are not apparent and the matrix appears glassy (*hyal* = glass, transparent) blue-white when viewed by the unaided eye. Chondrocytes account for only 1–10% of the cartilage volume (Figure 4.8g).

Hyaline cartilage provides firm support with some pliability. It covers the ends of long bones as *articular cartilage*, providing springy pads that absorb compression at joints. Hyaline cartilage also supports the tip of the nose, connects the ribs to the sternum, and supports most of the respiratory system passages. Most of the embryonic skeleton consists of hyaline cartilage before bone forms. Skeletal hyaline cartilage persists during childhood as the *epiphyseal plates* (e″pĭ-fis′e-ul), actively growing regions near the ends of long bones.

Elastic Cartilage   Histologically, **elastic cartilage** (Figure 4.8h) is nearly identical to hyaline cartilage. However, elastic cartilage has many more elastic fibers. Found where strength and exceptional stretchability are needed, elastic cartilage forms the "skeletons" of the external ear (the pinna) and the epiglottis (the flap that covers the opening to the respiratory passageway when we swallow).

Fibrocartilage   Structurally, **fibrocartilage** is intermediate between hyaline cartilage and dense regular connective tissues. Its rows of chondrocytes (a cartilage feature) alternate with rows of thick collagen fibers (characteristic of dense regular connective tissue) (Figure 4.8i). Because it is compressible and resists tension well, fibrocartilage is found where strong support and the ability to withstand heavy pressure are required: for example, the intervertebral discs (resilient cushions between the bony vertebrae) and the spongy cartilages of the knee (menisci) (see Figure 6.1, p. 175).

4

(g) Cartilage: hyaline

Description: Amorphous but firm matrix; collagen fibers form an imperceptible network; chondroblasts produce the matrix and when mature (chondrocytes) lie in lacunae.

Function: Supports and reinforces; serves as resilient cushion; resists compressive stress.

Location: Forms most of the embryonic skeleton; covers the ends of long bones in joint cavities; forms costal cartilages of the ribs; cartilages of the nose, trachea, and larynx.

Costal cartilages

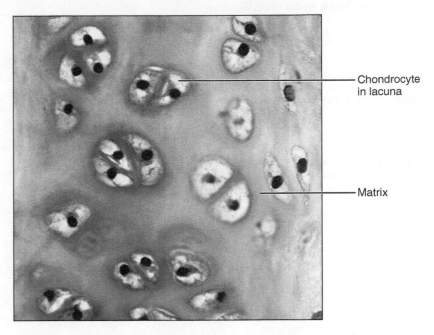

Chondrocyte in lacuna

Matrix

Photomicrograph: Hyaline cartilage from a costal cartilage of a rib (470×).

(h) Cartilage: elastic

Description: Similar to hyaline cartilage, but more elastic fibers in matrix.

Function: Maintains the shape of a structure while allowing great flexibility.

Location: Supports the external ear (pinna); epiglottis.

Chondrocyte in lacuna

Matrix

Photomicrograph: Elastic cartilage from the human ear pinna; forms the flexible skeleton of the ear (800×).

Figure 4.8 *(continued)* **(g)** and **(h)** Cartilage. (For related images, see *A Brief Atlas of the Human Body*, Plates 17 and 18.)

(i) Cartilage: fibrocartilage

Description: Matrix similar to but less firm than that in hyaline cartilage; thick collagen fibers predominate.

Function: Tensile strength allows it to absorb compressive shock.

Location: Intervertebral discs; pubic symphysis; discs of knee joint.

Intervertebral discs

Chondrocytes in lacunae

Collagen fiber

Photomicrograph: Fibrocartilage of an intervertebral disc (125×). Special staining produced the blue color seen.

Figure 4.8 *(continued)* **Connective tissues. (i)** Cartilage. (For a related image, see *A Brief Atlas of the Human Body*, Plate 19.)

Bone (Osseous Tissue)

Because of its rocklike hardness, **bone**, or **osseous tissue** (os'e-us), has an exceptional ability to support and protect body structures. Bones of the skeleton also provide cavities for storing fat and synthesizing blood cells. Bone matrix is similar to that of cartilage but is harder and more rigid because, in addition to its more abundant collagen fibers, bone has an added matrix element—inorganic calcium salts (bone salts).

Osteoblasts produce the organic portion of the matrix, and then bone salts are deposited on and between the fibers. Mature bone cells, or **osteocytes**, reside in the lacunae within the matrix they have made (Figure 4.8j). A cross section of bone tissue reveals closely packed structural units called *osteons* formed of concentric rings of bony matrix (lamellae) surrounding central canals containing the blood vessels and nerves serving the bone. Unlike cartilage, the next firmest connective tissue, bone is well supplied by invading blood vessels.

Blood

Blood, the fluid within blood vessels, is the most atypical connective tissue. It does *not* connect things or give mechanical support. It is classified as a connective tissue because it develops from mesenchyme and consists of *blood cells*, surrounded by a nonliving fluid matrix called *blood plasma* (Figure 4.8k).

The vast majority of blood cells are red blood cells, or erythrocytes, but scattered white blood cells and platelets (needed for blood clotting) are also seen. The "fibers" of blood are soluble protein molecules that precipitate, forming visible fiberlike structures during blood clotting. Blood functions as the transport vehicle for the cardiovascular system, carrying nutrients, wastes, respiratory gases, and many other substances throughout the body.

☑ **Check Your Understanding**

13. Which connective tissue has a soft weblike matrix capable of serving as a fluid reservoir?
14. What type of connective tissue is damaged when you cut your index finger tendon?
15. John wants to become a professional basketball player. Unfortunately he is short for his age and his epiphyseal plates have already fused. What type of connective tissue forms the epiphyseal plates?

For answers, see Appendix H.

Muscle Tissue

✓ Compare and contrast the structures and body locations of the three types of muscle tissue.

Muscle tissues are highly cellular, well-vascularized tissues that are responsible for most types of body movement. Muscle cells possess **myofilaments**, elaborate versions of the *actin* and *myosin* filaments that bring about movement or contraction in all

(j) Others: bone (osseous tissue)

Description: Hard, calcified matrix containing many collagen fibers; osteocytes lie in lacunae. Very well vascularized.

Function: Supports and protects (by enclosing); provides levers for the muscles to act on; stores calcium and other minerals and fat; marrow inside bones is the site for blood cell formation (hematopoiesis).

Location: Bones

Central canal

Lacunae

Lamella

Photomicrograph: Cross-sectional view of bone (125×).

(k) Connective tissue: blood

Description: Red and white blood cells in a fluid matrix (plasma).

Function: Transport respiratory gases, nutrients, wastes, and other substances.

Location: Contained within blood vessels.

Red blood cells (erythrocytes)

White blood cells:
• Lymphocyte
• Neutrophil

Plasma

Photomicrograph: Smear of human blood (1670×); shows two white blood cells surrounded by red blood cells.

Figure 4.8 *(continued)* **(j)** Bone. (For a related image, see *A Brief Atlas of the Human Body*, Plate 20.) **(k)** Blood. (For related images, see *A Brief Atlas of the Human Body*, Plates 22–27.)

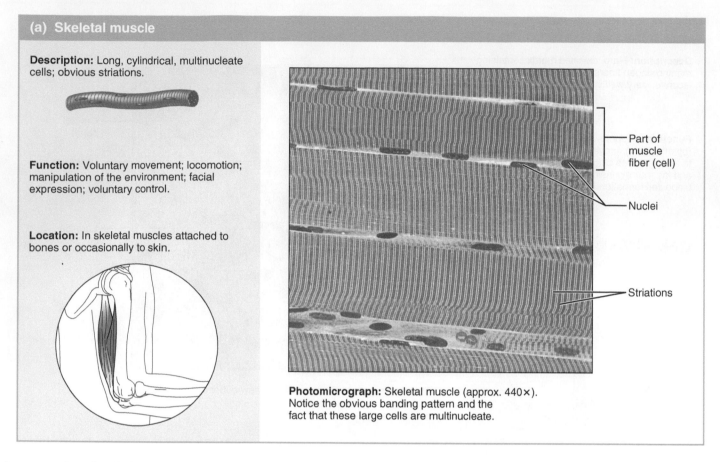

(a) Skeletal muscle

Description: Long, cylindrical, multinucleate cells; obvious striations.

Function: Voluntary movement; locomotion; manipulation of the environment; facial expression; voluntary control.

Location: In skeletal muscles attached to bones or occasionally to skin.

Part of muscle fiber (cell)

Nuclei

Striations

Photomicrograph: Skeletal muscle (approx. 440×). Notice the obvious banding pattern and the fact that these large cells are multinucleate.

Figure 4.9 Muscle tissues. (a) Skeletal muscle tissue. (For a related image, see *A Brief Atlas of the Human Body*, Plate 28.)

cell types. There are three kinds of muscle tissue: skeletal, cardiac, and smooth.

Skeletal Muscle

Skeletal muscle tissue is packaged by connective tissue sheets into organs called *skeletal muscles* that are attached to the bones of the skeleton. These muscles form the flesh of the body, and as they contract they pull on bones or skin, causing body movements.

Skeletal muscle cells, also called **muscle fibers**, are long, cylindrical cells that contain many peripherally located nuclei. Their obvious banded, or striated, appearance reflects the precise alignment of their myofilaments **(Figure 4.9a)**.

Cardiac Muscle

Cardiac muscle is found only in the walls of the heart. Its contractions help propel blood through the blood vessels to all parts of the body. Like skeletal muscle cells, cardiac muscle cells are striated. However, cardiac cells differ structurally in that they are

- Generally uninucleate (one nucleus) with the nucleus situated centrally

- Branching cells that fit together tightly at unique junctions called **intercalated discs** (in-ter'kah-la"ted) (Figure 4.9b)

Smooth Muscle

Smooth muscle is so named because its cells have no visible striations. Individual smooth muscle cells are spindle shaped and contain one centrally located nucleus (Figure 4.9c). Smooth muscle is found mainly in the walls of hollow organs other than the heart (digestive and urinary tract organs, uterus, and blood vessels). It squeezes substances through these organs by alternately contracting and relaxing.

Because skeletal muscle contraction is under our conscious control, skeletal muscle is often referred to as **voluntary muscle**, and the other two types are called **involuntary muscle** because we do not consciously control them. We describe skeletal muscle and smooth muscle in detail in Chapter 9, and cardiac muscle in Chapter 18.

☑ Check Your Understanding

16. You are looking at muscle tissue through the microscope and you see striped branching cells that connect with one another. What type of muscle are you viewing?

17. Which muscle type(s) is voluntary? Which is injured when you pull a muscle while exercising?

For answers, see Appendix H.

(b) Cardiac muscle

Description: Branching, striated, generally uninucleate cells that interdigitate at specialized junctions (intercalated discs).

Function: As it contracts, it propels blood into the circulation; involuntary control.

Location: The walls of the heart.

Intercalated discs

Striations

Nucleus

Photomicrograph: Cardiac muscle (900×); notice the striations, branching of cells, and the intercalated discs.

(c) Smooth muscle

Description: Spindle-shaped cells with central nuclei; no striations; cells arranged closely to form sheets.

Function: Propels substances or objects (foodstuffs, urine, a baby) along internal passageways; involuntary control.

Location: Mostly in the walls of hollow organs.

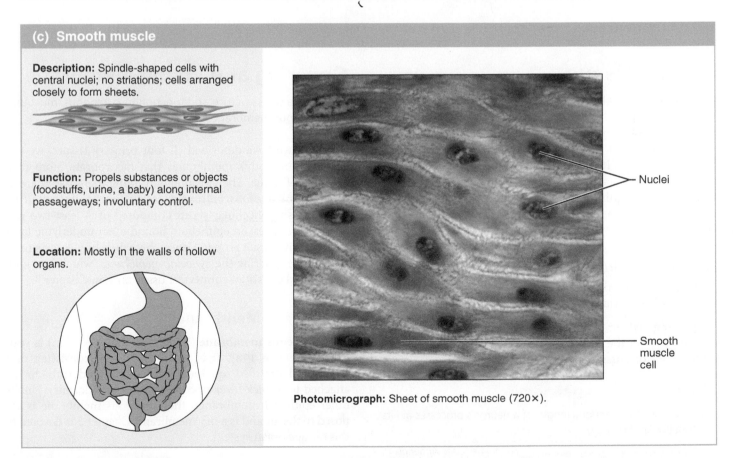

Nuclei

Smooth muscle cell

Photomicrograph: Sheet of smooth muscle (720×).

Figure 4.9 *(continued)* **(b)** Cardiac muscle tissue. (For a related image, see *A Brief Atlas of the Human Body*, Plate 31.) **(c)** Smooth muscle tissue. (For a related image, see *A Brief Atlas of the Human Body*, Plate 32.

Nervous tissue

Description: Neurons are branching cells; cell processes that may be quite long extend from the nucleus-containing cell body; also contributing to nervous tissue are nonexcitable supporting cells.

Neuron processes — Axon Dendrites — Cell body

Function: Neurons transmit electrical signals from sensory receptors and to effectors (muscles and glands) which control their activity; supporting cells support and protect neurons.

Location: Brain, spinal cord, and nerves.

Nuclei of supporting cells

Cell body of a neuron

Neuron processes

Photomicrograph: Neurons (350×)

Figure 4.10 **Nervous tissue.** (For a related image, see *A Brief Atlas of the Human Body*, Plate 33.)

Nervous Tissue

✓ Indicate the general characteristics of nervous tissue.

Nervous tissue is the main component of the nervous system—the brain, spinal cord, and nerves—which regulates and controls body functions. It contains two major cell types: neurons and supporting cells.

Neurons are highly specialized nerve cells that generate and conduct nerve impulses **(Figure 4.10)**. Typically, they are branching cells with cytoplasmic extensions or processes that enable them to

- Respond to stimuli (via processes called *dendrites*)
- Transmit electrical impulses over substantial distances within the body (via processes called *axons*)

Supporting cells are nonconducting cells that support, insulate, and protect the delicate neurons. Chapter 11 presents a more complete discussion of nervous tissue.

☑ **Check Your Understanding**

18. How does the extended length of a neuron's processes aid its function in the body?

For answers, see Appendix H.

Covering and Lining Membranes

✓ Describe the structure and function of cutaneous, mucous, and serous membranes.

Now that we have described all four primary tissues, we can consider the body's membranes that incorporate more than one type of tissue. The covering and lining membranes are of three types: *cutaneous*, *mucous*, or *serous*. Essentially they all are continuous multicellular sheets composed of at least two primary tissue types: an epithelium bound to an underlying layer of connective tissue proper. Hence, these membranes are simple organs. We describe the *synovial membranes*, which line joint cavities and consist of connective tissue only, in Chapter 8.

Cutaneous Membrane

The **cutaneous membrane** (ku-ta′ne-us; *cutis* = skin) is your skin **(Figure 4.11a)**. It is an organ system consisting of a keratinized stratified squamous epithelium (epidermis) firmly attached to a thick layer of connective tissue (dermis). Unlike other epithelial membranes, the cutaneous membrane is exposed to the air and is a dry membrane. Chapter 5 is devoted to this unique organ system.

(a) Cutaneous membrane

The cutaneous membrane (the skin) covers the body surface.

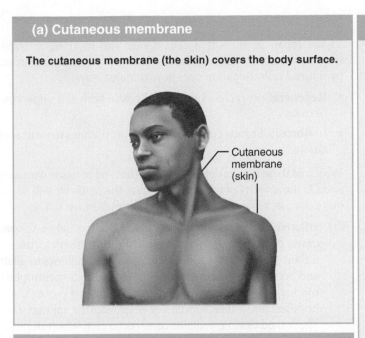

Cutaneous membrane (skin)

(b) Mucous membranes

Mucous membranes line body cavities that are open to the exterior.

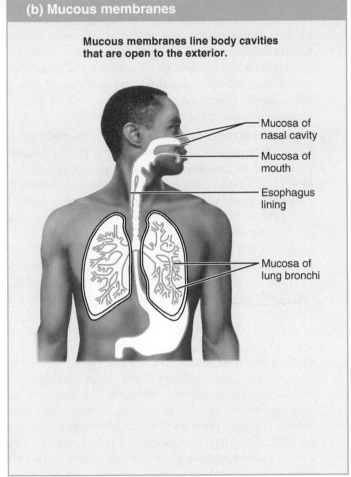

Mucosa of nasal cavity

Mucosa of mouth

Esophagus lining

Mucosa of lung bronchi

(c) Serous membranes

Serous membranes line body cavities that are closed to the exterior.

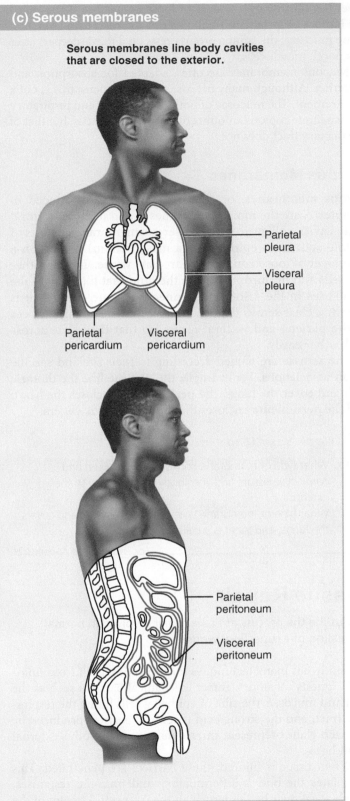

Parietal pleura

Visceral pleura

Parietal pericardium

Visceral pericardium

Parietal peritoneum

Visceral peritoneum

Figure 4.11 Classes of membranes.

Mucous Membranes

Mucous membranes, or **mucosae** (mu-ko′se), line all body cavities that open to the outside of the body, such as the hollow organs of the digestive, respiratory, and urogenital tracts (Figure 4.11b).

In all cases, they are "wet," or moist, membranes bathed by secretions or, in the case of the urinary mucosa, urine. Notice that the term *mucosa* refers to the location of the membrane, *not* its cell composition, which varies. However, most mucosae contain either stratified squamous or simple columnar epithelia. The epithelial

4

sheet lies directly over a layer of loose connective tissue called the **lamina propria** (lam′ĭ-nah pro′pre-ah; "one's own layer"). In some mucosae, the lamina propria rests on a third (deeper) layer of smooth muscle cells.

Mucous membranes are often adapted for absorption and secretion. Although many mucosae secrete mucus, this is not a requirement. The mucosae of both the digestive and respiratory tracts secrete copious amounts of lubricating mucus, but that of the urinary tract does not.

Serous Membranes

Serous membranes, or **serosae** (se-ro′se), introduced in Chapter 1, are the moist membranes found in closed ventral body cavities (Figure 4.11c). A serous membrane consists of simple squamous epithelium (a mesothelium) resting on a thin layer of loose connective (areolar) tissue. The mesothelial cells add hyaluronic acid to the fluid that filters from the capillaries in the associated connective tissue. The result is the thin, clear *serous fluid* that lubricates the facing surfaces of the parietal and visceral layers, so that they slide across each other easily.

The serosae are named according to their site and specific organ associations. For example, the **pleurae** line the thoracic wall and cover the lungs; the **pericardium** encloses the heart; and the **peritoneum** encloses the abdominopelvic viscera.

☑ Check Your Understanding

19. What type of membrane consists of epithelium and connective tissue, and lines body cavities open to the exterior?
20. What type of membrane lines the thoracic walls and covers the lungs, and what is it called?

_____ *For answers, see Appendix H.*

Tissue Repair

✓ Outline the process of tissue repair involved in normal healing of a superficial wound.

The body has many techniques for protecting itself from uninvited "guests" or injury. Intact mechanical barriers such as the skin and mucosae, the cilia of epithelial cells lining the respiratory tract, and the strong acid (chemical barrier) produced by stomach glands represent three defenses at the body's external boundaries.

When tissue is injured, these barriers are penetrated. This stimulates the body's inflammatory and immune responses, which wage their battles largely in the connective tissues of the body. The *inflammatory response* is a relatively nonspecific reaction that develops quickly wherever tissues are injured, while the *immune response* is extremely specific, but takes longer to swing into action. We consider the inflammatory and immune responses in detail in Chapter 21.

Steps of Tissue Repair

Tissue repair requires that cells divide and migrate, activities that are initiated by growth factors (wound hormones) released by injured cells. Repair occurs in two major ways:

- **Regeneration** replaces destroyed tissue with the same kind of tissue.

- In **fibrosis**, fibrous connective tissue proliferates to form **scar tissue**.

Which of these occurs depends on (1) the type of tissue damaged and (2) the severity of the injury. In skin, the tissue we will use as our example, repair involves both activities **(Figure 4.12)**.

① **Inflammation sets the stage.** Tissue trauma causes injured tissue cells, macrophages, mast cells, and others to release inflammatory chemicals, which cause the capillaries to dilate and become very permeable. White blood cells (neutrophils, monocytes) and plasma fluid rich in clotting proteins, antibodies, and other substances seep into the injured area. The leaked clotting proteins construct a clot, which stops the loss of blood, holds the edges of the wound together, and effectively walls in, or isolates, the injured area, preventing bacteria, toxins, or other harmful substances from spreading to surrounding tissues. The part of the clot exposed to air quickly dries and hardens, forming a *scab*. The inflammatory events leave behind excess fluid, bits of destroyed cells, and other debris, which are eventually removed via lymphatic vessels or phagocytized by macrophages.

② **Organization restores the blood supply.** Even while the inflammatory process is going on, the first phase of tissue repair, called **organization**, begins. During organization the blood clot is replaced by **granulation tissue**, a delicate pink tissue composed of several elements. It contains capillaries that grow in from nearby areas and lay down a new capillary bed. Granulation tissue is actually named for these capillaries, which protrude nublike from its surface, giving it a granular appearance. These capillaries are fragile and bleed freely, as we see when someone picks at a scab. Proliferating fibroblasts in granulation tissue produce growth factors as well as new collagen fibers to bridge the gap. Some of these fibroblasts have contractile properties that allow them to pull the margins of the wound together or to pull existing blood vessels into the healing wound. As organization proceeds, macrophages digest the original blood clot and collagen fiber deposit continues. The granulation tissue, destined to become scar tissue (a permanent fibrous patch), is highly resistant to infection because it produces bacteria-inhibiting substances. As a rule, wound healing is a self-limited response. Once enough matrix has accumulated in the injured area, the fibroblasts either revert to the resting stage or undergo apoptosis.

③ **Regeneration and fibrosis effect permanent repair.** During organization, the surface epithelium begins to *regenerate*, growing under the scab, which soon detaches. As the fibrous tissue beneath matures and contracts, the regenerating

Scab

Blood clot in incised wound

Epidermis

Vein

Regenerating epithelium

Inflammatory chemicals

Migrating white blood cell

Artery

Area of granulation tissue ingrowth

Fibroblast

Macrophage

Budding capillary

Regenerated epithelium

Fibrosed area

① **Inflammation sets the stage:**
- Severed blood vessels bleed.
- Inflammatory chemicals are released.
- Local blood vessels become more permeable, allowing white blood cells, fluid, clotting proteins, and other plasma proteins to seep into the injured area.
- Clotting occurs; surface dries and forms a scab.

② **Organization restores the blood supply:**
- The clot is replaced by granulation tissue, which restores the vascular supply.
- Fibroblasts produce collagen fibers that bridge the gap.
- Macrophages phagocytize dead and dying cells and other debris.
- Surface epithelial cells multiply and migrate over the granulation tissue.

③ **Regeneration and fibrosis effect permanent repair:**
- The fibrosed area matures and contracts; the epithelium thickens.
- A fully regenerated epithelium with an underlying area of scar tissue results.

Figure 4.12 Tissue repair of a nonextensive skin wound: regeneration and fibrosis.

epithelium thickens until it finally resembles the adjacent skin. The end result is a fully regenerated epithelium, and an underlying area of scar tissue. The scar may be invisible, or visible as a thin white line, depending on the severity of the wound.

The repair process that we have just described follows healing of a wound (cut, scrape, puncture) that breaches an epithelial barrier. In simple *infections* (a pimple or sore throat), healing is solely by regeneration. Only severe (destructive) infections lead to clot formation or scarring.

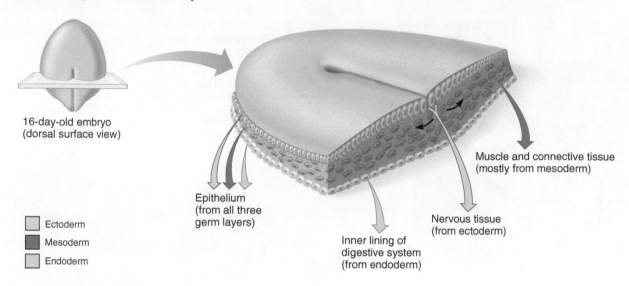

16-day-old embryo
(dorsal surface view)

Ectoderm
Mesoderm
Endoderm

Epithelium
(from all three
germ layers)

Muscle and connective tissue
(mostly from mesoderm)

Nervous tissue
(from ectoderm)

Inner lining of
digestive system
(from endoderm)

Figure 4.13 Embryonic germ layers and the primary tissue types they produce. The three embryonic layers collectively form the very early embryonic body.

Regenerative Capacity of Different Tissues

Tissues vary widely in their capacity for regeneration. Epithelial tissues, bone, areolar connective tissue, dense irregular connective tissue, and blood-forming tissue regenerate extremely well. Smooth muscle and dense regular connective tissue have a moderate capacity for regeneration, but skeletal muscle and cartilage have a weak regenerative capacity. Cardiac muscle and the nervous tissue in the brain and spinal cord have virtually no *functional* regenerative capacity, and they are routinely replaced by scar tissue. However, recent studies show that some unexpected (and highly selective) cellular division occurs in both these tissues after damage, and efforts are under way to coax them to regenerate better.

In nonregenerating tissues and in exceptionally severe wounds, fibrosis totally replaces the lost tissue. Over a period of months, the fibrous mass shrinks and becomes more and more compact. The resulting scar appears as a pale, often shiny area composed mostly of collagen fibers. Scar tissue is strong, but it lacks the flexibility and elasticity of most normal tissues. Also, it cannot perform the normal functions of the tissue it has replaced.

Homeostatic Imbalance 4.3

Scar tissue that forms in the wall of the urinary bladder, heart, or other muscular organ may severely hamper the organ's function. The normal shrinking of the scar reduces the internal volume and may hinder or even block substances from moving through a hollow organ. Scar tissue hampers muscle's ability to contract and may interfere with its normal excitation by the nervous system. In the heart, these problems may lead to progressive heart failure. In irritated visceral organs, particularly following abdominal surgery, *adhesions* may form as the newly forming scar tissue connects adjacent organs together. Such adhesions can prevent the normal shifting about (churning) of loops of the intestine, dangerously obstructing the flow of foodstuffs. Adhesions can also restrict heart movements and immobilize joints. +

✓ Check Your Understanding

21. What are the three main steps of tissue repair?
22. Why does a deep injury to the skin result in abundant scar tissue?

For answers, see Appendix H.

Developmental Aspects of Tissues

✓ Indicate the embryonic origin of each tissue class.

✓ Briefly describe tissue changes that occur with age.

One of the first events of embryonic development is the formation of the three **primary germ layers**, which lie one atop the next like a three-layered cellular pancake. From superficial to deep, these layers are the **ectoderm**, **mesoderm** (mez'o-derm), and **endoderm** (Figure 4.13). These primary germ layers then specialize to form the four primary tissues—epithelium, nervous tissue, muscle, and connective tissues—that make up all body organs.

By the end of the second month of development, the primary tissues have appeared, and all major organs are in place. In general, tissue cells remain mitotic and produce the rapid growth that occurs before birth. The division of nerve cells, however, stops or nearly stops during the fetal period. After birth, the cells of most other tissues continue to divide until adult body size is achieved. Cellular division then slows greatly, although many tissues retain some ability to regenerate.

In adults, only epithelia and blood-forming tissues are highly mitotic. Some tissues that regenerate through life, such as the glandular cells of the liver, do so through division of their mature (specialized) cells. Others, like the epidermis of the skin and cells lining the intestine, have abundant *stem cells*, relatively undifferentiated cells that divide as necessary to produce new cells.

Cancer—The Intimate Enemy

The word cancer elicits dread in everyone. Why does cancer strike some and not others?

Although once perceived as disorganized cell growth, this disease is now known to be a logical, coordinated process in which a precise sequence of tiny alterations changes a normal cell into a killer.

When cells fail to follow normal controls of cell division and multiply excessively, an abnormal mass of proliferating cells called a **neoplasm** (ne'o-plazm, "new growth") results. Neoplasms are classified as **benign** ("kindly") or **malignant** ("bad"). A benign neoplasm is strictly a local affair. Its cells remain compacted, are often encapsulated, tend to grow slowly, and seldom kill their hosts if removed before they compress vital organs.

In contrast, cancers are malignant neoplasms, nonencapsulated masses that grow relentlessly. Their cells resemble immature cells, and they invade their surroundings rather than pushing them aside, as reflected in the name cancer, from the Latin word for "crab." Whereas normal cells become fatally "homesick" and die when they lose contact with the surrounding matrix, malignant cells tend to break away from the parent mass—the primary tumor—and travel via blood or lymph to other body organs, where they form secondary cancer masses.

This capability for traveling to other parts of the body, called **metastasis** (mĕ-tas'tah-sis), probably has a lot to do with signaling molecules and the cell-surface glycoproteins the cancer cells bear. Metastasis and invasiveness distinguish cancer cells from the cells of benign neoplasms. Cancer cells consume an exceptional amount of the body's nutrients, leading to weight loss and tissue wasting that contribute to death.

Carcinogenesis

Autopsies on individuals aged 50–70 who died of another cause have revealed that most of us have microscopic (but dormant) in situ (confined to origin site) neoplasms. So what changes a normal cell into a cancerous one? Some physical factors (radiation, mechanical trauma), certain viral infections, chronic inflammations, and many chemicals (tobacco tars, saccharine, some natural food chemicals).

All these factors cause *mutations*—changes in DNA that alter the expression of certain genes. However, not all carcinogens do damage because most are eliminated by peroxisomal or lysosomal enzymes or by the immune system. Furthermore, one mutation usually isn't enough. It takes several genetic changes to transform (convert) a normal cell into a cancerous cell.

The discovery of **oncogenes** (Greek *onco* = tumor), or cancer-causing genes, in rapidly spreading cancers provided a clue to the role of genes in cancer. **Proto-oncogenes**, benign forms of oncogenes in normal cells, were discovered later. Proto-oncogenes code for proteins that are essential for cell division, growth, and cellular adhesion, among other things. Many proto-oncogenes have fragile sites that break when exposed to carcinogens, converting them to oncogenes. Failure to code for certain proteins may lead to loss of an enzyme that controls an important metabolic process. Oncogenes may also "switch on" dormant genes that allow cells to become invasive and metastasize. Known oncogenes now number over 100.

Oncogenes have been detected in only 15–20% of human cancers, so investigators were not too surprised by the discovery of **tumor suppressor genes**, or **anti-oncogenes**, which suppress cancer by inactivating carcinogens, aiding DNA repair, or enhancing the immune system's counterattack. In fact, over half of all cancers involve malfunction or loss of just 2 of the 15 identified tumor suppressor genes—*p53* and *p16*. This is not surprising when you learn that *p53* prompts most cells to make proteins that stop cell division in stressed cells by promoting apoptosis or cell cycle arrest.

Furthermore, although each type of cancer is genetically distinct, human cancers appear to share a master set of genes—an activated group of 67 genes—and almost all cancer cells have gained or lost entire chromosomes. Whatever genetic factors are at work, the "seeds" of cancer appear to be in our own genes. Cancer is an intimate enemy indeed.

Let's look at the carcinogenesis of colorectal cancer, one of the best-understood human cancers. As with most cancers, a metastasis develops gradually. One of the first signs is a polyp (see photo on p. 146), a small benign growth consisting of apparently normal mucosa cells. As cell division continues, the polyp enlarges, becoming an adenoma (a term for any neoplasm of glandular epithelium). As various tumor suppressor genes are inactivated and the *K-ras* oncogene is mobilized, the mutations pile up and the adenoma becomes increasingly abnormal. The final consequence is colon carcinoma, a form of cancer that metastasizes quickly.

Cancer Prevalence

Almost half of all Americans develop cancer in their lifetime and a fifth of us will die of it. Cancer can arise from almost any cell type, but the most common cancers originate in the skin, lung, colon, breast, and prostate. Although stomach and colon cancer incidence is down, skin and lymphoid cancer rates are up.

Many cancers are preceded by observable lumps or other structural changes in tissue—for instance, *leukoplakia*, white patches in the mouth caused by the chronic irritation of ill-fitting dentures or heavy smoking. Although these lesions sometimes progress to cancer, in many cases they remain stable or even revert to normal if the environmental irritant is removed.

Diagnosis and Staging

Screening procedures are vital for early detection. Examples include *mammography* (X-ray examination of the breasts), examining breasts or testicles for lumps, examining the blood for cancer markers, and checking fecal samples for blood.

Unfortunately, most cancers are diagnosed only after symptoms have already appeared. In this case diagnosis is usually by **biopsy**: removing a tissue sample surgically and examining it microscopically for malignant cells. Increasingly, diagnosis includes chemical or genetic analysis of the sample—typing cancer cells by which genes are switched on or off, a technique described below.

Physical and histological examinations, lab tests, and imaging techniques (MRI, CT) can determine the extent of the disease (size of the neoplasm, degree of metastasis, etc.). Then, the cancer is assigned a **stage** from 1 to 4 according to the probability of cure. Stage 1 has the best probability of cure, stage 4 the worst.

Cancer Treatments

Most cancers are removed surgically if possible. To destroy metastasized cells, surgery is commonly followed by X irradiation and/or treatment with radioisotopes and chemotherapy (treatment with cytotoxic drugs). Recently, some oncologists have been using heat therapy (a slight upward temperature change) to make cancer cells more vulnerable to chemotherapy or radiation.

Chemotherapy is beset with the problem of resistance. Some cancer cells can eject the drugs in tiny bubbles or flattened vesicles dubbed exosomes, and these cells proliferate, forming new tumors that are resistant to chemotherapy. Furthermore, anticancer drugs have unpleasant side effects—nausea, vomiting, hair loss—because they kill *all* rapidly dividing cells, including normal tissue cells. The anticancer drugs also can damage the brain, producing a phenomenon called chemobrain—mental fuzziness and memory loss reported by many cancer patients. X rays also have side effects because, in passing through the body, they destroy healthy tissue as well as cancer cells.

Promising New Therapies

Traditional cancer treatments—"cut, burn, and poison"—are widely recognized as crude and painful. Promising new therapies focus on

- *Interrupting the signaling pathways that fuel cancer growth.* Imatinib (brand name Gleevec) incapacitates a mutated enzyme that triggers uncontrolled division of cells in two rare blood and digestive system cancers. Trastuzumab (Herceptin) is used to treat breast cancer. These

drugs can provide a few extra weeks of life, before their protective effects wear off and the disease progresses again.

- *Delivering treatments more precisely to the cancer while sparing normal tissue.* One approach is to inject the patient with tiny drug-coated metal beads; then a powerful magnet positioned over the cancer guides the beads to the tumor. Or, a patient might take light-sensitive drugs that are drawn naturally into rapidly dividing cancer cells. Then, exposure to certain frequencies of laser light sets off reactions that kill the malignant cells. Proton therapy delivers highly targeted killing doses of protons (radiation) with incredible precision and effectiveness. Unlike X rays, which pass through the cancer and onward through the patient's body, protons can be slowed down and even directed to stop in the neoplasm.

- *Using genetically modified immune cells to target cancer cells.* One promising technique harvests a patient's most aggressive cancer-killing immune cells (T lymphocytes), inserts modified genes into them that make them even more efficient, multiplies the cells in the lab, and infuses them back into the patient.

- *Testing genotypes.* A few major cancer centers are beginning to genotype (test for genetic markers) every patient's tumor. The hope is to match personalized markers with drugs tailored to go after the tumor's genetic weak spot. For example, taxol, quite successful in treating breast and ovarian cancer, works only against tumors with a specific genetic makeup.

A polyp in the colon

Other experimental treatments seek to starve cancer cells by cutting off their blood supply, fix defective tumor suppressor genes and oncogenes, destroy cancer cells with viruses, or signal cancer cells to commit suicide by apoptosis. A cancer vaccine (TRICOM) contains genetically engineered viruses carrying genes for a cancer protein called carcinoembryonic antigen (CEA). When CEA proteins are delivered into the patient's body, they stimulate an immune response that orchestrates an attack on all CEA-bearing cancer cells.

At present, about half of all cancer cases are cured. Although average survival rates have not increased, cancer patients' quality of life has improved in the last decade. We can offer better treatments for cancer-associated pain, and antinausea drugs and other helpful medicines can soothe the side effects of chemotherapy.

Given good nutrition, good circulation, and relatively infrequent wounds and infections, our tissues normally function efficiently through youth and middle age. But with increasing age, epithelia thin and are more easily breached. Tissue repair is less efficient, and bone, muscle, and nervous tissues begin to atrophy, particularly when a person is not physically active. These events are due partly to decreased circulatory efficiency, which reduces delivery of nutrients to the tissues, but in some cases, diet is a contributing factor. As income declines or as chewing becomes more difficult, older people tend to eat soft foods, which may be low in protein and vitamins. As a result, tissue health suffers.

Another problem of aging tissues is the likelihood of DNA mutations in the most actively mitotic cells, which increases the risk of cancer (see *A Closer Look* on p. 145).

☑ Check Your Understanding

23. What are the names of the three embryonic germ layers?
24. Which germ layer gives rise to the nervous system?
25. Which two tissue types remain highly mitotic throughout life?

For answers, see Appendix H.

As we have seen, body cells combine to form four discrete tissue types: epithelial, connective, nervous, and muscle tissues. The cells making up each of these tissues share certain features but are by no means identical. They "belong" together because they have basic functional similarities. The important concept to carry away with you is that tissues, despite their unique abilities, cooperate to keep the body safe, healthy, and whole.

Chapter Summary

 For more chapter study tools, go to the Study Area of MasteringA&P at **www.masteringaandp.com**.
There you will find:

- Interactive Physiology **iP**
- A&PFlix **A&PFlix**
- Practice Anatomy Lab **PAL**
- PhysioEx **PEx**
- Videos, Practice Quizzes and Tests, MP3 Tutor Sessions, Case Studies, and much more!

Tissues are collections of structurally similar cells with related functions. The four primary tissues are epithelial, connective, nervous, and muscle tissues.

Preparing Human Tissue for Microscopy (pp. 117–118)

1. Preparation of tissues for microscopic examination involves cutting thin sections of the tissue and using dyes to stain the tissue. Minor distortions called artifacts can be introduced by the tissue preparation process.

Epithelial Tissue (pp. 118–126)

1. Epithelial tissue is the covering, lining, and glandular tissue of the body. Its functions include protection, absorption, excretion, filtration, secretion, and sensory reception.

Special Characteristics of Epithelium (pp. 118–119)

2. Epithelial tissues exhibit specialized contacts, polarity, avascularity, support from connective tissue, and high regenerative capacity.

Classification of Epithelia (pp. 119–124)

3. Epithelium is classified by arrangement as simple (one layer) or stratified (more than one layer) and by cell shape as squamous, cuboidal, or columnar. The terms denoting cell shape and arrangement are combined to describe the epithelium fully.

4. Simple squamous epithelium is a single layer of squamous cells. Highly adapted for filtration and exchange of substances, it forms walls of air sacs of the lungs and lines blood vessels. It contributes to serosae as mesothelium and lines all hollow circulatory system organs as endothelium.

5. Simple cuboidal epithelium, commonly active in secretion and absorption, is found in glands and in kidney tubules.

6. Simple columnar epithelium, specialized for secretion and absorption, consists of a single layer of tall columnar cells that exhibit microvilli and often mucus-producing cells. It lines most of the digestive tract.

7. Pseudostratified columnar epithelium is a simple columnar epithelium that appears stratified. Its ciliated variety, rich in mucus-secreting cells, lines most of the upper respiratory passages.

8. Stratified squamous epithelium is multilayered; cells at the free surface are squamous. It is adapted to resist abrasion. It lines the esophagus and vagina; its keratinized variety forms the skin epidermis.

9. Stratified cuboidal epithelia are rare in the body, and are found chiefly in ducts of large glands. Stratified columnar epithelium has a very limited distribution, found mainly in the male urethra and at transition areas between other epithelia types.

10. Transitional epithelium is a modified stratified squamous epithelium, adapted for responding to stretch. It lines hollow urinary system organs.

Glandular Epithelia (pp. 124–126)

11. A gland is one or more cells specialized to secrete a product.

12. On the basis of site of product release, glands are classified as exocrine or endocrine. Glands are classified structurally as multicellular or unicellular.

13. Unicellular glands, typified by goblet cells and mucous cells, are mucus-secreting single-celled glands.

14. Multicellular exocrine glands are classified according to duct structure as simple or compound, and according to the structure of their secretory parts as tubular, alveolar, or tubuloalveolar.

15. Multicellular exocrine glands of humans are classified functionally as merocrine or holocrine.

Connective Tissue (pp. 127–136)

1. Connective tissue is the most abundant and widely distributed tissue of the body. Its functions include binding and support, protection, insulation, fat storage, and transportation (blood).

Common Characteristics of Connective Tissue (p. 127)

2. Connective tissues originate from embryonic mesenchyme and have a matrix. Depending on type, a connective tissue may be well vascularized (most), poorly vascularized (dense connective tissue), or avascular (cartilage).

Structural Elements of Connective Tissue (pp. 127–129)

3. The structural elements of all connective tissues are extracellular matrix and cells.

4. The extracellular matrix consists of ground substance and fibers (collagen, elastic, and reticular). It may be fluid, gel-like, or firm.

5. Each connective tissue type has a primary cell type that can exist as a mitotic, matrix-secreting cell (blast) or as a mature cell (cyte) responsible for maintaining the matrix. The undifferentiated cell type of connective tissue proper is the fibroblast; that of cartilage is the chondroblast; that of bone is the osteoblast; and that of blood-forming tissue is the hematopoietic stem cell (see Chapter 17).

Types of Connective Tissue (pp. 129–136)

6. Embryonic connective tissue is called mesenchyme.

7. Connective tissue proper consists of loose and dense varieties. The loose connective tissues are
   - Areolar: gel-like ground substance; all three fiber types loosely interwoven; a variety of cells; forms the lamina propria and soft packing around body organs; the prototype.
   - Adipose: consists largely of adipocytes; scant matrix; insulates and protects body organs; provides reserve energy fuel. Brown fat is more important for generating body heat.
   - Reticular: finely woven reticular fibers in soft ground substance; the stroma of lymphoid organs and bone marrow.

8. Dense connective tissue proper includes
   - Dense regular: dense parallel bundles of collagen fibers; few cells, little ground substance; high tensile strength; forms tendons, ligaments, aponeuroses; in cases where this tissue also contains numerous elastic fibers it is called elastic connective tissue.
   - Dense irregular: like regular variety, but fibers are arranged in different planes; resists tension exerted from many

different directions; forms the dermis of the skin and organ capsules.

9. Cartilage exists as
   - Hyaline: firm ground substance containing collagen fibers; resists compression well; found in fetal skeleton, at articulating surfaces of bones, and trachea; most abundant type.
   - Elastic cartilage: elastic fibers predominate; provides flexible support of the external ear and epiglottis.
   - Fibrocartilage: parallel collagen fibers; provides support with compressibility; forms intervertebral discs and knee cartilages.
10. Bone (osseous tissue) consists of a hard, collagen-containing matrix embedded with calcium salts; forms the bony skeleton.
11. Blood consists of blood cells in a fluid matrix (plasma).

Muscle Tissue (pp. 136–139)

1. Muscle tissue consists of elongated cells specialized to contract and cause movement.
2. Based on structure and function, the muscle tissues are
   - Skeletal muscle: attached to and moves the bony skeleton; cells are cylindrical and striated.
   - Cardiac muscle: forms the walls of the heart; pumps blood; cells are branched and striated.
   - Smooth muscle: in the walls of hollow organs; propels substances through the organs; cells are spindle shaped and lack striations.

Nervous Tissue (p. 140)

1. Nervous tissue forms organs of the nervous system. It is composed of neurons and supporting cells.

2. Neurons are branching cells that receive and transmit electrical impulses. They are involved in body regulation. Supporting cells support and protect neurons.

iP Nervous System I; Topic: Anatomy Review, pp. 1, 3.

Covering and Lining Membranes (pp. 140–142)

1. Membranes are simple organs, consisting of an epithelium bound to an underlying connective tissue layer. They include mucosae, serosae, and the cutaneous membrane.

Tissue Repair (pp. 142–144)

1. Inflammation is the body's response to injury. Tissue repair begins during the inflammatory process. It may lead to regeneration, fibrosis, or both.
2. Tissue repair begins with organization, during which the blood clot is replaced by granulation tissue. If the wound is small and the damaged tissue is actively mitotic, the tissue will regenerate and cover the fibrous tissue. When a wound is extensive or the damaged tissue amitotic, it is repaired only by fibrous connective (scar) tissue.

Developmental Aspects of Tissues (pp. 144–146)

1. Epithelium arises from all three primary germ layers (ectoderm, mesoderm, endoderm); muscle and connective tissue from mesoderm; and nervous tissue from ectoderm.
2. The decrease in mass and viability seen in most tissues during old age often reflects circulatory deficits or poor nutrition.

Review Questions

Multiple Choice/Matching

(Some questions have more than one correct answer. Select the best answer or answers from the choices given.)

1. Use the key to classify each of the following described tissue types into one of the four major tissue categories.

   Key: **(a)** connective tissue   **(c)** muscle
         (b) epithelium   **(d)** nervous tissue

   _____ **(1)** Tissue type composed largely of nonliving extracellular matrix; important in protection and support

   _____ **(2)** The tissue immediately responsible for body movement

   _____ **(3)** The tissue that enables us to be aware of the external environment and to react to it

   _____ **(4)** The tissue that lines body cavities and covers surfaces

2. An epithelium that has several layers, with an apical layer of flattened cells, is called (choose all that apply): **(a)** ciliated, **(b)** columnar, **(c)** stratified, **(d)** simple, **(e)** squamous.

3. Match the epithelial types named in column B with the appropriate description(s) in column A.

Column A	Column B
_____ **(1)** Lines most of the digestive tract	**(a)** pseudostratified ciliated columnar
_____ **(2)** Lines the esophagus	**(b)** simple columnar
_____ **(3)** Lines much of the respiratory tract	**(c)** simple cuboidal
_____ **(4)** Forms the walls of the air sacs of the lungs	**(d)** simple squamous
	(e) stratified columnar
_____ **(5)** Found in urinary tract organs	**(f)** stratified squamous
_____ **(6)** Endothelium and mesothelium	**(g)** transitional

4. The gland type that secretes products such as milk, saliva, bile, or sweat through a duct is **(a)** an endocrine gland, **(b)** an exocrine gland.

5. The membrane which lines body cavities that open to the exterior is a(n) **(a)** endothelium, **(b)** cutaneous membrane, **(c)** mucous membrane, **(d)** serous membrane.

6. Scar tissue is a variety of **(a)** epithelium, **(b)** connective tissue, **(c)** muscle tissue, **(d)** nervous tissue, **(e)** all of these.

Short Answer Essay Questions

7. Define tissue.
8. Name four important functions of epithelial tissue and provide at least one example of a tissue that exemplifies each function.
9. Describe the criteria used to classify covering and lining epithelia.
10. Explain the functional classification of multicellular exocrine glands and supply an example for each class.
11. Provide examples from the body that illustrate four of the major functions of connective tissue.
12. Name the primary cell type in connective tissue proper; in cartilage; in bone.
13. Name the two major components of matrix and, if applicable, subclasses of each component.
14. Matrix is extracellular. How does the matrix get to its characteristic position?

15. Name the specific connective tissue type found in the following body locations: (a) forming the soft packing around organs, (b) supporting the ear pinna, (c) forming "stretchy" ligaments, (d) first connective tissue in the embryo, (e) forming the intervertebral discs, (f) covering the ends of bones at joint surfaces, (g) main component of subcutaneous tissue.

16. What is the function of macrophages?

17. Differentiate between the roles of neurons and the supporting cells of nervous tissue.

18. Compare and contrast skeletal, cardiac, and smooth muscle tissue relative to structure, body location, and specific function.

19. Describe the process of tissue repair, making sure you indicate factors that influence this process.

20. Indicate which primary tissue classes derive from each embryonic germ layer.

21. In what ways are adipose tissue and bone similar? How are they different?

Critical Thinking and Clinical Application Questions

1. John sustained a severe injury during football practice and is told that he has a torn knee cartilage. Can he expect a quick, uneventful recovery? Explain your response.

2. The epidermis (epithelium of the cutaneous membrane or skin) is a keratinized stratified squamous epithelium. Explain why that epithelium is much better suited for protecting the body's external surface than a mucosa consisting of a simple columnar epithelium would be.

3. Your friend is trying to convince you that if the ligaments binding the bones together at your freely movable joints (such as your knee, shoulder, and hip joints) contained more elastic fibers, you would be much more flexible. Although there is some truth to this statement, such a condition would present serious problems. Why?

4. In adults, over 90% of all cancers are either adenomas (adenocarcinomas) or carcinomas. (See Related Clinical Terms for this chapter.) In fact, cancers of the skin, lung, colon, breast, and prostate are all in these categories. Which one of the four basic tissue types gives rise to most cancers? Why do you think this is so?

5. Cindy, an overweight high school student, is overheard telling her friend that she's going to research how she can transform some of her white fat to brown fat. What is her rationale here (assuming it is possible)?

6. Mrs. Delancy went to the local meat market and bought a beef tenderloin (cut from the loin, the region along the steer's vertebral column) and some tripe (cow's stomach). What type of muscle was she preparing to eat in each case?

AT THE CLINIC

Related Clinical Terms

Adenoma (ad″ĕ-no′mah; *aden* = gland, *oma* = tumor) Any neoplasm of glandular epithelium, benign or malignant. The malignant type is more specifically called adenocarcinoma.

Autopsy (aw′top-se) Examination of the body, its organs, and its tissues after death to determine the actual cause of death; also called postmortem examination and necropsy.

Carcinoma (kar″sĭ-no′mah; *karkinos* = crab, cancer) Cancer arising in an epithelium; accounts for 90% of human cancers.

Healing by first intention The simplest type of healing; occurs when the edges of the wound are brought together by sutures, staples, or other means used to close surgical incisions. Only small amounts of granulation tissue need be formed.

Healing by second intention The wound edges remain separated, and relatively large amounts of granulation tissue bridge the gap; the manner in which unattended wounds heal. Healing is slower than in wounds in which the edges are brought together, and larger scars result.

Keloid (ke′loid) Abnormal proliferation of connective tissue during healing of skin wounds; results in large, unsightly mass of scar tissue at the skin surface.

Lesion (le′zhun; "wound") Any injury, wound, or infection that affects tissue over an area of a definite size (as opposed to being widely spread throughout the body).

Marfan's syndrome Genetic disease resulting in abnormalities of connective tissues due to a defect in fibrillin, a protein that is associated with elastin in elastic fibers. Clinical signs include loose-jointedness, long limbs and spiderlike fingers and toes,

visual problems, and weakened blood vessels (especially the aorta) due to poor connective tissue reinforcement.

Osteogenesis imperfecta (brittle bone disease) An inherited condition that causes defective collagen production. Because collagen reinforces many body structures including bones, the result is weak bones that break easily. It is not unusual for its victims to have 30 or more fractures during their lifetime. Occurs in 1 out of 20,000 births. Misdiagnosis results in many infants coming to the ER with multiple fractures being treated as battered babies.

Pathology (pah-thol′o-je) Scientific study of changes in organs and tissues produced by disease.

Pus A collection of tissue fluid, bacteria, dead and dying tissue cells, white blood cells, and macrophages in an inflamed area.

Sarcoma (sar-ko′mah; *sarkos* = flesh; *oma* = tumor) Cancer arising in the mesenchyme-derived tissues, that is, in connective tissues and muscle.

Scurvy A nutritional deficiency caused by lack of adequate vitamin C needed to synthesize collagen; signs and symptoms include blood vessel disruption, delay in wound healing, weakness of scar tissue, and loosening of teeth.

VAC (vacuum-assisted closure) Innovative healing process for open-skin wounds and skin ulcers. Often induces healing when all other methods fail. Involves covering the wound with a special sponge, and then applying suction through the sponge. In response to the subsequent skin stretching, fibroblasts in the wound form more collagen tissue and new blood vessels proliferate, bringing more blood into the injured area, which also promotes healing.

The Integumentary System

Would you be enticed by an ad for a coat that is waterproof, stretchable, washable, and permanent-press, that automatically repairs small cuts, rips, and burns? How about one that's guaranteed to last a lifetime? Sounds too good to be true, but you already have such a coat—your skin.

The skin and its derivatives (sweat and oil glands, hairs, and nails) make up a complex set of organs that serves several functions, mostly protective. Together, these organs form the **integumentary system** (in-teg″u-men′tar-e).

The Skin

✓ Name the tissue types composing the epidermis and dermis. List the major layers of each and describe the functions of each layer.

✓ Describe the factors that normally contribute to skin color. Briefly describe how changes in skin color may be used as clinical signs of certain disease states.

Figure 5.1 Skin structure. Three-dimensional view of the skin and underlying subcutaneous tissue. The epidermal and dermal layers have been pulled apart at the right corner to reveal the dermal papillae.

The skin receives little respect from its inhabitants, but architecturally it is a marvel. It covers the entire body, has a surface area of 1.2 to 2.2 square meters, weighs 4 to 5 kilograms (4–5 kg = 9–11 lb), and accounts for about 7% of total body weight in the average adult. Also called the integument ("covering"), the skin multitasks. Its functions go well beyond serving as a bag for body contents. Pliable yet tough, it takes constant punishment from external agents. Without our skin, we would quickly fall prey to bacteria and perish from water and heat loss.

Varying in thickness from 1.5 to 4.0 millimeters (mm) or more in different parts of the body, the skin is composed of two distinct regions **(Figure 5.1)**:

- The *epidermis* (ep″ĭ-der′mis), composed of epithelial cells, is the outermost protective shield of the body (*epi* = upon).

- The underlying *dermis,* making up the bulk of the skin, is a tough, leathery layer composed mostly of fibrous connective tissue.

Only the dermis is vascularized. Nutrients reach the epidermis by diffusing through the tissue fluid from blood vessels in the dermis.

The subcutaneous tissue just deep to the skin is known as the **hypodermis** (Figure 5.1). Strictly speaking, the hypodermis is not part of the skin, but it shares some of the skin's protective functions. The hypodermis, also called **superficial fascia** because it is superficial to the tough connective tissue wrapping (fascia) of the skeletal muscles, consists mostly of adipose tissue.

Besides storing fat, the hypodermis anchors the skin to the underlying structures (mostly to muscles), but loosely enough that the skin can slide relatively freely over those structures. Sliding skin protects us by ensuring that many blows just glance off our bodies. Because of its fatty composition, the hypodermis also acts as a shock absorber and an insulator that reduces heat loss. The hypodermis thickens markedly when a person gains weight. In females, this "extra" subcutaneous fat accumulates first in the thighs and breasts, but in males it first collects in the anterior abdomen (as a "beer belly").

Epidermis

Structurally, the **epidermis** is a keratinized stratified squamous epithelium consisting of four distinct cell types and four or five distinct layers.

Cells of the Epidermis

The cells populating the epidermis include *keratinocytes*, *melanocytes*, *dendritic cells*, and *tactile cells*.

Keratinocytes The chief role of **keratinocytes** (kĕ-rat′ĭ-no-sītz″; "keratin cells") is to produce **keratin**, the fibrous protein that helps give the epidermis its protective properties (Greek *kera* = horn) (**Figure 5.2b**, orange cells). Most epidermal cells are keratinocytes.

Tightly connected to one another by desmosomes, the keratinocytes arise in the deepest part of the epidermis from a cell layer called the stratum basale. These cells undergo almost continuous mitosis in response to prompting by epidermal growth factor, a peptide produced by various cells throughout the body. As these cells are pushed upward by the production of new cells beneath them, they make the keratin that eventually dominates their cell contents. By the time the keratinocytes reach the skin surface, they are dead, scalelike structures that are little more than keratin-filled plasma membranes.

Millions of dead keratinocytes rub off every day, giving us a totally new epidermis every 25 to 45 days, but cell production and keratin formation is accelerated in body areas regularly subjected to friction, such as the hands and feet. Persistent friction (from a poorly fitting shoe, for example) causes a thickening of the epidermis called a *callus*.

Melanocytes **Melanocytes** (mel′ah-no-sītz), the spider-shaped epithelial cells that synthesize the pigment **melanin** (mel′ah-nin; *melan* = black), are found in the deepest layer of the epidermis (Figure 5.2b, gray cells). As melanin is made, it accumulates in membrane-bound granules called *melanosomes* that motor proteins move along actin filaments to the ends of the melanocyte's processes (the "spider arms"). From there they are transferred to a number of nearby keratinocytes (4 to 10 depending on body area). The melanin granules accumulate on the superficial, or "sunny," side of the keratinocyte nucleus, forming a pigment shield that protects the nucleus from the damaging effects of ultraviolet (UV) radiation in sunlight.

Dendritic Cells The star-shaped **dendritic cells** arise from bone marrow and migrate to the epidermis. Also called **Langerhans cells** (lahng′er-hanz) after a German anatomist, they ingest foreign substances and are key activators of our immune system, as described later in this chapter. Their slender processes extend among the surrounding keratinocytes, forming a more or less continuous network (Figure 5.2b, purple cell).

Tactile Cells Occasional **tactile (Merkel) cells** are present at the epidermal-dermal junction. Shaped like a spiky hemisphere (Figure 5.2b, blue cell), each tactile cell is intimately associated with a disclike sensory nerve ending. The combination, called a *tactile* or *Merkel disc*, functions as a sensory receptor for touch.

Layers of the Epidermis

Variation in epidermal thickness determines if skin is *thick* or *thin*. In **thick skin**, which covers areas subject to abrasion—the palms, fingertips, and soles of the feet—the epidermis consists of five layers, or strata (stra′tah; "bed sheets"). From deep to superficial,

these layers are stratum basale, stratum spinosum, stratum granulosum, stratum lucidum, and stratum corneum. In thin skin, which covers the rest of the body, the stratum lucidum appears to be absent and the other strata are thinner (Figure 5.2a, b).

Note that the terms "thick skin" and "thin skin" are really misnomers because they refer to the epidermis only. Indeed, the thickest skin in the body is on the upper back.

Stratum Basale (Basal Layer) The **stratum basale** (stra′tum bah-sa′le), the deepest epidermal layer, is attached to the underlying dermis along a wavy borderline that reminds one of corrugated cardboard. For the most part, it consists of a single row of stem cells—a continually renewing cell population—representing the youngest keratinocytes. The many mitotic nuclei seen in this layer reflect the rapid division of these cells and account for its alternate name, **stratum germinativum** (jer′mĭ-nă″tiv-um; "germinating layer"). Each time one of these basal cells divides, one daughter cell is pushed into the cell layer just above to begin its specialization into a mature keratinocyte. The other daughter cell remains in the basal layer to continue the process of producing new keratinocytes.

Some 10–25% of the cells in the stratum basale are melanocytes, and their branching processes extend among the surrounding cells, reaching well into the more superficial stratum spinosum layer. Occasional tactile cells also occur in this stratum.

Stratum Spinosum (Prickly Layer) The **stratum spinosum** (spi′no-sum; "prickly") is several cell layers thick. These cells contain a weblike system of intermediate filaments, mainly tension-resisting bundles of pre-keratin filaments, which span their cytosol to attach to desmosomes. Looking like tiny versions of the spiked iron balls used in medieval warfare, the keratinocytes in this layer appear to have spines, causing them to be called *prickle cells*. The spines do not exist in the living cells; they are artifacts that arise during tissue preparation when these cells shrink but their numerous desmosomes hold tight. Scattered among the keratinocytes are melanin granules and dendritic cells, which are most abundant in this epidermal layer.

Stratum Granulosum (Granular Layer) The thin **stratum granulosum** (gran″u-lo′sum) consists of four to six cell layers in which keratinocyte appearance changes drastically, and the process of **keratinization** (in which the cells fill with the protein keratin) begins. These cells flatten, their nuclei and organelles begin to disintegrate, and they accumulate two types of granules. The *keratohyaline granules* (ker″ah-to-hi′ah-lin) help to form keratin in the upper layers, as we will see.

The *lamellar granules* (lam′el-ar; "a small plate") contain a water-resistant glycolipid that is spewed into the extracellular space and is a major factor in slowing water loss across the epidermis. The plasma membranes of these cells thicken as cytosol proteins bind to the inner membrane face and lipids released by the lamellar granules coat their external surfaces. These events produce an epidermal water barrier and make the cells more resistant to destruction. So, you might say that keratinocytes "toughen up" to make the outer strata the strongest skin region.

Like all epithelia, the epidermis relies on capillaries in the underlying connective tissue (the dermis in this case) for its nutrients. Above the stratum granulosum, the epidermal cells are

Figure 5.2 The main structural features of the skin epidermis.

(a) Photomicrograph of the four major epidermal layers (200×). (b) Diagram showing these four layers and the distribution of different cell types. The four cell types are keratinocytes (orange), melanocytes (gray), dendritic cells (purple), and tactile cells (blue). A sensory nerve ending (yellow), extending from the dermis (pink), is shown associated with the tactile cell forming a tactile disc (touch receptor). Notice that numerous desmosomes join the keratinocytes together. The stratum lucidum, found only in thick skin, is not illustrated here.

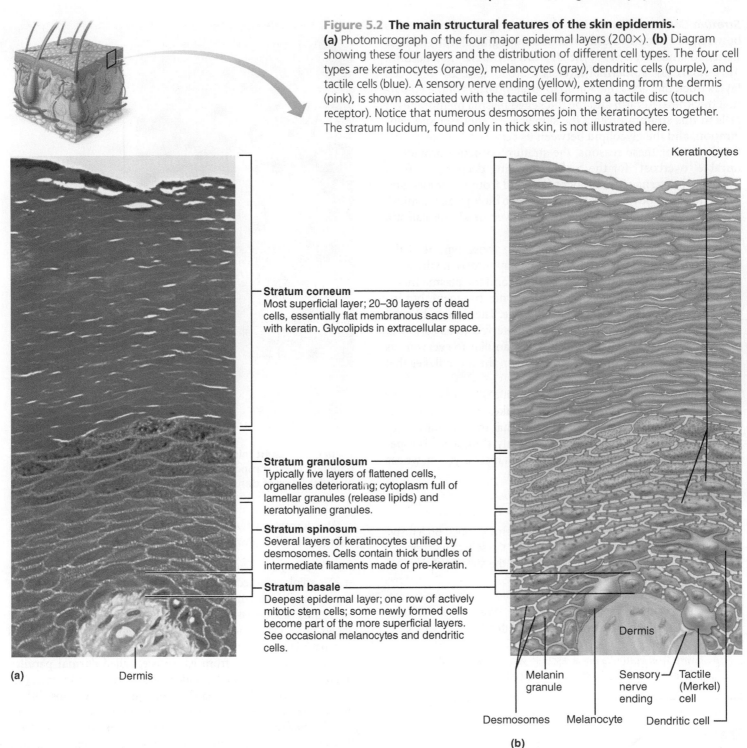

Keratinocytes

Stratum corneum
Most superficial layer; 20–30 layers of dead cells, essentially flat membranous sacs filled with keratin. Glycolipids in extracellular space.

Stratum granulosum
Typically five layers of flattened cells, organelles deteriorating; cytoplasm full of lamellar granules (release lipids) and keratohyaline granules.

Stratum spinosum
Several layers of keratinocytes unified by desmosomes. Cells contain thick bundles of intermediate filaments made of pre-keratin.

Stratum basale
Deepest epidermal layer; one row of actively mitotic stem cells; some newly formed cells become part of the more superficial layers. See occasional melanocytes and dendritic cells.

(a) Dermis

Melanin granule   Dermis   Sensory nerve ending   Tactile (Merkel) cell

Desmosomes   Melanocyte   Dendritic cell

(b)

too far from the dermal capillaries and the glycolipids coating their external surfaces cut them off from nutrients, so they die. This is a normal sequence of events.

Stratum Lucidum (Clear Layer) Through the light microscope, the **stratum lucidum** (loo′sid-um; "light"), visible only in thick skin, is a thin translucent band just above the stratum granulosum. Considered by some to be a subdivision of the superficial stratum corneum, it consists of two or three rows of clear, flat, dead keratinocytes with indistinct boundaries. Here, or in the stratum corneum above, the gummy substance of the keratohyaline granules clings to the keratin filaments in the cells, causing them to aggregate in large, cable-like, parallel arrays of intermediate filaments called *tonofilaments*.

Stratum Corneum (Horny Layer)   An abrupt transition occurs between the nucleated cells of the stratum granulosum and the flattened anucleate cells of the **stratum corneum** (kor′ne-um). This outermost epidermal layer is a broad zone 20 to 30 cell layers thick that accounts for up to three-quarters of the epidermal thickness. Keratin and the thickened plasma membranes of cells in this stratum protect the skin against abrasion and penetration, and the glycolipid between its cells nearly waterproofs this layer. For these reasons, the stratum corneum provides a durable "overcoat" for the body, protecting deeper cells from the hostile external environment (air) and from water loss, and rendering the body relatively insensitive to biological, chemical, and physical assaults. It is amazing that even dead cells can still play so many roles.

The differentiation from basal cells to those typical of the stratum corneum is a specialized form of apoptosis in which the nucleus and other organelles break down and the plasma membrane thickens. So, the terminal cells do not fragment, but instead eventually slough off the skin surface. The shingle-like cell remnants of the stratum corneum are referred to as *cornified,* or *horny, cells* (*cornu* = horn). They are familiar to everyone as dandruff, shed from the scalp, and dander, the loose flakes that slough off dry skin.

The average person's skin sheds some 50,000 dead cells every minute and 18 kg (40 lb) of these skin flakes in a lifetime, providing a lot of fodder for the dust mites that inhabit our homes and bed linens. The saying "Beauty is only skin deep" is especially interesting in light of the fact that nearly everything we see when we look at someone is dead!

☑ Check Your Understanding

1. While walking barefoot in a barn, Jeremy stepped on a rusty nail that penetrated the epidermis on the sole of his foot. Name the layers the nail pierced from the superficial skin surface to the junction with the dermis.
2. The stratum basale is also called the stratum germinativum, a name that refers to its major function. What is that function?
3. Why are the desmosomes connecting the keratinocytes so important?
4. Given that epithelia are avascular, which layer would you expect to have the best-nourished cells?

For answers, see Appendix H.

Dermis

The **dermis** (*derm* = skin), the second major skin region, is strong, flexible connective tissue. Its cells are typical of those found in any connective tissue proper: fibroblasts, macrophages, and occasional mast cells and white blood cells. Its semifluid matrix, embedded with fibers, binds the entire body together like a body stocking. It is your "hide" and corresponds exactly to animal hides used to make leather.

The dermis has a rich supply of nerve fibers, blood vessels, and lymphatic vessels. The major portions of hair follicles, as well as oil and sweat glands, derive from epidermal tissue but reside in the dermis.

Figure 5.3   Light micrograph of the dermis identifying the papillary layer composed of areolar connective tissue and the reticular layer of dense irregular connective tissue (110×).

The dermis has two layers, the papillary and reticular, which abut one another along an indistinct boundary **(Figure 5.3)**.

Papillary Layer   The thin superficial **papillary layer** (pap′il-er-e) is areolar connective tissue in which fine interlacing collagen and elastic fibers form a loosely woven mat that is heavily invested with small blood vessels. The looseness of this connective tissue allows phagocytes and other defensive cells to wander freely as they patrol the area for bacteria that have breached the skin.

Peglike projections from its surface, called **dermal papillae** (pah-pil′e; *papill* = nipple), indent the overlying epidermis (see Figure 5.1). Many dermal papillae contain capillary loops. Others house free nerve endings (pain receptors) and touch receptors called *tactile* or *Meissner's corpuscles* (mīs′nerz kor′pus-lz). Note that tactile cells and tactile corpuscles are different structures. (We consider them in more detail in Chapter 13.) In thick skin, such as the palms of the hands and soles of the feet, these papillae lie atop larger mounds called *dermal ridges*, which in turn cause the overlying epidermis to form *epidermal ridges* **(Figure 5.4a)**. Collectively, these skin ridges, referred to as **friction ridges**, are assumed to enhance the gripping ability of the fingers and feet like tire treads help grip the road. Recent studies indicate that they also contribute to our sense of touch by amplifying vibrations detected by the large lamellar corpuscles (receptors) in the dermis.

Openings of
sweat gland ducts   Friction ridges

(a) Friction ridges of fingertip (SEM 12×)

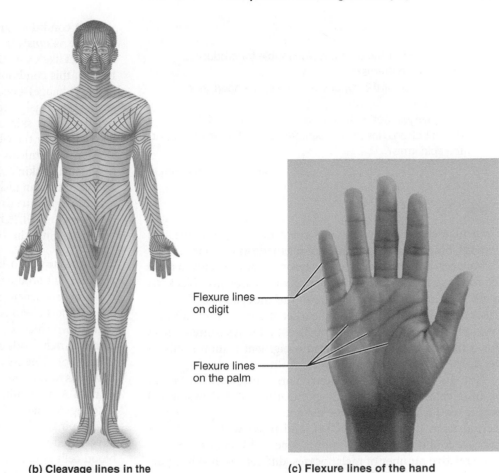

(b) Cleavage lines in the reticular dermis

Flexure lines on digit

Flexure lines on the palm

(c) Flexure lines of the hand

Figure 5.4 Dermal modifications result in characteristic skin markings.
(a) Scanning electron micrograph of friction ridges (epidermal ridges topping the deeper dermal papillary ridges). Notice the sweat duct openings along the crests of the ridges, which are responsible for fingerprints.
(b) Cleavage (tension) lines represent separations between underlying collagen fiber bundles in the reticular region of the dermis. They tend to run circularly around the trunk and longitudinally in the limbs.
(c) Flexure lines form where the dermis is closely attached to the underlying fascia.

Friction ridge patterns are genetically determined and unique to each of us. Because sweat pores open along their crests, our fingertips leave identifying films of sweat called *fingerprints* on almost anything we touch.

Reticular Layer The deeper **reticular layer**, accounting for about 80% of the thickness of the dermis, is coarse, irregularly arranged, dense fibrous connective tissue (Figure 5.3). The network of blood vessels that nourishes this layer, the *cutaneous plexus*, lies between this layer and the hypodermis. Its extracellular matrix contains pockets of adipose cells and thick bundles of interlacing collagen fibers. The collagen fibers run in various planes, but most run parallel to the skin surface. Separations, or less dense regions, between these bundles form **cleavage (tension) lines** in the skin. These externally invisible lines tend to run longitudinally in the skin of the head and limbs and in circular patterns around the neck and trunk (Figure 5.4b).

Cleavage lines are important to surgeons because when an incision is made *parallel* to these lines, the skin gapes less and heals more readily. The collagen fibers of the dermis give skin strength and resiliency that prevent most jabs and scrapes from penetrating the dermis. In addition, collagen binds water, helping to keep skin hydrated. Elastic fibers provide the stretch-recoil properties of skin.

Flexure lines, a third type of skin marking, are dermal folds that occur at or near joints, where the dermis is tightly secured to deeper structures. (Notice the deep creases on your palms.) Since the skin cannot slide easily to accommodate joint movement in such regions, the dermis folds and deep skin creases form (Figure 5.4c). Flexure lines are also visible on the wrists, fingers, soles, and toes.

Homeostatic Imbalance 5.1

Extreme stretching of the skin, such as during pregnancy, can tear the dermis, leaving silvery white scars called *striae* (stri′e; "streaks"), commonly called "stretch marks." Short-term but acute trauma (as from a burn or wielding a hoe) can cause a *blister*, a fluid-filled pocket that separates the epidermal and dermal layers. ✚

☑ Check Your Understanding

5. Which layer of the dermis is responsible for producing fingerprint patterns?

6. Which tissue of the hypodermis makes it a good shock absorber?

7. You have just gotten a paper cut. It is very painful, but it doesn't bleed. Has the cut penetrated into the dermis or just the epidermis?

For answers, see Appendix H.

Skin Color

Three pigments contribute to skin color: melanin, carotene, and hemoglobin. Of these, only melanin is made in the skin.

Melanin is a polymer made of tyrosine amino acids. Its two forms range in color from reddish yellow to brownish black. Its synthesis depends on an enzyme in melanocytes called tyrosinase (ti-ro′sĭ-nās) and, as noted earlier, it passes from melanocytes to the basal keratinocytes. Eventually, lysosomes break down the melanosomes, so melanin pigment is found only in the deeper layers of the epidermis.

Human skin comes in different colors. However, distribution of those colors is not random—populations of darker-skinned people tend to be found nearer the equator (where greater protection from the sun is needed), and those with the lightest skin are found closer to the poles. Since all humans have the same relative number of melanocytes, differences in skin coloring reflect the kind and amount of melanin made and retained. Melanocytes of black- and brown-skinned people produce many more and darker melanosomes than those of fair-skinned individuals, and their keratinocytes retain it longer. *Freckles* and *pigmented nevi* (moles) are local accumulations of melanin.

When we expose our skin to sunlight, keratinocytes secrete chemicals that stimulate melanocytes. Prolonged sun exposure causes a substantial melanin buildup, which helps protect the DNA of viable skin cells from UV radiation by absorbing the rays and dissipating the energy as heat. Indeed, the initial signal for speeding up melanin synthesis seems to be a faster repair rate of DNA that has suffered photodamage (*photo* = light). In all but the darkest people, this defensive response causes skin to darken visibly (tanning occurs).

⚖ Homeostatic Imbalance 5.2

Despite melanin's protective effects, excessive sun exposure eventually damages the skin. It causes elastic fibers to clump, which results in leathery skin; temporarily depresses the immune system; and can alter the DNA of skin cells leading to skin cancer. The fact that dark-skinned people get skin cancer less often than fair-skinned people and get it in areas with less pigment—the soles of the feet and nail beds—attests to melanin's effectiveness as a natural sunscreen.

Ultraviolet radiation has other consequences as well, such as destroying the body's folic acid stores necessary for DNA synthesis. This can have serious consequences, particularly in pregnant women because the deficit may impair the development of the embryo's nervous system.

One condition sun exposure does not cause, regardless of its name, is *sunspots*, small circular white spots on the skin that stand out like a sore thumb in tanned skin. Actually a fungus infection, this condition—more accurately called *tinea versicolor* (*vers* = change)—occurs mainly on the arms, legs, upper chest, and back. Largely a cosmetic problem, its growth is encouraged by oily, sweaty skin. Antifungal medication works, but it takes a long time for the white patches to become pigmented again.

Many chemicals induce photosensitivity; that is, they heighten the skin's sensitivity to UV radiation and can cause an unsightly skin rash. Such substances include some antibiotic and antihistamine drugs, and many chemicals in perfumes and detergents. Small, itchy blisters erupt all over the body. Then the peeling begins—in sheets! ✚

Carotene (kar′o-tēn) is a yellow to orange pigment found in certain plant products such as carrots. It tends to accumulate in the stratum corneum and in fatty tissue of the hypodermis. Its color is most obvious in the palms and soles, where the stratum corneum is thickest, and most intense when large amounts of carotene-rich foods are eaten. However, the yellowish tinge of the skin of some Asian peoples is due to variations in melanin, as well as to carotene. In the body, carotene can be converted to vitamin A, a vitamin that is essential for normal vision, as well as for epidermal health.

The pinkish hue of fair skin reflects the crimson color of the oxygenated pigment **hemoglobin** (he′mo-glo″bin) in the red blood cells circulating through the dermal capillaries. Because Caucasian skin contains only small amounts of melanin, the epidermis is nearly transparent and allows hemoglobin's color to show through.

⚖ Homeostatic Imbalance 5.3

When hemoglobin is poorly oxygenated, both the blood and the skin of Caucasians appear blue, a condition called *cyanosis* (si″ah-no′sis; *cyan* = dark blue). Skin often becomes cyanotic during heart failure and severe respiratory disorders. In dark-skinned individuals, the skin does not appear cyanotic because of the masking effects of melanin, but cyanosis is apparent in their mucous membranes and nail beds (the same sites where the red cast of oxygenated blood is normally visible).

Many alterations in skin color signal certain disease states or even emotional states:

- *Redness*, or *erythema* (er″ĭ-the′mah): Reddened skin may indicate embarrassment (blushing), fever, hypertension, inflammation, or allergy.

- *Pallor*, or *blanching*: During fear, anger, and certain other types of emotional stress, some people become pale. Pale skin may also signify anemia or low blood pressure.

- *Jaundice* (jawn′dis), or *yellow cast*: An abnormal yellow skin tone usually signifies a liver disorder, in which yellow bile pigments accumulate in the blood and are deposited in body tissues. [Normally, the liver cells secrete the bile pigments (bilirubin) as a component of bile.]

- *Bronzing*: A bronze, almost metallic appearance of the skin is a sign of Addison's disease, in which the adrenal cortex produces inadequate amounts of its steroid hormones; or a sign of pituitary gland tumors that inappropriately secrete melanocyte-stimulating hormone (MSH).

- *Black-and-blue marks*, or *bruises*: Black-and-blue marks reveal where blood escaped from the circulation and clotted beneath the skin. Such clotted blood masses are called hematomas (he″mah-to′mah; "blood swelling"). ✚

☑ **Check Your Understanding**

8. Melanin and carotene are two pigments that contribute to skin color. What is the third and where is it found?

9. What is cyanosis and what does it indicate?

10. Which alteration in skin color may indicate a liver disorder?

For answers, see Appendix H.

Appendages of the Skin

✓ List the parts of a hair follicle and explain the function of each part. Also describe the functional relationship of arrector pili muscles to the hair follicles.

✓ Name the regions of a hair and explain the basis of hair color. Describe the distribution, growth, replacement, and changing nature of hair during the life span.

✓ Describe the structure of nails.

✓ Compare the structure and locations of sweat and oil glands. Also compare the composition and functions of their secretions.

✓ Compare and contrast eccrine and apocrine glands.

Along with the skin itself, the integumentary system includes several derivatives of the epidermis. These **skin appendages** include hair and hair follicles, nails, sweat glands, and sebaceous (oil) glands. Each plays a unique role in maintaining body homeostasis.

A key step in beginning to form any of the skin's appendages is formation of an epithelial bud. This process is stimulated by a reduced production of cell adhesion factor (cadherin). Once the cell-to-cell attractions are broken, the cells can move about and rearrange themselves, allowing an epithelial bud to form.

Hairs and Hair Follicles

Hair is an important part of our body image—consider, for example, the spiky hair style of punk rockers and the flowing, glossy manes of some high-fashion models. Millions of hairs are distributed over our entire skin surface except our palms, soles, lips, nipples, and parts of the external genitalia (the head of the penis, for instance). Although hair helps to keep other mammals warm, our sparse body hair is far less luxuriant and useful. Its main function in humans is to sense insects on the skin before they bite or sting us. Hair on the scalp guards the head against physical trauma, heat loss, and sunlight. (Pity the bald man.) Eyelashes shield the eyes, and nose hairs filter large particles like lint and insects from the air we inhale.

Structure of a Hair

Hairs, or **pili** (pi′li), are flexible strands produced by hair follicles and consist largely of dead, keratinized cells. The *hard keratin* that dominates hairs and nails has two advantages over the *soft keratin* found in typical epidermal cells: (1) It is tougher and more durable, and (2) its individual cells do not flake off.

The chief regions of a hair are the *shaft*, the portion in which keratinization is complete, and the *root*, where keratinization is still ongoing. The shaft, which projects from the skin, extends about halfway down the portion of the hair embedded in the skin **(Figure 5.5)**. The root is the remainder of the hair deep within the follicle. If the shaft is flat and ribbonlike in cross section, the hair is kinky; if it is oval, the hair is silky and wavy; if it is perfectly round, the hair is straight and tends to be coarse.

A hair has three concentric layers of keratinized cells: the medulla, cortex, and cuticle (Figure 5.5a, b).

- The *medulla* (mĕ-dul′ah; "middle"), its central core, consists of large cells and air spaces. The medulla, which is the only part of the hair that contains soft keratin, is absent in fine hairs.

- The *cortex*, a bulky layer surrounding the medulla, consists of several layers of flattened cells.

- The outermost **cuticle** is formed from a single layer of cells overlapping one another like shingles on a roof. This arrangement helps separate neighboring hairs so the hair does not mat. (Hair conditioners smooth out the rough surface of the cuticle and make our hair look shiny.) The most heavily keratinized part of the hair, the cuticle provides strength and helps keep the inner layers tightly compacted.

  Because it is subjected to the most abrasion, the cuticle tends to wear away at the tip of the hair shaft, allowing keratin fibrils in the cortex and medulla to frizz out, creating "split ends."

Hair pigment is made by melanocytes at the base of the hair follicle and transferred to the cortical cells. Various proportions of melanins of different colors (yellow, rust, brown, and black) combine to produce hair color from blond to pitch black. Additionally, red hair is colored by the iron-containing pigment *trichosiderin*. When melanin production decreases (mediated by delayed-action genes) and air bubbles replace melanin in the hair shaft, hair turns gray or white.

Structure of a Hair Follicle

Hair follicles (*folli* = bag) fold down from the epidermal surface into the dermis. In the scalp, they may even extend into the hypodermis. The deep end of the follicle, located about 4 mm (1/6 in.) below the skin surface, expands to form a **hair bulb** (Figure 5.5c, d). A knot of sensory nerve endings called a **hair follicle receptor**, or **root hair plexus**, wraps around each hair bulb (see Figure 5.1). Bending the hair stimulates these endings. Consequently, our hairs act as sensitive touch receptors.

- Feel the tickle as you run your hand over the hairs on your forearm.

5

Follicle wall
- Peripheral connective tissue (fibrous) sheath
- Glassy membrane
- Epithelial root sheath
  - External root sheath
  - Internal root sheath

Hair
- Cuticle
- Cortex
- Medulla

(a) Diagram of a cross section of a hair within its follicle

(b) Photomicrograph of a cross section of a hair and hair follicle (100×)

Hair shaft

Arrector pili

Sebaceous gland

Hair root

Hair bulb

Follicle wall
- Peripheral connective tissue (fibrous) sheath
- Glassy membrane
- Epithelial root sheath
  - External root sheath
  - Internal root sheath

Hair root
- Cuticle
- Cortex
- Medulla

Hair matrix

Hair papilla

Melanocyte

Subcutaneous adipose tissue

(c) Diagram of a longitudinal view of the expanded hair bulb of the follicle, which encloses the matrix

(d) Photomicrograph of longitudinal view of the hair bulb in the follicle (160×)

Figure 5.5 Skin appendages: Structure of a hair and hair follicle.

A *hair papilla*, a nipple-like bit of dermal tissue, protrudes into the hair bulb. This papilla contains a knot of capillaries that supplies nutrients to the growing hair and signals it to grow. Except for its location, this papilla is similar to the dermal papillae underlying other epidermal regions.

The wall of a hair follicle is composed of an outer **peripheral connective tissue sheath** (or *fibrous sheath*), derived from the dermis; a thickened basal lamina called the *glassy membrane*; and an inner **epithelial root sheath**, derived mainly from an invagination of the epidermis (Figure 5.5). The epithelial root sheath, which has external and internal parts, thins as it approaches the hair bulb, so that only a single layer of epithelial cells covers the papilla.

The cells that compose the **hair matrix**, or actively dividing area of the hair bulb that produces the hair, originate in a region called the *hair bulge* located a fraction of a millimeter above the hair bulb. When chemical signals diffusing from the hair papilla reach the hair bulge, some of its cells migrate toward the papilla, where they divide to produce the hair cells. As the matrix produces new hair cells, the older part of the hair is pushed upward, and its fused cells become increasingly keratinized and die.

Associated with each hair follicle is a bundle of smooth muscle cells called an **arrector pili** (ah-rek′tor pi′li; "raiser of hair") muscle. As you can see in Figure 5.1, most hair follicles approach the skin surface at a slight angle. The arrector pili muscle is attached in such a way that its contraction pulls the hair follicle upright and dimples the skin surface to produce goose bumps in response to cold temperatures or fear. This "hair-raising" response is not very useful to humans, with our short sparse hairs, but it is an important way for other animals to retain heat and protect themselves. Furry animals stay warmer by trapping a layer of insulating air in their fur; and a scared animal with its hair on end looks larger and more formidable to its enemy. The more important role of the arrector pili in humans is that its contractions force sebum out of hair follicles to the skin surface where it acts as a skin lubricant.

Types and Growth of Hair

Hairs come in various sizes and shapes, but as a rule they can be classified as vellus or terminal. The body hair of children and adult females is pale, fine **vellus hair** (vel′us; *vell* = wool, fleece). The coarser, longer hair of the eyebrows and scalp is **terminal hair**, which may also be darker.

At puberty, terminal hairs appear in the axillary and pubic regions of both sexes and on the face and chest (and typically the arms and legs) of males. These terminal hairs grow in response to the stimulating effects of androgens (of which *testosterone* is the most important), and when male hormones are present in large amounts, terminal hair growth is luxuriant.

Many factors influence hair growth and density, especially nutrition and hormones. Poor nutrition means poor hair growth, whereas conditions that increase local dermal blood flow (such as chronic physical irritation or inflammation) may enhance local hair growth. Many old-time bricklayers who carried their hod on one shoulder all the time developed one hairy shoulder. Undesirable hair growth (such as on a woman's upper lip) may be arrested by *electrolysis* or laser treatments, which use electricity or light energy, respectively, to destroy the hair roots.

Homeostatic Imbalance 5.4

In women, both the ovaries and the adrenal glands normally produce small amounts of androgens. Excessive hairiness, or **hirsutism** (her′soot-izm; *hirsut* = hairy), as well as other signs of masculinization, may result from an adrenal gland or ovarian tumor that secretes abnormally large amounts of androgens. Since few women want a beard or hairy chest, such tumors are surgically removed as soon as possible. ✚

The rate of hair growth varies from one body region to another and with sex and age, but it averages 2.5 mm per week. Each follicle goes through *growth cycles.* In each cycle, an active growth phase, ranging from weeks to years, is followed by a regressive phase. During the regressive phase, the hair matrix cells die and the follicle base and hair bulb shrivel somewhat, dragging the hair papilla upward to abut the region of the follicle that does not regress. The follicle then enters a resting phase for one to three months. After the resting phase, the cycling part of the follicle regenerates and activated bulge cells migrate toward the papilla. As a result, the matrix proliferates again and forms a new hair to replace the old one that has fallen out or will be pushed out by the new hair.

The life span of hairs varies and appears to be controlled by a slew of proteins. The follicles of the scalp remain active for six to ten years before becoming inactive for a few months. Because only a small percentage of the hair is shed at any one time, we lose an average of 90 scalp hairs daily. The follicles of the eyebrow hairs remain active for only three to four months, which explains why your eyebrows are never as long as the hairs on your head.

Hair Thinning and Baldness

A follicle has only a limited number of cycles in it. Given ideal conditions, hair grows fastest from the teen years to the 40s, and then its growth slows. The fact that hairs are shed faster than they are replaced leads to hair thinning and some degree of baldness, or **alopecia** (al″o-pe′she-ah), in both sexes. By age 35, noticeable hair loss occurs in 40% of men, and by age 60 that number jumps to 85%. Much less dramatic in women, the process usually begins at the anterior hairline and progresses posteriorly. Coarse terminal hairs are replaced by vellus hairs, and the hair becomes increasingly wispy.

True, or *frank, baldness* is a different story entirely. The most common type, **male pattern baldness**, is a genetically determined, sex-influenced condition. It is thought to be caused by a delayed-action gene that "switches on" in adulthood and changes the response of the hair follicles to DHT (dihydrotestosterone), a metabolite of testosterone. As a result, the follicular growth cycles become so short that many hairs never even emerge from their follicles before shedding, and those that do are fine vellus hairs that look like peach fuzz in the "bald" area.

Until recently, the only cure for male pattern baldness was drugs that inhibit testosterone production, but they also cause loss of sex drive—a trade-off few men would choose. Quite by accident, it was discovered that minoxidil (Rogaine), a drug used to reduce high blood pressure, has the interesting side effect in some bald men (and balding women) of stimulating hair regrowth. Although its results are variable, minoxidil is available over the counter in dropper bottles or spray form for application to the scalp. Finasteride (better known as Propecia), according to some the most promising cure for male pattern baldness, has had moderate success. Available only by prescription in once-a-day pill form, it must be taken for the rest of a person's life. Once the patient stops taking it, all of the new growth falls out.

Homeostatic Imbalance 5.5

Hair thinning can be induced by a number of factors that upset the normal balance between hair loss and replacement. Outstanding examples are acutely high fever, surgery, severe emotional trauma, and certain drugs (excessive vitamin A, some antidepressants and blood thinners, anabolic steroids, and most chemotherapy drugs). Protein-deficient diets and lactation lead to hair thinning because new hair growth stops when protein needed for keratin synthesis is not available or is being used for milk production. In all of these cases, hair regrows if the cause is removed or corrected.

In the rare condition *alopecia areata*, the immune system attacks the follicles and the hair falls out in patches. But again, the follicles survive. Hair loss due to severe burns, excessive radiation, or other factors that eliminate the follicles is permanent. ✚

☑ Check Your Understanding

11. What are the concentric regions of a hair shaft, from the outside in?
12. Why is having your hair cut painless?
13. What is the role of an arrector pili muscle?
14. What is the function of the hair papilla?

_____ *For answers, see Appendix H.*

Nails

A **nail** is a scalelike modification of the epidermis that forms a clear protective covering on the dorsal surface of the distal part of a finger or toe **(Figure 5.6)**. Nails, which correspond to the hooves or claws of other animals, are useful as "tools" to help pick up small objects or scratch an itch.

In contrast to *soft keratin* of the epidermis, nails (like hairs) contain *hard keratin*. Each nail has a *free edge*, a *nail plate* or *body* (visible attached portion), and a proximal *root* (embedded in the skin). The deeper layers of the epidermis extend beneath the nail as the *nail bed*, and the nail itself corresponds to the superficial keratinized layers. The thickened proximal portion of the nail bed, called the **nail matrix**, is responsible for nail growth. As the nail cells produced by the matrix become heavily keratinized, the nail body slides distally over the nail bed.

Nails normally appear pink because of the rich bed of capillaries in the underlying dermis. However, the region that lies over the thick nail matrix appears as a white crescent called the *lunule* (lu'nool; "little moon"). The proximal and lateral borders of the nail are overlapped by skin folds, called **nail folds**. The proximal nail fold projects onto the nail body as the **cuticle** or **eponychium** (ep″o-nik′e-um; "on the nail"). The thickened region beneath the free edge of the nail where dirt and debris tend to accumulate is the **hyponychium** ("below nail"), informally called the quick. It secures the free edge of the nail plate at the fingertip.

Changes in nail appearance can help diagnose certain conditions. For example, yellow-tinged nails may indicate a respiratory or thyroid gland disorder, while thickened yellow nails may signal a fungus infection. An outward concavity of the nail (spoon nail) may signal an iron deficiency, and horizontal lines (Beau's lines) across the nails may hint of malnutrition.

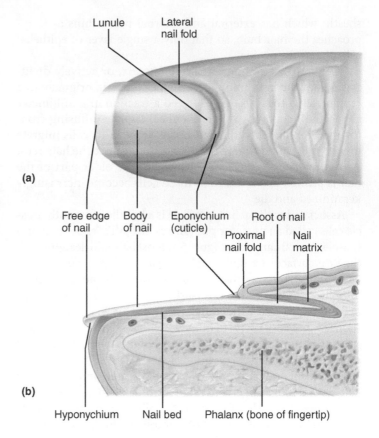

(a)

(b)

Lunule   Lateral nail fold

Free edge of nail   Body of nail   Eponychium (cuticle)   Root of nail

Proximal nail fold   Nail matrix

Hyponychium   Nail bed   Phalanx (bone of fingertip)

Figure 5.6 Skin appendages: Structure of a nail. (a) Surface view of the distal part of a finger. **(b)** Sagittal section of the fingertip. The nail matrix that forms the nail lies beneath the lunule.

☑ Check Your Understanding

15. Why is the lunule of a nail white instead of pink like the rest of the nail?
16. Why are nails so hard?

_____ *For answers, see Appendix H.*

Sweat (Sudoriferous) Glands

Sweat glands, also called **sudoriferous glands** (su″do-rif′er-us; *sudor* = sweat), are distributed over the entire skin surface except the nipples and parts of the external genitalia. Their number is staggering—up to 3 million per person.

We have two types of sweat glands: eccrine and apocrine. In both types, the secretory cells are associated with myoepithelial cells, specialized cells that contract when stimulated by the nervous system. Their contraction forces the sweat into and through the gland's duct system to the skin surface.

Eccrine (Merocrine) Sweat Glands

Eccrine sweat glands (ek′rin; "secreting"), also called **merocrine sweat glands**, are far more numerous and are particularly abundant on the palms, soles of the feet, and forehead. Each is a simple, coiled, tubular gland. The secretory part lies coiled in the dermis, and the duct extends to open in a funnel-shaped *pore* (*por* = channel) at the skin surface **(Figure 5.7b)**.

Sebaceous
gland

Sweat
pore

Dermal
connective
tissue

Sebaceous
gland duct

Hair in
hair follicle

Eccrine
gland

Duct

Dermal connective
tissue

Secretory cells

**(a) Photomicrograph of a sectioned
sebaceous gland (90×)**

**(b) Photomicrograph of a sectioned
eccrine gland (140×)**

Figure 5.7 Skin appendages: Cutaneous glands.

(These sweat pores are different from the so-called pores of a person's complexion, which are actually the external outlets of hair follicles.)

Eccrine gland secretion, commonly called sweat, is a hypotonic filtrate of the blood that passes through the secretory cells of the sweat glands and is released by exocytosis. It is 99% water, with some salts (mostly sodium chloride), vitamin C, antibodies, a microbe-killing peptide dubbed *dermcidin*, and traces of metabolic wastes (urea, uric acid, and ammonia). The exact composition depends on heredity and diet. Small amounts of ingested drugs may also be excreted by this route. Normally, sweat is acidic with a pH between 4 and 6.

The sympathetic division of the autonomic nervous system, over which we have little control, regulates sweating. Its major role is to prevent the body from overheating. Heat-induced sweating begins on the forehead and spreads inferiorly over the remainder of the body. Emotionally induced sweating—the so-called "cold sweat" brought on by fright or nervousness—begins on the palms, soles, and axillae (armpits) and then spreads to other body areas.

Apocrine Sweat Glands

Apocrine sweat glands (ap′o-krin), approximately 2000 of them, are largely confined to the axillary and anogenital areas. In spite of their name, they are merocrine glands, which release their product by exocytosis like the eccrine sweat glands. Larger than eccrine glands, they lie deeper in the dermis or even in the hypodermis, and their ducts empty into hair follicles.

Apocrine secretion contains the same basic components as true sweat, plus fatty substances and proteins. Consequently, it is viscous and sometimes has a milky or yellowish color. The secretion is odorless, but when bacteria on the skin decompose its organic molecules, it takes on a musky and generally unpleasant odor, the basis of body odor.

Apocrine glands begin functioning at puberty under the influence of the male sex hormones (*androgens*) and play little role in maintaining a constant body temperature. Their precise function is not yet known, but they are activated by sympathetic nerve fibers during pain and stress. Because sexual foreplay increases their activity, and they enlarge and recede with the phases of a woman's menstrual cycle, they may be the human equivalent of other animals' sexual scent glands.

Ceruminous glands (sĕ-roo′mĭ-nus; *cera* = wax) are modified apocrine glands found in the lining of the external ear canal. Their secretion mixes with sebum produced by nearby sebaceous glands to form a sticky, bitter substance called *cerumen*, or earwax, that is thought to deter insects and block entry of foreign material.

Mammary glands, another variety of specialized sweat glands, secrete milk. Although they are properly part of the integumentary system, we will consider the mammary glands in Chapter 27 with female reproductive organs.

Sebaceous (Oil) Glands

The **sebaceous glands** (se-ba′shus; "greasy"), or **oil glands** (Figure 5.7a), are simple branched alveolar glands that are found all over the body except in the thick skin of the palms and soles. They are small on the body trunk and limbs, but quite large on the face, neck, and upper chest. These glands secrete an oily substance called **sebum** (se′bum). The central cells of the alveoli accumulate oily lipids until they become so engorged that they burst, so functionally these glands are *holocrine glands* (see p. 125). The accumulated lipids and cell fragments constitute sebum.

Most, but not all, sebaceous glands develop as outgrowths of hair follicles and secrete sebum into a hair follicle, or occasionally to a pore on the skin surface. Arrector pili contractions force sebum out of the hair follicles to the skin surface. Sebum softens and lubricates the hair and skin, prevents hair from becoming brittle, and slows water loss from the skin when external humidity is low. Perhaps even more important is its *bactericidal* (bacterium-killing) action.

Hormones, especially androgens, stimulate the secretion of sebum. Sebaceous glands are relatively inactive during childhood but are activated in both sexes during puberty, when androgen production begins to rise.

Homeostatic Imbalance 5.6

If accumulated sebum blocks a sebaceous gland duct, a *whitehead* appears on the skin surface. If the material oxidizes and dries, it darkens to form a *blackhead*. *Acne* is an active inflammation of the sebaceous glands accompanied by "pimples" (pustules or cysts) on the skin. It is usually caused by bacterial infection, particularly by staphylococcus, and can range from mild to severe, leading to permanent scarring.

Overactive sebaceous glands can cause *seborrhea* (seb″o-re′ah; "fast-flowing sebum"), known as "cradle cap" in infants. Seborrhea begins on the scalp as pink, raised lesions that gradually become yellow to brown and begin to slough off oily scales. ✚

☑ Check Your Understanding

17. Which cutaneous glands are associated with hair follicles?
18. When Anthony returned home from a run in 85°F weather, his face was dripping with sweat. Why?
19. What is the difference between heat-induced sweating and a "cold sweat," and which variety of sweat gland is involved?
20. Sebaceous glands are not found in thick skin. Why is their absence in those body regions desirable?

For answers, see Appendix H.

Functions of the Integumentary System

✓ Describe how the skin accomplishes at least five different functions.

First and foremost, our skin is a barrier. Like the skin of a grape, it keeps its contents juicy and whole. The skin is also a master at self (wound) repair, and interacts immediately with other body systems by making potent molecules, all the while protecting deeper tissues from damaging external agents. Even this short list hints that the skin and its derivatives perform a variety of functions, including: protection, body temperature regulation, cutaneous sensation, metabolic functions, blood reservoir, and excretion.

Protection

Given its superficial location, the skin is our most vulnerable organ system, exposed to microorganisms, abrasion, temperature extremes, and harmful chemicals. The skin constitutes at least three types of barriers: chemical, physical, and biological.

Chemical Barriers

Chemical barriers include skin secretions and melanin. Although the skin's surface teems with bacteria, the low pH of skin secretions—the so-called **acid mantle**—retards their multiplication. In addition, dermcidin in sweat and bactericidal substances in sebum kill many bacteria outright. Skin cells also secrete natural antibiotics called *defensins* that literally punch holes in bacteria, making them look like sieves. Wounded skin releases large quantities of protective peptides called *cathelicidins* that are particularly effective in preventing infection by group A streptococcus bacteria.

As discussed earlier, melanin provides a chemical pigment shield to prevent UV damage to skin cells.

Physical Barriers

The continuity of skin and the hardness of its keratinized cells provide physical barriers. As a physical barrier, the skin is a remarkable compromise. A thicker epidermis would be more impenetrable, but we would pay the price in loss of suppleness and agility.

The outstanding barrier capacity of the skin arises from the structure of its stratum corneum, which has been compared to bricks and mortar. Multiple layers of dead flat cells are the bricks and the glycolipids surrounding them are the mortar. Epidermal continuity works hand in hand with the acid mantle and certain chemicals in skin secretions to ward off bacterial invasion. The water-resistant glycolipids of the epidermis block most diffusion of water and water-soluble substances between cells, preventing both their loss from and entry into the body through the skin. However, there is a continual small loss of water through the epidermis, and if immersed in water (other than salt water), the skin will take in some water and swell slightly.

Substances that *do* penetrate the skin in limited amounts include

- *Lipid-soluble substances*, such as oxygen, carbon dioxide, fat-soluble vitamins (A, D, E, and K), and steroids (estrogens)
- *Oleoresins* (o″le-o-rez′inz) of certain plants, such as poison ivy and poison oak
- *Organic solvents*, such as acetone, dry-cleaning fluid, and paint thinner, which dissolve the cell lipids
- *Salts of heavy metals*, such as lead and mercury
- Selected drugs (nitroglycerine, nicotine, seasickness medications)

■ Drug agents called *penetration enhancers* that help ferry other drugs into the body

Alcoholic drinks dramatically enhance skin permeability for at least 24 hours after their ingestion.

Homeostatic Imbalance 5.7

Organic solvents and heavy metals are devastating to the body and can be lethal. Passage of organic solvents through the skin into the blood can shut down the kidneys and also cause brain damage. Absorption of lead results in anemia and neurological defects. These substances should never be handled with bare hands. ✚

Biological Barriers

Biological barriers include the dendritic cells of the epidermis, macrophages in the dermis, and DNA itself.

Dendritic cells are active elements of the immune system. To activate the immune response, the foreign substances, or *antigens*, must be presented to specialized white blood cells called lymphocytes. In the epidermis, the dendritic cells play this role.

Dermal macrophages constitute a second line of defense to dispose of viruses and bacteria that manage to penetrate the epidermis. They, too, act as antigen "presenters."

Although melanin provides a fairly good chemical sunscreen, DNA itself is a remarkably effective biologically based sunscreen. Electrons in DNA molecules absorb UV radiation and transfer it to the atomic nuclei, which heat up and vibrate vigorously. Since the heat dissipates to surrounding water molecules instantaneously, the DNA converts potentially destructive radiation into harmless heat.

Body Temperature Regulation

The body works best when its temperature remains within homeostatic limits. Like car engines, we need to get rid of the heat generated by our internal reactions. As long as the external temperature is lower than body temperature, the skin surface loses heat to the air and to cooler objects in its environment, just as a car radiator loses heat to the air and other nearby parts.

Under normal resting conditions, and as long as the environmental temperature is below 31–32°C (88–90°F), sweat glands secrete about 500 ml (0.5 L) of sweat per day. This routine and unnoticeable sweating is called *insensible perspiration*. When body temperature rises, the nervous system stimulates dermal blood vessels to dilate and the sweat glands into vigorous secretory activity. Indeed, on a hot day, sweat becomes noticeable and can account for the loss of up to 12 L (about 3 gallons) of body water in one day. This visible output of sweat is called *sensible perspiration*. Evaporation of sweat from the skin surface dissipates body heat and efficiently cools the body, preventing overheating.

When the external environment is cold, dermal blood vessels constrict. Their constriction causes the warm blood to bypass the skin temporarily and allows skin temperature to drop to that of the external environment. This slows passive heat loss from the body, conserving body heat. Chapter 24 discusses body temperature regulation.

Cutaneous Sensation

The skin is richly supplied with **cutaneous sensory receptors**, which are actually part of the nervous system. The cutaneous receptors are classified as *exteroceptors* (ek″ster-o-sep′torz) because they respond to stimuli arising outside the body. For example, tactile (Meissner's) corpuscles (in the dermal papillae) and tactile discs allow us to become aware of a caress or the feel of our clothing against our skin, whereas lamellar (also called Pacinian) corpuscles (in the deeper dermis or hypodermis) alert us to bumps or contacts involving deep pressure. Hair follicle receptors report on wind blowing through our hair and a playful tug on a pigtail. Free nerve endings that meander throughout the skin sense painful stimuli (irritating chemicals, extreme heat or cold, and others). We defer detailed discussion of these cutaneous receptors to Chapter 13.

Figure 5.1 illustrates all the cutaneous receptors mentioned above except for tactile corpuscles, which are found only in skin that lacks hairs, and tactile cells, shown in Figure 5.2b.

Metabolic Functions

The skin is a chemical factory, fueled in part by the sun's rays. When sunlight bombards the skin, modified cholesterol molecules are converted to a vitamin D precursor, which is transported via the blood to other body areas to be ultimately converted to vitamin D, which plays various roles in calcium metabolism. For example, calcium cannot be absorbed from the digestive tract without vitamin D.

Among its other metabolic functions, the epidermis makes chemical conversions that supplement those of the liver. For example, keratinocyte enzymes can

■ "Disarm" many cancer-causing chemicals that penetrate the epidermis

■ Convert some harmless chemicals into carcinogens

■ Activate some steroid hormones—for instance, they can transform cortisone applied to irritated skin into hydrocortisone, a potent anti-inflammatory drug

Skin cells also make several biologically important proteins, including collagenase, an enzyme that aids the natural turnover of collagen (and deters wrinkles).

Blood Reservoir

The dermal vascular supply is extensive and can hold about 5% of the body's entire blood volume. When other body organs, such as vigorously working muscles, need a greater blood supply, the nervous system constricts the dermal blood vessels. This constriction shunts more blood into the general circulation, making it available to the muscles and other body organs.

Excretion

The body eliminates limited amounts of nitrogen-containing wastes (ammonia, urea, and uric acid) in sweat, although most such wastes are excreted in urine. Profuse sweating is an important avenue for water and salt (sodium chloride) loss.

(a) Basal cell carcinoma

(b) Squamous cell carcinoma

(c) Melanoma

Figure 5.8 Photographs of skin cancers.

☑ **Check Your Understanding**

21. What chemicals produced in the skin help provide barriers to bacteria? List at least three and explain how the chemicals are protective.
22. Which epidermal cells play a role in body immunity?
23. How is sunlight important to bone health?
24. How does the skin contribute to body metabolism?

_____

For answers, see Appendix H.

Homeostatic Imbalances of Skin

✓ Summarize the characteristics of the three major types of skin cancers.

✓ Explain why serious burns are life threatening. Describe how to determine the extent of a burn and differentiate first-, second-, and third-degree burns.

Loss of homeostasis in body cells and organs reveals itself on the skin, sometimes in startling ways. The skin can develop more than 1000 different conditions and ailments. The most common skin disorders are bacterial, viral, or yeast infections. Related Clinical Terms on pp. 171–172 summarizes a number of these. Less common, but far more damaging to body well-being, are skin cancer and burns, considered next.

Skin Cancer

One in five Americans develops skin cancer at some point. Most tumors that arise in the skin are benign and do not spread (metastasize) to other body areas. (A wart, a neoplasm caused by a virus, is one example.) However, some skin tumors are malignant, or cancerous, and invade other body areas.

The single most important risk factor for skin cancer is overexposure to the UV radiation in sunlight, which damages DNA bases. Adjacent pyrimidine bases often respond by fusing, forming lesions called *dimers*. UV radiation also appears to disable a tumor suppressor gene [*p53* or the patched (*ptc*) gene]. In limited numbers of cases, however, frequent irritation of the skin by infections, chemicals, or physical trauma seems to be a predisposing factor.

Interestingly, sunburned skin accelerates its production of Fas, a protein that causes genetically damaged skin cells to commit suicide, reducing the risk of mutations that will cause sun-linked skin cancer. The death of these gene-damaged cells causes the skin to peel after a sunburn.

There is no such thing as a "healthy tan," but the good news for sun worshippers is the newly developed skin lotions that can fix damaged DNA before the involved cells become cancerous. These lotions contain tiny oily vesicles (liposomes) filled with enzymes that initiate repair of the DNA mutations most commonly caused by sunlight. The liposomes penetrate the epidermis and enter the keratinocytes, ultimately making their way into the nuclei to bind to specific sites where two DNA bases have fused. There, by selectively cutting the DNA strands, they begin a DNA repair process that is completed by cellular enzymes.

The three major forms of skin cancer are basal cell carcinoma, squamous cell carcinoma, and melanoma.

Basal Cell Carcinoma

Basal cell carcinoma (kar″sĭ-no′mah), the least malignant and most common, accounts for nearly 80% of cases. Stratum basale cells proliferate, invading the dermis and hypodermis. The cancer lesions occur most often on sun-exposed areas of the face and appear as shiny, dome-shaped nodules that later develop a central ulcer with a pearly, beaded edge **(Figure 5.8a)**. Basal cell carcinoma is relatively slow-growing, and metastasis seldom occurs before it is noticed. Full cure by surgical excision is the rule in 99% of cases.

Squamous Cell Carcinoma

Squamous cell carcinoma, the second most common skin cancer, arises from the keratinocytes of the stratum spinosum. The lesion appears as a scaly reddened papule (small, rounded elevation) that arises most often on the head (scalp, ears, and lower lip), and hands (Figure 5.8b). It tends to grow rapidly and metastasize if not removed. If it is caught early and removed surgically or by radiation therapy, the chance of complete cure is good.

Melanoma

Melanoma (mel″ah-no′mah), cancer of melanocytes, is the most dangerous skin cancer because it is highly metastatic and resistant to chemotherapy. It accounts for only 2–3% of skin cancers, but its incidence is increasing rapidly (by 3–8% per year in the United States). Melanoma can begin wherever there is pigment. Most such cancers appear spontaneously, and about one-third develop from preexisting moles. It usually appears as a spreading brown to black patch (Figure 5.8c) that metastasizes rapidly to surrounding lymph and blood vessels.

The key to surviving melanoma is early detection. The chance of survival is poor if the lesion is over 4 mm thick. The usual therapy for melanoma is wide surgical excision accompanied by immunotherapy (immunizing the body against its cancer cells).

The American Cancer Society suggests that we regularly examine our skin for new moles or pigmented spots. Apply the **ABCD rule** for recognizing melanoma:

Asymmetry: The two sides of the pigmented spot or mole do not match.

Border irregularity: The borders of the lesion exhibit indentations.

Color: The pigmented spot contains several colors (blacks, browns, tans, and sometimes blues and reds).

Diameter: The spot is larger than 6 mm in diameter (the size of a pencil eraser).

Some experts add an E, for elevation above the skin surface.

Burns

Burns are a devastating threat to the body primarily because of their effects on the skin. A **burn** is tissue damage inflicted by intense heat, electricity, radiation, or certain chemicals, all of which denature cell proteins and kill cells in the affected areas.

The immediate threat to life resulting from severe burns is a catastrophic loss of body fluids containing proteins and electrolytes. This leads to dehydration and electrolyte imbalance, and then renal failure (kidney shutdown) and circulatory shock (inadequate blood circulation due to reduced blood volume). To save the patient, the lost fluids must be replaced immediately via the intravenous (IV) route.

Evaluating Burns

In adults, the volume of fluid lost can be estimated by computing the percentage of body surface burned using the **rule of nines**. This method divides the body into 11 areas, each accounting for 9% of total body area, plus an additional area surrounding the genitals accounting for 1% of body surface area (Figure 5.9). The rule of nines is only approximate, so special tables are used when greater accuracy is desired.

Burn patients also need thousands of extra food calories daily to replace lost proteins and allow tissue repair. No one can eat enough food to provide these calories, so burn patients are given supplementary nutrients through gastric tubes and IV lines. After the initial crisis has passed, infection becomes the main threat and sepsis (widespread bacterial infection) is the leading cause of death in burn victims. Burned skin

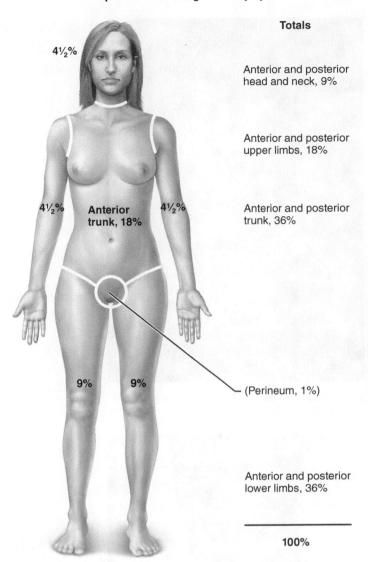

Figure 5.9 Estimating the extent and severity of burns using the rule of nines. Surface area values for the anterior body surface are indicated on the human figure. Total surface area (anterior and posterior body surfaces) for each body region is indicated to the right of the figure.

is sterile for about 24 hours. Thereafter, bacteria, fungi, and other pathogens easily invade areas where the skin barrier is destroyed, and they multiply rapidly in the nutrient-rich environment of dead tissues. Adding to this problem is the fact that the immune system becomes deficient within one to two days after severe burn injury.

Burns are classified according to their severity (depth) as first-, second-, or third-degree burns. In **first-degree burns**, only the epidermis is damaged. Symptoms include localized redness, swelling, and pain. First-degree burns tend to heal in two to three days without special attention. Sunburn is usually a first-degree burn.

(a) Skin bearing partial thickness burn (1st- and 2nd-degree burns)

(b) Skin bearing full thickness burn (3rd-degree burn)

Figure 5.10 Partial thickness and full thickness burns.

Second-degree burns injure the epidermis and the upper region of the dermis. Symptoms mimic those of first-degree burns, but blisters also appear. The burned area is red and painful, but skin regeneration occurs with little or no scarring within three to four weeks if care is taken to prevent infection. First- and second-degree burns are referred to as *partial-thickness burns* **(Figure 5.10a)**.

Third-degree burns are *full-thickness burns*, involving the entire thickness of the skin (Figure 5.10b). The burned area appears gray-white, cherry red, or blackened, and initially there is little or no edema. Since the nerve endings have been destroyed, the burned area is not painful. Although skin might eventually regenerate by proliferating epithelial cells at the edges of the burn or stem cells in hair follicles, it is usually impossible to wait that long because of fluid loss and infection. Skin grafting is advised.

In general, burns are considered critical if any of the following conditions exists:

- Over 25% of the body has second-degree burns
- Over 10% of the body has third-degree burns
- There are third-degree burns of the face, hands, or feet

Facial burns introduce the possibility of burned respiratory passageways, which can swell and cause suffocation. Burns at joints are also troublesome because scar tissue can severely limit joint mobility.

Treating Burns

To prepare a burned area for a skin graft, the *eschar* (es′kar), or burned skin, must first be debrided (removed). To prevent infection and fluid loss, the area is then flooded with antibiotics and covered temporarily with a synthetic membrane, animal (pig) skin, cadaver skin, or "living bandage" made from the thin amniotic sac membrane that surrounds a fetus. Then healthy skin is transplanted to the burned site. Unless the graft is taken from the patient (an autograft), however, there is a good chance that the patient's immune system will reject it (see p. 790 in Chapter 21). Even if the graft "takes," extensive scar tissue often forms in the burned areas.

An exciting technique eliminates many of the traditional problems of skin grafting and rejection. Synthetic skin—a silicone "epidermis" bound to a spongy "dermal" layer composed of collagen and ground cartilage—is applied to the debrided area. In time, the patient's own dermal tissue absorbs and replaces the artificial one. Then the silicone sheet is peeled off and replaced with a network of epidermal cells cultured from the patient's own skin. The body does not reject this artificial skin, which saves lives and results in minimal scarring. However, it is more likely to become infected than is an autograft.

☑ Check Your Understanding

25. Which type of skin cancer develops from the youngest epidermal cells?
26. What name is given to the rule for recognizing the signs of melanoma?

27. The healing of burns and epidermal regeneration is usually uneventful unless the burn is a third-degree burn. What accounts for this difference?

28. Although the anterior head and face represent only a small percentage of the body surface, burns to this area are often more serious than those to the body trunk. Why?

For answers, see Appendix H.

Developmental Aspects of the Integumentary System

✓ Describe and attempt to explain the causes of changes that occur in the skin from birth to old age.

The epidermis develops from the embryonic ectoderm, and the dermis and hypodermis develop from mesoderm. By the end of the fourth month of development, the skin is fairly well formed. The epidermis has all its strata, dermal papillae are obvious, fingerprints have developed, and rudimentary epidermal derivatives have formed by downward projections of cells from the basal layer. During the fifth and sixth months, the fetus is covered with a downy coat of delicate colorless hairs called the *lanugo coat* (lah-nu′go; "wool"). This hairy cloak is shed by the seventh month, and vellus hairs appear.

From Infancy to Adulthood

When a baby is born, its skin is covered with *vernix caseosa* (ver′-niks kă-se-o′sah; "varnish of cheese"), a white, cheesy-looking substance produced by the sebaceous glands that protects the fetus's skin within the water-filled amnion. The newborn's skin is very thin and often has accumulations in the sebaceous glands on the forehead and nose that appear as small white spots called *milia* (mil′e-ah). These normally disappear by the third week after birth.

During infancy and childhood, the skin thickens, and more subcutaneous fat is deposited. Although we all have approximately the same number of sweat glands, the number that function increases in the first two years after birth and is determined by climate. For this reason, people who grow up in hot climates have more active sweat glands than those raised in cooler areas of the world.

During adolescence, the skin and hair become oilier as sebaceous glands are activated, and acne may appear. Acne generally subsides in early adulthood, and skin reaches its optimal appearance when we reach our 20s and 30s. Thereafter, the skin starts to show the effects of cumulative environmental assaults (abrasion, wind, sun, chemicals). Scaling and various kinds of skin inflammation, or **dermatitis** (der″mah-ti′tis), become more common.

Aging Skin

As old age approaches, the rate of epidermal cell replacement slows, the skin thins, and its susceptibility to bruises and other injuries increases. The lubricating substances produced by the skin glands that make young skin so soft become deficient. Skin becomes dry and itchy, although people with naturally oily skin seem to postpone this dryness until later in life. Elastic fibers clump, and collagen fibers become fewer and stiffer. The subcutaneous fat layer diminishes, leading to the intolerance to cold so common in elderly people. Additionally, declining levels of sex hormones result in similar fat distribution in elderly men and women.

The decreasing elasticity of the skin, along with the loss of subcutaneous tissue, inevitably leads to wrinkling. Decreasing numbers of melanocytes and dendritic cells enhance the risk and incidence of skin cancer in this age group. As a rule, redheads and fair-skinned individuals, who have less melanin to begin with, show age-related changes more rapidly than do those with darker skin and hair.

By age 50, the number of active hair follicles has declined by two-thirds and continues to fall, resulting in hair thinning. Hair loses its luster in old age, and the delayed-action genes responsible for graying and male pattern baldness become active.

Although there is no known way to avoid skin aging, one of the best ways to slow the process is to shield your skin from both the UVA (aging rays) and UVB (rays that burn) of the sun. Aged skin that has been protected from the sun, while it grows thinner and loses some elasticity, still remains unwrinkled and unmarked. Wear protective clothing and apply sunscreens or sunblocks with a sun protection factor (SPF) of 15 or higher. Remember, the same sunlight that produces that fashionable tan also causes the sagging, blotchy, wrinkled skin of old age complete with pigmented "liver spots." Much of this havoc is due to UVA activation of enzymes called matrix metalloproteinases, which degrade collagen and other dermal components. A drug called tretinoin, related to vitamin A, inhibits these enzymes and is used in some skin creams to slow photo-aging. Good nutrition, plenty of fluids, and cleanliness may also delay the process.

☑ **Check Your Understanding**

29. What is the source of vernix caseosa that covers the skin of the newborn baby?

30. What change in the skin leads to cold intolerance in the elderly?

31. How does UV radiation contribute to skin wrinkles?

For answers, see Appendix H.

The skin is only about as thick as a paper towel—not too impressive as organ systems go. Yet, when it is severely damaged, nearly every body system reacts. Metabolism accelerates or may be impaired, immune system changes occur, bones may soften, the cardiovascular system may fail—the list goes on and on. On the other hand, when the skin is intact and performing its functions, the body as a whole benefits. *System Connections* on p. 168 summarizes homeostatic interrelationships between the integumentary system and other organ systems.

Homeostatic Interrelationships Between the Integumentary System and Other Body Systems

- Nervous system regulates diameter of blood vessels in skin; activates sweat glands, contributing to thermoregulation; interprets cutaneous sensation; activates arrector pili muscles

Endocrine System   Chapter 16

- Skin protects endocrine organs; converts some hormones to their active forms; synthesizes a vitamin D precursor
- Androgens produced by the endocrine system activate sebaceous glands and are involved in regulating hair growth

Cardiovascular System   Chapters 17–19

- Skin protects cardiovascular organs; prevents fluid loss from body; serves as blood reservoir
- Cardiovascular system transports oxygen and nutrients to skin and removes wastes from skin; provides substances needed by skin glands to make their secretions

Lymphatic System/Immunity   Chapters 20–21

- Skin protects lymphatic organs; prevents pathogen invasion; dendritic cells and macrophages help activate the immune system
- Lymphatic system prevents edema by picking up excessive leaked fluid; immune system protects skin cells

Respiratory System   Chapter 22

- Skin protects respiratory organs; hairs in nose help filter out dust from inhaled air
- Respiratory system furnishes oxygen to skin cells and removes carbon dioxide via gas exchange with blood

Digestive System   Chapter 23

- Skin protects digestive organs; provides vitamin D needed for calcium absorption; performs some of the same chemical conversions as liver cells
- Digestive system provides needed nutrients to the skin

Urinary System   Chapters 25–26

- Skin protects urinary organs; excretes salts and some nitrogenous wastes in sweat
- Urinary system activates vitamin D precursor made by keratinocytes; disposes of nitrogenous wastes of skin metabolism

Reproductive System   Chapter 27

- Skin protects reproductive organs; cutaneous receptors respond to erotic stimuli; highly modified sweat glands (mammary glands) produce milk
- During pregnancy, skin stretches to accommodate growing fetus; changes in skin pigmentation may occur

Skeletal System   Chapters 6–8

- Skin protects bones; skin synthesizes a vitamin D precursor needed for normal calcium absorption and deposit of bone (calcium) salts, which make bones hard
- Skeletal system provides support for skin

Muscular System   Chapters 9–10

- Skin protects muscles
- Active muscles generate large amounts of heat, which increases blood flow to the skin and may activate sweat glands in skin

Nervous System   Chapters 11–15

- Skin protects nervous system organs; cutaneous sensory receptors for touch, pressure, pain, and temperature located in skin (see Figure 5.1)

Access more System Connections in the Study Area at **www.masteringaandp.com**.

168

Chapter Summary

 For more chapter study tools, go to the Study Area of MasteringA&P at **www.masteringaandp.com**.
There you will find:

- Interactive Physiology **iP**
- A&PFlix **A&PFlix**
- Practice Anatomy Lab **PAL**
- PhysioEx **PEx**
- Videos, Practice Quizzes and Tests, MP3 Tutor Sessions, Case Studies, and much more!

The Skin   (pp. 150–157)

1. The skin, or integument, is composed of two discrete tissue layers, an outer epidermis and a deeper dermis, resting on subcutaneous tissue, the hypodermis.

Epidermis   (pp. 151–154)

2. The epidermis is an avascular, keratinized sheet of stratified squamous epithelium. Most epidermal cells are keratinocytes. Scattered among the keratinocytes in the deepest epidermal layers are melanocytes, dendritic cells, and tactile cells.

3. From deep to superficial, the strata, or layers of the epidermis, are the basale, spinosum, granulosum, lucidum, and corneum. The stratum lucidum is absent in thin skin. The mitotically active stratum basale is the source of new cells for epidermal growth. The most superficial layers are increasingly keratinized and less viable.

Dermis   (pp. 154–156)

4. The dermis, composed mainly of dense, irregular connective tissue, is well supplied with blood vessels, lymphatic vessels, and nerves. Cutaneous receptors, glands, and hair follicles reside within the dermis.

5. The more superficial papillary layer exhibits dermal papillae that protrude into the epidermis above, as well as dermal ridges. Dermal ridges and epidermal ridges together form the friction ridges that produce fingerprints.

6. In the deeper, thicker reticular layer, the connective tissue fibers are much more densely interwoven. Less dense regions between the collagen bundles produce cleavage, or tension, lines in the skin. Points of tight dermal attachment to the hypodermis produce dermal folds, or flexure lines.

Skin Color   (pp. 156–157)

7. Skin color reflects the amount of pigments (melanin and carotene) in the skin and the oxygenation level of hemoglobin in blood.

8. Melanin production is stimulated by exposure to ultraviolet radiation in sunlight. Melanin, produced by melanocytes and transferred to keratinocytes, protects the keratinocyte nuclei from the damaging effects of UV radiation.

9. Skin color is affected by emotional state. Alterations in normal skin color (jaundice, bronzing, erythema, and others) may indicate certain disease states.

Appendages of the Skin   (pp. 157–162)

1. Skin appendages, which derive from the epidermis, include hairs and hair follicles, nails, and glands (sweat and sebaceous).

Hairs and Hair Follicles   (pp. 157–160)

2. A hair, produced by a hair follicle, consists of heavily keratinized cells. A typical hair has a central medulla, a cortex, and an outer cuticle and root and shaft portions. Hair color reflects the amount and kind of melanin present.

3. A hair follicle consists of an inner epithelial root sheath and an outer peripheral connective tissue sheath derived from the dermis. The base of the hair follicle is a hair bulb with a matrix that produces the hair. A hair follicle is richly vascularized and well supplied with nerve fibers. Arrector pili muscles pull the follicles into an upright position, producing goose bumps, and propel sebum to the skin surface when they contract.

4. Except for hairs of the scalp and around the eyes, hairs formed initially are fine vellus hairs; at puberty, under the influence of androgens, coarser, darker terminal hairs appear in the axillae and the genital region.

5. The rate of hair growth varies in different body regions and with sex and age. Differences in life span of hairs account for differences in length on different body regions. Hair thinning reflects factors that lengthen follicular resting periods, age-related atrophy of hair follicles, and a delayed-action gene.

Nails   (p. 160)

6. A nail is a scalelike modification of the epidermis that covers the dorsum of a finger (or toe) tip. The actively growing region is the nail matrix.

Sweat (Sudoriferous) Glands   (pp. 160–161)

7. Eccrine (merocrine) sweat glands, with a few exceptions, are distributed over the entire body surface. Their primary function is thermoregulation. They are simple coiled tubular glands that secrete a salt solution containing small amounts of other solutes. Their ducts usually empty to the skin surface via pores.

8. Apocrine sweat glands, which may function as scent glands, are found primarily in the axillary and anogenital areas. Their secretion is similar to eccrine secretion, but it also contains proteins and fatty substances on which bacteria thrive.

Sebaceous (Oil) Glands   (pp. 161–162)

9. Sebaceous glands occur all over the body surface except for the palms and soles. They are simple alveolar glands; their oily holocrine secretion is called sebum. Sebaceous gland ducts usually empty into hair follicles.

10. Sebum lubricates the skin and hair, prevents water loss from the skin, and acts as a bactericidal agent. Sebaceous glands are activated (at puberty) and controlled by androgens.

Functions of the Integumentary System   (pp. 162–164)

1. Protection. The skin protects by chemical barriers (the antibacterial nature of sebum, defensins, cathelicidins, the acid mantle, and the UV shield of melanin), physical barriers (the hardened keratinized and lipid-rich surface), and biological barriers (dendritic cells, macrophages, and DNA).

2. Body temperature regulation. The skin vasculature and sweat glands, regulated by the nervous system, play an important role in maintaining body temperature homeostasis.

3. Cutaneous sensation. Cutaneous sensory receptors respond to temperature, touch, pressure, and pain stimuli.

5

4. Metabolic functions. A vitamin D precursor is synthesized from cholesterol by epidermal cells. Skin cells also play a role in some chemical conversions.
5. Blood reservoir. The extensive vascular supply of the dermis allows the skin to act as a blood reservoir.
6. Excretion. Sweat contains small amounts of nitrogenous wastes and plays a minor role in excretion.

Homeostatic Imbalances of Skin (pp. 164–167)

1. The most common skin disorders result from infections.

Skin Cancer (pp. 164–165)

2. The most common cause of skin cancer is exposure to ultraviolet radiation.
3. Basal cell carcinoma and squamous cell carcinoma are cured if they are removed before metastasis. Melanoma, a cancer of melanocytes, is less common but more dangerous.

Burns (pp. 165–166)

4. In severe burns, the initial threat is loss of protein- and electrolyte-rich body fluids, which may lead to circulatory collapse. The second threat is overwhelming bacterial infection.
5. The extent of a burn may be evaluated by using the rule of nines. The severity of burns is indicated by the terms first degree, second

degree, and third degree. Third-degree burns are full-thickness burns that require grafting for successful recovery.

Developmental Aspects of the Integumentary System (p. 167)

1. The epidermis develops from embryonic ectoderm; the dermis (and hypodermis) develops from mesoderm.
2. The fetus exhibits a downy lanugo coat. Fetal sebaceous glands produce vernix caseosa, which helps protect the fetus's skin from its watery environment.

From Infancy to Adulthood (p. 167)

3. A newborn's skin is thin. During childhood the skin thickens and more subcutaneous fat is deposited. At puberty, sebaceous glands are activated and terminal hairs appear in greater numbers.

Aging Skin (p. 167)

4. In old age, the rate of epidermal cell replacement declines and the skin and hair thin. Skin glands become less active. Loss of collagen and elastic fibers and subcutaneous fat leads to wrinkling; delayed-action genes cause graying and balding. Photodamage is a major cause of skin aging.

Review Questions

Multiple Choice/Matching

(Some questions have more than one correct answer. Select the best answer or answers from the choices given.)

1. Which epidermal cell type is most numerous? (a) keratinocyte, (b) melanocyte, (c) dendritic cell, (d) tactile cell.
2. Which cell functions as part of the immune system? (a) keratinocyte, (b) melanocyte, (c) dendritic cell, (d) tactile cell.
3. The epidermis provides a physical barrier due largely to the presence of (a) melanin, (b) carotene, (c) collagen, (d) keratin.
4. Skin color is determined by (a) the amount of blood, (b) pigments, (c) oxygenation level of the blood, (d) all of these.
5. The sensations of touch and pressure are picked up by receptors located in (a) the stratum spinosum, (b) the dermis, (c) the hypodermis, (d) the stratum corneum.
6. Which is not a true statement about the papillary layer of the dermis? (a) it is largely areolar connective tissue, (b) it is most responsible for the toughness of the skin, (c) it contains nerve endings that respond to stimuli, (d) it is highly vascular.
7. Skin surface markings that reflect points of tight dermal attachment to underlying tissues are called (a) tension lines, (b) papillary ridges, (c) flexure lines, (d) dermal papillae.
8. Which of the following is not an epidermal derivative? (a) hair, (b) sweat gland, (c) sensory receptor, (d) sebaceous gland.
9. An arrector pili muscle (a) is associated with each sweat gland, (b) can cause a hair to stand up straight, (c) enables each hair to be stretched when wet, (d) provides new cells for continued growth of its associated hair.
10. The product of this type of sweat gland includes protein and lipid substances that become odoriferous as a result of bacterial action: (a) apocrine gland, (b) eccrine gland, (c) sebaceous gland, (d) pancreatic gland.
11. Sebum (a) lubricates the surface of the skin and hair, (b) consists of cell fragments and fatty substances, (c) in excess may cause seborrhea, (d) all of these.
12. The rule of nines is helpful clinically in (a) diagnosing skin cancer, (b) estimating the extent of a burn, (c) estimating how serious a cancer is, (d) preventing acne.

Short Answer Essay Questions

13. Which epidermal cells are also called prickle cells? Which contain keratohyaline and lamellar granules?
14. Is a bald man really hairless? Explain.
15. You go to the beach to swim on an extremely hot, sunny summer afternoon. Describe two ways in which your integumentary system acts to preserve homeostasis during your outing.
16. Distinguish clearly between first-, second-, and third-degree burns.
17. Describe the process of hair formation, and list several factors that may influence (a) growth cycles and (b) hair texture.
18. What color does carotene impart to the skin?
19. Why does skin wrinkle and what factors accelerate the wrinkling process?
20. Explain each of these familiar phenomena in terms of what you learned in this chapter: (a) pimples, (b) dandruff, (c) greasy hair and "shiny nose," (d) stretch marks from gaining weight, (e) freckles.
21. Count Dracula, the most famous vampire, rumored to have killed at least 200,000 people, was based on a real person who lived in eastern Europe about 600 years ago. He was indeed a "monster," although he was not a real vampire. The historical Count Dracula may have suffered from which of the following? (Hint: See Related Clinical Terms.) (a) porphyria, (b) EB, (c) halitosis, (d) vitiligo. Explain your answer.

22. Why are there no skin cancers that originate from stratum corneum cells?

23. A man got his finger caught in a machine at the factory. The damage was less serious than expected, but the entire nail was torn off his right index finger. The parts lost were the body, root, bed, matrix, and eponychium of the nail. First, define each of these parts. Then, tell if this nail is likely to grow back.

24. On an outline diagram of the human body, mark off various regions according to the rule of nines. What percentage of the total body surface is affected if the skin over the following body parts is burned? (a) the entire posterior trunk and buttocks, (b) an entire lower limb, (c) the entire front of the left upper limb.

25. A common belief is that having your hair cut makes it become thicker. Explain why this belief is not true.

Critical Thinking and Clinical Application Questions

1. Dean, a 40-year-old aging beach boy, is complaining to you that although his suntan made him popular when he was young, now his face is all wrinkled, and he has several darkly pigmented moles that are growing rapidly and are as big as large coins. He shows you the moles, and immediately you think "ABCD." What does that mean and why should he be concerned?

2. Victims of third-degree burns demonstrate the loss of vital functions performed by the skin. What are the two most important problems encountered clinically with such patients? Explain each in terms of the absence of skin.

3. Thelma, a 30-year-old resident of a mental hospital, has an abnormal growth of hair on the dorsum of her right index finger. The orderly comments that she gnaws on that finger continuously. What do you think is the relationship between Thelma's gnawing activity and her hairy finger?

4. A model is concerned about a new scar on her abdomen. She tells her surgeon that there is practically no scar from the appendix operation done when she was 16, but this new gallbladder scar is "gross." Her appendectomy scar is small, obliquely located on the inferior abdominal surface, and very indistinct. By contrast, the gallbladder scar is large, lumpy, and runs at right angles to the central axis of the body trunk. Can you explain why the scars are so different?

5. Osteomalacia, a condition of soft bones, is prevalent in Muslim countries that decree that their women wear the burka, a garment that covers all but their eyes. What is the cause and effect here?

6. Mrs. Gaucher received second-degree burns on her abdomen when she dropped a kettle of boiling water. She asked her doctor (worriedly) if she would need a skin graft. What do you think he told her?

AT THE CLINIC

Related Clinical Terms

Albinism (al′bĭ-nizm; *alb* = white) Inherited condition in which melanocytes do not synthesize melanin owing to a lack of tyrosinase. An albino's skin is pink, the hair pale or white, and the irises of the eyes unpigmented or poorly so.

Boils and carbuncles (kar′bung-klz; "little glowing embers") Inflammation of hair follicles and sebaceous glands in which an infection has spread to the underlying hypodermis; common on the dorsal neck. Carbuncles are composite boils. A common cause is bacterial infection.

Cold sores (fever blisters) Small fluid-filled blisters that itch and smart; usually occur around the lips and in the mucosa of the mouth; caused by a herpes simplex infection. The virus localizes in a cutaneous nerve, where it remains dormant until activated by emotional upset, fever, or UV radiation.

Contact dermatitis Itching, redness, and swelling, progressing to blister formation; caused by exposure of the skin to chemicals (e.g., poison ivy oleoresin) that provoke an allergic response in sensitive individuals.

Decubitus ulcer (de-ku′bĭ-tus) Localized breakdown and ulceration of skin due to interference with its blood supply. Usually occurs over a bony prominence, such as the hip or heel, that is subjected to continuous pressure; also called a bedsore.

Dermatology The branch of medicine that studies and treats disorders of the skin.

Eczema (ek′ze-mah) A skin rash characterized by itching, blistering, oozing, and scaling of the skin. A common allergic reaction in children, but also occurs (typically in a more severe form) in adults. Frequent causes include allergic reactions to certain foods (fish, eggs, and others) or to inhaled dust or pollen. Treated by methods used for other allergic disorders.

Epidermolysis bullosa (EB) A group of hereditary disorders characterized by inadequate or faulty synthesis of keratin, collagen, and/or basement membrane "cement" that results in lack of cohesion between layers of the skin and mucosa. A simple touch causes layers to separate and blister. For this reason, EB victims are called "touch-me-nots." In severe cases fatal blistering occurs in major vital organs. Because the blisters rupture easily, victims suffer frequent infections. Treatments are aimed at relieving the symptoms and preventing infection.

Impetigo (im″pĕ-ti′go; *impet* = an attack) Pink, fluid-filled, raised lesions (common around the mouth and nose) that develop a yellow crust and eventually rupture. Caused by staphylococcus infection, it is contagious, and common in school-age children.

Porphyria (por-fer′e-ah; "purple") An inherited condition in which certain enzymes needed to form the heme of hemoglobin of blood are lacking. Without these enzymes, metabolic intermediates of the heme pathway called porphyrins build up, spill into the circulation, and eventually cause lesions throughout the body, especially when exposed to sunlight. The skin becomes lesioned and scarred; fingers, toes, and nose are disfigured; gums degenerate and teeth become prominent. Believed to be the basis of folklore about vampires.

Psoriasis (so-ri′ah-sis) A chronic autoimmune condition characterized by raised, reddened epidermal patches covered with silvery scales that itch or burn, crack, and sometimes bleed or become infected. When severe, it may be disfiguring and

Related Clinical Terms *(continued)*

debilitating. Trauma, infection, hormonal changes, or stress often trigger the autoimmune attacks. Cortisone-containing topicals (medications applied to the skin surface) may control mild cases. For more severe cases, self-injected drugs called biologicals and/or phototherapy with UV light in conjunction with chemotherapeutic drugs provides some relief.

Rosacea (ro-za′she-ah) A chronic skin eruption produced by dilated small blood vessels of the face, particularly the nose and cheeks. Papules and acne-like pustules may or may not occur. More common in women, but tends to be more severe when it occurs in men. Cause is unknown, but stress, some endocrine disorders, and anything that produces flushing (hot beverages, alcohol, sunlight, etc.) can aggravate this condition.

Vitiligo (vit″ĭ-li′go; *viti* = a vine, winding) The most prevalent skin pigmentation disorder, characterized by a loss of melanocytes

and uneven dispersal of melanin, so that unpigmented skin regions (light spots) are surrounded by normally pigmented areas. An autoimmune disorder.

Scleroderma (*scler* = hard) An autoimmune disorder characterized by stiff, hardened skin due to abnormal amounts of collagen in the dermis that severely limit joint movements and facial expressions. A classic sign of the disorder is Raynaud disease in which the fingers and toes become white and painful because of poor blood flow to those areas. The fibrosis that occurs in systemic cases may affect a variety of organs including the lungs, eventually leading to suffocation, and the kidneys, leading to renal hypertension because of blood vessel constriction and occlusion. Environmental factors including organic solvents, asbestos, and even silicone breast implants have all been suspect scleroderma triggers.

5

Case Study   Integumentary System

A terrible collision between a trailer truck and a bus has occurred on Route 91. Several of the passengers are rushed to area hospitals for treatment. We will follow a few of these people in clinical case studies that will continue through the book from one organ system to the next.

Examination of Mrs. DeStephano, a 45-year-old woman, reveals several impairments of homeostasis. Relative to her integumentary system, the following comments are noted on her chart:

- Epidermal abrasions of the right arm and shoulder
- Severe lacerations of the right cheek and temple
- Cyanosis apparent

The lacerated areas are cleaned, sutured (stitched), and bandaged by the emergency room (ER) personnel, and Mrs. DeStephano is admitted for further tests.

Relative to her signs:

1. What protective mechanisms are impaired or deficient in the abraded areas?

2. Assuming that bacteria are penetrating the dermis in these areas, what remaining skin defenses might act to prevent further bacterial invasion?

3. What benefit is conferred by suturing the lacerations? (Hint: See Chapter 4, p. 149, Related Clinical Terms, healing by first intention.)

4. Mrs. DeStephano's cyanotic skin may hint at what additional problem (and impairment of what body systems or functions)?

(Answers in Appendix H)

6

Bones and Skeletal Tissues

A ll of us have heard the expressions "bone tired" and "bag of bones"—rather unflattering and inaccurate images of one of our most phenomenal tissues and our main skeletal elements. Our brains, not our bones, convey feelings of fatigue. As for "bag of bones," they are indeed more prominent in some of us, but without bones to form our internal supporting skeleton we would all creep along the ground like slugs, lacking any definite shape or form. Along with its bones, the skeleton contains resilient cartilages, which we briefly discuss in this chapter. However, our major focus is the structure and function of bone tissue and the dynamics of its formation and remodeling throughout life.

Skeletal Cartilages

✓ Describe the functional properties of the three types of cartilage tissue.

✓ Locate the major cartilages of the adult skeleton.

✓ Explain how cartilage grows.

The human skeleton is initially made up of cartilages and fibrous membranes, but bone soon replaces most of these early supports. The few cartilages that remain in adults are found mainly in regions where flexible skeletal tissue is needed.

Basic Structure, Types, and Locations

A **skeletal cartilage** is made of some variety of *cartilage tissue* molded to fit its body location and function. Cartilage consists primarily of water, which accounts for its resilience, that is, its ability to spring back to its original shape after being compressed.

The cartilage, which contains no nerves or blood vessels, is surrounded by a layer of dense irregular connective tissue, the *perichondrium* (per″ĭ-kon′dre-um; "around the cartilage"). The perichondrium acts like a girdle to resist outward expansion when the cartilage is compressed. Additionally, the perichondrium contains the blood vessels from which nutrients diffuse through the matrix to reach the cartilage cells internally. This mode of nutrient delivery limits cartilage thickness.

As we described in Chapter 4, there are three types of cartilage tissue in the body: hyaline, elastic, and fibrocartilage. The skeletal cartilages include examples from all three. All three types have the same basic components—cells called *chondrocytes*, encased in small cavities (lacunae) within an *extracellular matrix* containing a jellylike ground substance and fibers.

Hyaline Cartilages

Hyaline cartilages, which look like frosted glass when freshly exposed, provide support with flexibility and resilience. They are the most abundant skeletal cartilages. Their chondrocytes are spherical (see Figure 4.8g), and the only fiber type in their matrix is fine collagen fibers (which are undetectable microscopically). Colored blue in **Figure 6.1**, skeletal hyaline cartilages include

- *Articular cartilages*, which cover the ends of most bones at movable joints

- *Costal cartilages*, which connect the ribs to the sternum (breastbone)

- *Respiratory cartilages*, which form the skeleton of the *larynx* (*voicebox*) and reinforce other respiratory passageways

- *Nasal cartilages*, which support the external nose

Elastic Cartilages

Elastic cartilages resemble hyaline cartilages (see Figure 4.8h), but they contain more stretchy elastic fibers and so are better able to stand up to repeated bending. They are found in only two skeletal locations, shown in green in Figure 6.1—the external ear and the epiglottis (the flap that bends to cover the opening of the larynx each time we swallow).

Fibrocartilages

Highly compressible with great tensile strength, **fibrocartilages** consist of roughly parallel rows of chondrocytes alternating with thick collagen fibers (see Figure 4.8i). Fibrocartilages occur in sites that are subjected to both pressure and stretch, such as the padlike cartilages (menisci) of the knee and the discs between vertebrae, colored red in Figure 6.1.

Growth of Cartilage

Unlike bone, which has a hard matrix, cartilage has a flexible matrix which can accommodate mitosis. It is the ideal tissue to use to rapidly lay down the embryonic skeleton and to provide for new skeletal growth.

Cartilage grows in two ways. In **appositional growth** (ap″o-zish′un-al; "growth from outside"), cartilage-forming cells in the surrounding perichondrium secrete new matrix against the external face of the existing cartilage tissue. In **interstitial growth** (in″ter-stish′al; "growth from inside"), the lacunae-bound chondrocytes divide and secrete new matrix, expanding the cartilage from within. Typically, cartilage growth ends during adolescence when the skeleton stops growing.

Under certain conditions—during normal bone growth in youth and during old age, for example—cartilage can become calcified (hardened due to deposit of calcium salts). Note, however, that calcified cartilage is not bone; cartilage and bone are always distinct tissues.

☑ Check Your Understanding

1. Which type of cartilage is most plentiful in the adult body?
2. What two body structures contain flexible elastic cartilage?
3. Cartilage grows by interstitial growth. What does this mean?

For answers, see Appendix H.

Classification of Bones

✓ Name the major regions of the skeleton and describe their relative functions.

✓ Compare and contrast the four bone classes and provide examples of each class.

The 206 named bones of the human skeleton are divided into two groups: axial and appendicular.

The **axial skeleton** forms the long axis of the body and includes the bones of the skull, vertebral column, and rib cage, shown in orange in Figure 6.1. Generally speaking these bones protect, support, or carry other body parts.

The **appendicular skeleton** (ap″en-dik′u-lar) consists of the bones of the upper and lower limbs and the girdles (shoulder bones and hip bones) that attach the limbs to the axial skeleton (colored gold in Figure 6.1). Bones of the limbs help us move from place to place (locomotion) and manipulate our environment.

Bones come in many sizes and shapes. For example, the pisiform bone of the wrist is the size and shape of a pea, whereas the femur (thigh bone) is nearly 2 feet long in some people and has a large, ball-shaped head. The unique shape of each bone fulfills a particular need. The femur, for example, withstands great pressure, and its hollow-cylinder design provides maximum strength with minimum weight to accommodate our upright posture.

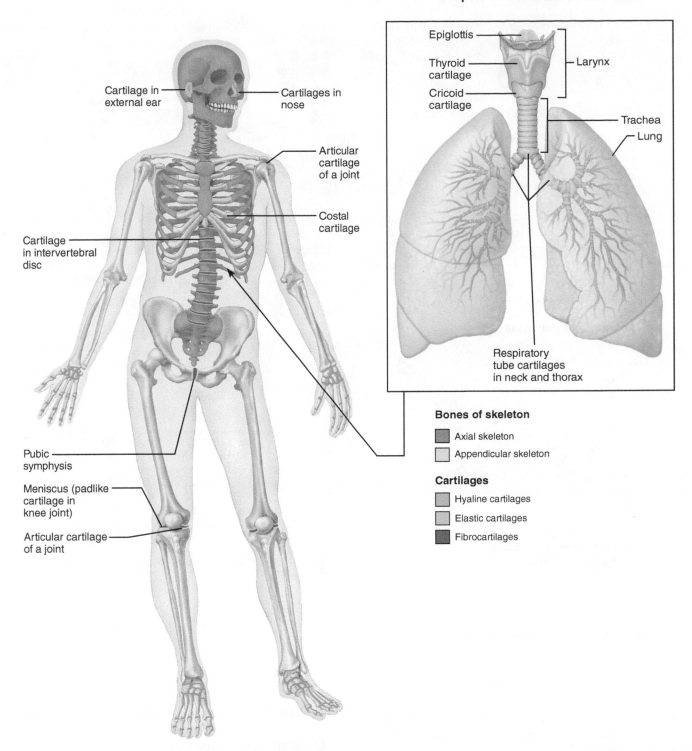

Figure 6.1 The bones and cartilages of the human skeleton. The cartilages that support the respiratory tubes and larynx are drawn separately at the right.

Generally, bones are classified by their shape as long, short, flat, or irregular (Figure 6.2).

- **Long bones**, as their name suggests, are considerably longer than they are wide (Figure 6.2a). A long bone has a shaft plus two ends which are often expanded. All limb bones except the patella (kneecap) and the wrist and ankle bones are long bones. Notice that these bones are named for their elongated

shape, *not* their overall size. The three bones in each of your fingers are long bones, even though they are small.

- **Short bones** are roughly cube shaped. The bones of the wrist and ankle are examples (Figure 6.2d). **Sesamoid bones** (ses'ah-moid; "shaped like a sesame seed") are a special type of short bone that form in a tendon (for example, the patella). They vary in size and number in different individuals. Some

6

(a) Long bone (humerus)

(b) Irregular bone (vertebra), right lateral view

(c) Flat bone (sternum)

(d) Short bone (talus)

Figure 6.2 Classification of bones on the basis of shape.

sesamoid bones act to alter the direction of pull of a tendon. The function of others is not known.

- **Flat bones** are thin, flattened, and usually a bit curved. The sternum (breastbone), scapulae (shoulder blades), ribs, and most skull bones are flat bones (Figure 6.2c).

- **Irregular bones** have complicated shapes that fit none of the preceding classes. Examples include the vertebrae and the hip bones (Figure 6.2b).

☑ **Check Your Understanding**

4. What are the components of the axial skeleton?
5. Contrast the general function of the axial skeleton to that of the appendicular skeleton.
6. What bone class do the ribs and skull bones fall into?

For answers, see Appendix H.

Functions of Bones

✓ List and describe seven important functions of bones.

Our bones perform seven important functions:

- **Support.** Bones provide a framework that supports the body and cradles its soft organs. For example, bones of lower limbs act as pillars to support the body trunk when we stand, and the rib cage supports the thoracic wall.

- **Protection.** The fused bones of the skull protect the brain. The vertebrae surround the spinal cord, and the rib cage helps protect the vital organs of the thorax.

- **Movement.** Skeletal muscles, which attach to bones by tendons, use bones as levers to move the body and its parts. As a result, we can walk, grasp objects, and breathe. The design of joints determines the types of movement possible.

- **Mineral and growth factor storage.** Bone is a reservoir for minerals, most importantly calcium and phosphate. The stored minerals are released into the bloodstream in their ionic form as needed for distribution to all parts of the body. Indeed, "deposits" and "withdrawals" of minerals to and from the bones go on almost continuously. Additionally, mineralized bone matrix stores important growth factors.

- **Blood cell formation.** Most blood cell formation, or **hematopoiesis** (hem″ah-to-poi-e′sis), occurs in the red marrow cavities of certain bones.

- **Triglyceride (fat) storage.** Fat, a source of energy for the body, is stored in bone cavities.

- **Hormone production.** Bones produce osteocalcin, a hormone which not only helps regulate bone formation, but also protects against obesity, glucose intolerance, and diabetes mellitus. (Osteocalcin is discussed further in Chapter 16.)

☑ **Check Your Understanding**

7. What is the functional relationship between skeletal muscles and bones?
8. What two types of substances are stored in bone matrix?
9. Describe two functions of a bone's marrow cavities.

For answers, see Appendix H.

Bone Structure

✓ Describe the gross anatomy of a typical flat bone and a long bone. Indicate the locations and functions of red and yellow marrow, articular cartilage, periosteum, and endosteum.

✓ Indicate the functional importance of bone markings.

✓ Describe the histology of compact and spongy bone.

✓ Discuss the chemical composition of bone and the advantages conferred by its organic and inorganic components.

Because they contain different types of tissue, bones are organs. (Recall that an organ contains several different tissues.) Although bone (osseous) tissue dominates bones, they also contain nervous tissue in their nerves, cartilage in their articular cartilages, fibrous connective tissue lining their cavities, and muscle and epithelial tissues in their blood vessels. We will consider bone structure at three levels: gross, microscopic, and chemical.

Gross Anatomy

Bone Textures: Compact and Spongy Bone

Every bone has a dense outer layer that looks smooth and solid to the naked eye. This external layer is **compact bone** (Figures 6.3 and 6.4). Internal to this is **spongy bone** (also called *trabecular bone*), a honeycomb of small needle-like or flat pieces called **trabeculae** (trah-bek′u-le; "little beams"). In living bones the open spaces between trabeculae are filled with red or yellow bone marrow.

Figure 6.3 Flat bones consist of a layer of spongy bone sandwiched between two thin layers of compact bone. (Photomicrograph at bottom, 25×)

Structure of Short, Irregular, and Flat Bones

Short, irregular, and flat bones share a simple design: They all consist of thin plates of spongy bone covered by compact bone. These plates are covered outside and inside by connective tissue membranes, respectively the periosteum and endosteum (described on pp. 178–179). However, these bones are not cylindrical and so they have no shaft or epiphyses. They contain bone marrow (between their trabeculae), but no well-defined marrow cavity. Where they form movable joints with their neighbors, hyaline cartilage covers their surfaces.

Figure 6.3 shows a typical flat bone of the skull. In flat bones, the spongy bone is called the **diploë** (dip′lo-e; "folded") and the whole arrangement resembles a stiffened sandwich.

Structure of a Typical Long Bone

With few exceptions, all long bones have the same general structure: a shaft, bone ends, and membranes **(Figure 6.4)**.

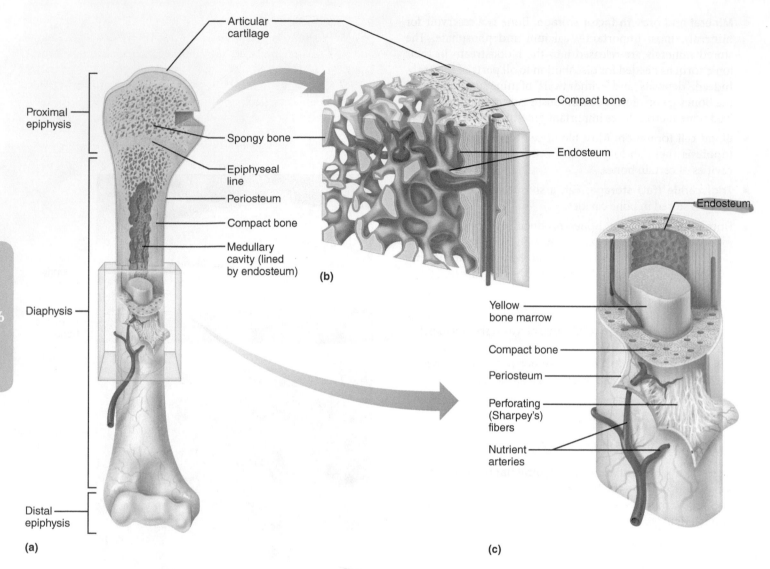

Figure 6.4 The structure of a long bone (humerus of arm). (a) Anterior view with bone sectioned frontally to show the interior at the proximal end. **(b)** Enlarged view of spongy bone and compact bone of the epiphysis of (a). (For related images, see *A Brief Atlas of the Human Body*, Plates 20 and 21.) **(c)** Enlarged cross-sectional view of the shaft (diaphysis) of (a). Note that the external surface of the diaphysis is covered by periosteum, but the articular surface of the epiphysis is covered with hyaline cartilage.

Diaphysis   A tubular **diaphysis** (di-af′ĭ-sis; *dia* = through, *physis* = growth), or shaft, forms the long axis of the bone. It is constructed of a relatively thick *collar* of compact bone that surrounds a central **medullary cavity** (med′u-lar-e; "middle"), or *marrow cavity*. In adults, the medullary cavity contains fat (yellow marrow) and is called the **yellow marrow cavity**.

Epiphyses   The **epiphyses** (e-pif′ĭ-sēz; singular: epiphysis) are the bone ends (*epi* = upon). In many cases, they are broader than the diaphysis. An outer shell of compact bone forms the epiphysis exterior and their interior contains spongy bone. A thin layer of articular (hyaline) cartilage covers the joint surface of each epiphysis, cushioning the opposing bone ends during movement and absorbing stress.

Between the diaphysis and each epiphysis of an adult long bone is an **epiphyseal line**, a remnant of the **epiphyseal plate**, a disc of hyaline cartilage that grows during childhood to lengthen the bone. The flared portion of the bone where the diaphysis and epiphysis meet, whether it is the epiphyseal plate or line, is sometimes called the *metaphysis* (*meta* = between).

Membranes   A glistening white, double-layered membrane called the **periosteum** (per″e-os′te-um; *peri* = around, *osteo* = bone) covers the external surface of the entire bone except the joint surfaces. The outer *fibrous layer* of the periosteum is dense irregular connective tissue. The inner *osteogenic layer*, abutting the bone surface, consists primarily of primitive stem cells, *osteogenic cells*, that give rise to all bone cells except bone-destroying cells. These cell types are described shortly.

The periosteum is richly supplied with nerve fibers and blood vessels, which pass through the shaft to enter the marrow cavity via **nutrient foramina** (fo-ra′me-nah; "openings"). *Perforating (Sharpey's) fibers*—tufts of collagen fibers that extend from its fibrous layer into the bone matrix—secure the periosteum to the underlying bone (Figure 6.4). The periosteum also provides anchoring points for tendons and ligaments. At these points the perforating fibers are exceptionally dense.

A delicate connective tissue membrane called the **endosteum** (en-dos′te-um; "within the bone") covers internal bone surfaces (Figure 6.4). The endosteum covers the trabeculae of spongy bone and lines the canals that pass through the compact bone. Like the periosteum, the endosteum contains osteogenic cells that can differentiate into other bone cells.

Location of Hematopoietic Tissue in Bones

Hematopoietic tissue, **red marrow**, is typically found within the trabecular cavities of spongy bone of long bones and in the diploë of flat bones. For this reason, both these cavities are often called **red marrow cavities**. In newborn infants, the medullary cavity of the diaphysis and all areas of spongy bone contain red bone marrow. In most adult long bones, the fat-containing medullary cavity extends well into the epiphysis, and little red marrow is present in the spongy bone cavities. For this reason, blood cell production in adult long bones routinely occurs only in the heads of the femur and humerus (the long bone of the arm).

The red marrow found in the diploë of flat bones (such as the sternum) and in some irregular bones (such as the hip bone) is much more active in hematopoiesis. When clinicians suspect problems with the blood-forming tissue, they obtain red marrow samples from these sites. However, yellow marrow in the medullary cavity can revert to red marrow if a person becomes very anemic and needs more red blood cells.

Bone Markings

The external surfaces of bones are rarely smooth and featureless. Instead, they display projections, depressions, and openings. These **bone markings** serve as sites of muscle, ligament, and tendon attachment, as joint surfaces, or as conduits for blood vessels and nerves.

Projections—bone markings that bulge outward from the surface—include heads, trochanters, spines, and others. Each has distinguishing features and functions. In most cases, bone projections indicate the stresses created by muscles attached to and pulling on them or are modified surfaces where bones meet and form joints.

Bone markings that are depressions and openings include fossae (singular: fossa), sinuses, foramina (singular: foramen), and grooves. They usually allow nerves and blood vessels to pass. Table 6.1 describes the most important types of bone markings. Familiarize yourself with these terms because you will meet them again as identifying marks of the individual bones studied in the lab.

Microscopic Anatomy of Bone

Cells of Bone Tissue

Five major cell types populate bone tissue: osteogenic cells, osteoblasts, osteocytes, bone lining cells, and osteoclasts. All of these except for the osteoclasts originate from mesenchymal cells. Each cell type is essentially a specialized form of the same basic cell type that transforms to a mature or functional form that serves bone growth in some specific way (Figure 6.5). Bone cells, like other connective tissue cells, are surrounded by an extracellular matrix of their making.

Osteogenic Cells Osteogenic cells, also called **osteoprogenitor cells**, are mitotically active stem cells found in the membranous periosteum and endosteum. In growing bones they are flattened or squamous cells. When stimulated, these cells differentiate into osteoblasts or bone lining cells (see below), while others persist as osteogenic cells.

Osteoblasts Osteoblasts are bone-forming cells that secrete the bone matrix. Like their close relatives, the fibroblasts and chondroblasts, they are actively mitotic. The unmineralized bone matrix they secrete includes collagen (90% of bone protein) and calcium-binding proteins that make up the initial unmineralized bone, or *osteoid*. As described later, osteoblasts also play a role in matrix calcification.

(a) **Osteogenic cell**	(b) **Osteoblast**	(c) **Osteocyte**	(d) **Osteoclast**
Stem cell	Matrix-synthesizing cell responsible for bone growth	Mature bone cell that monitors and maintains the mineralized bone matrix	Bone-resorbing cell

Figure 6.5 Comparison of different types of bone cells. The bone lining cell, similar in appearance to the osteogenic cell and similar to the osteocyte in function, is not illustrated.

Table 6.1	Bone Markings	
NAME OF BONE MARKING	**DESCRIPTION**	**ILLUSTRATIONS**
Projections That Are Sites of Muscle and Ligament Attachment		
Tuberosity (too"bĕ-ros'ĭ-te)	Large rounded projection; may be roughened	
Crest	Narrow ridge of bone; usually prominent	
Trochanter (tro-kan'ter)	Very large, blunt, irregularly shaped process (the only examples are on the femur)	
Line	Narrow ridge of bone; less prominent than a crest	
Tubercle (too'ber-kl)	Small rounded projection or process	
Epicondyle (ep"ĭ-kon'dĭl)	Raised area on or above a condyle	
Spine	Sharp, slender, often pointed projection	
Process	Any bony prominence	
Projections That Help to Form Joints		
Head	Bony expansion carried on a narrow neck	
Facet	Smooth, nearly flat articular surface	
Condyle (kon'dĭl)	Rounded articular projection	
Ramus (ra'mus)	Armlike bar of bone	
Depressions and Openings		
For Passage of Blood Vessels and Nerves		
Groove	Furrow	
Fissure	Narrow, slitlike opening	
Foramen (fo-ra'men)	Round or oval opening through a bone	
Notch	Indentation at the edge of a structure	
Others		
Meatus (me-a'tus)	Canal-like passageway	
Sinus	Cavity within a bone, filled with air and lined with mucous membrane	
Fossa (fos'ah)	Shallow, basinlike depression in a bone, often serving as an articular surface	

When actively depositing matrix, osteoblasts are cube shaped. When inactive, they resemble the flattened osteogenic cells or may differentiate into bone lining cells. When the osteoblasts become completely surrounded by the matrix being secreted, they become osteocytes.

Osteocytes The spidery **osteocytes** (Figure 6.5) are mature bone cells that occupy spaces (lacunae) that conform to their shape. Osteocytes monitor and maintain the bone matrix. If they die, the surrounding matrix is resorbed. Osteocytes also act as stress or strain "sensors" and respond to mechanical stimuli (bone loading, bone deformation, weightlessness). They communicate this information to the cells responsible for bone remodeling (osteoblasts and osteoclasts) so that bone matrix can be made or degraded as necessary to preserve calcium homeostasis. We discuss the bone-destroying *osteoclast* on p. 187 when we explore bone remodeling.

Bone Lining Cells   **Bone lining cells** are flat cells found on bone surfaces where bone remodeling is not going on. Like osteocytes, they are thought to help maintain the matrix. Bone lining cells on the external bone surface are also called *periosteal cells*, whereas those lining internal surfaces are called *endosteal cells*.

Osteoclasts   Derived from the same hematopoietic stem cells that differentiate into macrophages, **osteoclasts** are giant multinucleate cells located at sites of bone resorption. When actively resorbing (breaking down) bone, the osteoclasts rest in a shallow depression called a *resorption bay* and exhibit a distinctive *ruffled border* which directly contacts the bone. The deep plasma membrane infoldings of the ruffled border tremendously increase the surface area for enzymatically degrading the bones and seal off that area from the surrounding matrix.

Compact Bone

Although compact bone looks solid, a microscope reveals that it is riddled with passageways that serve as conduits for nerves and blood vessels (see Figure 6.7).

Osteon (Haversian System)   The structural unit of compact bone is called either the **osteon** (os'te-on) or the **Haversian system** (ha-ver'zhen). Each osteon is an elongated cylinder oriented parallel to the long axis of the bone. Functionally, osteons are tiny weight-bearing pillars.

As shown in the "exploded" view in **Figure 6.6**, an osteon is a group of hollow tubes of bone matrix, one placed outside the next like the growth rings of a tree trunk. Each matrix tube is a **lamella** (lah-mel'ah; "little plate"), and for this reason compact bone is often called **lamellar bone**. Although all of the collagen fibers in a particular lamella run in a single direction, the collagen fibers in adjacent lamellae always run in different directions. This alternating pattern is beautifully designed to withstand torsion stresses—the adjacent lamellae reinforce one another to resist twisting. You can think of the osteon's design as a "twister resister."

Collagen fibers are not the only part of bone lamellae that are beautifully ordered. The tiny crystals of bone salts align between the collagen fibrils and thus also alternate their direction in adjacent lamellae.

Canals and Canaliculi   Running through the core of each osteon is the **central canal**, or **Haversian canal**, containing small blood vessels and nerve fibers that serve the osteon's cells. Canals of a second type called **perforating canals**, or **Volkmann's canals** (folk'mahnz), lie at right angles to the long axis of the bone and connect the blood and nerve supply of the periosteum to those in the central canals and the medullary cavity **(Figure 6.7a)**. Unlike the central canals of osteons, the perforating canals are not surrounded by concentric lamellae, but like all other internal bone cavities, these canals are lined with endosteum.

Spider-shaped osteocytes (Figures 6.5c and 6.7b) occupy **lacunae** (*lac* = hollow; *una* = little) at the junctions of the lamellae. Hairlike canals called *canaliculi* (kan"ah-lik'u-li) connect the lacunae to each other and to the central canal.

Figure 6.6 A single osteon. The osteon is drawn as if pulled out like a telescope to illustrate the individual lamellae.

The manner in which canaliculi are formed is interesting. When bone is forming, the osteoblasts secreting bone matrix surround blood vessels and maintain contact with one another and local osteocytes by tentacle-like projections containing gap junctions. Then, as the newly secreted matrix hardens and the maturing cells become trapped within it, a system of tiny canals—the *canaliculi* filled with tissue fluid and containing the osteocyte extensions—is formed. The canaliculi tie all the osteocytes in a mature osteon together, allowing them to communicate and permitting nutrients and wastes to be relayed from one osteocyte to the next throughout the osteon. Although bone matrix is hard and impermeable to nutrients, its canaliculi and cell-to-cell relays (via gap junctions) allow bone cells to be well nourished.

Interstitial and Circumferential Lamellae   Not all the lamellae in compact bone are part of complete osteons. Lying between intact osteons are incomplete lamellae called **interstitial lamellae** (in"ter-stish'al) (Figure 6.7c, right photomicrograph). They either fill the gaps between forming osteons or are remnants of osteons that have been cut through by bone remodeling (discussed later). **Circumferential lamellae**, located just deep to the periosteum and just superficial to the endosteum, extend around the entire circumference of the diaphysis (Figure 6.7a) and effectively resist twisting of the long bone.

Spongy Bone

In contrast to compact bone, spongy bone looks like a poorly organized, even haphazard, tissue (see Figure 6.4 and Figure 6.3b). However, the trabeculae in spongy bone align precisely along lines of stress and help the bone resist stress. These tiny bone struts are as carefully positioned as the cables on a suspension bridge.

6

Figure 6.7 Microscopic anatomy of compact bone. (a) Diagram of a pie-shaped segment of compact bone. **(b)** Close-up of a portion of one osteon. Note the position of osteocytes in the lacunae. **(c)** SEM (left) of cross-sectional view of an osteon (410×). Light photomicrograph (right) of a cross-sectional view of an osteon (410×).

Only a few cells thick, trabeculae contain irregularly arranged lamellae and osteocytes interconnected by canaliculi. No osteons are present. Nutrients reach the osteocytes of spongy bone by diffusing through the canaliculi from capillaries in the endosteum surrounding the trabeculae.

Chemical Composition of Bone

Bone contains both organic and inorganic substances. *Organic components* include bone cells and osteoid. Its *inorganic components* are mineral salts.

Organic Components

The organic components of bone include its cells (osteogenic cells, osteoblasts, osteocytes, bone-lining cells, and osteoclasts) and **osteoid** (os'te-oid), the organic part of the matrix. Osteoid, which makes up approximately one-third of the matrix, includes ground substance (composed of proteoglycans and glycoproteins) and collagen fibers, both of which are made and secreted by osteoblasts. These organic substances, particularly collagen, contribute both to a bone's structure and to the flexibility and tensile strength that allow it to resist stretch and twisting.

Bone's resilience is thought to come from *sacrificial bonds* in or between collagen molecules. These bonds stretch and break easily on impact, dissipating energy to prevent the force from rising to a fracture value. In the absence of continued or additional trauma, most of the sacrificial bonds re-form.

Inorganic Components

The balance of bone tissue (65% by mass) consists of inorganic *hydroxyapatites* (hi-drok"se-ap'ah-tītz), or *mineral salts*, largely calcium phosphates present as tiny, tightly packed, needle-like crystals in and around collagen fibers in the extracellular matrix. The crystals account for the most notable characteristic of bone—its exceptional hardness, which allows it to resist compression.

The proper combination of organic and inorganic matrix elements makes bone exceedingly durable and strong without being brittle. Healthy bone is half as strong as steel in resisting compression and fully as strong as steel in resisting tension.

Because of the mineral salts they contain, bones last long after death and provide an enduring "monument." In fact, skeletal remains many centuries old can still reveal the shapes and sizes of ancient peoples, the kinds of work they did, and many of the ailments they suffered, such as arthritis. *Growth arrest lines*, horizontal lines on long bones, provide visible proof of illness when the body uses nutrients to fight disease and the bones stop growing.

☑ Check Your Understanding

10. Are crests, tubercles, and spines bony projections or depressions?
11. How does the structure of compact bone differ from that of spongy bone when viewed with the naked eye?
12. Which membrane lines the internal canals and covers the trabeculae of a bone?
13. Which component of bone—organic or inorganic—makes it hard?
14. Which cell has a ruffled border and acts to break down bone matrix?

For answers, see Appendix H.

Bone Development

✓ Compare and contrast intramembranous ossification and endochondral ossification.

✓ Describe the process of long bone growth that occurs at the epiphyseal plates.

Ossification and **osteogenesis** (os"te-o-jen'ĕ-sis) are synonyms meaning the process of bone formation (*os* = bone, *genesis* = beginning). In embryos this process leads to the formation of the bony skeleton. Later another form of ossification known as *bone growth* goes on until early adulthood as the body increases in size. Bones are capable of growing thicker throughout life. However, ossification in adults serves mainly for bone *remodeling* and repair.

Formation of the Bony Skeleton

Before week 8, the skeleton of a human embryo is constructed entirely from fibrous membranes and hyaline cartilage. Bone tissue begins to develop at about this time and eventually replaces most of the existing fibrous or cartilage structures.

- In *endochondral ossification* (*endo* = within, *chondro* = cartilage), a bone develops by replacing hyaline cartilage. The resulting bone is called a **cartilage**, or **endochondral**, **bone**.

- In *intramembranous ossification*, a bone develops from a fibrous membrane and the bone is called a **membrane bone**.

The beauty of using flexible structures (membranes and cartilages) to fashion the embryonic skeleton is that they can accommodate mitosis. Were the early skeleton composed of calcified bone tissue from the outset, growth would be much more difficult.

Endochondral Ossification

Except for the clavicles, essentially all bones below the base of the skull form by **endochondral ossification** (en"do-kon'dral). Beginning late in the second month of development, this process uses hyaline cartilage "bones" formed earlier as models, or patterns, for bone construction. It is more complex than intramembranous ossification because the hyaline cartilage must be broken down as ossification proceeds.

For example, the formation of a long bone typically begins in the center of the hyaline cartilage shaft at a region called the **primary ossification center**. First, blood vessels infiltrate the perichondrium covering the hyaline cartilage "bone," converting it to a vascularized periosteum. As a result of this change in nutrition, the underlying mesenchymal cells specialize into osteoblasts. The stage is now set for ossification to begin **(Figure 6.8)**:

① **A bone collar forms around the diaphysis of the hyaline cartilage model.** Osteoblasts of the newly converted periosteum secrete osteoid against the hyaline cartilage diaphysis, encasing it in a cuff or collar of bone called the *periosteal bone collar*.

② **Cartilage in the center of the diaphysis calcifies and then develops cavities.** As the bone collar forms, chondrocytes within the shaft hypertrophy (enlarge) and signal the surrounding cartilage matrix to calcify. Then, because calcified cartilage matrix is impermeable to diffusing nutrients, the chondrocytes die and the matrix begins to deteriorate. This deterioration opens up cavities, but the bone collar stabilizes the hyaline cartilage model. Elsewhere, the cartilage remains healthy and continues to grow briskly, causing the cartilage model to elongate.

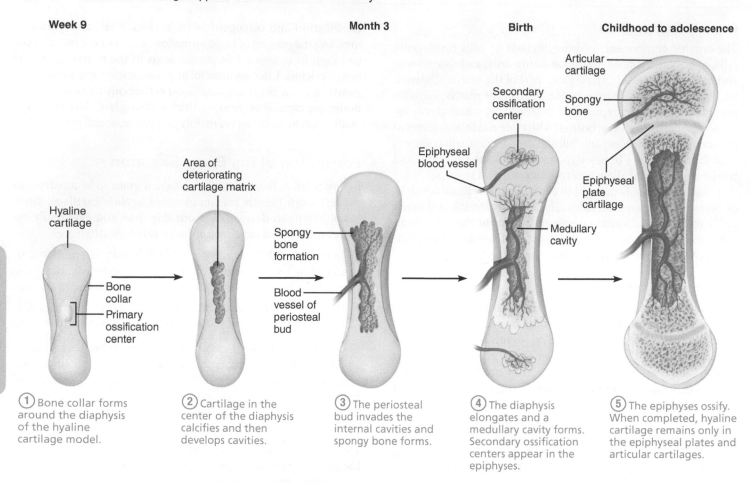

Week 9 | **Month 3** | **Birth** | **Childhood to adolescence**

① Bone collar forms around the diaphysis of the hyaline cartilage model.

② Cartilage in the center of the diaphysis calcifies and then develops cavities.

③ The periosteal bud invades the internal cavities and spongy bone forms.

④ The diaphysis elongates and a medullary cavity forms. Secondary ossification centers appear in the epiphyses.

⑤ The epiphyses ossify. When completed, hyaline cartilage remains only in the epiphyseal plates and articular cartilages.

Figure 6.8 Endochondral ossification in a long bone.

③ **The periosteal bud invades the internal cavities and spongy bone forms.** In month 3, the forming cavities are invaded by a collection of elements called the **periosteal bud**, which contains a nutrient artery and vein, nerve fibers, red marrow elements, osteogenic cells, and osteoclasts. The entering osteoclasts partially erode the calcified cartilage matrix, and the osteogenic cells become osteoblasts and secrete osteoid around the remaining calcified fragments of hyaline cartilage, forming bone-covered cartilage trabeculae. In this way, the earliest version of spongy bone forms in a developing long bone.

④ **The diaphysis elongates and a medullary cavity forms.** As the primary ossification center enlarges, osteoclasts break down the newly formed spongy bone and open up a medullary cavity in the center of the diaphysis. Throughout the fetal period (week 9 until birth), the rapidly growing epiphyses consist only of cartilage, and the hyaline cartilage models continue to elongate by division of viable cartilage cells at the epiphyses. Ossification "chases" cartilage formation along the length of the shaft as cartilage calcifies, erodes, and then is replaced by bony spicules on the epiphyseal surfaces facing the medullary cavity.

⑤ **The epiphyses ossify.** At birth, most of our long bones have a bony diaphysis surrounding remnants of spongy bone, a widening medullary cavity, and two cartilaginous epiphyses. Shortly before or after birth, **secondary ossification centers** appear in one or both epiphyses, and the epiphyses gain bony tissue. (Typically, the large long bones form secondary centers in both epiphyses, whereas the small long bones form only one secondary ossification center.) The cartilage in the center of the epiphysis calcifies and deteriorates, opening up cavities that allow a periosteal bud to enter. Then bone trabeculae appear, just as they did earlier in the primary ossification center.

In short bones, only the primary ossification center is formed. Most irregular bones develop from several distinct ossification centers.

Secondary ossification reproduces almost exactly the events of primary ossification, except that the spongy bone in the interior is retained and no medullary cavity forms in the epiphyses. When secondary ossification is complete, hyaline cartilage remains only at two places:

- On the epiphyseal surfaces, as the *articular cartilages*
- At the junction of the diaphysis and epiphysis, where it forms the *epiphyseal plates*

Labels for diagram 1:
- Mesenchymal cell
- Collagen fibril
- Ossification center
- Osteoid
- Osteoblast

① **Ossification centers appear in the fibrous connective tissue membrane.**
- Selected centrally located mesenchymal cells cluster and differentiate into osteoblasts, forming an ossification center that produces the first trabeculae of spongy bone.

Labels for diagram 2:
- Osteoblast
- Osteoid
- Osteocyte
- Newly calcified bone matrix

② **Osteoid is secreted within the fibrous membrane and calcifies.**
- Osteoblasts begin to secrete osteoid, which calcifies in a few days.
- Trapped osteoblasts become osteocytes.

Labels for diagram 3:
- Mesenchyme condensing to form the periosteum
- Trabeculae of woven bone
- Blood vessel

③ **Woven bone and periosteum form.**
- Accumulating osteoid is laid down between embryonic blood vessels in a manner that results in a network (instead of concentric lamellae) of trabeculae called woven bone.
- Vascularized mesenchyme condenses on the external face of the woven bone and becomes the periosteum.

Labels for diagram 4:
- Fibrous periosteum
- Osteoblast
- Plate of compact bone
- Diploë (spongy bone) cavities contain red marrow

④ **Lamellar bone replaces woven bone, just deep to the periosteum. Red marrow appears.**
- Trabeculae just deep to the periosteum thicken. Mature lamellar bone replaces them, forming compact bone plates.
- Spongy bone (diploë), consisting of distinct trabeculae, persists internally and its vascular tissue becomes red marrow.

Intramembranous Ossification

Intramembranous ossification forms the cranial bones of the skull (frontal, parietal, occipital, and temporal bones) and the clavicles. Most bones formed by this process are flat bones. At about week 8 of development, ossification begins within fibrous connective tissue membranes formed by *mesenchymal cells*. This process involves four major steps, depicted in **Figure 6.9**.

Postnatal Bone Growth

During infancy and youth, long bones lengthen entirely by interstitial growth of the epiphyseal plate cartilage and its replacement by bone, and all bones grow in thickness by appositional growth. Most bones stop growing during adolescence. However, some facial bones, such as those of the nose and lower jaw, continue to grow almost imperceptibly throughout life.

Growth in Length of Long Bones

Longitudinal bone growth mimics many of the events of endochondral ossification and depends on the presence of epiphyseal cartilage. The cartilage is relatively inactive on the side of the epiphyseal plate facing the epiphysis, a region called the *resting* or *quiescent zone*. But the epiphyseal plate cartilage abutting the diaphysis organizes into a pattern that allows fast, efficient growth. The cartilage cells here form tall columns, like coins in a stack. The cells at the "top" (epiphysis-facing) side of the stack abutting the resting zone comprise the *proliferation* or *growth zone* **(Figure 6.10)**. These cells divide quickly, pushing the epiphysis away from the diaphysis and lengthening the entire long bone.

Meanwhile, the older chondrocytes in the stack, which are closer to the diaphysis (*hypertrophic zone* in Figure 6.10), hypertrophy, and their lacunae erode and enlarge, leaving large interconnecting spaces. Subsequently, the surrounding cartilage matrix calcifies and these chondrocytes die and deteriorate, producing the *calcification zone*.

This leaves long slender spicules of calcified cartilage at the epiphysis-diaphysis junction, which look like stalactites hanging from the roof of a cave. These calcified spicules ultimately become part of the *ossification* or *osteogenic zone*, and are invaded by marrow elements from the medullary cavity. Osteoclasts partly erode the cartilage spicules, then osteoblasts quickly cover them with new bone, and ultimately spongy bone replaces them. Eventually as osteoclasts digest the spicule tips, the medullary cavity also lengthens. During growth, the epiphyseal plate maintains a constant thickness because the rate of cartilage growth on its epiphysis-facing side is balanced by its replacement with bony tissue on its diaphysis-facing side.

Longitudinal growth is accompanied by almost continuous remodeling of the epiphyseal ends to maintain the proportion between the diaphysis and epiphyses. Bone remodeling involves both new bone formation and bone resorption **(Figure 6.11)**.

Figure 6.9 **Intramembranous ossification.** Diagrams ③ and ④ represent much lower magnification than diagrams ① and ②.

Figure 6.10 Growth in length of a long bone occurs at the epiphyseal plate. The side of the epiphyseal plate facing the epiphysis contains resting cartilage cells. The cells of the epiphyseal plate proximal to the resting cartilage area are arranged in four zones—proliferation, hypertrophic, calcification, and ossification—from the region of the earliest stage of growth ① to the region where bone is replacing the cartilage ④ (115×).

We describe it in more detail later in conjunction with the changes that occur in adult bones.

As adolescence ends, the chondroblasts of the epiphyseal plates divide less often and the plates become thinner and thinner until they are entirely replaced by bone tissue. Longitudinal bone growth ends when the bone of the epiphysis and diaphysis fuses. This process, called *epiphyseal plate closure*, happens at about 18 years of age in females and 21 years of age in males. Once this has occurred, only the articular cartilage remains in bones. However, as noted earlier, an adult bone can still widen by appositional growth if stressed by excessive muscle activity or body weight.

Growth in Width (Thickness)

Growing bones widen as they lengthen. As with cartilages, bones increase in thickness or, in the case of long bones, diameter, by appositional growth. Osteoblasts beneath the periosteum secrete

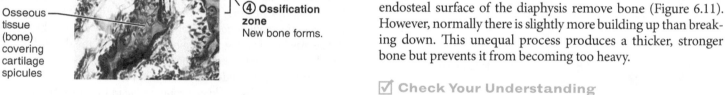

Figure 6.11 Long bone growth and remodeling during youth. The events at the left depict endochondral ossification that occurs at the articular cartilages and epiphyseal plates as the bone lengthens. Events at the right show bone remodeling during long bone growth to maintain proper bone proportions. The dashed red outline matches the view on the left.

bone matrix on the external bone surface as osteoclasts on the endosteal surface of the diaphysis remove bone (Figure 6.11). However, normally there is slightly more building up than breaking down. This unequal process produces a thicker, stronger bone but prevents it from becoming too heavy.

☑ Check Your Understanding

15. Bones don't begin with bone tissue. What do they begin with?
16. When describing endochondral ossification, some say "bone chases cartilage." What does that mean?
17. Where is the primary ossification center located in a long bone? Where is (are) the secondary ossification center(s) located?
18. As a long bone grows in length, what is happening in the hypertrophic zone of the epiphyseal plate?

For answers, see Appendix H.

Hormonal Regulation of Bone Growth

The bone growth that occurs until young adulthood is exquisitely controlled by a symphony of hormones. During infancy and childhood, the single most important stimulus of epiphyseal plate activity is *growth hormone* released by the anterior pituitary gland. Thyroid hormones modulate the activity of growth hormone, ensuring that the skeleton has proper proportions as it grows.

At puberty, male and female sex hormones (testosterone and estrogens, respectively) are released in increasing amounts. Initially these sex hormones promote the growth spurt typical of adolescence, as well as the masculinization or feminization of specific parts of the skeleton. Later the hormones induce epiphyseal closure, ending longitudinal bone growth.

Excesses or deficits of any of these hormones can result in abnormal skeletal growth. For example, hypersecretion of growth hormone in children results in excessive height (gigantism), and deficits of growth hormone or thyroid hormone produce characteristic types of dwarfism.

Bone Homeostasis: Remodeling and Repair

✓ Compare the locations and remodeling functions of the osteoblasts, osteocytes, and osteoclasts.

✓ Explain how hormones and physical stress regulate bone remodeling.

✓ Describe the steps of fracture repair.

Bones appear to be the most lifeless of body organs, and may even summon images of a graveyard. But as you have just learned, bone is a dynamic and active tissue, and small-scale changes in bone architecture occur continually. Every week we recycle 5–7% of our bone mass, and as much as half a gram of calcium may enter or leave the adult skeleton each day! Spongy bone is replaced every three to four years; compact bone, every ten years or so. This is fortunate because when bone remains in place for long periods more of the calcium salts crystallize (see description below) and the bone becomes more brittle—ripe conditions for fracture.

When we break bones—the most common disorder of bone homeostasis—they undergo a remarkable process of self-repair.

Bone Remodeling

In the adult skeleton, bone deposit and bone resorption occur at the surfaces of both the periosteum and the endosteum. Together, the two processes constitute **bone remodeling**. "Packets" of adjacent osteoblasts and osteoclasts called *remodeling units* coordinate bone remodeling (with help from the stress-sensing osteocytes).

In healthy young adults, total bone mass remains constant, an indication that the rates of bone deposit and resorption are essentially equal. Remodeling does not occur uniformly, however. For example, the distal part of the femur, or thigh bone, is fully replaced every five to six months, whereas its shaft is altered much more slowly.

Bone Deposit

An *osteoid seam*—an unmineralized band of gauzy-looking bone matrix 10–12 micrometers (μm) wide—marks areas of new matrix deposits by osteoblasts. Between the osteoid seam and the older mineralized bone, there is an abrupt transition called the *calcification front*. Because the osteoid seam is always of constant width and the change from unmineralized to mineralized matrix is sudden, it seems that the osteoid must mature for about a week before it can calcify.

The precise trigger for calcification is still controversial, but mechanical signals are definitely involved. One critical factor is the product of the local concentrations of calcium and phosphate (P_i) ions (the $Ca^{2+} \cdot P_i$ product) in the endosteal cavity. When the $Ca^{2+} \cdot P_i$ product reaches a certain level, tiny crystals of hydroxyapatite form spontaneously and catalyze further crystallization of calcium salts in the area. Other factors involved are matrix proteins that bind and concentrate calcium, and the enzyme *alkaline phosphatase* (shed in *matrix vesicles* by the osteoblasts), which is essential for mineralization. Once proper conditions are present, calcium salts are deposited all at once and with great precision throughout the "matured" matrix.

Bone Resorption

As noted earlier, the giant **osteoclasts** accomplish **bone resorption**. Osteoclasts move along a bone surface, digging depressions or grooves as they break down the bone matrix. The ruffled border of the osteoclast clings tightly to the bone, sealing off the area of bone destruction and secreting *lysosomal enzymes* that digest the organic matrix and *protons* (H^+). The resulting acidic brew in the resorption bay converts the calcium salts into soluble forms that pass easily into solution. Osteoclasts may also phagocytize the demineralized matrix and dead osteocytes. The digested matrix end products, growth factors, and dissolved minerals are then endocytosed, transported across the osteoclast (by transcytosis), and released at the opposite side. There they enter the interstitial fluid and then the blood.

When resorption of a given area of bone is completed, the osteoclasts undergo apoptosis. There is much to learn about osteoclast activation, but PTH and proteins secreted by T cells of the immune system appear to be important.

Control of Remodeling

Remodeling goes on continuously in the skeleton, regulated by genetic factors and two control loops that serve different "masters." One is a negative feedback hormonal loop that maintains Ca^{2+} homeostasis in the blood. The other involves responses to mechanical and gravitational forces acting on the skeleton.

The hormonal feedback becomes much more meaningful when you understand calcium's importance in the body. Ionic calcium is necessary for an amazing number of physiological processes, including transmission of nerve impulses, muscle contraction, blood coagulation, secretion by glands and nerve cells, and cell division.

The human body contains 1200–1400 g of calcium, more than 99% present as bone minerals. Most of the remainder is in body cells. Less than 1.5 g is present in blood, and the hormonal control loop normally maintains blood Ca^{2+} within the narrow range of 9–11 mg per dl (100 ml) of blood. Calcium is absorbed from the intestine under the control of vitamin D metabolites. The daily dietary calcium requirement is 400–800 mg from birth until age 10, and 1200–1500 mg from ages 11 to 24.

Hormonal Controls The hormonal controls primarily involve **parathyroid hormone (PTH)**, produced by the parathyroid glands. To a much lesser extent **calcitonin** (kal″sĭ-to′nin), produced by parafollicular cells (C cells) of the thyroid gland, may be involved.

Figure 6.12 **Parathyroid hormone (PTH) control of blood calcium levels.**

When blood levels of ionic calcium decline, PTH is released (**Figure 6.12**). The increased PTH level stimulates osteoclasts to resorb bone, releasing calcium into blood. Osteoclasts are no respecters of matrix age: When activated, they break down both old and new matrix. As blood concentrations of calcium rise, the stimulus for PTH release ends. The decline of PTH reverses its effects and causes blood Ca^{2+} levels to fall.

In humans, calcitonin appears to be a hormone in search of a function because its effects on calcium homeostasis are negligible. When administered at pharmacological (abnormally high) doses, it does lower blood calcium levels temporarily.

These hormonal controls act to preserve blood calcium homeostasis, not the skeleton's strength or well-being. In fact, if blood calcium levels are low for an extended time, the bones become so demineralized that they develop large, punched-out-looking holes. Thus, the bones serve as a storehouse from which ionic calcium is drawn as needed.

Homeostatic Imbalance 6.1

Minute changes from the homeostatic range for blood calcium can lead to severe neuromuscular problems ranging from hyperexcitability (when blood Ca^{2+} levels are too low) to nonresponsiveness and inability to function (with high blood Ca^{2+} levels). In addition, sustained high blood levels of Ca^{2+}, a condition known as *hypercalcemia* (hi″per-kal-se′me-ah), can lead to undesirable deposits of calcium salts in the blood vessels, kidneys, and other soft organs, which may hamper their function. ✚

Other hormones are also involved in modifying bone density and bone turnover. For example, *leptin*, a hormone released by adipose tissue, plays a role in regulating bone density. Best known for its effects on weight and energy balance (see pp. 940–941), in animal studies leptin appears to inhibit osteoblasts. It does so through an additional pathway mediated by the hypothalamus, which activates sympathetic nerves serving bones. However, the full scope of leptin's bone-modifying activity in humans is still being worked out.

It is also evident that the brain, intestine, and skeleton have ongoing conversations that help regulate the balance between bone formation and destruction, with serotonin serving as a hormonal go-between. *Serotonin* is better known as a neurotransmitter that regulates mood and sleep, but most of the body's serotonin is made in the gut (intestine) and the blood-brain barrier (see Chapter 12) bars it from entering the brain. The role of gut serotonin is still poorly understood. What is known is that when we eat, serotonin is secreted and circulated via the blood to the bones where it interferes with osteoblast activity. Reduction of bone turnover after eating may lock calcium in bone when new calcium is flooding into the bloodstream.

This is a troubling finding for those taking Prozac and other antidepressant drugs that inhibit serotonin uptake, making it more available to bone cells. Such patients have lower bone density and suffer more fractures than people not taking these drugs.

Response to Mechanical Stress The second set of controls regulating bone remodeling, bone's response to mechanical stress (muscle pull) and gravity, keeps the bones strong where stressors are acting.

Wolff's law holds that a bone grows or remodels in response to the demands placed on it. The first thing to understand is that a bone's anatomy reflects the common stresses it encounters. For example, a bone is loaded (stressed) whenever weight bears down on it or muscles pull on it. This loading is usually off center and tends to bend the bone. Bending compresses the bone on one side and subjects it to tension (stretching) on the other (**Figure 6.13**).

Load here
(body weight)

Head of
femur

Tension
here

Compression
here

Point of
no stress

Figure 6.13 Bone anatomy and bending stress. Body weight transmitted to the head of the femur (thigh bone) threatens to bend the bone along the indicated arc, compressing it on one side (converging arrows on right) and stretching it on the other side (diverging arrows on left). Because these two forces cancel each other internally, much less bone material is needed internally than superficially.

(a)

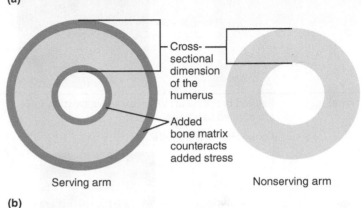

Cross-sectional dimension of the humerus

Added bone matrix counteracts added stress

Serving arm

Nonserving arm

(b)

Figure 6.14 Vigorous exercise can strengthen bone. The brown rings in (b) represent differences in the cross-sectional areas of the serving and nonserving arms of a professional tennis player. Average increases in bone rigidity and strength of 62% and 45%, respectively, were recorded in the serving arms. The structural changes were more pronounced in those who began training at an early age. *Source:* C. B. Ruff, "Gracilization of the Modern Human Skeleton," *American Scientist* 94(6): p. 513, Nov–Dec 2006.

As a result of these mechanical stressors, long bones are thickest midway along the diaphysis, exactly where bending stresses are greatest (bend a stick and it will split near the middle). Both compression and tension are minimal toward the center of the bone (they cancel each other out), so a bone can "hollow out" for lightness (using spongy bone instead of compact bone) without jeopardy.

Wolff's law also explains several other observations:

■ Handedness (being right or left handed) results in the bones of one upper limb being thicker than those of the less-used limb. Vigorous exercise of the most-used limb leads to large increases in bone strength **(Figure 6.14)**.

■ Curved bones are thickest where they are most likely to buckle.

■ The trabeculae of spongy bone form trusses, or struts, along lines of compression.

■ Large, bony projections occur where heavy, active muscles attach. The bones of weight lifters have enormous thickenings at the attachment sites of the most-used muscles.

Wolff's law also explains the featureless bones of the fetus and the atrophied bones of bedridden people—situations in which bones are not stressed.

How do mechanical forces communicate with the cells responsible for remodeling? Deforming a bone produces an electrical current. Because compressed and stretched regions are oppositely charged, it has been suggested that electrical signals direct remodeling. This principle underlies some of the devices used to speed bone repair and heal fractures. Fluid flows within the canaliculi also appear to provide stimuli that direct the remodeling process.

The skeleton is continuously subjected to both hormonal influences and mechanical forces. At the risk of constructing too large a building on too small a foundation, we can speculate that:

■ Hormonal controls determine *whether* and *when* remodeling occurs in response to changing blood calcium levels.

■ Mechanical stress determines *where* remodeling occurs.

For example, when bone must be broken down to increase blood calcium levels, PTH is released and targets the osteoclasts.

Table 6.2	Common Types of Fractures		
FRACTURE TYPE	**DESCRIPTION AND COMMENTS**	**FRACTURE TYPE**	**DESCRIPTION AND COMMENTS**
Comminuted	Bone fragments into three or more pieces. Particularly common in the aged, whose bones are more brittle	**Compression**	Bone is crushed. Common in porous bones (i.e., osteoporotic bones) subjected to extreme trauma, as in a fall
Spiral	Ragged break occurs when excessive twisting forces are applied to a bone. Common sports fracture	**Epiphyseal**	Epiphysis separates from the diaphysis along the epiphyseal plate. Tends to occur where cartilage cells are dying and calcification of the matrix is occurring
Depressed	Broken bone portion is pressed inward. Typical of skull fracture	**Greenstick**	Bone breaks incompletely, much in the way a green twig breaks. Only one side of the shaft breaks; the other side bends. Common in children, whose bones have relatively more organic matrix and are more flexible than those of adults

Crushed vertebra

Figure 6.15 **Stages in the healing of a bone fracture.**

However, mechanical forces determine which osteoclasts are most sensitive to PTH stimulation, so that bone in the least stressed areas (which is temporarily dispensable) is broken down.

Bone Repair

Despite their remarkable strength, bones are susceptible to **fractures**, or breaks. During youth, most fractures result from exceptional trauma that twists or smashes the bones (sports injuries, automobile accidents, and falls, for example). In old age, most fractures occur as bones thin and weaken.

Fracture Classification

Fractures may be classified by

- Position of the bone ends after fracture: In *nondisplaced fractures*, the bone ends retain their normal position. In *displaced fractures*, the bone ends are out of normal alignment.

- Completeness of the break: If the bone is broken through, the fracture is a *complete fracture*. If not, it is an *incomplete fracture*.

- Whether the bone ends penetrate the skin: If so, the fracture is an *open (compound) fracture*. If not, it is a *closed (simple) fracture*.

In addition to these three either-or classifications, all fractures can be described in terms of the location of the fracture, its external appearance, and/or the nature of the break **(Table 6.2)**.

Fracture Treatment and Repair

Treatment involves *reduction*, the realignment of the broken bone ends. In *closed (external) reduction*, the physician's hands coax the bone ends into position. In *open (internal) reduction*, the bone ends are secured together surgically with pins or wires.

After the broken bone is reduced, it is immobilized either by a cast or traction to allow healing. A simple fracture of small or medium-sized bones in young adults heals in six to eight weeks,

but it takes much longer for large, weight-bearing bones and for bones of elderly people (because of their poorer circulation).

Repair in a simple fracture involves four major stages **(Figure 6.15)**:

1. **A hematoma forms.** When a bone breaks, blood vessels in the bone and periosteum, and perhaps in surrounding tissues, are torn and hemorrhage. As a result, a **hematoma** (he"mah-to'mah), a mass of clotted blood, forms at the fracture site. Soon, bone cells deprived of nutrition die, and the tissue at the site becomes swollen, painful, and inflamed.

2. **Fibrocartilaginous callus forms.** Within a few days, several events lead to the formation of soft *granulation tissue*, also called the *soft callus* (kal'us; "hard skin"). Capillaries grow into the hematoma and phagocytic cells invade the area and begin cleaning up the debris. Meanwhile, fibroblasts and cartilage and osteogenic cells invade the fracture site from the nearby periosteum and endosteum and begin reconstructing the bone. The fibroblasts produce collagen fibers that span the break and connect the broken bone ends. Some precursor cells differentiate into chondroblasts that secrete cartilage matrix. Within this mass of repair tissue, osteoblasts begin forming spongy bone. The cartilage cells farthest from the capillaries secrete an externally bulging cartilaginous matrix that later calcifies. This entire mass of repair tissue, now called the **fibrocartilaginous callus**, splints the broken bone.

3. **Bony callus forms.** Within a week, new bone trabeculae appear in the fibrocartilaginous callus and gradually convert it to a **bony (hard) callus** of spongy bone. Bony callus formation continues until a firm union forms about two months later. This process generally repeats the events of endochondral ossification.

4. **Bone remodeling occurs.** Beginning during bony callus formation and continuing for several months after, the bony callus is remodeled. The excess material on the diaphysis exterior and within the medullary cavity is removed, and

compact bone is laid down to reconstruct the shaft walls. The final structure of the remodeled area resembles the original unbroken bony region because it responds to the same set of mechanical stressors.

☑ **Check Your Understanding**

19. If osteoclasts in a long bone are more active than osteoblasts, how will bone mass change?
20. Which stimulus—PTH (a hormone) or mechanical forces acting on the skeleton—is more important in maintaining homeostatic blood calcium levels?
21. How does an open fracture differ from a closed fracture?
22. How do bone growth and bone remodeling differ?

For answers, see Appendix H.

Homeostatic Imbalances of Bone

✓ Contrast the disorders of bone remodeling seen in osteoporosis, osteomalacia, and Paget's disease.

Imbalances between bone deposit and bone resorption underlie nearly every disease that affects the human skeleton.

Osteomalacia and Rickets

Osteomalacia (os"te-o-mah-la′she-ah; "soft bones") includes a number of disorders in which the bones are poorly mineralized. Osteoid is produced, but calcium salts are not adequately deposited, so bones are soft and weak. The main symptom is pain when weight is put on the affected bones.

Rickets is the analogous disease in children. Because young bones are still growing rapidly, rickets is much more severe than adult osteomalacia. Bowed legs and deformities of the pelvis, skull, and rib cage are common. Because the epiphyseal plates cannot calcify, they continue to widen, and the ends of long bones become visibly enlarged and abnormally long.

Osteomalacia and rickets are caused by insufficient calcium in the diet or by a vitamin D deficiency. Drinking vitamin D–fortified milk and exposing the skin to sunlight (which spurs the body to form vitamin D) usually cure these disorders. Although the seeming elimination of rickets in the United States has been heralded as a public health success, rickets still rears its head in isolated situations. For example, if a mother who breast-feeds her infant becomes vitamin D deficient because of sun-deprivation or dreary winter weather, the infant too will be vitamin D deficient and will develop rickets.

Osteoporosis

For most of us, the phrase "bone problems of the elderly" brings to mind the stereotype of a victim of osteoporosis—a hunched-over old woman shuffling behind her walker. **Osteoporosis** (os"te-o-po-ro′sis) refers to a group of diseases in which bone resorption outpaces bone deposit. The bones become so fragile

(a) Normal bone

(b) Osteoporotic bone

Figure 6.16 The contrasting architecture of normal versus osteoporotic bone. Scanning electron micrographs, 300×.

that something as simple as a hearty sneeze or stepping off a curb can cause them to break. The composition of the matrix remains normal but bone mass declines, and the bones become porous and light **(Figure 6.16)**.

Even though osteoporosis affects the entire skeleton, the spongy bone of the spine is most vulnerable, and compression fractures of the vertebrae are common. The femur, particularly its neck, is also very susceptible to fracture (a *broken hip*) in people with osteoporosis.

Risk Factors for Osteoporosis

Osteoporosis occurs most often in the aged, particularly in postmenopausal women. Although men develop it to a lesser degree, 30% of American women between the ages of 60 and 70 have osteoporosis, and 70% have it by age 80. Moreover, 30% of all Caucasian women (the most susceptible group) will experience a bone fracture due to osteoporosis.

Sex hormones—androgens in males and estrogens in females—help maintain the health and normal density of the skeleton by restraining osteoclasts and promoting deposit of new bone. After menopause, however, estrogen secretion wanes, and estrogen deficiency is strongly implicated in osteoporosis in older women.

Several other factors can contribute to osteoporosis:

- Petite body form
- Insufficient exercise to stress the bones
- A diet poor in calcium and protein
- Abnormal vitamin D receptors
- Smoking (which reduces estrogen levels)
- Hormone-related conditions such as hyperthyroidism, low blood levels of thyroid-stimulating hormone, and diabetes mellitus

Osteoporosis can develop at any age as a result of immobility. It can also occur in males with prostate cancer who are being treated with androgen-suppressing drugs.

Treating Osteoporosis

Osteoporosis has traditionally been treated with calcium and vitamin D supplements, weight-bearing exercise, and *hormone (estrogen) replacement therapy (HRT)*. Frustratingly, HRT slows the loss of bone but does not reverse it. Additionally, because of the increased risk of heart attack, stroke, and breast cancer associated with estrogen replacement therapy, it is a controversial treatment these days. Although not a substitute for HRT, estrogenic compounds in soy products (principally the isoflavones daidzein and genistein) offer a good addition or adjunct for some patients.

Newer drugs are available. Bisphosphonates decrease osteoclast activity and number, and partially reverse osteoporosis in the spine. Selective estrogen receptor modulators (SERMs), such as raloxifene, dubbed "estrogen light," mimic estrogen's beneficial bone-sparing properties without targeting the uterus or breast. Additionally, *statins*, drugs used to lower cholesterol levels, have an unexpected side effect of increasing bone mineral density up to 8% over four years. The monoclonal antibody drug *denosumab* significantly reduces fractures in men fighting prostate cancer and improves bone density in the elderly.

Preventing Osteoporosis

How can osteoporosis be prevented (or at least delayed)? The first requirement is to get enough calcium while your bones are still increasing in density (bones reach their peak density during early adulthood). Second, keep in mind that excessive intake of carbonated beverages and alcohol leaches minerals from bone and decreases bone density. Finally, get plenty of weight-bearing exercise (walking, jogging, tennis, etc.) throughout life. This will increase bone mass above normal values and provide a greater buffer against age-related bone loss.

Paget's Disease

Often discovered by accident when X rays are taken for some other reason, **Paget's disease** (paj′ets) is characterized by excessive and haphazard bone deposit and resorption. The newly formed bone, called *Pagetic bone*, is hastily made and has an abnormally high ratio of spongy bone to compact bone. This,

along with reduced mineralization, causes a spotty weakening of the bones. Late in the disease, osteoclast activity wanes, but osteoblasts continue to work, often forming irregular bone thickenings or filling the marrow cavity with Pagetic bone.

Paget's disease may affect any part of the skeleton, but it is usually a localized condition. The spine, pelvis, femur, and skull are most often involved and become increasingly deformed and painful. It rarely occurs before age 40, and it affects about 3% of North American elderly people. Its cause is unknown, but a virus may trigger it. Drug therapies include calcitonin (administered by a nasal inhaler), and the newer bisphosphonates, which have shown success in preventing bone breakdown.

☑ Check Your Understanding

23. Which bone disorder is characterized by excessive deposit of weak, poorly mineralized bone?
24. What are three measures that may help to maintain healthy bone density?
25. What name is given to "adult rickets"?

For answers, see Appendix H.

Developmental Aspects of Bones: Timing of Events

✓ Describe the timing and cause of changes in bone architecture and bone mass throughout life.

Bones are on a precise schedule from the time they form until death. The mesoderm germ layer gives rise to embryonic mesenchymal cells, which in turn produce the membranes and cartilages that form the embryonic skeleton. These structures then ossify according to an amazingly predictable timetable that allows fetal age to be determined easily from either X rays or sonograms. Although each bone has its own developmental schedule, most long bones begin ossifying by 8 weeks after conception and have well-developed primary ossification centers by 12 weeks **(Figure 6.17)**.

Birth to Young Adulthood

At birth, most long bones of the skeleton are well ossified except for their epiphyses. After birth, secondary ossification centers develop in a predictable sequence. The epiphyseal plates persist and provide for long bone growth all through childhood and the sex hormone–mediated growth spurt at adolescence. By age 25, nearly all bones are completely ossified and skeletal growth ceases.

Age-Related Changes in Bone

In children and adolescents, bone formation exceeds bone resorption. In young adults, these processes are in balance, and in old age, resorption predominates. Despite the environmental factors (discussed earlier) that influence bone density, genetics still plays the major role in determining how much a person's bone density will change over a lifetime. A single gene that codes for vitamin D's cellular docking site helps determine both

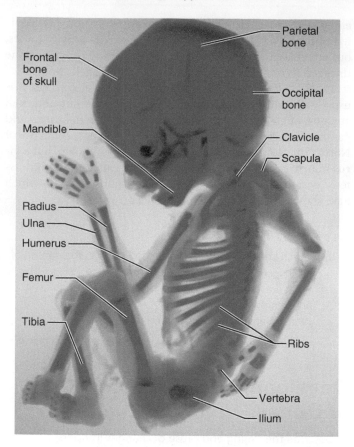

Figure 6.17 **Fetal primary ossification centers at 12 weeks.**
The darker areas indicate primary ossification centers in the skeleton
of a 12-week-old fetus.

the tendency to accumulate bone mass during early life and a
person's risk of osteoporosis later in life.

Beginning in the fourth decade of life, bone mass decreases
with age. The only exception appears to be in bones of the skull.
Among young adults, skeletal mass is generally greater in males
than in females. Age-related bone loss is faster in whites than in
blacks (who have greater bone density to begin with) and faster
in females than in males.

Qualitative changes also occur: More osteons remain incompletely formed, mineralization is less complete, and the amount
of nonviable bone increases, reflecting a diminished blood supply to the bones in old age. These age-related changes are also
bad news because fractures heal more slowly in old people.

Electrical stimulation of fracture sites and daily ultrasound
treatments hasten repair and healing. Presumably electrical
fields inhibit PTH stimulation of osteoclasts and induce formation of growth factors that stimulate osteoblasts.

☑ Check Your Understanding

26. What is the status of bone structure at birth?
27. The decrease in bone mass that begins in the fourth decade
of life affects nearly all bones. What are the exceptions?

For answers, see Appendix H.

This chapter has examined skeletal cartilages and bones—their
architecture, composition, and dynamic nature. We have also discussed the role of bones in maintaining overall body homeostasis,
as summarized in *System Connections*. Now we are ready to look
at the individual bones of the skeleton and how they contribute to
its functions, both collectively and individually.

Chapter Summary

 For more chapter study tools, go to the Study Area of
MasteringA&P at **www.masteringaandp.com**.
There you will find:

- Interactive Physiology **iP**
- A&PFlix **A&PFlix**
- Practice Anatomy Lab **PAL**
- PhysioEx **PEx**
- Videos, Practice Quizzes and Tests, MP3 Tutor Sessions, Case
  Studies, and much more!

Skeletal Cartilages   (pp. 173–174)

Basic Structure, Types, and Locations   (p. 174)

1. A skeletal cartilage exhibits chondrocytes housed in lacunae
   (cavities) within the extracellular matrix (ground substance and
   fibers). It contains large amounts of water (which accounts for its
   resilience), lacks nerve fibers, is avascular, and is surrounded by a
   fibrous perichondrium that resists expansion.
2. Hyaline cartilages appear glassy; the fibers are collagenous. They
   provide support with flexibility and resilience and are the most

abundant skeletal cartilages, accounting for the articular, costal,
respiratory, and nasal cartilages.

3. Elastic cartilages contain abundant elastic fibers, in addition to
   collagen fibers, and are more flexible than hyaline cartilages. They
   support the outer ear and epiglottis.
4. Fibrocartilages, which contain thick collagen fibers, are the
   most compressible cartilages and resist stretching. They form
   intervertebral discs and knee joint cartilages.

Growth of Cartilage   (p. 174)

5. Cartilages grow from within (interstitial growth) and by adding
   new cartilage tissue at the periphery (appositional growth).

Classification of Bones   (pp. 174–176)

1. Bones are classified as long, short, flat, or irregular on the basis of
   their shape and their proportion of compact or spongy bone.

Functions of Bones   (pp. 176–177)

1. Bones give the body shape; protect and support body organs;
   provide levers for muscles to pull on; store calcium and other
   minerals; store growth factors and triglyceride; and are the site of
   blood cell and osteocalcin production.

Homeostatic Interrelationships Between the Skeletal System and Other Body Systems

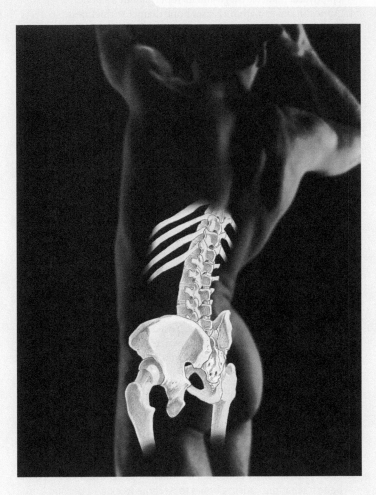

Integumentary System   Chapter 5

- Skeletal system provides support for body organs including the skin
- Skin provides vitamin D needed for proper calcium absorption and use

Muscular System   Chapters 9–10

- Skeletal system provides levers plus ionic calcium for muscle activity
- Muscle pull on bones increases bone strength and viability; helps determine bone shape

Nervous System   Chapters 11–15

- Skeletal system protects brain and spinal cord; provides depot for calcium ions needed for neural function
- Nerves innervate bone and joint capsules, providing for pain and joint sense

Endocrine System   Chapter 16

- Skeletal system provides some bony protection; stores calcium needed for second-messenger signaling mechanisms
- Hormones regulate uptake and release of calcium from bone; promote long bone growth and maturation

Cardiovascular System   Chapters 17–19

- Bone marrow cavities provide site for blood cell formation; matrix stores calcium needed for cardiac muscle activity
- Cardiovascular system delivers nutrients and oxygen to bones; carries away wastes

Lymphatic System/Immunity   Chapters 20–21

- Skeletal system provides some protection to lymphatic organs; bone marrow is site of origin for lymphocytes involved in immune response
- Lymphatic system drains leaked tissue fluids; immune cells protect against pathogens

Respiratory System   Chapter 22

- Skeletal system protects lungs by enclosure (rib cage)
- Respiratory system provides oxygen; disposes of carbon dioxide

Digestive System   Chapter 23

- Skeletal system provides some bony protection to intestines, pelvic organs, and liver
- Digestive system provides nutrients needed for bone health and growth

Urinary System   Chapters 25–26

- Skeletal system protects pelvic organs (urinary bladder, etc.)
- Urinary system activates vitamin D; disposes of nitrogenous wastes

Reproductive System   Chapter 27

- Skeletal system protects some reproductive organs by enclosure
- Gonads produce hormones that influence the form of the skeleton and epiphyseal closure

6

Bone Structure   (pp. 177–183)

Gross Anatomy   (pp. 177–179)

1. Flat bones consist of two thin plates of compact bone enclosing a diploë (spongy bone layer). Short and irregular bones resemble flat bones structurally.
2. A long bone is composed of a diaphysis (shaft) and epiphyses (ends). The medullary cavity of the diaphysis contains yellow marrow; the epiphyses contain spongy bone. The epiphyseal line is the remnant of the epiphyseal plate. Periosteum covers the diaphysis; endosteum lines inner bone cavities. Hyaline cartilage covers joint surfaces.
3. In adults, hematopoietic tissue (red marrow) is found within the diploë of flat bones and occasionally within the epiphyses of long bones. In infants, red marrow is also found in the medullary cavity.
4. Bone markings are important anatomical landmarks that reveal sites of muscle attachment, points of articulation, and sites of blood vessel and nerve passage.

Microscopic Anatomy of Bone   (pp. 179–182)

5. There are five types of bone cells—osteogenic cells (bone stem cells), osteoblasts (matrix-synthesizing cells), osteocytes (bone matrix maintenance cells), bone lining cells (line surfaces where no bone activity is ongoing), and osteoclasts (bone destruction cells).
6. The structural unit of compact bone, the osteon, consists of a central canal surrounded by concentric lamellae of bone matrix. Osteocytes, embedded in lacunae, are connected to each other and the central canal by canaliculi.
7. Spongy bone has slender trabeculae containing irregular lamellae, which enclose red marrow–filled cavities.

Chemical Composition of Bone   (pp. 182–183)

8. Bone is composed of living cells and matrix. The extracellular matrix includes osteoid, organic substances that are secreted by osteoblasts and give the bone tensile strength. Its inorganic (mineral) components, the hydroxyapatites (calcium salts), make bone hard.

Bone Development   (pp. 183–187)

Formation of the Bony Skeleton   (pp. 183–185)

1. Intramembranous ossification forms the clavicles and most skull bones. The ground substance of the bone matrix is deposited between collagen fibers within the fibrous membrane to form bone. Eventually, compact bone plates enclose the diploë.
2. Most bones are formed by endochondral ossification of a hyaline cartilage model. Osteoblasts beneath the periosteum secrete bone matrix on the cartilage model, forming the bone collar. As the cartilage model deteriorates, internal cavities open up, allowing periosteal bud entry. Bone matrix is deposited around the cartilage remnants but is later broken down.

Postnatal Bone Growth   (pp. 185–187)

3. Long bones increase in length by interstitial growth of the epiphyseal plate cartilage and its replacement by bone.
4. Appositional growth increases bone diameter/thickness.

Bone Homeostasis: Remodeling and Repair   (pp. 187–192)

Bone Remodeling   (pp. 187–191)

1. Bone is continually deposited and resorbed in response to hormonal and mechanical stimuli. Together these processes constitute bone remodeling.
2. An unmineralized osteoid seam appears at areas of new bone deposit; calcium salts are deposited a few days later.
3. Osteoclasts release lysosomal enzymes and acids on bone surfaces to be resorbed. The dissolved products are transcytosed to the opposite face of the osteoclast for release to the extracellular fluid.
4. The hormonal controls of bone remodeling serve blood calcium homeostasis. When blood calcium levels decline, PTH is released and stimulates osteoclasts to digest bone matrix, releasing ionic calcium. As blood calcium levels rise, PTH secretion declines.
5. Mechanical stress and gravity acting on the skeleton help maintain skeletal strength. Bones thicken, develop heavier prominences, or rearrange their trabeculae in sites where stressed.

Bone Repair   (pp. 191–192)

6. Fractures are treated by open or closed reduction. The healing process involves formation of a hematoma, a fibrocartilaginous callus, a bony callus, and bone remodeling, in succession.

Homeostatic Imbalances of Bone   (pp. 192–193)

1. Imbalances between bone formation and resorption underlie all skeletal disorders.
2. Osteomalacia and rickets occur when bones are inadequately mineralized. The bones become soft and deformed. The most frequent cause is inadequate vitamin D.
3. Osteoporosis is any condition in which bone breakdown outpaces bone formation, causing bones to become weak and porous. Postmenopausal women are particularly susceptible.
4. Paget's disease is characterized by excessive and abnormal bone remodeling.

Developmental Aspects of Bones: Timing of Events (pp. 193–194)

1. Osteogenesis is predictable and precisely timed.
2. Longitudinal long bone growth continues until the end of adolescence. Skeletal mass increases dramatically during puberty and adolescence, when formation exceeds resorption.
3. Bone mass is fairly constant in young adulthood, but beginning in the 40s, bone resorption exceeds formation.

Review Questions

Multiple Choice/Matching

(Some questions have more than one correct answer. Select the best answer or answers from the choices given.)

1. Which is a function of the skeletal system? (a) support, (b) hematopoietic site, (c) storage, (d) providing levers for muscle activity, (e) all of these.
2. A bone with approximately the same width, length, and height is most likely (a) a long bone, (b) a short bone, (c) a flat bone, (d) an irregular bone.
3. The shaft of a long bone is properly called the (a) epiphysis, (b) periosteum, (c) diaphysis, (d) compact bone.
4. Sites of hematopoiesis include all but (a) red marrow cavities of spongy bone, (b) the diploë of flat bones, (c) medullary cavities in bones of infants, (d) medullary cavities in bones of a healthy adult.

5. An osteon has **(a)** a central canal carrying blood vessels, **(b)** concentric lamellae, **(c)** osteocytes in lacunae, **(d)** canaliculi that connect lacunae to the central canal, **(e)** all of these.

6. The organic portion of matrix is important in providing all but **(a)** tensile strength, **(b)** hardness, **(c)** ability to resist stretch, **(d)** flexibility.

7. The flat bones of the skull develop from **(a)** areolar tissue, **(b)** hyaline cartilage, **(c)** fibrous connective tissue, **(d)** compact bone.

8. The remodeling of bone is a function of which cells? **(a)** chondrocytes and osteocytes, **(b)** osteoblasts and osteoclasts, **(c)** chondroblasts and osteoclasts, **(d)** osteoblasts and osteocytes.

9. Bone remodeling in adults is regulated and directed mainly by **(a)** growth hormone, **(b)** thyroid hormones, **(c)** sex hormones, **(d)** mechanical stress, **(e)** PTH.

10. Where within the epiphyseal plate are the dividing cartilage cells located? **(a)** nearest the shaft, **(b)** in the marrow cavity, **(c)** farthest from the shaft, **(d)** in the primary ossification center.

11. Wolff's law is concerned with **(a)** calcium homeostasis of the blood, **(b)** the shape of a bone being determined by mechanical stresses placed on it, **(c)** the electrical charge on bone surfaces.

12. Formation of the bony callus in fracture repair is followed by **(a)** hematoma formation, **(b)** fibrocartilaginous callus formation, **(c)** bone remodeling, **(d)** formation of granulation tissue.

13. The fracture type in which the bone ends are incompletely separated is **(a)** greenstick, **(b)** compound, **(c)** simple, **(d)** comminuted, **(e)** compression.

14. The disorder in which bones are porous and thin but bone composition is normal is **(a)** osteomalacia, **(b)** osteoporosis, **(c)** Paget's disease.

Short Answer Essay Questions

15. Compare bone to cartilage tissue relative to its resilience, speed of regeneration, and access to nutrients.

16. Describe in proper sequence the events of endochondral ossification.

17. Osteocytes residing in lacunae of osteons of healthy compact bone are located quite a distance from the blood vessels in the central canals, yet they are well nourished. How can this be explained?

18. As we grow, our long bones increase in diameter, but the thickness of the compact bone of the shaft remains relatively constant. Explain this phenomenon.

19. Describe the process of new bone formation in an adult bone. Use the terms osteoid seam and calcification front in your discussion.

20. Compare and contrast controls of bone remodeling exerted by hormones and by mechanical and gravitational forces, including the actual purpose of each control system and changes in bone architecture that might occur.

21. (a) During what period of life does skeletal mass increase dramatically? Begin to decline? (b) Why are fractures most common in elderly individuals? (c) Why are greenstick fractures most common in children?

22. Yolanda is asked to review a bone slide that her professor has set up under the microscope. She sees concentric layers surrounding a central cavity. Is this bone section taken from the diaphysis or the epiphyseal plate of the specimen?

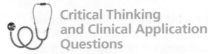

Critical Thinking and Clinical Application Questions

1. Following a motorcycle accident, a 22-year-old man was rushed to the emergency room. X rays revealed a spiral fracture of his right tibia (main bone of the leg). Two months later, X rays revealed good bony callus formation. What is bony callus?

2. Mrs. Abbruzzo brought her 4-year-old daughter to the doctor, complaining that she didn't "look right." The child's forehead was enlarged, her rib cage was knobby, and her lower limbs were bent and deformed. X rays revealed very thick epiphyseal plates. Mrs. Abbruzzo was advised to increase dietary amounts of vitamin D and milk and to "shoo" the girl outside to play in the sun. Considering the child's signs and symptoms, what disease do you think she has? Explain the doctor's instructions.

3. You overhear some anatomy students imagining out loud what their bones would look like if they had compact bone on the inside and spongy bone on the outside, instead of the other way around. You tell them that such imaginary bones would be poorly designed mechanically and would break easily. Explain your reason for saying this.

4. What would a long bone look like at the end of adolescence if bone remodeling did not occur?

5. Why do you think wheelchair-bound people with paralyzed lower limbs have thin, weak bones of the leg and thigh?

6. Jay Beckenstein went to weight-lifting camp in the summer between seventh and eighth grade. He noticed that the camp trainer put tremendous pressure on him and his friends to improve their strength. After an especially vigorous workout, Jay's arm felt extremely sore and weak around the elbow. He went to the camp doctor, who took X rays and then told him that the injury was serious, for the "end of his upper arm bone was starting to twist off." What had happened? Could the same thing happen to Jay's 23-year-old sister, Trixie, who was also starting a program of weight lifting? Why or why not?

7. Old Norse stories tell of a famous Viking named Egil, who lived around 900 AD. His skull was greatly enlarged and misshapen, and the cranial bones were thickened (6 cm, more than 2 inches, thick). After he died, his skull was dug up and it withstood the blow of an ax without damage. In life, he had headaches from the pressure exerted by enlarged vertebrae on his spinal cord. So much blood was diverted to his bones to support their extensive remodeling that his fingers and toes always felt cold and his heart was damaged through overexertion. What bone disorder did Egil probably have?

AT THE CLINIC

Related Clinical Terms

Achondroplasia (a-kon″dro-pla′ze-ah; *a* = without; *chondro* = cartilage; *plasi* = mold, shape) A congenital condition involving defective cartilage and endochondral bone growth so that the limbs are too short but the membrane bones are of normal size; a type of dwarfism.

Bony spur Abnormal projection from a bone due to bony overgrowth; common in aging bones.

Ostealgia (os″te-al′je-ah; *algia* = pain) Pain in a bone.

Osteitis (os″te-i′tis; *itis* = inflammation) Inflammation of bony tissue.

Osteogenesis imperfecta Also called brittle bone disease, a disorder in which the bone matrix contains inadequate collagen, putting it at risk for shattering.

Osteomyelitis (os″te-o-mi″ě-li′tis) Inflammation of bone and bone marrow caused by pus-forming bacteria that enter the body via a wound (e.g., compound bone fracture), or spread from an infection near the bone. Commonly affects the long bones, causing acute pain and fever. May result in joint stiffness, bone destruction, and shortening of a limb. Treatment involves antibiotics, draining any abscesses (local collections of pus), and removing dead bone fragments (which prevent healing).

Osteosarcoma (os″te-o-sar-ko′mah) A form of bone cancer typically arising in a long bone of a limb and most often in those 10–25 years of age. Grows aggressively, painfully eroding the bone;

tends to metastasize to the lungs and cause secondary lung tumors. Usual treatment is amputation of the affected bone or limb, followed by chemotherapy and surgical removal of any metastases. Survival rate is about 50% if detected early.

Pathologic fracture Fracture in a diseased bone involving slight (coughing or a quick turn) or no physical trauma. For example, a hip bone weakened by osteoporosis may break and cause the person to fall, rather than breaking because of the fall.

Traction ("pulling") Placing sustained tension on a body region to keep the parts of a fractured bone in proper alignment. Also prevents spasms of skeletal muscles, which would separate the fractured bone ends or crush the spinal cord in the case of vertebral column fractures.

Case Study   Skeletal System

Remember Mrs. DeStephano? When we last heard about her she was being admitted for further studies. Relative to her skeletal system, the following notes have been added to her chart.

- Fracture of superior right tibia (shinbone of leg); skin lacerated; area cleaned and protruding bone fragments subjected to internal (open) reduction and casted
- Nutrient artery of tibia damaged
- Medial meniscus (fibrocartilage disc) of right knee joint crushed; knee joint inflamed and painful

Relative to these notes:

1. What type of fracture does Mrs. DeStephano have?

2. What problems can be predicted with such fractures and how are they treated?

3. What is internal reduction? Why was a cast applied?

4. Given an uncomplicated recovery, approximately how long should it take before Mrs. DeStephano has a good solid bony callus?

5. What complications might be predicted by the fact that the nutrient artery is damaged?

6. What new techniques might be used to enhance fracture repair if healing is delayed or impaired?

7. How likely is it that Mrs. DeStephano's knee cartilage will regenerate? Why?

(Answers in Appendix H)

7

The Skeleton

The word *skeleton* comes from the Greek word meaning "dried-up body" or "mummy," a rather unflattering description. Nonetheless, the human skeleton is a triumph of design and engineering that puts most skyscrapers to shame. It is strong, yet light, and almost perfectly adapted for the protective, locomotor, and manipulative functions it performs.

The **skeleton**, or **skeletal system**, composed of bones, cartilages, joints, and ligaments, accounts for about 20% of body mass (about 30 pounds in a 160-pound person). Bones make up most of the skeleton. Cartilages occur only in isolated areas, such as the nose, parts of the ribs, and the joints. Ligaments connect bones and reinforce joints, allowing required movements while restricting motions in other directions. Joints, the junctions between bones, provide for the remarkable mobility of the skeleton. We discuss joints and ligaments separately in Chapter 8.

PART 1
The Axial Skeleton

✓ Name the major parts of the axial and appendicular skeletons and describe their relative functions.

(a) Anterior view

(b) Posterior view

Figure 7.1 The human skeleton. Bones of the axial skeleton are colored green. Bones of the appendicular skeleton are gold.

As described in Chapter 6, the skeleton is divided into *axial* and *appendicular* portions (see Figures 6.1 and 7.1). The **axial skeleton** is structured from 80 bones segregated into three major regions: the *skull, vertebral column,* and *thoracic cage* **(Figure 7.1)**. This part of the skeleton (1) forms the longitudinal axis of the body, (2) supports the head, neck, and trunk, and (3) protects the brain, spinal cord, and the organs in the thorax. As we will see later in this chapter, the bones of the appendicular skeleton, which allow us to interact with and manipulate our environment, are appended to the axial skeleton.

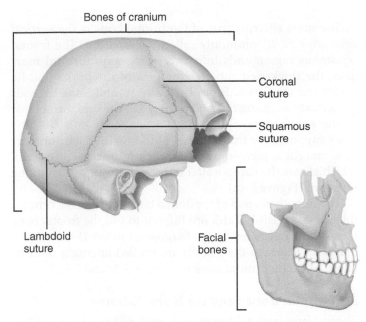

Bones of cranium

Coronal suture

Squamous suture

Lambdoid suture

Facial bones

(a) Cranial and facial divisions of the skull

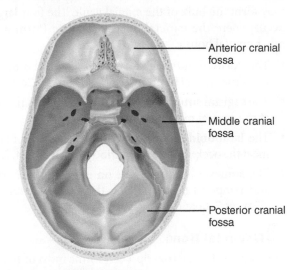

Anterior cranial fossa

Middle cranial fossa

Posterior cranial fossa

(b) Superior view of the cranial fossae

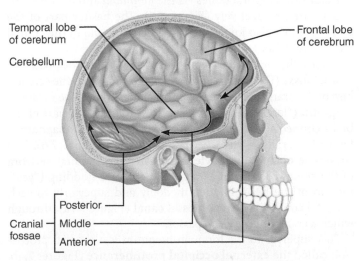

Temporal lobe of cerebrum

Cerebellum

Frontal lobe of cerebrum

Posterior

Cranial fossa — Middle

Anterior

(c) Lateral view of cranial fossae showing the contained brain regions

Figure 7.2 The skull: Cranial and facial divisions and fossae.

☑ **Check Your Understanding**

1. What are the three main parts of the axial skeleton?
2. Which part of the skeleton—axial or appendicular—is important in protecting internal organs?

For answers, see Appendix H.

The Skull

✓ Name, describe, and identify the skull bones. Identify their important markings.

✓ Compare and contrast the major functions of the cranium and the facial skeleton.

The **skull** is the body's most complex bony structure. It is formed by *cranial* and *facial bones*, 22 in all. The cranial bones, or **cranium** (kra'ne-um), enclose and protect the fragile brain and furnish attachment sites for head and neck muscles. The facial bones (1) form the framework of the face, (2) contain cavities for the special sense organs of sight, taste, and smell, (3) provide openings for air and food passage, (4) secure the teeth, and (5) anchor the facial muscles of expression, which we use to show our feelings. As you will see, the individual skull bones are well suited to their assignments.

Most skull bones are flat bones. Except for the mandible, which is connected to the rest of the skull by freely movable joints, all bones of the adult skull are firmly united by interlocking joints called **sutures** (soo'cherz). The suture lines have a saw-toothed or serrated appearance.

The major skull sutures, the *coronal, sagittal, squamous,* and *lambdoid sutures,* connect cranial bones (Figures 7.2a, 7.4b, and 7.5a). Most other skull sutures connect facial bones and are named according to the specific bones they connect.

Overview of Skull Geography

It is worth surveying basic skull "geography" before describing the individual bones. With the lower jaw removed, the skull resembles a lopsided, hollow, bony sphere. The facial bones form its anterior aspect, and the cranium forms the rest of the skull (Figure 7.2a).

The cranium can be divided into a vault and a base. The *cranial vault,* also called the *calvaria* (kal-va're-ah; "bald part of skull"), forms the superior, lateral, and posterior aspects of the skull, as well as the forehead. The *cranial base* forms the skull's inferior aspect. Internally, prominent bony ridges divide the base into three distinct "steps" or fossae—the *anterior, middle,* and *posterior cranial fossae* (Figure 7.2b and c). The brain sits snugly in these cranial fossae, completely enclosed by the cranial vault. Overall, the brain is said to occupy the *cranial cavity.*

In addition to the large cranial cavity, the skull has many smaller cavities. These include the middle and internal ear cavities (carved into the lateral side of its base) and, anteriorly, the

Figure 7.3 **Major cavities of the skull, frontal section.**

nasal cavity and the orbits (Figure 7.3). The *orbits* house the eyeballs. Several bones of the skull contain air-filled sinuses, which lighten the skull.

The skull also has about 85 named openings (foramina, canals, fissures, etc.). The most important of these provide passageways for the spinal cord, the major blood vessels serving the brain, and the 12 pairs of cranial nerves (numbered I through XII), which transmit information to and from the brain.

As you read about the bones of the skull, locate each bone on the different skull views in Figures 7.4, 7.5, and 7.6. The skull bones and their important markings are also summarized in Table 7.1 (pp. 216–217). The color-coded boxes before a bone's name in the text and in Table 7.1 correspond to the color of that bone in the figures. For example, note the color of the frontal bone in Table 7.1 and see how you can easily find it in Figures 7.4 and 7.5.

Cranium

The eight cranial bones are the paired parietal and temporal bones and the unpaired frontal, occipital, sphenoid, and ethmoid bones. Together, these construct the brain's protective bony "helmet." Because its superior aspect is curved, the cranium is self-bracing. This allows the bones to be thin, and, like an eggshell, the cranium is remarkably strong for its weight.

Frontal Bone

The shell-shaped **frontal bone** (Figures 7.4a, 7.5, and 7.7) forms the anterior cranium. It articulates posteriorly with the paired parietal bones via the prominent *coronal suture.*

The most anterior part of the frontal bone is the vertical *squamous part,* commonly called the *forehead.* The frontal squamous region ends inferiorly at the **supraorbital margins,** the thickened superior margins of the orbits that lie under the eyebrows. From here, the frontal bone extends posteriorly, forming the superior wall of the *orbits* and most of the **anterior cranial fossa** (Figure 7.7a and b). This fossa supports the frontal lobes of the brain. Each supraorbital margin is pierced by a **supraorbital foramen (notch),** which allows the supraorbital artery and nerve to pass to the forehead (Figure 7.4a).

The smooth portion of the frontal bone between the orbits is the **glabella** (glah-bel'ah). Just inferior to this the frontal bone meets the nasal bones at the *frontonasal suture* (Figure 7.4a). The areas lateral to the glabella are riddled internally with sinuses, called the **frontal sinuses** (Figures 7.5c and 7.3).

Parietal Bones and the Major Sutures

The two large **parietal bones** are curved, rectangular bones that form most of the superior and lateral aspects of the skull; hence they form the bulk of the cranial vault. The four largest sutures occur where the parietal bones articulate (form a joint) with other cranial bones:

- The **coronal suture** (kŏ-ro'nul), where the parietal bones meet the frontal bone anteriorly (Figures 7.2a and 7.5)
- The **sagittal suture,** where the parietal bones meet superiorly at the cranial midline (Figure 7.4b)
- The **lambdoid suture** (lam'doid), where the parietal bones meet the occipital bone posteriorly (Figures 7.2a, 7.4b, and 7.5)
- The **squamous suture** (one on each side), where a parietal and temporal bone meet on the lateral aspect of the skull (Figures 7.2a and 7.5)

Occipital Bone

The **occipital bone** (ok-sip'ĭ-tal) forms most of the skull's posterior wall and base. It articulates anteriorly with the paired parietal and temporal bones via the *lambdoid* and *occipitomastoid sutures,* respectively (Figure 7.5). The basilar part of the occipital bone also joins with the sphenoid bone in the cranial base (Figure 7.6a).

Internally, the occipital bone forms the walls of the **posterior cranial fossa** (Figures 7.7 and 7.2c), which supports the cerebellum of the brain. In the base of the occipital bone is the **foramen magnum** ("large hole") through which the inferior part of the brain connects with the spinal cord. The foramen magnum is flanked laterally by two occipital condyles (Figure 7.6). The rockerlike **occipital condyles** articulate with the first vertebra of the spinal column in a way that permits a nodding ("yes") motion of the head. Hidden medially and superiorly to each occipital condyle is a **hypoglossal canal** (Figure 7.7a), through which a cranial nerve (XII) passes.

Just superior to the foramen magnum is a median protrusion called the **external occipital protuberance** (Figures 7.4b, 7.5, and 7.6). You can feel this knoblike projection just below

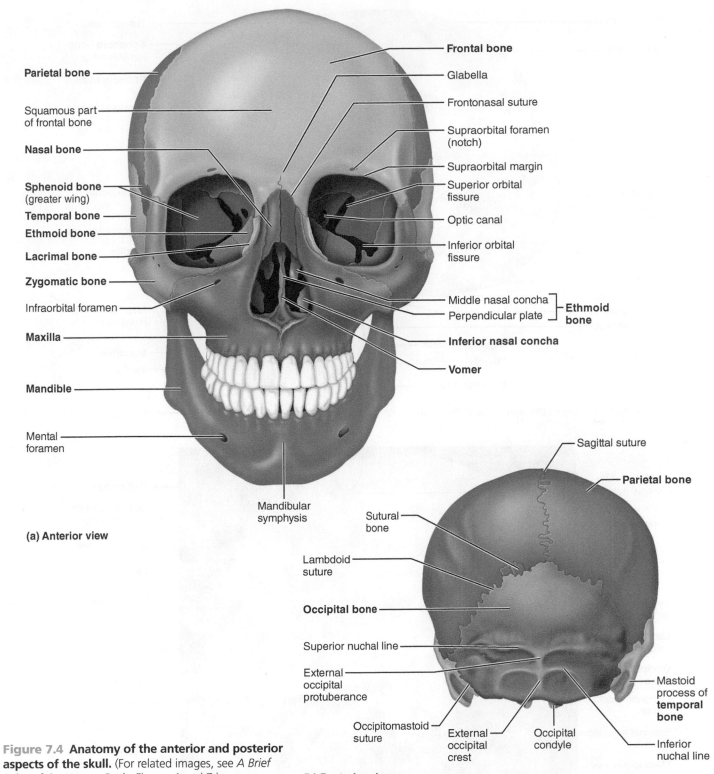

Parietal bone

Squamous part of frontal bone

Nasal bone

Sphenoid bone (greater wing)

Temporal bone

Ethmoid bone

Lacrimal bone

Zygomatic bone

Infraorbital foramen

Maxilla

Mandible

Mental foramen

Frontal bone

Glabella

Frontonasal suture

Supraorbital foramen (notch)

Supraorbital margin

Superior orbital fissure

Optic canal

Inferior orbital fissure

Middle nasal concha ⎫
Perpendicular plate ⎭ **Ethmoid bone**

Inferior nasal concha

Vomer

Mandibular symphysis

(a) Anterior view

Sagittal suture

Parietal bone

Sutural bone

Lambdoid suture

Occipital bone

Superior nuchal line

External occipital protuberance

Occipitomastoid suture

External occipital crest

Occipital condyle

Mastoid process of **temporal bone**

Inferior nuchal line

Figure 7.4 Anatomy of the anterior and posterior aspects of the skull. (For related images, see *A Brief Atlas of the Human Body*, Figures 1 and 7.)

(b) Posterior view

the most bulging part of your posterior skull. A number of inconspicuous ridges, the *external occipital crest* and the *superior* and *inferior nuchal lines* (nu′kal), mark the occipital bone near the foramen magnum. The external occipital crest secures the *ligamentum nuchae* (lig″ah-men′tum noo′ke;

nucha = back of the neck), a sheetlike elastic ligament that connects the vertebrae of the neck to the skull. The nuchal lines, and the bony regions between them, anchor many neck and back muscles. The superior nuchal line marks the upper limit of the neck.

(*Text continues on p. 208.*)

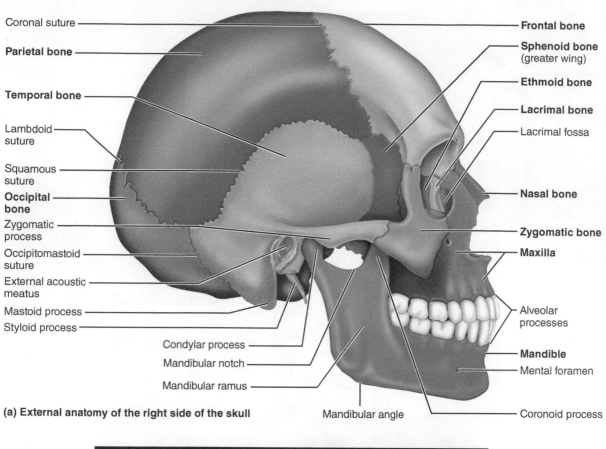

Coronal suture

Parietal bone

Temporal bone

Lambdoid
suture

Squamous
suture

**Occipital
bone**

Zygomatic
process

Occipitomastoid
suture

External acoustic
meatus

Mastoid process

Styloid process

Condylar process

Mandibular notch

Mandibular ramus

Frontal bone

Sphenoid bone
(greater wing)

Ethmoid bone

Lacrimal bone

Lacrimal fossa

Nasal bone

Zygomatic bone

Maxilla

Alveolar
processes

Mandible

Mental foramen

Coronoid process

Mandibular angle

(a) External anatomy of the right side of the skull

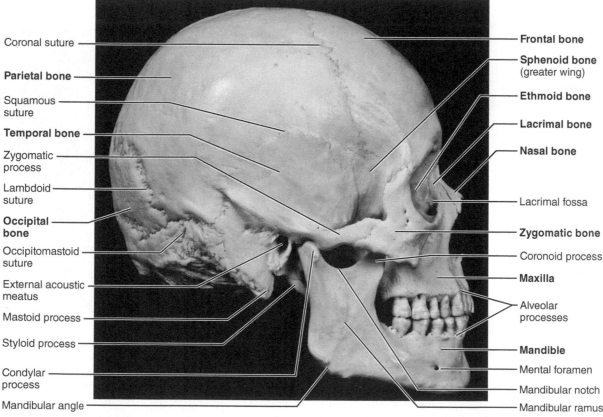

Coronal suture

Parietal bone

Squamous
suture

Temporal bone

Zygomatic
process

Lambdoid
suture

**Occipital
bone**

Occipitomastoid
suture

External acoustic
meatus

Mastoid process

Styloid process

Condylar
process

Mandibular angle

Frontal bone

Sphenoid bone
(greater wing)

Ethmoid bone

Lacrimal bone

Nasal bone

Lacrimal fossa

Zygomatic bone

Coronoid process

Maxilla

Alveolar
processes

Mandible

Mental foramen

Mandibular notch

Mandibular ramus

(b) Photograph of right side of skull

Figure 7.5 **Bones of the lateral aspect of the skull, external and internal views.**
(For related images, see *A Brief Atlas of the Human Body,* Figures 2 and 3.)

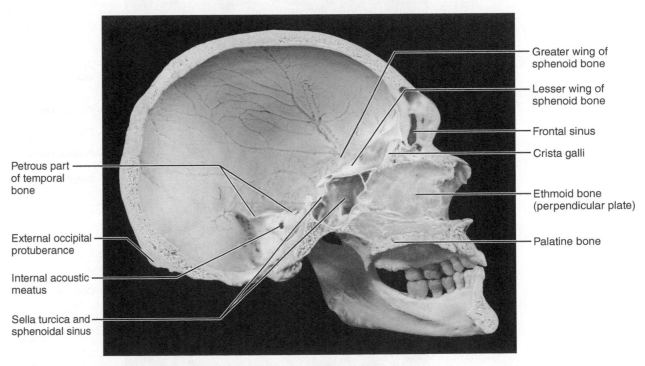

Parietal bone

Coronal suture

Frontal bone

Greater wing
Lesser wing
} Sphenoid bone

Frontal sinus

Crista galli

Nasal bone

Sphenoidal sinus

Ethmoid bone (perpendicular plate)

Vomer

Incisive fossa

Maxilla

Alveolar processes

Mandible

Squamous suture

Temporal bone

Lambdoid suture

Occipital bone

Occipitomastoid suture

External occipital protuberance

Internal acoustic meatus

Sella turcica of sphenoid bone

Pterygoid process of sphenoid bone

Mandibular foramen

Palatine bone

Palatine process of maxilla

(c) Midsagittal section showing the internal anatomy of the left half of skull

Greater wing of sphenoid bone

Lesser wing of sphenoid bone

Frontal sinus

Crista galli

Ethmoid bone (perpendicular plate)

Palatine bone

Petrous part of temporal bone

External occipital protuberance

Internal acoustic meatus

Sella turcica and sphenoidal sinus

(d) Photo of skull cut through the midline, same view as in (c)

Figure 7.5 *(continued)*

Maxilla
(palatine process)

Hard
palate

Palatine bone
(horizontal plate)

Zygomatic bone

Temporal bone
(zygomatic process)

Vomer

Mandibular
fossa

Styloid process

Mastoid process

Temporal bone
(petrous part)

Basilar part of the
occipital bone

Parietal bone

External occipital crest

External occipital
protuberance

Incisive fossa

Intermaxillary suture

Median palatine suture

Infraorbital foramen

Maxilla

Sphenoid bone
(greater wing)

Foramen ovale

Foramen spinosum

Foramen lacerum

Carotid canal

External acoustic meatus

Stylomastoid
foramen

Jugular foramen

Occipital condyle

Inferior nuchal line

Superior nuchal line

Occipital bone

Foramen magnum

(a) Inferior view of the skull (mandible removed)

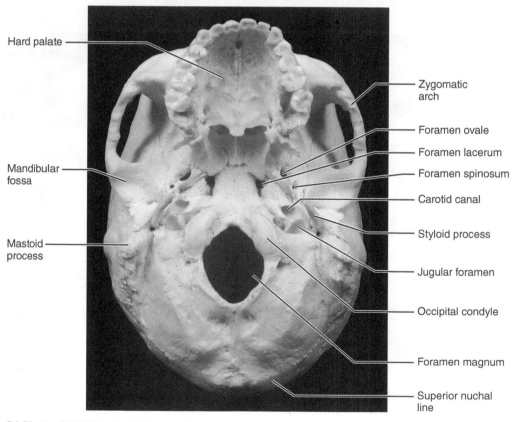

Hard palate

Mandibular
fossa

Mastoid
process

Zygomatic
arch

Foramen ovale

Foramen lacerum

Foramen spinosum

Carotid canal

Styloid process

Jugular foramen

Occipital condyle

Foramen magnum

Superior nuchal
line

(b) Photo of inferior view of the skull

Figure 7.6 Inferior aspect of the skull, mandible removed. (For related images, see
A Brief Atlas of the Human Body, Figure 4.)

View

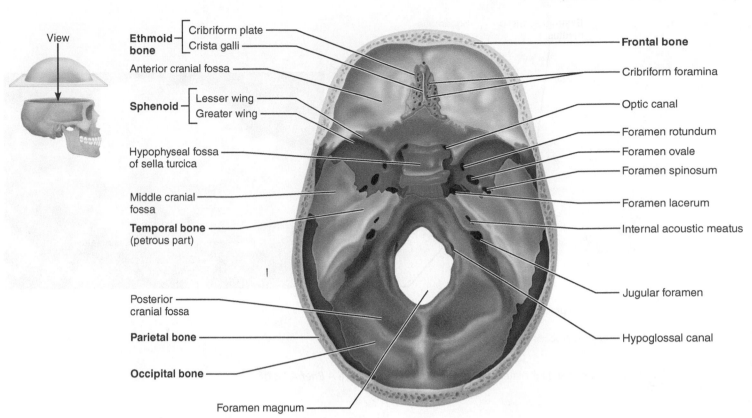

Ethmoid bone
— Cribriform plate
— Crista galli

Anterior cranial fossa

Sphenoid
— Lesser wing
— Greater wing

Hypophyseal fossa of sella turcica

Middle cranial fossa

Temporal bone (petrous part)

Posterior cranial fossa

Parietal bone

Occipital bone

Foramen magnum

Frontal bone

Cribriform foramina

Optic canal

Foramen rotundum

Foramen ovale

Foramen spinosum

Foramen lacerum

Internal acoustic meatus

Jugular foramen

Hypoglossal canal

7

(a) Superior view of the skull, calvaria removed

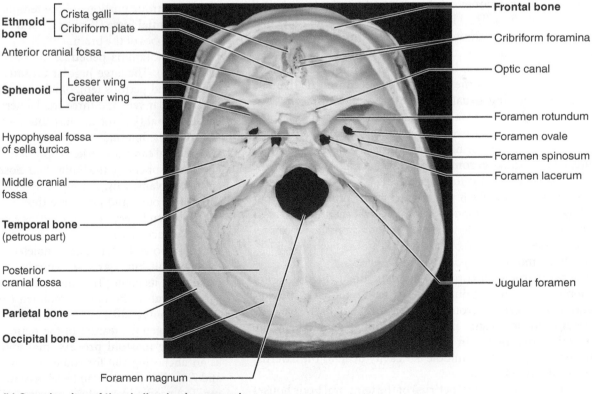

Ethmoid bone
— Crista galli
— Cribriform plate

Anterior cranial fossa

Sphenoid
— Lesser wing
— Greater wing

Hypophyseal fossa of sella turcica

Middle cranial fossa

Temporal bone (petrous part)

Posterior cranial fossa

Parietal bone

Occipital bone

Foramen magnum

Frontal bone

Cribriform foramina

Optic canal

Foramen rotundum

Foramen ovale

Foramen spinosum

Foramen lacerum

Jugular foramen

(b) Superior view of the skull, calvaria removed

Figure 7.7 **The base of the cranial cavity.** (For related images, see *A Brief Atlas of the Human Body*, Figure 5.)

Figure 7.8 The temporal bone. Right lateral view. (For related images, see *A Brief Atlas of the Human Body*, Figures 2 and 8.)

Temporal Bones

The two **temporal bones** are best viewed on the lateral skull surface (Figure 7.5). They lie inferior to the parietal bones and meet them at the squamous sutures. The temporal bones form the inferolateral aspects of the skull and parts of the cranial base. The use of the terms *temple* and *temporal*, from the Latin word *temporum*, meaning "time," came about because gray hairs, a sign of time's passing, usually appear first at the temples.

Each temporal bone has a complicated shape **(Figure 7.8)** and is described in terms of its three major parts, the *squamous, tympanic,* and *petrous parts*. The flaring **squamous part** abuts the squamous suture. It has a barlike **zygomatic process** that meets the zygomatic bone of the face anteriorly. Together, these two bony structures form the **zygomatic arch**, which you can feel as the projection of your cheek (*zygoma* = cheekbone). The small, oval **mandibular fossa** (man-dib′u-lar) on the inferior surface of the zygomatic process receives the condylar process of the mandible (lower jawbone), forming the freely movable *temporomandibular joint*.

The **tympanic part** (tim-pan′ik; "eardrum") (Figure 7.8) of the temporal bone surrounds the **external acoustic meatus**, or external ear canal, through which sound enters the ear. The external acoustic meatus and the eardrum at its deep end are part of the *external ear*. In a dried skull, the eardrum has been removed and part of the middle ear cavity deep to the external meatus can also be seen.

The thick **petrous part** (pet′rus) of the temporal bone houses the *middle* and *internal ear cavities*, which contain sensory receptors for hearing and balance. Extending from the occipital bone posteriorly to the sphenoid bone anteriorly, it contributes to the cranial base (Figures 7.6 and 7.7). In the floor of the cranial cavity, the petrous part of the temporal bone looks like a miniature mountain ridge (*petrous* = rocky). The posterior slope of this ridge lies in the posterior cranial fossa; the anterior slope is in the middle cranial fossa. Together, the sphenoid bone and the petrous portions of the temporal bones construct the **middle cranial fossa** (Figures 7.7 and 7.2b), which supports the temporal lobes of the brain.

Several foramina penetrate the bone of the petrous region (Figure 7.6). The large **jugular foramen** at the junction of the occipital and petrous temporal bones allows passage of the internal jugular vein and three cranial nerves (IX, X, and XI). The **carotid canal** (kar-rot′id), just anterior to the jugular foramen, transmits the internal carotid artery into the cranial cavity. The two internal carotid arteries supply blood to over 80% of the cerebral hemispheres of the brain; their closeness to the internal ear cavities explains why, during excitement or exertion, we sometimes hear our rapid pulse as a thundering sound in the head. The **foramen lacerum** (la′ser-um) is a jagged opening (*lacerum* = torn or lacerated) between the petrous temporal bone and the sphenoid bone. It is almost completely closed by cartilage in a living person, but it is conspicuous in a dried skull, and students usually ask its name. The **internal acoustic meatus**, positioned superolateral to the jugular foramen (Figures 7.5c and d, and 7.7), transmits cranial nerves VII and VIII.

A conspicuous feature of the petrous part of the temporal bone is the **mastoid process** (mas′toid; "breast"), which acts as an anchoring site for some neck muscles (Figures 7.5, 7.6, and 7.8). This process can be felt as a lump just posterior to the ear. The needle-like **styloid process** (sti′loid; "stakelike") is an attachment point for several tongue and neck muscles and for a ligament that secures the hyoid bone of the neck to the skull (see Figure 7.15). The **stylomastoid foramen**, between the styloid and mastoid processes, allows cranial nerve VII (the facial nerve) to leave the skull (Figure 7.6).

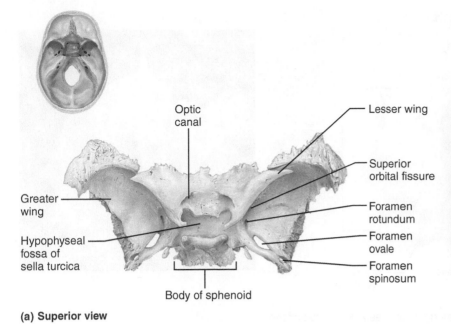

(a) Superior view

Optic canal

Lesser wing

Greater wing

Superior orbital fissure

Hypophyseal fossa of sella turcica

Foramen rotundum

Foramen ovale

Foramen spinosum

Body of sphenoid

(b) Posterior view

Body of sphenoid

Lesser wing

Greater wing

Superior orbital fissure

Pterygoid process

Figure 7.9 The sphenoid bone. (For related images, see *A Brief Atlas of the Human Body*, Figures 5 and 9).

Homeostatic Imbalance 7.1

The mastoid process is full of air cavities (sinuses) called **mastoid air cells**. Their position adjacent to the middle ear cavity (a high-risk area for infections spreading from the throat) puts them at risk for infection themselves. A mastoid sinus infection, or *mastoiditis*, is notoriously difficult to treat. Because the mastoid air cells are separated from the brain by only a very thin bony plate, mastoid infections may spread to the brain as well. Surgical removal of the mastoid process was once the best way to prevent life-threatening brain inflammations in people susceptible to repeated bouts of mastoiditis. Today, antibiotic therapy is the treatment of choice. ✚

Sphenoid Bone

The bat-shaped **sphenoid bone** (sfe′noid; *sphen* = wedge) spans the width of the middle cranial fossa (Figure 7.7). The sphenoid is considered the keystone of the cranium because it forms a central wedge that articulates with all other cranial bones. It is a challenging bone to study because of its complex shape. As shown in **Figure 7.9**, it consists of a central body and three pairs of processes: the greater wings, lesser wings, and pterygoid processes (ter′ĭ-goid). Within the **body** of the sphenoid are the paired **sphenoidal sinuses** (see Figures 7.5c and d, and 7.14).

The superior surface of the body bears a saddle-shaped prominence, the **sella turcica** (sel′ah ter′sĭ-kah), meaning "Turk's saddle." The seat of this saddle, called the **hypophyseal fossa**, forms a snug enclosure for the pituitary gland (hypophysis).

The **greater wings** project laterally from the sphenoid body, forming parts of (1) the middle cranial fossa (Figures 7.7 and 7.2b), (2) the posterior walls of the orbits (Figure 7.4a), and (3) the external wall of the skull, where they are seen as flag-shaped, bony areas medial to the zygomatic arch (Figure 7.5). The hornlike **lesser wings** form part of the floor of the anterior cranial fossa (Figure 7.7) and part of the medial walls of the orbits. The trough-shaped **pterygoid processes** project inferiorly

Crista galli

Cribriform plate with cribriform foramina

Orbital plate

Left lateral mass

Ethmoidal air cells

Perpendicular plate

Middle nasal concha

Figure 7.10 The ethmoid bone. Anterior view. (For related images, see *A Brief Atlas of the Human Body*, Figures 3 and 10.)

from the junction of the body and greater wings (Figure 7.9b). They anchor the pterygoid muscles, which are important in chewing.

A number of openings in the sphenoid bone are visible in Figures 7.7 and 7.9. The **optic canals** lie anterior to the sella turcica; they allow the optic nerves (cranial nerves II) to pass to the eyes. On each side of the sphenoid body is a crescent-shaped row of four openings. The anteriormost of these, the **superior orbital fissure**, is a long slit between the greater and lesser wings. It allows cranial nerves that control eye movements (III, IV, VI) to enter the orbit. This fissure is most obvious in an anterior view of the skull (Figure 7.4; see also Figure 7.9b). The **foramen rotundum** and **foramen ovale** (o-va'le) provide passageways for branches of cranial nerve V (the maxillary and mandibular nerves, respectively) to reach the face (Figure 7.7). The foramen rotundum is in the medial part of the greater wing and is usually oval, despite its name meaning "round opening." The foramen ovale, a large, oval foramen posterior to the foramen rotundum, is also visible in an inferior view of the skull (Figure 7.6). Posterolateral to the foramen ovale is the small **foramen spinosum** (Figure 7.7); it transmits the *middle meningeal artery*, which serves the internal faces of some cranial bones.

Ethmoid Bone

Like the temporal and sphenoid bones, the delicate **ethmoid bone** has a complex shape **(Figure 7.10)**. Lying between the sphenoid and the nasal bones of the face, it is the most deeply situated bone of the skull. It forms most of the bony area between the nasal cavity and the orbits.

The superior surface of the ethmoid is formed by the paired horizontal **cribriform plates** (krib'rĭ-form) (see also Figure 7.7), which help form the roof of the nasal cavities and the floor of the anterior cranial fossa. The cribriform plates are punctured by tiny holes (*cribr* = sieve) called *cribriform foramina* that allow the filaments of the olfactory nerves to pass from the smell

receptors in the nasal cavities to the brain. Projecting superiorly between the cribriform plates is a triangular process called the **crista galli** (kris'tah gah'le; "rooster's comb"). The outermost covering of the brain (the dura mater) attaches to the crista galli and helps secure the brain in the cranial cavity.

The **perpendicular plate** of the ethmoid bone projects inferiorly in the median plane and forms the superior part of the nasal septum, which divides the nasal cavity into right and left halves (Figure 7.5c and d). Flanking the perpendicular plate on each side is a **lateral mass** riddled with sinuses called **ethmoidal air cells** (Figures 7.10 and 7.14), for which the bone itself is named (*ethmos* = sieve). Extending medially from the lateral masses, the delicately coiled **superior** and **middle nasal conchae** (kong'ke; *concha* = shell), named after the conch shells found on warm ocean beaches, protrude into the nasal cavity (Figures 7.10 and 7.13a). The lateral surfaces of the ethmoid's lateral masses are called **orbital plates** because they contribute to the medial walls of the orbits.

Sutural Bones

Sutural bones are tiny, irregularly shaped bones or bone clusters that occur within sutures, most often in the lambdoid suture (Figure 7.4b). Structurally unimportant, their number varies, and not all skulls exhibit them. The significance of these tiny bones is unknown.

☑ Check Your Understanding

3. Look at Figure 7.4. Which of the skull bones illustrated in view (a) are cranial bones?
4. Which bone forms the crista galli?
5. Which skull bones house the external ear canals?
6. What bones abut one another at the sagittal suture? At the lambdoid suture?

For answers, see Appendix H.

Mandibular fossa
of temporal bone

Temporomandibular
joint

Mandibular notch

Coronoid
process

Condylar
process

Mandibular foramen

Ramus
of
mandible

Alveolar
process

Mental
foramen

Mandibular
angle

Body of mandible

(a) Mandible, right lateral view

Articulates with
frontal bone

Frontal process

Orbital surface

Zygomatic
process
(cut)

Infraorbital
foramen

Anterior nasal
spine

Alveolar
process

(b) Maxilla, right lateral view

(c) Maxilla, photo of right lateral view

Figure 7.11 Detailed anatomy of the mandible and the maxilla. (For related images, see *A Brief Atlas of the Human Body*, Figures 11 and 12.)

Facial Bones

The facial skeleton is made up of 14 bones (see Figures 7.4a and 7.5a), of which only the mandible and the vomer are unpaired. The maxillae, zygomatics, nasals, lacrimals, palatines, and inferior nasal conchae are paired bones. As a rule, the facial skeleton of men is more elongated than that of women. Women's faces tend to be rounder and less angular.

Mandible

The U-shaped **mandible** (man′dĭ-bl), or lower jawbone (Figures 7.4a and 7.5, and **Figure 7.11a**), is the largest, strongest bone of the face. It has a body, which forms the chin, and two upright *rami* (*rami* = branches). Each ramus meets the body posteriorly at a **mandibular angle**. At the superior margin of

each ramus are two processes separated by the **mandibular notch**. The anterior **coronoid process** (kor′o-noid; "crown-shaped") is an insertion point for the large temporalis muscle that elevates the lower jaw during chewing. The posterior **condylar process** articulates with the mandibular fossa of the temporal bone, forming the *temporomandibular joint* on the same side.

The mandibular **body** anchors the lower teeth. Its superior border, called the **alveolar process** (al-ve′o-lar), contains the sockets (*dental alveoli*) in which the teeth are embedded. In the midline of the mandibular body is a slight ridge, the **mandibular symphysis** (sim′fih-sis), indicating where the two mandibular bones fused during infancy (Figure 7.4a).

Large **mandibular foramina**, one on the medial surface of each ramus, permit the nerves responsible for tooth sensation to pass to the teeth in the lower jaw. Dentists inject lidocaine into these foramina to prevent pain while working on the lower teeth. The **mental foramina**, openings on the lateral aspects of the mandibular body, allow blood vessels and nerves to pass to the skin of the chin (*ment* = chin) and lower lip.

Maxillary Bones

The **maxillary bones**, or **maxillae** (mak-sil'le; "jaws") (Figures 7.4 to 7.6 and 7.11b and c), are fused medially. They form the upper jaw and the central portion of the facial skeleton. All facial bones except the mandible articulate with the maxillae. Hence, the maxillae are considered the keystone bones of the facial skeleton.

The maxillae carry the upper teeth in their **alveolar processes**. Just inferior to the nose the maxillae meet medially, forming the pointed **anterior nasal spine** at their junction. The **palatine processes** (pă'lah-tĭn) of the maxillae project posteriorly from the alveolar processes and fuse medially at the *intermaxillary suture*, forming the anterior two-thirds of the hard palate, or bony roof of the mouth (Figures 7.5c and d and 7.6). Just posterior to the teeth is a midline foramen, called the **incisive fossa**, which serves as a passageway for blood vessels and nerves.

The **frontal processes** extend superiorly to the frontal bone, forming part of the lateral aspects of the bridge of the nose (Figures 7.4a and 7.11b). The regions that flank the nasal cavity laterally contain the **maxillary sinuses** (see Figure 7.14), the largest of the paranasal sinuses. They extend from the orbits to the roots of the upper teeth. Laterally, the maxillae articulate with the zygomatic bones via their **zygomatic processes**.

The **inferior orbital fissure** is located deep within the orbit (Figure 7.4a) at the junction of the maxilla with the greater wing of the sphenoid. It permits the zygomatic nerve, the maxillary nerve (a branch of cranial nerve V), and blood vessels to pass to the face. Just below the eye socket on each side is an **infraorbital foramen** that allows the infraorbital nerve (a continuation of the maxillary nerve) and artery to reach the face.

Zygomatic Bones

The irregularly shaped **zygomatic bones** (Figures 7.4a, 7.5a, and 7.6) are commonly called the cheekbones (*zygoma* = cheekbone). They articulate with the zygomatic processes of the temporal bones posteriorly, the zygomatic processes of the frontal bone superiorly, and with the zygomatic processes of the maxillae anteriorly. The zygomatic bones form the prominences of the cheeks and part of the inferolateral margins of the orbits.

Nasal Bones

The thin, basically rectangular **nasal bones** (na'zal) are fused medially, forming the bridge of the nose (Figures 7.4a and 7.5a). They articulate with the frontal bone superiorly, the maxillary bones laterally, and the perpendicular plate of the ethmoid bone posteriorly. Inferiorly they attach to the cartilages that form most of the skeleton of the external nose.

Lacrimal Bones

The delicate, fingernail-shaped **lacrimal bones** (lak'rĭ-mal) contribute to the medial walls of each orbit (Figures 7.4a and 7.5a). They articulate with the frontal bone superiorly, the ethmoid bone posteriorly, and the maxillae anteriorly. Each lacrimal bone contains a deep groove that helps form a **lacrimal fossa**. The lacrimal fossa houses the *lacrimal sac*, part of the passageway that allows tears to drain from the eye surface into the nasal cavity (*lacrima* = tears).

Palatine Bones

Each L-shaped **palatine bone** is fashioned from two bony plates, the *horizontal* and *perpendicular* (see Figures 7.13a and 7.6a), and has three important articular processes, the *pyramidal*, *sphenoidal*, and *orbital*. The **horizontal plates**, joined at the median palatine suture, complete the posterior portion of the hard palate. The superiorly projecting **perpendicular (vertical) plates** form part of the posterolateral walls of the nasal cavity and a small part of the orbits.

Vomer

The slender, plow-shaped **vomer** (vo'mer; "plow") lies in the nasal cavity, where it forms part of the nasal septum (see Figures 7.4a and 7.13b). It is described below in connection with the nasal cavity.

Inferior Nasal Conchae

The paired **inferior nasal conchae** are thin, curved bones in the nasal cavity. They project medially from the lateral walls of the nasal cavity, just inferior to the middle nasal conchae of the ethmoid bone (see Figures 7.4a and 7.13a). They are the largest of the three pairs of conchae and, like the others, they form part of the lateral walls of the nasal cavity.

☑ Check Your Understanding

7. Women with prominent (high) cheekbones are often considered beautiful by the modeling industry. What bones are the "cheekbones"?
8. Johnny was vigorously exercising the only joints in the skull that are freely movable. What would you guess he was doing?
9. What bones are the keystone bones of the facial skeleton?

For answers, see Appendix H.

Special Characteristics of the Orbits and Nasal Cavity

✓ Define the bony boundaries of the orbits, nasal cavity, and paranasal sinuses.

Two restricted skull regions, the orbits and the nasal cavity, are formed from an amazing number of bones. Even though we have already described the individual bones forming these structures, we give a brief summary here to pull the parts together.

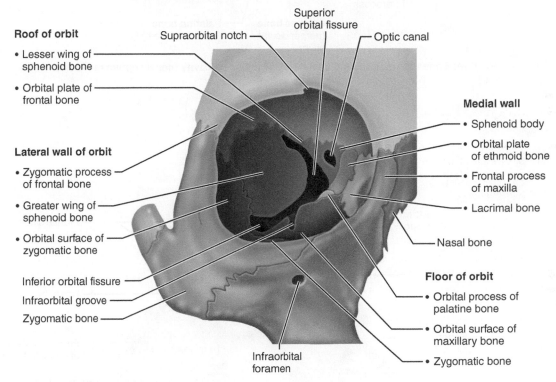

(a) Photograph, right orbit

Roof of orbit
- Lesser wing of sphenoid bone
- Orbital plate of frontal bone

Supraorbital notch

Superior orbital fissure

Optic canal

Medial wall
- Sphenoid body
- Orbital plate of ethmoid bone
- Frontal process of maxilla
- Lacrimal bone
- Nasal bone

Lateral wall of orbit
- Zygomatic process of frontal bone
- Greater wing of sphenoid bone
- Orbital surface of zygomatic bone

Inferior orbital fissure

Infraorbital groove

Zygomatic bone

Infraorbital foramen

Floor of orbit
- Orbital process of palatine bone
- Orbital surface of maxillary bone
- Zygomatic bone

(b) Contribution of each of the seven bones forming the right orbit

Figure 7.12 Bones that form the orbits. (For a related image, see *A Brief Atlas of the Human Body,* Figure 14.)

The Orbits

The cone-shaped **orbits** are bony cavities in which the eyes are firmly encased and cushioned by fatty tissue. The muscles that move the eyes and the tear-producing lacrimal glands are also housed in the orbits. The walls of each orbit are formed by parts of seven bones—the frontal, sphenoid, zygomatic, maxilla, palatine, lacrimal, and ethmoid bones. Their relationships are shown in **Figure 7.12.** Also seen in the orbits are the superior and inferior orbital fissures and the optic canals, described earlier.

The Nasal Cavity

The **nasal cavity** is constructed of bone and hyaline cartilage **(Figure 7.13).** The *roof* of the nasal cavity is formed by the cribriform plates of the ethmoid. The *lateral walls* are largely shaped by the superior and middle conchae of the ethmoid bone, the perpendicular plates of the palatine bones, and the inferior nasal conchae. The depressions under cover of the conchae on the lateral walls are called *meatuses* (*meatus* = passage), so there are superior, middle, and inferior meatuses. The *floor* of the nasal cavity is formed by the palatine processes of the

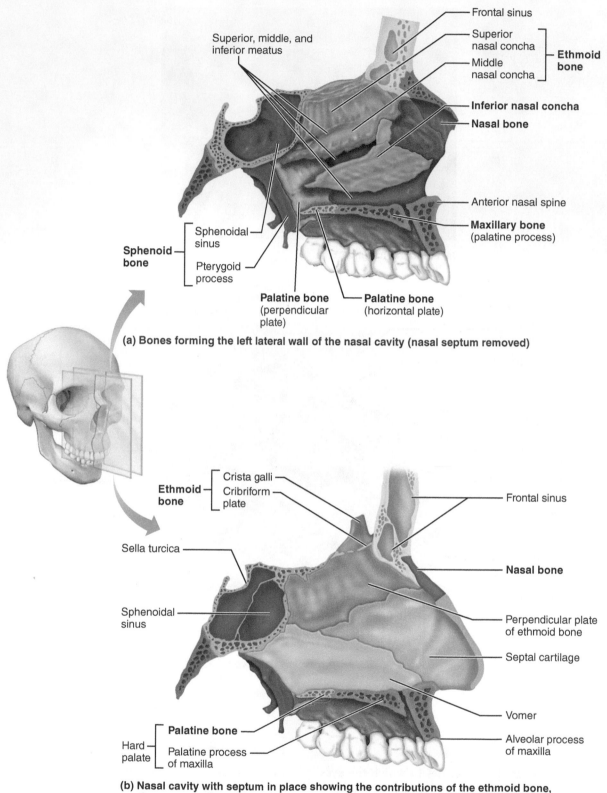

(a) Bones forming the left lateral wall of the nasal cavity (nasal septum removed)

(b) Nasal cavity with septum in place showing the contributions of the ethmoid bone, the vomer, and septal cartilage

Figure 7.13 Bones of the nasal cavity. (For a related image, see *A Brief Atlas of the Human Body*, Figure 15.)

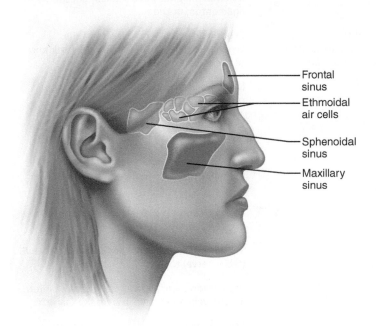

Frontal
sinus

Ethmoidal
air cells
(sinus)

Sphenoidal
sinus

Maxillary
sinus

(a) Anterior aspect

Frontal
sinus

Ethmoidal
air cells

Sphenoidal
sinus

Maxillary
sinus

(b) Medial aspect

Figure 7.14 Paranasal sinuses.

maxillae and the palatine bones. The nasal cavity is divided into right and left parts by the *nasal septum*. The bony portion of the septum is formed by the vomer inferiorly and the perpendicular plate of the ethmoid bone superiorly (Figure 7.13b). A sheet of cartilage called the *septal cartilage* completes the septum anteriorly.

The nasal septum and conchae are covered with a mucus-secreting mucosa that moistens and warms the entering air and helps cleanse it of debris. The scroll-shaped conchae increase the turbulence of air flowing through the nasal cavity. This swirling forces more of the inhaled air into contact with the warm, damp mucosa and encourages trapping of airborne particles (dust, pollen, bacteria) in the sticky mucus.

Greater horn

Lesser horn

Body

Figure 7.15 The hyoid bone, anterior view.

Paranasal Sinuses

Five skull bones—the frontal, sphenoid, ethmoid, and paired maxillary bones—contain mucosa-lined, air-filled sinuses that give them a rather moth-eaten appearance in an X-ray image. These particular sinuses are called **paranasal sinuses** because they cluster around the nasal cavity **(Figure 7.14)**.

Small openings connect the sinuses to the nasal cavity and act as "two-way streets": Air enters the sinuses from the nasal cavity, and mucus formed by the sinus mucosae drains into the nasal cavity. The mucosa of the sinuses also helps to warm and humidify inspired air. The paranasal sinuses lighten the skull and enhance the resonance of the voice.

☑ Check Your Understanding

10. What bones contain the paranasal sinuses?
11. The perpendicular plates of the palatine bones and the superior and middle conchae of the ethmoid bone form a substantial part of the nasal cavity walls. Which bone forms the roof of that cavity?
12. What bone forms the bulk of the orbit floor and what sense organ is found in the orbit of a living person?

For answers, see Appendix H.

The Hyoid Bone

Though not really part of the skull, the **hyoid bone** (hi'oid; "U-shaped") lies just inferior to the mandible in the anterior neck, and looks like a miniature version of it **(Figure 7.15)**. The hyoid bone is unique in that it is the only bone of the body that does not articulate directly with any other bone. Instead, it is anchored by the narrow *stylohyoid ligaments* to the styloid processes of the temporal bones. Horseshoe-shaped, with a body and two pairs of *horns*, or *cornua*, the hyoid bone acts as a movable base for the tongue. Its body and greater horns are attachment points for neck muscles that raise and lower the larynx during swallowing and speech.

(Text continues on p. 218.)

Table 7.1	Bones of the Skull	
BONE COLOR CODE*	**COMMENTS**	**IMPORTANT MARKINGS**
Cranial Bones		
Frontal (1) (Figures 7.4a, 7.5, and 7.7)	Forms forehead, superior part of orbits, and most of the anterior cranial fossa; contains sinuses	**Supraorbital foramina (notches):** allow the supraorbital arteries and nerves to pass
Parietal (2) (Figures 7.4 and 7.5)	Form most of the superior and lateral aspects of the skull	
Occipital (1) (Figures 7.4b, 7.5, 7.6, and 7.7)	Forms posterior aspect and most of the base of the skull	**Foramen magnum:** allows passage of the spinal cord from the brain stem to the vertebral canal
		Hypoglossal canals: allow passage of the hypoglossal nerves (cranial nerve XII)
		Occipital condyles: articulate with the atlas (first vertebra)
		External occipital protuberance and **nuchal lines:** sites of muscle attachment
		External occipital crest: attachment site of ligamentum nuchae
Temporal (2) (Figures 7.5, 7.6, 7.7, and 7.8)	Form inferolateral aspects of the skull and contribute to the middle cranial fossa; have squamous, tympanic, and petrous parts	**Zygomatic process:** helps to form the zygomatic arch, which forms the prominence of the cheek
		Mandibular fossa: articular point of the condylar process of the mandible
		External acoustic meatus: canal leading from the external ear to the eardrum
		Styloid process: attachment site for several neck muscles and for a ligament to the hyoid bone
		Mastoid process: attachment site for several neck and tongue muscles
		Stylomastoid foramen: allows cranial nerve VII (facial nerve) to pass
		Jugular foramen: allows passage of the internal jugular vein and cranial nerves IX, X, and XI
		Carotid canal: allows passage of the internal carotid artery
Sphenoid (1) (Figures 7.4a, 7.5, 7.6, 7.7, and 7.9)	Keystone of the cranium; contributes to the middle cranial fossa and orbits; main parts are the body, greater wings, lesser wings, and pterygoid processes	**Sella turcica:** hypophyseal fossa portion is the seat of the pituitary gland
		Optic canals: allow passage of optic nerves (cranial nerves II) and the ophthalmic arteries
		Superior orbital fissures: allow passage of cranial nerves III, IV, VI, part of V (ophthalmic division), and ophthalmic vein
		Foramen rotundum (2): allows passage of the maxillary division of cranial nerve V
		Foramen ovale (2): allows passage of the mandibular division of cranial nerve V
		Foramen spinosum (2): allows passage of the middle meningeal artery

Table 7.1 (continued)

BONE COLOR CODE*	COMMENTS	IMPORTANT MARKINGS
Ethmoid (1) (Figures 7.4a, 7.5, 7.7, 7.10, and 7.14)	Helps to form the anterior cranial fossa; forms part of the nasal septum and the lateral walls and roof of the nasal cavity; contributes to the medial wall of the orbit	**Crista galli:** attachment point for the falx cerebri, a dural membrane fold **Cribriform plates:** allow passage of filaments of the olfactory nerves (cranial nerve I) **Superior** and **middle nasal conchae:** form part of lateral walls of nasal cavity; increase turbulence of air flow
Auditory ossicles (malleus, incus, and stapes) (2 each)	Found in middle ear cavity; involved in sound transmission; see Figure 15.24b, p. 571	
Facial Bones		
Mandible (1) (Figures 7.4a, 7.5, and 7.11a)	The lower jaw	**Coronoid processes:** insertion points for the temporalis muscles **Condylar processes:** articulate with the temporal bones in the temporomandibular joints of the jaw **Mandibular symphysis:** medial fusion point of the mandibular bones **Dental alveoli:** sockets for the teeth **Mandibular foramina:** permit the inferior alveolar nerves to pass **Mental foramina:** allow blood vessels and nerves to pass to the chin and lower lip
Maxilla (2) (Figures 7.4a, 7.5, 7.6, and 7.11b)	Keystone bones of the face; form the upper jaw and parts of the hard palate, orbits, and nasal cavity walls	**Dental alveoli:** sockets for teeth **Zygomatic processes:** help form the zygomatic arches **Palatine processes:** form the anterior hard palate; meet medially in intermaxillary suture **Frontal process:** forms part of lateral aspect of bridge of nose **Incisive fossa:** permits blood vessels and nerves to pass through anterior hard palate (fused palatine processes) **Inferior orbital fissure:** permits maxillary branch of cranial nerve V, the zygomatic nerve, and blood vessels to pass **Infraorbital foramen:** allows passage of infraorbital nerve to skin of face
Zygomatic (2) (Figures 7.4a, 7.5a, and 7.6a)	Form the cheeks and part of the orbits	
Nasal (2) (Figures 7.4a and 7.5)	Form the bridge of the nose	
Lacrimal (2) (Figures 7.4a and 7.5a)	Form part of the medial orbit walls	**Lacrimal fossa:** houses the lacrimal sac, which helps to drain tears into the nasal cavity
Palatine (2) (Figures 7.5c, 7.6a, and 7.13)	Form posterior part of the hard palate and a small part of nasal cavity and orbit walls	**Median palatine suture:** medial fusion point of the horizontal plates of the palatine bones, which form the posterior part of the hard palate
Vomer (1) (Figures 7.4a and 7.13b)	Inferior part of the nasal septum	
Inferior nasal concha (2) (Figures 7.4a and 7.13a)	Form part of the lateral walls of the nasal cavity	

*The color code beside each bone name corresponds to the bone's color in Figures 7.4 to 7.13. The number in parentheses ( ) following the bone name indicates the total number of such bones in the body.

The Vertebral Column

General Characteristics

✓ Describe the structure of the vertebral column, list its components, and describe its curvatures.

✓ Indicate a common function of the spinal curvatures and the intervertebral discs.

Some people think of the **vertebral column** as a rigid supporting rod, but this is inaccurate. Also called the **spine** or **spinal column**, the vertebral column consists of 26 irregular bones connected in such a way that a flexible, curved structure results (**Figure 7.16**).

Serving as the axial support of the trunk, the spine extends from the skull to the pelvis, where it transmits the weight of the trunk to the lower limbs. It also surrounds and protects the delicate spinal cord and provides attachment points for the ribs and for the muscles of the back and neck.

In the fetus and infant, the vertebral column consists of 33 separate bones, or **vertebrae** (ver'tĕ-bre). Inferiorly, nine of these eventually fuse to form two composite bones, the sacrum and the tiny coccyx. The remaining 24 bones persist as individual vertebrae separated by intervertebral discs.

Regions and Curvatures

The vertebral column is about 70 cm (28 inches) long in an average adult and has five major regions (Figure 7.16). The seven vertebrae of the neck are the **cervical vertebrae** (ser'vĭ-kal), the next 12 are the **thoracic vertebrae** (tho-ras'ik), and the five supporting the lower back are the **lumbar vertebrae** (lum'bar). Remembering common meal times—7 AM, 12 noon, and 5 PM—will help you recall the number of bones in these three regions of the spine. The vertebrae become progressively larger from the cervical to the lumbar region, as they must support greater and greater weight.

Inferior to the lumbar vertebrae is the **sacrum** (sa'krum), which articulates with the hip bones of the pelvis. The terminus of the vertebral column is the tiny **coccyx** (kok'siks).

All of us have the same number of cervical vertebrae. Variations in numbers of vertebrae in other regions occur in about 5% of people.

When you view the vertebral column from the side, you can see the four curvatures that give it its S, or sinusoid, shape. The **cervical** and **lumbar curvatures** are concave posteriorly; the **thoracic** and **sacral curvatures** are convex posteriorly. These curvatures increase the resilience and flexibility of the spine, allowing it to function like a spring rather than a rigid rod.

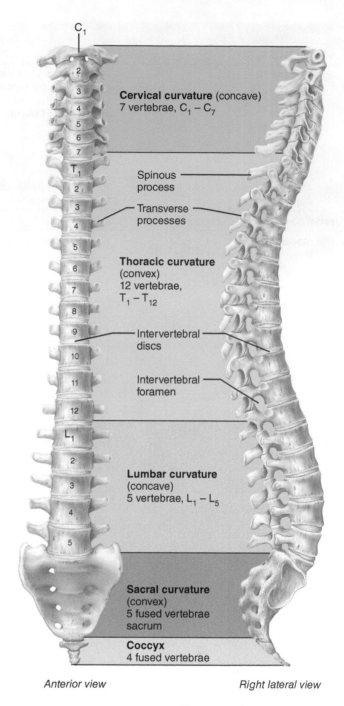

Cervical curvature (concave)
7 vertebrae, $C_1 - C_7$

Spinous process

Transverse processes

Thoracic curvature (convex)
12 vertebrae, $T_1 - T_{12}$

Intervertebral discs

Intervertebral foramen

Lumbar curvature (concave)
5 vertebrae, $L_1 - L_5$

Sacral curvature (convex)
5 fused vertebrae sacrum

Coccyx
4 fused vertebrae

Anterior view   Right lateral view

Figure 7.16 The vertebral column. Notice the curvatures in the lateral view. (The terms convex and concave refer to the curvature of the posterior aspect of the vertebral column.) (For a related image, see *A Brief Atlas of the Human Body*, Figure 17.)

⚒ Homeostatic Imbalance 7.2

There are several types of abnormal spinal curvatures (**Figure 7.17**). Some are congenital (present at birth); others result from disease, poor posture, or unequal muscle pull on the spine. *Scoliosis* (sko"le-o'sis), literally, "twisted disease," is an abnormal *lateral* curvature that occurs most often in the thoracic region. It is quite common during late childhood, particularly in girls, for some unknown reason. Other, more severe cases result from abnormal vertebral structure, lower limbs of unequal length, or muscle paralysis. If muscles on one side of the body are nonfunctional, those of the opposite side exert an unopposed pull on the spine and force it out of alignment. Scoliosis is treated (with body braces or surgically) before growth ends to prevent permanent deformity and breathing difficulties due to a compressed lung.

Kyphosis (ki-fo'sis), or hunchback, is a *dorsally* exaggerated *thoracic* curvature. It is particularly common in elderly people because of osteoporosis, but may also reflect tuberculosis of the spine, rickets, or osteomalacia.

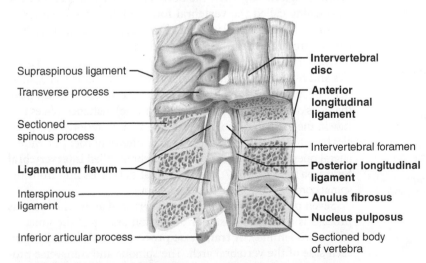

(a) Scoliosis   **(b) Kyphosis**   **(c) Lordosis**

Figure 7.17 Abnormal spinal curvatures.

Lordosis, or swayback, is an accentuated *lumbar* curvature. It, too, can result from spinal tuberculosis or osteomalacia. Temporary lordosis is common in those carrying a large load up front, such as men with "potbellies" and pregnant women. In an attempt to preserve their center of gravity, these individuals automatically throw back their shoulders, accentuating their lumbar curvature. ✚

Ligaments

Like a tall, tremulous TV transmitting tower, the vertebral column cannot possibly stand upright by itself. It must be held in place by an elaborate system of cable-like supports. In the case of the vertebral column, straplike ligaments and the trunk muscles assume this role.

The major supporting ligaments are the **anterior** and **posterior longitudinal ligaments** (Figure 7.18). These run as continuous bands down the front and back surfaces of the vertebrae from the neck to the sacrum. The broad anterior ligament is strongly attached to both the bony vertebrae and the discs. Along with its supporting role, it prevents hyperextension of the spine (bending too far backward). The posterior ligament, which resists hyperflexion of the spine (bending too sharply forward), is narrow and relatively weak. It attaches only to the discs. However, the **ligamentum flavum**, which connects adjacent vertebrae, contains elastic connective tissue and is especially strong. It stretches as we bend forward and then recoils when we resume an erect posture. Short ligaments connect each vertebra to those immediately above and below.

Intervertebral Discs

Each **intervertebral disc** is a cushionlike pad composed of two parts. The inner gelatinous **nucleus pulposus** (pul-po′sus; "pulp") acts like a rubber ball, giving the disc its elasticity and compressibility. Surrounding the nucleus pulposus is a strong collar composed of collagen fibers superficially and fibrocartilage internally, the **anulus fibrosus** (an′u-lus fi-bro′sus; "ring of fibers") (Figure 7.18a, c). The anulus fibrosus limits the expansion of the nucleus pulposus when the spine is compressed. It also acts like a woven strap to bind successive vertebrae together, withstands twisting forces, and resists tension in the spine.

Sandwiched between the bodies of neighboring vertebrae, the intervertebral discs act as shock absorbers during walking, jumping, and running. They allow the spine to flex and extend, and to a lesser extent to bend laterally. At points of compression, the discs flatten and bulge out a bit between the vertebrae. The discs are thickest in the lumbar and cervical regions, which enhances the flexibility of these regions.

Collectively the discs account for about 25% of the height of the vertebral column. They flatten somewhat during the course of the day, so we are always a few millimeters shorter at night than when we awake in the morning.

⚖ Homeostatic Imbalance 7.3

Severe or sudden physical trauma to the spine—for example, from bending forward while lifting a heavy object—may result in herniation of one or more discs. A **herniated** (**prolapsed**)

(a) Median section of three vertebrae, illustrating the composition of the discs and the ligaments

Supraspinous ligament
Transverse process
Sectioned spinous process
Ligamentum flavum
Interspinous ligament
Inferior articular process
Intervertebral disc
Anterior longitudinal ligament
Intervertebral foramen
Posterior longitudinal ligament
Anulus fibrosus
Nucleus pulposus
Sectioned body of vertebra

(b) Anterior view of part of the spinal column, showing the anterior longitudinal ligament

Posterior longitudinal ligament
Anterior longitudinal ligament
Body of a vertebra
Intervertebral disc

Figure 7.18 Ligaments and fibrocartilage discs uniting the vertebrae.

Vertebral spinous process
(posterior aspect of vertebra)

Spinal nerve root

Transverse process

Herniated portion of disc

Anulus fibrosus of disc

Spinal cord

Nucleus pulposus of disc

Nucleus pulposus of intact disc

Herniated nucleus pulposus

(c) Superior view of a herniated intervertebral disc

(d) MRI of lumbar region of vertebral column in sagittal section showing herniated disc

Figure 7.18 *(continued)* **Ligaments and fibrocartilage discs uniting the vertebrae.**

disc (commonly called a *slipped disc*) usually involves rupture of the anulus fibrosus followed by protrusion of the spongy nucleus pulposus through the anulus (Figure 7.18c, d). If the protrusion presses on the spinal cord or on spinal nerves exiting from the cord, numbness or excruciating pain may result.

Herniated discs are generally treated with moderate exercise, massage, heat therapy, and painkillers. If this fails, the protruding disc may have to be removed surgically and a bone graft done to fuse the adjoining vertebrae. For those preferring to avoid general anesthesia, part of the disc can be vaporized with a laser in an outpatient procedure called percutaneous laser disc decompression that takes only 30 to 40 minutes. If necessary, tears in the anulus can be sealed by electrothermal means at the same time. The patient leaves with only an adhesive bandage to mark the spot. ✚

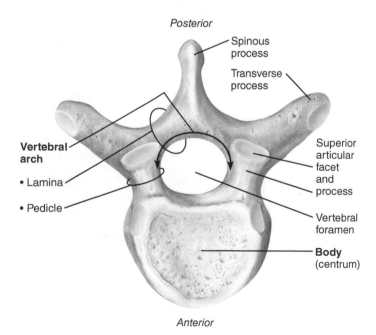

Posterior

Spinous process

Transverse process

Vertebral arch

• Lamina

• Pedicle

Superior articular facet and process

Vertebral foramen

Body (centrum)

Anterior

Figure 7.19 Typical vertebral structures. Superior view of a thoracic vertebra. Only bone features are illustrated in this and subsequent bone figures in this chapter. Articular cartilage is not depicted.

☑ **Check Your Understanding**

13. What are the five major regions of the vertebral column?
14. In which two of these regions is the vertebral column concave posteriorly?
15. Besides the spinal curvatures, which skeletal elements help to make the vertebral column flexible?

For answers, see Appendix H.

General Structure of Vertebrae

✓ Discuss the structure of a typical vertebra and describe regional features of cervical, thoracic, and lumbar vertebrae.

All vertebrae have a common structural pattern **(Figure 7.19)**. Each vertebra consists of a **body**, or **centrum**, anteriorly and a **vertebral arch** posteriorly. The disc-shaped body is the weight-bearing region. Together, the body and vertebral arch enclose an opening called the **vertebral foramen**. Successive vertebral foramina of the articulated vertebrae form the long **vertebral canal**, through which the spinal cord passes.

The vertebral arch is a composite structure formed by two pedicles and two laminae. The **pedicles** (ped′ĭ-kelz; "little feet"), short bony pillars projecting posteriorly from the vertebral body, form the sides of the arch. The **laminae** (lam′ĭ-ne), flattened plates that fuse in the median plane, complete the arch posteriorly. The pedicles have notches on their superior and inferior borders, providing lateral openings between adjacent vertebrae called **intervertebral foramina** (see Figure 7.16). The spinal nerves issuing from the spinal cord pass through these foramina.

Seven processes project from the vertebral arch. The **spinous process** is a median posterior projection arising at the junction of the two laminae. A **transverse process** extends laterally from each side of the vertebral arch. The spinous and transverse processes are attachment sites for muscles that move the vertebral column and for ligaments that stabilize it. The paired **superior** and **inferior articular processes** protrude superiorly and inferiorly,

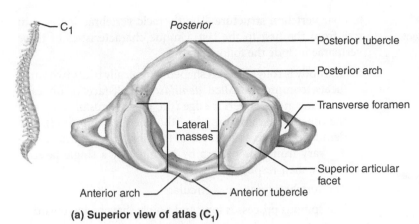

(a) Superior view of atlas (C₁)

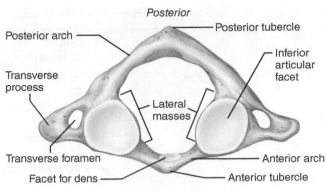

(b) Inferior view of atlas (C₁)

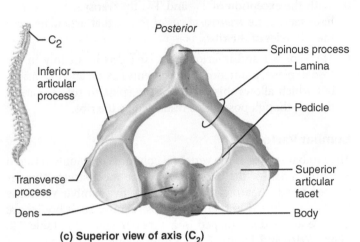

(c) Superior view of axis (C₂)

Figure 7.20 The first and second cervical vertebrae. (For a related image, see *A Brief Atlas of the Human Body*, Figure 18.)

respectively, from the pedicle-lamina junctions. The smooth joint surfaces of the articular processes, called *facets* ("little faces"), are covered with hyaline cartilage. The inferior articular processes of each vertebra form movable joints with the superior articular processes of the vertebra immediately below. Thus, successive vertebrae join both at their bodies and at their articular processes.

Regional Vertebral Characteristics

Beyond their common structural features, vertebrae exhibit variations that allow different regions of the spine to perform slightly different functions and movements. In general, movements that can occur between vertebrae are (1) flexion and extension (anterior bending and posterior straightening of the spine), (2) lateral flexion (bending the *upper body* to the right or left), and (3) rotation (in which vertebrae rotate on one another in the longitudinal axis of the spine). The regional vertebral characteristics described in this section are illustrated and summarized in **Table 7.2** on p. 223.

Cervical Vertebrae

The seven cervical vertebrae, identified as C₁–C₇, are the smallest, lightest vertebrae (see Figure 7.16). The first two (C₁ and C₂) are unusual and we will skip them for the moment. The "typical"

cervical vertebrae (C₃–C₇) have the following distinguishing features (see Figure 7.21 and Table 7.2):

- The body is oval—wider from side to side than in the anteroposterior dimension.
- Except in C₇, the spinous process is short, projects directly back, and is *bifid* (bi′fid), or split at its tip.
- The vertebral foramen is large and generally triangular.
- Each transverse process contains a **transverse foramen** through which the vertebral arteries pass to service the brain.

The spinous process of C₇ is not bifid and is much larger than those of the other cervical vertebrae (see Figure 7.21a). Because its spinous process is palpable through the skin, C₇ can be used as a landmark for counting the vertebrae and is called the **vertebra prominens** ("prominent vertebra").

The first two cervical vertebrae, the atlas and the axis, are somewhat more robust than the typical cervical vertebra. They have no intervertebral disc between them, and they are highly modified, reflecting their special functions. The **atlas** (C₁) has no body and no spinous process **(Figure 7.20a and b)**. Essentially, it is a ring of bone consisting of *anterior* and *posterior arches* and a *lateral mass* on each side. Each lateral mass has articular facets on both its superior and inferior surfaces. The superior articular facets receive the occipital condyles of the skull—they "carry" the skull, just as Atlas supported the heavens in Greek mythology. These joints allow you to nod "yes." The inferior articular facets form joints with the axis (C₂) below.

The **axis**, which has a body and the other typical vertebral processes, is not as specialized as the atlas. In fact, its only unusual feature is the knoblike **dens** (denz; "tooth") projecting superiorly from its body. The dens is actually the "missing" body of the atlas, which fuses with the axis during embryonic development. Cradled in the anterior arch of the atlas by the transverse ligament **(Figure 7.21a)**, the dens acts as a pivot for the rotation of the atlas. Hence, this joint allows you to rotate your head from side to side to indicate "no."

Thoracic Vertebrae

The 12 thoracic vertebrae (T₁–T₁₂) all articulate with the ribs (see Table 7.2, Figure 7.16, and Figure 7.21b). The first looks much like C₇, and the last four show a progression toward

(a) Cervical vertebrae

- Dens of axis
- Transverse ligament of atlas
- **C$_1$ (atlas)**
- **C$_2$ (axis)**
- **C$_3$**
- Inferior articular process
- Bifid spinous process
- Transverse processes
- **C$_7$ (vertebra prominens)**

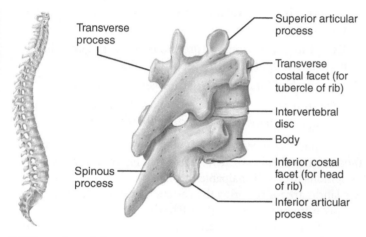

(b) Thoracic vertebrae

- Transverse process
- Superior articular process
- Transverse costal facet (for tubercle of rib)
- Intervertebral disc
- Body
- Spinous process
- Inferior costal facet (for head of rib)
- Inferior articular process

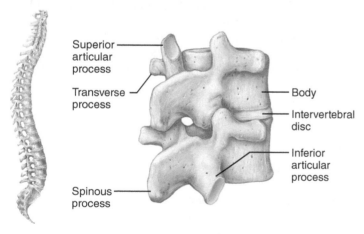

(c) Lumbar vertebrae

- Superior articular process
- Transverse process
- Body
- Intervertebral disc
- Inferior articular process
- Spinous process

Figure 7.21 Posterolateral views of articulated vertebrae. Notice the bulbous tip on the spinous process of C$_7$, the vertebra prominens. (For a related image, see *A Brief Atlas of the Human Body*, Figures 19, 20, and 21.)

lumbar vertebral structure. The thoracic vertebrae increase in size from the first to the last. Unique characteristics of these vertebrae include the following:

- The body is roughly heart shaped. It typically bears two small facets, commonly called *demifacets* (half-facets), on each side, one at the superior edge (the *superior costal facet*) and the other at the inferior edge (the *inferior costal facet*). The demifacets receive the heads of the ribs. (The bodies of T$_{10}$–T$_{12}$ vary from this pattern by having only a single facet to receive their respective ribs.)
- The vertebral foramen is circular.
- The spinous process is long and points sharply downward.
- With the exception of T$_{11}$ and T$_{12}$, the transverse processes have facets, the *transverse costal facets*, that articulate with the tubercles of the ribs.
- The superior and inferior articular facets lie mainly in the frontal plane, a situation that prevents flexion and extension, but which allows this region of the spine to rotate. Lateral flexion, though possible, is restricted by the ribs.

Lumbar Vertebrae

The lumbar region of the vertebral column, commonly referred to as the small of the back, receives the most stress. The enhanced weight-bearing function of the five lumbar vertebrae (L$_1$–L$_5$) is reflected in their sturdier structure. Their bodies are massive and kidney shaped in a superior view (see Table 7.2, Figure 7.16, and Figure 7.21). Other characteristics typical of these vertebrae:

- The pedicles and laminae are shorter and thicker than those of other vertebrae.
- The spinous processes are short, flat, and hatchet shaped and are easily seen when a person bends forward. These processes are robust and project directly backward, adaptations for the attachment of the large back muscles.
- The vertebral foramen is triangular.
- The orientation of the facets of the articular processes of the lumbar vertebrae differs substantially from that of the other vertebra types (see Table 7.2). These modifications lock the lumbar vertebrae together and provide stability by preventing rotation of the lumbar spine. Flexion and extension are possible (as when you do sit-ups), as is lateral flexion.

Sacrum

The triangular sacrum, which shapes the posterior wall of the pelvis, is formed by five fused vertebrae (S$_1$–S$_5$) in adults (**Figure 7.22**, and see Figure 7.16). It articulates superiorly (via its **superior articular processes**) with L$_5$ and inferiorly with the coccyx. Laterally, the sacrum articulates, via its **auricular surfaces**, with the two hip bones to form the **sacroiliac joints** (sa″kro-il′e-ak) of the pelvis.

The **sacral promontory** (prom′on-tor″e; "high point of land projecting into the sea"), the anterosuperior margin of the first sacral vertebra, bulges anteriorly into the pelvic cavity. The body's center of gravity lies about 1 cm posterior to this

Table 7.2 **Regional Characteristics of Cervical, Thoracic, and Lumbar Vertebrae**

CHARACTERISTIC	CERVICAL (3–7)	THORACIC	LUMBAR
Body	Small, wide side to side	Larger than cervical; heart shaped; bears two costal facets	Massive; kidney shaped
Spinous process	Short; bifid; projects directly posterior	Long; sharp; projects inferiorly	Short; blunt; rectangular; projects directly posteriorly
Vertebral foramen	Triangular	Circular	Triangular
Transverse processes	Contain foramina	Bear facets for ribs (except T_{11} and T_{12})	Thin and tapered
Superior and inferior articular processes	Superior facets directed superoposteriorly	Superior facets directed posteriorly	Superior facets directed posteromedially (or medially)
	Inferior facets directed inferoanteriorly	Inferior facets directed anteriorly	Inferior facets directed anterolaterally (or laterally)
Movements allowed	Flexion and extension; lateral flexion; rotation; the spine region with the greatest range of movement	Rotation; lateral flexion possible but restricted by ribs; flexion and extension limited	Flexion and extension; some lateral flexion; rotation prevented

Superior View

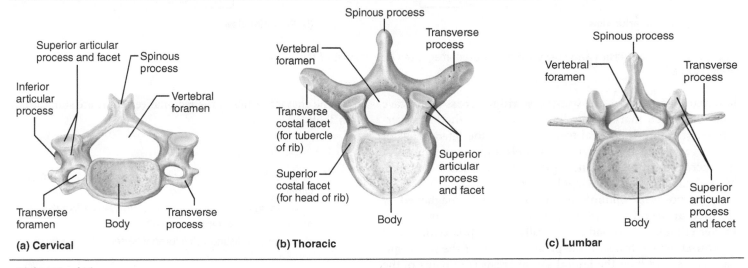

(a) Cervical

(b) Thoracic

(c) Lumbar

Right Lateral View

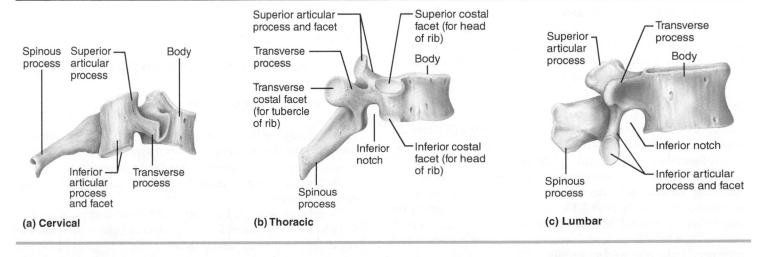

(a) Cervical

(b) Thoracic

(c) Lumbar

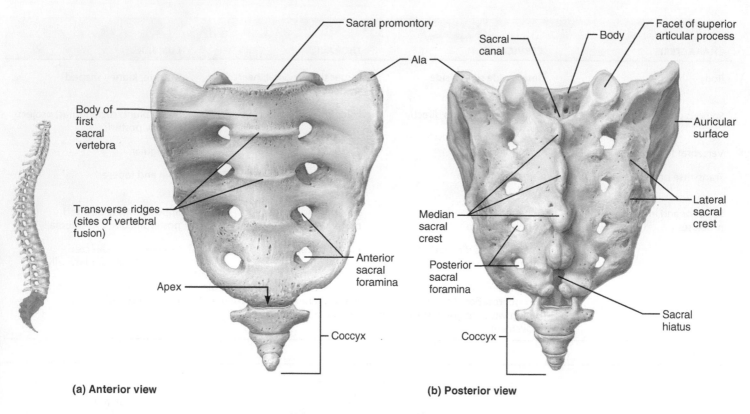

(a) Anterior view

(b) Posterior view

Figure 7.22 **The sacrum and coccyx.** (For a related image, see *A Brief Atlas of the Human Body*, Figure 22.)

landmark. Four ridges, the **transverse ridges**, cross its concave anterior aspect, marking the lines of fusion of the sacral vertebrae. The **anterior sacral foramina** lie at the lateral ends of these ridges and transmit blood vessels and anterior rami of the sacral spinal nerves. The regions lateral to these foramina expand superiorly as the winglike **alae**.

In its posterior midline the sacral surface is roughened by the **median sacral crest** (the fused spinous processes of the sacral vertebrae). This is flanked laterally by the **posterior sacral foramina**, which transmit the posterior rami of the sacral spinal nerves, and then the **lateral sacral crests** (remnants of the transverse processes of S_1–S_5).

The vertebral canal continues inside the sacrum as the **sacral canal**. Since the laminae of the fifth (and sometimes the fourth) sacral vertebrae fail to fuse medially, an enlarged external opening called the **sacral hiatus** (hi-a′tus; "gap") is obvious at the inferior end of the sacral canal.

Coccyx

The coccyx, our tailbone, is a small triangular bone (Figure 7.22, and see Figure 7.16). It consists of four (or in some cases three or five) vertebrae fused together. The coccyx articulates superiorly with the sacrum. (The name *coccyx* is from the Greek word meaning "cuckoo" and was so named because of its fancied resemblance to a bird's beak.) Except for the slight support the coccyx affords the pelvic organs, it is a nearly useless bone. Occasionally, a baby is born with an unusually long coccyx, which may need to be removed surgically.

The characteristics of the regional vertebrae are summarized in Table 7.2.

☑ **Check Your Understanding**

16. What is the normal number of cervical vertebrae? Of thoracic vertebrae?
17. How would a complete fracture of the dens affect the mobility of the vertebral column?
18. How can you distinguish a lumbar vertebra from a thoracic vertebra?

For answers, see Appendix H.

The Thoracic Cage

✓ Name and describe the bones of the thoracic cage (bony thorax).

✓ Differentiate true from false ribs.

Anatomically, the thorax is the chest, and its bony underpinnings are called the **thoracic cage** or *bony thorax*. Elements of the thoracic cage include the thoracic vertebrae posteriorly, the ribs laterally, and the sternum and costal cartilages anteriorly. The costal cartilages secure the ribs to the sternum **(Figure 7.23a)**.

Roughly cone shaped with its broad dimension positioned inferiorly, the bony thorax forms a protective cage around the vital organs of the thoracic cavity (heart, lungs, and great blood vessels), supports the shoulder girdles and upper limbs, and provides

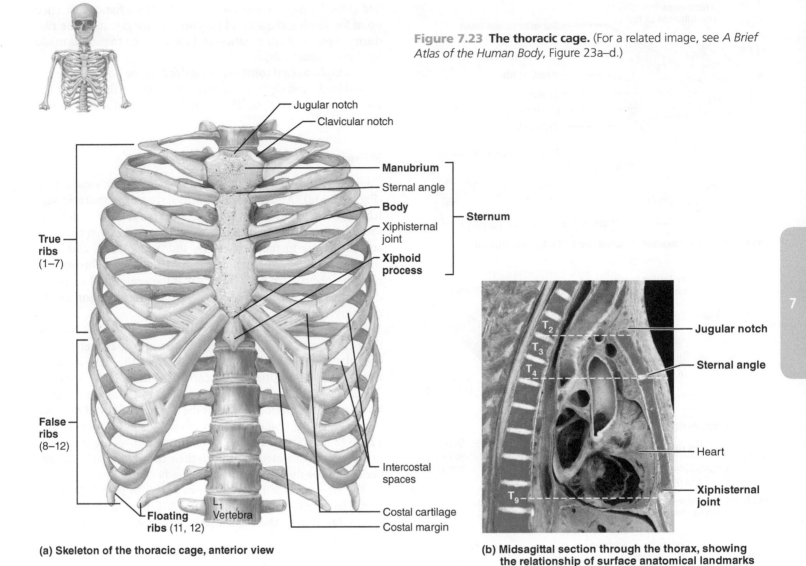

Figure 7.23 The thoracic cage. (For a related image, see *A Brief Atlas of the Human Body*, Figure 23a–d.)

Jugular notch
Clavicular notch
Manubrium
Sternal angle
Body
Xiphisternal joint
Xiphoid process
Sternum

True ribs (1–7)

False ribs (8–12)

Intercostal spaces

L₁ Vertebra
Floating ribs (11, 12)
Costal cartilage
Costal margin

(a) Skeleton of the thoracic cage, anterior view

T₂
T₃
T₄
T₉

Jugular notch
Sternal angle
Heart
Xiphisternal joint

(b) Midsagittal section through the thorax, showing the relationship of surface anatomical landmarks of the thorax to the vertebral column

attachment points for many muscles of the neck, back, chest, and shoulders. The *intercostal spaces* between the ribs are occupied by the intercostal muscles, which lift and then depress the thorax during breathing.

Sternum

The **sternum** (breastbone) lies in the anterior midline of the thorax. Vaguely resembling a dagger, it is a flat bone approximately 15 cm (6 inches) long, resulting from the fusion of three bones: the manubrium, the body, and the xiphoid process. The *manubrium* (mah-nu′bre-um; "knife handle") is the superior portion, which is shaped like the knot in a necktie. The manubrium articulates via its **clavicular notches** (klah-vik′u-lar) with the clavicles (collarbones) laterally, and just below this, it also articulates with the first two pairs of ribs. The *body*, or midportion, forms the bulk of the sternum. The sides of the body are notched where it articulates with the costal cartilages of the second to seventh ribs. The *xiphoid process* (zif′oid; "swordlike") forms the inferior end of the

sternum. This small, variably shaped process is a plate of hyaline cartilage in youth, but it is usually ossified in adults over the age of 40. The xiphoid process articulates only with the sternal body and serves as an attachment point for some abdominal muscles.

Homeostatic Imbalance 7.4

In some people, the xiphoid process projects posteriorly. In such cases, blows to the chest can push the xiphoid into the underlying heart or liver, causing massive hemorrhage. ✚

The sternum has three important anatomical landmarks: the jugular notch, the sternal angle, and the xiphisternal joint (Figure 7.23). The easily palpated **jugular** (*suprasternal*) **notch** is the central indentation in the superior border of the manubrium. If you slide your finger down the anterior surface of your neck, it will land in the jugular notch. The jugular notch is generally in line with the disc between the second and third thoracic vertebrae and the point where the left common carotid artery issues from the aorta (Figure 7.23b).

(a) Vertebral and sternal articulations of a typical true rib

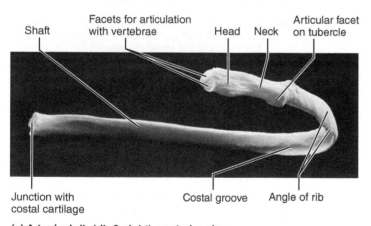

(b) Superior view of the articulation between a rib and a thoracic vertebra

(c) A typical rib (rib 6, right), posterior view

Figure 7.24 Ribs. All ribs illustrated in this figure are right ribs. (For a related image, see *A Brief Atlas of the Human Body,* Figure 23e and f.)

The **sternal angle** is felt as a horizontal ridge across the front of the sternum, where the manubrium joins the sternal body. This cartilaginous joint acts like a hinge, allowing the sternal body to swing anteriorly when we inhale. The sternal angle is in line with the disc between the fourth and fifth thoracic vertebrae

and at the level of the second pair of ribs. It is a handy reference point for finding the second rib and thus for counting the ribs during a physical examination and for listening to sounds made by specific heart valves.

The **xiphisternal joint** (zif″ĭ-ster′nul) is the point where the sternal body and xiphoid process fuse. It lies at the level of the ninth thoracic vertebra. The heart lies on the diaphragm just deep to this joint.

Ribs

Twelve pairs of **ribs** form the flaring sides of the thoracic cage (Figure 7.23a). All ribs attach posteriorly to the thoracic vertebrae (bodies and transverse processes) and curve inferiorly toward the anterior body surface. The superior seven rib pairs attach directly to the sternum by individual costal cartilages (bars of hyaline cartilage). These are **true** or **vertebrosternal ribs** (ver″tĕ-bro-ster′nal). (Notice that the anatomical name indicates the two attachment points of a rib—the posterior attachment given first.)

The remaining five pairs of ribs are called **false ribs** because they either attach indirectly to the sternum or entirely lack a sternal attachment. Rib pairs 8–10 attach to the sternum indirectly, each joining the costal cartilage immediately above it. These ribs are also called **vertebrochondral ribs** (ver″tĕ-bro-kon′dral). The inferior margin of the rib cage, or **costal margin**, is formed by the costal cartilages of ribs 7–10. Rib pairs 11 and 12 are called **vertebral ribs** or **floating ribs** because they have no anterior attachments. Instead, their costal cartilages lie embedded in the muscles of the lateral body wall.

The ribs increase in length from pair 1 to pair 7, then decrease in length from pair 8 to pair 12. Except for the first rib, which lies deep to the clavicle, the ribs are easily felt in people of normal weight.

A typical rib is a bowed flat bone (**Figure 7.24**). The bulk of a rib is simply called the *shaft.* Its superior border is smooth, but its inferior border is sharp and thin and has a *costal groove* on its inner face that lodges the intercostal nerves and blood vessels.

In addition to the shaft, each rib has a head, neck, and tubercle. The wedge-shaped *head,* the posterior end, articulates with the vertebral bodies by two facets: One joins the body of the same-numbered thoracic vertebra, the other articulates with the body of the vertebra immediately superior. The *neck* is the constricted portion of the rib just beyond the head. Lateral to this, the knoblike *tubercle* articulates with the costal facet of the transverse process of the same-numbered thoracic vertebra. Beyond the tubercle, the shaft angles sharply forward (at the angle of the rib) and then extends to attach to its costal cartilage anteriorly. The costal cartilages provide secure but flexible rib attachments to the sternum.

The first pair of ribs is quite atypical. They are flattened superiorly to inferiorly and are quite broad, forming a horizontal table that supports the subclavian blood vessels that serve the upper limbs. There are also other exceptions to the typical rib pattern. Rib 1 and ribs 10–12 articulate with only one vertebral body, and ribs 11 and 12 do not articulate with a vertebral transverse process.

Figure 7.25 The pectoral girdle and clavicle. (For a related image, see *A Brief Atlas of the Human Body*, Figure 24.)

(a) Articulated pectoral girdle

Acromio-clavicular joint

Clavicle

Scapula

(b) Right clavicle, superior view

Sternal (medial) end

Posterior

Anterior

Acromial (lateral) end

(c) Right clavicle, inferior view

Acromial end

Trapezoid line

Anterior

Sternal end

Posterior

Conoid tubercle

☑ **Check Your Understanding**

19. How does a true rib differ from a false rib?

20. What is the sternal angle and what is its clinical importance?

21. Besides the ribs and sternum, there is a third group of bones making up the thoracic cage. What is it?

For answers, see Appendix H.

PART 2
The Appendicular Skeleton

Bones of the limbs and their girdles are collectively called the **appendicular skeleton** because they are appended to the axial skeleton that forms the longitudinal axis of the body (see Figure 7.1). The yokelike *pectoral girdles* (pek'tor-al; "chest") attach the upper limbs to the body trunk. The more sturdy *pelvic girdle* secures the lower limbs. Although the bones of the upper and lower limbs differ in their functions and mobility, they have the same fundamental plan: Each limb is composed of three major segments connected by movable joints.

The appendicular skeleton enables us to carry out the movements typical of our freewheeling and manipulative lifestyle. Each time we take a step, throw a ball, or pop a caramel into our mouth, we are making good use of our appendicular skeleton.

The Pectoral (Shoulder) Girdle

✓ Identify bones forming the pectoral girdle and relate their structure and arrangement to the function of this girdle.

✓ Identify important bone markings on the pectoral girdle.

The **pectoral girdle**, or **shoulder girdle**, consists of the *clavicle* (klav'ĭ-kl) anteriorly and the *scapula* (skap'u-lah) posteriorly (**Figure 7.25** and Table 7.3 on p. 233). The paired pectoral girdles and their associated muscles form your shoulders. Although the term *girdle* usually signifies a beltlike structure encircling the body, a single pectoral girdle, or even the pair, does not quite satisfy this description. Anteriorly, the medial end of each clavicle joins the sternum; the distal ends of the clavicles meet the scapulae laterally. However, the scapulae fail to complete the ring posteriorly, because their medial borders do not join each other or the axial skeleton. Instead, the scapulae are attached to the thorax and vertebral column only by the muscles that clothe their surfaces.

The pectoral girdles attach the upper limbs to the axial skeleton and provide attachment points for many of the muscles that move the upper limbs. These girdles are very light and allow the upper limbs a degree of mobility not seen anywhere else in the body. This mobility is due to the following factors:

- Because only the clavicle attaches to the axial skeleton, the scapula can move quite freely across the thorax, allowing the arm to move with it.
- The socket of the shoulder joint (the scapula's glenoid cavity) is shallow and poorly reinforced, so it does not restrict the movement of the humerus (arm bone). Although this arrangement is good for flexibility, it is bad for stability: Shoulder dislocations are fairly common.

Clavicles

The **clavicles** ("little keys"), or collarbones, are slender, S-shaped bones that can be felt along their entire course as they extend horizontally across the superior thorax (Figure 7.25). Each clavicle is cone shaped at its medial **sternal end**, which attaches to the sternal manubrium, and flattened at its lateral **acromial end** (ah-kro′me-al), which articulates with the scapula. The medial two-thirds of the clavicle is convex anteriorly; its lateral third is concave anteriorly. Its superior surface is fairly smooth, but the inferior surface is ridged and grooved by ligaments and by the action of the muscles that attach to it. The *trapezoid line* and the *conoid tubercle*, for example, are anchoring points for a ligament that connects the clavicle to the scapula.

Besides anchoring many muscles, the clavicles act as braces: They hold the scapulae and arms out laterally, away from the narrower superior part of the thorax. This bracing function becomes obvious when a clavicle is fractured: The entire shoulder region collapses medially. The clavicles also transmit compression forces from the upper limbs to the axial skeleton, for example, when someone pushes a car to a gas station.

The clavicles are not very strong and are likely to fracture, for example, when a person uses outstretched arms to break a fall. The curves in the clavicle ensure that it usually fractures anteriorly (outward). If it were to collapse posteriorly (inward), bone splinters would damage the subclavian artery, which passes just deep to the clavicle to serve the upper limb. The clavicles are exceptionally sensitive to muscle pull and become noticeably larger and stronger in those who perform manual labor or athletics involving the shoulder and arm muscles.

Scapulae

The **scapulae**, or *shoulder blades*, are thin, triangular flat bones (Figure 7.25a and Figure 7.26). Interestingly, their name derives from a word meaning "spade" or "shovel," for ancient cultures made spades from the shoulder blades of animals. The scapulae lie on the dorsal surface of the rib cage, between ribs 2 and 7.

Each scapula has three borders. The *superior border* is the shortest, sharpest border. The *medial*, or *vertebral*, *border* parallels the vertebral column. The thick *lateral*, or *axillary*, *border* abuts the armpit and ends superiorly in a small, shallow fossa, the **glenoid cavity** (gle′noid; "pit-shaped"). This cavity articulates with the humerus of the arm, forming the shoulder joint.

Like all triangles, the scapula has three corners or *angles*. The superior scapular border meets the medial border at the

superior angle and the lateral border at the *lateral angle*. The medial and lateral borders join at the *inferior angle*. The inferior angle moves extensively as the arm is raised and lowered, and is an important landmark for studying scapular movements.

The anterior, or costal, surface of the scapula is concave and relatively featureless. Its posterior surface bears a prominent **spine** that is easily felt through the skin. The spine ends laterally in an enlarged, roughened triangular projection called the **acromion** (ah-kro′me-on; "point of the shoulder"). The acromion articulates with the acromial end of the clavicle, forming the **acromioclavicular joint**.

Projecting anteriorly from the superior scapular border is the **coracoid process** (kor′ah-coid); *corac* means "beaklike," but this process looks more like a bent little finger. The coracoid process helps anchor the biceps muscle of the arm. It is bounded by the **suprascapular notch** (a nerve passage) medially and by the glenoid cavity laterally.

Several large fossae appear on both sides of the scapula and are named according to location. The *infraspinous* and *supraspinous fossae* are inferior and superior, respectively, to the spine. The *subscapular fossa* is the shallow concavity formed by the entire anterior scapular surface. Lying within these fossae are muscles with similar names.

☑ Check Your Understanding

22. What two bones construct each pectoral girdle?
23. Where is the single point of attachment of the pectoral girdle to the axial skeleton?
24. What is the major shortcoming of the flexibility allowed by the shoulder joint?

For answers, see Appendix H.

The Upper Limb

✓ Identify or name the bones of the upper limb and their important markings.

Thirty separate bones form the bony framework of each upper limb (see Figures 7.27 to 7.29, and Table 7.3 on p. 233). Each of these bones may be described regionally as a bone of the arm, forearm, or hand. (Keep in mind that anatomically the "arm" is only that part of the upper limb between the shoulder and elbow.)

Arm

The **humerus** (hu′mer-us), the sole bone of the arm, is a typical long bone (Figure 7.27). The largest, longest bone of the upper limb, it articulates with the scapula at the shoulder and with the radius and ulna (forearm bones) at the elbow.

At the proximal end of the humerus is its smooth, hemispherical **head**, which fits into the glenoid cavity of the scapula in a manner that allows the arm to hang freely at one's side. Immediately inferior to the head is a slight constriction, the **anatomical neck**. Just inferior to this are the lateral **greater tubercle** and the more medial **lesser tubercle**, separated by the **intertubercular sulcus**, or *bicipital groove* (bi-sip′ĭ-tal). These tubercles are sites of attachment of the rotator cuff muscles. The intertubercular sulcus guides

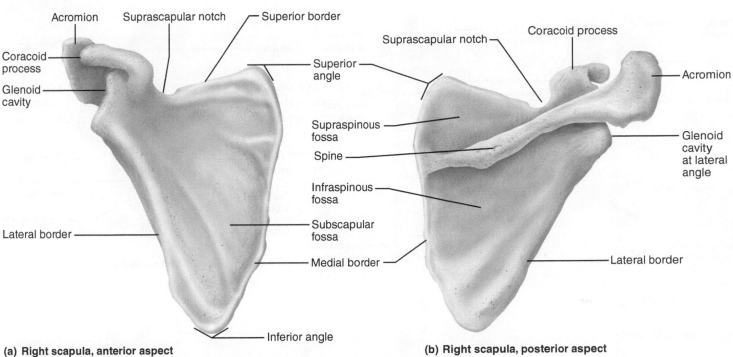

(a) Right scapula, anterior aspect

Acromion — Suprascapular notch — Superior border

Coracoid process

Glenoid cavity

Lateral border

Subscapular fossa

Medial border

Inferior angle

Suprascapular notch — Coracoid process

Superior angle

Acromion

Supraspinous fossa

Spine

Glenoid cavity at lateral angle

Infraspinous fossa

Lateral border

(b) Right scapula, posterior aspect

Supraspinous fossa

Infraspinous fossa

Subscapular fossa

Posterior   *Anterior*

Acromion

Spine

Infraspinous fossa

Supraspinous fossa

Supraglenoid tubercle

Coracoid process

Glenoid cavity

Infraglenoid tubercle

Subscapular fossa

Inferior angle

(c) Right scapula, lateral aspect

Figure 7.26 The scapula. View (c) is accompanied by a schematic representation of its orientation. (For a related image, see *A Brief Atlas of the Human Body*, Figure 24.)

Figure 7.27 **The humerus of the right arm and detailed views of articulation at the elbow.** (For a related image, see *A Brief Atlas of the Human Body*, Figure 25.)

(a) Anterior view

(b) Posterior view

(c) Anterior view at the elbow region

(d) Posterior view of extended elbow

a tendon of the biceps muscle of the arm to its attachment point at the rim of the glenoid cavity (the supraglenoid tubercle). Just distal to the tubercles is the **surgical neck**, so named because it is the most frequently fractured part of the humerus. About midway down the shaft on its lateral side is the V-shaped **deltoid tuberosity,** the roughened attachment site for the deltoid muscle of the shoulder. Nearby, the **radial groove** runs obliquely down the posterior aspect of the shaft, marking the course of the radial nerve, an important nerve of the upper limb.

At the distal end of the humerus are two condyles: a medial **trochlea** (trok′le-ah; "pulley"), which looks like an hourglass tipped on its side, and the lateral ball-like **capitulum** (kah-pit′u-lum). These condyles articulate with the ulna and the radius,

respectively (Figure 7.27c and d). The condyle pair is flanked by the **medial** and **lateral epicondyles** (muscle attachment sites). Directly above these epicondyles are the **medial and lateral supracondylar ridges**. The ulnar nerve, which runs behind the medial epicondyle, is responsible for the painful, tingling sensation you experience when you hit your "funny bone."

Superior to the trochlea on the anterior surface is the **coronoid fossa**; on the posterior surface is the deeper **olecranon fossa** (o-lek′rah-non). These two depressions allow the corresponding processes of the ulna to move freely when the elbow is flexed and extended. A small **radial fossa**, lateral to the coronoid fossa, receives the head of the radius when the elbow is flexed.

Figure 7.28 Radius and ulna of the right forearm. Note the structural details of the ulnar head and distal portion of radius and ulna. (For a related image, see *A Brief Atlas of the Human Body*, Figure 26.)

(a) Anterior view   (b) Posterior view

(c) Proximal portion of ulna, lateral view

(d) Distal ends of the radius and ulna at the wrist

Forearm

Two parallel long bones, the radius and the ulna, form the skeleton of the forearm, or *antebrachium* (an"te-bra′ke-um) **(Figure 7.28)**. Unless a person's forearm muscles are very bulky, these bones are easily palpated along their entire length. Their proximal ends articulate with the humerus; their distal ends form joints with bones of the wrist. The radius and ulna articulate with each other both proximally and distally at small **radioulnar joints** (ra"de-o-ul′nar), and they are connected along their entire length by a flat, flexible ligament, the **interosseous membrane** (in"ter-os′e-us; "between the bones").

In the anatomical position, the radius lies laterally (on the thumb side) and the ulna medially. However, when you rotate your forearm so that the palm faces posteriorly (a movement called pronation), the distal end of the radius crosses over the ulna and the two bones form an X (see Figure 8.6a, p. 259).

Ulna

The **ulna** (ul′nah; "elbow") is slightly longer than the radius. It has the main responsibility for forming the elbow joint with the humerus. Its proximal end looks like the adjustable end of a monkey wrench: It bears two prominent processes, the **olecranon** (elbow)

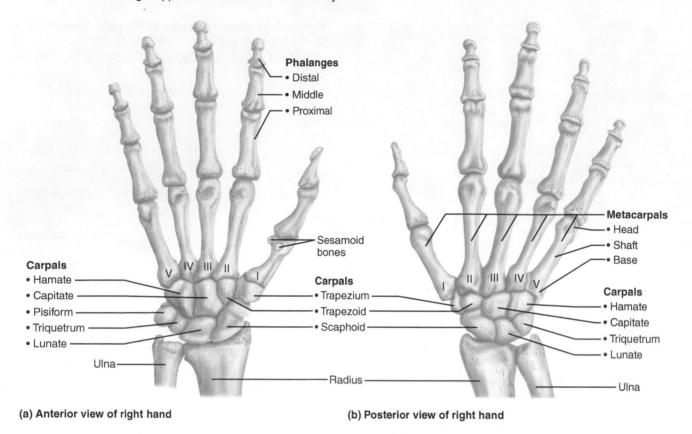

Phalanges
• Distal
• Middle
• Proximal

Sesamoid
bones

Carpals
• Hamate
• Capitate
• Pisiform
• Triquetrum
• Lunate

Ulna

V IV III II   I

Carpals
• Trapezium
• Trapezoid
• Scaphoid

Radius

(a) Anterior view of right hand

Metacarpals
• Head
• Shaft
• Base

I   II   III   IV   V

Carpals
• Hamate
• Capitate
• Triquetrum
• Lunate

Ulna

(b) Posterior view of right hand

Figure 7.29 Bones of the right hand. (For a related image, see *A Brief Atlas of the Human Body*, Figure 27.)

and the **coronoid process**, separated by a deep concavity, the **trochlear notch** (Figure 7.28c). Together, these two processes grip the trochlea of the humerus, forming a hinge joint that allows the forearm to be bent upon the arm (flexed), then straightened again (extended). When the forearm is fully extended, the olecranon "locks" into the olecranon fossa (Figure 7.27d), keeping the forearm from hyperextending (moving posteriorly beyond the elbow joint). The posterior olecranon forms the angle of the elbow when the forearm is flexed and is the bony part that rests on the table when you lean on your elbows. On the lateral side of the coronoid process is a small depression, the **radial notch**, where the ulna articulates with the head of the radius.

Distally the ulnar shaft narrows and ends in a knoblike **head** (Figure 7.28d). Medial to the head is the **ulnar styloid process**, from which a ligament runs to the wrist. The ulnar head is separated from the bones of the wrist by a disc of fibrocartilage and plays little or no role in hand movements.

Radius

The **radius** ("rod") is thin at its proximal end and wide distally—the opposite of the ulna. The **head** of the radius is shaped somewhat like the head of a nail (Figure 7.28). The superior surface of this head is concave, and it articulates with the capitulum of the humerus. Medially, the head articulates with the radial notch of the ulna (Figure 7.27c). Just inferior to the head is the rough **radial tuberosity**, which anchors the biceps muscle of the arm. Distally, where the radius is expanded, it has a medial

ulnar notch (Figure 7.28d), which articulates with the ulna, and a lateral **radial styloid process** (an anchoring site for ligaments that run to the wrist). Between these two markings, the radius is concave where it articulates with carpal bones of the wrist.

The ulna contributes more heavily to the elbow joint, and the radius is the major forearm bone contributing to the wrist joint. When the radius moves, the hand moves with it.

 Homeostatic Imbalance 7.5

Colles' fracture is a break in the distal end of the radius. It is a common fracture when a falling person attempts to break his or her fall with outstretched hands. ✚

Hand

The skeleton of the hand (**Figure 7.29**) includes the bones of the *carpus* (wrist); the bones of the *metacarpus* (palm); and the *phalanges* (bones of the fingers).

Carpus (Wrist)

A "wrist" watch is actually worn on the distal forearm (over the lower ends of the radius and ulna), not on the wrist at all. The true wrist, or carpus, is the proximal part of the structure we generally call our "hand." The carpus consists of eight marble-size short bones, or **carpals** (kar′palz), closely united by ligaments. Because gliding movements occur between these bones, the carpus as a whole is quite flexible.

Table 7.3   Bones of the Appendicular Skeleton, Part 1: Pectoral Girdle and Upper Limb

BODY REGION	BONES*	ILLUSTRATION	LOCATION	MARKINGS
Pectoral girdle (Figures 7.25, 7.26)	**Clavicle** (2)		Clavicle is in superoanterior thorax; articulates medially with sternum and laterally with scapula	Acromial end; sternal end
	Scapula (2)		Scapula is in posterior thorax; forms part of the shoulder; articulates with humerus and clavicle	Glenoid cavity; spine; acromion; coracoid process; infraspinous, supraspinous, and subscapular fossae
Upper limb Arm (Figure 7.27)	**Humerus** (2)		Humerus is sole bone of arm; between scapula and elbow	Head; greater and lesser tubercles; intertubercular sulcus; radial groove; deltoid tuberosity; trochlea; capitulum; coronoid and olecranon fossae; epicondyles; radial fossa
Forearm (Figure 7.28)	**Ulna** (2)		Ulna is the medial bone of forearm between elbow and wrist; with the humerus forms elbow joint	Coronoid process; olecranon; radial notch; trochlear notch; ulnar styloid process; head
	Radius (2)		Radius is the lateral bone of forearm; articulates with carpals to form part of the wrist joint	Head; radial tuberosity; radial styloid process; ulnar notch
Hand (Figure 7.29)	8 **Carpals** (16) scaphoid lunate triquetrum pisiform trapezium trapezoid capitate hamate		Carpals form a bony crescent at the wrist; arranged in two rows of four bones each	
	5 **Metacarpals** (10)		Metacarpals form the palm; one in line with each digit	
	14 **Phalanges** (28) distal middle proximal		Phalanges form the fingers; three in digits 2–5; two in digit 1 (the thumb)	

Anterior view of pectoral girdle and upper limb

*The number in parentheses ( ) following the bone name denotes the total number of such bones in the body.

7

The carpals are arranged in two irregular rows of four bones each (Figure 7.29). In the proximal row (lateral to medial) are the **scaphoid** (skaf′oid; "boat-shaped"), **lunate** (lu′nāt; "moon-like"), **triquetrum** (tri-kwet′rum; "triangular"), and **pisiform** (pi′sĭ-form; "pea-shaped"). Of these, all but the pisiform participate in forming the wrist joint. The carpals of the distal row (lateral to medial) are the **trapezium** (trah-pe′ze-um; "little table"), **trapezoid** (tră′peh-zoid; "four-sided"), **capitate** ("head-shaped"), and **hamate** (ham′āt; "hooked").

There are numerous memory-jogging phrases to help you recall the carpals in the order given above. If you don't have one, try: **S**ally **l**eft **t**he **p**arty **t**o **t**ake **C**indy **h**ome. As with all such memory jogs, the first letter of each word is the first letter of the term you need to remember.

Homeostatic Imbalance 7.6

The arrangement of its bones is such that the carpus is concave anteriorly and a ligament roofs over this concavity, forming the notorious *carpal tunnel*. Besides the median nerve (which supplies the lateral side of the hand), several long muscle tendons crowd into this tunnel. Overuse and inflammation of the tendons cause them to swell, compressing the median nerve, which causes tingling and numbness of the areas served, and movements of the thumb weaken. Pain is greatest at night. Those who repeatedly flex their wrists and fingers, such as those who work at computer keyboards all day, are particularly susceptible to this nerve impairment, called *carpal tunnel syndrome*. This condition is treated by splinting the wrist during sleep or by surgery. +

Metacarpus (Palm)

Five **metacarpals** radiate from the wrist like spokes to form the **metacarpus** or palm of the hand (*meta* = beyond). These small long bones are not named, but instead are numbered I to V from thumb to little finger. The **bases** of the metacarpals articulate with the carpals proximally and each other medially and laterally (Figure 7.29). Their bulbous **heads** articulate with the proximal phalanges of the fingers. When you clench your fist, the heads of the metacarpals become prominent as your *knuckles*.

Metacarpal I, associated with the thumb, is the shortest and most mobile. It occupies a more anterior position than the other metacarpals. Consequently, the joint between metacarpal I and the trapezium is a unique saddle joint that allows *opposition*, the action of touching your thumb to the tips of your other fingers.

Phalanges (Fingers)

The **fingers**, or **digits** of the upper limb, are numbered 1 to 5 beginning with the thumb, or **pollex** (pol′eks). In most people, the third finger is the longest. Each hand contains 14 miniature long bones called **phalanges** (fah-lan′jēz). Except for the thumb, each finger has three phalanges: *distal, middle,* and *proximal*. The thumb has no middle phalanx. [Phalanx (fa′langks; "a closely knit row of soldiers") is the singular term for phalanges.]

☑ Check Your Understanding

25. Which bones play the major role in forming the elbow joint?
26. Which bones of the upper limb have a styloid process?

27. Where are carpals found and what type of bone (short, irregular, long, or flat) are they?

For answers, see Appendix H.

The Pelvic (Hip) Girdle

✓ Name the bones contributing to the os coxae, and relate the pelvic girdle's strength to its function.

✓ Describe differences in the male and female pelves and relate these to functional differences.

The **pelvic girdle**, or **hip girdle**, attaches the lower limbs to the axial skeleton, transmits the full weight of the upper body to the lower limbs, and supports the visceral organs of the pelvis (Figures 7.30 and 7.31 and Table 7.4, p. 237). Unlike the pectoral girdle, which is sparingly attached to the thoracic cage, the pelvic girdle is secured to the axial skeleton by some of the strongest ligaments in the body. And unlike the shallow glenoid cavity of the scapula, the corresponding sockets of the pelvic girdle are deep and cuplike and firmly secure the head of the femur in place. Thus, even though both the shoulder and hip joints are ball-and-socket joints, very few of us can wheel or swing our legs about with the same degree of freedom as our arms. The pelvic girdle lacks the mobility of the pectoral girdle but is far more stable.

The pelvic girdle is formed by the sacrum* (a part of the axial skeleton) and a pair of **hip bones**, each also called an **os coxae** (ahs kok′se), or **coxal bone** (*coxa* = hip). Each hip bone unites with its partner anteriorly and with the sacrum posteriorly (Figure 7.30).

Each large, irregularly shaped hip bone consists of three separate bones during childhood: the ilium, ischium, and pubis (Figure 7.31). In adults, these bones are firmly fused and their boundaries are indistinguishable. Their names are retained, however, to refer to different regions of the composite hip bone.

At the point of fusion of the ilium, ischium, and pubis is a deep hemispherical socket called the **acetabulum** (as″ĕ-tab′u-lum; "vinegar cup") on the lateral surface of the pelvis (Figure 7.31). The acetabulum receives the head of the femur, or thigh bone, at this *hip joint*.

Ilium

The **ilium** (il′e-um; "flank") is a large flaring bone that forms the superior region of a coxal bone. It consists of a **body** and a superior winglike portion called the **ala** (a′lah). When you rest your hands on your hips, you are resting them on the thickened superior margins of the alae, the **iliac crests**, to which many muscles attach. Each iliac crest ends anteriorly in the blunt **anterior superior iliac spine** and posteriorly in the sharp **posterior superior iliac spine**.

Located below these are the less prominent *anterior* and *posterior inferior iliac spines*. All of these spines are attachment points for the muscles of the trunk, hip, and thigh. The anterior

---

*Some authorities do not consider the sacrum part of the pelvic girdle, but here we follow the convention in *Terminologia Anatomica*.

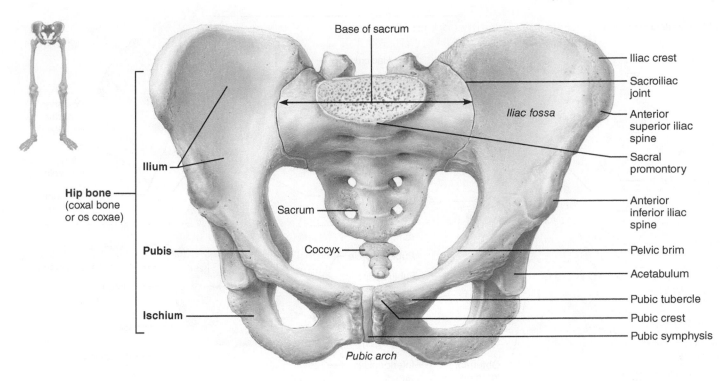

Figure 7.30 Pelvis. The pelvis consists of the two hip (coxal) bones, the sacrum, and the coccyx.

superior iliac spine is an especially important anatomical land-mark. It is easily felt through the skin and is visible in thin peo-ple. The posterior superior iliac spine is difficult to palpate, but its position is revealed by a skin dimple in the sacral region.

Just inferior to the posterior inferior iliac spine, the ilium indents deeply to form the **greater sciatic notch** (si-at′ik), through which the thick cordlike sciatic nerve passes to enter the thigh. The broad posterolateral surface of the ilium, the **glu-teal surface** (gloo′te-al), is crossed by three ridges, the **poste-rior**, **anterior**, and **inferior gluteal lines**, to which the gluteal (buttock) muscles attach.

The medial surface of the iliac ala exhibits a concavity called the **iliac fossa**. Posterior to this, the roughened **auricular surface** (aw-rik′u-lar; "ear-shaped") articulates with the same-named surface of the sacrum, forming the *sacroiliac joint* (Figure 7.30). The weight of the body is transmitted from the spine to the pelvis through the sacroiliac joints. Running inferiorly and anteriorly from the auricular surface is a robust ridge called the **arcuate line** (ar′ku-at; "bowed"). The arcuate line helps define the *pelvic brim*, the superior margin of the *true pelvis*, which we will discuss shortly. Anteriorly, the body of the ilium joins the pubis; inferiorly it joins the ischium.

Ischium

The **ischium** (is′ke-um; "hip") forms the posteroinferior part of the hip bone (Figures 7.30 and 7.31). Roughly L- or arc-shaped, it has a thicker, superior **body** adjoining the ilium and a thinner, inferior **ramus** (*ramus* = branch). The ramus joins the pubis anteriorly. The ischium has three important markings. Its **ischial spine** projects medially into the pelvic cavity and serves as a point of attachment of the *sacrospinous ligament* running from

the sacrum. Just inferior to the ischial spine is the **lesser sciatic notch**. A number of nerves and blood vessels pass through this notch to supply the anogenital area. The inferior surface of the ischial body is rough and grossly thickened as the **ischial tuber-osity**. When we sit, our weight is borne entirely by the ischial tuberosities, which are the strongest parts of the hip bones.

A massive ligament runs from the sacrum to each ischial tuberosity. This *sacrotuberous ligament* (not illustrated) helps hold the pelvis together. The ischial tuberosity is also a site of at-tachment of the large hamstring muscles of the posterior thigh.

Pubis

The **pubis** (pu′bis; "sexually mature"), or *pubic bone*, forms the anterior portion of the hip bone (Figures 7.30 and 7.31). In the an-atomical position, it lies nearly horizontally and the urinary blad-der rests upon it. Essentially, the pubis is V shaped with **superior** and **inferior pubic rami** issuing from its flattened medial **body**. The anterior border of the pubis is thickened to form the **pubic crest**. At the lateral end of the pubic crest is the **pubic tubercle**, one of the attachments for the *inguinal ligament*. As the two rami of the pubis run laterally to join with the body and ramus of the is-chium, they define a large opening in the hip bone, the **obturator foramen** (ob″tu-ra′tor), through which a few blood vessels and nerves pass. Although the obturator foramen is large, it is nearly closed by a fibrous membrane in life (*obturator* = closed up).

The bodies of the two pubic bones are joined by a fibrocarti-lage disc, forming the midline **pubic symphysis** joint. Inferior to this joint, the inferior pubic rami angle laterally, forming an inverted V-shaped arch called the **pubic arch** or **subpubic an-gle**. The acuteness of this arch helps to differentiate the male and female pelves.

(Text continues on p. 238.)

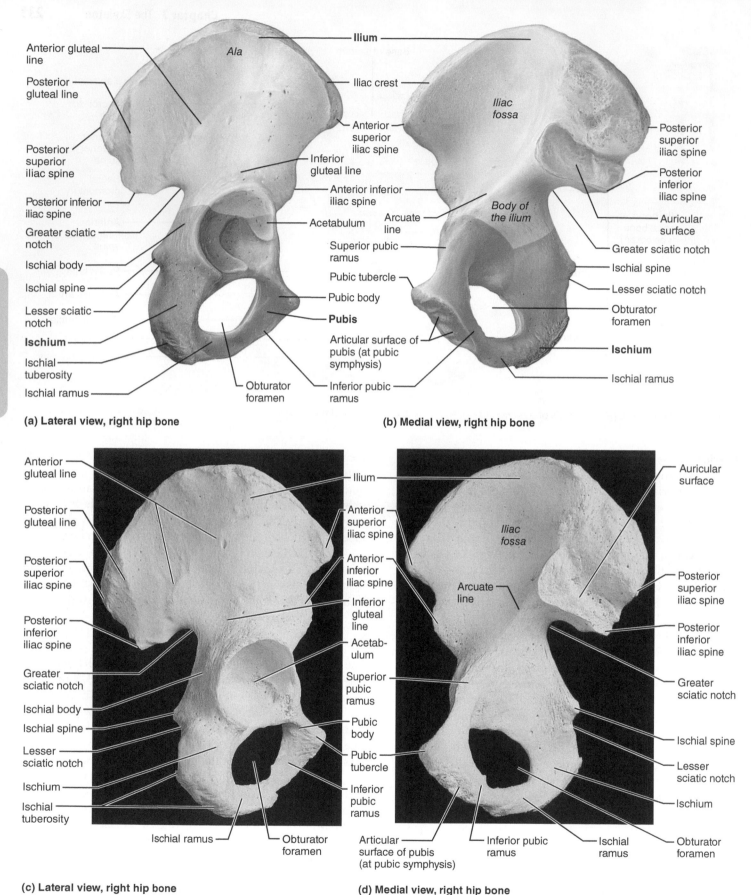

Figure 7.31 The hip (coxal) bones. Lateral and medial views of the right hip bone. The point of fusion of the ilium (gold), ischium (violet), and pubic (red) bones at the acetabulum is indicated in the diagrams (a, b). (For a related image, see *A Brief Atlas of the Human Body*, Figure 28.)

(a) Lateral view, right hip bone

Anterior gluteal line
Posterior gluteal line
Posterior superior iliac spine
Posterior inferior iliac spine
Greater sciatic notch
Ischial body
Ischial spine
Lesser sciatic notch
Ischium
Ischial tuberosity
Ischial ramus

Ala
Ilium
Iliac crest
Anterior superior iliac spine
Inferior gluteal line
Anterior inferior iliac spine
Acetabulum
Obturator foramen

(b) Medial view, right hip bone

Iliac fossa
Body of the ilium
Arcuate line
Superior pubic ramus
Pubic tubercle
Pubic body
Pubis
Articular surface of pubis (at pubic symphysis)
Inferior pubic ramus

Posterior superior iliac spine
Posterior inferior iliac spine
Auricular surface
Greater sciatic notch
Ischial spine
Lesser sciatic notch
Obturator foramen
Ischium
Ischial ramus

(c) Lateral view, right hip bone

Anterior gluteal line
Posterior gluteal line
Posterior superior iliac spine
Posterior inferior iliac spine
Greater sciatic notch
Ischial body
Ischial spine
Lesser sciatic notch
Ischium
Ischial tuberosity
Ischial ramus
Obturator foramen

Ilium
Anterior superior iliac spine
Anterior inferior iliac spine
Inferior gluteal line
Acetabulum
Superior pubic ramus
Pubic body
Pubic tubercle
Inferior pubic ramus

(d) Medial view, right hip bone

Arcuate line
Articular surface of pubis (at pubic symphysis)
Inferior pubic ramus

Auricular surface
Iliac fossa
Posterior superior iliac spine
Posterior inferior iliac spine
Greater sciatic notch
Ischial spine
Lesser sciatic notch
Ischium
Ischial ramus
Obturator foramen

7

Table 7.4 Comparison of the Male and Female Pelves

CHARACTERISTIC	FEMALE	MALE
General structure and functional modifications	Tilted forward; adapted for childbearing; true pelvis defines the birth canal; cavity of the true pelvis is broad, shallow, and has a greater capacity	Tilted less far forward; adapted for support of a male's heavier build and stronger muscles; cavity of the true pelvis is narrow and deep
Bone thickness	Less; bones lighter, thinner, and smoother	Greater; bones heavier and thicker, and markings are more prominent
Acetabula	Smaller; farther apart	Larger; closer
Pubic angle/arch	Broader (80° to 90°); more rounded	Angle is more acute (50° to 60°)
Anterior view		

Pelvic brim

Pubic arch

Sacrum	Wider; shorter; sacral curvature is accentuated	Narrow; longer; sacral promontory more ventral
Coccyx	More movable; projects inferiorly	Less movable; projects anteriorly
Greater sciatic notch	Wide and shallow	Narrow and deep
Left lateral view		

Pelvic inlet (brim)	Wider; oval from side to side	Narrow; basically heart shaped
Pelvic outlet	Wider; ischial tuberosities shorter, farther apart and everted	Narrower; ischial tuberosities longer, sharper, and point more medially
Posteroinferior view		

Pelvic Structure and Childbearing

The deep, basinlike structure formed by the hip bones, sacrum, and coccyx is called the **pelvis** or the *bony pelvis*. The differences between the male and female pelves are striking. The female pelvis is modified for childbearing: It tends to be wider, shallower, lighter, and rounder than that of a male. The female pelvis not only accommodates a growing fetus, but it must be large enough to allow the infant's relatively large head to exit at birth. The major differences between the typical male and female pelves are summarized and illustrated in Table 7.4.

The pelvis is said to consist of a false (greater) pelvis and a true (lesser) pelvis separated by the **pelvic brim**, a continuous oval ridge that runs from the pubic crest through the arcuate line and sacral promontory (Figure 7.30). The **false pelvis**, that portion superior to the pelvic brim, is bounded by the alae of the ilia laterally and the lumbar vertebrae posteriorly. The false pelvis is really part of the abdomen and helps support the abdominal viscera. It does not restrict childbirth in any way.

The **true pelvis** is the region inferior to the pelvic brim that is almost entirely surrounded by bone. It forms a deep bowl containing the pelvic organs. Its dimensions, particularly those of its *inlet* and *outlet*, are critical to the uncomplicated delivery of a baby, and they are carefully measured by an obstetrician.

The **pelvic inlet** *is* the pelvic brim, and its widest dimension is from right to left along the frontal plane. As labor begins, an infant's head typically enters the inlet with its forehead facing one ilium and its occiput facing the other. A sacral promontory that is particularly large can impair the infant's entry into the true pelvis.

The **pelvic outlet**, illustrated in the photos at the bottom of Table 7.4, is the inferior margin of the true pelvis. It is bounded anteriorly by the pubic arch, laterally by the ischia, and posteriorly by the sacrum and coccyx. Both the coccyx and the ischial spines protrude into the outlet opening, so a sharply angled coccyx or unusually large spines can interfere with delivery. The largest dimension of the outlet is the anteroposterior diameter.

Generally, after the baby's head passes through the inlet, it rotates so that the forehead faces posteriorly and the occiput anteriorly, and this is the usual position of the baby's head as it leaves the mother's body (see Figure 28.18 ②). Thus, during birth, the infant's head makes a quarter turn to follow the widest dimensions of the true pelvis.

☑ Check Your Understanding

28. The ilium and pubis help to form the os coxae. What other bone is involved in forming the os coxae?
29. The pelvic girdle is a heavy, strong girdle. How does its structure reflect its function?
30. Which of the following terms or phrases refer to the female pelvis? Wider, shorter sacrum; cavity narrow and deep; narrow heart-shaped inlet; more movable coccyx; long ischial spines.

For answers, see Appendix H.

The Lower Limb

✓ Identify the lower limb bones and their important markings.

The lower limbs carry the entire weight of the erect body and are subjected to exceptional forces when we jump or run. Thus, it is not surprising that the bones of the lower limbs are thicker and stronger than comparable bones of the upper limbs. The three segments of each lower limb are the thigh, the leg, and the foot (see **Table 7.5** on p. 243).

Thigh

The **femur** (fe'mur; "thigh"), the single bone of the thigh **(Figure 7.32)**, is the largest, longest, strongest bone in the body. Its durable structure reflects the fact that the stress on the femur during vigorous jumping can reach 280 kg/cm^2 (about 2 tons per square inch)! The femur is clothed by bulky muscles that prevent us from palpating its course down the length of the thigh. Its length is roughly one-quarter of a person's height.

Proximally, the femur articulates with the hip bone and then courses medially as it descends toward the knee. This arrangement allows the knee joints to be closer to the body's center of gravity and provides for better balance. The medial course of the two femurs is more pronounced in women because of their wider pelvis, a situation that may contribute to the greater incidence of knee problems in female athletes.

The ball-like **head** of the femur has a small central pit called the **fovea capitis** (fo've-ah kă'pĭ-tis; "pit of the head"). The short *ligament of the head of the femur* runs from this pit to the acetabulum, where it helps secure the femur. The head is carried on a *neck* that angles *laterally* to join the shaft. This arrangement reflects the fact that the femur articulates with the lateral aspect (rather than the inferior region) of the pelvis. The neck is the weakest part of the femur and is often fractured, an injury commonly called a broken hip.

At the junction of the shaft and neck are the lateral **greater trochanter** (tro-kan'ter) and posteromedial **lesser trochanter**. These projections serve as sites of attachment for thigh and buttock muscles. The two trochanters are connected by the **intertrochanteric line** anteriorly and by the prominent **intertrochanteric crest** posteriorly.

Inferior to the intertrochanteric crest on the posterior shaft is the **gluteal tuberosity**, which blends into a long vertical ridge, the **linea aspera** (lin'e-ah as'per-ah; "rough line"), inferiorly. Distally, the linea aspera diverges, forming the **medial** and **lateral supracondylar lines**. All of these markings are sites of muscle attachment. Except for the linea aspera, the femur shaft is smooth and rounded.

Distally, the femur broadens and ends in the wheel-like **lateral** and **medial condyles**, which articulate with the tibia of the leg. The **medial** and **lateral epicondyles** (sites of muscle attachment) flank the condyles superiorly. On the superior part of the medial epicondyle is a bump, the **adductor tubercle**. The smooth **patellar surface**, between the condyles on the anterior femoral surface, articulates with the *patella* (pah-tel'ah), or kneecap (see Figure 7.32 and Table 7.5). Between the condyles on the posterior aspect of the femur is the deep, U-shaped

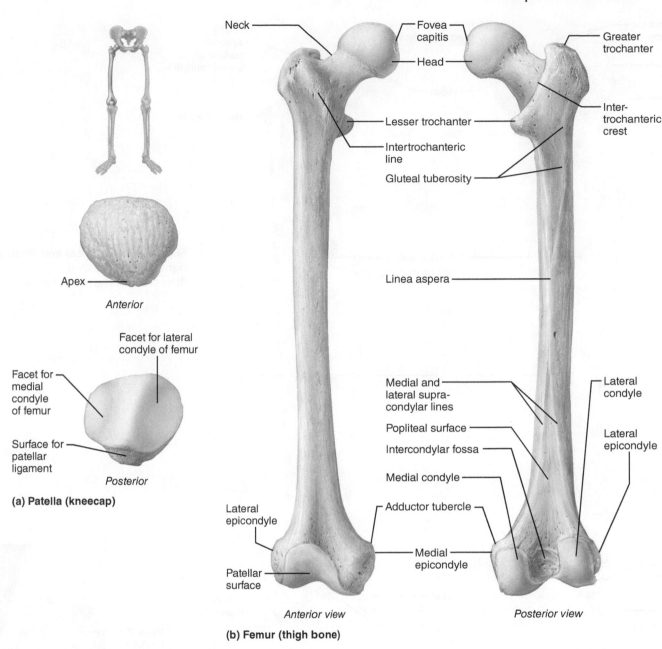

(a) Patella (kneecap)

Apex

Anterior

Facet for lateral condyle of femur

Facet for medial condyle of femur

Surface for patellar ligament

Posterior

Neck

Fovea capitis

Head

Greater trochanter

Lesser trochanter

Inter-trochanteric crest

Intertrochanteric line

Gluteal tuberosity

Linea aspera

Medial and lateral supra-condylar lines

Lateral condyle

Popliteal surface

Intercondylar fossa

Medial condyle

Lateral epicondyle

Adductor tubercle

Lateral epicondyle

Patellar surface

Medial epicondyle

Anterior view

Posterior view

(b) Femur (thigh bone)

Figure 7.32 Bones of the right knee and thigh. (For a related image, see *A Brief Atlas of the Human Body*, Figure 29.)

7

intercondylar fossa, and superior to that on the shaft is the smooth *popliteal surface*.

The **patella** ("small pan") is a triangular sesamoid bone enclosed in the (quadriceps) tendon that secures the anterior thigh muscles to the tibia. It protects the knee joint anteriorly and improves the leverage of the thigh muscles acting across the knee.

Leg

Two parallel bones, the tibia and fibula, form the skeleton of the leg, the region of the lower limb between the knee and the ankle **(Figure 7.33)**. These two bones are connected by an *interosseous membrane* and articulate with each other both proximally and distally. Unlike the joints between the radius and ulna of the forearm,

the *tibiofibular joints* (tib"e-o-fib′u-lar) of the leg allow essentially no movement. The bones of the leg thus form a less flexible but stronger and more stable limb than those of the forearm. The medial tibia articulates proximally with the femur to form the modified hinge joint of the knee and distally with the talus bone of the foot at the ankle. The fibula, by contrast, does not contribute to the knee joint and merely helps stabilize the ankle joint.

Tibia

The **tibia** (tib′e-ah; "shinbone") receives the weight of the body from the femur and transmits it to the foot. It is second only to the femur in size and strength. At its broad proximal end are the concave **medial** and **lateral condyles**, which look

7

Intercondylar eminence

Lateral condyle

Head

Superior tibiofibular joint

Articular surface of medial condyle

Medial condyle

Tibial tuberosity

Articular surface of lateral condyle

Head of fibula

Interosseous membrane

Anterior border

Fibula

Tibia

Fibula

Inferior tibiofibular joint

Lateral malleolus

Medial malleolus

Inferior articular surface

Lateral malleolus

(a) Anterior view

(b) Posterior view

Figure 7.33 The tibia and fibula of the right leg. (For a related image, see *A Brief Atlas of the Human Body,* Figure 30.)

Lateral condyle

Tibial tuberosity

Lateral condyle

Fibula articulates here

Line for soleus muscle

Parts of fractured fibula

(c) Anterior view, proximal tibia

(d) Posterior view, proximal tibia

(e) X ray of Pott's fracture of the fibula

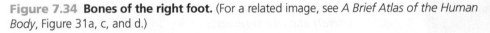

Phalanges
— Distal
— Middle
— Proximal

Metatarsals

I II III IV V

Medial cuneiform

Intermediate cuneiform

Navicular

Talus

Trochlea of talus

Lateral cuneiform

Cuboid

Tarsals

Calcaneus

(a) Superior view

Intermediate cuneiform

Navicular

Talus

Medial malleolar facet

Sustentaculum tali (talar shelf)

First metatarsal

Medial cuneiform

Calcaneus

Calcaneal tuberosity

(b) Medial view

Lateral malleolar facet

Navicular

Intermediate cuneiform

Lateral cuneiform

Talus

Calcaneus

Cuboid

Fifth metatarsal

(c) Lateral view

Figure 7.34 Bones of the right foot. (For a related image, see *A Brief Atlas of the Human Body*, Figure 31a, c, and d.)

like two huge checkers lying side by side. These are separated by an irregular projection, the **intercondylar eminence**. The tibial condyles articulate with the corresponding condyles of the femur. The inferior region of the lateral tibial condyle bears a facet that indicates the site of the *superior tibiofibular joint*. Just inferior to the condyles, the tibia's anterior surface displays the rough **tibial tuberosity**, to which the patellar ligament attaches.

The tibial shaft is triangular in cross section. Neither the tibia's sharp **anterior border** nor its medial surface is covered by muscles, so they can be felt just deep to the skin along their entire length. The anguish of a "bumped" shin is an experience familiar to nearly everyone. Distally the tibia is flat where it articulates with the talus bone of the foot. Medial to that joint surface is an inferior projection, the **medial malleolus** (mah-le′o-lus; "little hammer"), which forms the medial bulge of the ankle. The **fibular notch**, on the lateral surface of the tibia, participates in the *inferior tibiofibular joint*.

Fibula

The **fibula** (fib′u-lah; "pin") is a sticklike bone with slightly expanded ends. It articulates proximally and distally with the lateral aspects of the tibia. Its proximal end is its **head**; its distal end is the **lateral malleolus**. The lateral malleolus forms the conspicuous lateral ankle bulge and articulates with the talus. The fibular shaft is heavily ridged and appears to have been

twisted a quarter turn. The fibula does not bear weight, but several muscles originate from it.

Homeostatic Imbalance 7.7

A *Pott's fracture* occurs at the distal end of the fibula, the tibia, or both. It is a common sports injury. (See Figure 7.33e.) ✚

☑ Check Your Understanding

31. What lower limb bone is the second largest bone in the body?
32. Where is the medial malleolus located?
33. Which of the following sites is not a site of muscle attachment? Greater trochanter, lesser trochanter, gluteal tuberosity, lateral condyle.

For answers, see Appendix H.

Foot

The skeleton of the foot includes the bones of the *tarsus*, the bones of the *metatarsus*, and the *phalanges*, or toe bones (**Figure 7.34**). The foot has two important functions: It supports our body weight, and it acts as a lever to propel the body forward when we walk and run. A single bone could serve both purposes, but it would adapt poorly to uneven ground. Segmentation makes the foot pliable, avoiding this problem.

(a) Lateral aspect of right foot

- Medial longitudinal arch
- Transverse arch
- Lateral longitudinal arch

(b) X ray, medial aspect of right foot

Figure 7.35 Arches of the foot.

Tarsus

The **tarsus** is made up of seven bones called **tarsals** (tar′salz) that form the posterior half of the foot. It corresponds to the carpus of the hand. Body weight is carried primarily by the two largest, most posterior tarsals: the **talus** (ta′lus; "ankle"), which articulates with the tibia and fibula superiorly, and the strong **calcaneus** (kal-ka′ne-us; "heel bone"), which forms the heel of the foot and carries the talus on its superior surface. The thick *calcaneal*, or *Achilles*, *tendon* of the calf muscles attaches to the posterior surface of the calcaneus. The part of the calcaneus that touches the ground is the **calcaneal tuberosity**, and its shelflike projection that supports part of the talus is

the **sustentaculum tali** (sus″ten-tak′u-lum ta′le; "supporter of the talus") or **talar shelf**. The tibia articulates with the talus at the *trochlea* of the talus. The remaining tarsals are the lateral **cuboid**, the medial **navicular** (nah-vik′u-lar), and the anterior **medial**, **intermediate**, and **lateral cuneiform bones** (ku-ne′i-form; "wedge-shaped"). The cuboid and cuneiform bones articulate with the metatarsal bones anteriorly.

Metatarsus

The **metatarsus** consists of five small, long bones called **metatarsals**. These are numbered I to V beginning on the medial (great toe) side of the foot. The first metatarsal, which plays an important role in supporting body weight, is short and thick. The arrangement of the metatarsals is more parallel than that of the metacarpals of the hands. Distally, where the metatarsals articulate with the proximal phalanges of the toes, the enlarged head of the first metatarsal forms the "ball" of the foot.

Phalanges (Toes)

The 14 phalanges of the toes are a good deal smaller than those of the fingers and so are less nimble. But their general structure and arrangement are the same. There are three phalanges in each digit except for the great toe, the **hallux**. The hallux has only two, proximal and distal.

Arches of the Foot

A segmented structure can hold up weight only if it is arched. The foot has three arches: two *longitudinal arches* (*medial* and *lateral*) and one *transverse arch* (**Figure 7.35**), which account for its awesome strength. These arches are maintained by the interlocking shapes of the foot bones, by strong ligaments, and by the pull of some tendons during muscle activity. The ligaments and muscle tendons provide a certain amount of springiness. In general, the arches "give," or stretch slightly, when weight is applied to the foot and spring back when the weight is removed, which makes walking and running more economical in terms of energy use than would otherwise be the case.

If you examine your wet footprints, you will see that the medial margin from the heel to the head of the first metatarsal leaves no print. This is because the **medial longitudinal arch** curves well above the ground. The talus is the keystone of this arch, which originates at the calcaneus, rises toward the talus, and then descends to the three medial metatarsals.

The **lateral longitudinal arch** is very low. It elevates the lateral part of the foot just enough to redistribute some of the weight to the calcaneus and the head of the fifth metatarsal (to the ends of the arch). The cuboid is the keystone bone of this arch.

The two longitudinal arches serve as pillars for the **transverse arch**, which runs obliquely from one side of the foot to the other, following the line of the joints between the tarsals and metatarsals. Together, the arches of the foot form a half-dome that distributes about half of a person's standing and walking weight to the heel bones and half to the heads of the metatarsals.

Table 7.5   Bones of the Appendicular Skeleton, Part 2: Pelvic Girdle and Lower Limb

BODY REGION	BONES*	ILLUSTRATION	LOCATION	MARKINGS
Pelvic girdle (Figures 7.30, 7.31)	**Coxal** (2) (hip)		Each coxal (hip) bone is formed by the fusion of an ilium, ischium, and pubis; the coxal bones articulate anteriorly at the pubic symphysis and form sacroiliac joints with the sacrum posteriorly; girdle consisting of both coxal bones and the sacrum is basinlike	Iliac crest; anterior and posterior iliac spines; auricular surface; greater and lesser sciatic notches; obturator foramen; ischial tuberosity and spine; acetabulum; pubic arch; pubic crest; pubic tubercle
Lower limb Thigh (Figure 7.32)	**Femur** (2)		Femur is the sole bone of thigh; between hip joint and knee; largest bone of the body	Head; greater and lesser trochanters; neck; lateral and medial condyles and epicondyles; gluteal tuberosity; linea aspera
Kneecap (Figure 7.32)	**Patella** (2)		Patella is a sesamoid bone formed within the tendon of the quadriceps (anterior thigh) muscles	
Leg (Figure 7.33)	**Tibia** (2)		Tibia is the larger and more medial bone of leg; between knee and foot	Medial and lateral condyles; tibial tuberosity; anterior border; medial malleolus
	Fibula (2)		Fibula is the lateral bone of leg; sticklike	Head; lateral malleolus
Foot (Figure 7.34)	7 **Tarsals** (14) talus calcaneus navicular cuboid lateral cuneiform intermediate cuneiform medial cuneiform		Tarsals are seven bones forming the proximal part of the foot; the talus articulates with the leg bones at the ankle joint; the calcaneus, the largest tarsal, forms the heel	
	5 **Metatarsals** (10)		Metatarsals are five bones numbered I–V	
	14 **Phalanges** (28) distal middle proximal		Phalanges form the toes; three in digits 2–5, two in digit 1 (the great toe)	

* The number in parentheses ( ) following the bone name denotes the total number of such bones in the body.

Homeostatic Imbalance 7.8

Standing immobile for extended periods places excessive strain on the tendons and ligaments of the feet (because the muscles are inactive) and can result in fallen arches, or "flat feet," particularly if a person is overweight. Running on hard surfaces can also cause arches to fall unless the runner wears shoes that give proper arch support. ✚

The bones of the thigh, leg, and foot are summarized in Table 7.5.

☑ Check Your Understanding

34. Besides supporting our weight, what is a major function of the arches of the foot?
35. What are the two largest tarsal bones in each foot, and which one forms the heel of the foot?

For answers, see Appendix H.

Frontal suture

Frontal bone

Anterior fontanelle

Ossification center

Parietal bone

Posterior fontanelle

Occipital bone

(a) Superior view

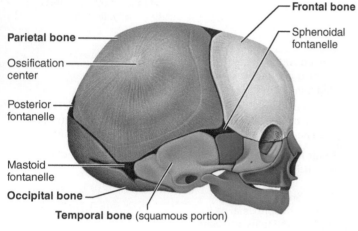

Frontal bone

Parietal bone

Sphenoidal fontanelle

Ossification center

Posterior fontanelle

Mastoid fontanelle

Occipital bone

Temporal bone (squamous portion)

(b) Lateral view

Figure 7.36 Skull of a newborn. Notice that the infant's skull has more bones than that of an adult. (For a related image, see *A Brief Atlas of the Human Body*, Figure 16.)

Developmental Aspects of the Skeleton

✓ Define fontanelles and indicate their significance.

✓ Describe how skeletal proportions change through life.

✓ Discuss how age-related skeletal changes may affect health.

The membrane bones of the skull start to ossify late in the second month of development. The rapid deposit of bone matrix at the ossification centers produces cone-shaped protrusions in the developing bones. At birth, the skull bones are still incomplete and are connected by as yet unossified remnants of fibrous membranes called **fontanelles** (fon"tah-nelz') (Figure 7.36). The fontanelles allow the infant's head to be compressed slightly during birth, and they accommodate brain growth in the fetus and infant. A baby's pulse can be felt surging in these "soft spots"; hence their name (*fontanelle* = little fountain). The large, diamond-shaped *anterior fontanelle* is palpable for 1½ to 2 years after birth. The others are replaced by bone by the end of the first year.

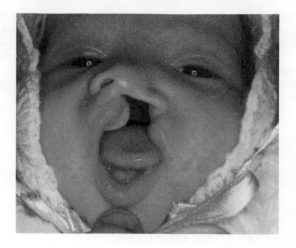

Figure 7.37 A baby born with a cleft lip and palate.

⚖ **Homeostatic Imbalance 7.9**

Several congenital abnormalities may distort the skull. Most common is *cleft palate*, a condition in which the right and left halves of the palate fail to fuse medially (Figure 7.37). The persistent opening between the oral and nasal cavities interferes with sucking and can lead to aspiration (inhalation) of food into the lungs and *aspiration pneumonia*.✚

The skeleton changes throughout life, but the changes in childhood are most dramatic. At birth, the baby's cranium is huge relative to its face, and several bones are still unfused (e.g., the mandible and frontal bones). The maxillae and mandible are foreshortened, and the contours of the face are flat (Figure 7.39). By 9 months after birth, the cranium is already half of its adult size (volume) because of the rapid growth of the brain. By 8 to 9 years, the cranium has almost reached adult proportions.

Between the ages of 6 and 13, the head appears to enlarge substantially as the face literally grows out from the skull. The jaws, cheekbones, and nose become more prominent. These facial changes are correlated with the expansion of the nose and paranasal sinuses, and development of the permanent teeth. Figure 7.39 tracks how differential bone growth alters body proportions throughout life.

Only the thoracic and sacral curvatures are well developed at birth. These so-called **primary curvatures** are convex posteriorly, and an infant's spine arches, like that of a four-legged animal (Figure 7.38).

The **secondary curvatures**—cervical and lumbar—are convex anteriorly and are associated with a child's development. They result from reshaping of the intervertebral discs rather than from modifications of the vertebrae. The cervical curvature is present before birth but is not pronounced until the baby starts to lift its head (at about 3 months). The lumbar curvature develops when the baby begins to walk (at about 12 months). The lumbar curvature positions the weight of the trunk over the body's center of gravity, providing optimal balance when standing.

Vertebral problems (scoliosis or lordosis; see Figure 7.17a and c) may appear during the early school years, when rapid growth of the limb bones stretches many muscles. During the

Figure 7.38 The C-shaped spine of a newborn infant.

preschool years, lordosis is often present, but this is usually rectified as the abdominal muscles become stronger and the pelvis tilts forward. The thorax grows wider, but a true "military posture" (head erect, shoulders back, abdomen in, and chest out) does not develop until adolescence.

⚖ Homeostatic Imbalance 7.10

The appendicular skeleton can also suffer from a number of congenital abnormalities. One that occurs in just over 1% of infants and is quite severe is *dysplasia of the hip* (dis-pla′ze-ah; "bad formation"). The acetabulum forms incompletely or the ligaments of the hip joint are loose, so the head of the femur slips out of its socket. Early treatment (a splint or harness to hold the femur in place or surgery to tighten hip ligaments) is essential to prevent permanent crippling. ✚

During youth, growth of the skeleton not only increases overall body height but also changes body proportions **(Figure 7.39)**. At birth, the head and trunk are approximately 1½ times as long as the lower limbs. The lower limbs grow more rapidly than the trunk from this time on, and by the age of 10, the head and trunk are approximately the same height as the lower limbs, a condition that persists thereafter. During puberty, the female pelvis broadens in preparation for childbearing, and the entire male skeleton becomes more robust. Once adult height is reached, a healthy skeleton changes very little until late middle age.

Old age affects many parts of the skeleton, especially the spine. As the discs become thinner, less hydrated, and less elastic, the risk of disc herniation increases. By 55 years, a loss of several centimeters in stature is common. Further shortening can be produced by osteoporosis of the spine or by kyphosis (called "dowager's hump" in the elderly; see Figure 7.17b). What was done during youth may be undone in old age as the vertebral column gradually resumes its initial arc shape.

The thorax becomes more rigid with age, largely because the costal cartilages ossify. This loss of rib cage elasticity causes shallow breathing, which leads to less efficient gas exchange.

Human newborn · Human adult

(a)

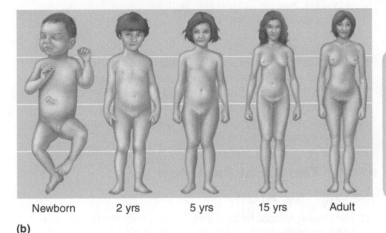

Newborn · 2 yrs · 5 yrs · 15 yrs · Adult

(b)

Figure 7.39 Different growth rates of body parts determine body proportions. (a) Differential growth transforms the rounded, foreshortened skull of a newborn to the sloping skull of an adult. **(b)** During growth of a human, the arms and legs grow faster than the head and trunk, as seen in this conceptualization of different-aged individuals all drawn at the same height.

All bones, you will recall, lose mass with age. Cranial bones lose less mass than most, but changes in facial contours with age are common. As the bony tissue of the jaws declines, the jaws look small and childlike once again. If the elderly person loses his or her teeth, this loss of bone from the jaws is accelerated, because the alveolar region bone is resorbed. As bones become more porous, they are more likely to fracture, especially the vertebrae and the neck of the femur.

☑ Check Your Understanding

36. What developmental events result in a dramatic enlargement of the facial skeleton between the ages of 6 and 13?
37. Under what conditions does the lumbar curvature of the spine develop?

For answers, see Appendix H.

Our skeleton is a marvelous substructure, to be sure, but it is much more than that. It is a protector and supporter of other body systems, and without it (and the joints considered in Chapter 8), our muscles would be almost useless. The homeostatic relationships between the skeletal system and other body systems are illustrated in *System Connections* in Chapter 6 (p. 195).

Chapter Summary

 For more chapter study tools, go to the Study Area of Mastering A&P at **www.masteringaandp.com**.
There you will find:

- Interactive Physiology **iP**
- A&PFlix *A&PFlix*
- Practice Anatomy Lab PAL
- PhysioEx **PEx**
- Videos, Practice Quizzes and Tests, MP3 Tutor Sessions, Case Studies, and much more!

1. The axial skeleton forms the longitudinal axis of the body. Its principal subdivisions are the skull, vertebral column, and thoracic cage. It provides support and protection (by enclosure).
2. The appendicular skeleton consists of the bones of the pectoral and pelvic girdles and the limbs. It allows mobility for manipulation and locomotion.

PART 1 The Axial Skeleton

The Skull (pp. 201–217)

1. The skull is formed by 22 bones. The cranium forms the vault and base of the skull, which protect the brain. The facial skeleton provides openings for the respiratory and digestive passages and attachment points for facial muscles.
2. Except for the temporomandibular joints, all bones of the adult skull are joined by immovable sutures.
3. **Cranium.** The eight bones of the cranium include the paired parietal and temporal bones and the single frontal, occipital, ethmoid, and sphenoid bones (see Table 7.1, pp. 216–217).
4. **Facial bones.** The 14 bones of the face include the paired maxillae, zygomatics, nasals, lacrimals, palatines, and inferior nasal conchae and the single mandible and vomer bones (Table 7.1).
5. **Orbits and nasal cavity.** Both the orbits and the nasal cavities are complicated bony regions formed of several bones.
6. **Paranasal sinuses.** Paranasal sinuses occur in the frontal, ethmoid, sphenoid, and maxillary bones.
7. **Hyoid bone.** The hyoid bone, supported in the neck by ligaments, serves as an attachment point for tongue and neck muscles.

The Vertebral Column (pp. 218–224)

1. **General characteristics.** The vertebral column includes 24 movable vertebrae (7 cervical, 12 thoracic, and 5 lumbar) and the sacrum and coccyx.
2. The fibrocartilage intervertebral discs act as shock absorbers and provide flexibility to the vertebral column.
3. The primary curvatures of the vertebral column are the thoracic and sacral; the secondary curvatures are the cervical and lumbar. Curvatures increase spine flexibility.
4. **General structure of vertebrae.** With the exception of C_1 and C_2, all vertebrae have a body, two transverse processes, two superior and two inferior articular processes, a spinous process, and a vertebral arch.
5. **Regional vertebral characteristics.** Special features distinguish the regional vertebrae (see Table 7.2, p. 223).

The Thoracic Cage (pp. 224–227)

1. The bones of the thoracic cage include the 12 rib pairs, the sternum, and the thoracic vertebrae. The thoracic cage protects the organs of the thoracic cavity.
2. **Sternum.** The sternum consists of the fused manubrium, body, and xiphoid process.
3. **Ribs.** The first seven rib pairs are called true ribs; the rest are called false ribs. Ribs 11 and 12 are floating ribs.

PART 2 The Appendicular Skeleton

The Pectoral (Shoulder) Girdle* (pp. 227–228)

1. Each pectoral girdle consists of one clavicle and one scapula. The pectoral girdles attach the upper limbs to the axial skeleton.
2. **Clavicles.** The clavicles hold the scapulae laterally away from the thorax. The sternoclavicular joints are the only attachment points of the pectoral girdle to the axial skeleton.
3. **Scapulae.** The scapulae articulate with the clavicles and with the humerus bones of the arms.

The Upper Limb* (pp. 228–234)

1. Each upper limb consists of 30 bones and is specialized for mobility.
2. **Arm/forearm/hand.** The skeleton of the arm is composed solely of the humerus; the skeleton of the forearm is composed of the radius and ulna; and the skeleton of the hand consists of the carpals, metacarpals, and phalanges.

The Pelvic (Hip) Girdle* (pp. 234–238)

1. The pelvic girdle, a heavy structure specialized for weight bearing, is composed of two hip bones and the sacrum. It secures the lower limbs to the axial skeleton.
2. Each hip bone consists of three fused bones: ilium, ischium, and pubis. The acetabulum occurs at the point of fusion.
3. **Ilium/ischium/pubis.** The ilium is the superior flaring portion of the hip bone. Each ilium forms a secure joint with the sacrum posteriorly. The ischium is a curved bar of bone; we sit on the ischial tuberosities. The V-shaped pubic bones articulate anteriorly at the pubic symphysis.
4. **Pelvic structure and childbearing.** The pelvis is the deep, basinlike structure formed by the hip bones, sacrum, and coccyx. The male pelvis is deep and narrow with larger, heavier bones than those of the female. The female pelvis, which forms the birth canal, is shallow and wide.

The Lower Limb* (pp. 238–243)

1. Each lower limb consists of the thigh, leg, and foot and is specialized for weight bearing and locomotion.
2. **Thigh.** The femur is the only bone of the thigh. Its ball-shaped head articulates with the acetabulum.
3. **Leg.** The bones of the leg are the tibia, which participates in forming both the knee and ankle joints, and the fibula.
4. **Foot.** The bones of the foot include the tarsals, metatarsals, and phalanges. The most important tarsals are the calcaneus (heel bone) and the talus, which articulates with the tibia superiorly.
5. The foot is supported by three arches (lateral, medial, and transverse) that distribute body weight to the heel and ball of the foot.

Developmental Aspects of the Skeleton (pp. 244–245)

1. Fontanelles, which allow brain growth and ease birth passage, are present in the skull at birth. Growth of the cranium after birth is related to brain growth. Increase in size of the facial skeleton follows tooth development and enlargement of nose and sinus cavities.

2. The vertebral column is C shaped at birth (thoracic and sacral curvatures are present); the secondary curvatures form when the baby begins to lift its head and walk.

3. Long bones continue to grow in length until late adolescence. The head and torso, initially 1½ times the length of the lower limbs, equal their length by the age of 10.

4. Changes in the female pelvis (preparatory for childbirth) occur during puberty.

5. Once at adult height, the skeleton changes little until late middle age. With old age, the intervertebral discs thin; this, along with osteoporosis, leads to a gradual loss in height and increased risk of disc herniation. Loss of bone mass increases the risk of fractures, and thoracic cage rigidity promotes breathing difficulties.

*For associated bone markings, see the pages indicated in the section heads.

Review Questions

Multiple Choice/Matching

(Some questions have more than one correct answer. Select the best answer or answers from the choices given.)

1. Match the bones in column B with their description in column A. (Note that some descriptions require more than a single choice.)

Column A	Column B
____ (1) connected by the coronal suture	(a) ethmoid
____ (2) keystone bone of cranium	(b) frontal
	(c) mandible
____ (3) keystone bone of the face	(d) maxillary
____ (4) form the hard palate	(e) occipital
____ (5) allows the spinal cord to pass	(f) palatine
____ (6) forms the chin	(g) parietal
____ (7) contain paranasal sinuses	(h) sphenoid
____ (8) contains mastoid sinuses	(i) temporal

2. Match the key terms with the bone descriptions that follow.

Key:

(a) clavicle   (b) ilium   (c) ischium
(d) pubis   (e) sacrum   (f) scapula
(g) sternum

____ (1) bone of the axial skeleton to which the pectoral girdle attaches
____ (2) markings include glenoid cavity and acromion
____ (3) features include the ala, crest, and greater sciatic notch
____ (4) doubly curved; acts as a shoulder strut
____ (5) hip bone that articulates with the axial skeleton
____ (6) the "sit-down" bone
____ (7) anteriormost bone of the pelvic girdle
____ (8) part of the vertebral column

3. Use key choices to identify the bone descriptions that follow.

Key:

(a) carpals   (b) femur   (c) fibula
(d) humerus   (e) radius   (f) tarsals
(g) tibia   (h) ulna

____ (1) articulates with the acetabulum and the tibia
____ (2) forms the lateral aspect of the ankle
____ (3) bone that "carries" the hand
____ (4) the wrist bones
____ (5) end shaped like a monkey wrench
____ (6) articulates with the capitulum of the humerus
____ (7) largest bone of this "group" is the calcaneus

Short Answer Essay Questions

4. Name the cranial and facial bones and compare and contrast the functions of the cranial and facial skeletons.

5. How do the relative proportions of the cranium and face of a fetus compare with those of an adult skull?

6. Name and diagram the normal vertebral curvatures. Which are primary and which are secondary curvatures?

7. List at least two specific anatomical characteristics each for typical cervical, thoracic, and lumbar vertebrae that would allow anyone to identify each type correctly.

8. What is the function of the intervertebral discs?

9. Distinguish between the anulus fibrosus and nucleus pulposus regions of a disc. Which provides durability and strength? Which provides resilience? Which part is involved in a "slipped" disc?

10. What is a true rib? A false rib?

11. The major function of the shoulder girdle is flexibility. What is the major function of the pelvic girdle? Relate these functional differences to anatomical differences seen in these girdles.

12. List three important differences between the male and female pelves.

13. Briefly describe the anatomical characteristics and impairment of function seen in cleft palate and hip dysplasia.

14. Compare a young adult skeleton to that of an extremely aged person relative to bone mass in general and the bony structure of the skull, thorax, and vertebral column in particular.

15. Peter Howell, a teaching assistant in the anatomy class, picked up a hip bone and pretended it was a telephone. He held the big hole in this bone right up to his ear and said, "Hello, obturator, obturator (operator, operator)." Name the structure he was helping the students to learn.

Critical Thinking and Clinical Application Questions

1. Justiniano worked in a poultry-packing plant where his job was cutting open chickens and stripping out their visceral organs. After work, he typed for long hours on his computer keyboard, writing a book about his work in the plant. Soon, his wrist

and hand began to hurt whenever he flexed it, and he began to awaken at night with pain and tingling on the thumb-half of his hand. What condition did he probably have?

2. Ralph had polio as a boy and was partially paralyzed in one lower limb for over a year. Although no longer paralyzed, he now has a severe lateral curvature of the lumbar spine. Explain what has happened and identify his condition.

3. Mary's grandmother slipped on a scatter rug and fell heavily to the floor. Her left lower limb was laterally rotated and noticeably shorter than the right, and when she attempted to get up, she winced with pain. Mary surmised that her grandmother might have "fractured her hip," which later proved to be true. What bone was probably fractured and at what site? Why is a "fractured hip" a common type of fracture in the elderly?

4. Mrs. Shea came up with what she considered to be a clever idea to bypass the long lines at Disney World. She had her husband rent a wheelchair and he wheeled her around from one exhibit to another for the better part of three days. As they sat on the plane, waiting to take off for Chicago, she complained to him that she had two sore spots on her buttocks. Why? What do you suppose would happen (to her buttocks) if she was wheeled around for a few more days?

AT THE CLINIC

Related Clinical Terms

Chiropractic (ki″ro-prak′tik) A system of treating disease by manipulating the vertebral column based on the idea that most diseases are due to pressure on nerves caused by faulty bone alignment; a specialist in this field is a chiropractor.

Clubfoot A relatively common congenital defect (one in 700 births) in which the soles of the feet face medially and the toes point inferiorly; may be genetically induced or reflect an abnormal position of the foot during fetal development.

Laminectomy Surgical removal of a vertebral lamina; most often done to relieve the symptoms of a ruptured disc.

Orthopedist (or″tho-pe′dist) or **orthopedic surgeon** A physician who specializes in restoring lost skeletal system function or repairing damage to bones and joints.

Pelvimetry Measurement of the dimensions of the inlet and outlet of the pelvis, usually to determine whether the pelvis is of adequate size to allow normal delivery of a baby.

Spina bifida (spi′nah bi′fi-dah; "cleft spine") Congenital defect of the vertebral column in which one or more of the vertebral arches are incomplete; ranges in severity from inconsequential to severe conditions that impair neural functioning and encourage nervous system infections.

Spinal fusion Surgical procedure involving insertion of bone chips (or crushed bone) to immobilize and stabilize a specific region of the vertebral column, particularly in cases of vertebral fracture and herniated discs.

Case Study Skeleton

Kayla Tanner, a 45-year-old mother of four, was a passenger on the bus involved in an accident on Route 91. When paramedics arrived on the scene, they found Mrs. Tanner lying on her side in the aisle. Upon examination, they found that her right thigh appeared shorter than her left thigh. They also noticed that even slight hip movement caused considerable pain. Suspecting a hip dislocation, they stabilized and transported her.

In the emergency department, doctors discovered a decreased ability to sense light touch in her right foot, and she was unable to move her toes or ankle. Dislocation of her right hip was confirmed by X ray. Mrs. Tanner was sedated to relax the muscles around the hip, and then doctors placed her in the supine position and performed a closed reduction ("popped" the femur back in place).

1. Mrs. Tanner's pelvic girdle contains a hemispherical socket at the point where her femur attaches. Name this structure.

2. Name the structure on the femur that forms the "ball" that fits into the "socket" you named in question 1.

3. There are three bones in the pelvic girdle that fuse together at a point within the structure that you named in question 1. Name those three bones.

4. Mrs. Tanner suffered an injury to the hip joint, but if you were asked to rest your hands on your hips, you would not actually touch this joint. What structure in the pelvic girdle would your hands be resting on?

5. The sedation that Mrs. Tanner was given was to relax the large muscles of the thigh and buttocks that attach to the proximal end of the femur. Name the structures on the femur where these muscles attach.

6. Mrs. Tanner's injury caused damage to the sciatic nerve that passes across the hip and down into the thigh, lower leg, and foot. Name the pelvic structure that this nerve passes through as it travels into the upper thigh.

(Answers in Appendix H)

$$8$$

Joints

Classification of Joints (pp. 249–250)

The graceful movements of ballet dancers and the rough-and-tumble grapplings of football players demonstrate the great variety of motion allowed by **joints**, or **articulations**—the sites where two or more bones meet. Our joints have two fundamental functions: They give our skeleton mobility, and they hold it together, sometimes playing a protective role in the process.

Joints are the weakest parts of the skeleton. Nonetheless, their structure resists various forces, such as crushing or tearing, that threaten to force them out of alignment.

Classification of Joints

✓ Define joint or articulation.

✓ Classify joints by structure and by function.

Joints are classified by structure and by function. The *structural classification* focuses on the material binding the bones together and whether or not a joint cavity is present. Structurally, there are *fibrous*, *cartilaginous*, and *synovial joints* (Table 8.1 on p. 253).

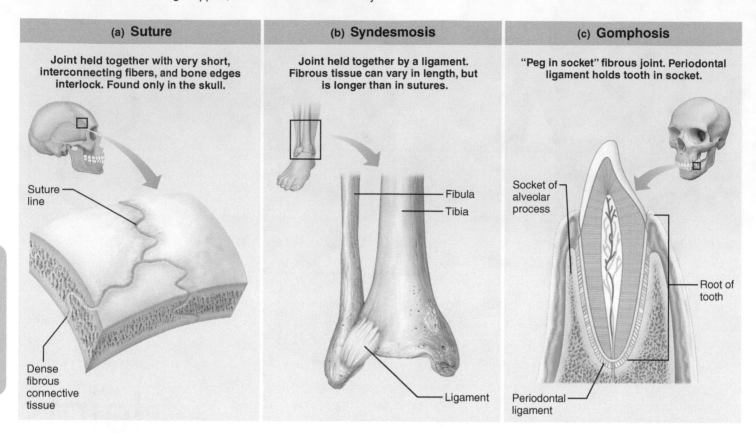

(a) Suture	(b) Syndesmosis	(c) Gomphosis
Joint held together with very short, interconnecting fibers, and bone edges interlock. Found only in the skull.	Joint held together by a ligament. Fibrous tissue can vary in length, but is longer than in sutures.	"Peg in socket" fibrous joint. Periodontal ligament holds tooth in socket.

Figure 8.1 Fibrous joints.

The *functional classification* is based on the amount of movement allowed at the joint. On this basis, there are **synarthroses** (sin″ar-thro′sēz; *syn* =together, *arthro* =joint), which are immovable joints; **amphiarthroses** (am″fe-ar-thro′sēz; *amphi* =on both sides), slightly movable joints; and **diarthroses** (di″ar-thro′sēz; *dia* =through, apart), or freely movable joints. Freely movable joints predominate in the limbs. Immovable and slightly movable joints are largely restricted to the axial skeleton. This localization of functional joint types is understandable because the less movable the joint, the more stable it is likely to be.

In general, fibrous joints are immovable, and synovial joints are freely movable. However, cartilaginous joints have both rigid and slightly movable examples. Since the structural categories are more clear-cut, we will use the structural classification in this discussion, indicating functional properties where appropriate.

Fibrous Joints

✓ Describe the general structure of fibrous joints. Name and give an example of each of the three common types of fibrous joints.

In **fibrous joints**, the bones are joined by fibrous tissue, namely dense fibrous connective tissue, and no joint cavity is present. The amount of movement allowed depends on the length of the connective tissue fibers uniting the bones. Most fibrous joints are immovable, although a few are slightly movable. The three types of fibrous joints are *sutures*, *syndesmoses*, and *gomphoses*.

Sutures

Sutures, literally "seams," occur only between bones of the skull **(Figure 8.1a)**. The wavy articulating bone edges interlock, and the junction is completely filled by a minimal amount of very short connective tissue fibers that are continuous with the periosteum. The result is nearly rigid splices that knit the bones together, yet allow the skull to expand as the brain grows during youth. During middle age, the fibrous tissue ossifies and the skull bones fuse into a single unit. At this stage, the closed sutures are more precisely called **synostoses** (sin″os-to′sēz), literally, "bony junctions." Because movement of the cranial bones would damage the brain, the immovable nature of sutures is a protective adaptation.

Syndesmoses

In **syndesmoses** (sin″des-mo′sēz), the bones are connected exclusively by *ligaments* (*syndesmos* =ligament), cords or bands of fibrous tissue. Although the connecting fibers are always longer than those in sutures, they vary quite a bit in length.

The amount of movement allowed at a syndesmosis depends on the length of the connecting fibers. If the fibers are short (as in the ligament connecting the distal ends of the tibia and fibula, Figure 8.1b), little or no movement is allowed, a characteristic best described as "give." If the fibers are long (as in the ligament-like interosseous membrane connecting the radius and ulna, Figure 7.28, p. 231), a large amount of movement is possible.

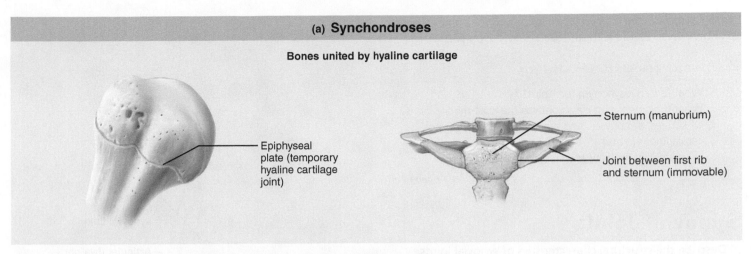

(a) Synchondroses

Bones united by hyaline cartilage

Epiphyseal plate (temporary hyaline cartilage joint)

Sternum (manubrium)

Joint between first rib and sternum (immovable)

(b) Symphyses

Bones united by fibrocartilage

Body of vertebra

Fibrocartilaginous intervertebral disc (sandwiched between hyaline cartilage)

Pubic symphysis

Figure 8.2 Cartilaginous joints.

Gomphoses

A **gomphosis** (gom-fo′sis) is a peg-in-socket fibrous joint (Figure 8.1c). The only example is the articulation of a tooth with its bony alveolar socket. The term *gomphosis* comes from the Greek *gompho*, meaning "nail" or "bolt," and refers to the way teeth are embedded in their sockets (as if hammered in). The fibrous connection in this case is the short **periodontal ligament** (Figure 23.11, p. 860).

Cartilaginous Joints

✓ Describe the general structure of cartilaginous joints. Name and give an example of each of the two common types of cartilaginous joints.

In **cartilaginous joints** (kar″tĭ-laj′ĭ-nus), the articulating bones are united by cartilage. Like fibrous joints, they lack a joint cavity and are not highly movable. The two types of cartilaginous joints are *synchondroses* and *symphyses*.

Synchondroses

A bar or plate of *hyaline cartilage* unites the bones at a **synchondrosis** (sin″kon-dro′sis; "junction of cartilage"). Virtually all synchondroses are synarthrotic.

The most common examples of synchondroses are the epiphyseal plates in long bones of children **(Figure 8.2a)**. Epiphyseal plates are temporary joints and eventually become synostoses. Another example of a synchondrosis is the immovable joint between the costal cartilage of the first rib and the manubrium of the sternum (Figure 8.2a).

Symphyses

A joint where *fibrocartilage* unites the bone is a **symphysis** (sim′fih-sis; "growing together"). Since fibrocartilage is compressible and resilient, it acts as a shock absorber and permits a limited amount of movement at the joint. Even though fibrocartilage is the main element of a symphysis, hyaline cartilage is also present in the form of articular cartilages on the bony surfaces. Symphyses are amphiarthrotic joints designed for strength with flexibility.

Examples include the intervertebral joints and the pubic symphysis of the pelvis (Figure 8.2b, and see Table 8.2 on p. 254).

see Table 8.2 on p. 254

☑ Check Your Understanding

1. What term is a synonym for "joint"?
2. What functional joint class contains the least-mobile joints?
3. Of sutures, symphyses, and synchondroses, which are cartilaginous joints?
4. How are joint mobility and stability related?

For answers, see Appendix H.

Synovial Joints

✓ Describe the structural characteristics of synovial joints.

✓ Compare the structures and functions of bursae and tendon sheaths.

✓ List three natural factors that stabilize synovial joints.

Synovial joints (si-no′ve-al; "joint eggs") are those in which the articulating bones are separated by a fluid-containing joint cavity. This arrangement permits substantial freedom of movement, and all synovial joints are freely movable diarthroses. Nearly all joints of the limbs—indeed, most joints of the body—fall into this class.

General Structure

Synovial joints have six distinguishing features (**Figure 8.3**):

- **Articular cartilage.** Glassy-smooth hyaline cartilage covers the opposing bone surfaces as **articular cartilage**. These thin (1 mm or less) but spongy cushions absorb compression placed on the joint and thereby keep the bone ends from being crushed.

- **Joint (articular) cavity.** A feature unique to synovial joints, the joint cavity is really just a potential space that contains a small amount of synovial fluid.

- **Articular capsule.** The joint cavity is enclosed by a two-layered **articular capsule**, or *joint capsule*. The tough external **fibrous layer** is composed of dense irregular connective tissue that is continuous with the periostea of the articulating bones. It strengthens the joint so that the bones are not pulled apart. The inner layer of the joint capsule is a **synovial membrane** composed of loose connective tissue. Besides lining the fibrous layer internally, it covers all internal joint surfaces that are not hyaline cartilage. The synovial membrane's function is to make synovial fluid.

- **Synovial fluid.** A small amount of slippery **synovial fluid** occupies all free spaces within the joint capsule. This fluid is derived largely by filtration from blood flowing through the capillaries in the synovial membrane. Synovial fluid has a viscous, egg-white consistency (*ovum* =egg) due to hyaluronic acid secreted by cells in the synovial membrane, but it thins and becomes less viscous during joint activity.

  Synovial fluid, which is also found *within* the articular cartilages, provides a slippery, weight-bearing film that reduces friction between the cartilages. Without this lubricant,

Figure 8.3 General structure of a synovial joint.

Labels: Ligament; Joint cavity (contains synovial fluid); Articular (hyaline) cartilage; Fibrous layer; Synovial membrane (secretes synovial fluid); Articular capsule; Periosteum

rubbing would wear away joint surfaces and excessive friction could overheat and destroy the joint tissues, essentially "cooking" them. The synovial fluid is forced from the cartilages when a joint is compressed; then as pressure on the joint is relieved, synovial fluid seeps back into the articular cartilages like water into a sponge, ready to be squeezed out again the next time the joint is loaded (put under pressure). This process, called *weeping lubrication*, lubricates the free surfaces of the cartilages and nourishes their cells. (Remember, cartilage is avascular.) Synovial fluid also contains phagocytic cells that rid the joint cavity of microbes and cellular debris.

- **Reinforcing ligaments.** Synovial joints are reinforced and strengthened by a number of bandlike **ligaments**. Most often, these are **capsular ligaments**, which are thickened parts of the fibrous layer. In other cases, they remain distinct and are found outside the capsule (as **extracapsular ligaments**) or deep to it (as **intracapsular ligaments**). Since intracapsular ligaments are covered with synovial membrane, they do not actually lie *within* the joint cavity.

  People said to be double-jointed amaze the rest of us by placing both heels behind their neck. However, they have the normal number of joints. It's just that their joint capsules and ligaments are more stretchy and loose than average.

- **Nerves and blood vessels.** Synovial joints are richly supplied with sensory nerve fibers that innervate the capsule. Some of

Table 8.1   Summary of Joint Classes

STRUCTURAL CLASS	STRUCTURAL CHARACTERISTICS	TYPES		MOBILITY
Fibrous	Bone ends/parts united by collagen fibers	Suture (short fibers)		Immobile (synarthrosis)
		Syndesmosis (longer fibers)		Slightly mobile (amphiarthrosis) and immobile
		Gomphosis (periodontal ligament)		Immobile
Cartilaginous	Bone ends/parts united by cartilage	Synchondrosis (hyaline cartilage)		Immobile
		Symphysis (fibrocartilage)		Slightly movable
Synovial	Bone ends/parts covered with articular cartilage and enclosed within an articular capsule lined with synovial membrane	1. Plane 2. Hinge 3. Pivot	4. Condylar 5. Saddle 6. Ball and socket	Freely movable (diarthrosis; movements depend on design of joint)

these fibers detect pain, as anyone who has suffered joint injury is aware, but most monitor joint position and stretch. Monitoring joint stretch is one of several ways the nervous system senses our posture and body movements (see p. 487). Synovial joints are also richly supplied with blood vessels, most of which supply the synovial membrane. There, extensive capillary beds produce the blood filtrate that is the basis of synovial fluid.

Besides the basic components described above, certain synovial joints have other structural features. Some, such as the hip and knee joints, have cushioning **fatty pads** between the fibrous layer and the synovial membrane or bone. Others have discs or wedges of fibrocartilage separating the articular surfaces. Where present, these **articular discs**, or **menisci** (mĕ-nis'ki; "crescents"), extend inward from the articular capsule and partially or completely divide the synovial cavity in two (see the menisci of the knee in Figure 8.8a, b, e, and f). Articular discs improve the fit between articulating bone ends, making the joint more stable and

minimizing wear and tear on the joint surfaces. Besides the knees, articular discs occur in the jaw and a few other joints (see notations in the Structural Type column in Table 8.2).

Bursae and Tendon Sheaths

Bursae and tendon sheaths are not strictly part of synovial joints, but they are often found closely associated with them **(Figure 8.4)**. Essentially bags of lubricant, they act as "ball bearings" to reduce friction between adjacent structures during joint activity. **Bursae** (ber'se; "purse") are flattened fibrous sacs lined with synovial membrane and containing a thin film of synovial fluid. They occur where ligaments, muscles, skin, tendons, or bones rub together.

A **tendon sheath** is essentially an elongated bursa that wraps completely around a tendon subjected to friction, like a bun around a hot dog. They are common where several tendons are crowded together within narrow canals (in the wrist region, for example).

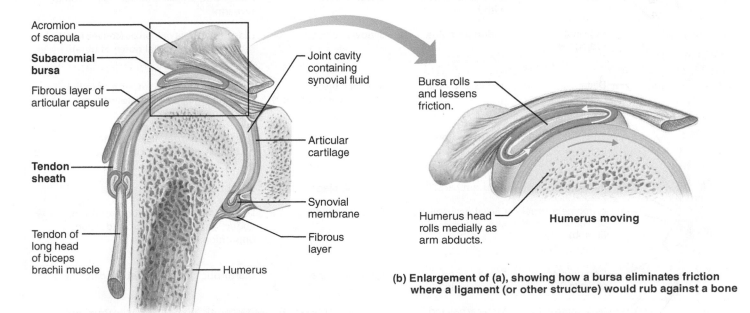

Acromion of scapula

Subacromial bursa

Fibrous layer of articular capsule

Joint cavity containing synovial fluid

Tendon sheath

Articular cartilage

Tendon of long head of biceps brachii muscle

Synovial membrane

Fibrous layer

Humerus

(a) Frontal section through the right shoulder joint

Bursa rolls and lessens friction.

Humerus head rolls medially as arm abducts.

Humerus moving

(b) Enlargement of (a), showing how a bursa eliminates friction where a ligament (or other structure) would rub against a bone

Figure 8.4   Bursae and tendon sheaths.

Table 8.2 Structural and Functional Characteristics of Body Joints

ILLUSTRATION	JOINT	ARTICULATING BONES	STRUCTURAL TYPE*	FUNCTIONAL TYPE; MOVEMENTS ALLOWED
	Skull	Cranial and facial bones	Fibrous; suture	Synarthrotic; no movement
	Temporo-mandibular	Temporal bone of skull and mandible	Synovial; modified hinge† (contains articular disc)	Diarthrotic; gliding and uniaxial rotation; slight lateral movement, elevation, depression, protraction, and retraction of mandible
	Atlanto-occipital	Occipital bone of skull and atlas	Synovial; condylar	Diarthrotic; biaxial; flexion, extension, lateral flexion, circumduction of head on neck
	Atlantoaxial	Atlas (C_1) and axis (C_2)	Synovial; pivot	Diarthrotic; uniaxial; rotation of the head
	Intervertebral	Between adjacent vertebral bodies	Cartilaginous; symphysis	Amphiarthrotic; slight movement
	Intervertebral	Between articular processes	Synovial; plane	Diarthrotic; gliding
	Costovertebral	Vertebrae (transverse processes or bodies) and ribs	Synovial; plane	Diarthrotic; gliding of ribs
	Sternoclavicular	Sternum and clavicle	Synovial; shallow saddle (contains articular disc)	Diarthrotic; multiaxial (allows clavicle to move in all axes)
	Sternocostal (first)	Sternum and rib 1	Cartilaginous; synchondrosis	Synarthrotic; no movement
	Sternocostal	Sternum and ribs 2–7	Synovial; double plane	Diarthrotic; gliding
	Acromio-clavicular	Acromion of scapula and clavicle	Synovial; plane (contains articular disc)	Diarthrotic; gliding and rotation of scapula on clavicle
	Shoulder (glenohumeral)	Scapula and humerus	Synovial; ball-and-socket	Diarthrotic; multiaxial; flexion, extension, abduction, adduction, circumduction, rotation of humerus
	Elbow	Ulna (and radius) with humerus	Synovial; hinge	Diarthrotic; uniaxial; flexion, extension of forearm
	Proximal radioulnar	Radius and ulna	Synovial; pivot	Diarthrotic; uniaxial; pivot (convex head of radius rotates in radial notch of ulna)
	Distal radioulnar	Radius and ulna	Synovial; pivot (contains articular disc)	Diarthrotic; uniaxial; rotation of radius around long axis of forearm to allow pronation and supination
	Wrist	Radius and proximal carpals	Synovial; condylar	Diarthrotic; biaxial; flexion, extension, abduction, adduction, circumduction of hand
	Intercarpal	Adjacent carpals	Synovial; plane	Diarthrotic; gliding
	Carpometacarpal of digit 1 (thumb)	Carpal (trapezium) and metacarpal 1	Synovial; saddle	Diarthrotic; biaxial; flexion, extension, abduction, adduction, circumduction, opposition of metacarpal I
	Carpometacarpal of digits 2–5	Carpal(s) and metacarpal(s)	Synovial; plane	Diarthrotic; gliding of metacarpals
	Metacarpo-phalangeal (knuckle)	Metacarpal and proximal phalanx	Synovial; condylar	Diarthrotic; biaxial; flexion, extension, abduction, adduction, circumduction of fingers
	Interphalangeal (finger)	Adjacent phalanges	Synovial; hinge	Diarthrotic; uniaxial; flexion, extension of fingers

Chapter 8 Joints **255**

Table 8.2 *(continued)*				
ILLUSTRATION	**JOINT**	**ARTICULATING BONES**	**STRUCTURAL TYPE***	**FUNCTIONAL TYPE; MOVEMENTS ALLOWED**
	Sacroiliac	Sacrum and coxal bone	Synovial; plane in childhood, increasingly fibrous in adult	Diarthrotic in child; amphiarthrotic in adult; (more movement during pregnancy)
	Pubic symphysis	Pubic bones	Cartilaginous; symphysis	Amphiarthrotic; slight movement (enhanced during pregnancy)
	Hip (coxal)	Hip bone and femur	Synovial; ball-and-socket	Diarthrotic; multiaxial; flexion, extension, abduction, adduction, rotation, circumduction of thigh
	Knee (tibiofemoral)	Femur and tibia	Synovial; modified hinge† (contains articular discs)	Diarthrotic; biaxial; flexion, extension of leg, some rotation allowed in flexed position
	Knee (femoropatellar)	Femur and patella	Synovial; plane	Diarthrotic; gliding of patella
	Superior tibiofibular	Tibia and fibula (proximally)	Synovial; plane	Diarthrotic; gliding of fibula
	Inferior tibiofibular	Tibia and fibula (distally)	Fibrous; syndesmosis	Synarthrotic; slight "give" during dorsiflexion
	Ankle	Tibia and fibula with talus	Synovial; hinge	Diarthrotic; uniaxial; dorsiflexion, and plantar flexion of foot
	Intertarsal	Adjacent tarsals	Synovial; plane	Diarthrotic; gliding; inversion and eversion of foot
	Tarsometatarsal	Tarsal(s) and metatarsal(s)	Synovial; plane	Diarthrotic; gliding of metatarsals
	Metatarso-phalangeal	Metatarsal and proximal phalanx	Synovial; condylar	Diarthrotic; biaxial; flexion, extension, abduction, adduction, circumduction of great toe
	Interpha-langeal (toe)	Adjacent phalanges	Synovial; hinge	Diarthrotic; uniaxial; flexion; extension of toes

*****Fibrous joints** indicated by orange circles; **cartilaginous joints** by blue circles; **synovial joints** by purple circles.
† These modified hinge joints are structurally bicondylar.

Factors Influencing the Stability of Synovial Joints

Because joints are constantly stretched and compressed, they must be stabilized so that they do not dislocate (come out of alignment). The stability of a synovial joint depends chiefly on three factors: the shapes of the articular surfaces; the number and positioning of ligaments; and muscle tone.

Articular Surfaces

The shapes of articular surfaces determine what movements are possible at a joint, but surprisingly, articular surfaces play only a minor role in joint stability. Many joints have shallow sockets or noncomplementary articulating surfaces ("misfits") that actually hinder joint stability. But when articular surfaces are large and fit snugly together, or when the socket is deep, stability is vastly improved. The ball and deep socket of the hip joint provide the best example of a joint made extremely stable by the shape of its articular surfaces.

Ligaments

The capsules and ligaments of synovial joints unite the bones and prevent excessive or undesirable motion. As a rule, the more ligaments a joint has, the stronger it is. However, when other stabilizing factors are inadequate, undue tension is placed on the ligaments and they stretch. Stretched ligaments stay stretched, like taffy, and a ligament can stretch only about 6% of its length before it snaps. Thus, when ligaments are the major means of bracing a joint, the joint is not very stable.

Muscle Tone

For most joints, the muscle tendons that cross the joint are the most important stabilizing factor. These tendons are kept taut at all times by the tone of their muscles. (*Muscle tone* is defined as low levels of contractile activity in relaxed muscles that keep the muscles healthy and ready to react to stimulation.) Muscle tone is extremely important in reinforcing the shoulder and knee joints and the arches of the foot.

☑ **Check Your Understanding**

5. What are the two layers of the articular capsule?
6. How do bursae and tendon sheaths improve joint function?
7. Generally speaking, what factor is most important in stabilizing synovial joints?
8. What is the importance of weeping lubrication?

For answers, see Appendix H.

Movements Allowed by Synovial Joints

✓ Name and describe (or perform) the common body movements.

✓ Name and provide examples of the six types of synovial joints based on the movement(s) allowed.

Every skeletal muscle of the body is attached to bone or other connective tissue structures at no fewer than two points. The muscle's **origin** is attached to the immovable (or less movable) bone. Its other end, the **insertion**, is attached to the movable bone. Body movement occurs when muscles contract across joints and their insertion moves toward their origin. The movements can be described in directional terms relative to the lines, or axes, around which the body part moves and the planes of space along which the movement occurs, that is, along the transverse, frontal, or sagittal plane. (See Chapter 1 to review these planes.)

Range of motion allowed by synovial joints varies from **non-axial movement** (slipping movements only, since there is no axis around which movement can occur) to **uniaxial movement** (movement in one plane) to **biaxial movement** (movement in two planes) to **multiaxial movement** (movement in or around all three planes of space and axes). Range of motion varies greatly in different people. In some, such as trained gymnasts or acrobats, range of joint movement may be extraordinary. The ranges of motion at the major joints are given in the far right column of Table 8.2.

There are three general types of movements: *gliding*, *angular movements*, and *rotation*. The most common body movements allowed by synovial joints are described next and illustrated in **Figure 8.5**.

Gliding Movements

Gliding occurs when one flat, or nearly flat, bone surface glides or slips over another (back-and-forth and side-to-side; Figure 8.5a) without appreciable angulation or rotation. Gliding occurs at the intercarpal and intertarsal joints, and between the flat articular processes of the vertebrae (Table 8.2).

Angular Movements

Angular movements (Figure 8.5b–e) increase or decrease the angle between two bones. These movements may occur in any plane of the body and include flexion, extension, hyperextension, abduction, adduction, and circumduction.

Figure 8.5 Movements allowed by synovial joints.

(a) Gliding movements at the wrist

(b) Angular movements: flexion, extension, and hyperextension of the neck

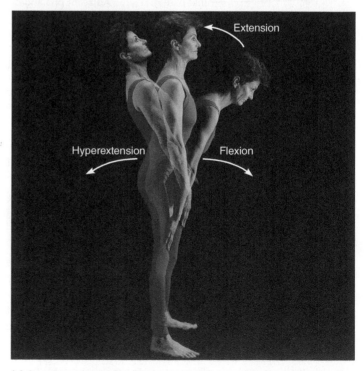

(c) Angular movements: flexion, extension, and hyperextension of the vertebral column

(d) Angular movements: flexion, extension, and hyperextension at the shoulder and knee

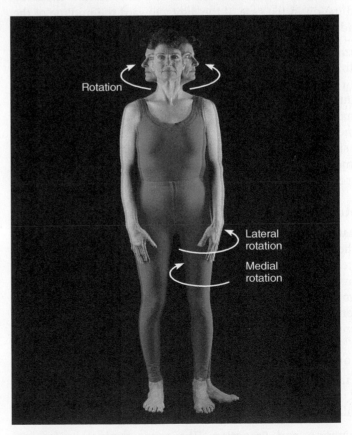

(e) Angular movements: abduction, adduction, and circumduction of the upper limb at the shoulder

(f) Rotation of the head, neck, and lower limb

Figure 8.5 *(continued)*

Flexion Flexion (flek'shun) is a bending movement, usually along the sagittal plane, that *decreases the angle* of the joint and brings the articulating bones closer together. Examples include bending the head forward on the chest (Figure 8.5b) and bending the body trunk or the knee from a straight to an angled position (Figure 8.5c and d). As a less obvious example, the arm is flexed at the shoulder when the arm is lifted in an anterior direction (Figure 8.5d).

Extension Extension is the reverse of flexion and occurs at the same joints. It involves movement along the sagittal plane that *increases the angle* between the articulating bones and typically straightens a flexed limb or body part. Examples include straightening a flexed neck, body trunk, elbow, or knee (Figure 8.5b–d). Continuing such movements beyond the anatomical position is called **hyperextension** (literally, "superextension") (Figure 8.5b–d).

Abduction Abduction ("moving away") is movement of a limb *away* from the midline or median plane of the body, along the frontal plane. Raising the arm or thigh laterally is an example of abduction (Figure 8.5e). For the fingers or toes, abduction means spreading them apart. In this case "midline" is the longest digit: the third finger or second toe. Notice, however, that lateral bending of the trunk away from the body midline in the frontal plane is called lateral flexion, not abduction.

Adduction Adduction ("moving toward") is the opposite of abduction, so it is the movement of a limb *toward* the body midline or, in the case of the digits, toward the midline of the hand or foot (Figure 8.5e).

Circumduction Circumduction (Figure 8.5e) is moving a limb so that it describes a cone in space (*circum* =around; *duco* =to draw). The distal end of the limb moves in a circle, while the point of the cone (the shoulder or hip joint) is more or less stationary. A pitcher winding up to throw a ball is actually circumducting his or her pitching arm. Because circumduction consists of flexion, abduction, extension, and adduction performed in succession, it is the quickest way to exercise the many muscles that move the hip and shoulder ball-and-socket joints.

Rotation

Rotation is the turning of a bone around its own long axis. It is the only movement allowed between the first two cervical vertebrae and is common at the hip (Figure 8.5f) and shoulder joints. Rotation may be directed toward the midline or away from it. For example, in *medial rotation* of the thigh, the femur's anterior surface moves toward the median plane of the body; *lateral rotation* is the opposite movement.

Special Movements

Certain movements do not fit into any of the above categories and occur at only a few joints. Some of these special movements are illustrated in **Figure 8.6**.

Supination and Pronation The terms **supination** (soo"pĭ-na'shun; "turning backward") and **pronation** (pro-na'shun; "turning forward") refer to the movements of the radius around the ulna (Figure 8.6a). Rotating the forearm laterally so that the palm faces anteriorly or superiorly is supination. In the anatomical position, the hand is supinated and the radius and ulna are parallel.

In pronation, the forearm rotates medially and the palm faces posteriorly or inferiorly. Pronation moves the distal end of the radius across the ulna so that the two bones form an X. This is the forearm's position when we are standing in a relaxed manner. Pronation is a much weaker movement than supination.

A trick to help you keep these terms straight: A *pro* basketball player pronates his or her forearm to dribble the ball.

Dorsiflexion and Plantar Flexion of the Foot The up-and-down movements of the foot at the ankle are given more specific names (Figure 8.6b). Lifting the foot so that its superior surface approaches the shin is **dorsiflexion** (corresponds to wrist extension), whereas depressing the foot (pointing the toes) is **plantar flexion** (corresponds to wrist flexion).

Inversion and Eversion Inversion and eversion are special movements of the foot (Figure 8.6c). In inversion, the sole of the foot turns medially. In eversion, the sole faces laterally.

Protraction and Retraction Nonangular anterior and posterior movements in a transverse plane are called **protraction** and **retraction**, respectively (Figure 8.6d). The mandible is protracted when you jut out your jaw and retracted when you bring it back.

Elevation and Depression Elevation means lifting a body part superiorly (Figure 8.6e). For example, the scapulae are elevated when you shrug your shoulders. Moving the elevated part inferiorly is **depression**. During chewing, the mandible is alternately elevated and depressed.

Opposition The saddle joint between metacarpal I and the trapezium allows a movement called **opposition** of the thumb (Figure 8.6f). This movement is the action taken when you touch your thumb to the tips of the other fingers on the same hand. It is opposition that makes the human hand such a fine tool for grasping and manipulating objects.

Types of Synovial Joints

Although all synovial joints have structural features in common, they do not have a common structural plan. Based on the shape of their articular surfaces, which in turn determine the movements allowed, synovial joints can be classified further into six major categories—plane, hinge, pivot, condylar (or ellipsoid), saddle, and ball-and-socket joints. The properties of these joints are summarized in *Focus on Types of Synovial Joints* **(Figure 8.7)** on pp. 260–261.

☑ Check Your Understanding

9. John bent over to pick up a dime. What movement was occurring at his hip joint, at his knees, and between his index finger and thumb?
10. On the basis of movement allowed, which of the following joints are uniaxial? Hinge, condylar, saddle, pivot.

For answers, see Appendix H.

(Text continues on p. 262.)

(a) Pronation (P) and supination (S)

(b) Dorsiflexion and plantar flexion

(c) Inversion and eversion

(d) Protraction and retraction

(e) Elevation and depression

(f) Opposition

Figure 8.6 **Special body movements.**

Figure 8.7 The shapes of the joint surfaces define the types of movements that can occur at a synovial joint; they also determine the classification of synovial joints into six structural types.

(a) Plane joint

Nonaxial movement

Metacarpals

Carpals

Flat articular surfaces

Gliding

Examples: Intercarpal joints, intertarsal joints, joints between vertebral articular surfaces

(b) Hinge joint

Uniaxial movement

Humerus

Ulna

Cylinder

Trough

Medial/lateral axis

Flexion and extension

Examples: Elbow joints, interphalangeal joints

(c) Pivot joint

Uniaxial movement

Ulna

Radius

Sleeve (bone and ligament)

Axle (rounded bone)

Vertical axis

Rotation

Examples: Proximal radioulnar joints, atlantoaxial joint

(d) Condylar joint

Biaxial movement

Phalanges

Metacarpals

Oval articular surfaces

Medial/ lateral axis

Anterior/ posterior axis

Flexion and extension

Adduction and abduction

Examples: Metacarpophalangeal (knuckle) joints, wrist joints

(e) Saddle joint

Biaxial movement

Metacarpal I

Trapezium

Articular surfaces are both concave and convex

Medial/ lateral axis

Anterior/ posterior axis

Adduction and abduction

Flexion and extension

Example: Carpometacarpal joints of the thumbs

(f) Ball-and-socket joint

Multiaxial movement

Cup (socket)

Spherical head (ball)

Scapula

Humerus

Medial/lateral axis

Anterior/posterior axis

Vertical axis

Flexion and extension

Adduction and abduction

Rotation

Examples: Shoulder joints and hip joints

(a) Sagittal section through the right knee joint

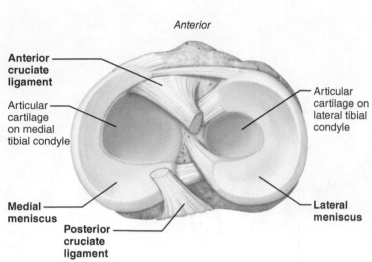

Anterior

(b) Superior view of the right tibia in the knee joint, showing the menisci and cruciate ligaments

(c) Anterior view of right knee

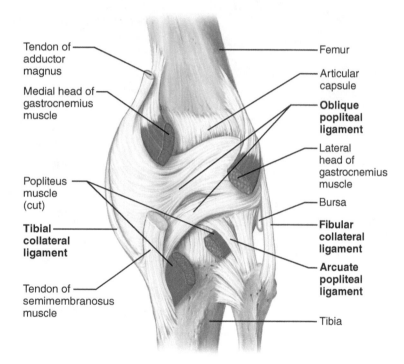

(d) Posterior view of the joint capsule, including ligaments

Figure 8.8 The knee joint.

Selected Synovial Joints

✓ Describe the elbow, knee, hip, jaw, and shoulder joints in terms of articulating bones, anatomical characteristics of the joint, movements allowed, and joint stability.

In this section, we examine five joints in detail: knee, elbow, shoulder, hip, and temporomandibular (jaw) joint. All have the six distinguishing characteristics of synovial joints, and we will not discuss these common features again. Instead, we will emphasize the unique structural features, functional abilities, and, in certain cases, functional weaknesses of each of these joints.

Knee Joint

The knee joint is the largest and most complex joint in the body (Figure 8.8). Despite its single joint cavity, the knee consists of three joints in one: an intermediate one between the patella and the lower end of the femur (the **femoropatellar joint**), and lateral and medial joints (collectively known as the **tibiofemoral joint**) between the femoral condyles above and the C-shaped **menisci**, or *semilunar cartilages*, of the tibia below (Figure 8.8b and e). Besides deepening the shallow tibial articular surfaces, the menisci help prevent side-to-side rocking of the femur on the tibia and absorb shock transmitted to the knee joint. However, the menisci are

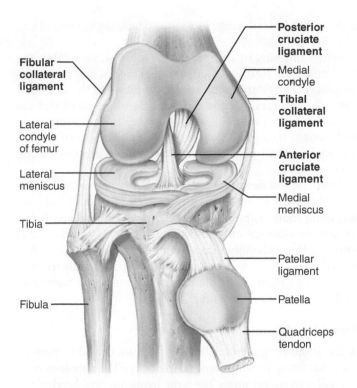

Posterior cruciate ligament

Fibular collateral ligament

Medial condyle

Tibial collateral ligament

Lateral condyle of femur

Anterior cruciate ligament

Lateral meniscus

Medial meniscus

Tibia

Fibula

Patellar ligament

Patella

Quadriceps tendon

(e) Anterior view of flexed knee, showing the cruciate ligaments (articular capsule removed, and quadriceps tendon cut and reflected distally)

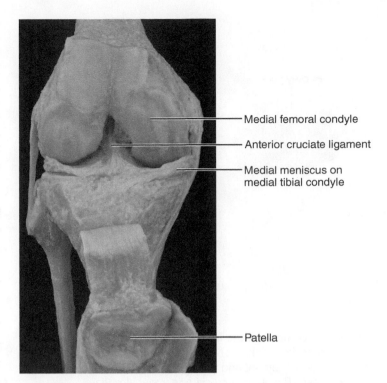

Medial femoral condyle

Anterior cruciate ligament

Medial meniscus on medial tibial condyle

Patella

(f) Photograph of an opened knee joint; view similar to (e)

Figure 8.8 *(continued)*

attached only at their outer margins and are frequently torn free.

The tibiofemoral joint acts primarily as a hinge, permitting flexion and extension. However, structurally it is a bicondylar joint. Some rotation is possible when the knee is partly flexed, and when the knee is extending. But, when the knee is fully extended, side-to-side movements and rotation are strongly resisted by ligaments and the menisci. The femoropatellar joint is a plane joint, and the patella glides across the distal end of the femur during knee flexion.

The knee joint is unique in that its joint cavity is only partially enclosed by a capsule. The relatively thin articular capsule is present only on the sides and posterior aspects of the knee, where it covers the bulk of the femoral and tibial condyles. Anteriorly, where the capsule is absent, three broad ligaments run from the patella to the tibia below. These are the **patellar ligament** flanked by the **medial** and **lateral patellar retinacula** (ret″ĭ-nak′u-lah; "retainers"), which merge imperceptibly into the articular capsule on each side (Figure 8.8c). The patellar ligament and retinacula are actually continuations of the tendon of the bulky quadriceps muscle of the anterior thigh. Physicians tap the patellar ligament to test the knee-jerk reflex.

The synovial cavity of the knee joint has a complicated shape, with several extensions that lead into "blind alleys." At least a dozen bursae are associated with this joint, some of which are shown in Figure 8.8a. For example, notice the *subcutaneous prepatellar bursa*, which is often injured when the knee is bumped anteriorly.

All three types of joint ligaments stabilize and strengthen the capsule of the knee joint. The ligaments of two of the types, capsular and extracapsular, all act to prevent hyperextension of the knee and are stretched taut when the knee is extended. These include the following:

- The extracapsular **fibular** and **tibial collateral ligaments** are also critical in preventing lateral or medial rotation when the knee is extended. The broad, flat tibial collateral ligament runs from the medial epicondyle of the femur to the medial condyle of the tibial shaft below and is fused to the medial meniscus (Figure 8.8c–e).

- The **oblique popliteal ligament** (pop″lĭ-te′al) is actually part of the tendon of the semimembranosus muscle that fuses with the joint capsule and helps stabilize the posterior aspect of the knee joint (Figure 8.8d).

- The **arcuate popliteal ligament** arcs superiorly from the head of the fibula over the popliteus muscle and reinforces the joint capsule posteriorly (Figure 8.8d).

The knee's *intracapsular ligaments* are called *cruciate ligaments* (kroo′she-āt) because they cross each other, forming an X (*cruci* =cross) in the notch between the femoral condyles. They act as restraining straps to help prevent anterior-posterior displacement of the articular surfaces and to secure the articulating bones when we stand (Figure 8.8a, b, e). Although these ligaments are in the joint capsule, they are *outside* the synovial cavity, and synovial membrane nearly covers their surfaces. Note that the two cruciate ligaments both run superiorly to the femur and are named for their *tibial* attachment site.

The **anterior cruciate ligament** attaches to the *anterior* intercondylar area of the tibia (Figure 8.8b). From there it passes posteriorly, laterally, and upward to attach to the femur on the medial side of its lateral condyle. This ligament prevents forward sliding of the tibia on the femur and checks hyperextension of the knee. It

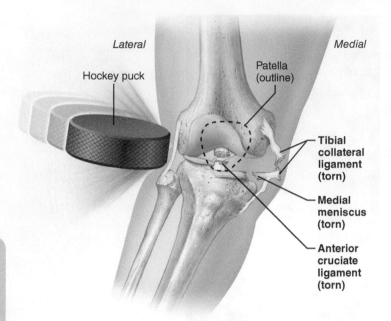

Lateral   *Medial*

Hockey puck

Patella
(outline)

Tibial
collateral
ligament
(torn)

Medial
meniscus
(torn)

Anterior
cruciate
ligament
(torn)

Figure 8.9 A common knee injury. Anterior view of a knee being hit by a hockey puck. Such blows to the lateral side tear both the tibial collateral ligament and the medial meniscus because the two are attached. The anterior cruciate ligament also tears.

is somewhat lax when the knee is flexed, and taut when the knee is extended.

The stronger **posterior cruciate ligament** is attached to the *posterior* intercondylar area of the tibia and passes anteriorly, medially, and superiorly to attach to the femur on the lateral side of the medial condyle (Figure 8.8a, b). This ligament prevents backward displacement of the tibia or forward sliding of the femur.

The knee capsule is heavily reinforced by muscle tendons. Most important are the strong tendons of the quadriceps muscles of the anterior thigh and the tendon of the semimembranosus muscle posteriorly (Figure 8.8c and d). The greater the strength and tone of these muscles, the less the chance of knee injury.

The knees have a built-in locking device that provides steady support for the body in the standing position. As we begin to stand up, the wheel-shaped femoral condyles roll like ball bearings across the tibial condyles and the flexed leg begins to extend at the knee. Because the lateral femoral condyle stops rolling before the medial condyle stops, the femur *spins* (rotates) medially on the tibia, until the cruciate and collateral ligaments of the knee are twisted and taut and the menisci are compressed. The tension in the ligaments effectively locks the joint into a rigid structure that cannot be flexed again until it is unlocked. This unlocking is accomplished by the popliteus muscle (see Figure 8.8d and Table 10.15, p. 370). It rotates the femur laterally on the tibia, causing the ligaments to become untwisted and slack.

Homeostatic Imbalance 8.1

Of all body joints, the knees are most susceptible to sports injuries because of their high reliance on nonarticular factors for stability and the fact that they carry the body's weight. The knee can absorb a vertical force equal to nearly seven times body weight. However, it is very vulnerable to *horizontal* blows, such

as those that occur during blocking and tackling in football and in ice hockey.

When thinking of common knee injuries, remember the 3 Cs: collateral ligaments, cruciate ligaments, and cartilages (menisci). Most dangerous are *lateral blows* to the extended knee. These forces tear the tibial collateral ligament and the medial meniscus attached to it, as well as the anterior cruciate ligament **(Figure 8.9)**. It is estimated that 50% of all professional football players have serious knee injuries during their careers.

Although less devastating than the injury just described, injuries that affect only the anterior cruciate ligament (ACL) are becoming more common, particularly as women's sports become more vigorous and competitive. Most ACL injuries occur when a runner changes direction quickly, twisting a hyperextended knee. A torn ACL heals poorly, so repair usually requires a graft taken from either the patellar ligament, the hamstring tendon, or the calcaneal tendon. ✚

Shoulder (Glenohumeral) Joint

In the shoulder joint, stability has been sacrificed to provide the most freely moving joint of the body. The shoulder joint is a ball-and-socket joint. The large hemispherical head of the humerus fits in the small, shallow glenoid cavity of the scapula **(Figure 8.10)**, like a golf ball sitting on a tee. Although the glenoid cavity is slightly deepened by a rim of fibrocartilage, the **glenoid labrum** (*labrum* =lip), it is only about one-third the size of the humeral head and contributes little to joint stability (Figure 8.10d).

The articular capsule enclosing the joint cavity (from the margin of the glenoid cavity to the anatomical neck of the humerus) is remarkably thin and loose, qualities that contribute to this joint's freedom of movement. The few ligaments reinforcing the shoulder joint are located primarily on its anterior aspect. The superiorly located **coracohumeral ligament** (kor′ah-ko-hu′mer-ul) provides the only strong thickening of the capsule and helps support the weight of the upper limb (Figure 8.10c). Three **glenohumeral ligaments** (glĕ″no-hu′mer-ul) strengthen the front of the capsule somewhat but are weak and may even be absent (Figure 8.10c, d).

Muscle tendons that cross the shoulder joint contribute most to this joint's stability. The "superstabilizer" is the tendon of the long head of the biceps brachii muscle of the arm (Figure 8.10c). This tendon attaches to the superior margin of the glenoid labrum, travels through the joint cavity, and then runs within the intertubercular sulcus of the humerus. It secures the head of the humerus against the glenoid cavity.

Four other tendons (and the associated muscles) make up the **rotator cuff**. This cuff encircles the shoulder joint and blends with the articular capsule. The muscles include the subscapularis, supraspinatus, infraspinatus, and teres minor. (The rotator cuff muscles are illustrated in Figure 10.15, p. 351.) The rotator cuff can be severely stretched when the arm is vigorously circumducted; this is a common injury of baseball pitchers. As noted in Chapter 7, shoulder dislocations are fairly common. Because the shoulder's reinforcements are weakest anteriorly and inferiorly, the humerus tends to dislocate in the forward and downward direction.

8

Acromion
of scapula

Coracoacromial
ligament

Subacromial
bursa

Fibrous layer of
articular capsule

Tendon
sheath

Tendon of
long head
of biceps
brachii muscle

Synovial cavity
of the glenoid
cavity containing
synovial fluid

Articular
cartilage

Synovial membrane

Fibrous layer of
articular capsule

Humerus

(a) Frontal section through right shoulder joint

(b) Cadaver photo corresponding to (a)

8

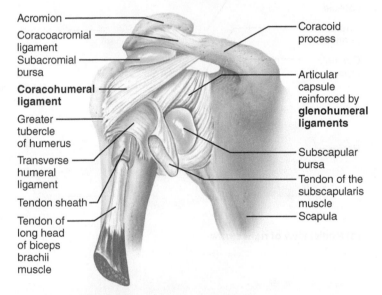

Acromion

Coracoacromial
ligament

Subacromial
bursa

**Coracohumeral
ligament**

Greater
tubercle
of humerus

Transverse
humeral
ligament

Tendon sheath

Tendon of
long head
of biceps
brachii
muscle

Coracoid
process

Articular
capsule
reinforced by
**glenohumeral
ligaments**

Subscapular
bursa

Tendon of the
subscapularis
muscle

Scapula

(c) Anterior view of right shoulder joint capsule

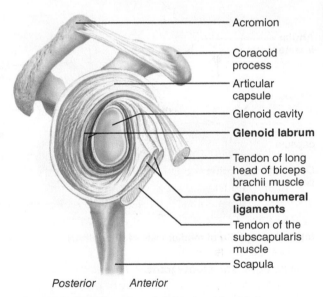

Acromion

Coracoid
process

Articular
capsule

Glenoid cavity

Glenoid labrum

Tendon of long
head of biceps
brachii muscle

**Glenohumeral
ligaments**

Tendon of the
subscapularis
muscle

Scapula

Posterior   *Anterior*

**(d) Lateral view of socket of right shoulder joint,
humerus removed**

Head of
humerus

Muscle of
rotator
cuff (cut)

Acromion
(cut)

Glenoid
cavity of
scapula

Capsule of
shoulder
joint
(opened)

(e) Anterior view of an opened shoulder joint

Figure 8.10 The shoulder joint.

8

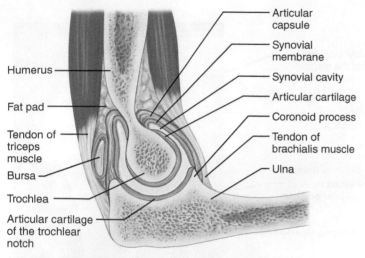

Articular capsule
Synovial membrane
Synovial cavity
Articular cartilage
Coronoid process
Tendon of brachialis muscle
Ulna
Humerus
Fat pad
Tendon of triceps muscle
Bursa
Trochlea
Articular cartilage of the trochlear notch

(a) Median sagittal section through right elbow (lateral view)

Humerus
Anular ligament
Radius
Lateral epicondyle
Articular capsule
Radial collateral ligament
Olecranon
Ulna

(b) Lateral view of right elbow joint

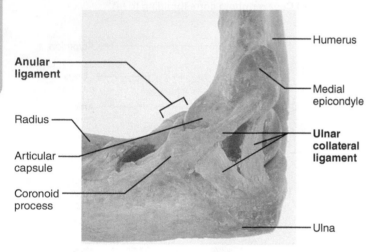

Humerus
Anular ligament
Medial epicondyle
Radius
Ulnar collateral ligament
Articular capsule
Coronoid process
Ulna

(c) Cadaver photo of medial view of right elbow

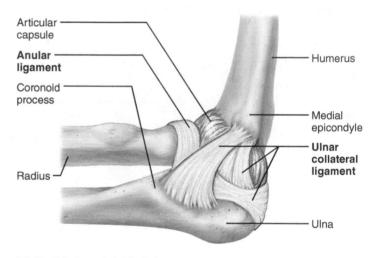

Articular capsule
Humerus
Anular ligament
Coronoid process
Medial epicondyle
Radius
Ulnar collateral ligament
Ulna

(d) Medial view of right elbow

Figure 8.11 The elbow joint.

Elbow Joint

Our upper limbs are flexible extensions that permit us to reach out and manipulate things in our environment. Besides the shoulder joint, the most prominent of the upper limb joints is the elbow. The elbow joint provides a stable and smoothly operating hinge that allows flexion and extension only **(Figure 8.11)**. Within the joint, both the radius and ulna articulate with the condyles of the humerus, but it is the close gripping of the trochlea by the ulna's trochlear notch that forms the "hinge" and stabilizes this joint (Figure 8.11a). A relatively lax articular capsule extends inferiorly from the humerus to the ulna and radius, and to the **anular ligament** (an′u-lar) surrounding the head of the radius (Figure 8.11b, c).

Anteriorly and posteriorly, the articular capsule is thin and allows substantial freedom for elbow flexion and extension. However, side-to-side movements are restricted by two strong capsular ligaments: the **ulnar collateral ligament** medially, and the **radial collateral ligament**, a triangular ligament on the lateral side (Figure 8.11b, c, and d). Additionally, tendons of several arm muscles, such as the biceps and triceps, cross the elbow joint and provide security.

The radius is a passive "onlooker" in the angular elbow movements. However, its head rotates within the anular ligament during supination and pronation of the forearm.

Hip Joint

The **hip** (coxal) **joint**, like the shoulder joint, is a ball-and-socket joint. It has a good range of motion, but not nearly as wide as the shoulder's range. Movements occur in all possible planes but are limited by the joint's strong ligaments and its deep socket.

The hip joint is formed by the articulation of the spherical head of the femur with the deeply cupped acetabulum of the hip bone **(Figure 8.12)**. The depth of the acetabulum is enhanced by a circular rim of fibrocartilage called the **acetabular labrum** (as″ĕ-tab′u-lar) (Figure 8.12a, b). The labrum's diameter is less than that of the head of the femur, and these articular surfaces fit snugly together, so hip joint dislocations are rare.

The thick articular capsule extends from the rim of the acetabulum to the neck of the femur and completely encloses the joint. Several strong ligaments reinforce the capsule of the hip joint.

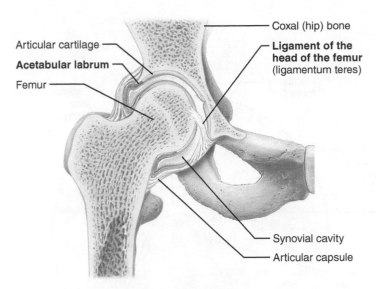

(a) Frontal section through the right hip joint

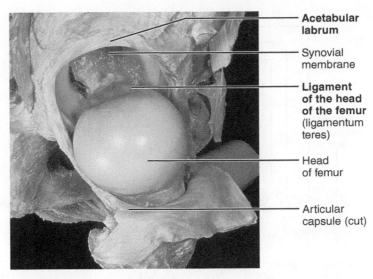

(b) Photo of the interior of the hip joint, lateral view

(c) Posterior view of right hip joint, capsule in place

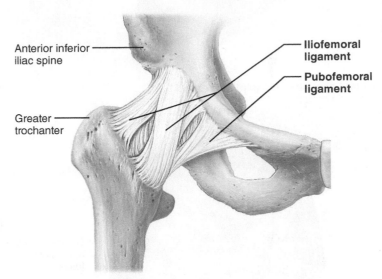

(d) Anterior view of right hip joint, capsule in place

Figure 8.12 The hip joint.

These include the **iliofemoral ligament** (il″e-o-fem′o-ral), a strong V-shaped ligament anteriorly; the **pubofemoral ligament** (pu″bo-fem′o-ral), a triangular thickening of the inferior part of the capsule; and the **ischiofemoral ligament** (is″ke-o-fem′o-ral), a spiraling posterior ligament (Figure 8.12c, d). These ligaments are arranged in such a way that they "screw" the femur head into the acetabulum when a person stands up straight, thereby providing more stability.

The **ligament of the head of the femur**, also called the *ligamentum teres*, is a flat intracapsular band that runs from the femur head to the lower lip of the acetabulum (Figure 8.12a, b). This ligament is slack during most hip movements, so it is not important in stabilizing the joint. In fact, its mechanical function (if any) is unclear, but it does contain an artery that helps supply the head of the femur. Damage to this artery may lead to severe arthritis of the hip joint.

Muscle tendons that cross the joint and the bulky hip and thigh muscles that surround it contribute to its stability and strength. In this joint, however, stability comes chiefly from the deep socket that securely encloses the femoral head and the strong capsular ligaments.

Temporomandibular Joint

The **temporomandibular joint** (TMJ), or jaw joint, is a modified hinge joint. It lies just anterior to the ear **(Figure 8.13)**. At this joint, the condylar process of the mandible articulates with the inferior surface of the squamous part of the temporal bone. The mandible's condylar process is egg shaped, whereas the articular surface of the temporal bone has a more complex shape. Posteriorly, it forms the concave **mandibular fossa**; anteriorly it forms a dense knob called the **articular tubercle**. The lateral aspect of the loose articular capsule that encloses the joint is thickened into a **lateral ligament**. Within the capsule, an articular disc divides the synovial cavity into superior and inferior compartments (Figure 8.13a, b).

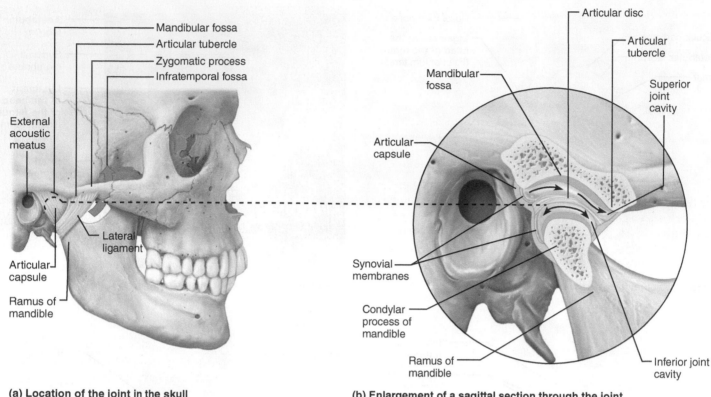

(a) Location of the joint in the skull

(b) Enlargement of a sagittal section through the joint

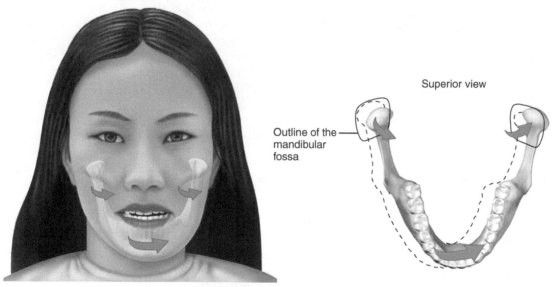

(c) Lateral excursion: lateral (side-to-side) movements of the mandible

Figure 8.13 The temporomandibular (jaw) joint. In **(b)**, note that the two parts of the joint cavity allow different movements, indicated by arrows. The inferior compartment of the joint cavity allows the condylar process of the mandible to rotate in opening and closing the mouth. The superior compartment lets the condylar process move forward to brace against the articular tubercle when the mouth opens wide, and also allows lateral excursion of this joint **(c)**.

Two distinct kinds of movement occur at the TMJ (Figure 8.13c). First, the concave inferior disc surface receives the condylar process of the mandible and allows the familiar hingelike movement of depressing and elevating the mandible while opening and closing the mouth. Second, the superior disc surface glides anteriorly along with the condylar process when the mouth is opened wide. This anterior movement braces the condylar process against the articular tubercle, so that the mandible is not forced through the thin roof of the mandibular fossa when one bites hard foods such as nuts or hard candies. The superior compartment also allows this joint to glide from side to side. As the posterior teeth are drawn into occlusion during grinding, the mandible moves with a side-to-side movement called *lateral excursion* (Figure 8.13c). This lateral jaw movement is unique to mammals and it is readily apparent in horses and cows as they chew.

Homeostatic Imbalance 8.2

Because of its shallow socket, the TMJ is the most easily dislocated joint in the body. Even a deep yawn can dislocate it. This joint almost always dislocates anteriorly, the condylar process of the mandible ending up in a skull region called the *infratemporal fossa* (Figure 8.13a). In such cases, the mouth remains wide open. To realign a dislocated TMJ, the physician places his or her thumbs in the patient's mouth between the lower molars and the cheeks, and then pushes the mandible inferiorly and posteriorly.

At least 5% of Americans suffer from painful temporomandibular disorders, the most common symptoms of which are pain in the ear and face, tenderness of the jaw muscles, popping sounds when the mouth opens, and joint stiffness. Usually caused by painful spasms of the chewing muscles, TMJ disorders often afflict people who grind their teeth; however, it can also result from jaw trauma or from poor occlusion of the teeth. Treatment usually focuses on getting the jaw muscles to relax by using massage, applying moist heat or ice, muscle-relaxant drugs, and adopting stress reduction techniques. For tooth grinders, use of a bite plate during sleep is generally recommended. ✚

☑ Check Your Understanding

11. Of the five joints studied in more detail—hip, shoulder, elbow, knee, and temporomandibular—which two have menisci? Which act mainly as a uniaxial hinge? Which depend mainly on muscles and their tendons for stability?

For answers, see Appendix H.

Homeostatic Imbalances of Joints

✓ Name the most common joint injuries and discuss the symptoms and problems associated with each.

✓ Compare and contrast the common types of arthritis.

✓ Describe the cause and consequences of Lyme disease.

Few of us pay attention to our joints unless something goes wrong with them. Although remarkably strong, joints are more likely to be injured by forces the bony skeleton can withstand. This is the price of our flexibility. Joint pain and malfunction can be caused by a number of factors besides traumatic injury, including inflammatory conditions and degenerative processes due to friction and wear.

Common Joint Injuries

For most of us, sprains and dislocations are the most common trauma-induced joint injuries, but cartilage injuries are equally threatening to athletes.

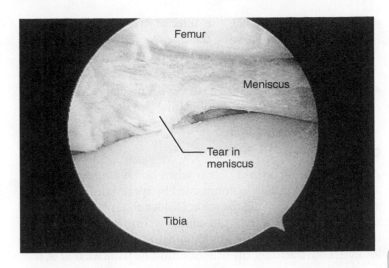

Figure 8.14 Arthroscopic photograph of a torn medial meniscus. (Courtesy of the author's tennis game.)

Cartilage Tears

Many aerobics devotees, encouraged to "feel the burn" during their workout, may feel the snap and pop of their overstressed cartilage instead. Although most cartilage injuries involve tearing of the knee menisci, tears and overuse damage to the articular cartilages of other joints is becoming increasingly common in competitive young athletes.

Cartilage tears typically occur when a meniscus is subjected to compression and shear stress at the same time. Cartilage is avascular and it rarely can obtain sufficient nourishment to repair itself, so it usually stays torn. Cartilage fragments (called loose bodies) can interfere with joint function by causing the joint to lock or bind, so most sports physicians recommend that the damaged cartilage be removed. Today, this can be done by **arthroscopic surgery** (ar-throskop'ik; "looking into joints"), a procedure that enables patients to be out of the hospital the same day. The arthroscope, a small instrument bearing a tiny lens and fiber-optic light source, enables the surgeon to view the joint interior, as in **Figure 8.14**. The surgeon can then repair a ligament, or remove cartilage fragments through one or more tiny slits, minimizing tissue damage and scarring. Removal of part of a meniscus does not severely impair knee joint mobility, but the joint is definitely less stable. Removal of the entire meniscus is an invitation to early onset of osteoarthritis in the joint. For younger patients a meniscal transplant may be an option to replace irreparably damaged cartilage. In the future, a tissue-engineered meniscus grown from your own stem cells may be implanted instead.

Sprains

In a **sprain**, the ligaments reinforcing a joint are stretched or torn. Common sites of sprains are the ankle, the knee, and the lumbar region of the spine. Partially torn ligaments will repair themselves, but they heal slowly because ligaments are so poorly vascularized. Sprains tend to be painful and immobilizing.

When ligaments are completely torn, there are three options:

- The torn ends of the ligament can be sewn together. This is difficult because trying to sew the hundreds of fibrous strands of a ligament together is like trying to sew two hairbrushes together.

- Certain ligaments, like the anterior cruciate ligament, are best repaired by replacing them with grafts. For example, a piece of tendon from a muscle can be attached to the articulating bones.

- For many ligaments, such as the knee's medial collateral ligament, we've come to realize that time and immobilization are just as effective as any surgical option.

Dislocations

A **dislocation (luxation)** occurs when bones are forced out of alignment. It is usually accompanied by sprains, inflammation, and difficulty in moving the joint. Dislocations may result from serious falls and are common contact sports injuries. Joints of the jaw, shoulders, fingers, and thumbs are most commonly dislocated. Like fractures, dislocations must be *reduced*; that is, the bone ends must be returned to their proper positions by a physician. *Subluxation* is a partial dislocation of a joint.

Repeat dislocations of the same joint are common because the initial dislocation stretches the joint capsule and ligaments. The resulting loose capsule provides poor reinforcement for the joint.

Inflammatory and Degenerative Conditions

Inflammatory conditions that affect joints include bursitis and tendonitis, various forms of arthritis, and Lyme disease.

Bursitis and Tendonitis

Bursitis is inflammation of a bursa and is usually caused by a blow or friction. Falling on one's knee may result in a painful bursitis of the prepatellar bursa, known as *housemaid's knee* or *water on the knee*. Prolonged leaning on one's elbows may damage the bursa close to the olecranon, producing *student's elbow*, or *olecranon bursitis*. Severe cases are treated by injecting anti-inflammatory drugs into the bursa. If excessive fluid accumulates, removing some fluid by needle aspiration may relieve the pressure.

Tendonitis is inflammation of tendon sheaths, typically caused by overuse. Its symptoms (pain and swelling) and treatment (rest, ice, and anti-inflammatory drugs) mirror those of bursitis.

Arthritis

The term **arthritis** describes over 100 different types of inflammatory or degenerative diseases that damage the joints. In all its forms, arthritis is the most widespread crippling disease in North America. One in five of us suffers its ravages. To a greater or lesser degree, all forms of arthritis have the same initial symptoms: pain, stiffness, and swelling of the joint.

Acute forms of arthritis usually result from bacterial invasion and are treated with antibiotics. Chronic forms of arthritis include osteoarthritis, rheumatoid arthritis, and gouty arthritis.

Osteoarthritis   Osteoarthritis (OA) is the most common chronic arthritis. A chronic (long-term) degenerative condition, OA is often called "wear-and-tear arthritis." OA is most prevalent in the aged and is probably related to the normal aging process (although it is seen occasionally in younger people and some forms have a genetic basis). More women than men are affected, but nearly half of us will develop this condition by the age of 85.

Current theory holds that normal joint use prompts the release of (metalloproteinase) enzymes that break down articular cartilage, especially its collagen fibrils. In healthy individuals, this damaged cartilage is eventually replaced, but in people with OA, more cartilage is destroyed than replaced. Although its specific cause is unknown, OA may reflect the cumulative effects of years of compression and abrasion acting at joint surfaces, causing excessive amounts of the cartilage-destroying enzymes to be released. The result is softened, roughened, pitted, and eroded articular cartilages. Because this process occurs most where an uneven orientation of forces cause extensive microdamage, badly aligned or overworked joints are likely to develop OA.

As the disease progresses, the exposed bone tissue thickens and forms bony spurs (osteophytes) that enlarge the bone ends and may restrict joint movement. Patients complain of stiffness on arising that lessens somewhat with activity. The affected joints may make a crunching noise, called *crepitus* (krep'ĭ-tus), as they move and the roughened articular surfaces rub together. The joints most often affected are those of the cervical and lumbar spine and the fingers, knuckles, knees, and hips.

The course of osteoarthritis is usually slow and irreversible. In many cases, its symptoms are controllable with a mild pain reliever like aspirin or acetaminophen, along with moderate activity to keep the joints mobile. Rubbing a hot-pepper substance called capsaicin on the skin over the painful joints helps lessen the pain of OA. Glucosamine and chondroitin sulfate, nutritional supplements consisting of macromolecules normally present in cartilage, have been widely used by arthritis sufferers. However, several recent studies suggest that these supplements are no more effective than placebos. Osteoarthritis is rarely crippling, but it can be, particularly when the hip or knee joints are involved.

Rheumatoid Arthritis   Rheumatoid arthritis (RA) (roo'mahtoid) is a chronic inflammatory disorder with an insidious onset. Though it usually arises between the ages of 30 and 50, it may occur at any age. It affects three times as many women as men. While not as common as osteoarthritis, rheumatoid arthritis affects millions, about 1% of all people.

In the early stages of RA, joint tenderness and stiffness are common. Many joints, particularly the small joints of the fingers, wrists, ankles, and feet, are afflicted at the same time and bilaterally. For example, if the right elbow is affected, most likely the left elbow is also affected. The course of RA is variable and marked by flare-ups (exacerbations) and remissions (*rheumat* =susceptible to change). Along with pain and swelling, its manifestations may include anemia, osteoporosis, muscle weakness, and cardiovascular problems.

RA is an *autoimmune disease*—a disorder in which the body's immune system attacks its own tissues. The initial trigger for this reaction is unknown, but various bacteria and viruses have been suspect. Perhaps these microorganisms bear molecules similar to some naturally present in the joints (possibly glycosaminoglycans, which are complex carbohydrates found in cartilage, joint fluid, and other connective tissues), and the immune system, once activated, attempts to destroy both.

RA begins with inflammation of the synovial membrane (*synovitis*) of the affected joints. Inflammatory cells (lymphocytes, macrophages, and others) migrate into the joint cavity from the blood and unleash a deluge of inflammatory chemicals

Joints: From Knights in Shining Armor to Bionic Humans

The technology for fashioning joints in medieval suits of armor developed over centuries. The technology for creating the prostheses (artificial joints) used in medicine today developed, in relative terms, in a flash—less than 60 years. Unlike the joints in medieval armor, which was worn outside the body, today's artificial joints must function inside the body. The history of joint prostheses dates to the 1940s and 1950s, when World War II and the Korean War left large numbers of wounded who needed artificial limbs. Today, nearly 1 million Americans per year receive a total joint replacement, mostly because of the destructive effects of osteoarthritis or rheumatoid arthritis.

To produce durable, mobile joints requires substances that are strong, nontoxic, and resistant to the corrosive effects of organic acids in blood. In 1963, Sir John Charnley, an English orthopedic surgeon, revolutionized the therapy of arthritic hips with an artificial hip design that is still in use today. His device consisted of a metal ball on a stem and a cup-shaped polyethylene plastic socket anchored to the pelvis by methyl methacrylate cement. This cement proved to be exceptionally strong and relatively problem free. Hip prostheses were followed by knee prostheses, but not until 10 years later did smoothly operating total knee joint replacements become a reality. Today, the metal parts of the prostheses are strong cobalt and titanium alloys, and the number of knee replacements equals the number of hip replacements.

Replacements are now available for many other joints, including fingers, elbows, and shoulders. Total hip and knee replacements last about 10 to 15 years in elderly patients who do not excessively stress the joint. Most such operations are done to reduce pain and restore about 80% of original joint function.

Replacement joints are not yet strong or durable enough for young, active people, but making them so is a major goal. Another problem is that the prostheses work loose over time, so researchers are seeking to enhance the fit between implant and bone. One solution is to strengthen the cement that

binds them (simply eliminating air bubbles from the cement increases its durability). Another solution is to use a cementless prosthesis, which allows the bone to grow into its surface, fixing it in place. In order for this to happen, a precise fit in the prosthesis and the bone must be achieved, something at which surgical robots such as ROBODOC excel.

Dramatic changes are also occurring in the way artificial joints are made. CAD/CAM (computer-aided design and computer-aided manufacturing) techniques have significantly reduced the time and cost of creating individualized joints. Fed the patient's X rays and medical information, the computer draws from a database of hundreds of normal joints and generates possible designs and modifications for a prosthesis. Once the best design is selected, the computer produces a program to direct the machines that make the prosthesis.

Joint replacement therapy is coming of age, but equally exciting are techniques that call on the ability of the patient's own tissues to regenerate.

- Bone marrow stimulation: Small holes poked through to the bone marrow allow mesenchymal stem cells from the

bone marrow to migrate into the joint and produce new cartilage.

- Osteochondral grafting: Healthy bone and cartilage are removed from one part of the body and transplanted to the injured joint.

- Autologous chondrocyte implantation: Healthy chondrocytes are removed from the body and seeded onto a supporting matrix of tissue-engineered collagen. When subjected to mechanical pressure in the lab, the cells produce new cartilage, which is then implanted.

- Mesenchymal stem cell regeneration: Undifferentiated mesenchymal cells are removed from bone marrow and placed in a gel, which is packed into an area of eroded cartilage.

These techniques offer hope for younger patients, since they could stave off the need for a joint prosthesis for several years.

And so, through the centuries, the focus has shifted from jointed armor to artificial joints that can be put inside the body to restore lost function. Modern technology has accomplished what the armor designers of the Middle Ages never dreamed of.

A hip prosthesis.

X ray of right knee showing total knee replacement prosthesis (co-designed by Kenneth Gustke, M.D., of Florida Orthopedic Institute).

Figure 8.15 A hand deformed by rheumatoid arthritis. Inflammation has enlarged the synovial joints.

that destroy body tissues when released inappropriately in large amounts as in RA. Synovial fluid accumulates, causing joint swelling, and in time, the inflamed synovial membrane thickens into a **pannus** ("rag"), an abnormal tissue that clings to the articular cartilages. The pannus erodes the cartilage (and sometimes the underlying bone) and eventually scar tissue forms and connects the bone ends. Later this scar tissue ossifies and the bone ends fuse together, immobilizing the joint. This end condition, called ankylosis (ang″kĭ-lo′sis; "stiff condition"), often produces bent, deformed fingers **(Figure 8.15)**. Not all cases of RA progress to the severely crippling ankylosis stage, but all cases do involve restriction of joint movement and extreme pain.

A wonder drug for RA sufferers is still undiscovered. The goal of current RA treatment is to go beyond simply alleviating the symptoms and instead to disrupt the relentless destruction of the joints by the autoimmune processes. Steroidal and nonsteroidal anti-inflammatory drugs decrease pain and inflammation, increasing joint mobility. More powerful immune suppressants (such as methotrexate) act to slow the autoimmune reaction. Several biologic agents are available to block the action of inflammatory chemicals. An important target of many of these agents is an inflammatory chemical called *tumor necrosis factor*, an important contributor to destruction of cartilage. Together, these drugs can dramatically slow the course of RA. As a last resort, replacing the joint with a joint prosthesis (artificial joint), may be an option to restore function (see *A Closer Look*, p. 271). Indeed, some RA sufferers have over a dozen artificial joints.

Gouty Arthritis Uric acid, a normal waste product of nucleic acid metabolism, is ordinarily excreted in urine without any problems. However, when blood levels of uric acid rise excessively (due to its excessive production or slow excretion), it may be deposited as needle-shaped urate crystals in the soft tissues of joints. An inflammatory response follows, leading to an agonizingly painful attack of **gouty arthritis** (gow′te), or **gout**. The initial attack typically affects one joint, often at the base of the great toe.

Gout is far more common in men than in women because men naturally have higher blood levels of uric acid (perhaps because estrogens increase the rate of its excretion). Because gout seems to run in families, genetic factors are definitely implicated.

Untreated gout can be very destructive; the articulating bone ends fuse and immobilize the joint. Fortunately, several drugs (colchicine, nonsteroidal anti-inflammatory drugs, glucocorticoids, and others) that terminate or prevent gout attacks are available. Patients are advised to drink plenty of water and to avoid alcohol excess (which promotes uric acid overproduction), and foods high in purine-containing nucleic acids, such as liver, kidneys, and sardines.

Lyme Disease

Lyme disease is an inflammatory disease caused by spirochete bacteria transmitted by the bite of ticks that live on mice and deer. It often results in joint pain and arthritis, especially in the knees, and is characterized by a skin rash, flu-like symptoms, and foggy thinking. If untreated, neurological disorders and irregular heartbeat may ensue.

Because symptoms vary from person to person, the disease is hard to diagnose. Antibiotic therapy is the usual treatment, but it takes a long time to kill the infecting bacteria.

☑ **Check Your Understanding**

12. What does the term "arthritis" mean?
13. How would you determine by looking at someone suffering from arthritis if he or she has OA or RA?
14. What is the cause of Lyme disease?

For answers, see Appendix H.

Developmental Aspects of Joints

✓ Discuss factors that promote or disturb joint homeostasis.

As bones form from mesenchyme in the embryo, the joints develop in parallel. By week 8, the synovial joints resemble adult joints in form and arrangement, and synovial fluid is being secreted. During childhood, a joint's size, shape, and flexibility are modified by use. Active joints have thicker capsules and ligaments, and larger bony supports.

Injuries aside, relatively few interferences with joint function occur until late middle age. Eventually advancing years take their toll and ligaments and tendons shorten and weaken. The intervertebral discs become more likely to herniate, and osteoarthritis rears its ugly head. Many people have osteoarthritis by the time they are in their 70s. The middle years also see an increased incidence of rheumatoid arthritis.

Exercise that coaxes joints through their full range of motion, such as regular stretching and aerobics, is the key to postponing the immobilizing effects of aging on ligaments and tendons, to keeping cartilages well nourished, and to strengthening the muscles that stabilize the joints. The key word for exercising is "prudently," because excessive or abusive use of the joints guarantees early onset of osteoarthritis. The buoyancy of water relieves much of the stress on weight-bearing joints, and people who swim or exercise in a pool often retain good joint function as long as they live. As with so many medical problems, it is easier to prevent joint problems than to cure or correct them.

☑ **Check Your Understanding**

15. What is the effect of regular exercise on joint health and structure?

For answers, see Appendix H.

The importance of joints is obvious: The skeleton's ability to protect other organs and to move smoothly reflects their presence. Now that we are familiar with joint structure and with the movements that joints allow, we are ready to consider how the muscles attached to the skeleton cause body movements by acting across its joints.

Chapter Summary

 For more chapter study tools, go to the Study Area of MasteringA&P at **www.masteringaandp.com**.
There you will find:

- Interactive Physiology **iP**
- A&PFlix **A&PFlix**
- Practice Anatomy Lab **PAL**
- PhysioEx **PEx**
- Videos, Practice Quizzes and Tests, MP3 Tutor Sessions, Case Studies, and much more!

1. Joints, or articulations, are sites where bones meet. Their functions are to hold bones together and to allow various degrees of skeletal movement.

Classification of Joints (pp. 249–250)

1. Joints are classified structurally as fibrous, cartilaginous, or synovial. They are classed functionally as synarthrotic, amphiarthrotic, or diarthrotic.

Fibrous Joints (pp. 250–251)

1. Fibrous joints occur where bones are connected by fibrous tissue; no joint cavity is present. Nearly all fibrous joints are synarthrotic.
2. **Sutures/syndesmoses/gomphoses.** The major types of fibrous joints are sutures, syndesmoses, and gomphoses.

Cartilaginous Joints (pp. 251–252)

1. In cartilaginous joints, the bones are united by cartilage; no joint cavity is present.
2. **Synchondroses/symphyses.** Cartilaginous joints include synchondroses and symphyses. Synchondroses are synarthrotic; all symphyses are amphiarthrotic.

Synovial Joints (pp. 252–269)

1. Most body joints are synovial joints, all of which are diarthrotic.

General Structure (pp. 252–253)

2. All synovial joints have a joint cavity enclosed by a fibrous layer lined with synovial membrane and reinforced by ligaments; articulating bone ends covered with articular cartilage; and synovial fluid in the joint cavity. Some (e.g., the knee) contain fibrocartilage discs that absorb shock.

Bursae and Tendon Sheaths (p. 253)

3. Bursae are fibrous sacs lined with synovial membrane and containing synovial fluid. Tendon sheaths are similar to bursae but are cylindrical structures that surround muscle tendons. Both allow adjacent structures to move smoothly over one another.

Factors Influencing the Stability of Synovial Joints (pp. 255–256)

4. Articular surfaces providing the most stability have large surfaces and deep sockets and fit snugly together.
5. Ligaments prevent undesirable movements and reinforce the joint.
6. The tone of muscles whose tendons cross the joint is the most important stabilizing factor in many joints.

Movements Allowed by Synovial Joints (pp. 256–258)

7. When a skeletal muscle contracts, the insertion (movable attachment) moves toward the origin (immovable attachment).
8. Synovial joints differ in their range of motion. Motion may be nonaxial (gliding), uniaxial (in one plane), biaxial (in two planes), or multiaxial (in all three planes).
9. Three common types of movements can occur when muscles contract across joints: (a) gliding movements, (b) angular movements (which include flexion, extension, abduction, adduction, and circumduction), and (c) rotation.
10. Special movements include supination and pronation, inversion and eversion, protraction and retraction, elevation and depression, opposition, dorsiflexion and plantar flexion.

Types of Synovial Joints (p. 258)

11. The six major categories of synovial joints are plane joints (nonaxial movement), hinge joints (uniaxial), pivot joints (uniaxial, rotation permitted), condylar joints (biaxial with angular movements in two planes), saddle joints (biaxial, like condylar joints, but with freer movement), and ball-and-socket joints (multiaxial and rotational movement).

Selected Synovial Joints (pp. 262–269)

12. The knee joint is the largest joint in the body. It is a hinge joint formed by the articulation of the tibial and femoral condyles (and anteriorly by the patella and patellar surface of the femur). Extension, flexion, and (some) rotation are allowed. Its articular surfaces are shallow and condylar. C-shaped menisci deepen the articular surfaces. The joint cavity is enclosed by a capsule only on the sides and posterior aspect. Several ligaments help prevent displacement of the joint surfaces. Muscle tone of the quadriceps and semimembranosus muscles is important in knee stability.
13. The shoulder joint is a ball-and-socket joint formed by the glenoid cavity of the scapula and the humeral head. The most freely movable joint of the body, it allows all angular and rotational movements. Its articular surfaces are shallow. Its capsule is lax and poorly reinforced by ligaments. The tendons of the biceps brachii and rotator cuff muscles help to stabilize it.
14. The elbow is a hinge joint in which the ulna (and radius) articulates with the humerus, allowing flexion and extension. Its articular surfaces are highly complementary and are the most important factor contributing to joint stability.
15. The hip joint is a ball-and-socket joint formed by the acetabulum of the hip bone and the femoral head. It is highly adapted for

8

weight bearing. Its articular surfaces are deep and secure. Its capsule is heavy and strongly reinforced by ligaments.

16. The temporomandibular joint is formed by (1) the condylar process of the mandible and (2) the mandibular fossa and articular tubercle of the temporal bone. This joint allows both a hingelike opening and closing of the mouth and an anterior gliding of the mandible. It often dislocates anteriorly and exhibits a number of TMJ disorders.

Homeostatic Imbalances of Joints (pp. 269–272)

Common Joint Injuries (pp. 269–270)

1. Cartilage injuries, particularly of the knee, are common in contact sports and may result from excessive compression and shear stress. The avascular cartilage is unable to repair itself.
2. Sprains involve stretching or tearing of joint ligaments. Because ligaments are poorly vascularized, healing is slow.
3. Dislocations involve displacement of the articular surfaces of bones. They must be reduced.

Inflammatory and Degenerative Conditions (pp. 270–272)

4. Bursitis and tendonitis are inflammations of a bursa and a tendon sheath, respectively.

5. Arthritis is joint inflammation or degeneration accompanied by stiffness, pain, and swelling. Acute forms generally result from bacterial infection. Chronic forms include osteoarthritis, rheumatoid arthritis, and gouty arthritis.
6. Osteoarthritis is a degenerative condition most common in the aged. Spine, knees, hips, knuckles, and fingers are most affected.
7. Rheumatoid arthritis, the most crippling arthritis, is an autoimmune disease involving severe inflammation of the joints.
8. Gouty arthritis, or gout, is joint inflammation caused by the deposit of urate salts in soft joint tissues.
9. Lyme disease is an infectious disease caused by the bite of a tick infected with spirochete bacteria.

Developmental Aspects of Joints (pp. 272–273)

1. Joints form from mesenchyme and in tandem with bone development in the embryo.
2. Excluding traumatic injury, joints usually function well until late middle age, at which time symptoms of connective tissue stiffening and osteoarthritis begin to appear. Prudent exercise delays these effects, whereas excessive exercise promotes the early onset of arthritis.

Review Questions

Multiple Choice/Matching

(Some questions have more than one correct answer. Select the best answer or answers from the choices given.)

1. Match the key terms to the appropriate descriptions.

   Key: (a) fibrous joints   (b) cartilaginous joints
         (c) synovial joints

   _____ (1) exhibit a joint cavity
   _____ (2) types are sutures and syndesmoses
   _____ (3) bones connected by collagen fibers
   _____ (4) types include synchondroses and symphyses
   _____ (5) all are diarthrotic
   _____ (6) many are amphiarthrotic
   _____ (7) bones connected by a disc of hyaline cartilage or fibrocartilage
   _____ (8) nearly all are synarthrotic
   _____ (9) shoulder, hip, jaw, and elbow joints

2. Freely movable joints are (a) synarthroses, (b) diarthroses, (c) amphiarthroses.
3. Anatomical characteristics shared by all synovial joints include all except (a) articular cartilage, (b) a joint cavity, (c) an articular capsule, (d) presence of fibrocartilage.
4. Factors that influence the stability of a synovial joint include (a) shape of articular surfaces, (b) presence of strong reinforcing ligaments, (c) tone of surrounding muscles, (d) all of these.
5. The description "Articular surfaces deep and secure; capsule heavily reinforced by ligaments and muscle tendons; extremely stable joint" best describes (a) the elbow joint, (b) the hip joint, (c) the knee joint, (d) the shoulder joint.
6. Ankylosis means (a) twisting of the ankle, (b) tearing of ligaments, (c) displacement of a bone, (d) immobility of a joint due to fusion of its articular surfaces.
7. An autoimmune disorder in which joints are affected bilaterally and which involves pannus formation and gradual joint immobilization is (a) bursitis, (b) gout, (c) osteoarthritis, (d) rheumatoid arthritis.

Short Answer Essay Questions

8. Define joint.
9. Discuss the relative value (to body homeostasis) of immovable, slightly movable, and freely movable joints.
10. Compare the structure, function, and common body locations of bursae and tendon sheaths.
11. Joint movements may be nonaxial, uniaxial, biaxial, or multiaxial. Define what each of these terms means.
12. Compare and contrast the paired movements of flexion and extension with adduction and abduction.
13. How does rotation differ from circumduction?
14. Name two types of uniaxial, biaxial, and multiaxial joints.
15. What is the specific role of the menisci of the knee? Of the anterior and posterior cruciate ligaments?
16. The knee has been called "a beauty and a beast." Provide several reasons that might explain the negative (beast) part of this description.
17. Why are sprains and cartilage injuries a particular problem?
18. List the functions of the following elements of a synovial joint: fibrous layer of the capsule, synovial fluid, articular cartilage.

Critical Thinking and Clinical Application Questions

1. Sophie worked cleaning homes for 30 years so she could send her two children to college. Several times, she had been forced to call her employers to tell them she could not come in to work because one of her kneecaps was swollen and painful. What is Sophie's condition, and what probably caused it?

2. As Harry was running down the road, he tripped and his left ankle twisted violently to the side. When he picked himself up, he was unable to put any weight on that ankle. The diagnosis was severe dislocation and sprains of the left ankle. The orthopedic surgeon stated that she would perform a closed reduction of the dislocation and attempt ligament repair by using arthroscopy. (a) Is the ankle joint normally a stable joint? (b) What does its stability depend on? (c) What is a closed reduction? (d) Why is ligament repair necessary? (e) What does arthroscopy entail? (f) How will the use of this procedure minimize Harry's recuperation time (and suffering)?

3. Mrs. Bell, a 45-year-old woman, appeared at her physician's office complaining of unbearable pain in the interphalangeal joint of her right great toe. The joint was red and swollen. When asked about previous episodes, she recalled a similar attack two years earlier that disappeared as suddenly as it had come. Her diagnosis was arthritis. (a) What type? (b) What is the precipitating cause of this particular type of arthritis?

4. Grace heard on the evening TV news that the deer population in her state had been increasing rapidly in the past few years and it was common knowledge that deer walked the streets at night. After the program, she suddenly exclaimed, "So that's why those three boys in my son's class got Lyme disease last year." Explain what she meant by that comment.

5. Tony Bowers, an exhausted biology student, was attending a lecture. After 30 minutes or so, he lost interest and began to doze. As the lecture ended, the hubbub aroused him and he let go with a tremendous yawn. To his great distress, he couldn't close his mouth—his lower jaw was "stuck" open. What do you think had happened?

AT THE CLINIC

Related Clinical Terms

Ankylosing spondylitis (ang′kĭ-lōz″ing spon″dĭ-li′tis; *ankyl* = crooked, bent; *spondyl* =vertebra) A variant of rheumatoid arthritis that chiefly affects males; it usually begins in the sacroiliac joints and progresses superiorly along the spine. The vertebrae become interconnected by fibrous tissue, causing the spine to become rigid ("poker back").

Arthrology (ar-throl′o-je; *logos* =study) The study of joints.

Arthroplasty ("joint reforming") Replacing a diseased joint with an artificial joint.

Chondromalacia patellae (kon-dro-mal-a′sĭ-ah; "softening of cartilage by the patella") Damage and softening of the articular cartilages on the posterior patellar surface and the anterior surface of the distal femur; most often seen in adolescent athletes. Produces a sharp pain in the knee when the leg is extended (in climbing stairs, for example). May result when the quadriceps femoris, the main group of muscles on the anterior thigh, pulls unevenly on the patella, persistently rubbing it against the femur in the knee joint; often corrected by exercises that strengthen weakened parts of the quadriceps muscles.

Rheumatism A term used by laypeople to indicate disease involving muscle or joint pain; consequently may be used to apply to arthritis, bursitis, etc.

Synovitis (sin″o-vi′tis) Inflammation of the synovial membrane of a joint. Caused by injury, infection, or arthritis. Excess synovial fluid accumulates in the joint cavity, a condition called *effusion* that causes the joint to swell, limiting joint movement.

Case Study — Joints

In the previous chapter, you met Kayla Tanner, a 45-year-old mother of four who suffered a dislocated right hip in the bus accident on Route 91. Prior to the closed reduction, the doctors noted that her right thigh was flexed at the hip, adducted, and medially rotated. After the reduction, the hip was put through a gentle range of motion (ROM) to assess the joint. A widened joint space in the postreduction X ray showed that the reduction was not complete, but no bone fragments were visible in the joint space. Mrs. Tanner was scheduled for immediate surgery.

The surgeons discovered that the acetabular labrum was detached from the rim of the acetabulum and was lying deep within the joint space. The detached portion of the labrum was excised, and the hip was surgically reduced. During the early healing phase (first two weeks), Mrs. Tanner was kept in traction with the hip abducted.

1. Joints can be classified by structure and by function. How would you structurally and functionally classify the joint involved in the injury in this case?

2. Name the six distinguishing features that define the structural classification of the joint involved in this injury.

3. The doctors noted that there were no bone fragments in the joint space. What is normally found in this space?

4. Surgeons had to remove a portion of Mrs. Tanner's acetabular labrum. What is this structure and what function does it supply at this joint?

5. The doctors noted that Mrs. Tanner's thigh was flexed at the hip, adducted, and medially rotated. Describe what this means in terms of the position of her leg.

6. Hip dislocations can be classified as anterior or posterior depending on which direction the head of the femur is facing after it dislocates. Based on the description you provided in question 5, which type of dislocation did Mrs. Tanner suffer?

7. In order to assess the joint as part of Mrs. Tanner's rehabilitation, clinicians would want to assess all of the movements that normally occur at the hip. List all the movements that the clinicians will need to assess.

(Answers in Appendix H)

Muscles and Muscle Tissue

B ecause flexing muscles look like mice scurrying beneath the skin, some scientist long ago dubbed them *muscles*, from the Latin *mus* meaning "little mouse." Indeed, we tend to think of the rippling muscles of professional boxers or weight lifters when we hear the word *muscle*. But muscle is also the dominant tissue in the heart and in the walls of other hollow organs. In all its forms, muscle tissue makes up nearly half the body's mass.

Muscles are distinguished by their ability to transform chemical energy (ATP) into directed mechanical energy. In so doing, they become capable of exerting force.

Overview of Muscle Tissues

✓ Compare and contrast the three basic types of muscle tissue.

✓ List four important functions of muscle tissue.

Types of Muscle Tissue

Chapter 4 introduced the three types of muscle tissue—*skeletal, cardiac,* and *smooth.* Now we are ready to describe each type in detail, but before we do, let's introduce some terminology.

- Skeletal and smooth muscle cells (but not cardiac muscle cells) are elongated, and for this reason, they are called **muscle fibers.**

- Whenever you see the prefixes **myo** or **mys** (both are word roots meaning "muscle") or **sarco** (flesh), the reference is to muscle. For example, the plasma membrane of muscle cells is called the *sarcolemma* (sar″ko-lem′ah), literally, "muscle" (sarco) "husk" (lemma), and muscle cell cytoplasm is called *sarcoplasm.*

Okay, let's get to it.

Skeletal Muscle

Skeletal muscle tissue is packaged into the *skeletal muscles,* organs that attach to and cover the bony skeleton. Skeletal muscle fibers are the longest muscle cells and have obvious stripes called *striations* (see Figure 4.9a, p. 138). Although it is often activated by reflexes, skeletal muscle is called **voluntary muscle** because it is the only type subject to conscious control.

- When you think of skeletal muscle tissue, the key words to keep in mind are *skeletal, striated,* and *voluntary.*

Skeletal muscle is responsible for overall body mobility. It can contract rapidly, but it tires easily and must rest after short periods of activity. Nevertheless, it can exert tremendous power, a fact revealed by reports of people lifting cars to save their loved ones. Skeletal muscle is also remarkably adaptable. For example, your forearm muscles can exert a force of a fraction of an ounce to pick up a paper clip—or a force of about 6 pounds to pick up this book!

Cardiac Muscle

Cardiac muscle tissue occurs only in the heart (the body's blood pump), where it constitutes the bulk of the heart walls. Like skeletal muscle cells, cardiac muscle cells are striated (see Figure 4.9b, p. 139), but cardiac muscle is not voluntary. Indeed, it can and does contract without being stimulated by the nervous system. Most of us have no conscious control over how fast our heart beats.

- Key words to remember for cardiac muscle are *cardiac, striated,* and *involuntary.*

Cardiac muscle usually contracts at a fairly steady rate set by the heart's pacemaker, but neural controls allow the heart to speed up for brief periods, as when you race across the tennis court to make that overhead smash.

Smooth Muscle

Smooth muscle tissue is found in the walls of hollow visceral organs, such as the stomach, urinary bladder, and respiratory passages. Its role is to force fluids and other substances through internal body channels. Like skeletal muscle, smooth muscle consists of elongated cells, but smooth muscle has no striations (see Figure 4.9c, p. 139).

Like cardiac muscle, smooth muscle is not subject to voluntary control. Its contractions are slow and sustained.

- We can describe smooth muscle tissue as *visceral, nonstriated,* and *involuntary.*

Special Characteristics of Muscle Tissue

What enables muscle tissue to perform its duties? Four special characteristics are key.

Excitability, also termed **responsiveness,** is the ability to receive and respond to a stimulus, that is, any change in the environment either inside or outside the body. In the case of muscle, the stimulus is usually a chemical—for example, a neurotransmitter released by a nerve cell, or a local change in pH. The response (sometimes separated out as an additional characteristic called conductivity) is to generate an electrical impulse that travels along the plasma membrane of the muscle cell and causes the cell to contract.

Contractility is the ability to shorten forcibly when adequately stimulated. This ability sets muscle apart from all other tissue types.

Extensibility is the ability to extend or stretch. Muscle cells shorten when contracting, but they can stretch, even beyond their resting length, when relaxed.

Elasticity is the ability of a muscle cell to recoil and resume its resting length after stretching.

Muscle Functions

Muscle performs at least four important functions for the body. It produces movement, maintains posture, stabilizes joints, generates heat, and more.

Producing Movement

Just about all movements of the human body and its parts result from muscle contraction. Skeletal muscles are responsible for all locomotion (moving from place to place) and manipulation. They enable you to respond quickly to changes in the external environment—for example, jump out of the way of a car, direct your eyes, and smile or frown.

Blood courses through your body because of the rhythmically beating cardiac muscle of your heart and the smooth muscle in the walls of your blood vessels, which helps maintain blood pressure. Smooth muscle in organs of the digestive, urinary, and reproductive tracts propels, or squeezes, substances (foodstuffs, urine, semen) through the organs and along the tract.

Maintaining Posture and Body Position

We are rarely aware of the skeletal muscles that maintain body posture. Yet these muscles function almost continuously, making one tiny adjustment after another to counteract the never-ending downward pull of gravity.

Stabilizing Joints

Even as muscles pull on bones to cause movement, they stabilize and strengthen the joints of the skeleton (Chapter 8).

Generating Heat

Muscles generate heat as they contract. This heat is vitally important in maintaining normal body temperature. Because skeletal muscle accounts for at least 40% of body mass, it is the muscle type most responsible for generating heat.

Additional Functions of Muscle

What else do muscles do? Skeletal muscles protect the more fragile internal organs (the viscera) by enclosing them. Smooth muscle forms valves to regulate the passage of substances through internal body openings, dilates and constricts the pupils of your eyes, and forms the arrector pili muscles attached to hair follicles.

◼ ◼ ◼

In this chapter, we examine the structure and function of skeletal muscle. Then we consider smooth muscle more briefly, largely by comparing it with skeletal muscle. We describe cardiac muscle in detail in Chapter 18, but for easy comparison, Table 9.3 on p. 310 summarizes the characteristics of all three muscle types.

☑ Check Your Understanding

1. When describing muscle, what does "striated" mean?
2. Harry is pondering an exam question that asks, "Which muscle type has elongated cells and is found in the walls of the urinary bladder?" How should he respond?

For answers, see Appendix H.

Skeletal Muscle

✓ Describe the gross structure of a skeletal muscle.

✓ Describe the microscopic structure and functional roles of the myofibrils, sarcoplasmic reticulum, and T tubules of skeletal muscle fibers.

✓ Describe the sliding filament model of muscle contraction.

For easy reference, Table 9.1 on p. 283 summarizes the levels of skeletal muscle organization, gross to microscopic, that we describe in the following sections.

Gross Anatomy of a Skeletal Muscle

Each **skeletal muscle** is a discrete organ, made up of several kinds of tissues. Skeletal muscle fibers predominate, but blood vessels, nerve fibers, and substantial amounts of connective tissue are also present. We can easily examine a skeletal muscle's shape and its attachments in the body without a microscope.

Nerve and Blood Supply

In general, one nerve, one artery, and one or more veins serve each muscle. These structures all enter or exit near the central part of the muscle and branch profusely through its connective tissue sheaths (described below). Unlike cells of cardiac and smooth muscle tissues, which can contract without nerve

stimulation, every skeletal muscle fiber is supplied with a nerve ending that controls its activity.

Skeletal muscle has a rich blood supply. This is understandable because contracting muscle fibers use huge amounts of energy and require almost continuous delivery of oxygen and nutrients via the arteries. Muscle cells also give off large amounts of metabolic wastes that must be removed through veins if contraction is to remain efficient. Muscle capillaries, the smallest of the body's blood vessels, are long and winding and have numerous cross-links, features that accommodate changes in muscle length. They straighten when the muscle stretches and contort when the muscle contracts.

Connective Tissue Sheaths

In an intact muscle, several different connective tissue sheaths wrap individual muscle fibers. Together these connective tissue sheaths support each cell and reinforce and hold together the muscle as a whole, preventing the bulging muscles from bursting during exceptionally strong contractions.

Let's consider these connective tissue sheaths from external to internal (see **Figure 9.1** and the top three rows of Table 9.1).

- **Epimysium.** The **epimysium** (ep"ĭ-mis'e-um; meaning "outside the muscle") is an "overcoat" of dense irregular connective tissue that surrounds the whole muscle. Sometimes it blends with the deep fascia that lies between neighboring muscles or the superficial fascia deep to the skin.
- **Perimysium and fascicles.** Within each skeletal muscle, the muscle fibers are grouped into **fascicles** (fas'ĭ-klz; "bundles") that resemble bundles of sticks. Surrounding each fascicle is a layer of fibrous connective tissue called **perimysium** (per"ĭ-mis'e-um; meaning "around the muscle [fascicles]").
- **Endomysium.** The **endomysium** (en"do-mis'e-um; meaning "within the muscle") is a wispy sheath of connective tissue that surrounds each individual muscle fiber. It consists of fine areolar connective tissue.

As shown in Figure 9.1, all of these connective tissue sheaths are continuous with one another as well as with the tendons that join muscles to bones. When muscle fibers contract, they pull on these sheaths, which transmit the pulling force to the bone to be moved. The sheaths contribute somewhat to the natural elasticity of muscle tissue, and also provide entry and exit routes for the blood vessels and nerve fibers that serve the muscle.

Attachments

Recall from Chapter 8 that most skeletal muscles span joints and attach to bones (or other structures) in at least two places. When a muscle contracts, the movable bone, the muscle's **insertion**, moves toward the immovable or less movable bone, the muscle's **origin**. In the muscles of the limbs, the origin typically lies proximal to the insertion.

Muscle attachments, whether origin or insertion, may be direct or indirect.

- In **direct**, or **fleshy**, **attachments**, the epimysium of the muscle is fused to the periosteum of a bone or perichondrium of a cartilage.

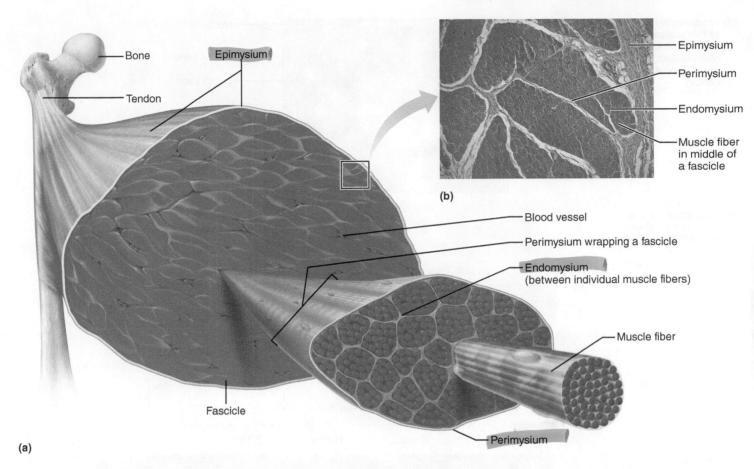

Figure 9.1 Connective tissue sheaths of skeletal muscle: epimysium, perimysium, and endomysium. (b) Photomicrograph of a cross section of part of a skeletal muscle (30×). (For a related image, see *A Brief Atlas of the Human Body*, Plate 29.)

- In **indirect attachments**, the muscle's connective tissue wrappings extend beyond the muscle either as a ropelike **tendon** (Figure 9.1a) or as a sheetlike **aponeurosis** (ap″o-nu-ro′sis). The tendon or aponeurosis anchors the muscle to the connective tissue covering of a skeletal element (bone or cartilage) or to the fascia of other muscles.

Indirect attachments are much more common because of their durability and small size. Tendons are mostly tough collagen fibers which can withstand the abrasion of rough bony projections that would tear apart the more delicate muscle tissues. Because of their relatively small size, more tendons than fleshy muscles can pass over a joint—so tendons also conserve space.

Before moving on to microscopic anatomy, you may want to review the top three rows of Table 9.1.

Microscopic Anatomy of a Skeletal Muscle Fiber

Each skeletal muscle fiber is a long cylindrical cell with multiple oval nuclei just beneath its **sarcolemma** or plasma membrane (Figure 9.2b). Skeletal muscle fibers are huge cells. Their diameter typically ranges from 10 to 100 μm—up to ten times that of an average body cell—and their length is phenomenal, some up to 30 cm long. Their large size and multiple nuclei are not surprising once you learn that hundreds of embryonic cells fuse to produce each fiber.

Sarcoplasm, the cytoplasm of a muscle cell, is similar to the cytoplasm of other cells, but it contains unusually large amounts of **glycosomes** (granules of stored glycogen that provide glucose during muscle cell activity) and **myoglobin**, a red pigment that stores oxygen. Myoglobin is similar to hemoglobin, the pigment that transports oxygen in blood.

In addition to the usual organelles, a muscle cell contains three structures that are highly modified: myofibrils, sarcoplasmic reticulum, and T tubules. Let's look at these structures more closely because they play important roles in muscle contraction.

Myofibrils

A single muscle fiber contains hundreds to thousands of rodlike **myofibrils** that run parallel to its length (Figure 9.2b). The myofibrils, each 1–2 μm in diameter, are so densely packed in the fiber that mitochondria and other organelles appear to be squeezed between them. They account for about 80% of cellular volume.

(a) Photomicrograph of **portions of two isolated muscle fibers** (700×). Notice the obvious striations (alternating dark and light bands).

Nuclei

Dark A band

Light I band

Fiber

(b) Diagram of **part of a muscle fiber** showing the myofibrils. One **myofibril** extends from the cut end of the fiber.

Sarcolemma

Mitochondrion

Myofibril

Dark A band   Light I band   Nucleus

Thin (actin) filament

Z disc   H zone   Z disc

(c) Small part of one **myofibril enlarged to show the myofilaments** responsible for the banding pattern. Each **sarcomere** extends from one Z disc to the next.

Thick (myosin) filament

I band   A band   I band   M line

Sarcomere

Z disc   M line   Z disc

(d) Enlargement of one sarcomere (sectioned lengthwise). Notice the myosin heads on the thick filaments.

Thin (actin) filament

Elastic (titin) filaments

Thick (myosin) filament

(e) Cross-sectional view of a sarcomere cut through in different locations.

Myosin filament

Actin filament

I band
thin filaments only

H zone
thick filaments only

M line
thick filaments linked by accessory proteins

Outer edge of A band
thick and thin filaments overlap

Figure 9.2 Microscopic anatomy of a skeletal muscle fiber. (For a related image, see *A Brief Atlas of the Human Body*, Plate 28.)

Myofibrils contain the contractile elements of skeletal muscle cells, the sarcomeres, which contain even smaller rodlike structures called *myofilaments*. Table 9.1 (bottom three rows; p. 283) summarizes these structures, which we discuss next.

Striations, Sarcomeres, and Myofilaments Striations, a repeating series of dark and light bands, are evident along the length of each myofibril. In an intact muscle fiber, the dark **A bands** and light **I bands** are nearly perfectly aligned, giving the cell its striated appearance.

As illustrated in Figure 9.2c:

- Each dark A band has a lighter region in its midsection called the **H zone** (H for *helle*; "bright").

- Each H zone is bisected vertically by a dark line called the **M line** (*M* for middle) formed by molecules of the protein myomesin.

- Each light I band also has a midline interruption, a darker area called the **Z disc** (or Z line).

- The region of a myofibril between two successive Z discs is a **sarcomere** (sar′ko-měr; literally, "muscle segment"). Averaging 2 μm long, a sarcomere is the smallest contractile unit of a muscle fiber—the *functional unit* of skeletal muscle. It contains an A band flanked by half an I band at each end. Within each myofibril, the sarcomeres align end to end like boxcars in a train.

If we examine the banding pattern of a myofibril at the molecular level, we see that it arises from orderly arrangement of even smaller structures within the sarcomeres. These smaller structures, the **myofilaments** or **filaments**, are the muscle equivalents of the actin- or myosin-containing microfilaments described in Chapter 3. As you will recall, the proteins actin and myosin play a role in motility and shape change in virtually every cell in the body. This property reaches its highest development in the contractile muscle fibers.

The central **thick filaments** containing myosin (red) extend the entire length of the A band (Figure 9.2c and d). They are connected in the middle of the sarcomere at the M line. The more lateral **thin filaments** containing actin (blue) extend across the I band and partway into the A band. The Z disc, a coin-shaped sheet composed largely of the protein alpha-actinin, anchors the thin filaments. We describe the third type of myofilament illustrated in Figure 9.2d, the *elastic filament*, in the next section. Intermediate (desmin) filaments (not illustrated) extend from the Z disc and connect each myofibril to the next throughout the width of the muscle cell.

Looking at the banding pattern more closely, we see that the H zone of the A band appears less dense because the thin filaments do not extend into this region. The M line in the center of the H zone is slightly darker because of the fine protein strands there that hold adjacent thick filaments together. The myofilaments are connected to the sarcolemma and held in alignment at the Z discs and the M lines.

A longitudinal view of the myofilaments (Figure 9.2d) is a bit misleading because it looks as if each thick (red) filament interdigitates with only four thin (blue) filaments. The cross section of a sarcomere on the far right in Figure 9.2e shows an area where thick and thin filaments overlap. Notice that a hexagonal arrangement of six thin filaments surrounds each thick filament, and three thick filaments enclose each thin filament.

Molecular Composition of Myofilaments Muscle contraction depends on the myosin- and actin-containing myofilaments. As noted earlier, thick filaments (about 16 nm in diameter) are composed primarily of the protein **myosin**. Each myosin molecule consists of two heavy and four light polypeptide chains, and has a rodlike tail attached by a flexible hinge to two globular *heads* **(Figure 9.3)**. The tail consists of two intertwined helical polypeptide heavy chains.

The globular heads, each associated with two light chains, are the "business end" of myosin. During contraction, they link the thick and thin filaments together, forming **cross bridges** **(Figure 9.4** on p. 284), and swivel around their point of attachment. As we will explain shortly, these cross bridges act as motors to generate force.

Each thick filament contains about 300 myosin molecules bundled together, with their tails forming the central part of the thick filament and their heads facing outward at the end of each thick filament (Figure 9.3). As a result, the central portion of a thick filament (in the H zone) is smooth, but its ends are studded with a staggered array of myosin heads. The heads bear actin and ATP-binding sites and also have intrinsic ATPase activity that splits ATP to generate energy for muscle contraction.

The thin filaments (7–8 nm thick) are composed chiefly of the protein **actin** (blue in Figure 9.3). Actin has kidney-shaped polypeptide subunits, called *globular actin* or *G actin*, which bear the active sites to which the myosin heads attach during contraction. In the thin filaments, G actin subunits are polymerized into long actin filaments called *filamentous*, or *F, actin*. Two intertwined actin filaments, resembling a twisted double strand of pearls, form the backbone of each thin filament (Figure 9.3).

Thin filaments also contain several regulatory proteins.

- Polypeptide strands of **tropomyosin** (tro″po-mi′o-sin), a rod-shaped protein, spiral about the actin core and help stiffen and stabilize it. Successive tropomyosin molecules are arranged end to end along the actin filaments, and in a relaxed muscle fiber, they block myosin-binding sites on actin so that myosin heads on the thick filaments cannot bind to the thin filaments.

- **Troponin** (tro′po-nin), the other major protein in thin filaments, is a globular three-polypeptide complex (Figure 9.3). One of its polypeptides (TnI) is an inhibitory subunit that binds to actin. Another (TnT) binds to tropomyosin and helps position it on actin. The third (TnC) binds calcium ions.

Both troponin and tropomyosin help control the myosin-actin interactions involved in contraction. Several other proteins help form the structure of the myofibril.

- The **elastic filament** we referred to earlier is composed of the giant protein **titin** (Figure 9.2d). Titin extends from the Z disc to the thick filament, and then runs within the thick filament (forming its core) to attach to the M line. It holds

Figure 9.3 Composition of thick and thin filaments.

the thick filaments in place, thus maintaining the organization of the A band, and helps the muscle cell spring back into shape after stretching. (The part of the titin that spans the I bands is extensible, unfolding when the muscle stretches and recoiling when the tension is released.) Titin does not resist stretching in the ordinary range of extension, but it stiffens as it uncoils, helping the muscle resist excessive stretching, which might pull the sarcomeres apart.

- Another important structural protein is **dystrophin**, which links the thin filaments to the integral proteins of the

sarcolemma (which in turn are anchored to the extracellular matrix).

- Other proteins that bind filaments or sarcomeres together and maintain their alignment include *nebulin, myomesin,* and *C proteins.*

Sarcoplasmic Reticulum and T Tubules

Skeletal muscle fibers contain two sets of intracellular tubules that help regulate muscle contraction: (1) the sarcoplasmic reticulum and (2) T tubules.

Table 9.1 Structure and Organizational Levels of Skeletal Muscle

STRUCTURE AND ORGANIZATIONAL LEVEL	DESCRIPTION	CONNECTIVE TISSUE WRAPPINGS
Muscle (organ) Epimysium, Muscle, Tendon, Fascicle	A muscle consists of hundreds to thousands of muscle cells, plus connective tissue wrappings, blood vessels, and nerve fibers.	Covered externally by the epimysium
Fascicle (a portion of the muscle) Part of fascicle, Perimysium, Muscle fiber	A fascicle is a discrete bundle of muscle cells, segregated from the rest of the muscle by a connective tissue sheath.	Surrounded by perimysium
Muscle Fiber (cell) Nucleus, Endomysium, Sarcolemma, Part of muscle fiber, Myofibril	A muscle fiber is an elongated multinucleate cell; it has a banded (striated) appearance.	Surrounded by endomysium
Myofibril or Fibril (complex organelle composed of bundles of myofilaments) Sarcomere	Myofibrils are rodlike contractile elements that occupy most of the muscle cell volume. Composed of sarcomeres arranged end to end, they appear banded, and bands of adjacent myofibrils are aligned.	—
Sarcomere (a segment of a myofibril) Sarcomere Thin (actin) filament, Thick (myosin) filament	A sarcomere is the contractile unit, composed of myofilaments made up of contractile proteins.	—
Myofilament or Filament (extended macromolecular structure) Thick filament, Head of myosin molecule, Thin filament, Actin molecules	Contractile myofilaments are of two types—thick and thin. Thick filaments contain bundled myosin molecules; thin filaments contain actin molecules (plus other proteins). The sliding of the thin filaments past the thick filaments produces muscle shortening. Elastic filaments (not shown here) maintain the organization of the A band and provide elastic recoil when muscle contraction ends.	—

9

Thin filament (actin) Myosin heads Thick filament (myosin)

Figure 9.4 Myosin heads forming cross bridges that generate muscular contractile force. Part of a sarcomere is seen in a transmission electron micrograph (277,000×).

Sarcoplasmic Reticulum Shown in blue in **Figure 9.5**, the **sarcoplasmic reticulum (SR)** is an elaborate smooth endoplasmic reticulum. Its interconnecting tubules surround each myofibril the way the sleeve of a loosely crocheted sweater surrounds your arm.

Most SR tubules run longitudinally along the myofibril, communicating with each other at the H zone. Others called **terminal cisterns** ("end sacs") form larger, perpendicular cross channels at the A band–I band junctions and they always occur in pairs. Closely associated with the SR are large numbers of mitochondria and glycogen granules, both involved in producing the energy used during contraction.

The SR regulates intracellular levels of ionic calcium. It stores calcium and releases it on demand when the muscle fiber is stimulated to contract. As you will see, calcium provides the final "go" signal for contraction.

T Tubules At each A band–I band junction, the sarcolemma of the muscle cell protrudes deep into the cell interior, forming an elongated tube called the **T tubule** (T for "transverse"). The T tubules, shown in gray in Figure 9.5, tremendously increase the muscle fiber's surface area. Possibly the result of fusing tubelike caveolae (inpocketings of the sarcolemma), the *lumen* (cavity) of the T tubule is continuous with the extracellular space.

Along its length, each T tubule runs between the paired terminal cisterns of the SR, forming **triads**, successive groupings of the three membranous structures (terminal cistern, T tubule, and terminal cistern). As they pass from one myofibril to the next, the T tubules also encircle each sarcomere.

Muscle contraction is ultimately controlled by nerve-initiated electrical impulses that travel along the sarcolemma. Because T tubules are continuations of the sarcolemma, they conduct impulses to the deepest regions of the muscle cell and every sarcomere. These impulses signal for the release of calcium from the adjacent terminal cisterns. Think of the T tubules as a rapid telegraph system that ensures that every myofibril in the muscle fiber contracts at virtually the same time.

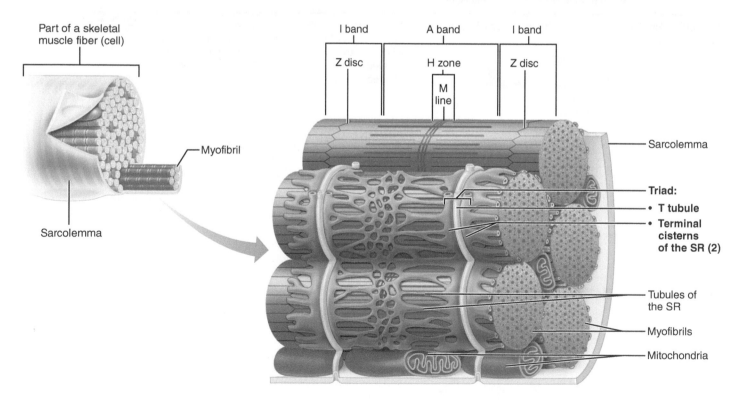

Figure 9.5 Relationship of the sarcoplasmic reticulum and T tubules to myofibrils of skeletal muscle. The tubules of the SR (blue) fuse to form a net of communicating channels at the level of the H zone and the saclike terminal cisterns abutting the A-I junctions. The T tubules (gray) are inward invaginations of the sarcolemma that run deep into the cell between the terminal cisterns. (See detailed view in Figure 9.11, pp. 290–291.) Sites of close contact of these three elements (terminal cistern, T tubule, and terminal cistern) are called triads.

Triad Relationships The roles of the T tubules and SR in providing signals for contraction are tightly linked. At the triads, where these organelles come into closest contact, integral proteins (some from the T tubule and others from the SR) protrude into the intermembrane spaces. The protruding integral proteins of the T tubule act as voltage sensors. Those of the SR form gated channels through which the terminal cisterns release Ca^{2+}. We will return to their interaction shortly.

Sliding Filament Model of Contraction

We almost always think "shortening" when we hear the word **contraction**, but to physiologists the term refers only to the activation of myosin's cross bridges, which are the force-generating sites. Shortening occurs if and when the cross bridges generate enough tension on the thin filaments to exceed the forces that oppose shortening. Contraction ends when the cross bridges become inactive, the tension declines, and then the muscle fiber relaxes.

In a relaxed muscle fiber, the thin and thick filaments overlap only at the ends of the A band (**Figure 9.6 ①**). The **sliding filament model of contraction** states that during contraction the thin filaments slide past the thick ones so that the actin and myosin filaments overlap to a greater degree:

- When the nervous system stimulates muscle fibers, the myosin heads on the thick filaments latch onto myosin-binding sites on actin in the thin filaments, and the sliding begins.

- These cross bridge attachments form and break several times during a contraction, acting like tiny ratchets to generate tension and propel the thin filaments toward the center of the sarcomere.

- As this event occurs simultaneously in sarcomeres throughout the cell, the muscle cell shortens.

- Notice that as the thin filaments slide centrally, the Z discs to which they attach are pulled *toward* the M line (Figure 9.6 ②). Overall, as a muscle cell shortens: (1) the I bands shorten, (2) the distance between successive Z discs shortens, (3) the H zones disappear, and (4) the contiguous A bands move closer together but their length does not change.

☑ Check Your Understanding

3. How does the term epimysium relate to the role and position of this connective tissue sheath?
4. Which myofilaments have binding sites for calcium? What specific molecule binds calcium?
5. Which region or organelle—cytosol, mitochondrion, or SR—contains the highest concentration of calcium ions in a resting muscle fiber? Which structure provides the ATP needed for muscle activity?

For answers, see Appendix H.

Physiology of Skeletal Muscle Fibers

✓ Explain how muscle fibers are stimulated to contract by describing events that occur at the neuromuscular junction.

✓ Describe how an action potential is generated.

① Fully relaxed sarcomere of a muscle fiber

② Fully contracted sarcomere of a muscle fiber

Figure 9.6 Sliding filament model of contraction. The numbers indicate events in a ① relaxed and a ② fully contracted sarcomere. At full contraction, the Z discs abut the thick filaments and the thin filaments overlap each other. The photomicrographs (top view in each case) show enlargements of 33,000×.

✓ Follow the events of excitation-contraction coupling that lead to cross bridge activity.

The sliding filament model tells us how a muscle fiber contracts, but what induces it to contract in the first place? For a skeletal muscle fiber to contract:

1. The fiber must be activated, that is, stimulated by a nerve ending so that a change in membrane potential occurs.
2. Next, it must generate an electrical current, called an **action potential**, in its sarcolemma.

Phase 1
Motor neuron stimulates muscle fiber (see Figure 9.8).

- Action potential (AP) arrives at axon terminal at neuromuscular junction
- ACh released; binds to receptors on sarcolemma
- Ion permeability of sarcolemma changes
- Local change in membrane voltage (depolarization) occurs
- Local depolarization (end plate potential) ignites AP in sarcolemma

Phase 2:
Excitation-contraction coupling occurs (see Figures 9.9 and 9.11).

- AP travels across the entire sarcolemma
- AP travels along T tubules
- SR releases Ca^{2+}; Ca^{2+} binds to troponin; myosin-binding sites (active sites) on actin exposed
- Myosin heads bind to actin; contraction begins

Figure 9.7 The phases leading to muscle fiber contraction.

3. The action potential is automatically propagated along the sarcolomma.
4. Then, intracellular calcium ion levels must rise briefly, providing the final trigger for contraction.

Steps 1 and 2, activation, occur at the neuromuscular junction and set the stage for the events that follow. Steps 3 and 4, which link the electrical signal to contraction, are called excitation-contraction coupling. **Figure 9.7** summarizes this series of events into two major phases, which we consider in detail below.

The Nerve Stimulus and Events at the Neuromuscular Junction

The nerve cells that activate skeletal muscle fibers are called *somatic motor neurons*, or *motor neurons of the somatic (voluntary) nervous system*. These motor neurons "reside" in the brain or spinal cord, but their long threadlike extensions called axons travel, bundled within nerves, to the muscle cells they serve.

The axon of each motor neuron divides profusely as it enters the muscle. Each axon ending gives off several short, curling branches that collectively form an elliptical **neuromuscular junction,** or **end plate**, with a single muscle fiber.

As a rule, each muscle fiber has only one neuromuscular junction, located approximately midway along its length. The axon terminal and the muscle fiber are exceedingly close (50–80 nm apart), but they remain separated by a space, the **synaptic cleft** (Figure 9.8), which is filled with a gel-like extracellular substance rich in glycoproteins and collagen fibers.

Within the moundlike axon terminal are **synaptic vesicles**, small membranous sacs containing the neurotransmitter **acetylcholine** (as″ĕ-til-ko′lēn), or **ACh**. The trough-like part of the muscle fiber's sarcolemma that helps form the neuromuscular junction is highly folded. These **junctional folds** provide a large surface area for the millions of **ACh receptors** located there. Hence, the neuromuscular junction includes the axon terminals, the synaptic cleft, and the junctional folds of the sarcolemma.

How does a motor neuron stimulate a skeletal muscle fiber? The simplest explanation is:

- When a nerve impulse reaches the end of an axon, the axon terminal releases ACh into the synaptic cleft.
- ACh diffuses across the cleft and attaches to ACh receptors on the sarcolemma of the muscle fiber.
- ACh binding triggers electrical events that ultimately generate an action potential.

Focus on Events at the Neuromuscular Junction (**Figure 9.8**) covers this process step by step. Study this figure before continuing.

After ACh binds to the ACh receptors, its effects are quickly terminated by **acetylcholinesterase** (as″ĕ-til-ko″lin-es′ter-ās), an enzyme located in the synaptic cleft. Acetylcholinesterase breaks down ACh to its building blocks, acetic acid and choline. This removal of ACh prevents continued (and most likely undesirable) muscle fiber contraction in the absence of additional nervous system stimulation.

Homeostatic Imbalance 9.1

Many toxins, drugs, and diseases interfere with events at the neuromuscular junction. For example, *myasthenia gravis* (*asthen* = weakness; *gravi* = heavy), a disease characterized by drooping upper eyelids, difficulty swallowing and talking, and generalized muscle weakness, involves a shortage of ACh receptors. Serum analysis reveals antibodies to ACh receptors, suggesting that myasthenia gravis is an autoimmune disease. Although normal numbers of receptors are initially present, they appear to be destroyed as the disease progresses. ✚

Generation of an Action Potential Across the Sarcolemma

Like the plasma membranes of all cells, a resting sarcolemma is *polarized*. That is, a voltmeter would show there is a potential difference (voltage) across the membrane and the inside is negative relative to the outer membrane face. (Chapter 3 describes the resting membrane potential.)

An action potential (AP) is the result of a predictable sequence of electrical changes. Once initiated, they occur along

Figure 9.8 When a nerve impulse reaches a neuromuscular junction, acetylcholine (ACh) is released. Upon binding to sarcolemma receptors, ACh causes a change in sarcolemma permeability leading to a change in membrane potential.

A&P Flix *Available at www.masteringaandp.com*

Action potential (AP)

Myelinated axon of motor neuron

Axon terminal of **neuromuscular junction**

Sarcolemma of the muscle fiber

① Action potential arrives at axon terminal of motor neuron.

causes a change in voltage

② Voltage-gated Ca^{2+} channels open. Ca^{2+} enters the axon terminal moving down its electochemical gradient.

Ca^{2+}

Ca^{2+}

Synaptic vesicle containing ACh

Axon terminal of motor neuron

Synaptic cleft

③ Ca^{2+} entry causes ACh (a neurotransmitter) to be released by exocytosis.

Fusing synaptic vesicles

ACh

Junctional folds of sarcolemma

④ ACh diffuses across the synaptic cleft and binds to its receptors on the sarcolemma.

Sarcoplasm of muscle fiber

⑤ ACh binding opens ion channels in the receptors that allow simultaneous passage of Na^+ into the muscle fiber and K^+ out of the muscle fiber. More Na^+ ions enter than K^+ ions exit, which produces a local change in the membrane potential called the end plate potential.

Na^+ K^+

Postsynaptic membrane ion channel opens; ions pass.

⑥ ACh effects are terminated by its breakdown in the synaptic cleft by acetylcholinesterase and diffusion away from the junction.

ACh

Degraded ACh

Na^+

Ion channel closes; ions cannot pass.

Phospholipids

Acetylcholinesterase

K^+

9

Ca²⁺

Synaptic cleft

ACh-containing synaptic vesicle

Ca²⁺

Axon terminal of neuromuscular junction

Wave of depolarization

① An end plate potential is generated at the neuromuscular junction (see Figure 9.8).

② **Depolarization: Generating and propagating an action potential (AP).** The local depolarization current spreads to adjacent areas of the sarcolemma. This opens voltage-gated sodium channels there, so Na⁺ enters following its electrochemical gradient and initiates the AP. The AP is propagated as its local depolarization wave spreads to adjacent areas of the sarcolemma, opening voltage-gated channels there. Again Na⁺ diffuses into the cell following its electrochemical gradient.

Figure 9.9 Summary of events in the generation and propagation of an action potential in a skeletal muscle fiber.

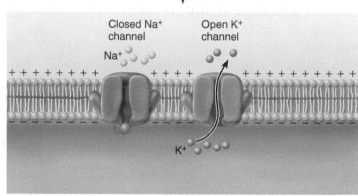

③ **Repolarization: Restoring the sarcolemma to its initial polarized state (negative inside, positive outside).** Repolarization occurs as Na⁺ channels close (inactivate) and voltage-gated K⁺ channels open. Because K⁺ concentration is substantially higher inside the cell than in the extracellular fluid, K⁺ diffuses rapidly out of the muscle fiber.

the entire surface of the sarcolemma. Essentially three steps are involved **(Figure 9.9)**:

① **Generation of an end plate potential.** Binding of ACh molecules to ACh receptors at the neuromuscular junction opens *chemically (ligand) gated ion channels* that allow Na⁺ and K⁺ to pass (also see Figure 9.8). Because the driving force for Na⁺ is greater than that for K⁺, more Na⁺ diffuses in than K⁺ diffuses out. A transient change in membrane potential occurs as the interior of the sarcolemma becomes less negative, an event called depolarization. Initially, depolarization is a local event called an **end plate potential**.

② **Depolarization: Generation and propagation of an action potential.** The end plate potential (local depolarization at the neuromuscular junction) ignites an action potential by spreading to adjacent membrane areas and opening voltage-gated sodium channels there. Na⁺ enters, following its electrochemical gradient, and once a certain

membrane voltage, referred to as *threshold*, is reached, an action potential is generated (initiated).

The action potential *propagates* (moves along the length of the sarcolemma) in all directions from the neuromuscular junction, just as ripples move away from a pebble dropped into a stream. As it propagates, the local depolarization wave of the AP spreads to adjacent areas of the sarcolemma and opens voltage-gated sodium channels there. Again, Na⁺, normally restricted from entering, diffuses into the cell following its electrochemical gradient.

③ **Repolarization: Restoring the sarcolemma to its initial polarized state.** The repolarization wave, like the depolarization wave, is a consequence of changes in membrane permeability. In this case, Na⁺ channels close and voltage-gated K⁺ channels open. Since the potassium ion concentration is substantially higher inside the cell than in the extracellular fluid, K⁺ diffuses rapidly out of the muscle fiber, restoring negatively charged conditions inside (also see Figure 9.10).

During repolarization, a muscle fiber is said to be in a **refractory period**, because the cell cannot be stimulated again until repolarization is complete. Note that repolarization restores only the *electrical conditions* of the resting (polarized) state. The ATP-dependent Na^+-K^+ pump restores the *ionic conditions* of the resting state, but hundreds of action potentials can occur before ionic imbalances interfere with contractile activity.

Once initiated, the action potential is unstoppable. It ultimately results in contraction of the muscle fiber. Although the action potential itself lasts only a few milliseconds (ms), the contraction phase of a muscle fiber may persist for 100 ms or more and far outlasts the electrical event that triggers it.

Excitation-Contraction Coupling

Excitation-contraction (E-C) coupling is the sequence of events by which transmission of an action potential along the sarcolemma causes myofilaments to slide. The action potential is brief and ends well before any signs of contraction are obvious.

As you will see, the electrical signal does not act directly on the myofilaments. Instead, it causes the rise in intracellular levels of calcium ions, which allows the filaments to slide.

Focus on Excitation-Contraction Coupling (Figure 9.11) on pp. 290–291 illustrates the steps in this process. This Focus feature also reveals how the integral proteins of the T tubules and terminal cisterns in the triads interact to provide the Ca^{2+} necessary for contraction to occur. Make sure you understand this material before continuing.

Summary: Channels Involved in Initiating Muscle Contraction

So let's summarize what has to happen to excite a muscle cell, starting from the nerve ending. Essentially this process activates four sets of ion channels:

1. The process begins when the nerve impulse reaches the axon terminal and opens voltage-gated calcium channels in the axonal membrane. Calcium entry triggers release of ACh into the synaptic cleft.
2. Released ACh binds to ACh receptors in the sarcolemma, opening chemically gated Na^+-K^+ channels. Greater influx of Na^+ causes a local voltage change (the end plate potential).
3. Local depolarization opens voltage-gated sodium channels in the neighboring region of the sarcolemma. This allows more sodium to enter, which further depolarizes the sarcolemma, generating and propagating an AP.
4. Transmission of the AP along the T tubules changes the shape of voltage-sensitive proteins in the T tubules, which in turn stimulate SR calcium release channels to release Ca^{2+} into the cytosol.

Muscle Fiber Contraction: Cross Bridge Cycling

As we have noted, cross bridge formation (attachment of myosin heads to actin) requires Ca^{2+}. Let's look more closely at how calcium ions promote muscle cell contraction.

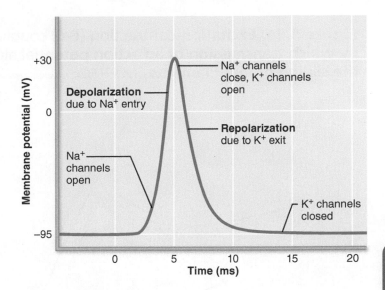

Figure 9.10 Action potential tracing indicates changes in Na^+ and K^+ ion channels.

When intracellular calcium levels are low, the muscle cell is relaxed, and tropomyosin molecules physically block the active (myosin-binding) sites on actin. As Ca^{2+} levels rise, the ions bind to regulatory sites on troponin. To activate its group of seven actins, a troponin must bind two calcium ions, change shape, and then roll tropomyosin into the groove of the actin helix, away from the myosin-binding sites. In short, the tropomyosin "blockade" is removed when sufficient calcium is present. Once binding sites on actin are exposed, the events of the cross bridge cycle occur in rapid succession, as depicted in *Focus on the Cross Bridge Cycle* (Figure 9.12) on p. 292.

The thin filaments continue to slide as long as the calcium signal and adequate ATP are present. When nerve impulses arrive rapidly, intracellular Ca^{2+} levels soar due to successive "puffs" or rounds of Ca^{2+} released from the SR. In such cases, the muscle cells do not completely relax between successive stimuli and contraction is stronger and more sustained (within limits) until nervous stimulation ceases.

As the Ca^{2+} pumps of the SR reclaim calcium ions from the cytosol and troponin again changes shape, tropomyosin again blocks actin's myosin-binding sites. The contraction ends, and the muscle fiber relaxes.

When the cycle is ready to start again, the myosin head is in its upright high-energy configuration (see step 4 in Focus Figure 9.12), ready to take another "step" and attach to an actin site farther along the thin filament. This "walking" of the myosin heads along the adjacent thin filaments during muscle shortening is much like a centipede's gait. The thin filaments cannot slide backward as the cycle repeats again and again because some myosin heads ("legs") are always in contact with actin (the "ground"). Contracting muscles routinely shorten by 30–35% of their total resting length, so each myosin cross bridge attaches and detaches many times during a single contraction. It is likely that only half of the myosin heads of a thick filament are pulling at the same instant. The others are randomly seeking their next binding site.

(Text continues on p. 293.)

Figure 9.11 Excitation-contraction (E-C) coupling is the sequence of events by which transmission of an action potential along the sarcolemma leads to the sliding of myofilaments. *A&PFlix* Available at www.masteringaandp.com

Setting the stage
The events at the neuromuscular junction (NMJ) set the stage for E-C coupling by providing excitation. Released acetylcholine binds to receptor proteins on the sarcolemma and triggers an action potential in a muscle fiber.

Axon terminal of motor neuron at NMJ

Synaptic cleft

ACh

Action potential is generated

Sarcolemma

T tubule

Terminal cistern of SR

Ca^{2+}

Triad

Muscle fiber

One sarcomere

One myofibril

Steps in E-C Coupling:

Sarcolemma

Voltage-sensitive tubule protein

T tubule

Ca²⁺ release channel

Terminal cistern of SR

Ca²⁺

Actin

Troponin

Tropomyosin blocking active sites

Myosin

Ca²⁺

Active sites exposed and ready for myosin binding

Myosin cross bridge

① The action potential (AP) propagates along the sarcolemma and down the T tubules.

② Calcium ions are released. Transmission of the AP along the T tubules of the triads causes the voltage-sensitive tubule proteins to change shape. This shape change opens the Ca²⁺ release channels in the terminal cisterns of the sarcoplasmic reticulum (SR), allowing Ca²⁺ to flow into the cytosol.

③ Calcium binds to troponin and removes the blocking action of tropomyosin. When Ca²⁺ binds, troponin changes shape, exposing binding sites for myosin (active sites) on the thin filaments.

④ Contraction begins: Myosin binding to actin forms cross bridges and contraction (cross bridge cycling) begins. At this point, E-C coupling is over.

The aftermath

When the muscle AP ceases, the voltage-sensitive tubule proteins return to their original shape, closing the Ca²⁺ release channels of the SR. Ca²⁺ levels in the sarcoplasm fall as Ca²⁺ is continually pumped back into the SR by active transport. Without Ca²⁺, the blocking action of tropomyosin is restored, myosin-actin interaction is inhibited, and relaxation occurs. Each time an AP arrives at the neuromuscular junction, the sequence of E-C coupling is repeated.

Figure 9.12 The cross bridge cycle is the series of events during which myosin heads pull thin filaments toward the center of the sarcomere. *A&PFlix* *Available at www.masteringaandp.com*

1 **Cross bridge formation.** Energized myosin head attaches to an actin myofilament, forming a cross bridge.

2 **The power (working) stroke.** ADP and P_i are released and the myosin head pivots and bends, changing to its bent low-energy state. As a result it pulls the actin filament toward the M line.

In the absence of ATP, myosin heads will not detach, causing rigor mortis.

3 **Cross bridge detachment.** After ATP attaches to myosin, the link between myosin and actin weakens, and the myosin head detaches (the cross bridge "breaks").

4 **Cocking of the myosin head.** As ATP is hydrolyzed to ADP and P_i, the myosin head returns to its prestroke high-energy, or "cocked," position.*

*This cycle will continue as long as ATP is available and Ca^{2+} is bound to troponin.

Except for the brief period following muscle cell excitation, calcium ion concentrations in the cytosol are kept almost undetectably low. There is a reason for this: Sustained high calcium activates apoptosis, leading to cell death.

⟍ Homeostatic Imbalance 9.2

Rigor mortis (death rigor) illustrates the fact that cross bridge detachment is ATP driven. Most muscles begin to stiffen 3 to 4 hours after death. Peak rigidity occurs at 12 hours and then gradually dissipates over the next 48 to 60 hours. Dying cells are unable to exclude calcium (which is in higher concentration in the extracellular fluid), and the calcium influx into muscle cells promotes formation of myosin cross bridges. Shortly after breathing stops, ATP synthesis ceases, but ATP continues to be consumed and cross bridge detachment is impossible. Actin and myosin become irreversibly cross-linked, producing the stiffness of rigor mortis, which gradually disappears as muscle proteins break down after death. ✚

☑ Check Your Understanding

6. What are the three structural components of a neuromuscular junction?
7. What is the final trigger for contraction? What is the initial trigger?
8. What prevents the filaments from sliding back to their original position each time a myosin cross bridge detaches from actin?
9. What would happen if a muscle fiber suddenly ran out of ATP when sarcomeres had only partially contracted?

For answers, see Appendix H.

Contraction of a Skeletal Muscle

✓ Define motor unit and muscle twitch, and describe the events occurring during the three phases of a muscle twitch.

✓ Explain how smooth, graded contractions of a skeletal muscle are produced.

✓ Differentiate between isometric and isotonic contractions.

In its relaxed state, a muscle is soft and unimpressive, not what you would expect of a prime mover of the body. However, within a few milliseconds, it can contract to become a hard elastic structure with dynamic characteristics that intrigue not only biologists but engineers and physicists as well.

Before we consider muscle contraction on the organ level, let's note a few principles of muscle mechanics.

- The principles governing contraction of a single muscle fiber and of a skeletal muscle consisting of a large number of fibers are pretty much the same.

- The force exerted by a contracting muscle on an object is called **muscle tension**. The opposing force exerted on the muscle by the weight of the object to be moved is called the **load**.

- A contracting muscle does not always shorten and move the load. If muscle tension develops but the load is not moved, the contraction is called *isometric* ("same measure")—think

of trying to lift a 2000-lb car. If the muscle tension developed overcomes the load and muscle shortening occurs, the contraction is *isotonic* ("same tension"), as when you lift a 5-lb sack of sugar. We will describe isometric and isotonic contractions in detail, but for now the important thing to remember when reading the accompanying graphs is this: *Increasing muscle tension* is measured for isometric contractions, whereas the *amount of muscle shortening* (distance in millimeters) is measured for isotonic contractions.

- A skeletal muscle contracts with varying force and for different periods of time in response to stimuli of varying frequencies and intensities. To understand how this occurs, we must look at the nerve-muscle functional unit called a *motor unit*. This is our next topic.

The Motor Unit

Each muscle is served by at least one *motor nerve*, and each motor nerve contains axons (fibrous extensions) of up to hundreds of motor neurons. As an axon enters a muscle, it branches into a number of terminals, each of which forms a neuromuscular junction with a single muscle fiber. A **motor unit** consists of one motor neuron and all the muscle fibers it innervates, or supplies **(Figure 9.13)**. When a motor neuron fires (transmits an action potential), all the muscle fibers it innervates contract.

The number of muscle fibers per motor unit may be as high as several hundred or as few as four. Muscles that exert fine control (such as those controlling the fingers and eyes) have small motor units. By contrast, large, weight-bearing muscles, whose movements are less precise (such as the hip muscles), have large motor units. The muscle fibers in a single motor unit are not clustered together but are spread throughout the muscle. As a result, stimulation of a single motor unit causes a weak contraction of the *entire* muscle.

The Muscle Twitch

Muscle contraction is easily investigated in the laboratory using an isolated muscle. The muscle is attached to an apparatus that produces a **myogram**, a recording of contractile activity. The line recording the activity is called a *tracing*.

A **muscle twitch** is a motor unit's response to a single action potential of its motor neuron. The muscle fibers contract quickly and then relax. Every twitch myogram has three distinct phases **(Figure 9.14a)**.

1. **Latent period.** The **latent period** is the first few milliseconds following stimulation when excitation-contraction coupling is occurring. During this period, cross bridges begin to cycle but muscle tension is not yet measurable and the myogram does not show a response.

2. **Period of contraction.** During the period of contraction, cross bridges are active, from the onset to the peak of tension development, and the myogram tracing rises to a peak. This period lasts 10–100 ms. If the tension (pull) becomes great enough to overcome the resistance of the load, the muscle shortens.

3. **Period of relaxation.** This final phase, lasting 10–100 ms, is initiated by reentry of Ca^{2+} into the SR. Because contractile force is declining, muscle tension decreases to zero and

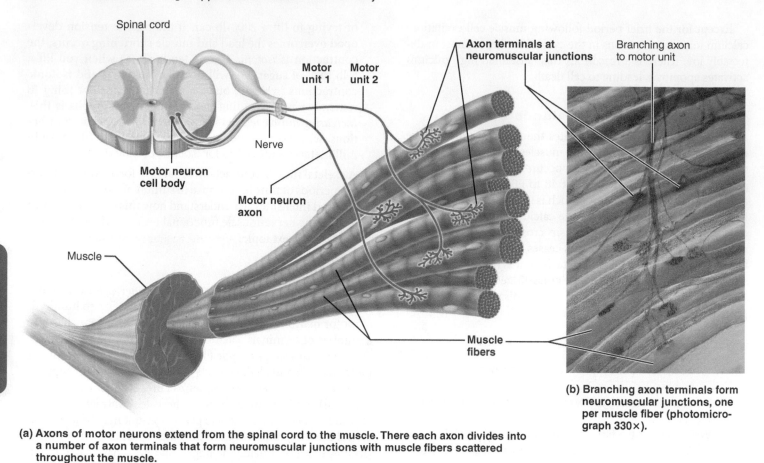

(a) Axons of motor neurons extend from the spinal cord to the muscle. There each axon divides into a number of axon terminals that form neuromuscular junctions with muscle fibers scattered throughout the muscle.

(b) Branching axon terminals form neuromuscular junctions, one per muscle fiber (photomicrograph 330×).

Figure 9.13 **A motor unit consists of one motor neuron and all the muscle fibers it innervates.** (For a related image, see *A Brief Atlas of the Human Body*, Plate 30.)

the tracing returns to the baseline. If the muscle shortened during contraction, it now returns to its initial length. Notice that a muscle contracts faster than it relaxes, as revealed by the asymmetric nature of the myogram tracing.

As you can see in Figure 9.14b, twitch contractions of some muscles are rapid and brief, as with the muscles controlling eye movements. In contrast, the fibers of fleshy calf muscles (gastrocnemius and soleus) contract more slowly and remain contracted for much longer periods. These differences between muscles reflect variations in enzymes and metabolic properties of the myofibrils.

Graded Muscle Responses

Muscle twitches—like those single, jerky contractions provoked in a laboratory—may result from certain neuromuscular problems, but this is *not* the way our muscles normally operate. Instead, healthy muscle contractions are relatively smooth and vary in strength as different demands are placed on them. These variations, needed for proper control of skeletal movement, are referred to as **graded muscle responses**.

In general, muscle contraction can be graded in two ways: by changing the frequency of stimulation, and by changing the strength of stimulation.

Muscle Response to Changes in Stimulus Frequency The nervous system achieves greater muscular force by increasing the firing rate of motor neurons. For example, if two identical stimuli (electrical shocks or nerve impulses) are delivered to a muscle in rapid succession, the second twitch will be stronger than the first. On a myogram the second twitch will appear to ride on the shoulders of the first (Figure 9.15a, b).

This phenomenon, called **wave** or **temporal summation**, occurs because the second contraction occurs before the muscle has completely relaxed. Because the muscle is already partially contracted and more calcium is being squirted into the cytosol to replace that being reclaimed by the SR, muscle tension produced during the second contraction causes more shortening than the first. In other words, the contractions are added together. (However, the refractory period is always honored. Thus, if a second stimulus arrives before repolarization is complete, no wave summation occurs.)

If the stimulus strength is held constant and the muscle is stimulated at an increasingly faster rate: (1) the relaxation time between twitches becomes shorter and shorter, (2) the concentration of Ca^{2+} in the cytosol rises higher and higher, and (3) the degree of wave summation becomes greater and greater, progressing to a sustained but quivering contraction referred to as **unfused** or **incomplete tetanus** (Figure 9.15b).

(a) Myogram showing the three phases of an isometric twitch

(b) Comparison of the relative duration of twitch responses of three muscles

Figure 9.14 The muscle twitch.

Finally, as the stimulation frequency continues to increase, muscle tension increases until it reaches maximal tension. At this point all evidence of muscle relaxation disappears and the contractions fuse into a smooth, sustained contraction plateau called **fused** or **complete tetanus** (tet′ah-nus; *tetan* = rigid, tense) (Figure 9.15c). (Note that this term is often confused with the bacterial disease called tetanus that causes severe involuntary contractions.) In the real world, fused tetanus happens infrequently, for example, when someone shows superhuman strength by lifting a fallen tree limb off a companion.

Vigorous muscle activity cannot continue indefinitely. Prolonged tetanus inevitably leads to muscle fatigue, a situation in which the muscle cannot contract and its tension drops to zero.

(a) A single stimulus is delivered. The muscle contracts and relaxes.

(b) If another stimulus is applied before the muscle relaxes completely, then more tension results. This is wave (or temporal) summation and results in unfused (or incomplete) tetanus.

(c) At higher stimulus frequencies, there is no relaxation at all between stimuli. This is fused (complete) tetanus.

Figure 9.15 A muscle's response to changes in stimulation frequency. (Note that tension is measured in grams.)

9

Figure 9.16 Relationship between stimulus intensity (graph at top) and muscle tension (tracing below). Below threshold voltage, the tracing shows no muscle response (stimuli 1 and 2). Once threshold (3) is reached, increases in voltage excite (recruit) more and more motor units until the maximal stimulus is reached (7). Further increases in stimulus voltage produce no further increase in contractile strength.

Muscle Response to Changes in Stimulus Strength Wave summation contributes to contractile force, but its primary function is to produce smooth, continuous muscle contractions by rapidly stimulating a specific number of muscle cells. **Recruitment**, also called **multiple motor unit summation**, controls the force of contraction more precisely. In the laboratory, recruitment is achieved by delivering shocks of increasing voltage to the muscle, calling more and more muscle fibers into play.

- Stimuli that produce no observable contractions are **subthreshold stimuli**.

- The stimulus at which the first observable contraction occurs is called the **threshold stimulus** (Figure 9.16). Beyond this point, the muscle contracts more and more vigorously as the stimulus strength increases.

- The **maximal stimulus** is the strongest stimulus that increases contractile force. It represents the point at which all the muscle's motor units are recruited.

Figure 9.17 The size principle of recruitment. Recruitment of motor neurons controlling skeletal muscle fibers is orderly and follows the size principle.

Increasing the stimulus intensity beyond the maximal stimulus does not produce a stronger contraction. In the body, the same phenomenon is caused by neural activation of an increasingly large number of motor units serving the muscle.

The recruitment process is not random. Instead it is dictated by the *size principle* (Figure 9.17). In any muscle:

- The motor units with the smallest muscle fibers are activated first because they are controlled by the smallest, most highly excitable motor neurons.

- As motor units with larger and larger muscle fibers begin to be excited, contractile strength increases.

- The largest motor units, containing large, coarse muscle fibers, have as much as 50 times the contractile force of the smallest ones. They are controlled by the largest, least excitable (highest-threshold) neurons and are activated only when the most powerful contraction is necessary.

Why is the size principle important? It allows the increases in force during weak contractions (for example, those that maintain posture or slow movements) to occur in small steps, whereas gradations in muscle force are progressively greater when large amounts of force are needed for vigorous activities such as jumping or running. The size principle explains how the same hand that lightly pats your cheek can deliver a stinging slap at the volleyball during a match.

Although *all* the motor units of a muscle may be recruited simultaneously to produce an exceptionally strong contraction, motor units are more commonly activated asynchronously. At a given instant, some are in tetanus (usually unfused tetanus) while others are resting and recovering. This technique helps prolong a strong contraction by preventing or delaying fatigue. It also explains how weak contractions promoted by infrequent stimuli can remain smooth.

Figure 9.18 Isotonic (concentric) and isometric contractions.

Isotonic and Isometric Contractions

As noted earlier, there are two main categories of contractions—*isotonic* and *isometric*. In **isotonic contractions** (*iso* = same; *ton* = tension), muscle length changes and moves a load. Once sufficient tension has developed to move the load, the tension remains relatively constant through the rest of the contractile period (**Figure 9.18a**).

Isotonic contractions come in two "flavors"—*concentric* and *eccentric*. **Concentric contractions** are those in which the muscle shortens and does work, such as picking up a book or

kicking a ball. Concentric contractions are probably more familiar, but **eccentric contractions**, in which the muscle generates force as it lengthens, are equally important for coordination and purposeful movements.

Eccentric contractions occur in your calf muscle, for example, as you walk up a steep hill. Eccentric contractions are about 50% more forceful than concentric ones at the same load and more often cause delayed-onset muscle soreness. (Consider how your calf muscles *feel* the day after hiking up that hill.) The reason is unclear, but it may be that the muscle stretching that occurs during eccentric contractions causes microtears in the muscles.

Biceps curls provide a simple example of how concentric and eccentric contractions work together in our everyday activities. When you flex your elbow to raise this textbook to your shoulder, the biceps muscle in your arm is contracting concentrically. When you straighten your arm to return the book to the desktop, the isotonic contraction of your biceps is eccentric. Basically, eccentric contractions put the body in position to contract concentrically. All jumping and throwing activities involve both types of contraction.

In **isometric contractions** (*metric* = measure), tension may build to the muscle's peak tension-producing capacity, but the muscle *neither shortens nor lengthens* (Figure 9.18b). Isometric contractions occur when a muscle attempts to move a load that is greater than the force (tension) the muscle is able to develop—think of trying to lift a piano single-handedly. Muscles contract isometrically when they act primarily to maintain upright posture or to hold joints stationary while movements occur at other joints.

Consider a knee bend. When you squat for a few seconds, the quadriceps muscles of your anterior thigh contract isometrically to hold your knee in the flexed position. When you start to rise to the upright position, they continue to contract isometrically until their tension exceeds the load (weight of your upper body). At that point muscle shortening (concentric contraction) begins. So the quadriceps contractile sequence for a deep knee bend from start to finish is (1) flex knee (eccentric), (2) hold squat position (isometric), (3) extend knee (isometric, then concentric). Of course, this list does not even begin to consider the isometric contractions of the posterior thigh muscles or of the trunk muscles that maintain a relatively erect trunk posture during this movement.

Electrochemical and mechanical events occurring within a muscle are identical in both isotonic and isometric contractions. However, the results are different. In isotonic contractions, the thin filaments slide. In isometric contractions, the cross bridges generate force but do *not* move the thin filaments, so there is no change in the banding pattern from that of the resting state. (You could say that they are "spinning their wheels" on the same actin binding sites.)

Muscle Tone

Skeletal muscles are described as voluntary, but even relaxed muscles are almost always slightly contracted, a phenomenon called **muscle tone**. Muscle tone is due to spinal reflexes that activate first one group of motor units and then another in response to activated stretch receptors in the muscles. Muscle tone does not produce active movements, but it keeps the muscles firm, healthy, and ready to respond to stimulation. Skeletal muscle tone also helps stabilize joints and maintain posture.

☑ **Check Your Understanding**

10. What is a motor unit?
11. What is happening in the muscle during the latent period of a twitch contraction?
12. Jay is competing in a chin-up competition. What type of muscle contractions are occurring in his biceps muscles

immediately after he grabs the bar? As his body begins to move upward toward the bar? When his body begins to approach the mat?

For answers, see Appendix H.

Muscle Metabolism

✓ Describe three ways in which ATP is regenerated during skeletal muscle contraction.

✓ Define EPOC and muscle fatigue. List possible causes of muscle fatigue.

Providing Energy for Contraction

As a muscle contracts, ATP supplies the energy to move and detach cross bridges, operate the calcium pump in the SR, and return Na^+ and K^+ to the cell exterior and interior respectively after excitation-contraction coupling. Surprisingly, muscles store very limited reserves of ATP—4 to 6 seconds' worth at most, just enough to get you going. Because ATP is the *only* energy source used directly for contractile activities, it must be regenerated as fast as it is broken down if contraction is to continue.

Fortunately, after ATP is hydrolyzed to ADP and inorganic phosphate in muscle fibers, it is regenerated within a fraction of a second by one or more of the three pathways summarized in **Figure 9.19**: (1) direct phosphorylation of ADP by creatine phosphate, (2) anaerobic, glycolysis, which converts glucose to lactic acid, and (3) aerobic respiration. All body cells use glycolysis and aerobic respiration to produce ATP, so we touch on them here but describe them in detail later, in Chapter 24.

Direct Phosphorylation of ADP by Creatine Phosphate (Figure 9.19a) As we begin to exercise vigorously, the demand for ATP soars and consumes the ATP stored in working muscles within a few twitches. Then **creatine phosphate (CP)** (kre'ahtin), a unique high-energy molecule stored in muscles, is tapped to regenerate ATP while the metabolic pathways adjust to the suddenly higher demand for ATP.

Coupling CP with ADP transfers energy and a phosphate group from CP to ADP to form ATP almost instantly:

$$\text{Creatine phosphate} + \text{ADP} \xrightarrow{\text{creatine kinase}} \text{creatine} + \text{ATP}$$

Muscle cells store two to three times more CP than ATP. The CP-ADP reaction, catalyzed by the enzyme **creatine kinase**, is so efficient that the amount of ATP in muscle cells changes very little during the initial period of contraction.

Together, stored ATP and CP provide for maximum muscle power for about 15 seconds—long enough to energize a 100-meter dash (slightly longer if the activity is less vigorous). The coupled reaction is readily reversible, and to keep CP "on tap," CP reserves are replenished during periods of rest or inactivity.

Anaerobic Pathway: Glycolysis and Lactic Acid Formation (Figure 9.19b) As stored ATP and CP are exhausted, more ATP is generated by breaking down (catabolizing) glucose obtained from the blood or glycogen stored in the muscle. The initial phase of glucose breakdown is **glycolysis** (gli-kol'ĭ-sis;

Figure 9.19 Pathways for regenerating ATP during muscle activity. The fastest pathway is direct phosphorylation **(a)**, and the slowest is aerobic respiration **(c)**.

"sugar splitting"). This pathway occurs in both the presence and the absence of oxygen, but because it does not use oxygen, it is an anaerobic (an-a′er-ōb-ik; "without oxygen") pathway. During glycolysis, glucose is broken down to two *pyruvic acid* molecules, releasing enough energy to form small amounts of ATP (2 ATP per glucose).

Ordinarily, pyruvic acid produced during glycolysis then enters the mitochondria and reacts with oxygen to produce still more ATP in the oxygen-using pathway called aerobic respiration, described shortly. But when muscles contract vigorously and contractile activity reaches about 70% of the maximum possible (for example, when you run 600 meters with maximal effort), the bulging muscles compress the blood vessels within them, impairing blood flow and oxygen delivery. Under these anaerobic conditions, most of the pyruvic acid produced during glycolysis is converted into **lactic acid**, and the overall process is referred to as **anaerobic glycolysis**. Thus, during oxygen deficit, lactic acid is the end product of cellular metabolism of glucose.

Most of the lactic acid diffuses out of the muscles into the bloodstream. Subsequently, the liver, heart, or kidney cells pick up the lactic acid and use it as an energy source. Additionally, liver cells can reconvert it to pyruvic acid or glucose and release it back into the bloodstream for muscle use, or convert it to glycogen for storage.

The anaerobic pathway harvests only about 5% as much ATP from each glucose molecule as the aerobic pathway, but it produces ATP about 2½ times faster. For this reason, when large amounts of ATP are needed for moderate periods (30–40 seconds) of strenuous muscle activity, glycolysis can provide most of the ATP needed as long as the required fuels and enzymes are available. Together, stored ATP and CP and the glycolysis–lactic acid pathway can support strenuous muscle activity for nearly a minute.

Although anaerobic glycolysis readily fuels spurts of vigorous exercise, it has shortcomings. Huge amounts of glucose are used to produce relatively small harvests of ATP, and the accumulating lactic acid is partially responsible for muscle soreness during intense exercise.

Aerobic Respiration (Figure 9.19c)   Because the amount of creatine phosphate is limited, muscles must metabolize nutrients to transfer energy from foodstuffs to ATP. During rest and light to moderate exercise, even if prolonged, 95% of the ATP used for muscle activity comes from aerobic respiration. **Aerobic respiration** occurs in the mitochondria, requires oxygen, and involves a sequence of chemical reactions that break the bonds of fuel molecules and release energy to make ATP.

Aerobic respiration, which includes glycolysis and the reactions that take place in the mitochondria, breaks down glucose entirely. Water, carbon dioxide, and large amounts of ATP are its final products.

$$\text{Glucose} + \text{oxygen} \longrightarrow \text{carbon dioxide} + \text{water} + \text{ATP}$$

The carbon dioxide released diffuses out of the muscle tissue into the blood, to be removed from the body by the lungs.

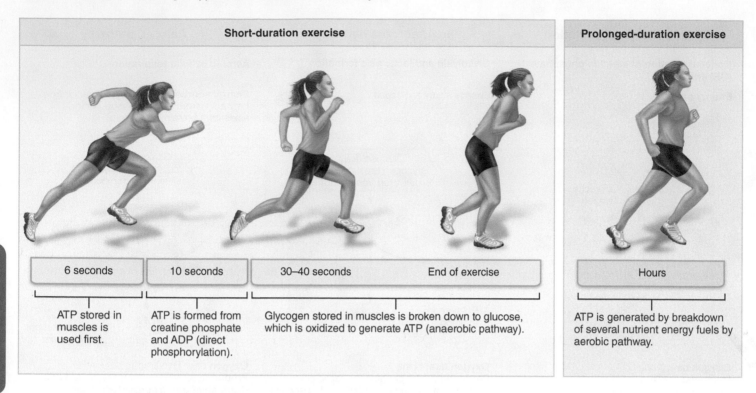

Short-duration exercise				Prolonged-duration exercise
6 seconds	10 seconds	30–40 seconds	End of exercise	Hours
ATP stored in muscles is used first.	ATP is formed from creatine phosphate and ADP (direct phosphorylation).	Glycogen stored in muscles is broken down to glucose, which is oxidized to generate ATP (anaerobic pathway).		ATP is generated by breakdown of several nutrient energy fuels by aerobic pathway.

Figure 9.20 Comparison of energy sources used during short-duration exercise and prolonged-duration exercise.

As exercise begins, muscle glycogen provides most of the fuel. Shortly thereafter, bloodborne glucose, pyruvic acid from glycolysis, and free fatty acids are the major sources of fuels. After about 30 minutes, fatty acids become the major energy fuels. Aerobic respiration provides a high yield of ATP (about 32 ATP per glucose), but it is slow because of its many steps and it requires continuous delivery of oxygen and nutrient fuels to keep it going.

Energy Systems Used During Sports Which pathways predominate during exercise? As long as a muscle cell has enough oxygen, it will form ATP by the aerobic pathway. When ATP demands are within the capacity of the aerobic pathway, light to moderate muscular activity can continue for several hours in well-conditioned individuals **(Figure 9.20)**. However, when exercise demands begin to exceed the ability of the muscle cells to carry out the necessary reactions quickly enough, anaerobic pathways begin to contribute more and more of the total ATP generated. The length of time a muscle can continue to contract using aerobic pathways is called **aerobic endurance**, and the point at which muscle metabolism converts to anaerobic glycolysis is called **anaerobic threshold**.

Activities that require a surge of power but last only a few seconds, such as weight lifting, diving, and sprinting, rely entirely on ATP and CP stores. The more on-and-off or burstlike activities of tennis, soccer, and a 100-meter swim appear to be fueled almost entirely by anaerobic glycolysis (Figure 9.20). Prolonged activities such as marathon runs and jogging, where endurance rather than power is the goal, depend mainly on aerobic respiration using both glucose and fatty acids as fuels.

Levels of CP and ATP don't change much during prolonged exercise because ATP is generated at the same rate as it is used—a "pay as you go" system. Compared to anaerobic energy production, aerobic generation of ATP is relatively slow, but the ATP harvest is enormous.

Muscle Fatigue

Muscle fatigue is a state of *physiological inability to contract* even though the muscle still may be receiving stimuli. Although many factors appear to contribute to fatigue, its specific causes are not fully understood. Most experimental evidence indicates that fatigue is due to a problem in excitation-contraction coupling or, in rare cases, problems at the neuromuscular junction. Availability of ATP declines during contraction, but it is abnormal for a muscle to totally run out of ATP. So, lack of ATP is not a fatigue-producing factor in moderate exercise.

Several ionic imbalances contribute to muscle fatigue. As action potentials are transmitted, potassium is lost from the muscle cells, and accumulates in the fluids of the T tubules. This ionic change disturbs the membrane potential of the muscle cells and halts Ca^{2+} release from the SR.

Theoretically, in short-duration exercise, an accumulation of inorganic phosphate (P_i) from CP and ATP breakdown may interfere with calcium release from the SR. Alternatively, it may interfere with the release of P_i from myosin and thus hamper myosin's power strokes. Lactic acid has long been assumed to be a major cause of fatigue, and excessive intracellular accumulation of lactic acid (which causes the muscles to ache) raises the concentration of H^+ and alters contractile proteins. However, pH is normally regulated within normal limits in all but the greatest degree of exertion. Additionally, lactic acid actually counteracts high K⁺ levels, which do lead to muscle fatigue (as noted above).

In general, intense exercise of short duration produces fatigue rapidly via ionic disturbances that alter E-C coupling, but recovery is also rapid. In contrast, the slow-developing fatigue of prolonged low-intensity exercise may require several hours for complete recovery. It appears that this type of exercise damages the SR, interfering with Ca^{2+} regulation and release, and therefore with muscle activation.

Excess Postexercise Oxygen Consumption (EPOC)

Whether or not fatigue occurs, vigorous exercise alters a muscle's chemistry dramatically. For a muscle to return to its resting state, all the following must occur:

- Its oxygen reserves in myoglobin must be replenished.
- The accumulated lactic acid must be reconverted to pyruvic acid.
- Glycogen stores must be replaced.
- ATP and creatine phosphate reserves must be resynthesized.

The use of these muscle stores during anaerobic exercise simply defers when the oxygen is consumed, because replacing them requires oxygen uptake and aerobic metabolism after exercise ends. Additionally, the liver must convert any lactic acid persisting in blood to glucose or glycogen. Once exercise stops, the repayment process begins.

The extra amount of oxygen that the body must take in for these restorative processes is called the **excess postexercise oxygen consumption (EPOC)**, formerly called the oxygen debt. EPOC represents the difference between the amount of oxygen needed for totally aerobic muscle activity and the amount actually used. All anaerobic sources of ATP used during muscle activity contribute to EPOC.

Heat Production During Muscle Activity

Only about 40% of the energy released during muscle contraction is converted to useful work (still, this percentage is significantly higher than that of many mechanical devices). The rest is given off as heat, which has to be dealt with to maintain body homeostasis.

When you exercise vigorously, you start to feel hot as the liberated heat warms your blood. Like a car's cooling system that dissipates heat, several homeostatic processes prevent heat in the body from building to dangerous levels. These processes include sweating and radiating heat from the skin surface.

Shivering represents the opposite side of homeostatic balance. In this case the body is too cold and muscle contractions are used to produce more heat.

☑ Check Your Understanding

13. When Eric returned from jogging, he was breathing heavily, sweating profusely, and complained that his legs ached and felt weak. His wife poured him a sports drink and urged him to take it easy until he could "catch his breath." On the basis of what you have learned about muscle energy metabolism, respond to the following questions: Why is Eric breathing heavily? Which ATP-generating pathway have his working muscles been using that makes him breathless? What metabolic products might account for his sore muscles and muscle weakness?

For answers, see Appendix H.

Force of Muscle Contraction

✓ Describe factors that influence the force, velocity, and duration of skeletal muscle contraction.

✓ Describe three types of skeletal muscle fibers and explain the relative value of each type.

The force of muscle contraction depends on the number of myosin cross bridges that are attached. This in turn is affected by four factors **(Figure 9.21)**: (1) number of muscle fibers stimulated, (2) relative size of the fibers, (3) frequency of stimulation, and (4) degree of muscle stretch. Let's examine the role of each factor.

Number of Muscle Fibers Recruited

As already discussed, the more motor units that are recruited, the greater the muscle force.

Size of Muscle Fibers

The bulkier the muscle (the greater its cross-sectional area), the more tension it can develop and the greater its strength, but there is more to it than this. As noted earlier, the large fibers of large motor units produce the most powerful movements. Regular resistance exercise increases muscle force by causing muscle cells to *hypertrophy* (hi-per′tro-fe), or increase in size.

Frequency of Stimulation

As a muscle begins to contract, the force generated by the cross bridges—the **internal tension**—stretches the connective tissue sheaths (noncontractile components). These in turn become taut and transfer their tension, called the **external tension**, to the load

| Large number of muscle fibers recruited | Large muscle fibers | High frequency of stimulation (wave summation and tetanus) | Muscle and sarcomere stretched to slightly over 100% of resting length |

↑ **Contractile force** (more cross bridges attached)

Figure 9.21 Factors that increase the force of skeletal muscle contraction.

Figure 9.22 Length-tension relationships of sarcomeres in skeletal muscles. A muscle generates maximum force when it is between 80 and 120% of its optimal resting length. Increases and decreases beyond this optimal range reduce its force and ability to generate tension.

(muscle insertion). When the contraction ends, the noncontractile components recoil and help return the muscle to its resting length.

Time is required to take up slack and stretch the noncontractile components, and while this is happening, the internal tension is already declining. So, in brief twitch contractions, the external tension is always less than the internal tension. However, when a muscle is stimulated rapidly, contractions are summed, becoming stronger and more vigorous and ultimately producing tetanus (see Figure 9.15).

During tetanic contractions more time is available to stretch the noncontractile components, and external tension approaches the internal tension. So, the more rapidly a muscle is stimulated, the greater the force it exerts.

Degree of Muscle Stretch

The optimal operating length for a muscle fiber is the length at which it can generate maximum force (Figure 9.21 and Figure 9.22). Within a sarcomere, the ideal **length-tension relationship** occurs when a muscle is slightly stretched and the thin and thick filaments overlap optimally, because this relationship permits sliding along nearly the entire length of the thin filaments.

If a muscle fiber stretches so much that the filaments do not overlap, the myosin heads have nothing to attach to and cannot generate tension. Alternatively, if the sarcomeres are so compressed and cramped that the Z discs abut the thick myofilaments, and the thin filaments touch and interfere with one another, little or no further shortening can occur.

If you stretch a muscle to various extents and stimulate it tetanically, the active tension the muscle can generate varies with length (Figure 9.22). A severely stretched muscle (say one over 180% of its optimal length) cannot develop tension. Likewise, at 75% of a muscle's resting length, its ability to generate force (or shorten) is limited because the actin myofilaments in its sarcomeres overlap and the thick filaments run into the Z discs, restricting further shortening.

In the body, skeletal muscles are maintained near their optimal operating length by the way they are attached to bones. The joints normally prevent bone movements that would stretch attached muscles beyond their optimal range.

Velocity and Duration of Contraction

Muscles vary in how fast they can contract and how long they can continue to contract before they fatigue. These characteristics are influenced by muscle fiber type, load, and recruitment.

Muscle Fiber Type

There are several ways of classifying muscle fibers, but learning about these classes will be easier if you pay attention to just two functional characteristics:

- **Speed of contraction.** On the basis of speed (velocity) of fiber shortening, there are **slow fibers** and **fast fibers**. The difference reflects how fast their myosin ATPases split ATP, and the pattern of electrical activity of their motor neurons. Contraction duration also varies with fiber type and depends on how quickly Ca^{2+} moves from the cytosol into the SR.

- **Major pathways for forming ATP.** The cells that rely mostly on the oxygen-using aerobic pathways for ATP generation are **oxidative fibers**. Those that rely more on anaerobic glycolysis are **glycolytic fibers**.

Using these two criteria, we can classify skeletal muscle cells as: **slow oxidative fibers**, **fast oxidative fibers**, or **fast glycolytic fibers**.

Table 9.2 gives details about each group, but a word to the wise: Do not approach this information by rote memorization—you'll just get frustrated. Instead, start with what you know for any category and see how the characteristics listed support that.

For example, think about a *slow oxidative fiber* (Table 9.2, first column, and Figure 9.23, right side). We can see that it

- Contracts *slowly* because its myosin ATPases are slow (a criterion)

- Depends on *oxygen* delivery and aerobic pathways (its major pathways for forming ATP give it *high oxidative capacity*—a criterion)

- Resists fatigue and has high endurance (typical of fibers that depend on aerobic metabolism)
- Is thin (a large amount of cytoplasm impedes diffusion of O_2 and nutrients from the blood)
- Has relatively little power (a thin cell can contain only a limited number of myofibrils)
- Has many mitochondria (actual sites of oxygen use)
- Has a rich capillary supply (the better to deliver bloodborne O_2)
- Is red (its color stems from an abundant supply of myoglobin, muscle's oxygen-binding pigment that stores O_2 reserves in the cell and helps O_2 diffuse through the cell)

Add these features together and you have a muscle fiber best suited to endurance-type activities.

Now think about a *fast glycolytic fiber* (Table 9.2, third column, and Figure 9.23, left side). In contrast, it

- Contracts *rapidly* due to the activity of fast myosin ATPases
- Does not use oxygen
- Depends on plentiful *glycogen* reserves for fuel rather than on blood-delivered nutrients
- Tires quickly because glycogen reserves are short-lived and lactic acid accumulates quickly, making it a fatigable fiber
- Has a large diameter, indicating the plentiful myofilaments that allow it to contract powerfully before it "poops out"

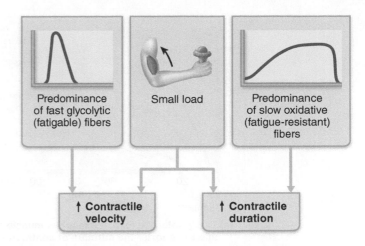

Figure 9.23 Factors influencing velocity and duration of skeletal muscle contraction.

- Has few mitochondria, little myoglobin and few capillaries (making it white), and is a much thicker cell (because it doesn't depend on continuous oxygen and nutrient diffusion from the blood)

For these reasons, a fast glycolytic fiber is best suited for short-term, rapid, intense movements (moving furniture across the room, for example).

Table 9.2	Structural and Functional Characteristics of the Three Types of Skeletal Muscle Fibers		
	SLOW OXIDATIVE FIBERS	**FAST OXIDATIVE FIBERS**	**FAST GLYCOLYTIC FIBERS**
Metabolic Characteristics			
Speed of contraction	Slow	Fast	Fast
Myosin ATPase activity	Slow	Fast	Fast
Primary pathway for ATP synthesis	Aerobic	Aerobic (some anaerobic glycolysis)	Anaerobic glycolysis
Myoglobin content	High	High	Low
Glycogen stores	Low	Intermediate	High
Recruitment order	First	Second	Third
Rate of fatigue	Slow (fatigue-resistant)	Intermediate (moderately fatigue-resistant)	Fast (fatigable)
Activities Best Suited For			
	Endurance-type activities—e.g., running a marathon; maintaining posture (antigravity muscles)	Sprinting, walking	Short-term intense or powerful movements, e.g., hitting a baseball
Structural Characteristics			
Color	Red	Red to pink	White (pale)
Fiber diameter	Small	Intermediate	Large
Mitochondria	Many	Many	Few
Capillaries	Many	Many	Few

(a) The greater the load, the less the muscle shortens and the shorter the duration of contraction

(b) The greater the load, the slower the contraction

Figure 9.24 Influence of load on duration and velocity of muscle contraction.

Finally, consider the less common intermediate muscle fiber types, called *fast oxidative fibers* (Table 9.2, middle column). They have many characteristics intermediate between the other two types (fiber diameter and power, for example). Like fast glycolytic fibers, they contract quickly, but like slow oxidative fibers, they are oxygen dependent and have a rich supply of myoglobin and capillaries.

Some muscles have a predominance of one fiber type, but most contain a mixture of fiber types, which gives them a range of contractile speeds and fatigue resistance. For example, a calf muscle can propel us in a sprint (using its white fast glycolytic fibers) or a long-distance race (making good use of its slow and fast oxidative fibers). But, as might be expected, all muscle fibers in a particular *motor unit* are of the same type.

Although everyone's muscles contain mixtures of the three fiber types, some people have relatively more of one kind. These differences are genetically initiated, but can be modified by exercise and no doubt determine athletic capabilities, such as endurance versus strength, to a large extent. For example, muscles of marathon runners have a high percentage of slow oxidative fibers (about 80%), while those of sprinters contain a higher percentage (about 60%) of fast oxidative and glycolytic fibers. Interconversion between the "fast" fiber types occurs as a result of specific exercise regimes, as we'll describe below.

Load

Because muscles are attached to bones, they are always pitted against some resistance, or load, when they contract. As you might expect, they contract fastest when there is no added load on them. A greater load results in a longer latent period, a slower contraction, and a shorter duration of contraction **(Figure 9.24)**. If the load exceeds the muscle's maximum tension, the speed of shortening is zero and the contraction is isometric (see Figure 9.18b).

Recruitment

In the same way that many hands on a project can get a job done more quickly and also can keep working longer, the more motor units that are contracting, the faster and more prolonged the contraction.

Adaptations to Exercise

✓ Compare and contrast the effects of aerobic and resistance exercise on skeletal muscles and on other body systems.

The amount of work a muscle does is reflected in changes in the muscle itself. When used actively or strenuously, muscles may become larger or stronger, or more efficient and fatigue resistant. Inactivity, on the other hand, *always* leads to muscle weakness and wasting.

Aerobic (Endurance) Exercise

Aerobic, or **endurance**, **exercise** such as swimming, jogging, fast walking, and biking results in several recognizable changes in skeletal muscles:

■ The number of capillaries surrounding the muscle fibers increases.

■ The number of mitochondria within the muscle fibers also increases.

■ The fibers synthesize more myoglobin.

These changes occur in all fiber types, but are most dramatic in slow oxidative fibers, which depend primarily on aerobic pathways. The changes result in more efficient muscle metabolism and in greater endurance, strength, and resistance to fatigue. Additionally, regular endurance exercise may convert fast glycolytic fibers into fast oxidative fibers.

Resistance Exercise

The moderately weak but sustained muscle activity required for endurance exercise does not promote significant skeletal muscle hypertrophy, even though the exercise may go on for hours. Muscle hypertrophy—think of the bulging biceps and chest muscles of a professional weight lifter—results mainly from high-intensity **resistance exercise** (typically under anaerobic conditions) such as weight lifting or isometric exercise, which pits muscles against high-resistance or immovable forces. Here strength, not stamina, is important, and a few minutes every other day is sufficient to allow a proverbial weakling to put on 50% more muscle within a year.

The additional muscle bulk largely reflects the increased size of individual muscle fibers (particularly the fast glycolytic variety) rather than an increased number of muscle fibers. [However, some of the bulk may result from longitudinal splitting of the fibers and subsequent growth of these "split" cells, or from the proliferation and fusion of satellite cells (see p. 312). The controversy is still raging.] Vigorously stressed muscle fibers also contain more mitochondria, form more myofilaments and myofibrils, store more glycogen, and develop more connective tissue between muscle cells.

Collectively these changes promote significant increases in muscle strength and size. Resistance activities can also convert fast oxidative fibers to fast glycolytic fibers. However, if the specific exercise routine is discontinued, the converted fibers revert to their original metabolic properties.

Resistance training can produce incredibly bulging muscles, but if done unwisely, some muscles may develop more than others. Because muscles work in antagonistic pairs or groups, opposing muscles must be equally strong to work together smoothly. When muscle training is not balanced, individuals can become *muscle-bound*, which means they lack flexibility, have a generally awkward stance, and are unable to make full use of their muscles.

A Balanced Exercise Program

Whatever the activity, exercise gains adhere to the *overload principle*. Forcing a muscle to work hard increases muscle strength and endurance. As muscles adapt to these greater demands, they must be overloaded even more to produce further gains.

However, always follow a heavy-workout day with a day of rest or an easy workout to let your muscles recover and repair themselves. Doing too much too soon, or ignoring the warning signs of muscle or joint pain, increases your risk of **overuse injuries** that may lead to lifetime disability.

Endurance and resistance exercises produce different patterns of muscular response, so it is important to know what your exercise goals are. Lifting weights will not improve your endurance for a triathlon. By the same token, jogging will do little to improve your muscle definition or enhance your strength for moving furniture. A program that alternates aerobic and anaerobic activities provides the best balance for optimal health.

Homeostatic Imbalance 9.3

To remain healthy, muscles must be active. Immobilization due to enforced bed rest or loss of neural stimulation results in *disuse atrophy* (degeneration and loss of mass), which begins almost as soon as the muscles are immobilized. Under such conditions, muscle strength can decline at the rate of 5% per day!

As noted earlier, even at rest, muscles receive weak intermittent stimuli from the nervous system. When totally deprived of neural stimulation, a paralyzed muscle may atrophy to one-quarter of its initial size. Fibrous connective tissue replaces the lost muscle tissue, making muscle rehabilitation impossible. +

☑ Check Your Understanding

16. How do aerobic and resistance exercise differ in their effects on muscle size and function?

For answers, see Appendix H.

Smooth Muscle

✓ Compare the gross and microscopic anatomy of smooth muscle cells to that of skeletal muscle cells.

✓ Compare and contrast the contractile mechanisms and the means of activation of skeletal and smooth muscles.

✓ Distinguish between unitary and multi unit smooth muscle structurally and functionally.

Except for the heart, which is made of cardiac muscle, the muscle in the walls of all the body's hollow organs is almost entirely smooth muscle. The chemical and mechanical events of contraction are essentially the same in all muscle tissues, but smooth muscle is distinctive in several ways, as summarized in **Table 9.3** on p. 310.

Microscopic Structure of Smooth Muscle Fibers

Smooth muscle fibers are spindle-shaped cells of variable size, each with one centrally located nucleus **(Figure 9.25b)**. Typically, they have a diameter of 5–10 μm and are 30–200 μm long. Skeletal muscle fibers are up to 10 times wider and thousands of times longer.

Smooth muscle lacks the coarse connective tissue sheaths seen in skeletal muscle. However, a small amount of fine connective tissue (endomysium), secreted by the smooth muscles themselves and containing blood vessels and nerves, is found between smooth muscle fibers.

Most smooth muscle is organized into sheets of closely apposed fibers. These sheets occur in the walls of all but the smallest blood vessels and in the walls of hollow organs of the respiratory, digestive, urinary, and reproductive tracts. In most cases, there are two sheets of smooth muscle with their fibers oriented at right angles to each other, as in the intestine (Figure 9.25).

- In the *longitudinal layer*, the muscle fibers run parallel to the long axis of the organ. Consequently, when these fibers contract, the organ dilates and shortens.

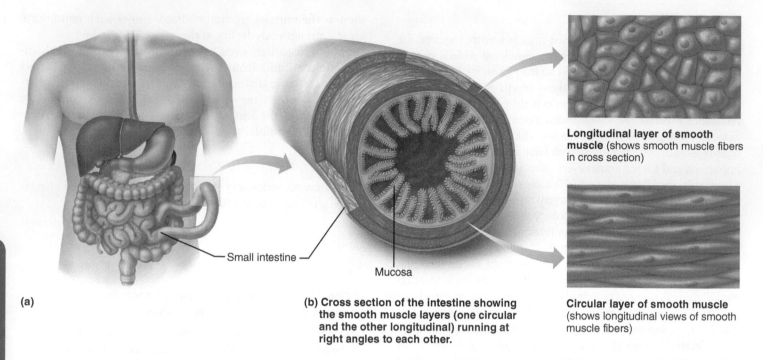

(a)

(b) **Cross section of the intestine showing the smooth muscle layers (one circular and the other longitudinal) running at right angles to each other.**

Longitudinal layer of smooth muscle (shows smooth muscle fibers in cross section)

Circular layer of smooth muscle (shows longitudinal views of smooth muscle fibers)

Figure 9.25 Arrangement of smooth muscle in the walls of hollow organs.

■ In the *circular layer*, the fibers run around the circumference of the organ. Contraction of this layer constricts the lumen of the organ and elongates the organ.

The alternating contraction and relaxation of these layers mixes substances in the lumen and squeezes them through the organ's internal pathway. This propulsive action is called **peristalsis** (per″ĭ-stal′sis; "around contraction"). Contraction of smooth muscle in the rectum, urinary bladder, and uterus helps those organs to expel their contents. Smooth muscle contraction also accounts for the constricted breathing of asthma and for stomach cramps.

Smooth muscle lacks the highly structured neuromuscular junctions of skeletal muscle. Instead, the innervating nerve fibers, which are part of the autonomic (involuntary) nervous system, have numerous bulbous swellings, called **varicosities** (Figure 9.26). The varicosities release neurotransmitter into a wide synaptic cleft in the general area of the smooth muscle cells. Such junctions are called **diffuse junctions**. Comparing the neural input to skeletal and smooth muscles, you could say that skeletal muscle gets priority mail while smooth muscle gets bulk mailings.

The sarcoplasmic reticulum of smooth muscle fibers is much less developed than that of skeletal muscle and lacks a specific pattern relative to the myofilaments. Some SR tubules of smooth muscle touch the sarcolemma at several sites, forming what resembles half-triads that may couple the action potential to calcium release from the SR.

T tubules are absent, but the sarcolemma has multiple **caveolae**, pouchlike infoldings that sequester bits of extracellular fluid containing a high concentration of Ca^{2+} close to the membrane (Figure 9.27a). Consequently, when calcium channels in the

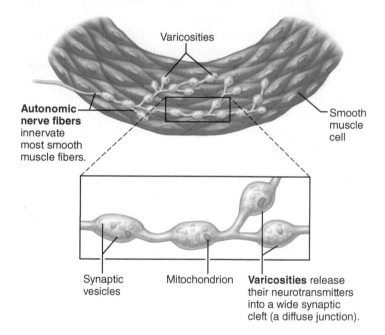

Varicosities

Autonomic nerve fibers innervate most smooth muscle fibers.

Smooth muscle cell

Synaptic vesicles

Mitochondrion

Varicosities release their neurotransmitters into a wide synaptic cleft (a diffuse junction).

Figure 9.26 Innervation of smooth muscle.

caveolae open, Ca^{2+} influx occurs rapidly. Although the SR *does* release some of the calcium that triggers contraction, most Ca^{2+} enters through calcium channels directly from the extracellular space. This situation is quite different from what we see in skeletal muscle, which does not depend on extracellular Ca^{2+} for excitation-contraction coupling. Contraction ends when cytoplasmic calcium is actively transported into the SR and out of the cell.

There are no striations in smooth muscle, as its name indicates, and therefore no sarcomeres. Smooth muscle fibers do contain interdigitating thick and thin filaments, but the myosin filaments are a lot shorter than the actin filaments and the type of myosin contained differs from skeletal muscle. The proportion and organization of smooth muscle myofilaments differ from skeletal muscle in the following ways:

- **Thick filaments are fewer but have myosin heads along their entire length.** The ratio of thick to thin filaments is much lower in smooth muscle than in skeletal muscle (1:13 compared to 1:2). However, thick filaments of smooth muscle contain actin-gripping myosin heads along their *entire length,* a feature that makes smooth muscle as powerful as a skeletal muscle of the same size. Also, in smooth muscle the myosin heads are oriented in one direction on one side of the filament and in the opposite direction on the other side.

- **No troponin complex in thin filaments.** As in skeletal muscle, tropomyosin mechanically stabilizes the thin filaments, but smooth muscle has no calcium-binding troponin complex. Instead, a protein called *calmodulin* acts as the calcium-binding site.

- **Thick and thin filaments arranged diagonally.** Bundles of contractile proteins crisscross within the smooth muscle cell so they spiral down the long axis of the cell like the stripes on a barber pole. Because of this diagonal arrangement, the smooth muscle cells contract in a twisting way so that they look like tiny corkscrews (Figure 9.27b).

- **Intermediate filament–dense body network.** Smooth muscle fibers contain a lattice-like arrangement of noncontractile *intermediate filaments* that resist tension. They attach at regular intervals to cytoplasmic structures called dense bodies (Figure 9.27). The **dense bodies**, which are also tethered to the sarcolemma, act as anchoring points for thin filaments and therefore correspond to Z discs of skeletal muscle.

The intermediate filament–dense body network forms a strong, cable-like intracellular cytoskeleton that harnesses the pull generated by the sliding of the thick and thin filaments. During contraction, areas of the sarcolemma between the dense bodies bulge outward, making the cell look puffy (Figure 9.27b). Dense bodies at the sarcolemma surface also bind the muscle cell to the connective tissue fibers outside the cell (endomysium) and to adjacent cells. This arrangement transmits the pulling force to the surrounding connective tissue and partly accounts for the synchronous contractions of most smooth muscle.

Contraction of Smooth Muscle

Mechanism of Contraction

In most cases, adjacent smooth muscle fibers exhibit slow, synchronized contractions, the whole sheet responding to a stimulus in unison. This synchronization reflects electrical coupling of smooth muscle cells by *gap junctions*, specialized cell connections described in Chapter 3. Skeletal muscle fibers are electrically isolated from one another, each stimulated to contract by its own neuromuscular junction. By contrast, gap junctions

(a) Relaxed smooth muscle fiber (note that gap junctions connect adjacent fibers)

(b) Contracted smooth muscle fiber

Figure 9.27 Intermediate filaments and dense bodies of smooth muscle fibers harness the pull generated by myosin cross bridges. Intermediate filaments attach to dense bodies throughout the sarcoplasm.

allow smooth muscles to transmit action potentials from fiber to fiber.

Some smooth muscle fibers in the stomach and small intestine are *pacemaker cells:* Once excited, they act as "drummers" to set the pace of contraction for the entire muscle sheet. These pacemakers have fluctuating membrane potentials and are self-excitatory, that is, they depolarize spontaneously in the absence of external stimuli. However, neural and chemical stimuli can modify both the rate and the intensity of smooth muscle contraction.

Contraction in smooth muscle is like contraction in skeletal muscle in the following ways:

- Actin and myosin interact by the sliding filament mechanism.
- The final trigger for contraction is a rise in the intracellular calcium ion level.
- ATP energizes the sliding process.

During excitation-contraction coupling, the tubules of the SR release Ca^{2+}, but, as mentioned above, Ca^{2+} also moves into the cell from the extracellular space via membrane channels. In all striated muscle types, calcium ions activate myosin by binding to troponin. In smooth muscle, calcium activates myosin by interacting with a regulatory molecule called **calmodulin**, a cytoplasmic calcium-binding protein. Calmodulin, in turn, interacts with a kinase enzyme called **myosin kinase** or **myosin light chain kinase** which phosphorylates the myosin, activating it **(Figure 9.28)**.

As in skeletal muscle, smooth muscle relaxes when intracellular Ca^{2+} levels drop—but getting smooth muscle to stop contracting is more complex. Events known to be involved include calcium detachment from calmodulin, active transport of Ca^{2+} into the SR and extracellular fluid, and dephosphorylation of myosin by a phosphorylase enzyme, which reduces the activity of the myosin ATPases.

9

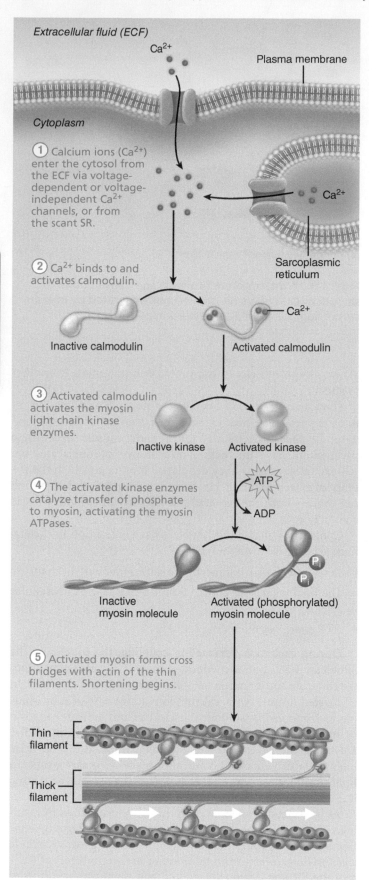

Extracellular fluid (ECF)

Ca²⁺

Plasma membrane

Cytoplasm

① Calcium ions (Ca²⁺) enter the cytosol from the ECF via voltage-dependent or voltage-independent Ca²⁺ channels, or from the scant SR.

Ca²⁺

Sarcoplasmic reticulum

② Ca²⁺ binds to and activates calmodulin.

Ca²⁺

Inactive calmodulin   Activated calmodulin

③ Activated calmodulin activates the myosin light chain kinase enzymes.

Inactive kinase   Activated kinase

ATP

ADP

④ The activated kinase enzymes catalyze transfer of phosphate to myosin, activating the myosin ATPases.

Pᵢ

Pᵢ

Inactive myosin molecule   Activated (phosphorylated) myosin molecule

⑤ Activated myosin forms cross bridges with actin of the thin filaments. Shortening begins.

Thin filament

Thick filament

Figure 9.28 Sequence of events in excitation-contraction coupling of smooth muscle.

Energy Efficiency of Smooth Muscle Contraction

Smooth muscle takes 30 times longer to contract and relax than does skeletal muscle, but it can maintain the same contractile tension for prolonged periods at less than 1% of the energy cost. If skeletal muscle is like a speedy windup car that quickly runs down, then smooth muscle is like a steady, heavy-duty engine that lumbers along tirelessly.

Part of the striking energy economy of smooth muscle is the sluggishness of its ATPases compared to those in skeletal muscle. Moreover, smooth muscle myofilaments may latch together during prolonged contractions, saving energy in that way as well. Smooth muscle cells may maintain that *latch state* even after myosin is dephosphorylated.

The smooth muscle in small arterioles and other visceral organs routinely maintains a moderate degree of contraction, called *smooth muscle tone*, day in and day out without fatiguing. Smooth muscle has low energy requirements, and as a rule, it makes enough ATP via aerobic pathways to keep up with the demand.

Regulation of Contraction

The contraction of smooth muscle can be regulated by nerves, hormones, or local chemical changes. Let's briefly consider each of these methods.

Neural Regulation   In some cases, the activation of smooth muscle by a neural stimulus is identical to that in skeletal muscle: Neurotransmitter binding generates an action potential, which is coupled to a rise in calcium ions in the cytosol. However, some types of smooth muscle respond to neural stimulation with graded potentials (local electrical signals) only.

Recall that all somatic nerve endings, that is, nerve endings that excite skeletal muscle, release the neurotransmitter acetylcholine. However, different autonomic nerves serving the smooth muscle of visceral organs release different neurotransmitters, each of which may excite or inhibit a particular group of smooth muscle cells.

The effect of a specific neurotransmitter on a smooth muscle cell depends on the type of receptor molecules on the cell's sarcolemma. For example, when acetylcholine binds to ACh receptors on smooth muscle in the bronchioles (small air passageways of the lungs), the response is strong contraction that narrows the bronchioles. When norepinephrine, released by a different type of autonomic nerve fiber, binds to norepinephrine receptors on the *same* smooth muscle cells, the effect is inhibitory—the muscle relaxes, which dilates the bronchioles. However, when norepinephrine binds to smooth muscle in the walls of most blood vessels, it stimulates the smooth muscle cells to contract and constrict the vessel.

Hormones and Local Chemical Factors   Some smooth muscle layers have no nerve supply at all. Instead, they depolarize spontaneously or in response to chemical stimuli that bind to G protein–linked receptors. Other smooth muscle cells respond to both neural and chemical stimuli.

Several chemical factors cause smooth muscle to contract or relax without an action potential by enhancing or inhibiting

Ca^{2+} entry into the sarcoplasm. They include certain hormones, histamine, excess carbon dioxide, low pH, and lack of oxygen. The direct response to these chemical stimuli alters smooth muscle activity according to local tissue needs and probably is most responsible for smooth muscle tone. For example, the hormone gastrin stimulates stomach smooth muscle to contract so it can churn foodstuffs more efficiently. We will consider activation of smooth muscle in specific organs as we discuss each organ in subsequent chapters.

Special Features of Smooth Muscle Contraction

Smooth muscle is intimately involved in the functioning of most hollow organs and has a number of unique characteristics. We have already considered some of these—smooth muscle tone, slow prolonged contractions, and low energy requirements. But smooth muscle also responds differently to stretch and can lengthen and shorten more than other muscle types. Let's take a look.

Response to Stretch Up to a point, when skeletal muscle is stretched, it responds with more vigorous contractions. Stretching of smooth muscle also provokes contraction, which automatically moves substances along an internal tract. However, the increased tension persists only briefly, and soon the muscle adapts to its new length and relaxes, while still retaining the ability to contract on demand.

This **stress-relaxation response** allows a hollow organ to fill or expand slowly to accommodate a greater volume without causing strong contractions that would expel its contents. This is an important attribute, because organs such as the stomach and intestines must store their contents long enough to digest and absorb the nutrients. Likewise, your urinary bladder must be able to store the continuously made urine until it is convenient to empty your bladder, or you would spend all your time in the bathroom.

Length and Tension Changes Smooth muscle stretches much more and generates more tension than skeletal muscles stretched to a comparable extent. As we saw in Figure 9.22, precise, highly organized sarcomeres limit how far a skeletal muscle can stretch before it is unable to generate force.

In contrast, the irregular, overlapping arrangement of smooth muscle filaments and the lack of sarcomeres allow them to generate considerable force, even when they are substantially stretched. The total length change that skeletal muscles can undergo and still function efficiently is about 60% (from 30% shorter to 30% longer than resting length), but smooth muscle can contract when it is anywhere from half to twice its resting length—a total range of 150%. This capability allows hollow organs to tolerate tremendous changes in volume without becoming flabby when they empty.

Hyperplasia All muscle cells can hypertrophy (increase in cell size), but certain smooth muscle fibers can also undergo *hyperplasia*, that is, they divide to increase their numbers. Consider the response of the uterus to the hormone estrogen. At puberty, girls' blood estrogen levels rise. As estrogen binds to uterine smooth muscle receptors, it stimulates the synthesis of more uterine smooth muscle, causing the uterus to grow to adult size. During pregnancy, high blood levels of estrogen stimulate uterine hyperplasia to accommodate the growing fetus.

Types of Smooth Muscle

The smooth muscle in different body organs varies substantially in its (1) fiber arrangement and organization, (2) innervation, and (3) responsiveness to various stimuli. For simplicity, however, smooth muscle is usually categorized into two major types: *unitary* and *multi unit*.

Unitary Smooth Muscle

Unitary smooth muscle, commonly called **visceral muscle** because it is in the walls of all hollow organs except the heart, is far more common. All the smooth muscle characteristics described so far pertain to unitary smooth muscle.

For example, the cells of unitary smooth muscle

- Are arranged in opposing (longitudinal and circular) sheets
- Are innervated by varicosities of autonomic nerve fibers and often exhibit rhythmic spontaneous action potentials
- Are electrically coupled by gap junctions and so contract as a unit (for this reason recruitment is not an option in unitary smooth muscle)
- Respond to various chemical stimuli

Multi Unit Smooth Muscle

The smooth muscles in the large airways to the lungs and in large arteries, the arrector pili muscles attached to hair follicles, and the internal eye muscles that adjust pupil size and allow the eye to focus visually are all examples of **multi unit smooth muscle**.

In contrast to unitary muscle, gap junctions and spontaneous depolarizations are rare. Like skeletal muscle, multi unit smooth muscle

- Consists of muscle fibers that are structurally independent of one another
- Is richly supplied with nerve endings, each of which forms a motor unit with a number of muscle fibers
- Responds to neural stimulation with graded contractions that involve recruitment

However, skeletal muscle is served by the somatic (voluntary) division of the nervous system. Multi unit smooth muscle, like unitary smooth muscle, is innervated by the autonomic (involuntary) division and also responds to hormones.

☑ **Check Your Understanding**

17. Compare the structures of skeletal and smooth muscle fibers.
18. Calcium is the trigger for contraction of all muscle types. How does its binding site differ in skeletal and smooth muscle fibers?
19. How does the stress-relaxation response suit the role of smooth muscle in hollow organs?

For answers, see Appendix H.

(Text continues on p. 312.)

Table 9.3	Comparison of Skeletal, Cardiac, and Smooth Muscle		
CHARACTERISTIC	**SKELETAL**	**CARDIAC**	**SMOOTH**
Body location	Attached to bones or (some facial muscles) to skin	Walls of the heart	Unitary muscle in walls of hollow visceral organs (other than the heart); multi unit muscle in intrinsic eye muscles, airways, large arteries
Cell shape and appearance	Single, very long, cylindrical, multinucleate cells with obvious striations	Branching chains of cells; uni- or binucleate; striations	Single, fusiform, uninucleate; no striations
Connective tissue components	Epimysium, perimysium, and endomysium	Endomysium attached to fibrous skeleton of heart	Endomysium
Presence of myofibrils composed of sarcomeres	Yes	Yes, but myofibrils are of irregular thickness	No, but actin and myosin filaments are present throughout; dense bodies anchor actin filaments
Presence of T tubules and site of invagination	Yes; two in each sarcomere at A-I junctions	Yes; one in each sarcomere at Z disc; larger diameter than those of skeletal muscle	No; only caveolae

Table 9.3 (continued)			
CHARACTERISTIC	**SKELETAL**	**CARDIAC**	**SMOOTH**
Elaborate sarcoplasmic reticulum	Yes	Less than skeletal muscle (1–8% of cell volume); scant terminal cisterns	Equivalent to cardiac muscle (1–8% of cell volume); some SR contacts the sarcolemma
Presence of gap junctions	No	Yes; at intercalated discs	Yes; in unitary muscle
Cells exhibit individual neuromuscular junctions	Yes	No	Not in unitary muscle; yes in multi unit muscle
Regulation of contraction	Voluntary via axon terminals of the somatic nervous system	Involuntary; intrinsic system regulation; also autonomic nervous system controls; hormones; stretch	Involuntary; autonomic nerves, hormones, local chemicals; stretch
Source of Ca²⁺ for calcium pulse	Sarcoplasmic reticulum (SR)	SR and from extracellular fluid	SR and from extracellular fluid
Site of calcium regulation	Troponin on actin-containing thin filaments	Troponin on actin-containing thin filaments	Calmodulin in the cytosol
Presence of pacemaker(s)	No	Yes	Yes (in unitary muscle only)
Effect of nervous system stimulation	Excitation	Excitation or inhibition	Excitation or inhibition
Speed of contraction	Slow to fast	Slow	Very slow
Rhythmic contraction	No	Yes	Yes in unitary muscle
Response to stretch	Contractile strength increases with degree of stretch (to a point)	Contractile strength increases with degree of stretch	Stress-relaxation response
Respiration	Aerobic and anaerobic	Aerobic	Mainly aerobic

Figure 9.29 **Myoblasts fuse to form a multinucleate skeletal muscle fiber.**

Developmental Aspects of Muscles

✓ Describe embryonic development of muscle tissues and the changes that occur in skeletal muscles with age.

With rare exceptions, all three types of muscle tissue develop from embryonic mesoderm cells called **myoblasts**. In forming skeletal muscle tissue, several myoblasts fuse to form multinuclear *myotubes* **(Figure 9.29)**. Integrins (cell adhesion proteins) in the myoblast membranes guide this process and soon functional sarcomeres appear. Skeletal muscle fibers are contracting by week 7 when the embryo is only about 2.5 cm (1 inch) long.

Initially, ACh receptors "sprout" over the entire surface of the developing myoblasts. As spinal nerves invade the muscle masses, the nerve endings target individual myoblasts and release the growth factor *agrin*. This chemical activates a muscle kinase (MuSK), which stimulates clustering and maintenance of ACh receptors at the newly forming neuromuscular junction in each muscle fiber. Then, the nerve endings release a different chemical that eliminates the receptor sites not innervated or stabilized by agrin.

Electrical activity in the neurons serving the muscle fibers also plays a critical role in muscle fiber maturation. As the somatic nervous system assumes control of muscle fibers, the number of fast and slow contractile fiber types is determined.

Myoblasts producing cardiac and smooth muscle cells do not fuse but develop gap junctions at a very early embryonic stage. Cardiac muscle is pumping blood just 3 weeks after fertilization. Specialized skeletal and cardiac muscle cells stop dividing early on but retain the ability to lengthen and thicken in a growing child and to hypertrophy in adults.

- *Satellite cells,* myoblast-like cells associated with skeletal muscle, help repair injured fibers and allow limited regeneration of dead skeletal muscle, a capability that declines with age.

- Cardiac muscle was thought to have no regenerative capability whatsoever, but recent studies suggest that cardiac cells do divide at a modest rate. Nonetheless, injured heart muscle is repaired mostly by scar tissue.

- Smooth muscles have a good regenerative capacity and smooth muscle cells of blood vessels divide regularly throughout life.

At birth, a baby's movements are uncoordinated and largely reflexive. Muscular development reflects the level of neuromuscular coordination, which develops in a head-to-toe and proximal-to-distal direction. In other words, a baby can lift its head before it can walk, and gross movements precede fine ones.

All through childhood, our control of our skeletal muscles becomes more and more sophisticated. By midadolescence, we reach the peak of our natural neural control of muscles, but can improve it by athletic or other types of training.

A frequently asked question is whether the strength difference between women and men has a biological basis. It does. Individuals vary, but on average, women's skeletal muscles make up approximately 36% of body mass, whereas men's account for about 42%. Men's greater muscular development is due primarily to the effects of testosterone on skeletal muscle, not to the effects of exercise. Body strength per unit muscle mass, however, is the same in both sexes. Strenuous muscle exercise causes more muscle enlargement in males than in females, again because of the influence of testosterone. Some athletes take large doses of synthetic male sex hormones ("steroids") to increase their muscle mass. *A Closer Look* discusses this illegal and physiologically dangerous practice.

Because of its rich blood supply, skeletal muscle is amazingly resistant to infection. Given good nutrition and moderate exercise, relatively few problems afflict skeletal muscles. However, muscular dystrophy, the world's most common genetic disorder, is a serious condition that deserves more than a passing mention.

Homeostatic Imbalance 9.4

The term **muscular dystrophy** refers to a group of inherited muscle-destroying diseases that generally appear during childhood. The affected muscles initially enlarge due to deposits of fat and connective tissue, but the muscle fibers atrophy and degenerate.

The most common and serious form is **Duchenne muscular dystrophy (DMD)**, which is inherited as a sex-linked recessive disease. It is expressed almost exclusively in males (one in every 3600 male births). This tragic disease is usually diagnosed when the boy is between 2 and 7 years old. Active, normal-appearing children become clumsy and fall frequently as their skeletal muscles weaken. The disease progresses relentlessly from the extremities upward, finally affecting the head and chest muscles and cardiac muscle. Victims rarely live beyond their early 20s, dying of respiratory failure.

DMD is caused by a defective gene for *dystrophin*, a cytoplasmic protein that links the cytoskeleton to the extracellular matrix and, like a girder, helps stabilize the sarcolemma. The fragile sarcolemma of DMD patients tears during contraction, allowing entry of excess Ca^{2+}. The deranged calcium homeostasis damages

Athletes Looking Good and Doing Better with Anabolic Steroids?

Society loves a winner and top athletes reap large social and monetary rewards. It is not surprising that some will grasp at anything that might increase their performance—including "juice," or anabolic steroids.

These drugs are variants of the male sex hormone testosterone engineered by pharmaceutical companies. They were introduced in the 1950s to treat anemia and certain muscle-wasting diseases and to prevent muscle atrophy in patients immobilized after surgery. Testosterone is responsible for the increase in muscle and bone mass and other physical changes that occur during puberty and converts boys into men.

Convinced that megadoses of steroids could produce enhanced masculinizing effects in grown men, many athletes and bodybuilders were using them by the early 1960s, a practice that is still going on. Investigations have stunned sports fans with revelations of steroid use by many elite athletes including Barry Bonds, formerly of the San Francisco Giants; Mark McGwire, formerly with the St. Louis Cardinals; and Marion Jones, one of the most celebrated women athletes of all time.

However, steroid use is not confined to professional athletes. It is estimated that nearly one in every 10 young men has tried them, and their use is also spreading among young women.

It is difficult to determine the extent of anabolic steroid use because most international competitions ban the use of drugs. Users (and prescribing physicians or drug dealers) are naturally reluctant to talk about it, and users stop doping before the event, aware that evidence of drug use is hard to find a week after they stop. Additionally, "underground" suppliers of performance-enhancing drugs keep producing new versions of designer steroids that evade standard antidoping tests. The Olympic Analytical Laboratory in Los Angeles

rocked the sports world when it revealed that a number of elite athletes tested positive for tetrahydrogestrinone (THG), a designer steroid not previously known or tested for.

There is little question that many professional bodybuilders and athletes competing in events that require muscle strength (e.g., shot put, discus throwing, and weight lifting) are heavy users. Football players have also admitted using steroids as an adjunct to training, diet, and psychological preparation for games. These athletes claim that anabolic steroids enhance muscle mass and strength, and raise oxygen-carrying capability owing to greater volume of red blood cells.

Typically, bodybuilders who use steroids combine high doses (up to 200 mg/day) via injection or transdermal skin patches with heavy resistance training. Intermittent use begins several months before an event, and commonly entails taking many anabolic steroid supplements (a method called stacking). They increase doses gradually as the competition nears.

Do the drugs do all that is claimed? Research studies report increased isometric strength and body weight in steroid users. While these are results weight lifters dream about, for runners and others requiring fine muscle coordination and endurance these changes may not translate into better performance. The "jury is still out" on this question.

Do the alleged advantages of steroids outweigh their risks? Absolutely not. Anabolic steroids cause: bloated faces (Cushingoid sign of steroid excess), acne and hair loss, shriveled testes and infertility, liver damage that promotes liver cancer, and changes in blood cholesterol levels that may predispose users to heart disease.

In addition, females can develop masculine characteristics such as smaller breasts, enlarged clitoris, excess body hair, and thinning scalp hair. The psychiatric

hazards of anabolic steroid use may be equally threatening: Recent studies indicate that one-third of users suffer serious mental problems. Depression, delusions, and manic behavior—in which users undergo Jekyll-and-Hyde personality swings and become extremely violent (termed 'roid rage)—are all common.

Another recent arrival on the scene, sold over the counter as a "nutritional performance-enhancer," is androstenedione, which is converted to testosterone in the body. Though it is taken orally (and the liver destroys much of it soon after ingestion), the few milligrams that survive temporarily boost testosterone levels. Reports of athletic wannabes from the fifth grade up sweeping the supplement off the drugstore shelves are troubling, particularly since it is not regulated by the U.S. Food and Drug Administration (FDA) and its long-term effects are unknown.

A study at Massachusetts General Hospital found that males who took androstenedione developed higher levels of the female hormone estrogen as well as testosterone, raising their risk of feminizing effects such as enlarged breasts. Youths with elevated levels of estrogen or testosterone may enter puberty early, stunting bone growth and leading to shorter-than-normal adult height.

Some people seem willing to try almost anything to win, short of killing themselves. Are they unwittingly doing this as well?

the contractile fibers, and inflammatory cells (macrophages and lymphocytes) accumulate in the surrounding connective tissue. As the regenerative capacity of the muscle is lost, and damaged cells undergo apoptosis, muscle mass drops.

There is still no cure for DMD. Current treatments are aimed at preventing or reducing spine and joint deformities and helping those with DMD remain mobile as long as possible. Thus far the only medication that has improved muscle strength and func-

tion is the steroid prednisone, but other immunosuppressant drugs may delay muscle deterioration.

One initially promising technique, *myoblast transfer therapy* (injecting healthy myoblast cells that fuse with diseased myoblasts) has been disappointing. Newer experimental therapies have reversed disease symptoms in dystrophic animal models. One of these involves injection of adeno-associated viruses carrying pared-down microdystrophin genes. A different approach

Homeostatic Interrelationships Between the Muscular System and Other Body Systems

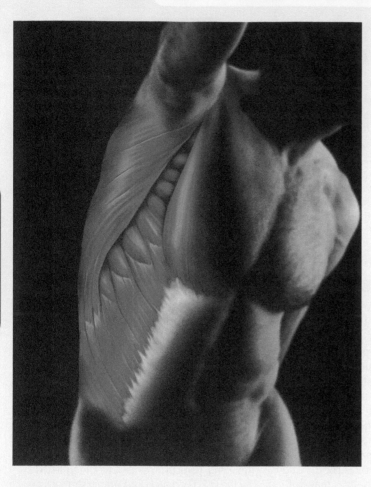

9

Endocrine System   Chapter 16

- Growth hormone and androgens influence skeletal muscle strength and mass; other hormones help regulate cardiac and smooth muscle activity

Cardiovascular System   Chapters 17–19

- Skeletal muscle activity increases efficiency of cardiovascular functioning; helps prevent atherosclerosis and causes cardiac hypertrophy
- Cardiovascular system delivers needed oxygen and nutrients to muscles

Lymphatic System/Immunity   Chapters 20–21

- Physical exercise may enhance or depress immunity depending on its intensity
- Lymphatic vessels drain leaked tissue fluids; immune system protects muscles from disease

Respiratory System   Chapter 22

- Muscular exercise increases respiratory capacity and efficiency of gas exchange
- Respiratory system provides oxygen and disposes of carbon dioxide

Digestive System   Chapter 23

- Physical activity increases gastrointestinal motility and elimination when at rest
- Digestive system provides nutrients needed for muscle health; liver metabolizes lactic acid

Urinary System   Chapters 25–26

- Physical activity promotes normal voiding behavior; skeletal muscle forms the voluntary sphincter of the urethra
- Urinary system disposes of nitrogenous wastes

Reproductive System   Chapter 27

- Skeletal muscle helps support pelvic organs (e.g., uterus); assists erection of penis and clitoris
- Testicular androgen promotes increased skeletal muscle

Integumentary System   Chapter 5

- Muscular exercise enhances circulation to skin and improves skin health
- Skin protects the muscles by external enclosure; helps dissipate heat generated by the muscles

Skeletal System   Chapters 6–8

- Skeletal muscle activity maintains bone health and strength
- Bones provide levers for muscle activity

Nervous System   Chapters 11–15

- Facial muscle activity allows emotions to be expressed
- Nervous system stimulates and regulates muscle activity
- Nervous system activity maintains muscle mass

Mastering A&P™ Access more System Connections in the Study Area at **www.masteringaandp.com**.

314

being tested is coaxing dystrophic muscles to produce more *utrophin*, a similar protein present in low amounts in adults but at much higher levels in fetal muscles. In mice at least, utrophin can compensate for dystrophin deficiency. ✚

As we age, the amount of connective tissue in our skeletal muscles increases, the number of muscle fibers decreases, and the muscles become stringier, or more sinewy. By age 30, even in healthy people, a gradual loss of muscle mass, called *sarcopenia* (sar-co-pe'ne-ah), begins. Apparently the same regulatory molecules (transcription factors, enzymes, hormones, and others) that promote muscle growth also oversee this type of muscle atrophy. Because skeletal muscles form so much of the body mass, body weight and muscle strength decline in tandem. By age 80, muscle strength usually decreases by about 50%. This "flesh wasting" condition has serious health implications for the elderly, particularly because falling becomes a common event.

Muscles can also suffer indirectly. Aging of the cardiovascular system affects nearly every organ in the body, and muscles are no exception. As atherosclerosis takes its toll and begins to block distal arteries, a circulatory condition called *intermittent claudication* (klaw"dĭ-ka'shun; "limping") occurs in some individuals. This condition restricts blood delivery to the legs, leading to excruciating pains in the leg muscles during walking, which forces the person to stop and rest.

But we don't have to slow up during old age. Regular exercise helps reverse sarcopenia, and frail elders who begin to "pump iron" (lift leg and hand weights) can rebuild muscle mass and dramatically increase their strength. Performing those lifting exercises rapidly can improve our ability to carry out the "explosive" movements needed to rise from a chair. Even moderate activity, like taking a walk daily, improves neuromuscular function and enhances independent living.

Smooth muscle is remarkably trouble free. Most problems that impair gastrointestinal function, for instance, stem from irritants such as excess alcohol, spicy foods, or bacterial infection. Under such conditions, smooth muscle motility increases in an attempt to rid the body of irritating agents, and diarrhea or vomiting occur.

☑ Check Your Understanding

20. How is the multinucleate condition achieved during development of skeletal muscle fibers?
21. What does it mean when we say "muscles get stringier with age"?
22. How can we defer (or reverse) some of the effects of age on skeletal muscles?

For answers, see Appendix H.

The capacity for movement is a property of all cells but, with the exception of muscle, these movements are largely restricted to intracellular events. Skeletal muscles, the major focus of this chapter, permit us to interact with our external environment in an amazing number of ways, and they also contribute to our internal homeostasis as summarized in *System Connections*.

In this chapter we have covered muscle anatomy from gross to molecular levels and have considered muscle physiology in some detail. Chapter 10 continues from this point to explain how skeletal muscles interact with bones and with each other, and then describes the individual skeletal muscles that make up the muscular system of the body.

Chapter Summary

 For more chapter study tools, go to the Study Area of MasteringA&P at **www.masteringaandp.com**.
There you will find:
- Interactive Physiology **iP**
- A&PFlix *A&PFlix*
- Practice Anatomy Lab PAL
- PhysioEx **PEx**
- Videos, Practice Quizzes and Tests, MP3 Tutor Sessions, Case Studies, and much more!

Overview of Muscle Tissues (pp. 276–278)

Types of Muscle Tissue (p. 277)

1. Skeletal muscle is attached to the skeleton, is striated, and can be controlled voluntarily.
2. Cardiac muscle forms the heart, is striated, and is controlled involuntarily.
3. Smooth muscle, located chiefly in the walls of hollow organs, is controlled involuntarily. Its fibers are not striated.

Special Characteristics of Muscle Tissue (p. 277)

4. Special functional characteristics of muscle include excitability, contractility, extensibility, and elasticity.

Muscle Functions (pp. 277–278)

5. Muscles move internal and external body parts, maintain posture, stabilize joints, generate heat, and protect some visceral organs.

Skeletal Muscle (pp. 278–305)

Gross Anatomy of a Skeletal Muscle (pp. 278–279)

1. Connective tissue coverings protect and strengthen skeletal muscle fibers (cells). Superficial to deep, these are epimysium, perimysium, and endomysium.
2. Skeletal muscle attachments (origins/insertions) may be direct or indirect via tendons or aponeuroses. Indirect attachments withstand friction better.

Microscopic Anatomy of a Skeletal Muscle Fiber (pp. 279–285)

3. Skeletal muscle fibers are long, striated, and multinucleate.
4. Myofibrils are contractile elements that occupy most of the cell volume. Their banded appearance results from a regular alternation of dark (A) and light (I) bands. Myofibrils are chains of sarcomeres; each sarcomere contains thick (myosin) and thin (actin) myofilaments arranged in a regular array. The heads of myosin molecules form cross bridges that interact with the thin filaments.
5. The sarcoplasmic reticulum (SR) is a system of membranous tubules surrounding each myofibril. Its function is to release and then sequester calcium ions.

6. T tubules are invaginations of the sarcolemma that run between the terminal cisterns of the SR. They allow an electrical stimulus to be delivered quickly deep into the cell.

Sliding Filament Model of Contraction (p. 285)

7. According to the sliding filament model, cross bridge (myosin head) activity of the thick filaments pulls the thin filaments toward the sarcomere centers.

Physiology of Skeletal Muscle Fibers (pp. 285–293)

8. Regulation of skeletal muscle cell contraction involves (a) generating and transmitting an action potential along the sarcolemma and (b) excitation-contraction coupling.

9. An end plate potential is set up when acetylcholine released by a nerve ending binds to ACh receptors on the sarcolemma, causing local changes in membrane permeability which allow ion flows that depolarize the membrane at that site.

10. The flow of current from the locally depolarized area spreads to the adjacent area of the sarcolemma, opening voltage-gated Na^+ channels, which allows Na^+ influx. These events generate the action potential. Once initiated, the action potential is self-propagating and unstoppable.

11. Then as the action potential travels away from a region, Na^+ channels close and voltage-gated K^+ channels open, repolarizing the membrane.

12. In excitation-contraction coupling the action potential is propagated down the T tubules, causing calcium to be released from the SR into the cytosol.

13. Sliding of the filaments is triggered by a rise in intracellular calcium ion levels. Troponin binding of calcium moves tropomyosin away from myosin-binding sites on actin, allowing cross bridge binding. Myosin ATPases split ATP, which energizes the power strokes. ATP binding to the myosin head is necessary for cross bridge detachment. Cross bridge activity ends when calcium is pumped back into the SR.

iP Muscular System; Topic: Sliding Filament Theory, pp. 18–29.

Contraction of a Skeletal Muscle (pp. 293–298)

14. A motor unit is one motor neuron and all the muscle cells it innervates. The neuron's axon has several branches, each of which forms a neuromuscular junction with one muscle cell.

15. A motor unit's response to a single brief threshold stimulus is a twitch. A twitch has three phases: latent (preparatory events occurring), contraction (the muscle tenses and may shorten), and relaxation (muscle tension declines and the muscle returns to its resting length).

16. Graded responses of muscles to rapid stimuli are wave summation and unfused and fused tetanus. A graded response to increasingly strong stimuli is multiple motor unit summation, or recruitment. The type and order of motor unit recruitment follows the size principle.

17. Isotonic contractions occur when the muscle shortens (concentric contraction) or lengthens (eccentric contraction) as the load is moved. Isometric contractions occur when muscle tension produces neither shortening nor lengthening.

iP Muscular System; Topic: Contraction of Motor Units, pp. 1–11.

Muscle Metabolism (pp. 298–301)

18. The energy source for muscle contraction is ATP, obtained from a coupled reaction of creatine phosphate with ADP and from aerobic and anaerobic metabolism of glucose.

19. When ATP is produced by anaerobic pathways, lactic acid accumulates and ionic imbalances disturb the membrane potential. To return the muscles to their resting state, ATP must be produced aerobically and used to regenerate creatine phosphate, glycogen reserves must be restored, and accumulated lactic acid must be metabolized. Oxygen used to accomplish this repayment is called excess postexercise oxygen consumption (EPOC).

20. Only about 40% of energy released during ATP hydrolysis powers contractile activity. The rest is liberated as heat.

iP Muscular System; Topic: Muscle Metabolism, pp. 1–7.

Force of Muscle Contraction (pp. 301–302)

21. The force of muscle contraction is affected by the number and size of contracting muscle cells (the more and the larger the cells, the greater the force), the frequency of stimulation, and the degree of muscle stretch.

22. In twitch contractions, the external tension exerted on the load is always less than the internal tension. When a muscle is tetanized, the external tension equals the internal tension.

23. When the thick and thin filaments are optimally overlapping, the muscle can generate maximum force. With excessive increase or decrease in muscle length, force declines.

Velocity and Duration of Contraction (pp. 302–304)

24. Factors determining the velocity and duration of muscle contraction include the load (the greater the load, the slower the contraction) and muscle fiber types.

25. The three types of muscle fibers are: (1) fast glycolytic (fatigable) fibers, (2) slow oxidative (fatigue-resistant) fibers, and (3) fast oxidative (fatigue-resistant) fibers. Most muscles contain a mixture of fiber types. The fast muscle fiber types can interconvert with certain exercise regimens.

Adaptations to Exercise (pp. 304–305)

26. Regular aerobic exercise gives skeletal muscles increased efficiency, endurance, strength, and resistance to fatigue.

27. In skeletal muscle, resistance exercises cause hypertrophy and large gains in strength.

28. Immobilizing muscles leads to muscle weakness and severe atrophy.

29. Improper training and excessive exercise result in overuse injuries, which may be disabling.

Smooth Muscle (pp. 305–311)

Microscopic Structure of Smooth Muscle Fibers (pp. 305–307)

1. A smooth muscle fiber is spindle shaped and uninucleate, and has no striations.

2. Smooth muscle cells are most often arranged in sheets. They lack elaborate connective tissue coverings.

3. The SR is poorly developed and T tubules are absent. Actin and myosin filaments are present, but sarcomeres are not. Intermediate filaments and dense bodies form an intracellular network that harnesses the pull generated during cross bridge activity and transfers it to the extracellular matrix.

Contraction of Smooth Muscle (pp. 307–309)

4. Smooth muscle fibers may be electrically coupled by gap junctions.

5. ATP energizes smooth muscle contraction, which is activated by a calcium pulse. However, calcium binds to calmodulin rather than to troponin (which is not present in smooth muscle fibers), and myosin must be phosphorylated to become active in contraction.

6. Smooth muscle contracts for extended periods at low energy cost and without fatigue.

7. Neurotransmitters of the autonomic nervous system may inhibit or stimulate smooth muscle fibers. Smooth muscle contraction may also be initiated by pacemaker cells, hormones, or local chemical factors that influence intracellular calcium levels, and by mechanical stretch.

8. Special features of smooth muscle contraction include the stress-relaxation response, the ability to generate large amounts of force when extensively stretched, and hyperplasia under certain conditions.

Types of Smooth Muscle   (p. 309)

9. Unitary smooth muscle has electrically coupled fibers that contract synchronously and often spontaneously.
10. Multi unit smooth muscle has independent, well-innervated fibers that lack gap junctions and pacemaker cells. Stimulation occurs via autonomic nerves (or hormones). Multi unit muscle contractions are rarely synchronous.

Developmental Aspects of Muscles   (pp. 312–313, 315)

1. Muscle tissue develops from embryonic mesoderm cells called myoblasts. Several myoblasts fuse to form a skeletal muscle fiber. Smooth and cardiac cells develop from single myoblasts and display gap junctions.
2. For the most part, specialized skeletal and cardiac muscle cells lose their ability to divide but retain the ability to hypertrophy. Smooth muscle regenerates well and undergoes hyperplasia.
3. Skeletal muscle development reflects maturation of the nervous system and occurs in head-to-toe and proximal-to-distal directions. Natural neuromuscular control reaches its peak in midadolescence.
4. Women's muscles account for about 36% of their total body weight and men's for about 42%, a difference due chiefly to the effects of male hormones on skeletal muscle growth.
5. Skeletal muscle is richly vascularized and quite resistant to infection, but in old age, skeletal muscles become fibrous, decline in strength, and atrophy. Regular exercise can offset some of these changes.

Review Questions

Multiple Choice/Matching

(Some questions have more than one correct answer. Select the best answer or answers from the choices given.)

1. The connective tissue covering that encloses the sarcolemma of an individual muscle fiber is called the (a) epimysium, (b) perimysium, (c) endomysium, (d) periosteum.
2. A fascicle is a (a) muscle, (b) bundle of muscle fibers enclosed by a connective tissue sheath, (c) bundle of myofibrils, (d) group of myofilaments.
3. Thick and thin myofilaments have different compositions. For each descriptive phrase, indicate whether the filament is (a) thick or (b) thin.

    ____ (1) contains actin
    ____ (2) contains ATPases
    ____ (3) attaches to the Z disc
    ____ (4) contains myosin
    ____ (5) contains troponin
    ____ (6) does not lie in the I band

4. The function of the T tubules in muscle contraction is to (a) make and store glycogen, (b) release Ca^{2+} into the cell interior and then pick it up again, (c) transmit the action potential deep into the muscle cells, (d) form proteins.
5. The sites where the motor nerve impulse is transmitted from the nerve endings to the skeletal muscle cell membranes are the (a) neuromuscular junctions, (b) sarcomeres, (c) myofilaments, (d) Z discs.
6. Contraction elicited by a single brief stimulus is called (a) a twitch, (b) wave summation, (c) multiple motor unit summation, (d) fused tetanus.
7. A smooth, sustained contraction resulting from very rapid stimulation of the muscle, in which no evidence of relaxation is seen, is called (a) a twitch, (b) wave summation, (c) multiple motor unit summation, (d) fused tetanus.
8. Characteristics of isometric contractions include all but (a) shortening, (b) increased muscle tension throughout the contraction phase, (c) absence of shortening, (d) used in resistance training.
9. During muscle contraction, ATP is provided by (a) a coupled reaction of creatine phosphate with ADP, (b) aerobic respiration of glucose, and (c) anaerobic glycolysis.

    ____ (1) Which provides ATP fastest?
    ____ (2) Which does (do) not require that oxygen be available?
    ____ (3) Which provides the highest yield of ATP per glucose molecule?
    ____ (4) Which results in the formation of lactic acid?
    ____ (5) Which has carbon dioxide and water products?
    ____ (6) Which is most important in endurance sports?

10. The neurotransmitter released by somatic motor neurons is (a) acetylcholine, (b) acetylcholinesterase, (c) norepinephrine.
11. The ions that enter the skeletal muscle cell during the generation of an action potential are (a) calcium ions, (b) chloride ions, (c) sodium ions, (d) potassium ions.
12. Myoglobin has a special function in muscle tissue. It (a) breaks down glycogen, (b) is a contractile protein, (c) holds a reserve supply of oxygen in the muscle.
13. Aerobic exercise results in all of the following except (a) increased cardiovascular system efficiency, (b) more mitochondria in the muscle cells, (c) increased size and strength of existing muscle cells, (d) increased neuromuscular system coordination.
14. The smooth muscle type found in the walls of digestive and urinary system organs and that exhibits gap junctions and pacemaker cells is (a) multi unit, (b) unitary.

Short Answer Essay Questions

15. Name and describe the four special functional abilities of muscle that are the basis for muscle response.
16. Distinguish between (a) direct and indirect muscle attachments and (b) a tendon and an aponeurosis.
17. (a) Describe the structure of a sarcomere and indicate the relationship of the sarcomere to myofilaments. (b) Explain the sliding filament model of contraction using appropriately labeled diagrams of a relaxed and a contracted sarcomere.
18. What is the importance of acetylcholinesterase in muscle cell contraction?
19. Explain how a slight (but smooth) contraction differs from a vigorous contraction of the same muscle. Use the concepts of multiple motor unit summation.
20. Explain what is meant by the term excitation-contraction coupling.
21. Define and draw a motor unit.
22. Describe the three distinct types of skeletal muscle fibers.
23. True or false: Most muscles contain a predominance of one skeletal muscle fiber type. Explain the reasoning behind your choice.
24. Describe some cause(s) of muscle fatigue and define this term clearly.

25. Define EPOC.
26. Smooth muscle has some unique properties, such as low energy usage, and the ability to maintain contraction over long periods. Tie these properties to the function of smooth muscle in the body.

Critical Thinking and Clinical Application Questions

1. Jim Fitch decided that his physique left much to be desired, so he joined a local health club and began to "pump iron" three times weekly. After three months of training, during which he lifted increasingly heavier weights, he noticed that his arm and chest muscles were substantially larger. Explain the structural and functional basis of these changes.

2. When a suicide victim was found, the coroner was unable to remove the drug vial clutched in his hand. Explain the reasons for this. If the victim had been discovered three days later, would the coroner have had the same difficulty? Explain.

3. Muscle-relaxing drugs are administered to a patient during major surgery. Which of the two chemicals described next would be a good skeletal muscle relaxant and why?
   - Chemical A binds to and blocks ACh receptors of muscle cells.
   - Chemical B floods the muscle cells' cytoplasm with Ca^{2+}.

4. Michael is answering a series of questions dealing with skeletal muscle cell excitation and contraction. In response to "What protein changes shape when Ca^{2+} binds to it?" he writes "tropomyosin." What should he have responded and what is the result of that calcium ion binding?

AT THE CLINIC

Related Clinical Terms

Fibromyositis (*fibro* = fiber; *itis* = inflammation) Also known as **fibromyalgia**; a group of conditions involving chronic inflammation of a muscle, its connective tissue coverings and tendons, and capsules of nearby joints. Symptoms are nonspecific and involve varying degrees of tenderness associated with specific trigger points, as well as fatigue and frequent awakening from sleep.

Hernia Protrusion of an organ through its body cavity wall. May be congenital (owing to failure of muscle fusion during development), but most often is caused by heavy lifting or obesity and subsequent muscle weakening.

Myalgia (mi-al′je-ah; *algia* = pain) Muscle pain resulting from any muscle disorder.

Myofascial pain syndrome Pain caused by a tightened band of muscle fibers, which twitch when the skin over them is touched. Mostly associated with overused or strained postural muscles.

Myopathy (mi-op′ah-the; *path* = disease, suffering) Any disease of muscle.

Myotonic dystrophy A form of muscular dystrophy that is less common than DMD; in the U.S. it affects about 14 of 100,000 people. Symptoms include a gradual reduction in muscle mass and control of the skeletal muscles, abnormal heart rhythm, and diabetes mellitus. May appear at any time; not sex-linked. Underlying genetic defect is multiple repeats of a particular gene

on chromosome 19. Because the number of repeats tends to increase from generation to generation, subsequent generations develop more severe symptoms. No effective treatment.

RICE Acronym for rest, ice, compression, and elevation. The standard treatment for a pulled muscle, or excessively stretched tendons or ligaments.

Spasm A sudden, involuntary twitch in smooth or skeletal muscle ranging from merely irritating to very painful; may be due to chemical imbalances. In spasms of the eyelid or facial muscles, called tics, psychological factors may be involved. Stretching and massaging the affected area may help end the spasm. A cramp is a prolonged spasm; usually occurs at night or after exercise.

Strain Commonly called a "pulled muscle," a strain is excessive stretching and possible tearing of a muscle due to muscle overuse or abuse. The injured muscle becomes painfully inflamed (myositis), and adjacent joints are usually immobilized.

Tetanus (1) A state of sustained contraction of a muscle that is a normal aspect of skeletal muscle functioning. (2) An acute infectious disease caused by the anaerobic bacterium *Clostridium tetani* and resulting in persistent painful spasms of some skeletal muscles. Progresses to fixed rigidity of the jaws (lockjaw) and spasms of trunk and limb muscles. Usually fatal due to respiratory failure.

Case Study Muscular System

Let's continue our tale of Mrs. DeStephano's medical problems, this time looking at the notes made detailing observations of her skeletal musculature.

- Severe lacerations of the muscles of the right leg and knee
- Damage to the blood vessels serving the right leg and knee
- Transection of the sciatic nerve (the large nerve serving most of the lower limb), just above the right knee

Her physician orders daily passive range-of-motion (ROM) exercise and electrical stimulation for her right leg and a diet high in protein, carbohydrates, and vitamin C.

1. Describe the step-by-step process of wound healing that will occur in her fleshy (muscle) wounds, and note the consequences of the specific restorative process that occurs.

2. What complications in healing can be anticipated owing to vascular (blood vessel) damage in the right leg?

3. What complications in muscle structure and function result from transection of the sciatic nerve? Why are passive ROM and electrical stimulation of her right leg muscles ordered?

4. Explain the reasoning behind the dietary recommendations.

(Answers in Appendix H)

10

The Muscular System

The human body enjoys an incredibly wide range of movements. The gentle blinking of your eye, standing on tiptoe, and wielding a sledgehammer are just a sample of the actions made possible by your muscular system.

Muscle tissue includes all contractile tissues (skeletal, cardiac, and smooth muscle), but when we study the muscular system, **skeletal muscles** take center stage. This chapter focuses on these muscular "machines" that enable us to perform so many different activities. However, before describing the individual muscles in detail, we will consider

- The manner in which muscles "play" with or against each other to bring about movement
- The criteria used for naming muscles
- The principles of leverage

Actions and Interactions of Skeletal Muscles

✓ Describe the functions of prime movers, antagonists, synergists, and fixators.

✓ Explain how a muscle's position relative to a joint affects its action.

The arrangement of body muscles permits them to work either together or in opposition to produce a wide variety of movements. As you eat, for example, you alternately raise your fork to your lips and lower it to your plate, and both sets of actions are accomplished by your arm and hand muscles. But muscles can only *pull*; they never *push*. Generally as a muscle shortens, its *insertion* (attachment on the movable bone) moves toward its *origin* (its fixed or immovable point of attachment). Whatever one muscle or muscle group can do, another muscle or group of muscles can "undo."

Muscles can be classified into four *functional* groups: prime movers, antagonists, synergists, and fixators. A muscle that has the major responsibility for producing a specific movement is a **prime mover**, or **agonist** (ag'o-nist; "leader"), of that movement. The pectoralis major muscle, which fleshes out the anterior chest (and inserts on the humerus), is a prime mover of arm flexion.

Muscles that oppose, or reverse, a particular movement are **antagonists** (an-tag'o-nists; "against the leaders"). When a prime mover is active, the antagonist muscles may stretch or remain relaxed. Usually, however, antagonists help to regulate the action of a prime mover by contracting slightly to provide some resistance, thus helping to prevent overshooting the mark or to slow or stop the movement. As you might expect, a prime mover and its antagonist are located on opposite sides of the joint across which they act, as shown in *Focus on Muscle Action* (Figure 10.1).

Antagonists can also be prime movers in their own right. For example, flexion of the arm by the pectoralis major muscle is antagonized by the latissimus dorsi, the prime mover for extending the arm.

In addition to agonists and antagonists, most movements involve the action of one or more **synergists** (sin'er-jists; *syn* = together, *erg* = work). Synergists help prime movers in one of these ways:

- Adding a little extra force to the same movement
- Reducing undesirable or unnecessary movements that might occur as the prime mover contracts

Let's look at the second function more closely. When a muscle crosses two or more joints, its contraction causes movement at all of the spanned joints unless other muscles act as joint stabilizers. For example, the finger flexor muscles cross both the wrist and the interphalangeal joints, but you can make a fist without bending your wrist because synergistic muscles stabilize the wrist. Additionally, as some flexors act, they may cause several other (undesirable) movements at the same joint. Synergists can prevent this, allowing all of the prime mover's force to be exerted in the desired direction.

When synergists immobilize a bone, or a muscle's origin so that the prime mover has a stable base on which to act, they are called **fixators** (fik'sa-terz). Recall from Chapter 7 that the scapula is held to the axial skeleton only by muscles and is quite freely movable. The fixator muscles that run from the axial skeleton to the scapula can immobilize the scapula so that only the desired movements occur at the mobile shoulder joint. Additionally, muscles that help maintain upright posture are fixators.

In summary, although prime movers seem to get all the credit for causing certain movements, antagonistic and synergistic muscles are also important in producing smooth, coordinated, and precise movements. Furthermore, a muscle may act as a prime mover in one movement, an antagonist for another movement, a synergist for a third movement, and so on.

Naming Skeletal Muscles

✓ List the criteria used in naming muscles. Provide an example to illustrate the use of each criterion.

Skeletal muscles are named according to a number of criteria. To simplify the task of learning muscle names and actions, pay attention to the following cues.

- **Muscle location.** Some muscle names indicate the bone or body region with which the muscle is associated.

  Examples: The temporalis (tem"por-ă'lis) muscle overlies the temporal bone, and intercostal (*costal* = rib) muscles run between the ribs.

- **Muscle shape.** Some muscles are named for their distinctive shapes.

  Examples: The deltoid (del'toid) muscle is roughly triangular (*deltoid* = triangle), and together the right and left trapezius (trah-pe'ze-us) muscles form a trapezoid.

- **Muscle size.** Terms such as *maximus* (largest), *minimus* (smallest), *longus* (long), and *brevis* (short) are often used in muscle names.

  Examples: The gluteus maximus and gluteus minimus are the large and small gluteus muscles, respectively.

- **Direction of muscle fibers.** The names of some muscles reveal the direction in which their fibers (and fascicles) run in reference to some imaginary line, usually the midline of the body or the longitudinal axis of a limb bone. In muscles with the term *rectus* (straight) in their names, the fibers run parallel to that imaginary line (axis). *Transversus* indicates that the muscle fibers run at right angles to that line, and *oblique* indicates that the fibers run obliquely to it.

  Examples: The rectus femoris (straight muscle of the thigh, or femur) and transversus abdominis (transverse muscle of the abdomen).

- **Number of origins.** When *biceps*, *triceps*, or *quadriceps* forms part of a muscle's name, you can assume that the muscle has two, three, or four origins, respectively.

  Example: The biceps brachii (bra'ke-i) muscle of the arm has two origins, or *heads*.

- **Location of the attachments.** Some muscles are named according to their points of origin and insertion. The origin is always named first.

  Example: The sternocleidomastoid (ster"no-kli"do-mas'toid) muscle of the neck has a dual origin on the sternum (*sterno*) and clavicle (*cleido*), and it inserts on the mastoid process of the temporal bone.

- **Muscle action.** When muscles are named for the movement they produce, action words such as *flexor*, *extensor*, or *adductor* appear in the muscle's name.

  Example: The adductor longus, located on the medial thigh, brings about thigh adduction. (To review the terminology for various actions, see Chapter 8, Figures 8.5, 8.6, pp. 256–259.)

Often, several criteria are combined in naming a muscle. For instance, the name *extensor carpi radialis longus* tells us the muscle's action (extensor), what joint it acts on (*carpi* = wrist), and that it lies close to the radius of the forearm (radialis). It also hints at the size (longus) relative to other wrist extensor muscles. Unfortunately, not all muscle names are this descriptive.

Figure 10.1   The action of a muscle can be inferred by the position of the muscle relative to the joint it crosses. (Examples given relate to the shoulder joint.) *A&P Flix*   Available at www.masteringaandp.com

(a) A muscle that crosses on the anterior side of a joint produces flexion*

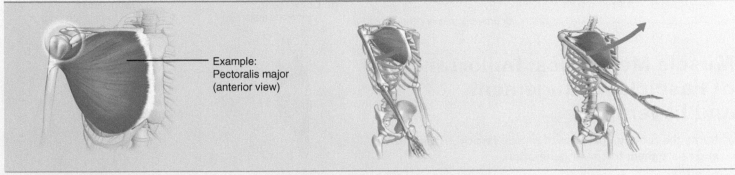

Example:
Pectoralis major
(anterior view)

(b) A muscle that crosses on the posterior side of a joint produces extension*

Example: Latissimus
dorsi (posterior view)

*The latissimus dorsi
is the antagonist of
the pectoralis major.*

(c) A muscle that crosses on the lateral side of a joint produces abduction

Example: Deltoid
middle fibers
(anterolateral view).

(d) A muscle that crosses on the medial side of a joint produces adduction

Example:
Teres major
(posterolateral view)

*The teres major
is the antagonist
of the deltoid.*

*These generalities do not apply to the knee and ankle because the lower limb is rotated during development. The muscles that cross these joints posteriorly produce flexion, and those that cross anteriorly produce extension.

☑ **Check Your Understanding**

1. The term "prime mover" is used in the business world to indicate people that get things done—the movers and shakers. What is its physiological meaning?
2. What criteria are used in naming each of the following muscles? Iliacus, adductor brevis, quadriceps femoris.

For answers, see Appendix H.

Muscle Mechanics: Importance of Fascicle Arrangement and Leverage

✓ Name the common patterns of muscle fascicle arrangement and relate them to power generation.

✓ Define lever, and explain how a lever operating at a mechanical advantage differs from one operating at a mechanical disadvantage.

✓ Name the three types of lever systems and indicate the arrangement of effort, fulcrum, and load in each. Also note the advantages of each type of lever system.

We discussed most factors contributing to muscle force and speed (load, fiber type, etc.) in Chapter 9 with two important exceptions—fascicle arrangement and lever systems. We attend to these factors next.

Arrangement of Fascicles

All skeletal muscles consist of fascicles (bundles of fibers), but fascicle arrangements vary, resulting in muscles with different shapes and functional capabilities. The most common patterns of fascicle arrangement are circular, convergent, parallel, and pennate **(Figure 10.2)**.

Circular

The fascicular pattern is **circular** when the fascicles are arranged in concentric rings (Figure 10.2a). Muscles with this arrangement surround external body openings, which they close by contracting. A general term for such muscles is *sphincters* ("squeezers"). Examples are the orbicularis muscles surrounding the eyes and the mouth.

Convergent

A **convergent** muscle has a broad origin, and its fascicles *converge* toward a single tendon of insertion. Such a muscle is triangular or fan shaped like the pectoralis major muscle of the anterior thorax (Figure 10.2b).

Parallel

In a **parallel** arrangement, the length of the fascicles runs parallel to the long axis of the muscle. Such muscles are either *straplike* like the sartorius muscle of the thigh (Figure 10.2d), or *spindle shaped* with an expanded belly (midsection), like

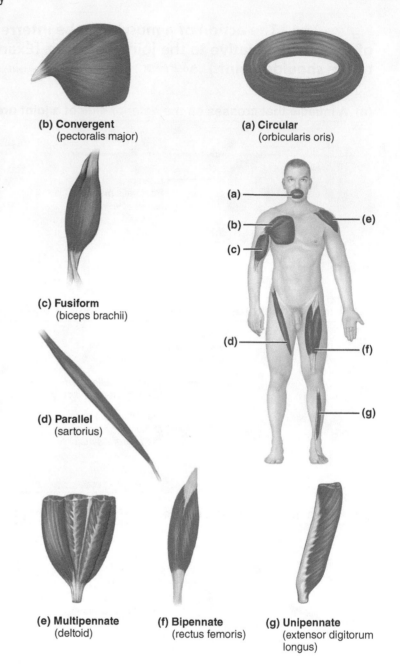

(b) Convergent
(pectoralis major)

(a) Circular
(orbicularis oris)

(c) Fusiform
(biceps brachii)

(d) Parallel
(sartorius)

(e) Multipennate
(deltoid)

(f) Bipennate
(rectus femoris)

(g) Unipennate
(extensor digitorum longus)

Figure 10.2 Patterns of fascicle arrangement in muscles.

the biceps brachii muscle of the arm (Figure 10.2c). However, some authorities classify spindle-shaped muscles into a separate class as **fusiform muscles**. This is the approach we use here in Figure 10.2.

Pennate

In a **pennate** (pen′ăt) pattern, the fascicles (and muscle fibers) are short and they attach obliquely (*penna* = feather) to a central tendon that runs the length of the muscle. Pennate muscles come in three forms:

■ *Unipennate*, in which the fascicles insert into only one side of the tendon, as in the extensor digitorum longus muscle of the leg (Figure 10.2g).

Effort x length of effort arm = load x length of load arm
(force x distance) = (resistance x distance)

10 x 25 = 1000 x 0.25
250 = 250

(a) Mechanical advantage with a power lever

Figure 10.3 Lever systems operating at a mechanical advantage and a mechanical disadvantage. The equation at the top expresses the relationships among the forces and relative distances in any lever system. **(a)** Mechanical advantage with a power lever. When using a jack, the load lifted is greater than the applied muscular effort. Only 10 kg of force (the effort) is needed to lift a 1000-kg car (the load).

(Figure continues on p. 324.)

■ *Bipennate*, in which the fascicles insert into the tendon from opposite sides so the muscle's "grain" resembles a feather (Figure 10.2f). The rectus femoris of the thigh is bipennate.

■ *Multipennate*, which looks like many feathers side by side, with all their quills inserted into one large tendon. The deltoid muscle, which forms the roundness of the shoulder, is multipennate (Figure 10.2e).

The arrangement of a muscle's fascicles determines its range of motion (the amount of movement produced when a muscle shortens) and its power. Because skeletal muscle fibers may shorten to about 70% of their resting length when they contract, the longer and the more nearly parallel the muscle fibers are to a muscle's long axis, the more the muscle can shorten. Muscles with parallel fascicle arrangements shorten the most, but are not usually very powerful. Muscle power depends more on the total number of muscle fibers in the muscle: The greater the number of muscle fibers, the greater the power. The stocky bipennate and multipennate muscles, which "pack in" the most fibers, shorten very little but are very powerful.

☑ **Check Your Understanding**

3. Of the muscles illustrated in Figure 10.2, which could shorten most? Which two would likely be most powerful? Why?

For answers, see Appendix H.

Lever Systems: Bone-Muscle Relationships

The operation of most skeletal muscles involves leverage—using a lever to move some object. A **lever** is a rigid bar that moves on a fixed point called the **fulcrum**, when a force is applied to it. The applied force, or **effort**, is used to move a resistance, or **load**. In your body, your joints are the fulcrums, and your bones act as levers. Muscle contraction provides the effort that is applied at the muscle's insertion point on a bone. The load is the bone itself, along with overlying tissues and anything else you are trying to move with that lever.

Levers: Power Versus Speed

A lever allows a given effort to move a heavier load, or to move a load farther or faster, than it otherwise could. If the load is close to the fulcrum and the effort is applied far from the fulcrum, a small effort exerted over a relatively large distance can move a large load over a small distance **(Figure 10.3a)**. Such lever is said to operate at a **mechanical advantage** and is commonly called a *power lever*. For example, as shown to the right in Figure 10.3a, a person can lift a car with a power lever, in this case, a jack. The car moves up only a small distance with each downward "push" of the jack handle, but relatively little muscle effort is needed.

If, on the other hand, the load is far from the fulcrum and the effort is applied near the fulcrum, the force exerted by the muscle must be greater than the load to be moved or supported (Figure 10.3b on p. 324). This lever system is a *speed lever* and operates at a **mechanical disadvantage**. Speed levers are useful because they allow a load to be moved rapidly over a large distance with a wide range of motion. Wielding a shovel is an example. As you can see, small differences in the site of a muscle's insertion (relative to the fulcrum or joint) can translate into large differences in the amount of force a muscle must generate to move a given load or resistance.

Regardless of type, all levers follow the same basic principle:

Effort farther than load from fulcrum = lever operates at a mechanical advantage

Effort nearer than load to fulcrum = lever operates at a mechanical disadvantage

(b) Mechanical disadvantage with a speed lever

Figure 10.3 *(continued)* **Lever systems operating at a mechanical advantage and a mechanical disadvantage.** **(b)** Mechanical disadvantage with a speed lever. When using a shovel to lift dirt, the muscular force is greater than the load lifted. A muscular force (effort) of 100 kg is used to lift 50 kg of dirt (the load). Levers operating at a mechanical disadvantage are common in the body.

Classes of Levers

Depending on the relative position of the three elements—effort, fulcrum, and load—a lever belongs to one of three classes.

In a **first-class lever**, the effort is applied at one end of the lever and the load is at the other, with the fulcrum somewhere between. Seesaws and scissors are first-class levers. First-class leverage also occurs when you lift your head off your chest **(Figure 10.4a)**. Some first-class levers in the body operate at a mechanical advantage (for strength), but others, such as the action of the triceps muscle in extending the forearm against resistance, operate at a mechanical disadvantage (for speed and distance).

In a **second-class lever**, the effort is applied at one end of the lever and the fulcrum is located at the other, with the load between them. A wheelbarrow demonstrates this type of lever system. Second-class levers are uncommon in the body, but the best example is the act of standing on your toes (Figure 10.4b). All second-class levers in the body work at a mechanical advantage because the muscle insertion is always farther from the fulcrum than is the load. Second-class levers are levers of strength, but speed and range of motion are sacrificed for that strength.

In a **third-class lever**, the effort is applied between the load and the fulcrum. These levers are speedy and always operate at a mechanical disadvantage—think of tweezers and forceps. Most skeletal muscles of the body act in third-class lever systems. An example is the activity of the biceps muscle of the arm, lifting the distal forearm and anything carried in the hand (Figure 10.4c). Third-class lever systems permit a muscle to be inserted very close to the joint across which movement occurs, which allows rapid, extensive movements (as in throwing) with relatively little shortening of the muscle. Muscles involved in third-class levers tend to be thicker and more powerful.

In conclusion, differences in the positioning of the three elements modify muscle activity with respect to speed of contraction, range of movement, and the weight of the load that can be lifted.

In lever systems that operate at a mechanical disadvantage (speed levers), force is lost but speed and range of movement are gained. Systems that operate at a mechanical advantage (power levers) are slower, more stable, and used where strength is a priority.

☑ **Check Your Understanding**

4. Which of the three lever systems involved in muscle mechanics would be the fastest lever—first-, second-, or third-class?
5. What benefit is provided by a lever that operates at a mechanical advantage?

For answers, see Appendix H.

Major Skeletal Muscles of the Body

✓ Name and identify the muscles described in Tables 10.1 to 10.17. State the origin, insertion, and action of each.

The grand plan of the muscular system is all the more impressive because of the sheer number of skeletal muscles in the body—more than 600 of them (many more than in **Figures 10.5** and **10.6** combined)! Remembering all the names, locations, and actions of these muscles is a monumental task. Take heart; here we consider only the principal muscles (approximately 125 pairs of them). Although this number is far fewer than 600, the job of learning about all these muscles will still require a concerted effort on your part.

Memorization will be easier if you apply what you learn in a practical, or clinical, way; that is, with a *functional anatomy focus*. Once you are satisfied that you have learned the name of a muscle and can identify it on a cadaver, model, or diagram, flesh out your learning by asking yourself, "What does it do?" [It might be a good idea to review body movements (pp. 256–259) before you get to this point.]

(Text continues on p. 328.)

(a) First-class lever

Arrangement of the elements is
load-fulcrum-effort

Example: scissors

In the body: A first-class lever system raises your head off your chest. The posterior neck muscles provide the effort, the atlanto-occipital joint is the fulcrum, and the weight to be lifted is the facial skeleton.

(b) Second-class lever

Arrangement of the elements is
fulcrum-load-effort

Example: wheelbarrow

In the body: Second-class leverage is exerted when you stand on tip-toe. The effort is exerted by the calf muscles pulling upward on the heel; the joints of the ball of the foot are the fulcrum; and the weight of the body is the load.

(c) Third-class lever

Arrangement of the elements is
load-effort-fulcrum

Example: tweezers or forceps

In the body: Flexing the forearm by the biceps brachii muscle exemplifies third-class leverage. The effort is exerted on the proximal radius of the forearm, the fulcrum is the elbow joint, and the load is the hand and distal end of the forearm.

10

Figure 10.4 Lever systems.

10

Facial
Epicranius, frontal belly
Orbicularis oculi
Zygomaticus
Orbicularis oris

Head
Temporalis
Masseter

Neck
Platysma
Sternohyoid
Sternocleidomastoid

Shoulder
Trapezius

Thorax
Pectoralis minor
Pectoralis major
Serratus anterior
Intercostals

Deltoid

Arm
Triceps brachii
Biceps brachii
Brachialis

Abdomen
Rectus abdominis
External oblique
Internal oblique
Transversus abdominis

Forearm
Pronator teres
Brachioradialis
Flexor carpi radialis
Palmaris longus

Pelvis/thigh
Iliopsoas
Pectineus

Thigh
Tensor fasciae latae
Sartorius
Adductor longus
Gracilis

Thigh
Rectus femoris
Vastus lateralis
Vastus medialis

Leg
Fibularis longus
Extensor digitorum longus
Tibialis anterior

Leg
Gastrocnemius
Soleus

Figure 10.5 Superficial muscles of the body: Anterior view. The abdominal surface has been partially dissected on the right side to show somewhat deeper muscles. (For a related image, see *A Brief Atlas of the Human Body*, Figure 33.)

Neck
Epicranius, occipital belly
Sternocleidomastoid
Trapezius

Shoulder
Deltoid
Infraspinatus
Teres major

Arm
Triceps brachii
Brachialis

Rhomboid major

Forearm
Brachioradialis

Latissimus dorsi

Extensor carpi radialis longus
Flexor carpi ulnaris
Extensor carpi ulnaris
Extensor digitorum

Hip
Gluteus medius

Gluteus maximus

Thigh
Iliotibial tract
Adductor magnus
Hamstrings:
Biceps femoris
Semitendinosus
Semimembranosus

Leg
Gastrocnemius

Soleus

Fibularis longus

Calcaneal (Achilles) tendon

Figure 10.6 Superficial muscles of the body: Posterior view. (For related images, see *A Brief Atlas of the Human Body*, Figures 32, 35, and 36.)

10

The tables that follow group the muscles of the body by function and by location, roughly from head to foot. Each table is keyed to a particular figure or group of figures illustrating the muscles it describes. The legend at the beginning of each table summarizes the types of movements produced by the muscles listed and gives pointers on the way those muscles interact with one another. The table itself describes each muscle's shape, location relative to other muscles, origin and insertion, primary actions, and innervation. (Some instructors want students to defer learning the muscle innervations until they study the nervous system, so check on what is expected of you in this regard.)

As you consider each muscle, we recommend the following plan of action:

1. Be alert to the information provided by the muscle's name.
2. Read its entire description and identify the muscle on the corresponding figure. If it's a superficial muscle, also identify it on Figure 10.5 or Figure 10.6. Doing so will help you to link the description in the table to a visual image of the muscle's location in the body.
3. Relate the muscle's attachments and location to its actions. This will focus your attention on functional details that often escape student awareness. For example, both the elbow and knee joints are hinge joints that allow flexion and extension. However, the knee flexes to the dorsum of the body (the calf moves toward the posterior thigh), whereas elbow flexion carries the forearm toward the anterior aspect of the arm. Therefore, leg flexors are located on the posterior thigh, while forearm flexors are found on the anterior aspect of the humerus. A visual example of this relationship is shown in Figure 10.1a and b with the action of the muscles acting at the shoulder. Because many muscles have several actions, we indicate the primary action of each muscle in blue type in the tables.
4. Finally, keep in mind the *best* way to learn muscle actions: Act out their movements yourself while feeling for the muscles contracting (bulging) beneath your skin.

Now you are ready to tackle these tables:

(Text continues on p. 382.)

10

MUSCLE GALLERY

| Table 10.1 | Muscles of the Head, Part I: Facial Expression   (Figure 10.7) |

The muscles that promote facial expression lie in the scalp and face just deep to the skin. They are thin and variable in shape and strength, and adjacent muscles tend to be fused. They are unusual muscles in that they insert into skin (or other muscles), not bones.

In the scalp, the main muscle is the **epicranius**, which has distinct anterior and posterior parts. The lateral scalp muscles are vestigial in humans. Muscles clothing the facial bones lift the eyebrows, flare the nostrils, open and close the eyes and mouth, and provide one of the best tools for influencing others—the smile. The tremendous importance of facial muscles in nonverbal communication becomes especially clear when they are paralyzed, as in some stroke victims and in the expressionless "mask" of patients with Parkinson's disease.

Cranial nerve VII, the *facial nerve*, innervates all muscles listed in this table (see Table 13.2).

Chapter 15 describes the external muscles of the eyes, which direct the eyeballs, and the levator palpebrae superioris muscles that raise the eyelids.

MUSCLE	DESCRIPTION	ORIGIN (O) AND INSERTION (I)	ACTION	NERVE SUPPLY
MUSCLES OF THE SCALP				
Epicranius (occipitofrontalis) (ep″ĭ-kra′ne-us; ok-sip″ĭ-to-fron-ta′lis) (*epi* = over; *cran* = skull)	Bipartite muscle consisting of the frontal and occipital bellies connected by the epicranial aponeurosis. The alternate actions of these two muscles pull scalp forward and backward.			
▪ **Frontal belly** (fron′tal) (*front* = forehead)	Covers forehead and dome of skull; no bony attachments	O—epicranial aponeurosis I—skin of eyebrows and root of nose	With aponeurosis fixed, raises the eyebrows (as in surprise). Wrinkles forehead skin horizontally	Facial nerve (cranial VII)
▪ **Occipital belly** (ok-sip″ĭ-tal′) (*occipito* = base of skull)	Overlies posterior occiput; by pulling on the epicranial aponeurosis, fixes origin of frontal belly	O—occipital and temporal bones I—epicranial aponeurosis	Fixes aponeurosis and pulls scalp posteriorly	Facial nerve
MUSCLES OF THE FACE				
Corrugator supercilii (kor′ah-ga-ter soo″per-sĭ′le-i) (*corrugo* = wrinkle; *supercilium* = eyebrow)	Small muscle; activity associated with that of orbicularis oculi	O—arch of frontal bone above nasal bone I—skin of eyebrow	Draws eyebrows together and inferiorly; wrinkles skin of forehead vertically (as in frowning)	Facial nerve

Figure 10.7 Lateral view of muscles of the scalp, face, and neck. (a) Photograph.

MUSCLE GALLERY

| Table 10.1 | Muscles of the Head, Part I: Facial Expression | (Figure 10.7) *(continued)* |

MUSCLE	DESCRIPTION	ORIGIN (O) AND INSERTION (I)	ACTION	NERVE SUPPLY
Orbicularis oculi (or-bik′u-lar-is ok′u-li) (*orb* = circular; *ocul* = eye)	Thin, flat sphincter muscle of eyelid; surrounds rim of the orbit	O—frontal and maxillary bones and ligaments around orbit I—tissue of eyelid	Closes eye; various parts can be activated individually; produces blinking and squinting; draws eyebrows inferiorly	Facial nerve (cranial VII)
Zygomaticus—major and minor (zi-go-mat′ĭ-kus) (*zygomatic* = cheekbone)	Muscle pair extending diagonally from cheekbone to corner of mouth	O—zygomatic bone I—skin and muscle at corner of mouth	Raises lateral corners of mouth upward (smiling muscle)	Facial nerve
Risorius (ri-zor′e-us) (*risor* = laughter)	Slender muscle inferior and lateral to zygomaticus	O—lateral fascia associated with masseter muscle I—skin at angle of mouth	Draws corner of lip laterally; tenses lips; synergist of zygomaticus	Facial nerve
Levator labii superioris (lĕva′tor la′be-i soo-per″e-or′is) (*leva* = raise; *labi* = lip; *superior* = above, over)	Thin muscle between orbicularis oris and inferior eye margin	O—zygomatic bone and infraorbital margin of maxilla I—skin and muscle of upper lip	Opens lips; raises and furrows upper lip	Facial nerve
Depressor labii inferioris (de-pres′or la′be-i in-fer″e-or′is) (*depressor* = depresses; *infer* = below)	Small muscle running from mandible to lower lip	O—body of mandible lateral to its midline I—skin and muscle of lower lip	Draws lower lip inferiorly (as in a pout)	Facial nerve
Depressor anguli oris (ang′gu-li or-is) (*angul* = angle, corner; *or* = mouth)	Small muscle lateral to depressor labii inferioris	O—body of mandible below incisors I—skin and muscle at angle of mouth below insertion of zygomaticus	Draws corners of mouth down and laterally (a "tragedy mask" grimace); zygomaticus antagonist	Facial nerve
Orbicularis oris	Complicated, multilayered muscle of the lips with fibers that run in many different directions; most run circularly	O—arises indirectly from maxilla and mandible; fibers blend with fibers of other facial muscles associated with the lips I—encircles mouth; inserts into muscle and skin at angles of mouth	Closes lips; purses and protrudes lips; kissing and whistling muscle	Facial nerve
Mentalis (men-ta′lis) (*ment* = chin)	One of the muscle pair forming a V-shaped muscle mass on chin	O—mandible below incisors I—skin of chin	Wrinkles chin; protrudes lower lip	Facial nerve
Buccinator (bu′sĭ-na″ter) (*bucc* = cheek or "trumpeter")	Thin, horizontal cheek muscle; principal muscle of cheek; deep to masseter (see also Figure 10.8)	O—molar region of maxilla and mandible I—orbicularis oris	Compresses cheek (as in whistling and sucking); trampoline-like action holds food between teeth during chewing; draws corner of mouth laterally; well developed in nursing infants	Facial nerve
Platysma (plah-tiz′mah) (*platy* = broad, flat)	Unpaired, thin, sheetlike superficial neck muscle; not strictly a head muscle, but plays a role in facial expression	O—fascia of chest (over pectoral muscles and deltoid) I—lower margin of mandible, and skin and muscle at corner of mouth	Tenses skin of neck (as during shaving); helps depress mandible; pulls lower lip back and down, producing downward sag of mouth	Facial nerve

MUSCLE GALLERY

Table 10.1 *(continued)*

(b)

Figure 10.7 *(continued)* **Lateral view of muscles of the scalp, face, and neck. (b)** Superficial muscles.

MUSCLE GALLERY

Table 10.2 Muscles of the Head, Part II: Mastication and Tongue Movement (Figure 10.8)

Four pairs of muscles are involved in mastication (chewing). All are innervated by the *mandibular branch* of *cranial nerve V*.

The prime movers of jaw closure (and biting) are the powerful **masseter** and **temporalis** muscles, which are easily palpated when the teeth are clenched (Figure 10.8a). The **pterygoid** muscles produce side-to-side grinding (Figure 10.8b). The **buccinator** muscles (see Table 10.1) also play a role in chewing. Normally, gravity is sufficient to depress the mandible, but if there is resistance to jaw opening, neck muscles such as the digastric and mylohyoid muscles (see Table 10.3) are activated.

The tongue is composed of muscle fibers that curl, squeeze, and fold the tongue during speaking and chewing. These **intrinsic tongue muscles** change the shape of the tongue and contribute to its exceptional nimbleness, but they do not really move the tongue. We discuss them in Chapter 23 with the digestive system.

In this table, we consider only the **extrinsic tongue muscles**, which anchor and move the tongue (Figure 10.8c). *Cranial nerve XII, the hypoglossal nerve,* innervates all extrinsic tongue muscles (see Table 13.2).

MUSCLE	DESCRIPTION	ORIGIN (O) AND INSERTION (I)	ACTION	NERVE SUPPLY
MUSCLES OF MASTICATION				
Masseter (mah-se'ter) (*maseter* = chewer)	Powerful muscle that covers lateral aspect of mandibular ramus	O—zygomatic arch and zygomatic bone I—angle and ramus of mandible	Prime mover of jaw closure; elevates mandible	Trigeminal nerve (cranial V)
Temporalis (tem"por-ă'lis) (*tempora* = time; pertaining to the temporal bone)	Fan-shaped muscle that covers parts of the temporal, frontal, and parietal bones	O—temporal fossa I—coronoid process of mandible via a tendon that passes deep to zygomatic arch	Closes jaw; elevates and retracts mandible; maintains position of the mandible at rest; deep anterior part may help protract mandible	Trigeminal nerve
Medial pterygoid (me'de-ul ter'ĭ-goid) (*medial* = toward median plane; *pterygoid* = winglike)	Deep two-headed muscle that runs along internal surface of mandible and is largely concealed by that bone	O—medial surface of lateral pterygoid plate of sphenoid bone, maxilla, and palatine bone I—medial surface of mandible near its angle	Acts with the lateral pterygoid muscle to protrude (pull anteriorly) the mandible and promote side-to-side (grinding) movements; synergist of temporalis and masseter muscles in elevation of the mandible	Trigeminal nerve
Lateral pterygoid (*lateral* = away from median plane)	Deep two-headed muscle; lies superior to medial pterygoid muscle	O—greater wing and lateral pterygoid plate of sphenoid bone I—condylar process of mandible and capsule of temporomandibular joint	Provides forward sliding and side-to-side grinding movements of the lower teeth; protrudes mandible	Trigeminal nerve
Buccinator	See Table 10.1	See Table 10.1	Compresses the cheek; keeps food between grinding surfaces of teeth during chewing	Facial nerve (cranial VII)
MUSCLES PROMOTING TONGUE MOVEMENTS (EXTRINSIC TONGUE MUSCLES)				
Genioglossus (je"ne-o-glah'sus) (*geni* = chin; *glossus* = tongue)	Fan-shaped muscle; forms bulk of inferior part of tongue; its attachment to mandible prevents tongue from falling backward and obstructing breathing	O—internal surface of mandible near symphysis I—inferior aspect of the tongue and body of hyoid bone	Protracts tongue; can depress or act in concert with other extrinsic muscles to retract tongue	Hypoglossal nerve (cranial XII)
Hyoglossus (hi'o-glos"us) (*hyo* = pertaining to hyoid bone)	Flat, quadrilateral muscle	O—body and greater horn of hyoid bone I—inferolateral tongue	Depresses tongue and draws its sides inferiorly	Hypoglossal nerve
Styloglossus (sti-lo-glah'sus) (*stylo* = pertaining to styloid process)	Slender muscle running superiorly to and at right angles to hyoglossus	O—styloid process of temporal bone I—inferolateral tongue	Retracts and elevates tongue	Hypoglossal nerve

MUSCLE GALLERY

Table 10.2 (continued)

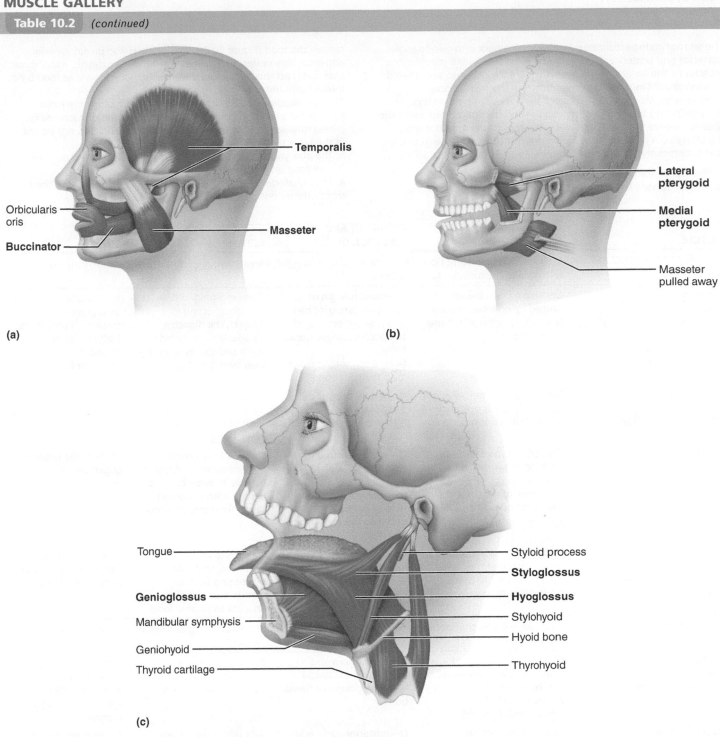

(a)

(b)

(c)

Figure 10.8 Muscles promoting mastication and tongue movements. (a) Lateral view of superficial muscles of mastication (temporalis, masseter, and buccinator muscles). **(b)** Lateral view of the deep chewing muscles. **(c)** Extrinsic muscles of the tongue and associated suprahyoid muscles of the throat.

10

MUSCLE GALLERY

Table 10.3	Muscles of the Anterior Neck and Throat: Swallowing (Figure 10.9)

The sternocleidomastoid muscle divides the neck into two triangles (anterior and posterior; Figure 10.9a). In this table, we consider the muscles of the *anterior* triangle, which are divided into **suprahyoid** and **infrahyoid muscles** (above and below the hyoid bone, respectively). Most of these muscles participate in swallowing.

Swallowing begins when the tongue and buccinator muscles of the cheeks squeeze the food back along the roof of the mouth toward the pharynx. A rapid series of sequential muscular movements in the posterior mouth and pharynx complete the process:

1. The *suprahyoid muscles* pull the hyoid bone superiorly and anteriorly toward the mandible, which widens the pharynx to receive the food (Figure 10.9c). The larynx is also pulled superiorly and anteriorly under the cover of the flaplike epiglottis, a maneuver that closes off the respiratory passageway (larynx) so that food is not inhaled into the lungs.

2. Small muscles that elevate the soft palate close off the nasal passages to prevent food from entering the superior nasal cavity. (These muscles, the *tensor* and *levator veli palatini*, are not described in the table but are illustrated in Figure 10.9c.)

3. The **pharyngeal constrictor muscles** in the wall of the pharynx propel food inferiorly into the esophagus.

4. The *infrahyoid muscles* pull the hyoid bone and larynx to their more inferior positions as swallowing ends.

MUSCLE	DESCRIPTION	ORIGIN (O) AND INSERTION (I)	ACTION	NERVE SUPPLY
SUPRAHYOID MUSCLES (soo″prah-hi′oid)	Muscles that help form floor of oral cavity, anchor tongue, elevate hyoid, and move larynx superiorly during swallowing; lie superior to hyoid bone			
Digastric (di-gas′trik) (*di* = two; *gaster* = belly)	Consists of two bellies united by an intermediate tendon, forming a V shape under the chin	O—lower margin of mandible (anterior belly) and mastoid process of temporal bone (posterior belly) I—by a connective tissue loop to hyoid bone	Open mouth and depress mandible; acting in concert, the digastric muscles elevate hyoid bone and steady it during swallowing and speech	Mandibular branch of trigeminal nerve (cranial V) for anterior belly; facial nerve (cranial VII) for posterior belly
Stylohyoid (sti″lo-hi′oid) (also see Figure 10.8)	Slender muscle below angle of jaw; parallels posterior belly of digastric muscle	O—styloid process of temporal bone I—hyoid bone	Elevates and retracts hyoid, thereby elongating floor of mouth during swallowing	Facial nerve
Mylohyoid (mi″lo-hi′oid) (*myle* = molar)	Flat, triangular muscle just deep to digastric muscle; this muscle pair make a sling that forms the floor of the anterior mouth	O—medial surface of mandible I—hyoid bone and median raphe (a median strip of connective tissue between the mylohyoid muscles)	Elevates hyoid bone and floor of mouth, enabling tongue to exert backward and upward pressure that forces food into pharynx	Mandibular branch of trigeminal nerve
Geniohyoid (je′ne-o-hi″oid) (also see Figure 10.8) (*geni* = chin)	Narrow muscle in contact with its partner medially; runs from chin to hyoid bone deep to mylohyoid	O—inner surface of mandibular symphysis I—hyoid bone	Pulls hyoid bone superiorly and anteriorly, shortening floor of mouth and widening pharynx to receive food	First cervical spinal nerve via hypoglossal nerve (cranial XII)
INFRAHYOID MUSCLES	Straplike muscles that depress the hyoid bone and larynx during swallowing and speaking (see also Figure 10.10c)			
Sternohyoid (ster″no-hi′oid) (*sterno* = sternum)	Most medial muscle of the neck: thin; superficial except inferiorly, where covered by sternocleidomastoid	O—manubrium and medial end of clavicle I—lower margin of hyoid bone	Depresses larynx and hyoid bone if mandible is fixed; may also flex skull	Cervical spinal nerves 1–3 (C_1–C_3) through ansa cervicalis (slender nerve root in cervical plexus)
Sternothyroid (ster′no-thi′roid) (*thyro* = thyroid cartilage)	Lateral and deep to sternohyoid	O—posterior surface of manubrium of sternum I—thyroid cartilage	Pulls larynx and hyoid bone inferiorly	As for sternohyoid
Omohyoid (o″mo-hi′oid) (*omo* = shoulder)	Straplike muscle with two bellies united by an intermediate tendon; lateral to sternohyoid	O—superior surface of scapula I—hyoid bone, lower border	Depresses and retracts hyoid bone	As for sternohyoid
Thyrohyoid (thi″ro-hi′oid) (also see Figure 10.8)	Appears as a superior continuation of sternothyroid muscle	O—thyroid cartilage I—hyoid bone	Depresses hyoid bone or elevates larynx if hyoid is fixed	First cervical nerve via hypoglossal nerve

10

MUSCLE GALLERY

Table 10.3   *(continued)*

MUSCLE	DESCRIPTION	ORIGIN (O) AND INSERTION (I)	ACTION	NERVE SUPPLY
PHARYNGEAL CONSTRICTOR MUSCLES (far-rin′je-al)				
Superior, middle, and inferior pharyngeal constrictor muscles	Three paired muscles whose fibers run circularly in pharynx wall; superior muscle is innermost and inferior one is outermost; substantial overlap	O—attached anteriorly to mandible and medial pterygoid plate (superior), hyoid bone (middle), and laryngeal cartilages (inferior) I—posterior median raphe of pharynx	Constrict pharynx during swallowing, which propels food to esophagus (via a massagelike action called peristalsis)	Pharyngeal plexus [branches of vagus nerve (X)]

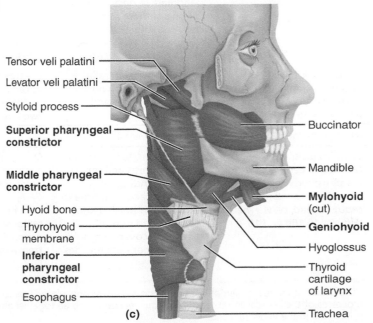

Figure 10.9 Muscles of the anterior neck and throat used in swallowing. (a) Anterior view of the suprahyoid and infrahyoid muscles. The sternocleidomastoid muscle (not involved in swallowing) is shown on the right side of the illustration to provide an anatomical landmark. Deeper neck muscles are illustrated on the left side. Note that a raphe is a seam of fibrous tissue. **(b)** Cadaver photo of suprahyoid and infrahyoid muscles. (For related images, see *A Brief Atlas of the Human Body*, Figures 44 and 45.) **(c)** Lateral view of the constrictor muscles of the pharynx shown in their proper anatomical relationship to the buccinator (a chewing muscle) and the hyoglossus muscle (which moves the tongue).

MUSCLE GALLERY

Table 10.4   Muscles of the Neck and Vertebral Column: Head Movements and Trunk Extension   (Figure 10.10)

Head movements

Muscles originating from the axial skeleton move the head. The major head flexors are the **sternocleidomastoid muscles** (Figure 10.10a, c), with help from the suprahyoid and infrahyoid muscles described in Table 10.3. Lateral head movements (rotating or tilting the head) result when the muscles on only one side of the neck contract. These actions are produced by the sternocleidomastoids and a number of deeper neck muscles, considered in this table. Head extension is aided by the trapezius muscles of the back, but the main extensors of the head are the **splenius** muscles deep to the trapezius muscles (Figure 10.10b).

Trunk extension

Trunk extension is brought about by the *deep* or *intrinsic back muscles* associated with the bony vertebral column. These muscles also maintain the normal curvatures of the spine, acting as postural muscles. As you consider these back muscles, keep in mind that they are deep. The superficial back muscles that cover them are concerned primarily with moving the shoulder girdle and upper limbs (see Tables 10.8 and 10.9).

The deep muscles of the back form a broad, thick column extending from the sacrum to the skull. Many muscles of varying length contribute to this mass. Think of each muscle as a string that when pulled causes one or several vertebrae to extend or to rotate on the vertebrae below. The largest deep back muscle group is the **erector spinae** group (Figure 10.10d). Because the origins and insertions of the different muscle groups overlap extensively, and many of these muscles are long, large regions of the vertebral column can be moved simultaneously and smoothly. Acting together, the deep back muscles extend (or hyperextend) the spine, but muscle contraction on only one side causes the spine to bend laterally (flex). Lateral flexion is automatically accompanied by some degree of rotation of the vertebral column. During vertebral movements, the articular facets of the vertebrae glide on each other.

In addition to the long back muscles, there are a number of short muscles that extend from one vertebra to the next. These small muscles act primarily as synergists in extending and rotating the spine and as spine stabilizers. They are not described in the table but you can deduce their actions by examining their origins and insertions in Figure 10.10e.

The trunk *muscles* that we consider in this table are extensors. The more superficial muscles, which have other functions, are considered in subsequent tables. For example, the anterior muscles of the abdominal wall that cause trunk *flexion* are described in Table 10.6.

MUSCLE	DESCRIPTION	ORIGIN (O) AND INSERTION (I)	ACTION	NERVE SUPPLY
ANTEROLATERAL NECK MUSCLES (Figure 10.10a and c)				
Sternocleidomastoid (ster"no-kli"do-mas'toid) (*sterno* = breastbone; *cleido* = clavicle; *mastoid* = mastoid process)	Two-headed muscle located deep to platysma on anterolateral surface of neck; fleshy parts on either side of neck delineate limits of anterior and posterior triangles; key muscular landmark in neck; spasms of one of these muscles may cause torticollis (wryneck)	O—manubrium of sternum and medial portion of clavicle I—mastoid process of temporal bone and superior nuchal line of occipital bone	Flexes and laterally rotates the head; simultaneous contraction of both muscles flexes neck, generally against resistance as when raising head when lying on back; acting alone, each muscle rotates head toward shoulder on opposite side and tilts or laterally flexes head to its own side	Accessory nerve (cranial nerve XI) and branches of cervical spinal nerves C_2 and C_3 (ventral rami)
Scalenes (ska'lēnz)— anterior, middle, and posterior (*scalene* = uneven)	Located more laterally than anteriorly on neck; deep to platysma and sternocleidomastoid	O—transverse processes of cervical vertebrae I—anterolaterally on first two ribs	Elevate first two ribs (aid in inspiration); flex and rotate neck	Cervical spinal nerves
INTRINSIC MUSCLES OF THE BACK (Figure 10.10b, d, e)				
Splenius (sple'ne-us)— capitis and cervicis portions (kă'pĭ-tis; ser-vis'us) (*splenion* = bandage; *caput* = head; *cervi* = neck) (Figures 10.10b and 10.7)	Broad bipartite superficial muscle (capitis and cervicis parts) extending from upper thoracic vertebrae to skull; capitis portion known as "bandage muscle" because it covers and holds down deeper neck muscles	O—ligamentum nuchae,* spinous processes of vertebrae C_7–T_6 I—mastoid process of temporal bone and occipital bone (capitis); transverse processes of C_2–C_4 vertebrae (cervicis)	Extend or hyperextend head; when splenius muscles on one side are activated, head rotates and bends laterally toward same side	Cervical spinal nerves (dorsal rami)

*The ligamentum nuchae (lig"ah-men'tum noo'ke) is a strong, elastic ligament extending from the occipital bone of the skull along the tips of the spinous processes of the cervical vertebrae. It binds the cervical vertebrae together and inhibits excessive head and neck flexion, thus preventing damage to the spinal cord in the vertebral canal.

MUSCLE GALLERY

Table 10.4 *(continued)*

1st cervical vertebra

Sternocleido-mastoid

Base of occipital bone

Mastoid process

Middle scalene

Anterior scalene

Posterior scalene

(a) Anterior

Mastoid process

Splenius capitis

Spinous processes of the vertebrae

Splenius cervicis

(b) Posterior

10

Platysma (cut)

Sternocleidomastoid (cut)

Internal jugular vein

Omohyoid

Sternohyoid

Sternothyroid

Sternocleidomastoid

Pectoralis major

(c)

Figure 10.10 Muscles of the neck and vertebral column that move the head and trunk. (For a related image, see *A Brief Atlas of the Human Body*, Plate 44.) **(a)** Muscles of the anterolateral neck; superficial platysma muscle and the deeper neck muscles removed. **(b)** Deep muscles of the posterior neck; superficial muscles removed. **(c)** Photograph of the anterior and lateral regions of the neck.

MUSCLE GALLERY

Table 10.4	Muscles of the Neck and Vertebral Column: Head Movements and Trunk Extension (Figure 10.10) *(continued)*

MUSCLE	DESCRIPTION	ORIGIN (O) AND INSERTION (I)	ACTION	NERVE SUPPLY
Erector spinae (e-rek′tor spi′ne) Also called **sacrospinalis** (Figure 10.10d, left side)	Prime mover of back extension. Each side consists of three columns—the iliocostalis, longissimus, and spinalis muscles—forming intermediate layer of intrinsic back muscles. Erector spinae provide resistance that helps control action of bending forward at the waist and act as powerful extensors to promote return to erect position. During full flexion (i.e., when touching fingertips to floor), erector spinae are relaxed and strain is borne entirely by ligaments of back. On reversing the movement, these muscles are initially inactive, and extension is initiated by hamstring muscles of thighs and gluteus maximus muscles of buttocks. As a result of this peculiarity, lifting a load or moving suddenly from a bent-over position can injure muscles and ligaments of back and intervertebral discs. Erector spinae muscles readily go into painful spasms following injury to back structures.			
▪ **Iliocostalis** (il″e-o-kos-tă′lis)—lumborum, thoracis, and cervicis portions (lum′bor-um; tho-ra′sis) (*ilio* = ilium; *cost* = rib; *thorac* = thorax)	Most lateral muscle group of erector spinae muscles; extend from pelvis to neck	O—iliac crests (lumborum); inferior 6 ribs (thoracis); ribs 3 to 6 (cervicis) I—angles of ribs (lumborum and thoracis); transverse processes of cervical vertebrae C_6–C_4 (cervicis)	Extend and laterally flex the vertebral column; maintain erect posture; acting on one side, bend vertebral column to same side	Spinal nerves (dorsal rami)
▪ **Longissimus** (lon-jis′ĭ-mus)—thoracis, cervicis, and capitis parts (*longissimus* = longest)	Intermediate tripartite muscle group of erector spinae; extend by many muscle slips from lumbar region to skull; mainly pass between transverse processes of vertebrae	O—transverse processes of lumbar through cervical vertebrae I—transverse processes of thoracic or cervical vertebrae and to ribs superior to origin as indicated by name; capitis inserts into mastoid process of temporal bone	Thoracis and cervicis act together to extend and laterally flex vertebral column; capitis extends head and turns the face toward same side	Spinal nerves (dorsal rami)
▪ **Spinalis** (spi-nă′lis)—thoracis and cervicis parts (*spin* = vertebral column, spine)	Most medial muscle column of erector spinae; cervicis usually rudimentary and poorly defined	O—spinous process of upper lumbar and lower thoracic vertebrae I—spinous process of upper thoracic and cervical vertebrae	Extends vertebral column	Spinal nerves (dorsal rami)
Semispinalis (sem′e-spĭ-nă′lis)—thoracis, cervicis, and capitis regions (*semi* = half) (Figure 10.10d, right side)	Composite muscle forming part of deep layer of intrinsic back muscles; extends from thoracic region to head	O—transverse processes of C_7–T_{12} I—occipital bone (capitis) and spinous processes of cervical (cervicis) and thoracic vertebrae T_1–T_4 (thoracis)	Extends vertebral column and head and rotates them to opposite side; acts synergistically with sternocleidomastoid muscles of opposite side	Spinal nerves (dorsal rami)
Quadratus lumborum (kwod-ra′tus lum-bor′um) (*quad* = four-sided; *lumb* = lumbar region) (See also Figure 10.20a)	Fleshy muscle forming part of posterior abdominal wall	O—iliac crest and lumbar fascia I—transverse processes of lumbar vertebrae L_1–L_4 and lower margin of 12th rib	Flexes vertebral column laterally when acting separately; when pair acts jointly, lumbar spine is extended and 12th rib is fixed; maintains upright posture; assists in forced inspiration	T_{12} and upper lumbar spinal nerves (ventral rami)

MUSCLE GALLERY

Table 10.4   (continued)

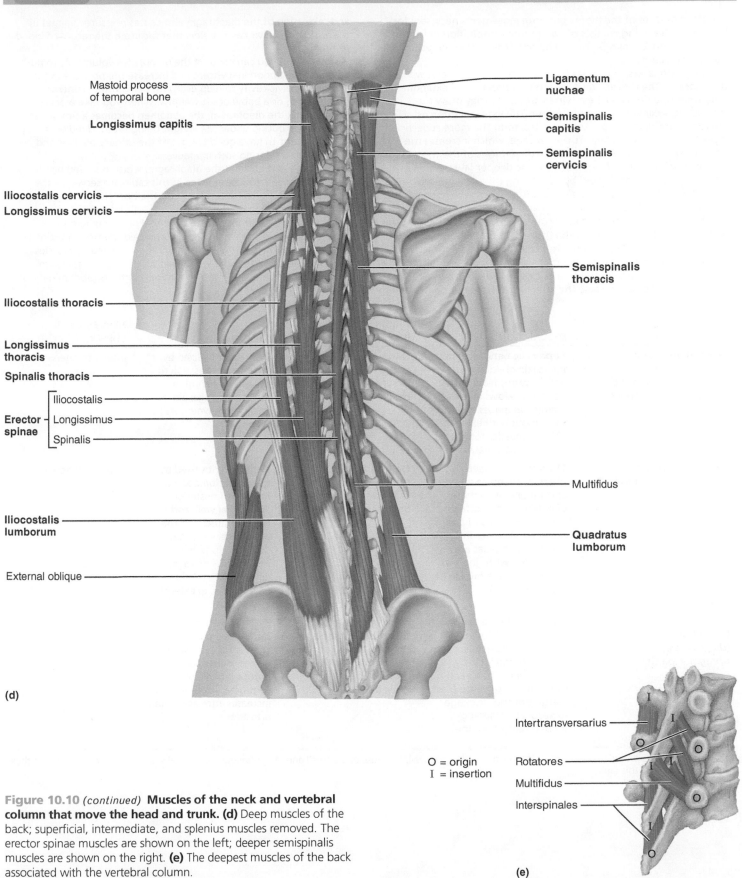

Mastoid process
of temporal bone

Longissimus capitis

Iliocostalis cervicis
Longissimus cervicis

Iliocostalis thoracis

Longissimus
thoracis

Spinalis thoracis

Erector
spinae
— Iliocostalis
— Longissimus
— Spinalis

Iliocostalis
lumborum

External oblique

**Ligamentum
nuchae**

**Semispinalis
capitis**

**Semispinalis
cervicis**

**Semispinalis
thoracis**

Multifidus

**Quadratus
lumborum**

(d)

O = origin
I = insertion

Intertransversarius

Rotatores

Multifidus

Interspinales

Figure 10.10 (continued) **Muscles of the neck and vertebral
column that move the head and trunk. (d)** Deep muscles of the
back; superficial, intermediate, and splenius muscles removed. The
erector spinae muscles are shown on the left; deeper semispinalis
muscles are shown on the right. **(e)** The deepest muscles of the back
associated with the vertebral column.

(e)

10

MUSCLE GALLERY

| **Table 10.5** | **Deep Muscles of the Thorax: Breathing** | **(Figure 10.11)** |

The deep muscles of the thorax promote movements necessary for breathing. Breathing consists of two phases—inspiration (inhaling) and expiration (exhaling)—caused by cyclic changes in the volume of the thoracic cavity.

Two main layers of muscles help form the anterolateral wall of the thorax.* The thoracic muscles are very short, most extending only from one rib to the next. On contraction, they draw the somewhat flexible ribs closer together. The **external intercostal muscles**, considered inspiratory muscles, form the more superficial layer (Figure 10.11a). They lift the rib cage, which increases the anterior to posterior and side-to-side dimensions of the thorax. The **internal intercostal muscles** form the deeper layer and may aid active (forced) expiration by depressing the rib cage. (However, quiet expiration is largely passive, resulting from relaxation of the external intercostals and diaphragm and elastic recoil of the lungs.)

The **diaphragm**, the most important muscle of inspiration, forms a muscular partition between the thoracic and abdominopelvic cavities (Figure 10.11b, c). In the relaxed state, the diaphragm is dome shaped. When it contracts it moves inferiorly and flattens, increasing the volume of the thoracic cavity, which draws air into the respiratory passageways. The alternating rhythmic contraction and relaxation of the diaphragm also causes pressure changes in the abdominopelvic cavity below that facilitate the return of blood to the heart.

In addition you can contract the diaphragm voluntarily to push down on the abdominal viscera and increase the pressure in the abdominopelvic cavity to help evacuate pelvic organ contents (urine, feces, or a baby) or lift weights. When you take a deep breath to fix the diaphragm, the abdomen becomes a firm pillar that will not buckle under the weight being lifted. Needless to say, it is important to have good control of the urinary bladder and anal sphincters during such maneuvers.

With the exception of the diaphragm, which is served by the *phrenic nerves*, the muscles listed in this table are served by the *intercostal nerves*, which run between the ribs.

Forced breathing (as during exercise) calls into play a number of other muscles that insert into the ribs. For example, during forced inspiration the scalene and sternocleidomastoid muscles of the neck help lift the ribs. Forced expiration is aided by muscles that pull the ribs inferiorly and those that push the diaphragm superiorly by compressing the abdominal contents (abdominal wall muscles).

MUSCLE	DESCRIPTION	ORIGIN (O) AND INSERTION (I)	ACTION	NERVE SUPPLY
External intercostals (in"ter-kos'talz) (*external* = toward the outside; *inter* = between; *cost* = rib)	11 pairs lie between ribs; fibers run obliquely (down and forward) from each rib to rib below; in lower intercostal spaces, fibers are continuous with external oblique muscle, forming part of abdominal wall	O—inferior border of rib above I—superior border of rib below	With first ribs fixed by scalene muscles, pull ribs toward one another to elevate rib cage; aid in inspiration; synergists of diaphragm	Intercostal nerves
Internal intercostals (*internal* = toward the inside, deep)	11 pairs lie between ribs; fibers run deep to and at right angles to those of external intercostals (i.e., run downward and posteriorly); lower internal intercostal muscles are continuous with fibers of internal oblique muscle of abdominal wall	O—superior border of rib below I—inferior border (costal groove) of rib above	With 12th ribs fixed by quadratus lumborum, muscles of posterior abdominal wall, and oblique muscles of the abdominal wall, they draw ribs together and depress rib cage; aid forced expiration; antagonistic to external intercostals	Intercostal nerves
Diaphragm (di'ah-fram) (*dia* = across; *phragm* = partition)	Broad muscle pierced by the aorta, inferior vena cava, and esophagus, forms floor of thoracic cavity; dome shaped in relaxed state; fibers converge from margins of thoracic cage toward a boomerang-shaped central tendon	O—inferior, internal surface of rib cage and sternum, costal cartilages of last six ribs and lumbar vertebrae I—central tendon	Prime mover of inspiration; flattens on contraction, increasing vertical dimensions of thorax; when strongly contracted, dramatically increases intra-abdominal pressure	Phrenic nerves

*Although there is a third (deepest) muscle layer of the thoracic wall, the muscles are small and discontinuous. Additionally, their function is unclear, so they are not included in this table.

MUSCLE GALLERY

Table 10.5 *(continued)*

Figure 10.11 Muscles of respiration. (a) Deep muscles of the thorax. The external intercostals (inspiratory muscles) are shown on the left and the internal intercostals (expiratory muscles) are shown on the right. These two muscle layers run obliquely and at right angles to each other. **(b)** Inferior view of the diaphragm, the prime mover of inspiration. Notice that its muscle fibers converge toward a central tendon, an arrangement that causes the diaphragm to flatten and move inferiorly as it contracts. **(c)** Photograph of the diaphragm, superior view.

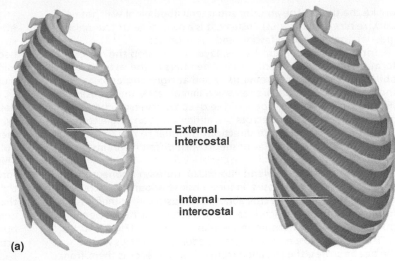

External intercostal

Internal intercostal

(a)

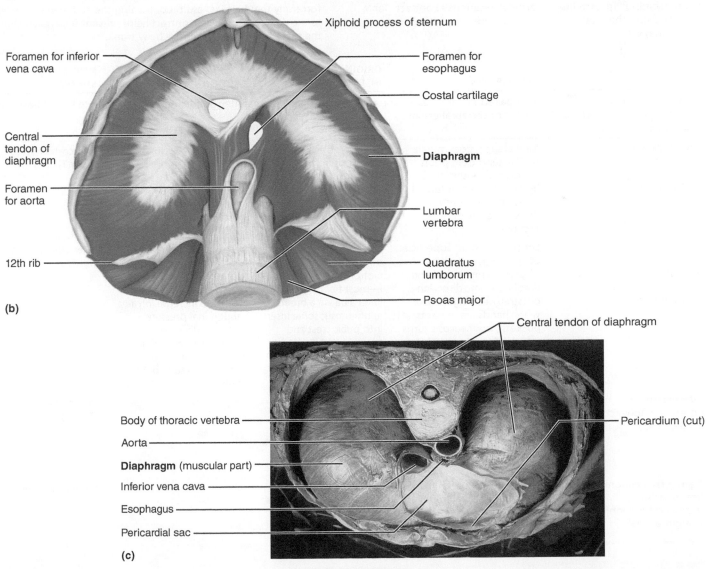

Xiphoid process of sternum

Foramen for inferior vena cava

Foramen for esophagus

Costal cartilage

Central tendon of diaphragm

Diaphragm

Foramen for aorta

Lumbar vertebra

12th rib

Quadratus lumborum

Psoas major

(b)

Central tendon of diaphragm

Pericardium (cut)

Body of thoracic vertebra

Aorta

Diaphragm (muscular part)

Inferior vena cava

Esophagus

Pericardial sac

(c)

MUSCLE GALLERY

Table 10.6 Muscles of the Abdominal Wall: Trunk Movements and Compression of Abdominal Viscera   (Figure 10.12)

Unlike the thorax, the anterior and lateral abdominal wall has no bony reinforcements (ribs). Instead, it is a composite of four paired muscles, their investing fasciae, and aponeuroses.

Three broad flat muscle pairs, layered one atop the next, form the lateral abdominal walls: The fibers of the **external oblique muscle** run inferomedially and at right angles to those of the **internal oblique**, which immediately underlies it (Figure 10.12a, b). The fibers of the deep **transversus abdominis muscle** run horizontally across the abdomen at an angle to both. This alternation of fascicle directions is similar to the construction of plywood (which is made of sheets with different grains) and provides great strength.

These three muscles blend into broad insertion aponeuroses anteriorly. The aponeuroses, in turn, enclose a fourth muscle pair medially, the straplike **rectus abdominis muscles**, and then fuse, forming the **linea alba** ("white line"), a tendinous raphe (seam) that runs from the sternum to the pubic symphysis (Figure 10.12a, c). The snug enclosure of the rectus abdominis muscles within the aponeuroses, the so-called *rectus sheath*, prevents them from "bowstringing" (protruding anteriorly) when they contract. Table 10.4 describes the quadratus lumborum muscles of the *posterior* abdominal wall.

The abdominal muscles protect and support the viscera most effectively when they are well toned. When weak or severely stretched (as during pregnancy), they allow the abdomen to become pendulous (i.e., to form a potbelly). Additional functions include lateral flexion and rotation of the trunk and flexion of the trunk against resistance (as in sit-ups).

During inspiration, the abdominal muscles relax, allowing the descending diaphragm to push the abdominal viscera inferiorly. When these abdominal muscles contract, several different activities may occur. For example, when they contract simultaneously, they pull the ribs inferiorly and compress the abdominal contents. This forces the visceral organs upward on the diaphragm, aiding forced expiration. When the abdominal muscles contract with the diaphragm and the glottis is closed (the Valsalva maneuver), the increased intra-abdominal pressure promotes urination, defecation, childbirth, vomiting, coughing, screaming, sneezing, burping, and nose blowing. (Next time you perform one of these activities, feel your abdominal muscles contract under your skin.)

These muscles also contract during heavy lifting— sometimes so forcefully that hernias result. Contracting the abdominal muscles as the deep back muscles contract helps prevent hyperextension of the spine and splints the entire body trunk.

MUSCLE	DESCRIPTION	ORIGIN (O) AND INSERTION (I)	ACTION	NERVE SUPPLY
MUSCLES OF THE ANTERIOR AND LATERAL ABDOMINAL WALL	Four paired flat muscles; important in supporting and protecting abdominal viscera; promote lateral flexion and flexion of vertebral column			
Rectus abdominis (rek'tus ab-dom'ĭ-nis) (*rectus* = straight; *abdom* = abdomen)	Medial superficial muscle pair; extend from pubis to rib cage; ensheathed by aponeuroses of lateral muscles; segmented by three tendinous inter-sections	O—pubic crest and symphysis I—xiphoid process and costal cartilages of ribs 5–7	Flex and rotate lumbar region of vertebral column; fix and depress ribs, stabilize pelvis during walking, increase intra-abdominal pressure; used in sit-ups, curls	Intercostal nerves (T$_6$ or T$_7$–T$_{12}$)
External oblique (o-blēk') (*external* = toward outside; *oblique* = running at an angle)	Largest and most superficial of the three lateral muscles; fibers run downward and medially (same direction outstretched fingers take when hands are in pants pockets); aponeurosis turns under inferiorly, forming inguinal ligament	O—by fleshy strips from outer surfaces of lower eight ribs I—most fibers insert into linea alba via a broad aponeurosis; some insert into pubic crest and tubercle and iliac crest	When pair contract simultaneously, flex vertebral column and compress abdominal wall and increase intra-abdominal pressure; acting individually, aid muscles of back in rotating trunk and flexing laterally; used in oblique curls	Intercostal nerves (T$_7$–T$_{12}$)
Internal oblique (*internal* = toward the inside; deep)	Most fibers run upward and medially; however, the muscle fans so its inferior fibers run downward and medially	O—lumbar fascia, iliac crest, and inguinal ligament I—linea alba, pubic crest, last three or four ribs, and costal margin	As for external oblique	Intercostal nerves (T$_7$–T$_{12}$) and L$_1$
Transversus abdominis (trans-ver'sus) (*transverse* = running straight across)	Deepest (innermost) muscle of abdominal wall; fibers run horizontally	O—inguinal ligament, lumbar fascia, cartilages of last six ribs; iliac crest I—linea alba, pubic crest	Compresses abdominal contents	Intercostal nerves (T$_7$–T$_{12}$) and L$_1$

MUSCLE GALLERY

Table 10.6 *(continued)*

Figure 10.12 Muscles of the abdominal wall. (a) Anterior view of the muscles forming the anterolateral abdominal wall; superficial muscles partially cut away to reveal the deeper muscles. **(b)** Lateral view of the trunk, illustrating the fiber direction and attachments of the abdominal muscles. Although shown in the same view, the rectus abdominis is deep to the fascia of the internal oblique muscle. **(c)** Transverse section through the anterolateral abdominal wall (midregion), showing how the aponeuroses of the lateral abdominal muscles contribute to the rectus abdominis sheath.

MUSCLE GALLERY

| Table 10.7 | Muscles of the Pelvic Floor and Perineum: Support of Abdominopelvic Organs | (Figure 10.13) |

Two paired muscles, the **levator ani** and **coccygeus**, form the funnel-shaped pelvic floor, or **pelvic diaphragm** (Figure 10.13a). This diaphragm (1) seals the inferior opening of the bony pelvis, (2) supports the pelvic organs, (3) lifts the pelvic floor superiorly to release feces, and (4) resists increased intra-abdominal pressure (which would expel contents of the urinary bladder, rectum, and uterus). The pelvic diaphragm is pierced by the rectum and urethra (urinary tube), and by the vagina in females.

The body region inferior to the pelvic diaphragm is the *perineum*. The **urogenital diaphragm** sits inferior to the muscles of the pelvic floor, and stretches between the two sides of the pubic arch in the anterior half of the perineum (Figure 10.13b). This thin

triangular sheet of muscle contains the **external urethral sphincter**, a sphincter muscle that surrounds the urethra and allows voluntary control of urination. Superficial to the urogenital diaphragm, and covered by the skin of the perineum, is the *superficial perineal space*, which contains muscles (**ischiocavernosus** and **bulbospongiosus**) that help maintain erection of the penis and clitoris (Figure 10.13c). In the posterior half of the perineum encircling the anus is the **external anal sphincter**, which allows voluntary control of defecation. Just anterior to this sphincter is the **central tendon of the perineum**, a strong tendon into which many of the perineal muscles insert.

MUSCLE	DESCRIPTION	ORIGIN (O) AND INSERTION (I)	ACTION	NERVE SUPPLY
MUSCLES OF THE PELVIC DIAPHRAGM (Figure 10.13a)				
Levator ani (lĕ-va′tor a′ne) (*levator* = raises; *ani* = anus)	Broad, thin, tripartite muscle (pubococcygeus, puborectalis, and iliococcygeus); its fibers extend inferomedially, forming a muscular "sling" around male prostate (or female vagina), urethra, and anorectal junction before meeting in the median plane	O—extensive linear origin inside pelvis from pubis to ischial spine I—inner surface of coccyx, levator ani of opposite side, and (in part) into the structures that penetrate it	Supports and maintains position of pelvic viscera; resists downward thrusts that accompany rises in intrapelvic pressure during coughing, vomiting, and expulsive efforts of abdominal muscles; forms sphincters at anorectal junction and vagina; lifts anal canal during defecation	S$_3$, S$_4$, and inferior rectal nerve (branch of pudendal nerve)
Coccygeus (kok-sij′e-us) (*coccy* = coccyx)	Small triangular muscle lying posterior to levator ani; forms posterior part of pelvic diaphragm	O—spine of ischium I—sacrum and coccyx	Supports pelvic viscera; supports coccyx and pulls it forward after it has been reflected posteriorly by defecation and childbirth	S$_4$ and S$_5$
MUSCLES OF THE UROGENITAL DIAPHRAGM (Figure 10.13b)				
Deep transverse perineal muscle (per″ĭ-ne′al) (*deep* = far from surface; *transverse* = across; *perine* = near anus)	Together the pair spans distance between ischial rami; in females, lies posterior to vagina	O—ischial rami I—midline central tendon of perineum; some fibers into vaginal wall in females	Supports pelvic organs; steadies central tendon	Pudendal nerve
External urethral sphincter (*sphin* = squeeze)	Muscle encircling urethra and vagina (female)	O—ischiopubic rami I—midline raphe	Constricts urethra; allows voluntary inhibition of urination; helps support pelvic organs	Pudendal nerve
MUSCLES OF THE SUPERFICIAL PERINEAL SPACE (Figure 10.13c)				
Ischiocavernosus (is″ke-o-kav″ern-o′sus) (*ischi* = hip; *caverna* = hollow chamber)	Runs from pelvis to base of penis or clitoris	O—ischial tuberosities I—crus of corpora cavernosa of male penis or female clitoris	Retards venous drainage and maintains erection of penis or clitoris	Pudendal nerve
Bulbospongiosus (bul″bo-spun″je-o′sus) (*bulbon* = bulb; *spongio* = sponge)	Encloses base of penis (bulb) in males and lies deep to labia in females	O—central tendon of perineum and midline raphe of penis I—anteriorly into corpora cavernosa of penis or clitoris	Empties male urethra; assists in erection of penis and of clitoris	Pudendal nerve
Superficial transverse perineal muscles (*superficial* = closer to surface)	Paired muscle bands posterior to urethral (and in females, vaginal) opening; variable; sometimes absent	O—ischial tuberosity I—central tendon of perineum	Stabilizes and strengthens central tendon of perineum	Pudendal nerve

MUSCLE GALLERY

Table 10.7 *(continued)*

Anterior

Levator ani
- Pubococcygeus
- Iliococcygeus

Symphysis pubis

Urogenital diaphragm

Urethra

Vagina

Anal canal

Obturator internus

Coccyx

Piriformis

Levator ani
Coccygeus
} **Pelvic diaphragm**

(a)   **Posterior**

Figure 10.13 Muscles of the pelvic floor and perineum. (a) Superior view of muscles of the pelvic diaphragm (levator ani and coccygeus) in a female pelvis. **(b)** Inferior view of muscles of the urogenital diaphragm of the perineum (external urethral sphincter and deep transverse perineal muscles). **(c)** Muscles of the superficial space of the perineum (ischiocavernosus, bulbospongiosus, and superficial transverse perineal muscle), which lie just deep to the skin of the perineum. Note that a raphe is a seam of fibrous tissue.

10

Inferior pubic ramus

External urethral sphincter

Deep transverse perineal muscle

Central tendon

Anus

External anal sphincter

Urethral opening

Vaginal opening

(b)   Male   Female

Penis

Midline raphe

Ischiocavernosus

Bulbospongiosus

Superficial transverse perineal muscle

Levator ani

Gluteus maximus

Anus

Clitoris

Urethral opening

Vaginal opening

(c)   Male   Female

MUSCLE GALLERY

Table 10.8	Superficial Muscles of the Anterior and Posterior Thorax: Movements of the Scapula and Arm (Figure 10.14)

Most superficial thorax muscles are *extrinsic shoulder muscles*, which run from the ribs and vertebral column to the shoulder girdle. They both fix the scapula in place and move it to increase the range of arm movements.

The anterior muscles of this group include the **pectoralis major**, **pectoralis minor**, **serratus anterior**, and **subclavius** (Figure 10.14a). Except for the pectoralis major, which inserts into the humerus, all muscles of the anterior group insert into the pectoral girdle.

The posterior muscles include the **latissimus dorsi** and **trapezius muscles** superficially and the underlying **levator scapulae** and **rhomboids** (Figure 10.14c). The latissimus dorsi, like the pectoralis major muscles anteriorly, insert into the humerus and are more concerned with moving the arm than the scapula, so we defer their consideration to Table 10.9 (arm-moving muscles).

The important movements of the pectoral girdle involve displacing the scapula, i.e., its elevation and depression, rotation, lateral (forward) movements, and medial (backward) movements. The clavicles rotate around their own axes to provide stability and precision to scapular movements.

Except for the serratus anterior, the anterior muscles stabilize and depress the shoulder girdle. Thus, most scapular movements are promoted by the serratus anterior muscles anteriorly and by posterior thoracic muscles. The arrangement of muscle attachments to the scapula is such that one muscle cannot bring about a simple (linear) movement on its own. To effect scapular movements, several muscles must act in combination.

The prime movers of shoulder (scapular) elevation are the superior trapezius fibers and the levator scapulae. When acting together to shrug the shoulder, their opposite rotational effects counterbalance each other. The scapula is depressed largely by gravity (weight of the arm), but when it is depressed against resistance, the inferior part of the trapezius, the pectoralis minor, and the serratus anterior (along with the latissimus dorsi, Table 10.9) are active. Anterolateral movements (abduction) of the scapula on the thorax wall, as in pushing or punching, mainly reflect serratus anterior activity. Posteromedial movement (adduction) of the scapula is effected mainly by the trapezius (midpart) and the rhomboids. Although the serratus anterior and trapezius muscles are antagonists in forward/backward movements of the scapulae, they act together to coordinate *rotational* scapular movements.

MUSCLE	DESCRIPTION	ORIGIN (O) AND INSERTION (I)	ACTION	NERVE SUPPLY
MUSCLES OF THE ANTERIOR THORAX (Figure 10.14a)				
Pectoralis minor (pek″to-ra′lis mi′nor) (*pectus* = chest, breast; *minor* = lesser)	Flat, thin muscle directly beneath and obscured by pectoralis major	O—anterior surfaces of ribs 3–5 (or 2–4) I—coracoid process of scapula	With ribs fixed, draws scapula forward and downward; with scapula fixed, draws rib cage superiorly	Medial and lateral pectoral nerves (C_6–C_8)
Serratus anterior (ser-a′tus) (*serratus* = saw)	Fan-shaped muscle; lies deep to scapula, deep and inferior to pectoral muscles on lateral rib cage; forms medial wall of axilla; origins have serrated (sawtooth) appearance; paralysis results in "winging" of vertebral border of scapula away from chest wall, making arm elevation impossible	O—by a series of muscle slips from ribs 1–8 (or 9) I—entire anterior surface of vertebral border of scapula	Rotates scapula so its inferior angle moves laterally and upward; prime mover to protract and hold scapula against chest wall; raises point of shoulder; important role in abducting and raising arm and in horizontal arm movements (pushing, punching); called "boxer's muscle"	Long thoracic nerve (C_5–C_7)
Subclavius (sub-kla′ve-us) (*sub* = under, beneath; *clav* = clavicle)	Small cylindrical muscle extending from rib 1 to clavicle	O—costal cartilage of rib 1 I—groove on inferior surface of clavicle	Helps stabilize and depress pectoral girdle	Nerve to subclavius (C_5 and C_6)

MUSCLE GALLERY

Table 10.8 (continued)

(a)

Sternocleidomastoid
Deltoid
Pectoralis major
Sternum
Biceps brachii

Subclavius
Clavicle
Subscapularis
Pectoralis minor
Coracobrachialis
Serratus anterior
Humerus

(b)

Sternocleidomastoid
Deltoid
Cephalic vein
Pectoralis major
External oblique

Subclavius
Pectoralis minor
Coracobrachialis
Biceps brachii
Internal intercostals (seen through external intercostal membranes)
Serratus anterior
Rectus abdominis

Figure 10.14 Superficial muscles of the thorax and shoulder acting on the scapula and arm. (a) Anterior view. The superficial muscles, which effect arm movements, are shown on the left side of the illustration. These muscles are removed on the right to show the muscles that stabilize or move the pectoral girdle. **(b)** Cadaver dissection, anterior view of superficial muscles of anterior thorax.

Table 10.8 Superficial Muscles of the Anterior and Posterior Thorax:
Movements of the Scapula and Arm   (Figure 10.14) *(continued)*

MUSCLE	DESCRIPTION	ORIGIN (O) AND INSERTION (I)	ACTION	NERVE SUPPLY
MUSCLES OF THE POSTERIOR THORAX (Figure 10.14c–e)				
Trapezius (trah-pe′ze-us) (*trapezion* = irregular four-sided figure)	Most superficial muscle of posterior thorax; flat and triangular in shape; upper fibers run inferiorly to scapula; middle fibers run horizontally to scapula; lower fibers run superiorly to scapula	O—occipital bone, ligamentum nuchae, and spinous processes of C_7 and all thoracic vertebrae I—a continuous insertion along acromion and spine of scapula and lateral third of clavicle	Stabilizes, raises, retracts, and rotates scapula; middle fibers retract (adduct) scapula; superior fibers elevate scapula (as in shrugging the shoulders) or help extend head with scapula fixed; inferior fibers depress scapula (and shoulder)	Accessory nerve (cranial nerve XI); C_3 and C_4
Levator scapulae (skap′u-le) (*levator* = raises)	Located at back and side of neck, deep to trapezius; thick straplike muscle	O—transverse processes of C_1–C_4 I—medial border of scapula, superior to spine	Elevates/adducts scapula in concert with superior fibers of trapezius; tilts glenoid cavity downward when scapula is fixed, flexes neck to same side	Cervical spinal nerves and dorsal scapular nerve (C_3–C_5)
Rhomboids (rom′boidz)—major and minor (*rhomboid* = diamond shaped)	Two roughly diamond-shaped muscles lying deep to trapezius and inferior to levator scapulae; rhomboid minor is the more superior muscle	O—spinous processes of C_7 and T_1 (minor) and spinous processes of T_2–T_5 (major) I—medial border of scapula	Stabilize scapula; act together (and with middle trapezius fibers) to retract (adduct) scapula, thus "squaring shoulders"; rotate scapula so that glenoid cavity is downward (as when lowering arm against resistance; e.g., paddling a canoe)	Dorsal scapular nerve (C_4 and C_5)

10

Trapezius

Deltoid

Rhomboid minor

Rhomboid major

Latissimus dorsi

Levator scapulae

Supraspinatus

Clavicle

Spine of scapula

Infraspinatus

Teres minor

Teres major

Humerus

(c)

Figure 10.14 *(continued)* **Superficial muscles of the thorax and shoulder acting on the scapula and arm.** **(c)** Posterior view. The superficial muscles are shown on the left side of the illustration. Superficial muscles are removed on the right side to reveal the deeper muscles acting on the scapula, and the rotator cuff muscles that help stabilize the shoulder joint.

MUSCLE GALLERY

Table 10.8 *(continued)*

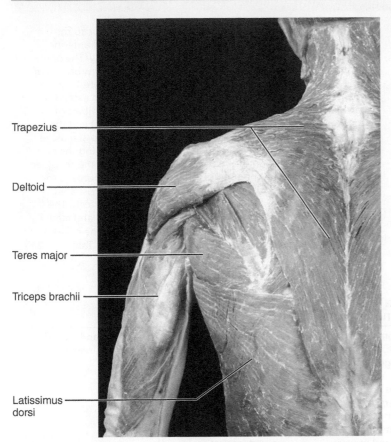

Trapezius

Deltoid

Teres major

Triceps brachii

Latissimus dorsi

(d)

Figure 10.14 *(continued)* **Superficial muscles of the thorax and shoulder acting on the scapula and arm. (d)** and **(e)** Cadaver dissections showing views similar to (c).

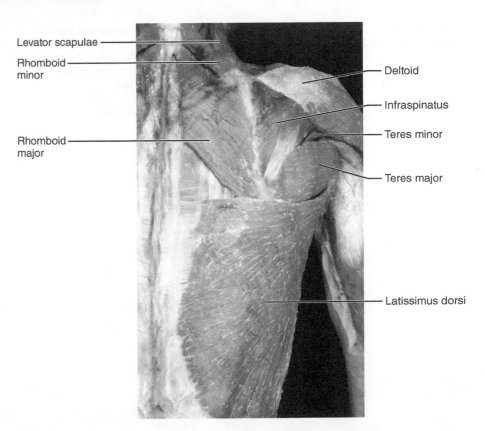

Levator scapulae

Rhomboid minor

Rhomboid major

Deltoid

Infraspinatus

Teres minor

Teres major

Latissimus dorsi

(e)

10

MUSCLE GALLERY

Recall that the ball-and-socket shoulder joint is the most flexible joint in the body, but pays the price of instability. Several muscles cross each shoulder joint to insert on the humerus. All muscles acting on the humerus originate from the pectoral girdle. However, two of these—the latissimus dorsi and pectoralis major—primarily originate on the axial skeleton.

Of the nine muscles covered here, only the **pectoralis major**, **latissimus dorsi**, and **deltoid muscles** are prime movers of arm movements (Figure 10.15a, b). The remaining six are synergists and fixators. Four of these, the **supraspinatus, infraspinatus, teres minor**, and **subscapularis** (marked with an asterisk* in Figure 10.15b, d), are *rotator cuff muscles*. They originate on the scapula, and their tendons blend with the fibrous capsule of the shoulder joint en route to the humerus. Although the rotator cuff muscles act as synergists in angular and rotational movements of the arm, their main function is to reinforce the capsule of the shoulder joint to prevent dislocation of the humerus. The remaining two muscles, the small **teres major** and **coracobrachialis**, cross the shoulder joint but do not reinforce it.

Generally speaking, muscles that originate *anterior* to the shoulder joint (pectoralis major, coracobrachialis, and anterior fibers of the deltoid) *flex* the arm, i.e., lift it anteriorly. The prime mover of arm flexion is the pectoralis major. The biceps brachii of the arm assists in this action (Figure 10.15a, c; see Table 10.10).

Muscles originating *posterior* to the shoulder joint extend the arm. These include the latissimus dorsi and posterior fibers of the deltoid muscles (both prime movers of arm extension) and the teres major. Note that the pectoralis and latissimus dorsi muscles are *antagonists* of one another in flexing and extending the arm.

The middle region of the fleshy deltoid muscle of the shoulder, which extends over the superolateral side of the humerus, is the prime mover of arm abduction. The main arm adductors are the pectoralis major anteriorly and latissimus dorsi posteriorly. The small muscles acting on the humerus promote lateral and medial rotation of the arm. The interactions among these nine muscles are complex and each contributes to several movements. Table 10.12 (Part I) summarizes their actions.

MUSCLE	DESCRIPTION	ORIGIN (O) AND INSERTION (I)	ACTION	NERVE SUPPLY
Pectoralis major (pek"to-ra'lis ma'jer) (*pectus* = breast, chest; *major* = larger)	Large, fan-shaped muscle covering superior portion of chest; forms anterior axillary fold; divided into clavicular and sternal parts	O—sternal end of clavicle, sternum, cartilage of ribs 1–6 (or 7), and aponeurosis of external oblique muscle I—fibers converge to insert by a short tendon into intertubercular sulcus and greater tubercle of humerus	Prime mover of arm flexion; rotates arm medially; adducts arm against resistance; with scapula (and arm) fixed, pulls rib cage upward, thus can help in climbing, throwing, pushing, and forced inspiration	Lateral and medial pectoral nerves (C_5–C_8 and T_1)
Deltoid (del'toid) (*delta* = triangular)	Thick, multipennate muscle forming rounded shoulder muscle mass; a common site for intramuscular injection, particularly in males, where it tends to be quite fleshy	O—embraces insertion of the trapezius; lateral third of clavicle; acromion and spine of scapula I—deltoid tuberosity of humerus	Prime mover of arm abduction when all its fibers contract simultaneously; antagonist of pectoralis major and latissimus dorsi, which adduct the arm; if only anterior fibers are active, can act powerfully in flexing and rotating humerus medially, therefore synergist of pectoralis major; if only posterior fibers are active, causes extension and lateral rotation of arm; active during rhythmic arm-swinging movements while walking	Axillary nerve (C_5 and C_6)

MUSCLE GALLERY

Table 10.9 (continued)

MUSCLE	DESCRIPTION	ORIGIN (O) AND INSERTION (I)	ACTION	NERVE SUPPLY
Latissimus dorsi (lah-tis′ĭ-mus dor′si) (*latissimus* = widest; *dorsi* = back)	Broad, flat, triangular muscle of lower back (lumbar region); extensive superficial origins; covered by trapezius superiorly; contributes to the posterior wall of axilla	O—indirect attachment via lumbodorsal fascia into spines of lower six thoracic vertebrae, lumbar vertebrae, lower 3 to 4 ribs, and iliac crest; also from scapula's inferior angle I—spirals around teres major to insert in floor of intertubercular sulcus of humerus	Prime mover of arm extension; powerful arm adductor; medially rotates arm at shoulder; depresses scapula; plays important role in lowering arm in a power stroke, as in striking a blow, hammering, swimming, and rowing; with arms fixed overhead, it pulls the rest of the body upward and forward	Thoracodorsal nerve (C_6–C_8)

(a) Anterior view

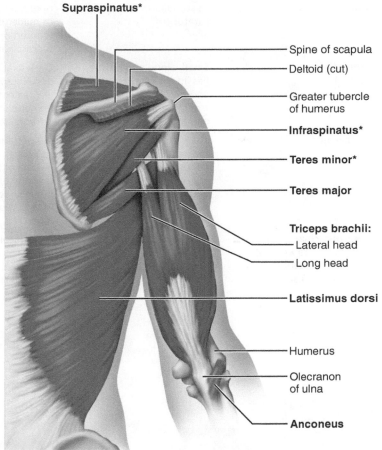

(b) Posterior view

Figure 10.15 Muscles crossing the shoulder and elbow joints, causing movements of the arm and forearm, respectively. (For related images, see *A Brief Atlas of the Human Body*, Figures 35 and 36.) **(a)** Superficial muscles of the anterior thorax, shoulder, and arm, anterior view. **(b)** Muscles of the posterior thorax and arm. The triceps brachii muscle of the posterior arm is shown in relation to the deep scapular muscles. The deltoid muscle of the shoulder and the trapezius muscle have been removed.

*Rotator cuff muscles

MUSCLE GALLERY

Table 10.9	Muscles Crossing the Shoulder Joint: Movements of the Arm (Humerus)		(Figure 10.15) (continued)

MUSCLE	DESCRIPTION	ORIGIN (O) AND INSERTION (I)	ACTION	NERVE SUPPLY
Subscapularis (sub-scap"u-lar'is) (*sub* = under; *scapular* = scapula)	Forms part of posterior wall of axilla; tendon of insertion passes in front of shoulder joint; a rotator cuff muscle	O—subscapular fossa of scapula I—lesser tubercle of humerus	Chief medial rotator of humerus; assisted by pectoralis major; helps hold head of humerus in glenoid cavity, stabilizing shoulder joint	Subscapular nerves (C_5–C_7)
Supraspinatus (soo"prah-spi-nah'tus) (*supra* = above, over; *spin* = spine)	Named for its location on posterior aspect of scapula; deep to trapezius; a rotator cuff muscle	O—supraspinous fossa of scapula I—superior part of greater tubercle of humerus	Initiates abduction; stabilizes shoulder joint; helps prevent downward dislocation of humerus, as when carrying a heavy suitcase	Suprascapular nerve
Infraspinatus (in"frah-spi-nah'tus) (*infra* = below)	Partially covered by deltoid and trapezius; named for its scapular location; a rotator cuff muscle	O—infraspinous fossa of scapula I—greater tubercle of humerus posterior to insertion of supraspinatus	Rotates humerus laterally; helps hold head of humerus in glenoid cavity, stabilizing the shoulder joint	Suprascapular nerve
Teres minor (te'rēz) (*teres* = round; *minor* = lesser)	Small, elongated muscle; lies inferior to infraspinatus and may be inseparable from that muscle; a rotator cuff muscle	O—lateral border of dorsal scapular surface I—greater tubercle of humerus inferior to infraspinatus insertion	Same action(s) as infraspinatus muscle	Axillary nerve
Teres major	Thick, rounded muscle; located inferior to teres minor; helps form posterior wall of axilla (along with latissimus dorsi and subscapularis)	O—posterior surface of scapula at inferior angle I—crest of lesser tubercle on anterior humerus; insertion tendon fused with that of latissimus dorsi	Extends, medially rotates, and adducts humerus; synergist of latissimus dorsi	Lower subscapular nerve (C_6 and C_7)
Coracobrachialis (kor"ah-ko-bra"ke-al'is) (*coraco* = coracoid; *brachi* = arm)	Small, cylindrical muscle	O—coracoid process of scapula I — medial surface of humerus shaft	Flexes and adducts humerus; synergist of pectoralis major	Musculocutaneous nerve (C_5–C_7)

Biceps brachii [Long head / Short head]

O = origin
I = insertion

(c)

Subscapularis*
Coracobrachialis
Brachialis

(d)

Figure 10.15 *(continued)* **Muscles crossing the shoulder and elbow joints, causing movements of the arm and forearm, respectively. (c)** The isolated biceps brachii muscle of the anterior arm. **(d)** The brachialis muscle and the coracobrachialis and subscapularis muscles shown in isolation in the diagram on the left, and in a dissection on the right.

*Rotator cuff muscles

MUSCLE GALLERY

| **Table 10.10** | **Muscles Crossing the Elbow Joint: Flexion and Extension of the Forearm** | **(Figure 10.15)** |

Muscles fleshing out the arm cross the elbow joint to insert on the forearm bones. Since the elbow is a hinge joint, movements promoted by these arm muscles are limited almost entirely to flexing and extending the forearm. Walls of fascia divide the arm into two muscle compartments—the *posterior extensors* and *anterior flexors*. The main forearm extensor is the bulky **triceps brachii** muscle, which forms nearly the entire musculature of the posterior compartment (Figure 10.15a, b).

All anterior arm muscles flex the forearm (elbow). In order of decreasing strength, these are the **brachialis, biceps brachii**, and **brachioradialis** (Figure 10.15a, c, d). The brachialis and biceps insert (respectively) into the ulna and radius and contract simultaneously during flexion; they are the chief forearm flexors. The biceps

brachii, a muscle that bulges when the forearm is flexed, is familiar to almost everyone. The brachialis, which lies deep to the biceps, is less known but is equally important in flexing the elbow. Because the brachioradialis arises from the distal humerus and inserts on the distal forearm, it resides mainly in the forearm. Its force is exerted far from the fulcrum, so the brachioradialis is a weak forearm flexor. The biceps muscle also supinates the forearm and is ineffective in flexing the elbow when the forearm *must* stay pronated. (This is why doing chin-ups with palms facing anteriorly is harder than with palms facing posteriorly.)

Table 10.12 (Part II) summarizes the actions of the muscles described here.

MUSCLE	DESCRIPTION	ORIGIN (O) AND INSERTION (I)	ACTION	NERVE SUPPLY
POSTERIOR MUSCLES				
Triceps brachii (tri′seps bra′ke-i) (*triceps* = three heads; *brachi* = arm)	Large fleshy muscle; the only muscle of posterior compartment of arm; three-headed origin; long and lateral heads lie superficial to medial head	O—long head: infraglenoid tubercle of scapula; lateral head: posterior shaft of humerus; medial head: posterior humeral shaft distal to radial groove I—by common tendon into olecranon of ulna	Powerful forearm extensor (prime mover, particularly medial head); antagonist of forearm flexors; long and lateral heads mainly active in extending the forearm against resistance; long head tendon may help stabilize shoulder joint and assist in arm adduction	Radial nerve (C_6–C_8)
Anconeus (an-ko′ne-us) (*ancon* = elbow) (see Figure 10.17)	Short triangular muscle; partially blended with distal end of triceps on posterior humerus	O—lateral epicondyle of humerus I—lateral aspect of olecranon of ulna	May control ulnar abduction during forearm pronation; synergist of triceps brachii in elbow extension	Radial nerve
ANTERIOR MUSCLES				
Biceps brachii (bi′seps) (*biceps* = two heads)	Two-headed fusiform muscle; bellies unite as insertion point is approached; tendon of long head helps stabilize shoulder joint	O—short head: coracoid process; long head: supraglenoid tubercle and lip of glenoid cavity; tendon of long head runs within capsule and into intertubercular sulcus of humerus I—by common tendon into radial tuberosity	Flexes elbow joint and supinates forearm; these actions usually occur at same time (e.g., when you open a bottle of wine, it turns the corkscrew and pulls the cork); weak flexor of arm at shoulder	Musculocutaneous nerve (C_5 and C_6)
Brachialis (bra′ke-al-is)	Strong muscle that is immediately deep to biceps brachii on distal humerus	O—front of distal humerus; embraces insertion of deltoid muscle I—coronoid process of ulna and capsule of elbow joint	A major forearm flexor (lifts ulna as biceps lifts the radius)	Musculocutaneous nerve
Brachioradialis (bra″ke-o-ra″de-al′is) (*radi* = radius, ray) (also see Figure 10.16)	Superficial muscle of lateral forearm; forms lateral boundary of cubital fossa; extends from distal humerus to distal forearm	O—lateral supracondylar ridge at distal end of humerus I—base of radial styloid process	Synergist in flexing forearm; acts to best advantage when forearm is partially flexed and semipronated; stabilizes elbow during rapid flexion *and* extension	Radial nerve (an important exception: the radial nerve typically serves extensor muscles)

10

MUSCLE GALLERY

Table 10.11 Muscles of the Forearm: Movements of the Wrist, Hand, and Fingers (Figures 10.16 and 10.17)

The many muscles in the forearm perform several basic functions. Some cause wrist movements, some move the fingers and thumb, and a few help pronate and supinate the forearms. In most cases, their fleshy portions contribute to the roundness of the proximal forearm and then they taper to long tendons distally to insert into the hand.

At the wrist, these tendons are securely anchored by bandlike thickenings of deep fascia called **flexor** and **extensor retinacula** ("retainers") (Figure 10.16a). These "wrist bands" keep the tendons from jumping outward when tensed. Crowded together in the wrist and palm, the muscle tendons are surrounded by slippery tendon sheaths that minimize friction as they slide against one another.

Although many forearm muscles arise from the humerus (and thus cross both the elbow and wrist joints), their actions on the elbow are slight. Flexion and extension are the movements typically effected at both the wrist and finger joints. In addition, the forearm muscles can abduct and adduct the wrist.

Fascia subdivides the forearm muscles into two main compartments: the *anterior flexors* and *posterior extensors*. Each has superficial and deep muscle layers. Most flexors in the anterior compartment arise from a common tendon on the humerus

and are innervated largely by the median nerve. Two anterior compartment muscles are not flexors but pronators, the **pronator teres** and **pronator quadratus** (Figure 10.16a–c). Pronation is one of the most important forearm movements.

Muscles of the posterior compartment extend the wrist and fingers. One exception is the **supinator** muscle, which assists the biceps brachii muscle of the arm in supinating the forearm (Figures 10.16b, c and 10.17b). (Also residing in the posterior compartment is the brachioradialis muscle, the weak elbow flexor considered in Table 10.10.) Most muscles of the posterior compartment arise from a common tendon on the humerus. The radial nerve supplies all posterior forearm muscles.

As described above, most muscles that move the hand are located in the forearm and "operate" the fingers via their long tendons, like operating a puppet by strings. This design makes the hand less bulky and enables it to perform finer movements. The hand movements promoted by the forearm muscles are assisted by the small *intrinsic* muscles of the hand, which control the most delicate and precise finger movements (see Table 10.13). Table 10.12 (Parts II and III) summarizes the actions of the forearm muscles.

MUSCLE	DESCRIPTION	ORIGIN (O) AND INSERTION (I)	ACTION	NERVE SUPPLY
PART I: ANTERIOR MUSCLES (Figure 10.16)	These eight muscles of the anterior fascial compartment are listed from the lateral to the medial aspect. Most arise from a common flexor tendon attached to the medial epicondyle of the humerus and have additional origins as well. Most of their tendons of insertion are held in place at the wrist by a thickening of deep fascia called the *flexor retinaculum*.			
Superficial Muscles				
Pronator teres (pro-na′tor te′rēz) (*pronation* = turning palm posteriorly, or down; *teres* = round)	Two-headed muscle; seen in superficial view between proximal margins of brachioradialis and flexor carpi radialis; forms medial boundary of cubital fossa	O—medial epicondyle of humerus; coronoid process of ulna I—by common tendon into lateral radius, midshaft	Pronates forearm; weak flexor of elbow	Median nerve
Flexor carpi radialis (flek′sor kar′pe ra″de-al′is) (*flex* = decrease angle between two bones; *carpi* = wrist; *radi* = radius)	Runs diagonally across forearm; midway, its fleshy belly is replaced by a flat tendon that becomes cordlike at wrist	O—medial epicondyle of humerus I—base of second and third metacarpals; insertion tendon easily seen and provides guide to position of radial artery at wrist (used for taking pulse)	Powerful flexor of wrist; abducts hand; weak synergist of elbow flexion	Median nerve
Palmaris longus (pahl-ma′ris lon′gus) (*palma* = palm; *longus* = long)	Small fleshy muscle with a long insertion tendon; often absent; may be used as guide to find median nerve that lies lateral to it at wrist	O—medial epicondyle of humerus I—palmar aponeurosis; (fascia of palm)	Tenses skin and fascia of palm during hand movements; weak wrist flexor; weak synergist for elbow flexion	Median nerve
Flexor carpi ulnaris (ul-na′ris) (*ulnar* = ulna)	Most medial muscle of this group; two-headed; ulnar nerve lies lateral to its tendon	O—medial epicondyle of humerus; olecranon and posterior surface of ulna I—pisiform and hamate bones and base of fifth metacarpal	Powerful flexor of wrist; also adducts hand in concert with extensor carpi ulnaris (posterior muscle); stabilizes wrist during finger extension	Ulnar nerve (C_7 and C_8)

MUSCLE GALLERY

Table 10.11 (continued)

MUSCLE	DESCRIPTION	ORIGIN (O) AND INSERTION (I)	ACTION	NERVE SUPPLY
Flexor digitorum superficialis (di"ji-tor'um soo"per-fish"e-al'is) (digit = finger, toe; superficial = close to surface)	Two-headed muscle; more deeply placed (therefore, actually forms an intermediate layer); overlain by muscles above but visible at distal end of forearm	O—medial epicondyle of humerus, coronoid process of ulna; shaft of radius I—by four tendons into middle phalanges of fingers 2–5	Flexes wrist and middle phalanges of fingers 2–5; the important finger flexor for speed and flexion against resistance	Median nerve (C_7, C_8, and T_1)
Deep Muscles				
Flexor pollicis longus (pah'li-kis) (pollix = thumb)	Partly covered by flexor digitorum superficialis; parallels flexor digitorum profundus laterally	O—anterior surface of radius and interosseous membrane I—distal phalanx of thumb	Flexes distal phalanx of thumb	Branch of median nerve (C_8, T_1)
Flexor digitorum profundus (pro-fun'dus) (profund = deep)	Extensive origin; overlain entirely by flexor digitorum superficialis	O—coronoid process, anteromedial surface of ulna, and interosseous membrane I—by four tendons into distal phalanges of fingers 2–5	Flexes distal interphalangeal joints; slow-acting flexor of any or all fingers; helps flex wrist	Medial half by ulnar nerve; lateral half by median nerve

Figure 10.16 Muscles of the anterior fascial compartment of the forearm acting on the right wrist and fingers. **(a)** Superficial view. **(b)** The brachioradialis, flexors carpi radialis and ulnaris, and palmaris longus muscles have been removed to reveal the flexor digitorum superficialis. **(c)** Deep muscles of the anterior compartment. The lumbricals and thenar muscles (intrinsic hand muscles) are also illustrated. (For a related image, see *A Brief Atlas of the Human Body*, Figure 37.)

MUSCLE GALLERY

Table 10.11	Muscles of the Forearm: Movements of the Wrist, Hand, and Fingers (Figures 10.16 and 10.17) *(continued)*

MUSCLE	DESCRIPTION	ORIGIN (O) AND INSERTION (I)	ACTION	NERVE SUPPLY
Pronator quadratus (kwod-ra′tus) (*quad* = square, four-sided)	Deepest muscle of distal forearm; passes downward and laterally; only muscle that arises solely from ulna and inserts solely into radius	O—distal portion of anterior ulnar shaft I—distal surface of anterior radius	Prime mover of forearm pronation; acts with pronator teres; also helps hold ulna and radius together	Median nerve (C_8 and T_1)
PART II: POSTERIOR MUSCLES (Figure 10.17)	These muscles of the posterior fascial compartment are listed from the lateral to the medial aspect. They are all innervated by the radial nerve or its branches. More than half of the posterior compartment muscles arise from a common extensor origin tendon attached to the posterior surface of the lateral epicondyle of the humerus and adjacent fascia. The extensor tendons are held in place at the posterior aspect of the wrist by the *extensor retinaculum,* which prevents "bowstringing" of these tendons when the wrist is hyperextended. The *extensor* muscles of the fingers end in a broad hood over the dorsal side of the digits, the extensor expansion.			

Superficial Muscles

MUSCLE	DESCRIPTION	ORIGIN (O) AND INSERTION (I)	ACTION	NERVE SUPPLY
Brachioradialis (see Table 10.10)	See Table 10.10	See Table 10.10	See Table 10.10	See Table 10.10
Extensor carpi radialis longus (ek-sten′sor) (*extend* = increase angle between two bones)	Parallels brachioradialis on lateral forearm, and may blend with it	O—lateral supracondylar ridge of humerus I—base of second metacarpal	Extends wrist in conjunction with extensor carpi ulnaris and abducts wrist in conjunction with flexor carpi radialis	Radial nerve (C_6 and C_7)
Extensor carpi radialis brevis (brĕ′vis) (*brevis* = short)	Shorter than extensor carpi radialis longus and lies deep to it	O—lateral epicondyle of humerus I—base of third metacarpal	Extends and abducts wrist; acts synergistically with extensor carpi radialis longus to steady wrist during finger flexion	Deep branch of radial nerve
Extensor digitorum	Lies medial to extensor carpi radialis brevis; a detached portion of this muscle, called *extensor digiti minimi,* extends little finger	O—lateral epicondyle of humerus I—by four tendons into extensor expansions and distal phalanges of fingers 2–5	Prime mover of finger extension; extends wrist; can abduct (flare) fingers	Posterior interosseous nerve, a branch of radial nerve (C_5 and C_6)
Extensor carpi ulnaris	Most medial of superficial posterior muscles; long, slender muscle	O—lateral epicondyle of humerus and posterior border of ulna I—base of fifth metacarpal	Extends wrist in conjunction with extensor carpi radialis and adducts wrist in conjunction with flexor carpi ulnaris	Posterior interosseous nerve

Deep Muscles

MUSCLE	DESCRIPTION	ORIGIN (O) AND INSERTION (I)	ACTION	NERVE SUPPLY
Supinator (soo″pĭ-na′tor) (*supination* = turning palm anteriorly or upward)	Deep muscle at posterior aspect of elbow; largely concealed by superficial muscles	O—lateral epicondyle of humerus; proximal ulna I—proximal end of radius	Assists biceps brachii to forcibly supinate forearm; works alone in slow supination; antagonist of pronator muscles	Posterior interosseous nerve
Abductor pollicis longus (ab-duk′tor) (*abduct* = movement away from median plane)	Lateral and parallel to extensor pollicis longus; just distal to supinator	O—posterior surface of radius and ulna; interosseous membrane I—base of first metacarpal and trapezium	Abducts and extends thumb	Posterior interosseous nerve
Extensor pollicis brevis and longus	Deep muscle pair with a common origin and action; overlain by extensor carpi ulnaris	O—dorsal shaft of radius and ulna; interosseous membrane I—base of proximal (brevis) and distal (longus) phalanx of thumb	Extends thumb	Posterior interosseous nerve

MUSCLE GALLERY

Table 10.11 *(continued)*

MUSCLE	DESCRIPTION	ORIGIN (O) AND INSERTION (I)	ACTION	NERVE SUPPLY
Extensor indicis (in'dĭ-kis) (*indicis* = index finger)	Tiny muscle arising close to wrist	O—posterior surface of distal ulna; interosseous membrane I—extensor expansion of index finger; joins tendon of extensor digitorum	Extends index finger and assists in extending wrist	Posterior interosseous nerve

(a)

(b)

Figure 10.17 Muscles of the posterior fascial compartment of the right forearm acting on the wrist and fingers. (a) Superficial muscles, posterior view. (For a related image, see *A Brief Atlas of the Human Body*, Figure 37b.) **(b)** Deep posterior muscles, superficial muscles removed. The interossei, the deepest layer of intrinsic hand muscles, are also illustrated.

MUSCLE GALLERY

Table 10.12 Summary: Actions of Muscles Acting on the Arm, Forearm, and Hand   (Figure 10.18)

PART I: Muscles Acting on the Arm (Humerus) (PM = Prime Mover)	Actions at the Shoulder					
	Flexion	Extension	Abduction	Adduction	Medial Rotation	Lateral Rotation
Pectoralis major	× (PM)			× (PM)	×	
Latissimus dorsi		× (PM)		× (PM)	×	
Teres major		×		×	×	
Deltoid	× (PM) (anterior fibers)	× (PM) (posterior fibers)	× (PM)		× (anterior fibers)	× (posterior fibers)
Subscapularis					× (PM)	
Supraspinatus			×			
Infraspinatus						× (PM)
Teres minor				× (weak)		× (PM)
Coracobrachialis	×			×		
Biceps brachii	× (weak)					
Triceps brachii				×		

PART II: Muscles Acting on the Forearm	Actions on the Forearm			
	Elbow Flexion	Elbow Extension	Pronation	Supination
Biceps brachii	× (PM)			×
Brachialis	× (PM)			
Triceps brachii		× (PM)		
Anconeus		×		
Pronator teres	× (weak)		×	
Pronator quadratus			× (PM)	
Supinator				×
Brachioradialis	×			

PART III: Muscles Acting on the Wrist and Fingers	Actions on the Wrist				Actions on the Fingers	
	Flexion	Extension	Abduction	Adduction	Flexion	Extension
Anterior Compartment						
Flexor carpi radialis	× (PM)		×			
Palmaris longus	× (weak)					
Flexor carpi ulnaris	× (PM)			×		
Flexor digitorum superficialis	× (PM)				×	
Flexor pollicis longus					× (thumb)	
Flexor digitorum profundus	×				×	
Posterior Compartment						
Extensor carpi radialis longus and brevis		×	×			
Extensor digitorum		× (PM)				× (and abducts)
Extensor carpi ulnaris		×		×		
Abductor pollicis longus			×		(abducts thumb)	
Extensor pollicis longus and brevis						× (thumb)
Extensor indicis		× (weak)				× (index finger)

10

MUSCLE GALLERY

Table 10.12 (continued)

Key:
- Extensors
- Flexors
- Others

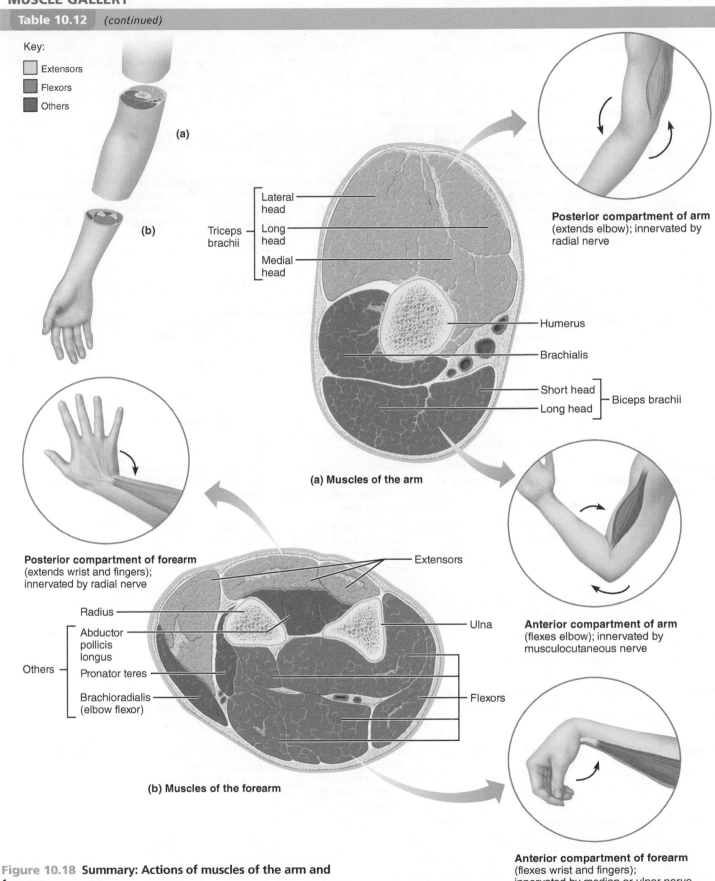

(a)

(b)

Triceps brachii
- Lateral head
- Long head
- Medial head

(a) Muscles of the arm

Humerus

Brachialis

Short head ⎤
Long head ⎦ Biceps brachii

Posterior compartment of arm (extends elbow); innervated by radial nerve

Anterior compartment of arm (flexes elbow); innervated by musculocutaneous nerve

Posterior compartment of forearm (extends wrist and fingers); innervated by radial nerve

Extensors

Radius

Others
- Abductor pollicis longus
- Pronator teres
- Brachioradialis (elbow flexor)

Ulna

Flexors

(b) Muscles of the forearm

Anterior compartment of forearm (flexes wrist and fingers); innervated by median or ulnar nerve

Figure 10.18 Summary: Actions of muscles of the arm and forearm.

MUSCLE GALLERY

Table 10.13 Intrinsic Muscles of the Hand: Fine Movements of the Fingers (Figure 10.19)

In this table we consider the small muscles that lie entirely in the hand. All are in the palm, none on the hand's dorsal side. All move the metacarpals and fingers. Small, weak muscles, they mostly control precise movements (such as threading a needle), leaving the powerful movements of the fingers ("power grip") to the forearm muscles.

The intrinsic muscles include the main abductors and adductors of the fingers, as well as muscles that produce the movement of opposition—moving the thumb toward the little finger—that enables you to grip objects. Many palm muscles are specialized to move the thumb, and surprisingly many move the little finger.

Thumb movements are defined differently from movements of other fingers because the thumb lies at a right angle to the rest of the hand. The thumb flexes by bending medially along the palm, not by bending anteriorly, as do the other fingers. (To demonstrate this difference, start with your hand in the anatomical position or

this will not be clear!) The thumb extends by pointing laterally (as in hitchhiking), not posteriorly, as do the other fingers. To abduct the fingers is to splay them laterally, but to abduct the thumb is to point it anteriorly. Adduction of the thumb brings it back posteriorly.

The intrinsic muscles of the palm are divided into three groups, those in

1. The *thenar eminence* (ball of the thumb)
2. The *hypothenar eminence* (ball of the little finger)
3. The midpalm

Thenar and hypothenar muscles are almost mirror images of each other, each containing a small flexor, an abductor, and an opponens muscle. The midpalmar muscles, called **lumbricals** and **interossei**, extend our fingers at the interphalangeal joints. The interossei are also the main finger abductors and adductors.

MUSCLE	DESCRIPTION	ORIGIN (O) AND INSERTION (I)	ACTION	NERVE SUPPLY
THENAR MUSCLES IN BALL OF THUMB (the'nar) (*thenar* = palm)				
Abductor pollicis brevis (*pollex* = thumb)	Lateral muscle of thenar group; superficial	O—flexor retinaculum and nearby carpals I—lateral base of thumb's proximal phalanx	Abducts thumb (at carpometacarpal joint)	Median nerve (C_8, T_1)
Flexor pollicis brevis	Medial and deep muscle of thenar group	O—flexor retinaculum and nearby carpals I—lateral side of base of proximal phalanx of thumb	Flexes thumb (at carpometacarpal and metacarpophalangeal joints)	Median (or occasionally ulnar) nerve (C_8, T_1)
Opponens pollicis (o-pōn'enz) (*opponens* = opposition)	Deep to abductor pollicis brevis, on metacarpal I	O—flexor retinaculum and trapezium I—whole anterior side of metacarpal I	Opposition: moves thumb to touch tip of little finger	Median (or occasionally ulnar) nerve
Adductor pollicis	Fan-shaped with horizontal fibers; distal to other thenar muscles; oblique and transverse heads	O—capitate bone and bases of metacarpals II–IV; front of metacarpal III I—medial side of base of proximal phalanx of thumb	Adducts and helps to oppose thumb	Ulnar nerve (C_8, T_1)
HYPOTHENAR MUSCLES IN BALL OF LITTLE FINGER				
Abductor digiti minimi (dǐ'jǐ-ti min'ǐ-mi) (*digiti minimi* = little finger)	Medial muscle of hypothenar group; superficial	O—pisiform bone I—medial side of proximal phalanx of little finger	Abducts little finger at metacarpophalangeal joint	Ulnar nerve
Flexor digiti minimi brevis	Lateral deep muscle of hypothenar group	O—hamate bone and flexor retinaculum I—same as abductor digiti minimi	Flexes little finger at metacarpophalangeal joint	Ulnar nerve
Opponens digiti minimi	Deep to abductor digiti minimi	O—same as flexor digiti minimi brevis I—most of length of medial side of metacarpal V	Helps in opposition: brings metacarpal V toward thumb to cup the hand	Ulnar nerve

MUSCLE GALLERY

Table 10.13   (continued)

Tendons of:
Flexor digitorum profundus
Flexor digitorum superficialis
Third lumbrical
Fourth lumbrical
Opponens digiti minimi
Flexor digiti minimi brevis
Abductor digiti minimi
Pisiform bone
Flexor carpi ulnaris tendon
Flexor digitorum superficialis tendons

Fibrous sheath
Second lumbrical
Dorsal interossei
First lumbrical
Adductor pollicis
Flexor pollicis brevis
Abductor pollicis brevis
Opponens pollicis
Flexor retinaculum
Abductor pollicis longus
Tendons of:
Palmaris longus
Flexor carpi radialis
Flexor pollicis longus

(a) First superficial layer

Flexor digitorum profundus tendon
Flexor digitorum superficialis tendon
Dorsal interossei
Adductor pollicis
Flexor pollicis brevis
Abductor pollicis brevis
Opponens pollicis
Flexor pollicis longus tendon

Palmar interossei
Opponens digiti minimi
Flexor digiti minimi brevis (cut)
Abductor digiti minimi (cut)

(b) Second layer

Palmar interossei

(c) Palmar interossei (isolated)

Dorsal interossei

(d) Dorsal interossei (isolated)

Figure 10.19 Hand muscles, ventral views of right hand.

MUSCLE GALLERY

Table 10.13 Intrinsic Muscles of the Hand: Fine Movements of the Fingers   (Figure 10.19) *(continued)*

MUSCLE	DESCRIPTION	ORIGIN (O) AND INSERTION (I)	ACTION	NERVE SUPPLY
MIDPALMAR MUSCLES				
Lumbricals (lum'brĭ-klz) (*lumbric* = earthworm)	Four worm-shaped muscles in palm, one to each finger (except thumb); unusual because they originate from the tendons of another muscle	O—lateral side of each tendon of flexor digitorum profundus in palm I—lateral edge of extensor expansion on proximal phalanx of fingers 2–5	Flex fingers at metacarpophalangeal joints but extend fingers at interphalangeal joints	Median nerve (lateral two) and ulnar nerve (medial two)
Palmar interossei (in"ter-os'e-i) (*interossei* = between bones)	Four long, cone-shaped muscles in the spaces between the metacarpals; lie ventral to the dorsal interossei	O—the side of each metacarpal that faces the midaxis of the hand (metacarpal III) but absent from metacarpal III I—extensor expansion on first phalanx of each finger (except finger 3), on side facing midaxis of hand	Adduct fingers: pull fingers in toward third digit; act with lumbricals to extend fingers at interphalangeal joints and flex them at metacarpophalangeal joints	Ulnar nerve
Dorsal interossei	Four bipennate muscles filling spaces between the metacarpals; deepest palm muscles, also visible on dorsal side of hand (Figure 10.17b)	O—sides of metacarpals I—extensor expansion over proximal phalanx of fingers 2–4 on side opposite midaxis of hand (finger 3), but on *both* sides of finger 3	Abduct (diverge) fingers; extend fingers at interphalangeal joints and flex them at metacarpophalangeal joints	Ulnar nerve

MUSCLE GALLERY

Table 10.14	**Muscles Crossing the Hip and Knee Joints: Movements of the Thigh and Leg (Figures 10.20 and 10.21)**

The muscles fleshing out the thigh are difficult to segregate into groups on the basis of action. Some thigh muscles act only at the hip joint, others only at the knee, while still others act at both joints. However, *most anterior* muscles of the hip and thigh flex the femur at the hip and extend the leg at the knee, producing the foreswing phase of walking. The *posterior* muscles of the hip and thigh, by contrast, mostly extend the thigh and flex the leg—the backswing phase of walking. A third group of muscles in this region, the *medial*, or *adductor*, muscles, all adduct the thigh; they have no effect on the leg.

In the thigh, the anterior, posterior, and adductor muscles are separated by walls of fascia into *anterior*, *posterior*, and *medial compartments* (see Figure 10.26a). The deep fascia of the thigh, the *fascia lata*, surrounds and encloses all three groups of muscles like a support stocking.

Movements of the thigh (occurring at the hip joint) are accomplished largely by muscles anchored to the pelvic girdle. Like the shoulder joint, the hip joint is a ball-and-socket joint permitting flexion, extension, abduction, adduction, circumduction, and rotation. Muscles effecting these movements are among the most powerful muscles of the body.

For the most part, the thigh *flexors* pass in front of the hip joint. The most important thigh flexors are the **iliopsoas** (the prime mover), **tensor fasciae latae**, and **rectus femoris** (Figure 10.20a). They are assisted in this action by the **adductor muscles** of the medial thigh and the straplike **sartorius**.

Thigh *extension* is effected primarily by the massive **hamstring muscles** of the posterior thigh (Figure 10.21a). During forceful extension, the **gluteus maximus** of the buttocks is called into play. Buttock muscles that lie lateral to the hip joint (**gluteus medius** and **minimus**) *abduct* the thigh (Figure 10.21c).

Thigh adduction is the role of the adductor muscles of the medial thigh. Abduction and adduction of the thighs are extremely important during walking to shift the trunk from side to side and balance the body's weight over the limb that is on the ground. Many different muscles bring about medial and lateral rotation of the thigh.

At the knee joint, flexion and extension are the main movements. The sole knee *extensor* is the **quadriceps femoris** muscle of the anterior thigh, the most powerful muscle in the body (Figure 10.20a). The quadriceps is antagonized by the hamstrings of the posterior compartment, which are the prime movers of knee flexion.

Table 10.17 (Part I) summarizes the actions of these muscles.

MUSCLE	DESCRIPTION	ORIGIN (O) AND INSERTION (I)	ACTION	NERVE SUPPLY
PART I: ANTERIOR AND MEDIAL MUSCLES (Figure 10.20)				
Origin on the Pelvis or Spine				
Iliopsoas (il″e-o-so′us)	Iliopsoas is a composite of two closely related muscles (iliacus and psoas major) whose fibers pass under the inguinal ligament (see Figure 10.12) to insert via a common tendon on the femur.			
▪ **Iliacus** (il-e-ak′us) (*iliac* = ilium)	Large, fan-shaped, more lateral muscle	O—iliac fossa and crest, ala of sacrum I—lesser trochanter of femur via iliopsoas tendon	Iliopsoas is the prime mover for flexing thigh, or for flexing trunk on thigh as during a bow	Femoral nerve (L$_2$ and L$_3$)
▪ **Psoas major** (so′us) (*psoa* = loin muscle; *major* = larger)	Longer, thicker, more medial muscle of the pair (butchers refer to this muscle as the tenderloin)	O—by fleshy slips from transverse processes, bodies, and discs of lumbar vertebrae and T$_{12}$ I—lesser trochanter of femur via iliopsoas tendon	As above; also flexes vertebral column laterally; important postural muscle	Ventral rami (L$_1$–L$_3$)
Sartorius (sar-tor′e-us) (*sartor* = tailor)	Straplike superficial muscle running obliquely across anterior surface of thigh to knee; longest muscle in body; crosses both hip and knee joints	O—anterior superior iliac spine I—winds around medial aspect of knee and inserts into medial aspect of proximal tibia	Flexes, abducts, and laterally rotates thigh; flexes knee (weak) as in a soccer kick; helps produce the cross-legged position	Femoral nerve

10

Table 10.14 Muscles Crossing the Hip and Knee Joints: Movements of the Thigh and Leg
(Figures 10.20 and 10.21) *(continued)*

Figure 10.20 Anterior and medial muscles promoting movements of the thigh and leg.
(For a related image, see *A Brief Atlas of the Human Body*, Figure 40.) **(a)** Anterior view of the deep muscles of the pelvis and superficial muscles of the right thigh. **(b)** Adductor muscles of the medial compartment of the thigh, isolated. **(c)** Vastus muscles of the quadriceps group, isolated.

10

MUSCLE GALLERY

Table 10.14	(continued)

Muscles of the Medial Compartment of the Thigh

Adductors (ah-duk'torz)	Large muscle mass consisting of three muscles (magnus, longus, and brevis) forming medial aspect of thigh; arise from inferior part of pelvis and insert at various levels on femur. All are used in movements that press thighs together, as when astride a horse; important in pelvic tilting movements that occur during walking and in fixing the hip when the knee is flexed and the foot is off the ground. Obturator nerve innervates entire group. Strain or stretching of this muscle group is called a "pulled groin."			
• **Adductor magnus** (mag'nus) (*adduct* = move toward midline; *magnus* = large)	Triangular muscle with a broad insertion; a composite muscle that is part adductor and part hamstring in action	O—ischial and pubic rami and ischial tuberosity I—linea aspera and adductor tubercle of femur	Anterior part adducts and medially rotates and flexes thigh; posterior part is a synergist of hamstrings to extend thigh	Obturator nerve and sciatic nerve (L_2–L_4)
• **Adductor longus** (*longus* = long)	Overlies middle aspect of adductor magnus; most anterior of adductor muscles	O—pubis near pubic symphysis I—linea aspera	Adducts, flexes, and medially rotates thigh	Obturator nerve (L_2–L_4)
• **Adductor brevis** (*brevis* = short)	In contact with obturator externus muscle; largely concealed by adductor longus and pectineus	O—body and inferior pubic ramus I—linea aspera above adductor longus	Adducts, flexes, and medially rotates thigh	Obturator nerve
Pectineus (pek-tin'e-us) (*pecten* = comb)	Short, flat muscle; overlies adductor brevis on proximal thigh; abuts adductor longus medially	O—pubis (and superior ramus) I—from lesser trochanter inferior to the linea aspera on posterior aspect of femur	Adducts, flexes, and medially rotates thigh	Femoral and sometimes obturator nerve
Gracilis (grah-si'lis) (*gracilis* = slender)	Long, thin, superficial muscle of medial thigh	O—inferior ramus and body of pubis and adjacent ischial ramus I—medial surface of tibia just inferior to its medial condyle	Adducts thigh, flexes and medially rotates leg, especially during walking	Obturator nerve

Muscles of the Anterior Compartment of the Thigh

Quadriceps femoris (kwod'rĭ-seps fem'o-ris)	Arises from four separate heads (*quadriceps* = four heads) that form the flesh of front and sides of thigh. These heads (rectus femoris, and lateral, medial, and intermediate vasti muscles) have a common insertion tendon, the *quadriceps tendon*, which inserts into the patella and then via the *patellar ligament* into tibial tuberosity. The quadriceps is a powerful knee extensor used in climbing, jumping, running, and rising from seated position. The tone of quadriceps plays important role in strengthening the knee joint. Femoral nerve innervates the group.			
• **Rectus femoris** (rek'tus) (*rectus* = straight; *femoris* = femur)	Superficial muscle of anterior thigh; runs straight down thigh; longest head and only muscle of group to cross hip joint	O—anterior inferior iliac spine and superior margin of acetabulum I—patella and tibial tuberosity via patellar ligament	Extends knee and flexes thigh at hip	Femoral nerve (L_2–L_4)
• **Vastus lateralis** (vas'tus lat"er-a'lis) (*vastus* = large; *lateralis* = lateral)	Largest head of the group, forms lateral aspect of thigh; a common intramuscular injection site, particularly in infants (who have poorly developed buttock and arm muscles)	O—greater trochanter, intertrochanteric line, linea aspera I—as for rectus femoris	Extends and stabilizes knee	Femoral nerve
• **Vastus medialis** (me"de-a'lis) (*medialis* = medial)	Forms inferomedial aspect of thigh	O—linea aspera, intertrochanteric and medial supracondylar lines I—as for rectus femoris	Extends knee	Femoral nerve

10

MUSCLE GALLERY

Table 10.14 Muscles Crossing the Hip and Knee Joints: Movements of the Thigh and Leg (Figures 10.20 and 10.21) *(continued)*

MUSCLE	DESCRIPTION	ORIGIN (O) AND INSERTION (I)	ACTION	NERVE SUPPLY
▪ **Vastus intermedius** (in"ter-me′de-us) (*intermedius* = intermediate)	Obscured by rectus femoris; lies between vastus lateralis and vastus medialis on anterior thigh	O—anterior and lateral surfaces of proximal femur shaft I—as for rectus femoris	Extends knee	Femoral nerve
Tensor fasciae latae (ten′sor fă′she-e la′te) (*tensor* = to make tense; *fascia* = band; *lata* = wide)	Enclosed between fascia layers of anterolateral aspect of thigh; functionally associated with medial rotators and flexors of thigh	O—anterior aspect of iliac crest and anterior superior iliac spine I—iliotibial tract*	Steadies the knee and trunk on thigh by making iliotibial tract taut; flexes and abducts thigh; rotates thigh medially	Superior gluteal nerve (L₄ and L₅)

PART II: POSTERIOR MUSCLES (Figure 10.21)

Gluteal Muscles—Origin on Pelvis

Gluteus maximus (gloo′te-us mak′sĭ-mus) (*glutos* = buttock; *maximus* = largest)	Largest and most superficial gluteus muscle; forms bulk of buttock mass; fibers are thick and coarse; important site of intramuscular injection (dorsal gluteal site); overlies large sciatic nerve; covers ischial tuberosity only when standing; when sitting, moves superiorly, leaving ischial tuberosity exposed in the subcutaneous position	O—dorsal ilium, sacrum, and coccyx I—gluteal tuberosity of femur; iliotibial tract	Major extensor of thigh; complex, powerful, and most effective when thigh is flexed and force is necessary, as in rising from a forward flexed position and in thrusting the thigh posteriorly in climbing stairs and running; generally inactive during standing and walking; laterally rotates and abducts thigh	Inferior gluteal nerve (L₅, S₁, and S₂)
Gluteus medius (me′de-us) (*medius* = middle)	Thick muscle largely covered by gluteus maximus; important site for intramuscular injections (ventral gluteal site); considered safer than dorsal gluteal site because less chance of injuring sciatic nerve	O—between anterior and posterior gluteal lines on lateral surface of ilium I—by short tendon into lateral aspect of greater trochanter of femur	Abducts and medially rotates thigh; steadies pelvis; its action is extremely important in walking; e.g., muscle of limb planted on ground tilts or holds pelvis in abduction so that pelvis on side of swinging limb does not sag and foot of swinging limb can clear the ground	Superior gluteal nerve (L₅, S₁)
Gluteus minimus (mĭ′nĭ-mus) (*minimus* = smallest)	Smallest and deepest gluteal muscle	O—between anterior and inferior gluteal lines on external surface of ilium I—anterior border of greater trochanter of femur	As for gluteus medius	Superior gluteal nerve (L₅, S₁)

Lateral Rotators

Piriformis (pir′ĭ-form-is) (*piri* = pear; *forma* = shape)	Pyramidal muscle located on posterior aspect of hip joint; inferior to gluteus minimus; issues from pelvis via greater sciatic notch	O—anterolateral surface of sacrum (opposite greater sciatic notch) I—superior border of greater trochanter of femur	Rotates extended thigh laterally; because inserted above head of femur, can also help abduct thigh when hip is flexed; stabilizes hip joint	S₁ and S₂, L₅

*The iliotibial tract is a thickened lateral portion of the *fascia lata* (the fascia that ensheathes all the muscles of the thigh). It extends as a tendinous band from the iliac crest to the knee (see Figure 10.21a).

MUSCLE GALLERY

Table 10.14   *(continued)*

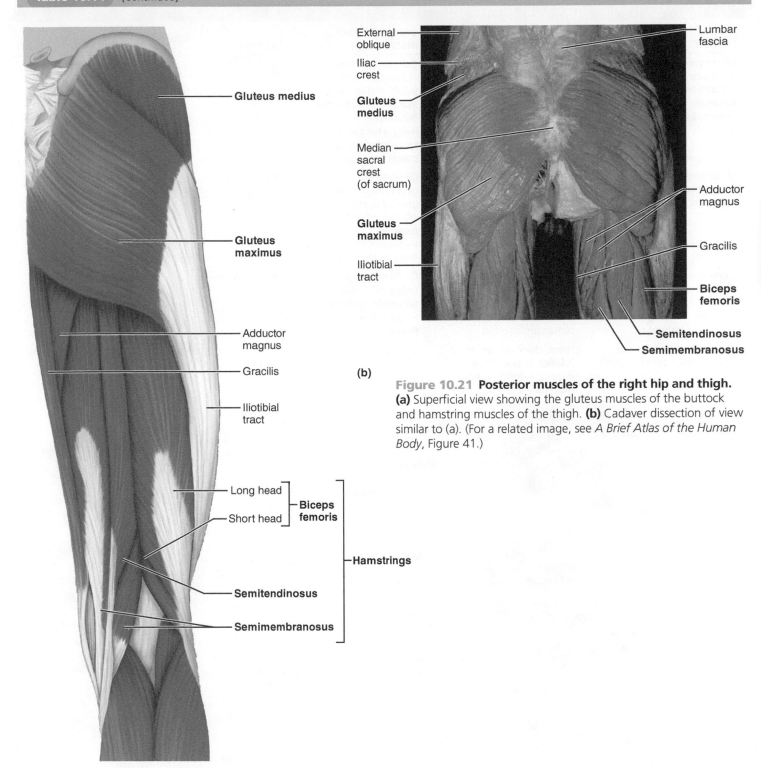

(a)

(b)

Figure 10.21 Posterior muscles of the right hip and thigh.
(a) Superficial view showing the gluteus muscles of the buttock and hamstring muscles of the thigh. **(b)** Cadaver dissection of view similar to (a). (For a related image, see *A Brief Atlas of the Human Body*, Figure 41.)

10

MUSCLE GALLERY

| Table 10.14 | Muscles Crossing the Hip and Knee Joints: Movements of the Thigh and Leg (Figures 10.20 and 10.21) *(continued)* | | | |

MUSCLE	DESCRIPTION	ORIGIN (O) AND INSERTION (I)	ACTION	NERVE SUPPLY
Obturator externus (ob″tu-ra′tor ek-ster′nus) (*obturator* = obturator foramen; *externus* = outside)	Flat, triangular muscle deep in superomedial aspect of thigh	O—outer surfaces of obturator membrane, pubis, and ischium, margins of obturator foramen I—by a tendon into trochanteric fossa of posterior femur	As for piriformis	Obturator nerve
Obturator internus (in-ter′nus) (*internus* = inside)	Surrounds obturator foramen within pelvis; leaves pelvis via lesser sciatic notch and turns acutely forward to insert on femur	O—inner surface of obturator membrane, greater sciatic notch, and margins of obturator foramen I—greater trochanter in front of piriformis	As for piriformis	L_5 and S_1
Gemellus (jĕ-mĕ′lis)— superior and inferior (*gemin* = twin, double; *superior* = above; *inferior* = below)	Two small muscles with common insertions and actions; considered extrapelvic portions of obturator internus	O—ischial spine (superior); ischial tuberosity (inferior) I—greater trochanter of femur	As for piriformis	L_5 and S_1
Quadratus femoris (*quad* = four-sided square)	Short, thick muscle; most inferior lateral rotator muscle; extends laterally from pelvis	O—ischial tuberosity I—intertrochanteric crest of femur	Rotates thigh laterally and stabilizes hip joint	L_5 and S_1

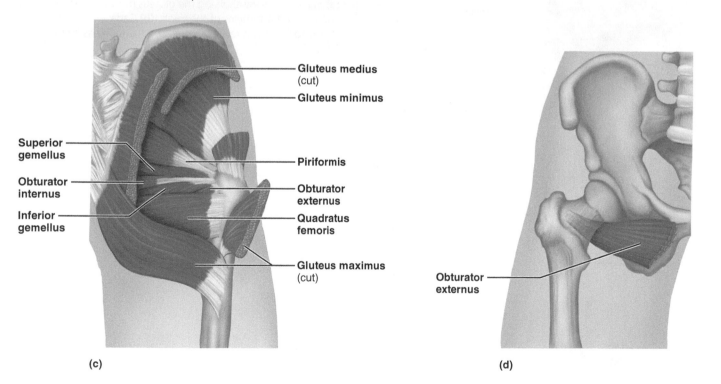

(c)

(d)

Figure 10.21 *(continued)* **Posterior muscles of the right hip and thigh. (c)** Deep muscles of the gluteal region, which act primarily to rotate the thigh laterally. The superficial gluteus maximus and medius have been removed. **(d)** Anterior view of the isolated obturator externus muscle.

MUSCLE GALLERY

Table 10.14 *(continued)*

MUSCLE	DESCRIPTION	ORIGIN (O) AND INSERTION (I)	ACTION	NERVE SUPPLY
Muscles of the Posterior Compartment of the Thigh				
Hamstrings	The hamstrings are fleshy muscles of the posterior thigh (biceps femoris, semitendinosus, and semimembranosus). They cross both the hip and knee joints and are prime movers of thigh extension and knee flexion. The group has a common origin site and is innervated by sciatic nerve (actually two nerves, the tibial and common fibular nerves wrapped in a common sheath). Ability of hamstrings to act on one of the two joints spanned depends on which joint is fixed—if knee is fixed (extended), they extend hip; if hip is extended, they flex knee. However, when hamstrings are stretched, they tend to restrict full accomplishment of antagonistic movement; e.g., if knees are fully extended, it is difficult to flex the hip fully (and touch your toes), and when the thigh is fully flexed as in kicking a football, it is almost impossible to extend the knee fully at the same time (without considerable practice). Name of this muscle group comes from old butchers' practice of using their tendons to hang hams for smoking. "Pulled hamstrings" are common sports injuries in those who run very hard, e.g., football halfbacks.			
▪ **Biceps femoris** (*biceps* = two heads)	Most lateral muscle of the group; arises from two heads	O—ischial tuberosity (long head); linea aspera, lateral supracondylar line, and distal femur (short head) I—common tendon passes downward and laterally (forming lateral border of popliteal fossa) to insert into head of fibula and lateral condyle of tibia	Extends thigh and flexes knee; laterally rotates leg, especially when knee is flexed	Sciatic nerve—tibial nerve to long head, common fibular nerve to short head (L_5–S_2)
▪ **Semitendinosus** (sem″e-ten″dĭ-no′sus) (*semi* = half; *tendinosus* = tendon)	Lies medial to biceps femoris; although its name suggests that this muscle is largely tendinous, it is quite fleshy; its long slender tendon begins about two-thirds of the way down thigh	O—ischial tuberosity in common with long head of biceps femoris I—medial aspect of upper tibial shaft	Extends thigh and flexes knee; with semimembranosus, medially rotates leg	Sciatic nerve—tibial nerve portion (L_5–S_2)
▪ **Semimembranosus** (sem″e-mem″-brah-no′sus) (*membranosus* = membrane)	Deep to semitendinosus	O—ischial tuberosity I—medial condyle of tibia; via oblique popliteal ligament to lateral condyle of femur	Extends thigh and flexes knee; medially rotates leg	Sciatic nerve—tibial nerve portion (L_5–S_2)

10

MUSCLE GALLERY

| Table 10.15 | Muscles of the Leg: Movements of the Ankle and Toes | (Figures 10.22 to 10.24) |

The deep fascia of the leg is continuous with the fascia lata that ensheathes the thigh. Like a snug "knee sock" beneath the skin, the leg fascia binds the leg muscles tightly, preventing excessive muscle swelling during exercise and aiding venous return. Its inward extensions segregate the leg muscles into *anterior, lateral,* and *posterior compartments* (see Figure 10.26b), each with its own nerve and blood supply. Distally the leg fascia thickens to form the **flexor, extensor,** and **fibular** (or peroneal) **retinacula,** "ankle brackets" that hold the tendons in place where they run to the foot (Figures 10.22a, 10.23a).

The various muscles of the leg promote movements at the ankle joint (dorsiflex and plantar flex), at the intertarsal joints (invert and evert the foot), and/or at the toes (flex and extend). Muscles in the *anterior extensor compartment of the leg* are primarily toe extensors and ankle dorsiflexors. Although dorsiflexion is not a powerful movement, it is important in preventing the toes from dragging during walking. Lateral compartment muscles are the **fibular,** formerly *peroneal (peron* = fibula), **muscles** that plantar flex and evert the foot. Muscles of the *posterior flexor compartment* primarily plantar flex the foot and flex the toes (Figure 10.24b–d). Plantar flexion is the most powerful movement of the ankle (and foot) because it lifts the entire weight of our body. It is essential for standing on tiptoe and provides the forward thrust when walking and running. The **popliteus muscle,** which crosses the knee, has a unique function. It "unlocks" the extended knee in preparation for flexion (Figure 10.24b, f).

We consider the tiny intrinsic muscles of the sole of the foot (lumbricals, interossei, and others) in Table 10.16.

Table 10.17 (Part II) summarizes the actions of the muscles in this table.

MUSCLE	DESCRIPTION	ORIGIN (O) AND INSERTION (I)	ACTION	NERVE SUPPLY
PART I: MUSCLES OF THE ANTERIOR COMPARTMENT (Figures 10.22 and 10.23)	All muscles of the anterior compartment dorsiflex the ankle and have a common innervation, the deep fibular nerve. Paralysis of the anterior muscle group causes *foot drop,* which requires that the leg be lifted unusually high during walking to prevent tripping over one's toes. One cause of "shin splints," also called anterior compartment syndrome, is painful inflammation of the anterior compartment muscles.			
Tibialis anterior (tib"e-a'lis) (*tibial* = tibia; *anterior* = toward the front)	Superficial muscle of anterior leg; laterally parallels sharp anterior margin of tibia	O—lateral condyle and upper 2/3 of tibial shaft; interosseous membrane I—by tendon into inferior surface of medial cuneiform and first metatarsal bone	Prime mover of dorsiflexion; inverts foot; helps support medial longitudinal arch of foot	Deep fibular nerve (L_4 and L_5)
Extensor digitorum longus (*extensor* = increases angle at a joint; *digit* = finger or toe; *longus* = long)	Unipennate muscle on anterolateral surface of leg; lateral to tibialis anterior muscle	O—lateral condyle of tibia; proximal 3/4 of fibula; interosseous membrane I—middle and distal phalanges of toes 2–5 via extensor expansion	Prime mover of toe extension (acts mainly at metatarsophalangeal joints); dorsiflexes foot	Deep fibular nerve (L_5 and S_1)
Fibularis (peroneus) tertius (fib-u-lar'ris ter'shus) (*fibular* = fibula; *tertius* = third)	Small muscle; usually continuous and fused with distal part of extensor digitorum longus; not always present	O—distal anterior surface of fibula and interosseous membrane I—tendon inserts on dorsum of fifth metatarsal	Dorsiflexes and everts foot	Deep fibular nerve (L_5 and S_1)
Extensor hallucis longus (hal'yu-kis) (*hallux* = great toe)	Deep to extensor digitorum longus and tibialis anterior; narrow origin	O—anteromedial fibula shaft and interosseous membrane I—tendon inserts on distal phalanx of great toe	Extends great toe; dorsiflexes foot	Deep fibular nerve (L_5 and S_1)

MUSCLE GALLERY

Table 10.15 *(continued)*

Fibularis longus

Gastrocnemius

Tibia

Tibialis anterior

Extensor digitorum longus

Soleus

Extensor hallucis longus

Fibularis tertius

Superior and inferior extensor retinacula

Extensor hallucis brevis

Extensor digitorum brevis

(a)

Figure 10.22 Muscles of the anterior compartment of the right leg. (a) Superficial view of anterior leg muscles. (For a related image, see *A Brief Atlas of the Human Body*, Figure 40.) **(b–d)** Some of the same muscles shown in isolation to visualize their origins and insertions.

O

O

Extensor hallucis longus

Fibularis tertius

I

I

(c)

O

Tibialis anterior

I

(b)

O

Extensor digitorum longus

O = origin
I = insertion

I

(d)

10

MUSCLE GALLERY

Table 10.15   Muscles of the Leg: Movements of the Ankle and Toes   (Figures 10.22 to 10.24) *(continued)*

O = origin
I = insertion

(a)

(b)

(c)

Figure 10.23 Muscles of the lateral compartment of the right leg.
(a) Superficial view of lateral aspect of the leg, illustrating positions of lateral compartment muscles (fibularis longus and brevis) relative to anterior and posterior leg muscles. **(b)** Isolated view of fibularis longus; inset illustrates the insertion of the fibularis longus on the plantar surface of the foot. **(c)** Isolated view of fibularis brevis. (For a related image, see *A Brief Atlas of the Human Body*, Figure 42.)

MUSCLE GALLERY

Table 10.15	(continued)			

MUSCLE	DESCRIPTION	ORIGIN (O) AND INSERTION (I)	ACTION	NERVE SUPPLY
PART II: MUSCLES OF THE LATERAL COMPARTMENT (Figures 10.23 and 10.24) These muscles have a common innervation, the superficial fibular nerve. Besides plantar flexion and foot eversion, these muscles stabilize the lateral ankle and lateral longitudinal arch of the foot.				
Fibularis (peroneus) longus (See also Figure 10.22)	Superficial lateral muscle; overlies fibula	O—head and upper portion of lateral fibula I—by long tendon that curves under foot to first metatarsal and medial cuneiform	Plantar flexes and everts foot; may help keep foot flat on ground	Superficial fibular nerve (L_5–S_2)
Fibularis (peroneus) brevis (*brevis* = short)	Smaller muscle; deep to fibularis longus; enclosed in a common sheath	O—distal fibula shaft I—by tendon running behind lateral malleolus to insert on proximal end of fifth metatarsal	Plantar flexes and everts foot	Superficial fibular nerve
PART III: MUSCLES OF THE POSTERIOR COMPARTMENT (Figure 10.24) The muscles of the posterior compartment have a common innervation, the tibial nerve. They act in concert to plantar flex the ankle.				
Superficial Muscles				
Triceps surae (tri″seps sur′e) (See also Figure 10.23)	Refers to muscle pair (gastrocnemius and soleus) that shapes the posterior calf and inserts via a common tendon into the calcaneus of the heel; this *calcaneal* or *Achilles tendon* is the largest tendon in the body. Prime movers of ankle plantar flexion.			
▪ **Gastrocnemius** (gas″truk-ne′me-us) (*gaster* = belly; *kneme* = leg)	Superficial muscle of pair; two prominent bellies that form proximal curve of calf	O—by two heads from medial and lateral condyles of femur I—posterior calcaneus via calcaneal tendon	Plantar flexes foot when knee is extended; because it also crosses knee joint, it can flex knee when foot is dorsiflexed	Tibial nerve (S_1, S_2)
▪ **Soleus** (so′le-us) (*soleus* = fish)	Broad, flat muscle, deep to gastrocnemius on posterior surface of calf	O—extensive origin from superior tibia, fibula, and interosseous membrane I—as for gastrocnemius	Plantar flexes foot; important locomotor and postural muscle during walking, running, and dancing	Tibial nerve
Plantaris (plan-tar′is) (*planta* = sole of foot)	Generally a small, feeble muscle, but varies in size and extent; may be absent	O—posterior femur above lateral condyle I—via a long, thin tendon into calcaneus or its tendon	Helps to flex knee and plantar flex foot	Tibial nerve
Deep Muscles (Figure 10.24c–f)				
Popliteus (pop-lit′e-us) (*poplit* = back of knee)	Thin, triangular muscle at posterior knee; passes inferomedially to tibial surface	O—lateral condyle of femur and lateral meniscus of knee I—proximal tibia	Flexes and rotates leg medially to unlock extended knee when flexion begins; with tibia fixed, rotates thigh laterally	Tibial nerve (L_4–S_1)
Flexor digitorum longus (*flexor* = decreases angle at a joint)	Long, narrow muscle; runs medial to and partially overlies tibialis posterior	O—extensive origin on the posterior tibia I—tendon runs behind medial malleolus and inserts into distal phalanges of toes 2–5	Plantar flexes and inverts foot; flexes toes; helps foot "grip" ground	Tibial nerve (L_5–S_2)
Flexor hallucis longus (See also Figure 10.23)	Bipennate muscle; lies lateral to inferior aspect of tibialis posterior	O—midshaft of fibula; interosseous membrane I—tendon runs under foot to distal phalanx of great toe	Plantar flexes and inverts foot; flexes great toe at all joints; "push off" muscle during walking	Tibial nerve (L_5–S_2)
Tibialis posterior (*posterior* = toward the back)	Thick, flat muscle deep to soleus; placed between posterior flexors	O—superior tibia and fibula and interosseous membrane I—tendon passes behind medial malleolus and under arch of foot; inserts into several tarsals and metatarsals II–IV	Prime mover of foot inversion; plantar flexes foot; stabilizes medial longitudinal arch of foot (as during ice skating)	Tibial nerve (L_4 and L_5)

10

MUSCLE GALLERY

Table 10.15   Muscles of the Leg: Movements of the Ankle and Toes   (Figures 10.22 to 10.24) *(continued)*

(a) Superficial view of the posterior leg.

(b) The gastrocnemius has been removed to show the soleus immediately deep to it.

Figure 10.24 **Muscles of the posterior compartment of the right leg.**

MUSCLE GALLERY

Table 10.15 (continued)

O = origin
I = insertion

Plantaris (cut)

Gastrocnemius
lateral head (cut)

Gastroc-
nemius
medial head
(cut)

Popliteus

Soleus (cut)

Tibialis posterior

Fibula

Fibularis
longus

Flexor
digitorum
longus

Flexor hallucis
longus

Fibularis brevis

Tendon of
tibialis posterior

Medial
malleolus

Calcaneal
tendon (cut)

Calcaneus

Tibialis
posterior

Popliteus

Flexor
hallucis
longus

Flexor
digitorum
longus

(c) The triceps surae has been removed to show the
deep muscles of the posterior compartment.

(d) Isolated tibialis
posterior.

(e) Isolated flexor
digitorum longus.

(f) Isolated
popliteus and
flexor hallucis
longus.

Figure 10.24 (continued)

MUSCLE GALLERY

Table 10.16	Intrinsic Muscles of the Foot: Toe Movement and Arch Support	(Figure 10.25)

The intrinsic muscles of the foot help to flex, extend, abduct, and adduct the toes. Collectively, along with the tendons of some leg muscles that enter the sole, the foot muscles help support the arches of the foot. There is a single muscle on the foot's dorsum (superior aspect), and several muscles on the plantar aspect (the sole). The plantar muscles occur in four layers, from superficial to deep. Overall, the foot muscles are remarkably similar to those in the palm of the hand.

MUSCLE	DESCRIPTION	ORIGIN (O) AND INSERTION (I)	ACTION	NERVE SUPPLY
MUSCLES ON DORSUM OF FOOT				
Extensor digitorum brevis (Figures 10.22a and 10.23a)	Small, four-part muscle on dorsum of foot; deep to the tendons of extensor digitorum longus; corresponds to the extensor indicis and extensor pollicis muscles of forearm	O—anterior part of calcaneus bone; extensor retinaculum I—base of proximal phalanx of great toe; extensor expansions on toes 2 to 4 or 5	Helps extend toes at metatarsophalangeal joints	Deep fibular nerve (L_5 and S_1)
MUSCLES ON SOLE OF FOOT—FIRST LAYER (MOST SUPERFICIAL) (Figure 10.25)				
Flexor digitorum brevis	Bandlike muscle in middle of sole; corresponds to flexor digitorum superficialis of forearm and inserts into digits in the same way	O—calcaneal tuberosity I—middle phalanx of toes 2–4	Helps flex toes	Medial plantar nerve (a branch of tibial nerve, S_1 and S_2)
Abductor hallucis (hal'yu-kis) (*hallux* = great toe)	Lies medial to flexor digitorum brevis (recall the similar thumb muscle, abductor pollicis brevis)	O—calcaneal tuberosity and flexor retinaculum I—proximal phalanx of great toe, medial side, in the tendon of flexor hallucis brevis)	Abducts great toe	Medial plantar nerve
Abductor digiti minimi	Most lateral of the three superficial sole muscles (recall similar abductor muscle in palm)	O—calcaneal tuberosity I—lateral side of base of little toe's proximal phalanx	Abducts and flexes little toe	Lateral plantar nerve (a branch of tibial nerve, S_1, S_2, and S_3)
MUSCLES ON SOLE OF FOOT—SECOND LAYER				
Flexor accessorius (quadratus plantae)	Rectangular muscle just deep to flexor digitorum brevis in posterior half of sole; two heads (see also Figure 10.25c)	O—medial and lateral sides of calcaneus I—tendon of flexor digitorum longus in midsole	Straightens out the oblique pull of flexor digitorum longus	Lateral plantar nerve
Lumbricals	Four little "worms" (like lumbricals in hand)	O—from each tendon of flexor digitorum longus I—extensor expansion on proximal phalanx of toes 2–5, medial side	By pulling on extensor expansion, flex toes at metatarsophalangeal joints and extend toes at interphalangeal joints	Medial plantar nerve (first lumbrical) and lateral plantar nerve (second to fourth lumbrical)

MUSCLE GALLERY

Table 10.16 *(continued)*

Tendon of
flexor hallucis longus

Lumbricals

Flexor hallucis
brevis

Flexor digiti
minimi brevis

Abductor hallucis

**Flexor digitorum
brevis**

Flexor accessorius

**Abductor digiti
minimi**

Calcaneal
tuberosity

(a) First layer (plantar aspect)

Lumbricals

Flexor hallucis
brevis

Flexor hallucis
longus tendon

Flexor digitorum
longus (tendon)

Flexor digiti
minimi brevis

Abductor digiti
minimi

Flexor accessorius

Fibularis longus (tendon)

Flexor digitorum
longus (tendon)

Flexor hallucis
longus (tendon)

(b) Second layer (plantar aspect)

Figure 10.25 Muscles of the right foot, plantar aspect. (For a related image, see *A Brief Atlas of the Human Body*, Figure 43.)

10

MUSCLE GALLERY

| Table 10.16 | Intrinsic Muscles of the Foot: Toe Movement and Arch Support | (Figure 10.25) *(continued)* | | |

MUSCLE	DESCRIPTION	ORIGIN (O) AND INSERTION (I)	ACTION	NERVE SUPPLY
MUSCLES ON SOLE OF FOOT—THIRD LAYER				
Flexor hallucis brevis	Covers metatarsal I; splits into two bellies—recall flexor pollicis brevis of thumb	O—lateral cuneiform and cuboid bones I—via two tendons onto base of the proximal phalanx of great toe; each insertion tendon contains a sesamoid bone	Flexes great toe's metatarsophalangeal joint	Medial plantar nerve
Adductor hallucis	Oblique and transverse heads; deep to lumbricals (recall adductor pollicis in thumb)	O—from bases of metatarsals II–IV and from fibularis longus tendon sheath (oblique head); from a ligament across metatarsophalangeal joints (transverse head) I—base of proximal phalanx of great toe, lateral side	Helps maintain the transverse arch of foot; weak adductor of great toe	Lateral plantar nerve (S_2 and S_3)
Flexor digiti minimi brevis	Covers metatarsal V (recall same muscle in hand)	O—base of metatarsal V and tendon sheath of fibularis longus I—base of proximal phalanx of toe 5	Flexes little toe at metatarsophalangeal joint	Lateral plantar nerve
MUSCLES ON SOLE OF FOOT—FOURTH LAYER (DEEPEST)				
Plantar (3) and dorsal interossei (4)	Similar to palmar and dorsal interossei of hand in locations, attachments, and actions; however, these muscles orient around the second digit, not the third	See palmar and dorsal interossei (Table 10.13)	See palmar and dorsal interossei (Table 10.13)	Lateral plantar nerve

10

MUSCLE GALLERY

Table 10.16   (continued)

Adductor hallucis
(transverse head)

Adductor hallucis
(oblique head)

Interosseous
muscles

**Flexor hallucis
brevis**

**Flexor digiti
minimi brevis**

Fibularis longus (tendon)

Flexor accessorius

Flexor digitorum
longus (tendon)

Flexor hallucis
longus (tendon)

(c) Third layer (plantar aspect)

Plantar
interossei

(d) Fourth layer (plantar aspect):
plantar interossei

Dorsal
interossei

(e) Fourth layer (dorsal aspect):
dorsal interossei

10

Figure 10.25 *(continued)* **Muscles of the right foot, plantar aspect.**

MUSCLE GALLERY

Table 10.17   Summary: Actions of Muscles Acting on the Thigh, Leg, and Foot   (Figure 10.26)

PART I: Muscles Acting on the Thigh and Leg (PM = Prime Mover)	Actions at the Hip Joint						Actions at the Knee	
	Flexion	Extension	Abduction	Adduction	Medial Rotation	Lateral Rotation	Flexion	Extension
Anterior and Medial Muscles								
Iliopsoas	× (PM)							
Sartorius	×		×			×	×	
Tensor fasciae latae	×		×		×			
Rectus femoris	×							× (PM)
Vastus muscles								× (PM)
Adductor magnus	×	×		×	×			
Adductor longus	×			×	×			
Adductor brevis	×			×	×			
Pectineus	×			×	×			
Gracilis				×	×		×	
Posterior Muscles								
Gluteus maximus		× (PM)	×			×		
Gluteus medius			× (PM)		×			
Gluteus minimus			×		×			
Piriformis			×			×		
Obturator internus			× (flexed) × (thigh)			×		
Obturator externus						×		
Gemelli						×		
Quadratus femoris						×		
Biceps femoris		× (PM)					× (PM)	
Semitendinosus		×					× (PM)	
Semimembranosus		×					× (PM)	
Gastrocnemius							×	
Plantaris							×	
Popliteus							× (and rotates leg medially)	

PART II: Muscles Acting on the Ankle and Toes	Actions at the Ankle Joint				Actions at the Toes	
	Plantar Flexion	Dorsiflexion	Inversion	Eversion	Flexion	Extension
Anterior Compartment						
Tibialis anterior		× (PM)	×			
Extensor digitorum longus		×				× (PM)
Fibularis tertius		×		×		
Extensor hallucis longus		×	× (weak)			× (great toe)
Lateral Compartment						
Fibularis longus and brevis	×			×		
Posterior Compartment						
Gastrocnemius	× (PM)					
Soleus	× (PM)					
Plantaris	×					
Flexor digitorum longus	×		×		× (PM)	
Flexor hallucis longus	×		×		× (great toe)	
Tibialis posterior	×		× (PM)			

MUSCLE GALLERY

Table 10.17 (continued)

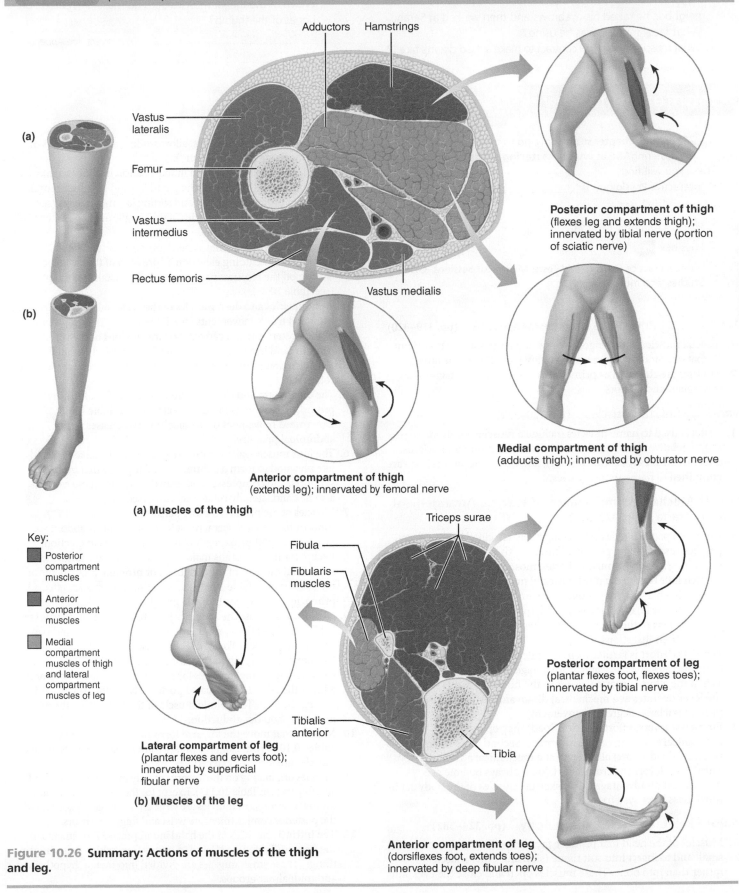

Adductors

Hamstrings

Vastus lateralis

Femur

Vastus intermedius

Rectus femoris

Vastus medialis

Posterior compartment of thigh (flexes leg and extends thigh); innervated by tibial nerve (portion of sciatic nerve)

Medial compartment of thigh (adducts thigh); innervated by obturator nerve

Anterior compartment of thigh (extends leg); innervated by femoral nerve

(a) Muscles of the thigh

Key:

■ Posterior compartment muscles

■ Anterior compartment muscles

■ Medial compartment muscles of thigh and lateral compartment muscles of leg

Triceps surae

Fibula

Fibularis muscles

Tibialis anterior

Tibia

Posterior compartment of leg (plantar flexes foot, flexes toes); innervated by tibial nerve

Lateral compartment of leg (plantar flexes and everts foot); innervated by superficial fibular nerve

(b) Muscles of the leg

Anterior compartment of leg (dorsiflexes foot, extends toes); innervated by deep fibular nerve

Figure 10.26 Summary: Actions of muscles of the thigh and leg.

10

☑ **Check Your Understanding**

6. As John listened to Roger's account of how he flirted with his neighbor, he raised his eyebrows and then winked at Sarah. What facial muscles was he using?

7. What muscles would you contract to make a "sad clown's face"?

8. How can the deltoid muscles both extend and flex the arm? Aren't these antagonistic movements?

9. Which of the thenar muscles does not have an insertion on bones of the thumb?

For answers, see Appendix H.

Chapter Summary

(MAP)™ For more chapter study tools, go to the Study Area of MasteringA&P at **www.masteringaandp.com**. There you will find:

- Interactive Physiology iP
- A&PFlix **A&PFlix**
- Practice Anatomy Lab PAL
- PhysioEx PEx
- Videos, Practice Quizzes and Tests, MP3 Tutor Sessions, Case Studies, and much more!

Actions and Interactions of Skeletal Muscles (pp. 319–320)

1. Skeletal muscles are arranged in opposing groups across body joints so that one group can reverse or modify the action of the other.

2. Muscles are classified as prime movers (agonists), antagonists, synergists, and fixators.

Naming Skeletal Muscles (pp. 320–322)

1. Criteria used to name muscles include a muscle's location, shape, relative size, fiber (fascicle) direction, number of origins, attachment sites (origin/insertion), and action. Several criteria are combined to name some muscles.

Muscle Mechanics: Importance of Fascicle Arrangement and Leverage (pp. 322–324)

1. Common patterns of fascicle arrangement are circular, convergent, parallel, fusiform, and pennate. Muscles with fibers that run parallel to the long axis of the muscle shorten most; stocky pennate muscles shorten little but are the most powerful muscles.

2. A lever is a bar that moves on a fulcrum. When an effort is applied to the lever, a load is moved. In the body, bones are the levers, joints are the fulcrums, and skeletal muscles exert the effort at their insertions.

3. When the effort is farther from the fulcrum than is the load, the lever operates at a mechanical advantage (it's slow and strong). When the effort is exerted closer to the fulcrum than is the load, the lever operates at a mechanical disadvantage (it's fast and promotes a large degree of movement).

4. First-class levers (effort-fulcrum-load) may operate at a mechanical advantage or disadvantage. Second-class levers (fulcrum-load-effort) all operate at a mechanical advantage. Third-class levers (fulcrum-effort-load) always operate at a mechanical disadvantage. Most skeletal muscles of the body act in third-class lever systems.

Major Skeletal Muscles of the Body (pp. 324–382)

1. Muscles of the head that produce facial expression tend to be small and to insert into soft tissue (skin and other muscles) rather than into bone. These muscles open and close the eyes and mouth, compress the cheeks, allow smiling and other types of facial language (see Table 10.1*).

2. Muscles of the head involved in mastication include the masseter and temporalis that elevate the mandible and two deep muscle pairs that promote grinding and sliding jaw movements (see Table 10.2*). Extrinsic muscles of the tongue anchor the tongue and control its movements.

3. Deep muscles of the anterior neck promote swallowing movements, including elevation/depression of the hyoid bone, closing off the respiratory passages, and peristalsis of the pharynx (see Table 10.3*).

4. Neck muscles and deep muscles of the vertebral column promote head and trunk movements (see Table 10.4*). The deep muscles of the posterior trunk can extend large regions of the vertebral column (and head) simultaneously. The anteriorly located sternocleidomastoid and scalene muscles effect head flexion and rotation.

5. The diaphragm and external intercostal muscles of the thorax promote movements of quiet breathing (see Table 10.5*). Downward movement of the diaphragm increases intra-abdominal pressure.

6. The four muscle pairs forming the abdominal wall are layered like plywood to form a natural muscular girdle that protects, supports, and compresses abdominal contents. These muscles also flex and laterally rotate the trunk (see Table 10.6*).

7. Muscles of the pelvic floor and perineum (see Table 10.7*) support the pelvic viscera, resist increases in intra-abdominal pressure, inhibit urination and defecation, and aid erection.

8. Except for the pectoralis major and the latissimus dorsi, the superficial muscles of the thorax fix or promote movements of the scapula (see Table 10.8*). Scapular movements are effected primarily by posterior thoracic muscles.

9. Nine muscles cross the shoulder joint to move the humerus (see Table 10.9*). Of these, seven originate on the scapula and two arise from the axial skeleton. Four muscles contribute to the "rotator cuff" helping to stabilize the multiaxial shoulder joint. Generally speaking, muscles located anteriorly flex, rotate, and adduct the arm. Those located posteriorly extend, rotate, and adduct the arm. The deltoid muscle of the shoulder is the prime mover of shoulder abduction.

10. Muscles that move the forearm form the flesh of the arm (see Table 10.10*). Anterior arm muscles are forearm flexors; posterior muscles are forearm extensors.

11. Muscles originating on the forearm mainly move the wrist, hand, and fingers (see Table 10.11*). Except for the two pronator muscles, the anterior forearm muscles are wrist and/or finger flexors; those of the posterior compartment are wrist and finger extensors.

12. The intrinsic muscles of the hand aid in precise movements of the fingers (Table 10.13*) and in opposition, which helps us grip things. These small muscles are divided into thenar, hypothenar, and midpalmar groups.

13. Muscles crossing the hip and knee joints move the thigh and leg (see Table 10.14*). Anteromedial muscles flex and/or adduct the thigh and flex the knee. Muscles of the posterior gluteal region extend and rotate the thigh. Posterior thigh muscles extend the hip and flex the knee.

14. Muscles in the leg act on the ankle and toes (see Table 10.15*). Anterior compartment muscles are largely ankle dorsiflexors.

Lateral compartment muscles are plantar flexors and foot everters. Those of the posterior leg are plantar flexors.

15. The intrinsic muscles of the foot (Table 10.16*) support the foot arches and help move the toes. Most occur in the sole, arranged in four layers. They resemble the small muscles in the palm of the hand.

*See specific table cited for detailed description of each muscle in the group.

Review Questions

Multiple Choice/Matching

(Some questions have more than one correct answer. Select the best answer or answers from the choices given.)

1. A muscle that assists an agonist by causing a like movement or by stabilizing a joint over which an agonist acts is a(n) **(a)** antagonist, **(b)** prime mover, **(c)** synergist, **(d)** agonist.

2. The arrangement of muscle fibers in which the fibers are arranged at an angle to a central longitudinal tendon is **(a)** circular, **(b)** longitudinal, **(c)** pennate, **(d)** parallel.

3. Match the muscle names in column B to the facial muscles described in column A.

Column A	Column B
____ (1) squints the eyes	**(a)** corrugator supercilii
____ (2) raises the eyebrows	**(b)** depressor anguli oris
____ (3) smiling muscle	**(c)** frontal belly of epicranius
____ (4) puckers the lips	
____ (5) pulls the scalp posteriorly	**(d)** occipital belly of epicranius
	(e) orbicularis oculi
	(f) orbicularis oris
	(g) zygomaticus

4. The prime mover of inspiration is the **(a)** diaphragm, **(b)** internal intercostals, **(c)** external intercostals, **(d)** abdominal wall muscles.

5. The arm muscle that both flexes the elbow and supinates the forearm is the **(a)** brachialis, **(b)** brachioradialis, **(c)** biceps brachii, **(d)** triceps brachii.

6. The chewing muscles that protrude the mandible and produce side-to-side grinding movements are the **(a)** buccinators, **(b)** masseters, **(c)** temporalis, **(d)** pterygoids.

7. Muscles that depress the hyoid bone and larynx include all but the **(a)** sternohyoid, **(b)** omohyoid, **(c)** geniohyoid, **(d)** sternothyroid.

8. Intrinsic muscles of the back that promote extension of the spine (or head) include all but **(a)** splenius muscles, **(b)** semispinalis muscles, **(c)** scalene muscles, **(d)** erector spinae.

9. Several muscles act to move and/or stabilize the scapula. Which of the following are small rectangular muscles that square the shoulders as they act together to retract the scapula? **(a)** levator scapulae, **(b)** rhomboids, **(c)** serratus anterior, **(d)** trapezius.

10. The quadriceps include all but **(a)** vastus lateralis, **(b)** vastus intermedius, **(c)** vastus medialis, **(d)** biceps femoris, **(e)** rectus femoris.

11. A prime mover of hip flexion is the **(a)** rectus femoris, **(b)** iliopsoas, **(c)** vastus muscles, **(d)** gluteus maximus.

12. The prime mover of hip extension *against* resistance is the **(a)** gluteus maximus, **(b)** gluteus medius, **(c)** biceps femoris, **(d)** semimembranosus.

13. Muscles that cause plantar flexion include all but the **(a)** gastrocnemius, **(b)** soleus, **(c)** tibialis anterior, **(d)** tibialis posterior, **(e)** fibularis muscles.

14. In walking, which two lower limb muscles keep the forward-swinging foot from dragging on the ground? **(a)** pronator teres and popliteus, **(b)** flexor digitorum longus and popliteus, **(c)** adductor longus and abductor digiti minimi in foot, **(d)** gluteus medius and tibialis anterior.

15. Which criterion (or criteria) is/are used in naming the gluteus medius? **(a)** relative size, **(b)** muscle location, **(c)** muscle shape, **(d)** action, **(e)** number of origins.

16. Which of the following is a large, deep muscle that protracts the scapula during punching? **(a)** serratus anterior, **(b)** rhomboids, **(c)** levator scapulae, **(d)** subscapularis.

Short Answer Essay Questions

17. Name four criteria used in naming muscles, and provide an example (other than those used in the text) that illustrates each criterion.

18. Differentiate between the arrangement of elements (load, fulcrum, and effort) in first-, second-, and third-class levers.

19. What does it mean when we say that a lever operates at a mechanical disadvantage, and what benefits does such a lever system provide?

20. Which muscles act to propel food down the length of the pharynx to the esophagus?

21. Name and describe the action of muscles used to shake your head no; to nod yes.

22. **(a)** Name the four muscle pairs that act in unison to compress the abdominal contents. **(b)** How does their arrangement (fiber direction) contribute to the strength of the abdominal wall? (c) Which of these muscles can effect lateral rotation of the spine? (d) Which can act alone to flex the spine?

23. List all six possible movements that can occur at the shoulder joint and name the prime mover(s) of each movement. Then name their antagonists.

24. **(a)** Name two forearm muscles that are powerful extensors and abductors of the wrist. **(b)** Name the sole forearm muscle that can flex the distal interphalangeal joints.

25. Name the muscles usually grouped together as the lateral rotators of the hip.

26. Name three thigh muscles that help you keep your seat astride a horse.

27. **(a)** Name three muscles or muscle groups used as sites for intramuscular injections. **(b)** Which of these is used most often in infants, and why?

28. Name two muscles in each of the following compartments or regions: (a) thenar eminence (ball of thumb), (b) posterior compartment of forearm, (c) anterior compartment of forearm—deep muscle group, (d) anterior muscle group in the arm,

10

(e) muscles of mastication, (f) third muscle layer of the foot, (g) posterior compartment of leg, (h) medial compartment of thigh, (i) posterior compartment of thigh.

Critical Thinking and Clinical Application Questions

1. Assume you have a 10-lb weight in your right hand. Explain why it is easier to flex the right elbow when your forearm is supinated than when it is pronated.

2. When Mrs. O'Brien returned to her doctor for a follow-up visit after childbirth, she complained that she was having problems controlling her urine flow (incontinent) when she sneezed. The physician asked his nurse to give Mrs. O'Brien instructions on how to perform exercises to strengthen the muscles of the pelvic floor. To which muscles was he referring?

3. Mr. Ahmadi, an out-of-shape 45-year-old man, was advised by his physician to lose weight and to exercise on a regular basis. He followed his diet faithfully and began to jog daily. One day, while on his morning jog, he heard a snapping sound that was immediately followed by a severe pain in his right lower calf. When his leg was examined, a gap was seen between his swollen upper calf region and his heel, and he was unable to plantar flex that ankle. What do you think happened? Why was the upper part of his calf swollen?

4. As Peter watched Sue walk down the runway at the fashion show, he contracted his right orbicularis oculi muscle, raised his arm, and contracted his opponens pollicis. Was he pleased or displeased with her performance? How do you know?

5. What type of lever system do the following activities describe? (a) The soleus muscle plantar flexes the foot. (b) The deltoid abducts the arm. (c) The triceps brachii is strained while doing pushups.

AT THE CLINIC

10

Related Clinical Terms

Charley horse A muscle contusion, i.e., tearing of muscle followed by bleeding into the tissues (hematoma) and severe, prolonged pain. A common contact sports injury; football players frequently suffer a charley horse of the quadriceps muscle of the thigh.

Electromyography Recording and interpretation of graphic records of the electrical activity of contracting muscles. Electrodes inserted into the muscles record the impulses that pass over muscle-cell membranes to stimulate contraction. The best and most important technique for determining the functions of muscles and muscle groups.

Hernia An abnormal protrusion of abdominal contents (typically coils of the small intestine) through a weak point in the muscles of the abdominal wall. Most often caused by increased intra-abdominal pressure during lifting or straining. The hernia penetrates the muscle wall but not the skin and so appears as a visible bulge in the body surface. Common abdominal hernias include the inguinal and umbilical hernias.

Quadriceps and hamstring strains Also called quad and hamstring pulls, these conditions involve tearing these muscles or their tendons; happen mainly in athletes who do not warm up properly and then fully extend their hip (quad pull) or knee (hamstring pull) quickly or forcefully (e.g., sprinters, tennis players). Not painful at first, but pain intensifies within three to six hours (30 minutes if the tearing is severe). After a week of rest, stretching is the best therapy.

Ruptured calcaneal tendon Although the calcaneal (Achilles) tendon is the largest, strongest tendon in the body, its rupture is surprisingly common, particularly in older people as a result of stumbling and in young sprinters when the tendon is traumatized during takeoff. The rupture is followed by abrupt pain; a gap is seen just above the heel, and the calf bulges as the triceps surae are released from their insertion. Plantar flexion is weak or impossible, but dorsiflexion is exaggerated. Usually repaired surgically.

Shin splints Common term for pain in the anterior compartment of the leg caused by irritation of the tibialis anterior muscle as might follow extreme or unusual exercise without adequate prior conditioning. Because it is tightly wrapped by fascia, the inflamed tibialis anterior cuts off its own circulation as it swells and presses painfully on its own nerves.

Tennis elbow Tenderness due to trauma or overuse of the tendon of origin of the forearm extensor muscles at the lateral epicondyle of the humerus. Caused and aggravated when these muscles contract forcefully to extend the hand at the wrist—as in executing a tennis backhand or lifting a loaded snow shovel. Despite its name, tennis elbow does not involve the elbow joint; most cases caused by work activities.

Torticollis (tor″tĭ-kol′is; *tort* = twisted) A twisting of the neck in which there is a chronic rotation and tilting of the head to one side, due to injury of the sternocleidomastoid muscle on one side; also called wryneck. Sometimes present at birth when the muscle fibers are torn during difficult delivery. Exercise that stretches the affected muscle is the usual treatment.

Case Study   Muscular System

In Chapters 7 and 8, you were introduced to Kayla Tanner, a 45-year-old mother of four who had suffered a dislocated right hip in the bus accident on Route 91. Six weeks after the injury, Mrs. Tanner reported that she was still unable to walk or run without hip pain, and had weakness in her hip, knee, and ankle. Mrs. Tanner walked with a limp that her doctors attributed to weaknesses in flexion at the knee, inversion of the foot, and plantar flexion.

Electromyography (which measures muscle electrical activity) and nerve conduction studies (which measure the speed of nerve impulses) revealed that Mrs. Tanner's sciatic nerve had been damaged as a result of her injuries—most likely as a result of the nerve being compressed when the hip was dislocated. This large nerve innervates a large number of lower limb muscles. Since her surgery, Mrs. Tanner has been undergoing intense physical therapy and has shown significant improvement.

1. During her initial visit with the physical therapist, Mrs. Tanner presented with significant "foot drop" (the inability to dorsiflex the foot when taking a step). Mrs. Tanner was asked to perform a variety of movements with her right lower extremity. The therapist focused her attention on the *prime movers* and *synergists* of the hip, knee, and ankle. What are "prime movers" and "synergists"?

2. In order to assess the function and strength of a specific muscle, a physical therapist will often apply resistance (push against the moving limb) to mimic the action of an *antagonist muscle*. What is an antagonist muscle, and why would the therapist mimic its action?

3. Mrs. Tanner's physical therapist performed a variety of assessments in order to establish a baseline from which her recovery could be measured. For each of the descriptions below, name the muscle (or muscles) that the therapist was assessing.
   a. With Mrs. Tanner in the seated position, the therapist positioned Mrs. Tanner's legs shoulder-width apart, then asked Mrs. Tanner to bring her feet together while the therapist applied resistance to the right leg.
   b. The therapist applied resistance to the top of Mrs. Tanner's foot and asked her to pull her forefoot up toward her shin.
   c. With Mrs. Tanner in the prone position (on her stomach), the therapist applied resistance to the leg while Mrs. Tanner was instructed to bring her heel up toward her buttocks (flex her knee).

4. Using descriptions similar to those listed in the question above, explain how you would assess the function of the following muscles.
   a. Extensor hallucis longus
   b. Fibularis (peroneus) longus
   c. Gastrocnemius

(Answers in Appendix H)

10

11

Fundamentals of the Nervous System and Nervous Tissue

Y ou are driving down the freeway, and a horn blares to your right. You immediately swerve to your left. Charlie leaves a note on the kitchen table: "See you later. Have the stuff ready at 6." You know the "stuff" is chili with taco chips. You are dozing but you awaken instantly when your infant son cries softly.

What do these three events have in common? They are all everyday examples of the functioning of your nervous system, which has your body cells humming with activity nearly all the time.

The **nervous system** is the master controlling and communicating system of the body. Every thought, action, and emotion reflects its activity. Its cells communicate by electrical and chemical signals, which are rapid and specific, and usually cause almost immediate responses.

We begin this chapter with a brief overview of the functions and organization of the nervous system. Then we focus on the functional anatomy of nervous tissue, especially the nerve cells, or *neurons*, which are the key to neural communication.

Functions and Divisions of the Nervous System

✓ List the basic functions of the nervous system.

✓ Explain the structural and functional divisions of the nervous system.

The nervous system has three overlapping functions, illustrated by the example of a thirsty person seeing and then lifting a glass of water (Figure 11.1):

1. **Sensory input.** The nervous system uses its millions of sensory receptors to monitor changes occurring both inside and outside the body. The gathered information is called **sensory input**.
2. **Integration.** The nervous system processes and interprets sensory input and decides what should be done at each moment—a process called **integration**.
3. **Motor output.** The nervous system activates *effector organs*—the muscles and glands—to cause a *response*, called **motor output.**

Here's another example: You are driving and see a red light ahead (sensory input). Your nervous system integrates this information (red light means "stop"), and your foot goes for the brake (motor output).

We have only one highly integrated nervous system. For convenience, it is divided into two principal parts, *central* and *peripheral*.

The **central nervous system (CNS)** consists of the *brain* and *spinal cord*, which occupy the dorsal body cavity. The CNS is the integrating and control center of the nervous system. It interprets sensory input and dictates motor output based on reflexes, current conditions, and past experience (Figure 11.2).

The **peripheral nervous system (PNS)** is the part of the nervous system *outside* the CNS. The PNS consists mainly of the nerves (bundles of axons) that extend from the brain and spinal cord. *Spinal nerves* carry impulses to and from the spinal cord, and *cranial nerves* carry impulses to and from the brain. These peripheral nerves serve as communication lines that link all parts of the body to the CNS.

The PNS has two functional subdivisions, as Figure 11.2 shows. The **sensory**, or **afferent**, **division** (af'er-ent; "carrying toward") consists of nerve fibers (axons) that convey impulses *to* the central nervous system from sensory receptors located throughout the body (see the blue fibers in Figure 11.2).

■ *Somatic sensory fibers* convey impulses from the skin, skeletal muscles, and joints (*soma* = body)

■ *Visceral sensory fibers* transmit impulses from the visceral organs (organs within the ventral body cavity)

The sensory division keeps the CNS constantly informed of events going on both inside and outside the body.

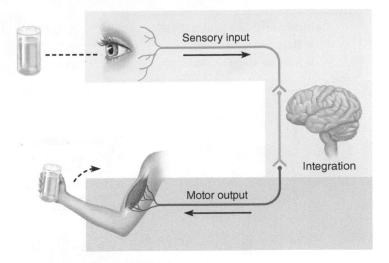

Figure 11.1 The nervous system's functions.

The **motor**, or **efferent**, **division** (ef'er-ent; "carrying away") of the PNS transmits impulses *from* the CNS to effector organs, which are the muscles and glands (see the red fibers in Figure 11.2). These impulses activate muscles to contract and glands to secrete. In other words, they *effect* (bring about) a motor response.

The motor division also has two main parts:

■ The **somatic nervous system** is composed of somatic motor nerve fibers that conduct impulses from the CNS to skeletal muscles. It is often referred to as the **voluntary nervous system** because it allows us to consciously control our skeletal muscles.

■ The **autonomic nervous system (ANS)** consists of visceral motor nerve fibers that regulate the activity of smooth muscles, cardiac muscles, and glands. *Autonomic* means "a law unto itself," and because we generally cannot control such activities as the pumping of our heart or the movement of food through our digestive tract, the ANS is also called the **involuntary nervous system**.

As we will describe in Chapter 14, the ANS has two functional subdivisions, the **sympathetic division** and the **parasympathetic division**. Typically these divisions work in opposition to each other—whatever one stimulates, the other inhibits.

☑ **Check Your Understanding**

1. What is meant by "integration," and does it primarily occur in the CNS or the PNS?
2. Which subdivision of the PNS is involved in (a) relaying the feeling of a "full stomach" after a meal, (b) contracting the muscles to lift your arm, and (c) increasing your heart rate?

For answers, see Appendix H.

Histology of Nervous Tissue

The nervous system consists mostly of nervous tissue, which is highly cellular. For example, less than 20% of the CNS is extracellular space, which means that the cells are densely packed

Figure 11.2 Levels of organization in the nervous system. The human nervous system is organized into two major divisions, the central nervous system (CNS) and peripheral nervous system (PNS). Visceral organs (primarily located in the ventral body cavity) are served by visceral sensory fibers and by motor fibers of the autonomic nervous system. The somata (limbs and body wall) are served by motor fibers of the somatic nervous system and by somatic sensory fibers. Arrows indicate the direction of nerve impulses. (Connections to spinal cord are not anatomically accurate.)

and tightly intertwined. Although it is very complex, nervous tissue is made up of just two principal types of cells:

- Supporting cells called *neuroglia*, small cells that surround and wrap the more delicate neurons

- *Neurons*, nerve cells that are excitable (responsive to stimuli) and transmit electrical signals

See Figure 4.10 on p. 140 to refresh your memory.

Neuroglia

✓ List the types of neuroglia and cite their functions.

Neurons associate closely with much smaller cells called **neuroglia** (nu-rog′le-ah; "nerve glue") or **glial cells** (gle′al). There are six types of neuroglia—four in the CNS and two in the PNS **(Figure 11.3)**. Once considered merely the "glue" or scaffolding that supports the neurons, neuroglia are now known to have many other important and unique functions.

Neuroglia in the CNS

Neuroglia in the CNS include *astrocytes*, *microglial cells*, *ependymal cells*, and *oligodendrocytes* (Figure 11.3a–d). Like neurons, most neuroglia have branching processes (extensions) and a central cell body. They can be distinguished, however, by their much smaller size and their darker-staining nuclei. They outnumber neurons in the CNS by about 10 to 1, and make up about half the mass of the brain.

Astrocytes Shaped like delicate branching sea anemones, **astrocytes** (as′tro-sītz; "star cells") are the most abundant and versatile glial cells. Their numerous radiating processes cling to neurons and their synaptic endings, and cover nearby capillaries. They support and brace the neurons and anchor them to their nutrient supply lines (Figure 11.3a).

Astrocytes play a role in making exchanges between capillaries and neurons, helping determine capillary permeability. They guide the migration of young neurons, and formation of synapses (junctions) between neurons. Astrocytes also control the chemical environment around neurons, where their most important job is "mopping up" leaked potassium ions and recapturing and recycling released neurotransmitters. Furthermore, astrocytes have been shown to respond to nearby nerve impulses and released neurotransmitters.

Connected by gap junctions, astrocytes signal each other both by taking in calcium, creating slow-paced intracellular calcium pulses (calcium waves), and by releasing extracellular chemical messengers. Recent research shows they also influence neuronal functioning and therefore participate in information processing in the brain.

Microglial Cells **Microglial cells** (mi-kro′gle-al) are small and ovoid with relatively long "thorny" processes (Figure 11.3b). Their processes touch nearby neurons, monitoring their health, and when they sense that certain neurons are injured or in other trouble, the microglial cells migrate toward them. Where invading microorganisms or dead neurons are present, the microglial cells transform into a special type of macrophage that phagocytizes the microorganisms or neuronal debris. This protective role of the microglial cells is important because cells of the immune system have limited access to the CNS.

Ependymal Cells **Ependymal cells** (ĕ-pen′dĭ-mul; "wrapping garment") range in shape from squamous to columnar, and many are ciliated (Figure 11.3c). They line the central cavities of the brain and the spinal cord, where they form a fairly permeable barrier between the cerebrospinal fluid that fills those cavities and the tissue fluid bathing the cells of the CNS. The beating of their cilia helps to circulate the cerebrospinal fluid that cushions the brain and spinal cord.

Figure 11.3 Neuroglia. (a–d) The four types of neuroglia of the CNS. **(e)** Neuroglia of the PNS.

(a) Astrocytes are the most abundant CNS neuroglia.

(b) Microglial cells are defensive cells in the CNS.

(c) Ependymal cells line cerebrospinal fluid–filled cavities.

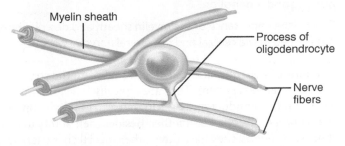

(d) Oligodendrocytes have processes that form myelin sheaths around CNS nerve fibers.

(e) Satellite cells and Schwann cells (which form myelin) surround neurons in the PNS.

Oligodendrocytes Though they also branch, the **oligodendrocytes** (ol″ĭ-go-den′dro-sīts) have fewer processes (*oligo* = few; *dendr* = branch) than astrocytes. Oligodendrocytes line up along the thicker nerve fibers in the CNS and wrap their processes tightly around the fibers, producing an insulating covering called a *myelin sheath* (Figure 11.3d).

Neuroglia in the PNS

The two kinds of PNS neuroglia—*satellite cells* and *Schwann cells*—differ mainly in location.

Satellite cells surround neuron cell bodies located in the peripheral nervous system (Figure 11.3e), and are thought to have many of the same functions in the PNS as astrocytes do in the CNS. Their name comes from a fancied resemblance to the moons (satellites) around a planet.

Schwann cells (also called *neurolemmocytes*) surround all nerve fibers in the PNS and form myelin sheaths around the thicker nerve fibers (Figure 11.3e and 11.4a). In this way, they are functionally similar to oligodendrocytes. (We describe the formation of myelin sheaths later in this chapter.) Schwann cells are vital to regeneration of damaged peripheral nerve fibers.

☑ **Check Your Understanding**

3. Which type of neuroglia controls the extracellular fluid environment around neuron cell bodies in the CNS? In the PNS?
4. Which two types of neuroglia form insulating coverings called myelin sheaths?

For answers, see Appendix H.

Neurons

✓ Define neuron, describe its important structural components, and relate each to a functional role.

✓ Differentiate between (1) a nerve and a tract, and (2) a nucleus and a ganglion.

✓ Explain the importance of the myelin sheath and describe how it is formed in the central and peripheral nervous systems.

The billions of **neurons**, also called *nerve cells*, are the structural units of the nervous system. They are typically large, highly specialized cells that conduct messages in the form of nerve impulses from one part of the body to another. Besides their ability to conduct nerve impulses, they have three other special characteristics:

- Neurons have *extreme longevity*. Given good nutrition, they can function optimally for a lifetime (over 100 years).

- Neurons are *amitotic*. As neurons assume their roles as communicating links of the nervous system, they lose their ability to divide. We pay a high price for this feature because neurons cannot be replaced if destroyed. There *are* exceptions to this rule. For example, olfactory epithelium and some hippocampal regions contain stem cells that can produce new neurons throughout life. (The hippocampus is a brain region involved in memory.)

- Neurons have an exceptionally *high metabolic rate* and require continuous and abundant supplies of oxygen and glucose. They cannot survive for more than a few minutes without oxygen.

Although neurons vary in structure, they all have a *cell body* and one or more slender *processes* (Figure 11.4).

Neuron Cell Body

The **neuron cell body** consists of a spherical nucleus with a conspicuous nucleolus surrounded by cytoplasm. Also called the **perikaryon** (*peri* = around, *kary* = nucleus) or **soma**, the cell body ranges in diameter from 5 to 140 μm. The cell body is the major *biosynthetic center* of a neuron and so it contains the usual organelles needed to synthesize proteins and other chemicals.

The neuron cell body's protein- and membrane-making machinery, consisting of clustered free ribosomes and rough endoplasmic reticulum (ER), is probably the most active and best developed in the body. This rough ER, also called the **chromatophilic substance** (*chromatophilic* = color loving) or *Nissl bodies* (nis′l), stains darkly with basic dyes. The Golgi apparatus is also well developed and forms an arc or a complete circle around the nucleus.

Mitochondria are scattered among the other organelles. Microtubules and **neurofibrils**, which are bundles of intermediate filaments (*neurofilaments*), are important in maintaining cell shape and integrity. They form a network throughout the cell body.

The cell body of some neurons also contains pigment inclusions. For example, some contain a black melanin, a red iron-containing pigment, or a golden-brown pigment called *lipofuscin* (lip″o-fu′sin). Lipofuscin, a harmless by-product of lysosomal activity, is sometimes called the "aging pigment" because it accumulates in neurons of elderly individuals.

The cell body is the focal point for the outgrowth of neuron processes during embryonic development. In most neurons, the plasma membrane of the cell body also acts as *part of the receptive region* that receives information from other neurons.

Most neuron cell bodies are located in the CNS, where they are protected by the bones of the skull and vertebral column. Clusters of cell bodies in the CNS are called **nuclei**, whereas those that lie along the nerves in the PNS are called **ganglia** (gang′gle-ah; *ganglion* = "knot on a string," "swelling").

Neuron Processes

Armlike **processes** extend from the cell body of all neurons. The brain and spinal cord (CNS) contain both neuron cell bodies and their processes. The PNS consists chiefly of neuron processes. Bundles of neuron processes are called **tracts** in the CNS and **nerves** in the PNS.

The two types of neuron processes, *dendrites* and *axons* (ak′sonz), differ in the structure and function of their plasma membranes. The convention is to describe these processes using a motor neuron as an example. We shall follow this practice, but keep in mind that many sensory neurons and some tiny CNS neurons differ from the "typical" pattern we present here.

Dendrites **Dendrites** of motor neurons are short, tapering, diffusely branching extensions. Typically, motor neurons have hundreds of twiglike dendrites clustering close to the cell body. Virtually all organelles present in the cell body also occur in dendrites.

Figure 11.4 Structure of a motor neuron. (a) Diagrammatic view. **(b)** Scanning electron micrograph showing the cell body and dendrites with obvious dendritic spines (2000×).

Dendrites, the main **receptive** or **input regions**, provide an enormous surface area for receiving signals from other neurons. In many brain areas, the finer dendrites are highly specialized for collecting information. They bristle with *dendritic spines*—thorny appendages having bulbous or spiky ends—which represent points of close contact (synapses) with other neurons (Figure 11.4b).

Dendrites convey incoming messages *toward* the cell body. These electrical signals are usually *not* action potentials (nerve impulses) but are short-distance signals called *graded potentials*, as we will describe shortly.

The Axon: Structure   Each neuron has a single **axon** (*axo* = axis, axle). The initial region of the axon arises from a cone-shaped area of the cell body called the **axon hillock** ("little hill") and then narrows to form a slender process that is uniform in diameter for the rest of its length (Figure 11.4a). In some neurons, the axon is very short or absent, but in others it accounts for nearly the entire length of the neuron. For example, axons of the motor neurons controlling the skeletal muscles of your great toe extend a meter or more (3–4 feet) from the lumbar region of your spine to your foot, making them among the longest cells in the body. Any long axon is called a **nerve fiber**.

Each neuron has only one axon, but axons may have occasional branches along their length. These branches, called **axon collaterals**, extend from the axon at more or less right angles. Whether an axon is undivided or has collaterals, it usually branches profusely at its end (terminus): 10,000 or more **terminal branches** (also called *terminal arborizations*) per neuron is not unusual. The knoblike distal endings of the terminal branches are called **axon terminals** or **terminal boutons** (boo-tonz'; "buttons"). Take your pick!

The Axon: Functional Characteristics   Functionally, the axon is the **conducting region** of the neuron (Figure 11.4). It *generates nerve impulses* and *transmits them*, typically away from the cell body, along the plasma membrane, or **axolemma** (ak"so-lem'ah). In motor neurons, the nerve impulse is generated at the junction of the axon hillock and axon (which for this reason is called the *trigger zone*) and conducted along the axon to the axon terminals, which are the **secretory region** of the neuron.

When the impulse reaches the axon terminals, it causes *neurotransmitters*—signaling chemicals usually stored in vesicles—to be released into the extracellular space. The neurotransmitters either excite or inhibit neurons (or effector cells) with which the axon is in close contact. Because each neuron both receives signals from and sends signals to scores of other neurons, it carries on "conversations" with many different neurons at the same time.

An axon contains the same organelles found in the dendrites and cell body with two important exceptions—it lacks rough

Schwann cell plasma membrane

Schwann cell cytoplasm

Axon

(1) A Schwann cell envelops an axon.

Schwann cell nucleus

(2) The Schwann cell then rotates around the axon, wrapping its plasma membrane loosely around it in successive layers.

Myelin sheath

(3) The Schwann cell cytoplasm is forced from between the membranes. The tight membrane wrappings surrounding the axon form the myelin sheath.

Schwann cell cytoplasm

(a) Myelination of a nerve fiber (axon)

Myelin sheath

Outer collar of perinuclear cytoplasm (of Schwann cell)

Axon

(b) Cross-sectional view of a myelinated axon (electron micrograph 24,000×)

Figure 11.5 Nerve fiber myelination by Schwann cells in the PNS.

endoplasmic reticulum and a Golgi apparatus, the structures involved with protein synthesis and packaging. Consequently, an axon depends (1) on its cell body to renew the necessary proteins and membrane components, and (2) on efficient transport

mechanisms to distribute them. Axons quickly decay if cut or severely damaged.

Transport Along the Axon Because axons are often very long, the task of moving molecules along their length might appear difficult. However, through the cooperative efforts of motor proteins and cytoskeletal elements (microtubules and actin filaments), substances travel continuously along the axon both away from and toward the cell body. Movement away from the cell body is *anterograde movement*, and that in the opposite direction is *retrograde movement*.

Substances moved in the anterograde direction include mitochondria, cytoskeletal elements, membrane components used to renew the axon plasma membrane, and enzymes needed to synthesize certain neurotransmitters. (Some neurotransmitters are synthesized in the cell body and then transported to the axon terminals.)

Substances transported through the axon in the retrograde direction are mostly organelles returning to the cell body to be degraded or recycled. Retrograde transport is also an important means of intracellular communication to "advise" the cell body of conditions at the axon terminals, and deliver to the cell body vesicles containing signal molecules (like nerve growth factor, which activates certain nuclear genes promoting growth).

One basic bidirectional transport mechanism appears to be responsible for axonal transport. It uses ATP-dependent "motor" proteins (kinesin and dynein), depending on the direction of transport. These proteins propel cellular components along the microtubules like trains along tracks at speeds up to 40 cm (15 inches) per day.

Homeostatic Imbalance 11.1

Certain viruses and bacterial toxins that damage neural tissues use retrograde axonal transport to reach the cell body. This transport mechanism has been demonstrated for polio, rabies, and herpes simplex viruses and for tetanus toxin. Researchers are investigating using retrograde transport to treat genetic diseases by introducing viruses containing "corrected" genes or microRNA to suppress defective genes. ✚

Myelin Sheath Many nerve fibers, particularly those that are long or large in diameter, are covered with a whitish, fatty (protein-lipoid), segmented **myelin sheath** (mi´ĕ-lin). Myelin protects and electrically insulates fibers, and it increases the transmission speed of nerve impulses. **Myelinated fibers** (axons bearing a myelin sheath) conduct nerve impulses rapidly, whereas **nonmyelinated fibers** conduct impulses more slowly. Note that myelin sheaths are associated only with axons. Dendrites are *always* nonmyelinated.

Myelination in the PNS Myelin sheaths in the PNS are formed by Schwann cells, which indent to receive an axon and then wrap themselves around it in a jelly roll fashion **(Figure 11.5)**. Initially the wrapping is loose, but the Schwann cell cytoplasm is gradually squeezed from between the membrane layers.

When the wrapping process is complete, many concentric layers of Schwann cell plasma membrane enclose the axon, much like gauze wrapped around an injured finger. This tight coil of wrapped membranes is the myelin sheath, and its thickness depends on the number of spirals. The nucleus and most of the cytoplasm of the Schwann cell end up as a bulge just external to the myelin sheath. This portion of the Schwann cell, next to the exposed part of its plasma membrane, is called the *outer collar of perinuclear cytoplasm* (formerly known as the *neurilemma*) (Figure 11.5b).

Plasma membranes of myelinating cells contain much less protein than the plasma membranes of most body cells. Channel and carrier proteins are notably absent, a characteristic that makes myelin sheaths exceptionally good electrical insulators. Another unique characteristic of these membranes is the presence of specific protein molecules that interlock to form a sort of molecular Velcro between adjacent myelin membranes.

Adjacent Schwann cells along an axon do not touch one another, so there are gaps in the sheath. These **myelin sheath gaps**, or **nodes of Ranvier** (ran′vē-ā″), occur at regular intervals (about 1 mm apart) along a myelinated axon. Axon collaterals can emerge from the axon at these gaps.

Sometimes Schwann cells surround peripheral nerve fibers but the coiling process does not occur. In such instances, a single Schwann cell can partially enclose 15 or more axons, each of which occupies a separate recess in the Schwann cell surface. Nerve fibers associated with Schwann cells in this manner are said to be *nonmyelinated* and are typically thin fibers.

Myelination in the CNS The central nervous system contains both myelinated and nonmyelinated axons. However, in the CNS, it is the oligodendrocytes that form myelin sheaths (Figure 11.3d).

Unlike a Schwann cell, which forms only one segment of a myelin sheath, an oligodendrocyte has multiple flat processes that can coil around as many as 60 axons at the same time. As in the PNS, myelin sheath gaps separate adjacent sections of an axon's myelin sheath. However, CNS myelin sheaths lack an outer collar of perinuclear cytoplasm because cell extensions do the coiling and the squeezed-out cytoplasm is forced back toward the centrally located nucleus instead of peripherally.

As in the PNS, the smallest-diameter axons are nonmyelinated. These nonmyelinated axons are covered by the long extensions of adjacent glial cells.

Regions of the brain and spinal cord containing dense collections of myelinated fibers are referred to as **white matter** and are primarily fiber tracts. **Gray matter** contains mostly nerve cell bodies and nonmyelinated fibers.

☑ Check Your Understanding

5. Which part of the neuron is its fiber? How do nerve fibers differ from the fibers of connective tissue (see Chapter 4) and the fibers in muscle (see Chapter 9)?
6. How does a nucleus within the brain differ from a nucleus within a neuron?
7. How is a myelin sheath formed in the CNS, and what is its function?

For answers, see Appendix H.

Classification of Neurons

✓ Classify neurons by structure and by function.

Neurons are classified both structurally and functionally. We describe both classifications here but use the functional classification in most discussions.

Structural Classification Neurons are grouped structurally according to the number of processes extending from their cell body. Three major neuron groups make up this classification: multipolar (*polar* = end, pole), bipolar, and unipolar neurons. (Table 11.1 is organized according to these three neuron types, and the top row shows their structures.)

Multipolar neurons have three or more processes—one axon and the rest dendrites. They are the most common neuron type in humans, with more than 99% of neurons belonging to this class. Multipolar neurons are the major neuron type in the CNS.

Bipolar neurons have two processes—an axon and a dendrite—that extend from opposite sides of the cell body. These rare neurons are found in some of the special sense organs. Examples include some neurons in the retina of the eye and in the olfactory mucosa.

Unipolar neurons have a single short process that emerges from the cell body and divides T-like into proximal and distal branches. The more distal process, the **peripheral process**, is often associated with a sensory receptor. The **central process** enters the CNS (Table 11.1). Unipolar neurons are more accurately called **pseudounipolar neurons** (*pseudo* = false) because they originate as bipolar neurons. Then, during early embryonic development, the two processes converge and partially fuse to form the short single process that issues from the cell body. Unipolar neurons are found chiefly in ganglia in the PNS, where they function as sensory neurons.

The fact that the fused peripheral and central processes of unipolar neurons are continuous and function as a single fiber might make you wonder whether they are axons or dendrites. The central process is definitely an axon because it conducts impulses away from the cell body (one definition of axon). However, the peripheral process is perplexing. Three facts favor classifying it as an axon: (1) It generates and conducts an impulse (functional definition of axon); (2) when large, it is heavily myelinated; and (3) it has a uniform diameter and is indistinguishable microscopically from an axon. However, the older definition of a dendrite as a process that transmits impulses *toward* the cell body interferes with that conclusion.

So which is it? In this book, we have chosen to emphasize the newer definition of an axon as generating and transmitting an impulse. For *unipolar neurons*, we will refer to the combined length of the peripheral and central process as an axon. In place of "dendrites," unipolar neurons have *receptive endings* (sensory terminals) at the end of the peripheral process.

Functional Classification This scheme groups neurons according to the direction in which the nerve impulse travels relative to the central nervous system. Based on this criterion, there are sensory neurons, motor neurons, and interneurons (Table 11.1, last row).

Table 11.1	Comparison of Structural Classes of Neurons	
	NEURON TYPE	
MULTIPOLAR	**BIPOLAR**	**UNIPOLAR (PSEUDOUNIPOLAR)**

Structural Class: Neuron Type According to the Number of Processes Extending from the Cell Body

Many processes extend from the cell body. All are dendrites except for a single axon.	Two processes extend from the cell body. One is a fused dendrite, the other is an axon.	One process extends from the cell body and forms central and peripheral processes, which together comprise an axon.

Relationship of Anatomy to the Three Functional Regions

■ Receptive region (receives stimulus).

☐ Conducting region (generates/transmits action potential).

■ Secretory region (axon terminals release neurotransmitters).

	(Many bipolar neurons do not generate action potentials. In those that do, the location of the trigger zone is not universal.)	

Relative Abundance and Location in Human Body

Most abundant in body. Major neuron type in the CNS.	Rare. Found in some special sensory organs (olfactory mucosa, eye, ear).	Found mainly in the PNS. Common only in dorsal root ganglia of the spinal cord and sensory ganglia of cranial nerves.

Structural Variations

Multipolar	Bipolar	Unipolar
		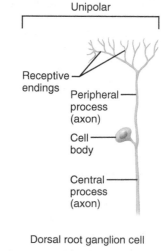
Purkinje cell of cerebellum Pyramidal cell	Olfactory cell Retinal cell	Dorsal root ganglion cell

Table 11.1 (continued)		
NEURON TYPE		
MULTIPOLAR	**BIPOLAR**	**UNIPOLAR (PSEUDOUNIPOLAR)**
Functional Class: Neuron Type According to Direction of Impulse Conduction		
1. Most multipolar neurons are **interneurons** that conduct impulses within the CNS, integrating sensory input or motor output. May be one of a chain of CNS neurons, or a single neuron connecting sensory and motor neurons. 2. Some multipolar neurons are **motor neurons** that conduct impulses along the efferent pathways from the CNS to an effector (muscle/gland).	Essentially all bipolar neurons are **sensory neurons** that are located in some special sense organs. For example, bipolar cells of the retina are involved with transmitting visual inputs from the eye to the brain (via an intermediate chain of neurons).	Most unipolar neurons are **sensory neurons** that conduct impulses along afferent pathways to the CNS for interpretation. (These sensory neurons are called primary or first-order sensory neurons.)

Sensory, or **afferent**, **neurons** transmit impulses from sensory receptors in the skin or internal organs *toward* or *into* the central nervous system. Except for certain neurons found in some special sense organs, virtually all sensory neurons are unipolar, and their cell bodies are located in sensory ganglia *outside* the CNS. Only the most distal parts of these unipolar neurons act as impulse receptor sites, and the peripheral processes are often very long. For example, fibers carrying sensory impulses from the skin of your great toe travel for more than a meter before they reach their cell bodies in a ganglion close to the spinal cord.

The receptive endings of some sensory neurons are naked, in which case those terminals themselves function as sensory receptors, but many sensory neuron endings bear receptors that include other cell types. We describe the various types of general sensory receptor end organs, such as those of the skin, in Chapter 13. The special sensory receptors (of the ear, eye, etc.) are the topic of Chapter 15.

Motor, or **efferent**, **neurons** carry impulses *away from* the CNS to the effector organs (muscles and glands) of the body periphery. Motor neurons are multipolar. Except for some neurons of the autonomic nervous system, their cell bodies are located in the CNS.

Interneurons, or *association neurons*, lie between motor and sensory neurons in neural pathways and shuttle signals through CNS pathways where integration occurs. Most interneurons are confined within the CNS. They make up over 99% of the neurons of the body, including most of those in the CNS.

Almost all interneurons are multipolar, but there is considerable diversity in both size and fiber-branching patterns. The Purkinje and pyramidal cells illustrated as structural variations in Table 11.1 are just two examples of their variety.

☑ **Check Your Understanding**

8. Which structural and functional type of neuron is activated first when you burn your finger? Which type is activated last to move your finger away from the source of heat?

For answers, see Appendix H.

Membrane Potentials

When a neuron is adequately stimulated, an electrical impulse is generated and conducted along the length of its axon. This response, called the *action potential* or *nerve impulse*, is always the same regardless of the source or type of stimulus, and it underlies virtually all functional activities of the nervous system.

In this section, we will consider how neurons are excited or inhibited and how they communicate with other cells. First, however, we need to explore some basic principles of electricity and revisit the resting membrane potential.

Basic Principles of Electricity

The human body is electrically neutral—it has the same number of positive and negative charges. However, there are regions where one type of charge predominates, making those regions positively or negatively charged. Because opposite charges attract each other, energy must be used (work must be done) to separate them. On the other hand, the coming together of opposite charges liberates energy that can be used to do work. For this reason, situations in which there are separated electrical charges of opposite sign have potential energy.

Figure 11.6 Operation of gated channels. (a) A chemically gated channel permeable to both Na^+ and K^+, and **(b)** a voltage-gated Na^+ channel.

Some Definitions: Voltage, Resistance, Current

Voltage, the measure of potential energy generated by separated charge, is measured in either *volts* (V) or *millivolts* (1 mV = 0.001 V). Voltage is always measured between two points and is called the **potential difference** or simply the **potential** between the points. The greater the difference in charge between two points, the higher the voltage.

The flow of electrical charge from one point to another is a **current**, and it can be used to do work—for example, to power a flashlight. The amount of charge that moves between the two points depends on two factors: voltage and resistance. **Resistance** is the hindrance to charge flow provided by substances through which the current must pass. Substances with high electrical resistance are *insulators*, and those with low resistance are *conductors*.

Ohm's law gives the relationship between voltage, current, and resistance:

$$\text{Current } (I) = \frac{\text{voltage } (V)}{\text{resistance } (R)}$$

Ohm's law tells us three things:

- Current (I) is directly proportional to voltage. The greater the voltage (potential difference), the greater the current.

- There is no net current flow between points that have the same potential, as you can see by inserting a value of 0 V into the equation.

- Current is inversely related to resistance: The greater the resistance, the smaller the current.

In the body, electrical currents reflect the flow of ions (rather than free electrons) across cellular membranes. (Unlike the electrons flowing along your house wiring, there are no free

electrons "running around" in a living system.) As we described in Chapter 3, there is a slight difference in the numbers of positive and negative ions on the two sides of cellular plasma membranes (there is a charge separation), so there is a potential across those membranes. The plasma membranes provide the resistance to current flow.

Role of Membrane Ion Channels

Recall that plasma membranes are peppered with a variety of membrane proteins that act as *ion channels*. Each of these channels is selective as to the type of ion (or ions) it allows to pass. For example, a potassium ion channel allows only potassium ions to pass.

Membrane channels are large proteins, often with several subunits, whose amino acid chains snake back and forth across the membrane. Some channels, **leakage** or **nongated channels**, are always open. Other channels are *gated*: Part of the protein forms a molecular "gate" that changes shape to open and close the channel in response to specific signals. There are three main types of gated channels:

- **Chemically gated**, or **ligand-gated**, **channels** open when the appropriate chemical (in this case a neurotransmitter) binds **(Figure 11.6a)**.

- **Voltage-gated channels** open and close in response to changes in the membrane potential (Figure 11.6b).

- **Mechanically gated channels** open in response to physical deformation of the receptor (as in sensory receptors for touch and pressure).

When gated ion channels open, ions diffuse quickly across the membrane following their electrochemical gradients, creating electrical currents and voltage changes across the membrane according to the rearranged Ohm's law equation:

$$\text{Voltage } (V) = \text{current } (I) \times \text{resistance } (R)$$

Ions move along chemical *concentration gradients* when they diffuse passively from an area of their higher concentration to an area of lower concentration. They move along *electrical gradients* when they move toward an area of opposite electrical charge. Together, electrical and concentration gradients constitute the **electrochemical gradient**. Ions flowing along electrochemical gradients underlie all electrical events in neurons.

The Resting Membrane Potential

✓ Define resting membrane potential and describe its electrochemical basis.

A voltmeter is used to measure the potential difference between two points. When one microelectrode of the voltmeter is inserted into a neuron and the other is in the extracellular fluid, it records a voltage across the membrane of approximately $-70\,\text{mV}$ **(Figure 11.7)**. The minus sign indicates that the cytoplasmic side (inside) of the membrane is negatively charged relative to the outside. This potential difference in a resting neuron (V_r) is called the **resting membrane potential**, and the membrane is said to be **polarized**. The value of the resting membrane potential varies (from -40 mV to -90 mV) in different types of neurons.

The resting potential exists only across the membrane. In other words, the bulk solutions inside and outside the cell are electrically neutral. Two factors generate the resting membrane potential: differences in the ionic composition of the intracellular and extracellular fluids, and differences in the permeability of the plasma membrane to those ions.

Differences in Ionic Composition

First, let's compare the ionic makeup of the intracellular and extracellular fluids, as shown in *Focus on Resting Membrane Potential* **(Figure 11.8)**. The cell cytosol contains a lower concentration of Na^+ and a higher concentration of K^+ than the extracellular fluid. Negatively charged (anionic) proteins (not shown) help to balance the positive charges of intracellular cations (primarily K^+). In the extracellular fluid, the positive charges of Na^+ and other cations are balanced chiefly by chloride ions (Cl^-). Although there are many other solutes (glucose, urea, and other ions) in both fluids, potassium (K^+) plays the most important role in generating the membrane potential.

Differences in Plasma Membrane Permeability

Next, let's consider the differential permeability of the membrane to various ions (Figure 11.8, bottom). At rest the membrane is impermeable to the large anionic cytoplasmic proteins, very slightly permeable to sodium, approximately 25 times more permeable to potassium than to sodium, and quite permeable to chloride ions. These resting permeabilities reflect the properties of the leakage ion channels in the membrane. Potassium ions diffuse out of the cell along their *concentration gradient* much

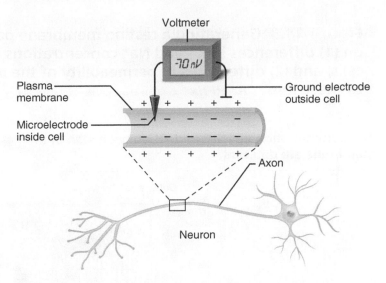

Figure 11.7 Measuring membrane potential in neurons. The potential difference between an electrode inside a neuron and the ground electrode in the extracellular fluid is approximately -70 mV (inside negative).

more easily than sodium ions can enter the cell along theirs. K^+ flowing out of the cell causes the cell to become more negative inside. Na^+ trickling into the cell makes the cell just slightly more positive than it would be if only K^+ flowed. Therefore, at resting membrane potential, the negative interior of the cell is due to a much greater ability for K^+ to diffuse out of the cell than for Na^+ to diffuse into the cell.

Because some K^+ is always leaking out of the cell and some Na^+ is always leaking in, you might think that the concentration gradients would eventually "run down," resulting in equal concentrations of Na^+ and K^+ inside and outside the cell. This does not happen because the ATP-driven sodium-potassium pump first ejects three Na^+ from the cell and then transports two K^+ back into the cell. In other words, the **sodium-potassium pump (Na^+-K^+ ATPase)** stabilizes the resting membrane potential by maintaining the concentration gradients for sodium and potassium.

☑ **Check Your Understanding**

9. For an open channel, what factors determine in which direction ions will move through that channel?

10. For which cation is there the greatest amount of leakage (through leakage channels) across the plasma membrane?

For answers, see Appendix H.

Membrane Potentials That Act as Signals

✓ Compare and contrast graded potentials and action potentials.

✓ Explain how action potentials are generated and propagated along neurons.

✓ Define absolute and relative refractory periods.

✓ Define saltatory conduction and contrast it to continuous conduction.

Figure 11.8 Generating a resting membrane potential depends on (1) differences in K⁺ and Na⁺ concentrations inside and outside cells, and (2) differences in permeability of the plasma membrane to these ions. *A&PFlix* Available at www.masteringaandp.com

The concentrations of Na⁺ and K⁺ on each side of the membrane are different.

The Na⁺ concentration is higher outside the cell.

The K⁺ concentration is higher inside the cell.

Na⁺-K⁺ pumps maintain the concentration gradients of Na⁺ and K⁺ across the membrane.

The permeabilities of Na⁺ and K⁺ across the membrane are different. In the next three panels, we will build the resting membrane potential step by step.

Suppose a cell has only K⁺ channels...

K⁺ loss through abundant leakage channels establishes a negative membrane potential. K⁺ flows down its large concentration gradient because the membrane is highly permeable to K⁺. As the positive K⁺ ions leak out, the negative voltage that develops on the membrane interior counteracts the concentration gradient, pulling K⁺ back into the cell. At -90 mV, the concentration and electrical gradients for K⁺ are balanced.

Now, let's add some Na⁺ channels to our cell...

Na⁺ entry through leakage channels reduces the negative membrane potential slightly. Na⁺ flows down its large concentration gradient, but the membrane is only slightly permeable to Na⁺. As a result, Na⁺ entering the cell makes the membrane potential slightly less negative than if there were only K⁺ channels.

Finally, let's add a pump to compensate for leaking ions.

Na⁺-K⁺ pumps maintain the concentration gradients, resulting in the resting membrane potential. A cell at rest is like a leaky boat that is constantly leaking K⁺ out and Na⁺ in through open channels. The "bailing pump" for this boat is the **Na⁺-K⁺ pump**, which counteracts the leaks by transporting Na⁺ out and K⁺ in.

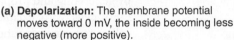

Depolarizing stimulus

(a) Depolarization: The membrane potential moves toward 0 mV, the inside becoming less negative (more positive).

Hyperpolarizing stimulus

(b) Hyperpolarization: The membrane potential increases, the inside becoming more negative.

Figure 11.9 Depolarization and hyperpolarization of the membrane. The resting membrane potential is approximately −70 mV (inside negative) in neurons.

Neurons use changes in their membrane potential as communication signals to receive, integrate, and send information. A change in membrane potential can be produced by (1) anything that alters ion concentrations on the two sides of the membrane, or (2) anything that changes membrane permeability to any ion. However, only permeability changes (changes in the number of open channels) are important for transferring information.

Changes in membrane potential can produce two types of signals:

- *Graded potentials*, which are usually incoming signals operating over short distances

- *Action potentials*, which are long-distance signals of axons

The terms *depolarization* and *hyperpolarization* describe changes in membrane potential *relative to resting membrane potential*. It is important to clearly understand these terms.

Depolarization is a decrease in membrane potential: The inside of the membrane becomes *less negative* (moves closer to zero) than the resting potential. For instance, a change in resting potential from −70 mV to −65 mV is a depolarization (Figure 11.9a). By convention, depolarization also includes events in which the membrane potential reverses and moves above zero to become positive.

Hyperpolarization is an increase in membrane potential: The inside of the membrane becomes *more negative* (moves further from zero) than the resting potential. For example, a change from −70 mV to −75 mV is hyperpolarization (Figure 11.9b). As we will describe shortly, depolarization increases the probability of producing nerve impulses, whereas hyperpolarization reduces this probability.

Graded Potentials

Graded potentials are short-lived, localized changes in membrane potential that can be either depolarizations or hyperpolarizations. These changes cause current flows that decrease in magnitude with distance. Graded potentials are called "graded" because their magnitude varies directly with stimulus strength. The stronger the stimulus, the more the voltage changes and the farther the current flows.

Graded potentials are triggered by some change (a stimulus) in the neuron's environment that opens gated ion channels. Graded potentials are given different names, depending on where they occur and the functions they perform.

- When the receptor of a sensory neuron is excited by some form of energy (heat, light, or other), the resulting graded potential is called a *receptor potential* or *generator potential*. We will consider these types of graded potentials in Chapter 13.

- When the stimulus is a neurotransmitter released by another neuron, the graded potential is called a *postsynaptic potential*, because the neurotransmitter is released into a fluid-filled gap called a synapse and influences the neuron beyond (post) the synapse.

Fluids inside and outside cells are fairly good conductors, and current, carried by ions, flows through these fluids whenever voltage changes. Suppose a stimulus depolarizes a small area of a neuron's plasma membrane (Figure 11.10a). Current (ions) flows on both sides of the membrane between the depolarized (active) membrane area and the adjacent polarized (resting) areas. Positive ions migrate toward more negative areas (the direction of cation movement is the direction of current flow),

(a) Depolarization: A small patch of the membrane (red area) depolarizes.

(b) Depolarization spreads: Opposite charges attract each other. This creates local currents (black arrows) that depolarize adjacent membrane areas, spreading the wave of depolarization.

(c) Membrane potential decays with distance: Because current is lost through the "leaky" plasma membrane, the voltage declines with distance from the stimulus (the voltage is *decremental*). Consequently, graded potentials are short-distance signals.

Figure 11.10 The spread and decay of a graded potential.

and negative ions simultaneously move toward more positive areas (Figure 11.10b).

For our patch of plasma membrane, positive ions (mostly K⁺) inside the cell move away from the depolarized area and accumulate on the neighboring membrane areas, where they neutralize negative ions. Meanwhile, positive ions on the outer membrane face move toward the region of reversed membrane polarity (the depolarized region), which is momentarily less positive. As these positive ions move, their "places" on the membrane become occupied by negative ions (such as Cl⁻ and HCO₃⁻), sort of like ionic musical chairs. In this way, at regions abutting the depolarized region, the inside becomes less negative and the outside becomes less positive. In other words, the

depolarization spreads as the neighboring membrane "patch" is, in turn, depolarized.

As just explained, the flow of current to adjacent membrane areas changes the membrane potential there as well. However, the plasma membrane is permeable like a leaky water hose, and most of the charge is quickly lost through leakage channels. Consequently, the current dies out within a few millimeters of its origin and is said to be *decremental* (Figure 11.10c).

Because the current dissipates quickly and decays (declines) with increasing distance from the site of initial depolarization, graded potentials can act as signals only over very short distances. Nonetheless, they are essential in initiating action potentials, the long-distance signals.

Action Potentials (AP)

The principal way neurons send signals over long distances is by generating and propagating (transmitting) action potentials. Only cells with *excitable membranes*—neurons and muscle cells—can generate action potentials.

An **action potential (AP)** is a brief reversal of membrane potential with a total amplitude (change in voltage) of about 100 mV (from −70 mV to +30 mV). Depolarization is followed by repolarization and often a short period of hyperpolarization. The whole event is over in a few milliseconds. Unlike graded potentials, action potentials do not decay with distance.

The events of action potential generation and transmission are identical in skeletal muscle cells and neurons. As we have noted, in a neuron, an AP is also called a **nerve impulse**, and is typically generated *only in axons*. A neuron generates a nerve impulse only when adequately stimulated. The stimulus changes the permeability of the neuron's membrane by opening specific voltage-gated channels on the axon.

These channels open and close in response to changes in the membrane potential. They are activated by local currents (graded potentials) that spread toward the axon along the dendritic and cell body membranes.

In many neurons, the transition from local graded potential to long-distance action potential takes place at the axon hillock. In sensory neurons, the action potential is generated by the peripheral (axonal) process just proximal to the receptor region. However, for simplicity, we will just use the term axon in our discussion. We'll look first at the generation of an action potential and then at its propagation.

Generation of an Action Potential *Focus on an Action Potential* (Figure 11.11) on pp. 402–403 describes how an action potential is generated. Let's start with a neuron in the resting (polarized) state.

① **Resting state: All gated Na⁺ and K⁺ channels are closed.** Only the leakage channels are open, maintaining resting membrane potential. Each Na⁺ channel has two gates: a voltage-sensitive *activation gate* that is closed at rest and responds to depolarization by opening, and an *inactivation gate* that blocks the channel once it is open. Thus, *depolarization opens and then inactivates sodium channels.*

Both gates must be open in order for Na$^+$ to enter, but the closing of *either* gate effectively closes the channel. By contrast, each active potassium channel has a single voltage-sensitive gate that is closed in the resting state and opens slowly in response to depolarization.

② **Depolarization: Na$^+$ channels open.** As local currents depolarize the axon membrane, the voltage-gated sodium channels open and Na$^+$ rushes into the cell. This influx of positive charge depolarizes that local patch of membrane further, opening more Na$^+$ channels so the cell interior becomes progressively less negative.

When depolarization at the stimulation site reaches a certain critical level called **threshold** (often between -55 and -50 mV), depolarization becomes self-generating, urged on by positive feedback. That is, after being initiated by the stimulus, depolarization is driven by the ionic currents created by Na$^+$ influx. As more Na$^+$ enters, the membrane depolarizes further and opens still more channels until all Na$^+$ channels are open. At this point, Na$^+$ permeability is about 1000 times greater than in a resting neuron. As a result, the membrane potential becomes less and less negative and then overshoots to about $+30$ mV as Na$^+$ rushes in along its electrochemical gradient. This rapid depolarization and polarity reversal produces the sharp upward *spike* of the action potential (Figure 11.11).

Earlier, we stated that membrane potential depends on membrane permeability, but here we say that membrane permeability depends on membrane potential. Can both statements be true? Yes, because these two relationships establish a *positive feedback cycle*: Increasing Na$^+$ permeability due to increased channel openings leads to greater depolarization, which increases Na$^+$ permeability, and so on. This explosive positive feedback cycle is responsible for the rising (depolarizing) phase of an action potential—it puts the "action" in the action potential.

③ **Repolarization: Na$^+$ channels are inactivating, and K$^+$ channels open.** The explosively rising phase of the action potential persists for only about 1 ms. It is self-limiting because the slow inactivation gates of the Na$^+$ channels begin to close at this point. As a result, the membrane permeability to Na$^+$ declines to resting levels, and the net influx of Na$^+$ stops completely. Consequently, the AP spike stops rising.

As Na$^+$ entry declines, the slow voltage-gated K$^+$ channels open and K$^+$ rushes out of the cell, following its electrochemical gradient. This restores the internal negativity of the resting neuron, an event called **repolarization**. Both the abrupt decline in Na$^+$ permeability and the increased permeability to K$^+$ contribute to repolarization.

④ **Hyperpolarization: Some K$^+$ channels remain open, and Na$^+$ channels reset.** The period of increased K$^+$ permeability typically lasts longer than needed to restore the resting state. As a result of the excessive K$^+$ efflux before the potassium channels close, a hyperpolarization is seen on the AP curve as a slight dip following the spike. Also at this point, the Na$^+$ channels begin to reset to their original position by changing shape to reopen their inactivation gates and close their activation gates.

Repolarization restores resting electrical conditions, but it does *not* restore resting ionic conditions. After repolarization, the *sodium-potassium pump* redistributes the ions. While it might appear that tremendous numbers of Na$^+$ and K$^+$ ions change places during an action potential, this is not the case. Only small amounts of sodium and potassium cross the membrane. (The Na$^+$ influx required to reach threshold produces only a 0.012% change in intracellular Na$^+$ concentration.) These small ionic changes are quickly corrected because an axon membrane has thousands of Na$^+$-K$^+$ pumps.

Threshold and the All-or-None Phenomenon Not all local depolarization events produce APs. The depolarization must reach threshold values if an axon is to "fire." What determines the *threshold point*?

One explanation is that threshold is the membrane potential at which the outward current created by K$^+$ movement is exactly equal to the inward current created by Na$^+$ movement. Threshold is typically reached when the membrane has been depolarized by 15 to 20 mV from the resting value. This depolarization status represents an unstable equilibrium state. If one more Na$^+$ enters, further depolarization occurs, opening more Na$^+$ channels and allowing more Na$^+$ to enter. If, on the other hand, one more K$^+$ leaves, the membrane potential is driven away from threshold, Na$^+$ channels close, and K$^+$ continues to diffuse outward until the potential returns to its resting value.

Recall that local depolarizations are graded potentials and their magnitude increases when stimuli become more intense. Brief weak stimuli (*subthreshold stimuli*) produce subthreshold depolarizations that are not translated into nerve impulses. On the other hand, stronger *threshold stimuli* produce depolarizing currents that push the membrane potential toward and beyond the threshold voltage. As a result, Na$^+$ permeability rises to such an extent that entering sodium ions "swamp" (exceed) the outward movement of K$^+$, establishing the positive feedback cycle and generating an AP.

The critical factor here is the total amount of current that flows through the membrane during a stimulus (electrical charge $\times$ time). Strong stimuli depolarize the membrane to threshold quickly. Weaker stimuli must be applied for longer periods to provide the crucial amount of current flow. Very weak stimuli do not trigger an AP because the local current flows they produce are so slight that they dissipate long before threshold is reached.

An AP is an **all-or-none phenomenon**: It either happens completely or doesn't happen at all. We can compare the generation of an AP to lighting a match under a small dry twig. The changes occurring where the twig is heated are analogous to the change in membrane permeability that initially allows more Na$^+$ to enter the cell. When that part of the twig becomes hot enough (when enough Na$^+$ enters the cell), it reaches the flash point (threshold) and the flame consumes the entire twig, even if you blow out the match. Similarly, the AP is generated and propagated whether or not the stimulus continues. But if you blow out the match before the twig reaches the threshold temperature, ignition will not take

(Text continues on p. 404.)

Figure 11.11 The action potential (AP) is a brief change in membrane potential in a "patch" of membrane that is depolarized by local currents.

A&P Flix *Available at www.masteringaandp.com*

The big picture
This graph shows how voltage changes over time at a given point inside an axon during the course of an action potential.

(1) Resting state. No ions move through voltage-gated channels.

(2) Depolarization is caused by Na⁺ flowing into the cell.

(3) Repolarization is caused by K⁺ flowing out of the cell.

(4) Hyperpolarization is caused by K⁺ continuing to leave the cell.

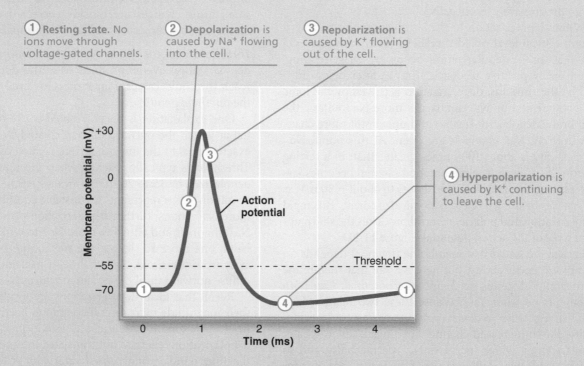

The AP is caused by permeability changes in the plasma membrane:
Relative membrane permeability tells you the relative number of ion channels that are open for each ion. Remember that open ion channels make the plasma membrane permeable to those ions.

Na⁺ channels open, causing depolarization.

K⁺ channels open later, over a longer time interval, causing repolarization and hyperpolarization.

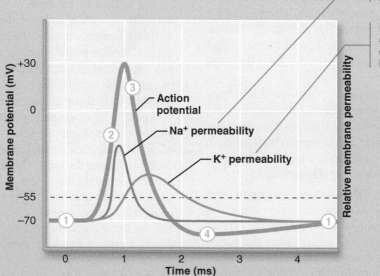

The key players

Voltage-gated Na⁺ channels have two gates and alternate between three different states.

Outside cell   Na⁺

Inside cell   Activation gate

Closed at the resting state, so no Na⁺ enters the cell through them

Na⁺

Opened by depolarization, allowing Na⁺ to enter the cell

Na⁺

Inactivation gate

Inactivated— channels automatically blocked by inactivation gates soon after they open

Voltage-gated K⁺ channels have one gate and two states.

Outside cell

Inside cell   K⁺

Closed at the resting state, so no K⁺ exits the cell through them

K⁺

Opened by depolarization, after a delay, allowing K⁺ to exit the cell

The events

Each step corresponds to one part of the AP graph.

Sodium channel   Na⁺   Potassium channel

Activation gates

Inactivation gate

K⁺

① **Resting state:** All gated Na⁺ and K⁺ channels are closed.

Na⁺

K⁺

④ **Hyperpolarization:** Some K⁺ channels remain open, and Na⁺ channels reset.

Na⁺

K⁺

② **Depolarization:** Na⁺ channels open.

Na⁺

K⁺

③ **Repolarization:** Na⁺ channels are inactivating, and K⁺ channels open.

(a) Time = 0 ms. Action potential has not yet reached the recording electrode.

(b) Time = 2 ms. Action potential peak reaches the recording electrode.

(c) Time = 4 ms. Action potential peak has passed the recording electrode. Membrane at the recording electrode is still hyperpolarized.

 Resting potential

 Peak of action potential

Hyperpolarization

Figure 11.12 Propagation of an action potential (AP). Recordings at three successive times as an AP propagates along an axon (from left to right). The arrows show the direction of local current flow generated by the movement of positive ions. This current brings the resting membrane at the leading edge of the AP to threshold, propagating the AP forward.

place. Likewise, if the number of Na$^+$ ions entering the cell is too low to achieve threshold, no AP will occur.

Propagation of an Action Potential If it is to serve as the neuron's signaling device, an AP must be **propagated** along the axon's entire length. As we have seen, the AP is generated by the influx of Na$^+$ through a given area of the membrane. This influx establishes local currents that depolarize adjacent membrane areas in the forward direction (away from the origin of the nerve impulse), which opens voltage-gated channels and triggers an action potential there **(Figure 11.12)**.

Because the area where the AP originated has just generated an AP, the sodium channels in that area are inactivated and no new AP is generated there. For this reason, the AP propagates away from its point of origin. (If an *isolated* axon is stimulated by an electrode, the nerve impulse will move away from the point of stimulus in all directions along the membrane.) In the body, APs are initiated at one end of the axon and conducted away from that point toward the axon's terminals. Once initiated, an AP is *self-propagating* and continues along the axon at a constant velocity—something like a domino effect.

Following depolarization, each segment of axon membrane repolarizes, which restores the resting membrane potential in that region. Because these electrical changes also set up local currents, the repolarization wave chases the depolarization wave down the length of the axon.

The propagation process we have just described occurs on nonmyelinated axons. On p. 405, we will describe propagation along myelinated axons.

Although the phrase *conduction of a nerve impulse* is commonly used, nerve impulses are not really conducted in the same way that an insulated wire conducts current. In fact, neurons are fairly poor conductors, and as noted earlier, local current flows decline with distance because the charges leak through the membrane. The expression *propagation of a nerve impulse* is more accurate, because the AP is *regenerated anew* at each membrane patch, and every subsequent AP is identical to the one that was generated initially.

Coding for Stimulus Intensity Once generated, all APs are independent of stimulus strength, and all APs are alike. So how can the CNS determine whether a particular stimulus is intense or weak—information it needs to initiate an appropriate response?

The answer is really quite simple: Strong stimuli generate nerve impulses more *often* in a given time interval than do weak stimuli. Stimulus intensity is coded for by the number of impulses per second—that is, by the *frequency of action potentials*—rather than by increases in the strength (amplitude) of the individual APs **(Figure 11.13)**.

Refractory Periods When a patch of neuron membrane is generating an AP and its voltage-gated sodium channels are open, the neuron cannot respond to another stimulus, no matter how

Figure 11.13 Relationship between stimulus strength and action potential frequency. APs are shown as vertical lines in the upper trace. The lower trace shows the intensity of the applied stimulus. A subthreshold stimulus does not generate an AP, but once threshold voltage is reached, the stronger the stimulus, the more frequently APs are generated.

Figure 11.14 Absolute and relative refractory periods in an AP.

strong. This period, from the opening of the Na⁺ channels until the Na⁺ channels begin to reset to their original resting state, is called the **absolute refractory period** (Figure 11.14). It ensures that each AP is a separate, *all-or-none event* and enforces one-way transmission of the AP.

The **relative refractory period** is the interval following the absolute refractory period. During the relative refractory period, most Na⁺ channels have returned to their resting state, some K⁺ channels are still open, and repolarization is occurring. During this time, the axon's threshold for AP generation is substantially elevated. A stimulus that would normally generate an AP is no longer sufficient, but an exceptionally strong stimulus can reopen the Na⁺ channels that have already returned to their resting state and generate another AP. Strong stimuli trigger more frequent APs by intruding into the relative refractory period.

Conduction Velocity How fast do APs travel? Conduction velocities of neurons vary widely. Nerve fibers that transmit impulses most rapidly (100 m/s or more) are found in neural pathways where speed is essential, such as those that mediate postural reflexes. Axons that conduct impulses more slowly typically serve internal organs (the gut, glands, blood vessels), where slower responses are not a handicap. The rate of impulse propagation depends largely on two factors:

■ **Axon diameter.** As a rule, the larger the axon's diameter, the faster it conducts impulses. Larger axons conduct more rapidly because they offer less resistance to the flow of local currents, bringing adjacent areas of the membrane to threshold more quickly.

■ **Degree of myelination.** Action potentials propagate because they are regenerated by voltage-gated channels in the membrane **(Figure 11.15a, b)**. In **continuous conduction**, AP propagation involving nonmyelinated axons, these channels

are immediately adjacent to each other. Continuous conduction is relatively slow.

The presence of a myelin sheath dramatically increases the rate of AP propagation. By acting as an insulator, myelin prevents almost all charge from leaking from the axon and allows the membrane voltage to change more rapidly. Current can pass through the membrane of a myelinated axon *only* at the myelin sheath gaps, where there is no myelin sheath and the axon is bare. Nearly all the voltage-gated Na⁺ channels are concentrated in these gaps.

When an AP is generated in a myelinated fiber, the local depolarizing current does not dissipate through the adjacent membrane regions, which are nonexcitable. Instead, the current is maintained and moves rapidly to the next myelin sheath gap, a distance of approximately 1 mm, where it triggers another AP. Consequently, APs are triggered only at the gaps, a type of conduction called **saltatory conduction** (*saltare* = to leap) because the electrical signal appears to jump from gap to gap along the axon (Figure 11.15c). Saltatory conduction is about 30 times faster than continuous conduction.

Homeostatic Imbalance 11.2

The importance of myelin to nerve transmission is painfully clear to people with demyelinating diseases such as **multiple sclerosis (MS)**. This autoimmune disease affects mostly young adults.

Multiple sclerosis gradually destroys myelin sheaths in the CNS, reducing them to nonfunctional hardened lesions called *scleroses*. The loss of myelin (a result of the immune system's attack on myelin proteins) shunts and short-circuits the current so that successive gaps are excited more and more slowly, and eventually impulse conduction ceases. However, the axons themselves are not damaged and growing numbers of Na⁺ channels appear spontaneously in the demyelinated fibers. This

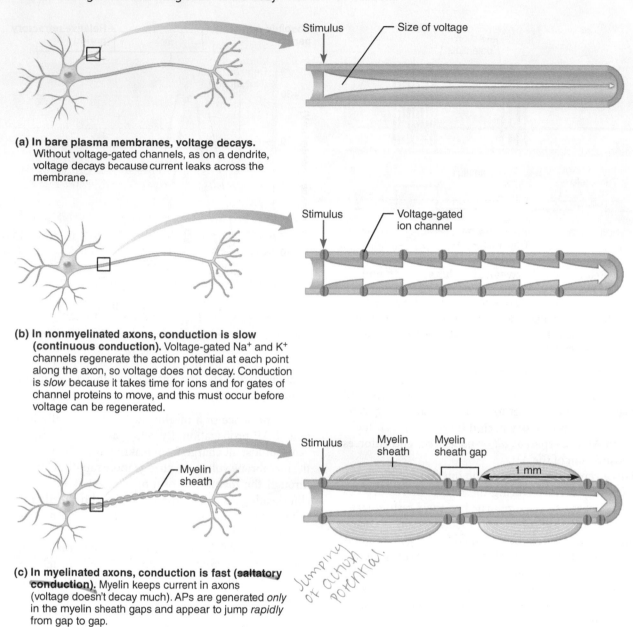

(a) In bare plasma membranes, voltage decays. Without voltage-gated channels, as on a dendrite, voltage decays because current leaks across the membrane.

(b) In nonmyelinated axons, conduction is slow (continuous conduction). Voltage-gated Na⁺ and K⁺ channels regenerate the action potential at each point along the axon, so voltage does not decay. Conduction is *slow* because it takes time for ions and for gates of channel proteins to move, and this must occur before voltage can be regenerated.

(c) In myelinated axons, conduction is fast (saltatory conduction). Myelin keeps current in axons (voltage doesn't decay much). APs are generated *only* in the myelin sheath gaps and appear to jump *rapidly* from gap to gap.

Figure 11.15 Action potential propagation in nonmyelinated and myelinated axons.

may account for the remarkably variable cycles of remission (symptom-free periods) and relapse (disability) typical of this disease. Common symptoms are visual disturbances (including blindness), problems controlling muscles (weakness, clumsiness, and ultimately paralysis), speech disturbances, and urinary incontinence.

The advent of drugs that modify the immune system's activity (such as interferons, glatiramer, and fingolimod) will continue to improve the lives of people with MS. These drugs seem to hold symptoms at bay, reducing complications and disability. Recent studies show that high blood levels of vitamin D reduce the risk of developing MS in the first place. ✚

Nerve fibers may be classified according to diameter, degree of myelination, and conduction speed.

- **Group A fibers** are mostly somatic sensory and motor fibers serving the skin, skeletal muscles, and joints. They have the largest diameter and thick myelin sheaths, and conduct impulses at speeds ranging up to 150 m/s (over 300 miles per hour).

- **Group B fibers**, lightly myelinated fibers of intermediate diameter, transmit impulses at an average rate of 15 m/s (about 30 mi/h).

- **Group C fibers** have the smallest diameter and are nonmyelinated. Consequently, they are incapable of saltatory conduction and conduct impulses at a leisurely pace—1 m/s (2 mi/h) or less.

The B and C fiber groups include autonomic nervous system motor fibers serving the visceral organs; visceral sensory fibers; and the smaller somatic sensory fibers transmitting sensory impulses from the skin (such as pain and small touch fibers).

What happens when an action potential arrives at the end of a neuron's axon? That is the subject of the next section.

Homeostatic Imbalance 11.3

A number of chemical and physical factors impair impulse propagation. Local anesthetics like those used by your dentist act by blocking voltage-gated Na^+ channels. As we have seen, no Na^+ entry—no AP.

Cold and continuous pressure interrupt blood circulation, hindering the delivery of oxygen and nutrients to neuron processes and impairing their ability to conduct impulses. For example, your fingers get numb when you hold an ice cube for more than a few seconds, and your foot "goes to sleep" when you sit on it. When you remove the cold object or pressure, impulses are transmitted again, leading to an unpleasant prickly feeling. ✚

☑ Check Your Understanding

11. Which is bigger, a graded potential or an action potential? Which travels farthest? Which initiates the other?

12. An action potential does not get smaller as it propagates along an axon. Why not?

13. Why does a myelinated axon conduct action potentials faster than a nonmyelinated axon?

14. If an axon receives two stimuli close together in time, only one AP occurs. Why?

For answers, see Appendix H.

The Synapse

✓ Define synapse. Distinguish between electrical and chemical synapses by structure and by the way they transmit information.

The operation of the nervous system depends on the flow of information through chains of neurons functionally connected by synapses. A **synapse** (sin′aps), from the Greek *syn*, "to clasp or join," is a junction that mediates information transfer from one neuron to the next or from a neuron to an effector cell—it's where the action is.

Synapses between the axon endings of one neuron and the dendrites of other neurons are **axodendritic synapses**. Those between axon endings of one neuron and cell bodies (soma) of other neurons are **axosomatic synapses** (Figure 11.16). Less common (and far less understood) are synapses between axons (*axoaxonal*), between dendrites (*dendrodendritic*), or between cell bodies and dendrites (*somatodendritic*).

The neuron conducting impulses toward the synapse is the **presynaptic neuron**, and the neuron transmitting the electrical signal away from the synapse is the **postsynaptic neuron.** At a given synapse, the presynaptic neuron sends the information, and the postsynaptic neuron receives the information. As you might anticipate, most neurons function as both presynaptic and postsynaptic neurons. Neurons have anywhere from 1000

to 10,000 axon terminals making synapses and are stimulated by an equal number of other neurons. Outside the central nervous system, the postsynaptic cell may be either another neuron or an effector cell (a muscle cell or gland cell).

Now let's look at the two varieties of synapses: *electrical* and *chemical*.

Electrical Synapses

Electrical synapses, the less common variety, consist of gap junctions like those found between certain other body cells. They contain protein channels, called connexons, that intimately connect the cytoplasm of adjacent neurons and allow ions and small molecules to flow directly from one neuron to the next. These neurons are *electrically coupled*, and transmission across these synapses is very rapid. Depending on the nature of the synapse, communication may be unidirectional or bidirectional.

A key feature of electrical synapses between neurons is that they provide a simple means of synchronizing the activity of all interconnected neurons. In adults, electrical synapses are found in regions of the brain responsible for certain stereotyped movements, such as the normal jerky movements of the eyes. They also occur in axoaxonal synapses in the hippocampus, a brain region intimately involved in emotions and memory.

Electrical synapses are far more abundant in embryonic nervous tissue, where they permit exchange of guiding cues during early neuronal development so that neurons can connect properly with one another. As the nervous system develops, chemical synapses replace some electrical synapses. Gap junctions also exist between glial cells of the CNS.

Chemical Synapses

In contrast to electrical synapses, which are specialized to allow the flow of ions between neurons, **chemical synapses** are specialized to allow the release and reception of chemical neurotransmitters. A typical chemical synapse is made up of two parts:

■ A knoblike *axon terminal* of the presynaptic neuron, which contains many tiny, membrane-bounded sacs called **synaptic vesicles**, each containing thousands of neurotransmitter molecules

■ A neurotransmitter *receptor region* on the postsynaptic neuron's membrane, usually located on a dendrite or the cell body

Although close to each other, presynaptic and postsynaptic membranes are always separated by the **synaptic cleft**, a fluid-filled space approximately 30 to 50 nm (about one-millionth of an inch) wide. (If an electrical synapse with its gap junctions is like the threshold of a doorway between neurons, a synaptic cleft is like a good-size lake between them.)

Because the current from the presynaptic membrane dissipates in the fluid-filled cleft, chemical synapses effectively prevent a nerve impulse from being *directly* transmitted from one neuron to another. Instead, an impulse is transmitted via a *chemical event* that depends on the release, diffusion, and receptor binding of neurotransmitter molecules and results in *unidirectional communication* between neurons.

(a)

Axodendritic synapses

Dendrites

Axosomatic synapses

Cell body

Axoaxonal synapses

Axon

Axon

Axosomatic synapses

Cell body (soma) of postsynaptic neuron

(b)

Figure 11.16 Synapses. (a) Axodendritic, axosomatic, and axoaxonal synapses. **(b)** Scanning electron micrograph of incoming fibers at axosomatic synapses (5300×).

In short, transmission of nerve impulses along an axon and across electrical synapses is a purely electrical event. However, chemical synapses convert the electrical signals to chemical signals (neurotransmitters) that travel across the synapse to the postsynaptic cells, where they are converted back into electrical signals.

Information Transfer Across Chemical Synapses

In Chapter 9 we introduced a specialized chemical synapse called a neuromuscular junction (p. 286). The chain of events that occurs at the neuromuscular junction is simply one example of the general process that we will discuss next and show in *Focus on a Chemical Synapse* **(Figure 11.17)**:

1. **Action potential arrives at axon terminal.** Neurotransmission at a chemical synapse begins with the arrival of an action potential at the presynaptic axon terminal.

2. **Voltage-gated Ca^{2+} channels open and Ca^{2+} enters the axon terminal.** Depolarization of the membrane by the action potential opens not only Na^+ channels but voltage-gated Ca^{2+} channels as well. During the brief time the Ca^{2+} channels are open, Ca^{2+} floods down its electrochemical gradient from the extracellular fluid into the terminal.

3. **Ca^{2+} entry causes synaptic vesicles to release neurotransmitter by exocytosis.** The surge of Ca^{2+} into the axon terminal acts as an intracellular messenger. A Ca^{2+}-sensing protein (*synaptotagmin*) binds Ca^{2+} and interacts with the SNARE proteins that control membrane fusion (see Figure 3.14). As a result, synaptic vesicles fuse with the axon membrane and empty their contents by exocytosis into the synaptic cleft. Ca^{2+} is then quickly removed from the terminal—either taken up into the mitochondria or ejected from the neuron by an active Ca^{2+} pump.

Figure 11.17 Chemical synapses transmit signals from one neuron to another using neurotransmitters.

A&P Flix   *Available at www.masteringaandp.com*

Presynaptic neuron

Postsynaptic neuron

Presynaptic neuron

① Action potential arrives at axon terminal.

② Voltage-gated Ca²⁺ channels open and Ca²⁺ enters the axon terminal.

Ca^{2+}

Ca^{2+}

Mitochondrion

Ca^{2+}

Ca^{2+}

Synaptic cleft

③ Ca²⁺ entry causes synaptic vesicles to release neurotransmitter by exocytosis

Axon terminal

Synaptic vesicles

④ Neurotransmitter diffuses across the synaptic cleft and binds to specific receptors on the postsynaptic membrane.

Postsynaptic neuron

Ion movement

Graded potential

Enzymatic degradation

Reuptake

Diffusion away from synapse

⑤ Binding of neurotransmitter opens ion channels, resulting in graded potentials.

⑥ Neurotransmitter effects are terminated by reuptake through transport proteins, enzymatic degradation, or diffusion away from the synapse.

For each nerve impulse reaching the presynaptic terminal, many vesicles (perhaps 300) empty into the synaptic cleft. The higher the impulse frequency (that is, the more intense the stimulus), the greater the number of synaptic vesicles that fuse and spill their contents, and the greater the effect on the postsynaptic cell.

④ **Neurotransmitter diffuses across the synaptic cleft and binds to specific receptors on the postsynaptic membrane.**

⑤ **Binding of neurotransmitter opens ion channels, creating graded potentials.** When neurotransmitter binds to the receptor protein, this receptor changes its three-dimensional shape. This change in turn opens ion channels and creates graded potentials. Postsynaptic membranes often contain receptor proteins and ion channels packaged together as chemically gated ion channels. Depending on the receptor protein to which the neurotransmitter binds and the type of channel the receptor controls, the postsynaptic neuron may be either excited or inhibited.

⑥ **Neurotransmitter effects are terminated.** The binding of a neurotransmitter to its receptor is reversible. As long as it is bound to a postsynaptic receptor, a neurotransmitter continues to affect membrane permeability and block reception of additional signals from presynaptic neurons. For this reason, some means of "wiping the postsynaptic slate clean" is necessary. The effects of neurotransmitters generally last a few milliseconds before being terminated in one of three ways, depending on the particular neurotransmitter:

- *Reuptake* by astrocytes or the presynaptic terminal, where the neurotransmitter is stored or destroyed by enzymes, as with norepinephrine

- *Degradation* by enzymes associated with the postsynaptic membrane or present in the synapse, as with acetylcholine

- *Diffusion* away from the synapse

Synaptic Delay

An impulse may travel at speeds of up to 150 m/s (300 mi/h) down an axon, but neural transmission across a chemical synapse is comparatively slow. It reflects the time required for neurotransmitter to be released, diffuse across the synaptic cleft, and bind to receptors. Typically, this **synaptic delay** lasts 0.3–5.0 ms, making transmission across the chemical synapse the *rate-limiting* (slowest) step of neural transmission. Synaptic delay helps explain why transmission along neural pathways involving only two or three neurons occurs rapidly, but transmission along multisynaptic pathways typical of higher mental functioning occurs much more slowly. However, in practical terms these differences are not noticeable.

☑ Check Your Understanding

15. What structure joins two neurons at an electrical synapse?
16. Events at a chemical synapse usually involve opening both voltage-gated ion channels and chemically gated ion channels. Where are these ion channels located and what causes each to open?

For answers, see Appendix H.

An EPSP is a local depolarization of the postsynaptic membrane that brings the neuron closer to AP threshold. Neurotransmitter binding opens chemically gated ion channels, allowing Na⁺ and K⁺ to pass through simultaneously.

(a) Excitatory postsynaptic potential (EPSP)

An IPSP is a local hyperpolarization of the postsynaptic membrane that drives the neuron away from AP threshold. Neurotransmitter binding opens K⁺ or Cl⁻ channels.

(b) Inhibitory postsynaptic potential (IPSP)

Figure 11.18 Postsynaptic potentials can be excitatory or inhibitory.

Postsynaptic Potentials and Synaptic Integration

✓ Distinguish between excitatory and inhibitory postsynaptic potentials.

✓ Describe how synaptic events are integrated and modified.

Many receptors on postsynaptic membranes at chemical synapses are specialized to open ion channels, in this way converting chemical signals to electrical signals. Unlike the voltage-gated ion channels responsible for APs, however, these chemically gated channels are relatively insensitive to changes in membrane potential. Consequently, channel opening at postsynaptic membranes cannot possibly become self-amplifying or self-generating. Instead, neurotransmitter receptors mediate graded potentials—local changes in membrane potential that are *graded* (vary in strength) according to the amount of neurotransmitter released and the time it remains in the area. **Table 11.2** compares graded potentials and action potentials.

Chemical synapses are either excitatory or inhibitory, depending on how they affect the membrane potential of the postsynaptic neuron.

Figure 11.19 Neural integration of EPSPs and IPSPs.

Excitatory Synapses and EPSPs

At excitatory synapses, neurotransmitter binding depolarizes the postsynaptic membrane. However, in contrast to what happens on axon membranes, *chemically gated* ion channels open on postsynaptic membranes (those of dendrites and neuronal cell bodies). Each channel allows Na^+ and K^+ to diffuse *simultaneously* through the membrane but in opposite directions.

Although this two-way cation flow may appear to be self-defeating when depolarization is the goal, remember that the electrochemical gradient for sodium is much steeper than that for potassium. As a result, Na^+ influx is greater than K^+ efflux, and *net* depolarization occurs.

If enough neurotransmitter binds, depolarization of the postsynaptic membrane can reach 0 mV, which is well above an axon's threshold (about -50 mV) for "firing off" an AP. However, unlike axons which have voltage-gated channels that make an AP possible, *postsynaptic membranes generally do not generate APs*. The dramatic polarity reversal seen in axons never occurs in membranes containing *only* chemically gated channels because the opposite movements of K^+ and Na^+ prevent excessive positive charge from accumulating inside the cell. For this reason, instead of APs, local graded depolarization events called **excitatory postsynaptic potentials (EPSPs)** occur at excitatory postsynaptic membranes **(Figure 11.18a)**.

Each EPSP lasts a few milliseconds and then the membrane returns to its resting potential. The only function of EPSPs is to help trigger an AP distally at the axon hillock of the postsynaptic neuron. Although currents created by individual EPSPs decline

with distance, they can and often do spread all the way to the axon hillock. If currents reaching the hillock are strong enough to depolarize the axon to threshold, axonal voltage-gated channels open and an AP is generated.

Inhibitory Synapses and IPSPs

Binding of neurotransmitters at inhibitory synapses *reduces* a postsynaptic neuron's ability to generate an AP. Most inhibitory neurotransmitters hyperpolarize the postsynaptic membrane by making the membrane more permeable to K^+ or Cl^-. Sodium ion permeability is not affected.

If K^+ channels open, K^+ moves out of the cell. If Cl^- channels open, Cl^- moves in. In either case, the charge on the inner face of the membrane becomes more negative. As the membrane potential increases and is driven farther from the axon's threshold, the postsynaptic neuron becomes *less and less likely* to "fire," and larger depolarizing currents are required to induce an AP. Hyperpolarizing changes in potential are called **inhibitory postsynaptic potentials (IPSPs)** (Figure 11.18b).

Integration and Modification of Synaptic Events

Summation by the Postsynaptic Neuron A single EPSP cannot induce an AP in the postsynaptic neuron **(Figure 11.19a)**. But if thousands of excitatory axon terminals fire on the same postsynaptic membrane, or if a small number of terminals deliver impulses rapidly, the probability of reaching threshold soars. EPSPs can add together, or **summate**, to influence the

Table 11.2	Comparison of Graded Potentials and Action Potentials	
	GRADED POTENTIAL (GP)	**ACTION POTENTIAL (AP)**
Location of event	Cell body and dendrites, typically	Axon hillock and axon

Distance traveled	Short distance—typically within cell body to axon hillock (0.1–1.0 mm)	Long distance—from trigger zone at axon hillock through entire length of axon (a few mm to over a meter)
Amplitude (size)	Various sizes (graded); decays with distance	Always the same size (all-or-none); does not decay with distance
Stimulus for opening ion channels	Chemical (neurotransmitter) or sensory stimulus (e.g., light, pressure, temperature)	Voltage (depolarization, triggered by GP reaching threshold)
Positive feedback cycle	Absent	Present
Repolarization	Voltage independent; occurs when stimulus is no longer present	Voltage regulated; occurs when Na⁺ channels inactivate and K⁺ channels open
Summation	Stimulus responses can summate to increase amplitude of graded potential	Does not occur; an all-or-none phenomenon

Temporal: increased frequency of stimuli

Spatial: stimuli from multiple sources

activity of a postsynaptic neuron. Otherwise, nerve impulses would never result.

Two types of summation occur: temporal and spatial.

■ **Temporal summation** (*temporal* = time) occurs when one or more presynaptic neurons transmit impulses in rapid-fire order and bursts of neurotransmitter are released in quick succession. The first impulse produces a small EPSP, and before it dissipates, successive impulses trigger more EPSPs. These summate, causing the postsynaptic membrane to depolarize much more than it would from a single EPSP (Figure 11.19b).

■ **Spatial summation** occurs when the postsynaptic neuron is stimulated simultaneously by a large number of terminals from one or, more commonly, many presynaptic neurons. Huge numbers of its receptors bind neurotransmitter and simultaneously initiate EPSPs, which summate and dramatically enhance depolarization (Figure 11.19c).

Although we have focused on EPSPs here, IPSPs also summate, both temporally and spatially. In this case, the postsynaptic neuron is inhibited to a greater degree.

Most neurons receive both excitatory and inhibitory inputs from thousands of other neurons. Additionally, the same axon may form different types of synapses (in terms

Table 11.2	(continued)			
	GRADED POTENTIAL (GP)			**ACTION POTENTIAL (AP)**
	POSTSYNAPTIC POTENTIAL (A TYPE OF GP)			
	EXCITATORY (EPSP)	**INHIBITORY (IPSP)**		
Function	Short-distance signaling; depolarization that spreads to axon hillock; moves membrane potential *toward* threshold for generating an AP	Short-distance signaling; hyperpolarization that spreads to axon hillock; moves membrane potential *away* from threshold for generating an AP		Long-distance signaling; constitutes the nerve impulse
Initial effect of stimulus	Opens chemically gated channels that allow simultaneous Na^+ and K^+ fluxes	Opens chemically gated K^+ or Cl^- channels		Opens voltage-gated channels; first opens Na^+ channels, then K^+ channels
Peak membrane potential	Depolarizes; moves toward 0 mV	Hyperpolarizes; moves toward −90 mV		+30 to +50 mV

of biochemical and electrical characteristics) with different types of target neurons. How is all this conflicting information sorted out?

Each neuron's axon hillock keeps a running account of all the signals it receives. Not only do EPSPs summate and IPSPs summate, but also EPSPs summate with IPSPs. If the stimulatory effects of EPSPs dominate the membrane potential enough to reach threshold, the neuron will fire. If summation yields only subthreshold depolarization or hyperpolarization, the neuron fails to generate an AP (Figure 11.19d).

However, partially depolarized neurons are **facilitated**—that is, more easily excited by successive depolarization events— because they are already near threshold. Thus, axon hillock membranes function as *neural integrators*, and their potential at any time reflects the sum of all incoming neural information.

Because EPSPs and IPSPs are graded potentials that decay the farther they spread, the most effective synapses are those closest to the axon hillock. Specifically, inhibitory synapses are most effective when located between the site of excitatory inputs

and the site of action potential generation (the axon hillock). Accordingly, inhibitory synapses occur most often on the cell body and excitatory synapses occur most often on the dendrites (Figure 11.19d).

Synaptic Potentiation Repeated or continuous use of a synapse (even for short periods) enhances the presynaptic neuron's ability to excite the postsynaptic neuron, producing larger-than-expected EPSPs. This phenomenon is called **synaptic potentiation**. The presynaptic terminals at such synapses contain relatively high Ca^{2+} concentrations, a condition that triggers the release of more neurotransmitter, which in turn produces larger EPSPs.

Synaptic potentiation also brings about Ca^{2+} influx via dendritic spines into the postsynaptic neuron. Brief high-frequency stimulation partially depolarizes the postsynaptic membrane. This partial depolarization causes certain chemically gated channels called *NMDA (N-methyl-D-aspartate) receptors* to allow Ca^{2+} to enter, something that only happens when the membrane is depolarized. As Ca^{2+} floods into the cell, it activates certain kinase enzymes that promote changes resulting in more effective responses to subsequent stimuli.

In some neurons, APs generated at the axon hillock propagate back up into the dendrites. This current flow may alter the effectiveness of synapses by opening voltage-gated Ca^{2+} channels, again allowing Ca^{2+} into the dendrites and promoting synaptic potentiation.

Synaptic potentiation can be viewed as a learning process that increases the efficiency of neurotransmission along a particular pathway. Indeed, the hippocampus of the brain, which plays a special role in memory and learning, exhibits an important type of synaptic plasticity called *long-term potentiation* (LTP).

Presynaptic Inhibition   Events at the presynaptic membrane can also influence postsynaptic activity. **Presynaptic inhibition** occurs when the release of excitatory neurotransmitter by one neuron is inhibited by the activity of another neuron via an axoaxonal synapse. More than one mechanism is involved, but the end result is that less neurotransmitter is released and bound, forming smaller EPSPs.

Notice that this is the opposite of what we see with synaptic potentiation. In contrast to postsynaptic inhibition by IPSPs, which decreases the excitability of the postsynaptic neuron, presynaptic inhibition decreases the excitatory stimulation of the postsynaptic neuron. In this way, presynaptic inhibition is like a functional synaptic "pruning."

☑ Check Your Understanding

17. Which ions flow through chemically gated channels to produce IPSPs? EPSPs?
18. What is the difference between temporal summation and spatial summation?

For answers, see Appendix H.

Neurotransmitters and Their Receptors

✓ Define neurotransmitter and name several classes of neurotransmitters.

Neurotransmitters, along with electrical signals, are the "language" of the nervous system—the means by which each neuron communicates with others to process and send messages to the rest of the body. Sleep, thought, rage, hunger, memory, movement, and even your smile reflect the "doings" of these versatile molecules. Most factors that affect synaptic transmission do so by enhancing or inhibiting neurotransmitter release or destruction, or by blocking their binding to receptors. Just as speech defects may hinder interpersonal communication, anything that interferes with neurotransmitter activity may short-circuit the brain's "conversations" or internal talk (see *A Closer Look* on pp. 418–419).

At present, more than 50 neurotransmitters or neurotransmitter candidates have been identified. Although some neurons produce and release only one kind of neurotransmitter, most make two or more and may release any one or all of them

at a given time. It appears that in most cases, different neurotransmitters are released at different stimulation frequencies, a restriction that avoids producing a jumble of nonsense messages. However, co-release of two neurotransmitters from the same vesicles has been documented. The coexistence of more than one neurotransmitter in a single neuron makes it possible for that cell to exert several influences rather than one discrete effect.

Neurotransmitters are classified chemically and functionally. Table 11.3 provides a detailed overview of neurotransmitters, and we describe some of them here. No one expects you to memorize this table at this point, but it will be a handy reference for you to look back at when you read about neurotransmitters in subsequent chapters.

Classification of Neurotransmitters by Chemical Structure

Neurotransmitters fall into several chemical classes based on molecular structure.

Acetylcholine

Acetylcholine (ACh) (as″ĕ-til-ko′lēn), the first neurotransmitter identified, is still the best understood because it is released at neuromuscular junctions, which are much easier to study than synapses buried in the CNS.

ACh is synthesized from acetic acid (as acetyl CoA) and choline by the enzyme *choline acetyltransferase*, then transported into synaptic vesicles for later release. Once released by the presynaptic terminal, ACh binds briefly to the postsynaptic receptors. Then it is released and degraded to acetic acid and choline by the enzyme **acetylcholinesterase (AChE)**, located in the synaptic cleft and on postsynaptic membranes. Presynaptic terminals recapture the released choline and reuse it to synthesize more ACh.

ACh is released by all neurons that stimulate skeletal muscles and by some neurons of the autonomic nervous system. ACh-releasing neurons are also found in the CNS.

Biogenic Amines

The **biogenic amines** (bi″o-jen′ik) include the **catecholamines** (kat″ĕ-kol′ah-mēnz), such as dopamine, norepinephrine (NE), and epinephrine, and the **indolamines**, which include serotonin and histamine. *Dopamine* and *NE* are synthesized from the amino acid tyrosine in a common pathway consisting of several steps. The epinephrine-releasing cells of the brain and adrenal medulla use the same pathway. *Serotonin* is synthesized from the amino acid tryptophan. *Histamine* is synthesized from the amino acid histidine.

Biogenic amine neurotransmitters are broadly distributed in the brain, where they play a role in emotional behavior and help regulate the biological clock. Additionally, some motor neurons of the autonomic nervous system release catecholamines, particularly NE. Imbalances of these neurotransmitters are associated with mental illness. For example, overactive dopamine signaling occurs in schizophrenia. Additionally, certain psychoactive

Table 11.3 Neurotransmitters and Neuromodulators

NEUROTRANSMITTER	FUNCTIONAL CLASSES	SITES WHERE SECRETED	COMMENTS
Acetylcholine (ACh)			
▪ At *nicotinic ACh receptors* (on skeletal muscles, autonomic ganglia, and in the CNS) ▪ At *muscarinic ACh receptors* (on visceral effectors and in the CNS)	Excitatory Direct action Excitatory or inhibitory depending on subtype of muscarinic receptor Indirect action via second messengers	CNS: widespread throughout cerebral cortex, hippocampus, and brain stem PNS: all neuromuscular junctions with skeletal muscle; some autonomic motor endings (all preganglionic and parasympathetic postganglionic fibers)	Effects prolonged when AChE blocked by nerve gas or organophosphate insecticides (malathion), leading to tetanic muscle spasms. Release inhibited by botulinum toxin; binding to nicotinic ACh receptors inhibited by curare (a muscle paralytic agent) and to muscarinic ACh receptors by atropine. ACh levels decrease in certain brain areas in Alzheimer's disease; nicotinic ACh receptors destroyed in myasthenia gravis. Binding of nicotine to nicotinic receptors in the brain enhances dopamine release, which may account for the behavioral effects of nicotine in smokers.
Biogenic Amines			
Norepinephrine (NE)	Excitatory or inhibitory depending on receptor type bound Indirect action via second messengers	CNS: brain stem, particularly in the locus coeruleus of the midbrain; limbic system; some areas of cerebral cortex PNS: main neurotransmitter of postganglionic neurons in the sympathetic nervous system	A "feel good" neurotransmitter. Release enhanced by amphetamines; removal from synapse blocked by tricyclic antidepressants [amitriptyline (Elavil) and others] and cocaine. Brain levels reduced by reserpine (an antihypertensive drug), leading to depression.
Dopamine	Excitatory or inhibitory depending on the receptor type bound Indirect action via second messengers	CNS: substantia nigra of midbrain; hypothalamus; the principal neurotransmitter of indirect motor pathways PNS: some sympathetic ganglia	A "feel good" neurotransmitter. Release enhanced by L-dopa and amphetamines; reuptake blocked by cocaine. Deficient in Parkinson's disease; dopamine neurotransmission increases in schizophrenia.
Serotonin (5-HT)	Mainly inhibitory Indirect action via second messengers; direct action at 5-HT$_3$ receptors	CNS: brain stem, especially midbrain; hypothalamus; limbic system; cerebellum; pineal gland; spinal cord	Plays a role in sleep, appetite, nausea, migraine headaches, and regulating mood. Drugs that block its uptake [fluoxetine (Prozac)] relieve anxiety and depression. Activity blocked by LSD and enhanced by ecstasy (MDMA).
Histamine	Excitatory or inhibitory depending on receptor type bound Indirect action via second messengers	CNS: hypothalamus	Involved in wakefulness, appetite control, and learning and memory. Also a paracrine (local signal) released from stomach (causes acid secretion) and connective tissue mast cells (mediates inflammation and vasodilation).
Amino Acids			
GABA (γ-aminobutyric acid)	Generally inhibitory Direct and indirect actions via second messengers	CNS: cerebral cortex, hypothalamus, Purkinje cells of cerebellum, spinal cord, granule cells of olfactory bulb, retina	Principal inhibitory neurotransmitter in the brain; important in presynaptic inhibition at axoaxonal synapses. Inhibitory effects augmented by alcohol, antianxiety drugs of the benzodiazepine class (e.g., Valium), and barbiturates, impairing motor coordination. Substances that block its synthesis, release, or action induce convulsions.

Table 11.3 Neurotransmitters and Neuromodulators *(continued)*

NEUROTRANSMITTER	FUNCTIONAL CLASSES	SITES WHERE SECRETED	COMMENTS
Amino Acids, continued			
Glutamate	Generally excitatory Direct action	CNS: spinal cord; widespread in brain where it represents the major excitatory neurotransmitter	Important in learning and memory. The "stroke neurotransmitter": excessive release produces excitotoxicity—neurons literally stimulated to death; most commonly caused by ischemia (oxygen deprivation, usually due to a blocked blood vessel).
Glycine	Generally inhibitory Direct action	CNS: spinal cord and brain stem, retina	Principal inhibitory neurotransmitter of the spinal cord. Strychnine blocks glycine receptors, resulting in uncontrolled convulsions and respiratory arrest.
Peptides			
Endorphins, e.g., beta endorphin, dynorphin, enkephalins	Generally inhibitory Indirect action via second messengers	CNS: widely distributed in brain; hypothalamus; limbic system; pituitary; spinal cord	Natural opiates; inhibit pain by inhibiting substance P. Effects mimicked by morphine, heroin, and methadone.
Tachykinins: substance P, neurokinin A (NKA)	Excitatory Indirect action via second messengers	CNS: basal nuclei, midbrain, hypothalamus, cerebral cortex PNS: certain sensory neurons of dorsal root ganglia (pain afferents), enteric neurons	Substance P mediates pain transmission in the PNS. In the CNS, tachykinins are involved in respiratory and cardiovascular controls and in mood.
Somatostatin	Generally inhibitory Indirect action via second messengers	CNS: hypothalamus, septum, basal nuclei, hippocampus, cerebral cortex Pancreas	Often released with GABA. A gut-brain peptide. Inhibits growth hormone release.
Cholecystokinin (CCK)	Generally excitatory Indirect action via second messengers	Throughout CNS Small intestine	Involved in anxiety, pain, memory. A gut-brain peptide hormone. Inhibits appetite.
Purines			
ATP	Excitatory or inhibitory depending on receptor type bound Direct and indirect actions via second messengers	CNS: basal nuclei, induces Ca^{2+} wave propagation in astrocytes PNS: dorsal root ganglion neurons	ATP released by sensory neurons (as well as that released by injured cells) provokes pain sensation.
Adenosine	Generally inhibitory Indirect action via second messengers	Throughout CNS and PNS	Caffeine (coffee), theophylline (tea), and theobromine (chocolate) stimulate by blocking brain adenosine receptors. May be involved in sleep-wake cycle and terminating seizures. Dilates arterioles, increasing blood flow to heart and other tissues as needed.
Gases and Lipids			
Nitric oxide (NO)	Excitatory or inhibitory Indirect action via second messengers	CNS: brain, spinal cord PNS: adrenal gland; nerves to penis	Its release potentiates stroke damage. Some types of male impotence treated by enhancing NO action [e.g., with sildenafil (Viagra)].
Carbon monoxide (CO)	Excitatory or inhibitory Indirect action via second messengers	Brain and some neuromuscular and neuroglandular synapses	
Endocannabinoids, e.g., 2-arachidonoylglycerol, anandamide	Inhibitory Indirect action via second messengers	Throughout CNS	Involved in memory (as a retrograde messenger), appetite control, nausea and vomiting, neuronal development. Receptors activated by THC, the principal active ingredient of cannabis. Receptors also found on immune cells.

11

drugs (LSD and mescaline) can bind to biogenic amine receptors and induce hallucinations.

Amino Acids

It is difficult to prove a neurotransmitter role when the suspect is an amino acid, because amino acids occur in all cells of the body and are important in many biochemical reactions. The amino acids for which a neurotransmitter role is certain include **glutamate**, **aspartate**, **glycine**, and **gamma (γ)-aminobutyric acid (GABA)**, but there may be others.

Peptides

The **neuropeptides**, essentially strings of amino acids, include a broad spectrum of molecules with diverse effects. For example, a neuropeptide called **substance P** is an important mediator of pain signals. By contrast, **endorphins**, which include **beta endorphin**, **dynorphin**, and **enkephalins** (en-kef′ah-linz), act as natural opiates, reducing our perception of pain under stressful conditions. Enkephalin activity increases dramatically in pregnant women in labor. Endorphin release is enhanced when an athlete gets a so-called second wind and is probably responsible for the "runner's high." Additionally, some researchers claim that the placebo effect is due to endorphin release. These painkilling neurotransmitters remained undiscovered until investigators began to ask why morphine and other opiates reduce anxiety and pain, and found that these drugs attach to the same receptors that bind natural opiates, producing similar but stronger effects.

Some neuropeptides, known as **gut-brain peptides**, are also produced by nonneural body tissues and are widespread in the gastrointestinal tract. Examples include somatostatin and cholecystokinin (CCK).

Purines

Purines are nitrogen-containing chemicals (such as guanine and adenine) that are breakdown products of nucleic acids. **Adenosine triphosphate (ATP)**, the cell's universal form of energy, is now recognized as a major neurotransmitter (perhaps the most primitive one) in both the CNS and PNS. Like the receptors for glutamate and acetylcholine, certain receptors produce fast excitatory responses when ATP binds, while other ATP receptors trigger slow, second-messenger responses. Upon binding to receptors on astrocytes, ATP mediates Ca^{2+} influx.

In addition to the neurotransmitter action of extracellular ATP, **adenosine**, a part of ATP, also acts outside of cells on adenosine receptors. Adenosine is a potent inhibitor in the brain. Caffeine's well-known stimulatory effects result from blocking these adenosine receptors.

Gases and Lipids

Not so long ago, it would have been scientific suicide to suggest that small, short-lived, toxic gas molecules might be neurotransmitters. Nonetheless, the discovery of these unlikely messengers has opened up a new chapter in the story of neurotransmission.

Gasotransmitters These gases—the so-called "gasotransmitters" nitric oxide, carbon monoxide, and hydrogen sulfide—defy all the classical descriptions of neurotransmitters. Rather than being stored in vesicles and released by exocytosis, they are synthesized on demand and diffuse out of the cells that make them. Instead of attaching to surface receptors, they zoom through the plasma membrane of nearby cells to bind with particular intracellular receptors.

Both **nitric oxide (NO)** and **carbon monoxide (CO)** activate *guanylyl cyclase*, the enzyme that makes the second messenger *cyclic GMP*. NO and CO are found in different brain regions and appear to act in different pathways, but their mode of action is similar. NO participates in a variety of processes in the brain, including the formation of new memories by increasing the strength of certain synapses. In this process, neurotransmitter binding to the postsynaptic receptors indirectly activates *nitric oxide synthase* (*NOS*), the enzyme that makes NO. The newly synthesized NO diffuses out of the postsynaptic cell back to the presynaptic terminal, where it activates guanylyl cyclase. In this way NO is thought to act as a retrograde messenger that sends a signal to increase synaptic strength.

Excessive release of NO contributes to much of the brain damage seen in stroke patients (see p. 463). In the myenteric plexus of the intestine, NO causes intestinal smooth muscle to relax.

Less is known about **hydrogen sulfide (H_2S)**, the most recently discovered gasotransmitter. Unlike NO and CO, it appears to act directly on ion channels and other proteins to alter their function.

Endocannabinoids Just as there are natural opiate neurotransmitters in the brain, our brains make natural neurotransmitters, the **endocannabinoids** (en″do-kă-nă′bĭ-noids), that act at the same receptors as tetrahydrocannabinol (THC), the active ingredient in marijuana. Their receptors, the *cannabinoid receptors*, are the most common G protein–linked receptors in the brain.

Like the gasotransmitters, the endocannabinoids are lipid soluble and are synthesized on demand, rather than stored and released from vesicles. Endocannabinoids are formed by clipping the cell's own plasma membrane lipids. The newly synthesized endocannabinoids diffuse freely from the postsynaptic neuron to their receptors on presynaptic terminals where they act as a retrograde messenger to decrease neurotransmitter release. Like NO, they are thought to be involved in learning and memory. We are only beginning to understand the many other processes these neurotransmitters may be involved in, which include neuronal development, controlling appetite, and suppressing nausea.

Classification of Neurotransmitters by Function

In this text we can only sample the incredible diversity of functions that neurotransmitters mediate. We limit our discussion here to two broad ways of classifying neurotransmitters according to function, adding more details in subsequent chapters.

Pleasure Me, Pleasure Me!

Sex! Drugs! Rock 'n' roll! Eat, drink, and be merry! Why do we find these activities so compelling? Our brains are wired to **reward** us with **pleasure** when we engage in behavior that is necessary for our own and our species' **survival**. This reward system consists of dopamine-releasing neurons in areas of the brain called the *ventral tegmental area* (VTA), the *nucleus accumbens*, and the *amygdala*.

Our ability to "feel good" involves brain neurotransmitters in this reward system. For example, the ecstasy of romantic love may be just a brain bath of glutamate and norepinephrine, which act on the reward system to release dopamine.

Unfortunately, drugs of abuse can subvert this powerful system. The 1930s songwriter Cole Porter knew what he was talking about when he wrote "I get a kick out of you," because these neurotransmitters are chemical cousins of the amphetamines. People who use "crystal meth" (methamphetamine) artificially stimulate their brains to provide their highly addictive pleasure flush. However, their pleasure is short-lived, because when the brain is flooded with neurotransmitter-like chemicals from the outside, it makes less of its own (why bother?).

Cocaine, another reward system titillater, has been around since ancient times. Once a toy of the rich, its granular form is inhaled, or "snorted." The laws of supply and demand have now brought cheaper cocaine to the masses, notably "crack"—a cheaper, more potent, smokable form of cocaine. For $50 or so, a novice user can experience a rush of intense pleasure. But crack is treacherous

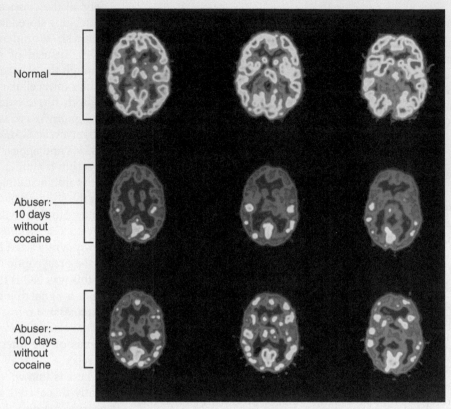

Normal

Abuser: 10 days without cocaine

Abuser: 100 days without cocaine

PET scans show that normal levels of brain activity (yellow and red) are depressed in cocaine users long after they stop using the drug.

and intensely addictive. It produces not only a higher high than the inhaled form of cocaine, but also a deeper crash that leaves the user desperate for more.

How does cocaine produce its effects? Basically, the drug stimulates the reward system and then "squeezes it dry." Cocaine produces its rush by hooking up to the dopamine reuptake transporter protein, blocking the reabsorption of dopamine. The neurotransmitter remains in the synapse and stimulates

the postsynaptic receptor cells again and again, allowing the body to feel its effects over a prolonged period. This sensation is accompanied by increases in heart rate, blood pressure, and sexual appetite.

As repeated doses of cocaine continue to block dopamine uptake, the body releases less and less dopamine and the reward system effectively goes dry. The cocaine user becomes anxious and, in a very real sense, unable to experience pleasure without the drug. The postsynaptic cells

---

The important idea to keep in mind is this: The function of a neurotransmitter is determined by the receptor to which it binds.

Effects: Excitatory Versus Inhibitory

Some neurotransmitters are excitatory (cause depolarization). Some are inhibitory (cause hyperpolarization). Others exert both effects, depending on the specific receptor types with which they interact.

For example, the amino acids GABA and glycine are usually inhibitory, whereas glutamate is typically excitatory (Table 11.3).

On the other hand, ACh and NE each bind to at least two receptor types that cause opposite effects. For example, acetylcholine is excitatory at neuromuscular junctions in skeletal muscle and inhibitory in cardiac muscle.

Actions: Direct Versus Indirect

Neurotransmitters that act *directly* are those that bind to and open ion channels. These neurotransmitters provoke rapid responses in postsynaptic cells by altering membrane potential. ACh and the amino acid neurotransmitters are typically direct-acting neurotransmitters.

become hypersensitive and sprout new receptors in a desperate effort to pick up dopamine signals. A vicious cycle of addiction begins: Cocaine is needed to experience pleasure, but using it suppresses dopamine release even more.

The dopamine effect alone is not enough to establish addiction. Another neurotransmitter, glutamate, which plays an important role in learning, is required to maintain addiction. Glutamate signaling seems to cause more permanent changes in the brain (synaptic potentiation) that lead to compulsive drug-seeking behaviors elicited by external cues. Take, for example, mice genetically engineered to lack a particular glutamate receptor (GluR5). These mice are perfectly willing to try cocaine but never become addicted. (Of course, no GluR5 means they're none too bright, either.)

Current thinking, then, is that the rush of pleasure on taking cocaine is due to dopamine. Glutamate, on the other hand, is thought to be responsible for the learning that makes true the perception "once an addict, always an addict." So strong is the combined dopamine and glutamate system that, even years later, certain settings can trigger intense cravings for the drug.

These out-of-control, desperate cravings are notoriously difficult to manage. Drug abusers call it "jonesing." Traditional antiaddiction drugs take so long to reduce the cravings that users commonly drop out of treatment programs.

How can we break this cycle of addiction? One way is to prevent cocaine from ever reaching the brain. Promising results have been obtained from a vaccine that prompts the immune system to bind cocaine molecules, preventing them from entering the brain. In a clinical trial, this vaccine dampened addicts' pleasurable responses to cocaine and reduced their use of the drug.

Another approach to breaking the addiction cycle is to even out the highs and lows experienced by the drug user by leveling out brain dopamine levels and keep the user from "crashing" so badly. Possibilities include using a much longer-acting inhibitor of dopamine reuptake or taking a drug that binds but only partially activates dopamine receptors.

A final approach to breaking the addiction cycle is to interrupt the learned reinforcement that brings on cravings. An effective ancient African folk remedy called ibogaine may do exactly this. However, ibogaine itself is too toxic for clinical use, as some unfortunate "underground" users have discovered. A close synthetic cousin, 18-methoxycoronaridine (18-MC) is much less toxic and promises to be effective against not only cocaine but also a number of other abused drugs. Future studies will show if it truly works.

The craving for drugs has made some addicts very creative home pharmacologists, willing to experiment with practically anything, no matter how toxic or dangerous, to get the "buzz" they need. A cheap mixture of cold medications, match heads, and iodine in acetone yields crystal meth—the highly addictive and once-again popular drug that wrecks people's lives and often explodes their home laboratories. Another creative mixture, with the street name of "ill face" or "illy," involves dipping marijuana in formaldehyde, drying and then smoking it. Other remarkable combinations are the "H-bomb" (ecstasy mixed with heroin), "A-bomb" (marijuana with heroin or opium), "sextasy" [ecstasy mixed with sildenafil (Viagra)], "octane" (PCP laced with gasoline), and "ozone" (marijuana, PCP, and crack in a cigarette).

Formaldehyde is known to cause cancer and gasoline damages the liver, but the real damage comes from the drugs themselves.

Take, for example, ecstasy, a drug that many of its users believe to be innocuous. In reality, ecstasy (MDMA) targets serotonin-releasing neurons. The "rush" of pleasure and energy that users feel is due to release of serotonin and other neurotransmitters. However, it damages and may destroy these neurons, causing the loss of verbal and spatial memory. Depression, sleeplessness, and memory problems may be permanent consequences—a steep price for a few moments of pleasure!

People who want pure, effective, and "safe" drugs of abuse don't get them on the street. They get them from doctors or "pill ladies" [female senior citizens who sell oxycodone (OxyContin), a powerful prescription opioid with effects similar to heroin]. Even people who would never dream of taking illicit drugs can be caught in the addictive cycle of prescription drugs. Prescribed legitimately to relieve severe pain, oxycodone is meant to be swallowed whole. Abusers crush the tablets and snort the powder or dissolve it in water and inject the solution. Abuse of oxycodone and its chemical cousin hydrocodone is spreading rapidly, doubling over the past four years. Medical examiners across North America report soaring rates of oxycodone-related emergency room visits and deaths. Indeed, emergency room visits caused by abuse of prescription or over-the-counter drugs now equal those for illicit drugs.

The brain, with its complex biochemistry, always circumvents attempts to keep it in a euphoric haze. Perhaps this means that pleasure must be transient by nature, experienced only against a background of its absence.

Neurotransmitters that act *indirectly* promote broader, longer-lasting effects by acting through intracellular *second-messenger* molecules, typically via G protein pathways (see Figure 3.16). In this way their action is similar to that of many hormones. The biogenic amines, neuropeptides, and dissolved gases are indirect neurotransmitters.

Neuromodulator is a term used to describe a chemical messenger released by a neuron that does not directly cause EPSPs or IPSPs but instead affects the strength of synaptic transmission. A neuromodulator may act presynaptically to influence the synthesis, release, degradation, or reuptake of neurotransmitter.

Alternatively, a neuromodulator may act postsynaptically by altering the sensitivity of the postsynaptic membrane to neurotransmitter.

Receptors for neuromodulators are not necessarily found at a synapse. Instead, a neuromodulator may be released from one cell to act at many cells in its vicinity, similar to paracrines (chemical messengers that act locally and are quickly destroyed). The distinction between neurotransmitters and neuromodulators is fuzzy, but chemical messengers such as NO, adenosine, and a number of neuropeptides are often referred to as neuromodulators.

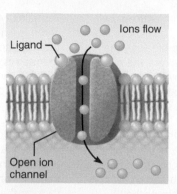

Figure 11.20 Direct neurotransmitter receptor mechanism: Channel-linked receptors. These chemically gated ion channels promote rapid synaptic transmission. In this case, ligand binding directly opens the channel.

Neurotransmitter Receptors

In Chapter 3, we introduced the various receptors involved in cell signaling. Now we are ready to pick up that thread again as we examine the action of receptors that bind neurotransmitters. For the most part, neurotransmitter receptors are either channel-linked receptors, which mediate fast synaptic transmission, or G protein–linked receptors, which oversee slow synaptic responses.

Recall from Chapter 3 that G protein signaling mechanisms are like a molecular relay race.

Channel-Linked Receptors: Mechanism of Action

Channel-linked receptors (*ionotropic receptors*) are ligand-gated ion channels that mediate direct neurotransmitter action. They are composed of several protein subunits in a "rosette" around a central pore. As the ligand binds to one (or more) receptor subunits, the proteins change shape. This event opens the central channel and allows ions to pass **(Figure 11.20)**. As a result, the membrane potential of the target cell changes.

Channel-linked receptors are always located precisely opposite sites of neurotransmitter release, and their ion channels open instantly upon ligand binding and remain open 1 ms or less while the ligand is bound. At excitatory receptor sites (nicotinic ACh channels and receptors for glutamate, aspartate, and ATP), the channel-linked receptors are cation channels that allow small cations (Na^+, K^+, Ca^{2+}) to pass, but Na^+ entry contributes most to membrane depolarization. Channel-linked receptors that respond to GABA and glycine, and allow Cl^- to pass, mediate fast inhibition (hyperpolarization).

G Protein–Linked Receptors: Mechanism of Action

Unlike responses to neurotransmitter binding at channel-linked receptors, which are immediate, simple, and brief, the activity mediated by **G protein–linked receptors** is indirect, complex, slow (hundreds of milliseconds or more), and often prolonged—ideal as a basis for some types of learning. Receptors in this class

Figure 11.21 Indirect neurotransmitter receptor mechanism: G protein–linked receptors. These receptors cause the formation of intracellular second messengers—cyclic AMP (cAMP) in this example—that indirectly bring about the cell's response.

are transmembrane protein complexes. They include muscarinic ACh receptors and those that bind the biogenic amines and neuropeptides. Because their effects tend to bring about widespread metabolic changes, G protein–linked receptors are commonly called *metabotropic receptors*.

When a neurotransmitter binds to a G protein–linked receptor, the G protein is activated (**Figure 11.21**). (To orient yourself, refer back to the simpler G protein explanation in Figure 3.16 on p. 82.) Activated G proteins typically work by controlling the production of second messengers such as **cyclic AMP**, **cyclic GMP**, **diacylglycerol**, or **Ca^{2+}**.

These second messengers, in turn, act as go-betweens to regulate (open or close) ion channels or activate kinase enzymes that initiate a cascade of enzymatic reactions in the target cells. Some second messengers modify (activate or inactivate) other proteins, including channel proteins, by attaching phosphate groups to them. Others interact with nuclear proteins that activate genes and induce synthesis of new proteins in the target cell.

☑ Check Your Understanding

19. ACh excites skeletal muscle and yet it inhibits heart muscle. How can this be?
20. Why is cyclic AMP called a second messenger?

For answers, see Appendix H.

Basic Concepts of Neural Integration

Until now, we have concentrated on the activities of individual neurons. However, neurons function in groups, and each group contributes to still broader neural functions. In this way, the organization of the nervous system is hierarchical.

Any time you have a large number of *anything*—people included—there must be *integration*. In other words, the parts must be fused into a smoothly operating whole.

In this section, we move to the first level of **neural integration**: *neuronal pools* and their patterns of communicating with other parts of the nervous system. In Chapter 12 we discuss the highest levels of neural integration—how we think and remember. With this understanding of the basics and of the larger picture, in Chapter 13 we examine how sensory inputs interface with motor activity.

Organization of Neurons: Neuronal Pools

✓ Describe common patterns of neuronal organization and processing.

The billions of neurons in the CNS are organized into **neuronal pools**. These functional groups of neurons integrate incoming information received from receptors or different neuronal pools and then forward the processed information to other destinations.

In a simple type of neuronal pool (**Figure 11.22**), one incoming presynaptic fiber branches profusely as it enters the pool and then synapses with several different neurons in the pool. When the incoming fiber is excited, it will excite some postsynaptic neurons and facilitate others. Neurons most likely

Figure 11.22 Simple neuronal pool. Postsynaptic neurons in the discharge zone receive more synapses and are more likely to discharge (generate APs). Postsynaptic neurons in the facilitated zone receive fewer synapses and are facilitated (brought closer to threshold).

to generate impulses are those closely associated with the incoming fiber, because they receive the bulk of the synaptic contacts. Those neurons are in the *discharge zone* of the pool.

Neurons farther from the center are not usually excited to threshold, but they are facilitated and can easily be brought to threshold by stimuli from another source. For this reason, the periphery of the pool is the *facilitated zone*. Keep in mind, however, that our figure is a gross oversimplification. Most neuronal pools consist of thousands of neurons and include inhibitory as well as excitatory neurons.

Types of Circuits

Individual neurons in a neuronal pool both send and receive information, and synaptic contacts may cause either excitation or inhibition. The patterns of synaptic connections in neuronal pools, called **circuits**, determine the pool's functional capabilities. **Figure 11.23** describes four basic circuit patterns and their properties: diverging, converging, reverberating, and parallel after-discharge circuits.

Patterns of Neural Processing

✓ Distinguish between serial and parallel processing.

Input processing is both *serial* and *parallel*. In serial processing, the input travels along one pathway to a specific destination. In parallel processing, the input travels along several different pathways to be integrated in different CNS regions. Each mode has unique advantages, but as an information processor, the brain derives its power from its ability to process in parallel.

Serial Processing

In **serial processing**, the whole system works in a predictable all-or-nothing manner. One neuron stimulates the next, which stimulates the next, and so on, eventually causing a specific, anticipated response. The most clear-cut examples of serial processing are spinal reflexes, but straight-through sensory

11

(a) Diverging circuit
• One input, many outputs
• An *amplifying* circuit
• **Example:** A single neuron in the brain can activate 100 or more motor neurons in the spinal cord and thousands of skeletal muscle fibers

(b) Converging circuit
• Many inputs, one output
• A *concentrating* circuit
• **Example:** Different sensory stimuli can all elicit the same memory

(c) Reverberating circuit
• Signal travels through a chain of neurons, each feeding back to previous neurons
• An *oscillating* circuit
• Controls rhythmic activity
• **Example:** Involved in breathing, sleep-wake cycle, and repetitive motor activities such as walking

(d) Parallel after-discharge circuit
• Signal stimulates neurons arranged in parallel arrays that eventually converge on a single output cell
• Impulses reach output cell at different times, causing a burst of impulses called an *after-discharge*
• **Example:** May be involved in exacting mental processes such as mathematical calculations

Figure 11.23 Types of circuits in neuronal pools.

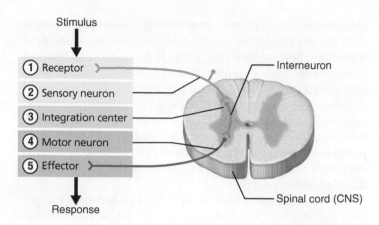

Figure 11.24 A simple reflex arc. Receptors detect a change in the internal or external environment that elicits a rapid stereotyped response. Effectors are muscles or glands.

pathways from receptors to the brain are also examples. Because reflexes are the functional units of the nervous system, it is important that you understand them early on.

Reflexes are rapid, automatic responses to stimuli, in which a particular stimulus always causes the same response. Reflex activity, which produces the simplest behaviors, is stereotyped and dependable. For example, if you touch a hot object you jerk your hand away, and an object approaching your eye triggers a blink. Reflexes occur over neural pathways called **reflex arcs** that have five essential components—receptor, sensory neuron, CNS integration center, motor neuron, and effector (**Figure 11.24**).

Parallel Processing

In **parallel processing**, inputs are segregated into many pathways, and different parts of the neural circuitry deal simultaneously with the information delivered by each pathway. For example, smelling a pickle (the input) may cause you to remember picking cucumbers on a farm; or it may remind you that you don't like pickles or that you must buy some at the market; or perhaps it will call to mind *all* these thoughts. For each person, parallel processing triggers unique pathways. The same stimulus—pickle smell, in our example—promotes many responses beyond simple awareness of the smell. Parallel processing is not repetitious because the circuits do different things with the information, and each pathway or "channel" is decoded in relation to all the others to produce a total picture.

Think, for example, about what happens when you step on something sharp while walking barefoot. The serially processed withdrawal reflex causes you to remove your foot immediately from the sharp object (painful stimulus). At the same time, pain and pressure impulses are speeding up to your brain along parallel pathways that allow you to decide whether to simply rub the hurt spot to soothe it or seek first aid.

Parallel processing is extremely important for higher-level mental functioning—for putting the parts together to understand the whole. For example, you can recognize a dollar bill in a split second. This task takes a serial-based computer a fairly long time, but your recognition is rapid because you use parallel processing. A single neuron sends information along several pathways instead of just one, so you process a large amount of information much more quickly.

☑ Check Your Understanding

21. Which types of neural circuits would give a prolonged output after a single input?
22. What pattern of neural processing occurs when your finger accidentally touches a hot grill? What is this response called?
23. What pattern of neural processing occurs when we smell freshly baked apple pie and remember Thanksgiving at our grandparents' house, the odor of freshly cooked turkey, sitting by the fire, and other such memories?

For answers, see Appendix H.

Developmental Aspects of Neurons

✓ Describe how neurons develop and form synapses.

We cover the nervous system in several chapters, so we limit our attention here to the development of neurons. Let's begin with two questions, How do neurons originate? and How do they mature?

The nervous system originates from a dorsal *neural tube* and the *neural crest*, formed from surface ectoderm (see Figure 12.33 ②, ③, p. 475). The neural tube, whose walls begin as a layer of *neuroepithelial* cells, becomes the CNS. The neuroepithelial cells then begin a three-phase process of differentiation, which occurs largely in the second month of development:

1. They *proliferate* to produce the appropriate number of cells needed for nervous system development.
2. The potential neurons, **neuroblasts**, become amitotic and *migrate* externally into their characteristic positions.
3. The neuroblasts sprout axons to *connect with* their functional targets and in so doing become neurons.

How does a neuroblast's growing axon "know" where to go—and once it gets there, where to make the proper connection? The growth of an axon toward an appropriate target requires multiple steps and is guided by multiple signals.

The growing tip of an axon, called a **growth cone**, is a prickly, fanlike structure that gives the axon the ability to interact with its environment (**Figure 11.25**). Extracellular and cell surface adhesion proteins such as laminin, integrin, and *nerve cell adhesion molecule* (*N-CAM*) provide anchor points for the growth cone, saying, "It's okay to grow here." *Neurotropins* are chemicals that signal to the growth cone "come this way" (netrin) or "go away" (ephrin, slit) or "stop here" (semaphorin). Throughout this growth and development, neurotrophic factors such as *nerve growth factor* (*NGF*) must be present to keep the neuroblast alive.

Failure of any of these guiding signals results in catastrophic developmental problems. For example, lack of N-CAM action causes developing neural tissue to fall into a tangled, spaghetti-like mass and hopelessly impairs neural function.

The growth cone gropes along like an amoeba, with oozing processes called *filopodia* which detect the guiding signals in the

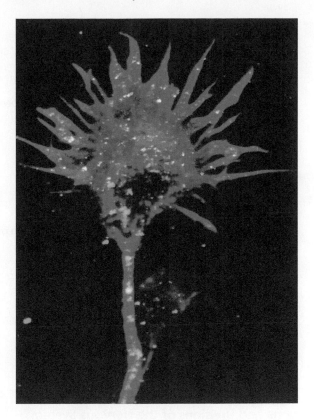

Figure 11.25 A neuronal growth cone. Fluorescent stains show the locations of cannabinoid receptors (green), tubulin (blue), and actin (pink) in this photomicrograph (1400×).

surrounding environment. Receptors for these signals generate various second messengers that cause the filopodia to move by rearranging their actin protein cores.

Once the axon reaches its target area, it must select the right site on the target cell to form a synapse. Special cell adhesion molecules couple the presynaptic and postsynaptic membranes together and generate intracellular signals that recruit vesicles containing preformed synaptic components. This results in the rapid formation of a synapse. In the brain and spinal cord, astrocytes provide both physical support and the cholesterol essential for constructing synapses. Both dendrites and astrocytes are active partners in the process of synapse formation. In the presence of thrombospondin released by astrocytes, dendrites actually reach out and grasp migrating axons, and synapses begin sprouting.

If neurons fail to make appropriate or functional synaptic contacts, they die. Besides cell death resulting from unsuccessful synapse formation, *apoptosis* (programmed cell death) is also a normal part of the developmental process. Of the neurons formed during the embryonic period, perhaps two-thirds die before we are born or shortly thereafter. Those that remain constitute most of our neural endowment for life.

The generally amitotic nature of neurons is important because their activity depends on the synapses they've formed, and if neurons were to divide, their connections might be hopelessly disrupted. This aside, there *do* appear to be some special neuronal populations where stem cells are found and new neurons can be formed—notably olfactory neurons and some cells of the hippocampus, a brain region involved in learning and memory.

☑ **Check Your Understanding**

24. What is the name of the growing tip of an axon that "sniffs out" where to go during development? What is the general name for the chemicals that tell it where to go?

For answers, see Appendix H.

In this chapter, we have examined how the amazingly complex neurons, via electrical and chemical signals, serve the body in a variety of ways. Some serve as "lookouts," others process information for immediate use or for future reference, and still others stimulate the body's muscles and glands into activity. With this background, we are ready to study the most sophisticated mass of neural tissue in the entire body—the brain (and its continuation, the spinal cord), the focus of Chapter 12.

Chapter Summary

 For more chapter study tools, go to the Study Area of MasteringA&P at **www.masteringaandp.com**. There you will find:

- Interactive Physiology **iP**
- A&PFlix **A&PFlix**
- Practice Anatomy Lab **PAL**
- PhysioEx **PEx**
- Videos, Practice Quizzes and Tests, MP3 Tutor Sessions, Case Studies, and much more!

Functions and Divisions of the Nervous System (p. 387)

1. The nervous system bears a major responsibility for maintaining body homeostasis. It monitors, integrates, and responds to information in the environment.
2. The nervous system is divided anatomically into the central nervous system (brain and spinal cord) and the peripheral nervous system (mainly cranial and spinal nerves).
3. The major functional divisions of the PNS are the sensory (afferent) division, which conveys impulses to the CNS, and the motor (efferent) division, which conveys impulses from the CNS.
4. The efferent division includes the somatic (voluntary) system, which serves skeletal muscles, and the autonomic (involuntary) system, which innervates smooth and cardiac muscle and glands.

Histology of Nervous Tissue (pp. 387–395)

Neuroglia (pp. 388–390)

1. Neuroglia (supporting cells) segregate and insulate neurons and assist neurons in various other ways.
2. CNS neuroglia include astrocytes, microglial cells, ependymal cells, and oligodendrocytes. PNS neuroglia include Schwann cells and satellite cells.

Neurons (pp. 390–395)

3. Neurons have a cell body and cytoplasmic processes called axons and dendrites.
4. A bundle of nerve fibers is called a tract in the CNS and a nerve in the PNS. A collection of cell bodies is called a nucleus in the CNS and a ganglion in the PNS.
5. The cell body is the biosynthetic (and receptive) center of the neuron. Except for those found in ganglia, cell bodies are found in the CNS.
6. Most neurons have many dendrites, receptive processes that conduct signals from other neurons toward the nerve cell body. With few exceptions, all neurons have one axon, which generates and conducts nerve impulses away from the nerve cell body. Axon terminals release neurotransmitter.

7. Bidirectional transport along axons uses ATP-dependent motor proteins "walking" along microtubule tracks. It moves vesicles, mitochondria, and cytosolic proteins toward the axon terminals and conducts substances destined for degradation back to the cell body.
8. Large nerve fibers (axons) are myelinated. The myelin sheath is formed in the PNS by Schwann cells and in the CNS by oligodendrocytes. The myelin sheath gaps are also called nodes of Ranvier. Nonmyelinated fibers are surrounded by supporting cells, but the membrane-wrapping process does not occur.
9. Anatomically, neurons are classified according to the number of processes issuing from the cell body as multipolar, bipolar, or unipolar.
10. Functionally, neurons are classified according to the direction of nerve impulse conduction. Sensory neurons conduct impulses toward the CNS, motor neurons conduct away from the CNS, and interneurons (association neurons) lie between sensory and motor neurons in the neural pathways.

iP Nervous System I; Topic: Anatomy Review, pp. 1–12.

Membrane Potentials (pp. 395–407)

Basic Principles of Electricity (pp. 395–397)

1. The measure of the potential energy of separated electrical charges is called voltage (V) or potential. Current (I) is the flow of electrical charge from one point to another. Resistance (R) is hindrance to current flow. Ohm's law gives the relationship among these: $I = V/R$.
2. In the body, ions provide the electrical charges; cellular plasma membranes provide resistance to ion flow. The membranes contain leakage channels (nongated, always open) and gated channels.

iP Nervous System I; Topic: Ion Channels, pp. 1–10.

The Resting Membrane Potential (p. 397)

3. A resting neuron exhibits a resting membrane potential, which is −70 mV (inside negative). It is due both to differences in sodium and potassium ion concentrations inside and outside the cell and to differences in permeability of the membrane to these ions.
4. The ionic concentration differences result from the operation of the sodium-potassium pump, which ejects 3 Na^+ from the cell for each 2 K^+ transported in.

iP Nervous System I; Topic: The Membrane Potential, pp. 1–16.

Membrane Potentials That Act as Signals (pp. 397–407)

5. Depolarization is a reduction in membrane potential (inside becomes less negative); hyperpolarization is an increase in membrane potential (inside becomes more negative).
6. Graded potentials are small, brief, local changes in membrane potential that act as short-distance signals. The current produced dissipates with distance.

11

7. An action potential (AP), or nerve impulse, is a large, but brief, depolarization signal (and polarity reversal) that underlies long-distance neural communication. It is an all-or-none phenomenon.

8. In the AP graph, an AP begins and ends at resting membrane potential. Depolarization to approximately $+30$ mV (inside positive) is caused by Na^+ influx. Depolarization ends when Na^+ channels inactivate. Repolarization and hyperpolarization are caused by K^+ efflux.

9. If threshold is reached, an AP is generated. If not, depolarization remains local.

10. In nerve impulse propagation, each AP provides the depolarizing stimulus for triggering an AP in the next membrane patch. Regions that have just generated APs are refractory; for this reason, the nerve impulse propagates in one direction only.

11. APs are independent of stimulus strength: Strong stimuli cause APs to be generated more frequently but not with greater amplitude.

12. During the absolute refractory period, a neuron cannot respond to another stimulus because it is already generating an AP. During the relative refractory period, the neuron's threshold is elevated because repolarization is ongoing.

13. In nonmyelinated fibers, APs are produced in a wave all along the axon, that is, by continuous conduction. In myelinated fibers, APs are generated only at myelin sheath gaps and are propagated more rapidly by saltatory conduction.

iP **Nervous System I; Topic: The Action Potential, pp. 1–18.**

The Synapse (pp. 407–414)

1. A synapse is a functional junction between neurons. The information-transmitting neuron is the presynaptic neuron; the information-receiving neuron is the postsynaptic neuron.

Electrical Synapses (p. 407)

2. Electrical synapses allow ions to flow directly from one neuron to another; the cells are electrically coupled.

Chemical Synapses (pp. 407–410)

3. Chemical synapses are sites of neurotransmitter release and binding. When the impulse reaches the presynaptic axon terminals, voltage-gated Ca^{2+} channels open, and Ca^{2+} enters the cell and mediates neurotransmitter release. Neurotransmitters diffuse across the synaptic cleft and attach to postsynaptic membrane receptors, opening ion channels. After binding, the neurotransmitters are removed from the synapse by diffusion, enzymatic breakdown, or reuptake into the presynaptic terminal or astrocytes.

iP **Nervous System II; Topics: Anatomy Review, pp. 1–9, Ion Channels, pp. 1–8, Synaptic Transmission, pp. 1–7.**

Postsynaptic Potentials and Synaptic Integration (pp. 410–414)

4. Binding of neurotransmitter at excitatory chemical synapses results in local graded potentials called EPSPs, caused by the opening of channels that allow simultaneous passage of Na^+ and K^+.

5. Neurotransmitter binding at inhibitory chemical synapses results in hyperpolarizations called IPSPs, caused by the opening of K^+ or Cl^- channels. IPSPs drive the membrane potential farther from threshold.

6. EPSPs and IPSPs summate temporally and spatially. The membrane of the axon hillock acts as a neuronal integrator.

7. Synaptic potentiation, which enhances the postsynaptic neuron's response, is produced by intense repeated stimulation. Ionic calcium appears to mediate such effects, which may be the basis of learning.

8. Presynaptic inhibition is mediated by axoaxonal synapses that reduce the amount of neurotransmitter released by the inhibited neuron.

iP **Nervous System II; Topic: Synaptic Potentials and Cellular Integration, pp. 1–10.**

Neurotransmitters and Their Receptors (pp. 414–421)

Classification of Neurotransmitters by Chemical Structure (pp. 414–417)

1. The major classes of neurotransmitters based on chemical structure are acetylcholine, biogenic amines, amino acids, peptides, purines, dissolved gases, and lipids.

Classification of Neurotransmitters by Function (pp. 417–419)

2. Functionally, neurotransmitters are classified as (1) inhibitory or excitatory (or both) and (2) direct or indirect action. Direct-acting neurotransmitters bind to and open ion channels. Indirect-acting neurotransmitters act through second messengers. Neuromodulators also act indirectly presynaptically or postsynaptically to change synaptic strength.

Neurotransmitter Receptors (pp. 420–421)

3. Neurotransmitter receptors are either channel-linked receptors that open ion channels, leading to fast changes in membrane potential, or G protein–linked receptors that oversee slow synaptic responses mediated by G proteins and intracellular second messengers. Second messengers most often activate kinases, which in turn act on ion channels or activate other proteins.

iP **Nervous System II; Topic: Synaptic Transmission, pp. 6–15.**

Basic Concepts of Neural Integration (pp. 421–423)

Organization of Neurons: Neuronal Pools (p. 421)

1. CNS neurons are organized into several types of neuronal pools, each with distinguishing patterns of synaptic connections called circuits.

Types of Circuits (p. 421)

2. The four basic circuit types are diverging, converging, reverberating, and parallel after-discharge.

Patterns of Neural Processing (pp. 421–423)

3. In serial processing, one neuron stimulates the next in sequence, producing specific, predictable responses, as in spinal reflexes. A reflex is a rapid, involuntary motor response to a stimulus.

4. Reflexes are mediated over neural pathways called reflex arcs. The minimum number of elements in a reflex arc is five: receptor, sensory neuron, integration center, motor neuron, and effector.

5. In parallel processing, which underlies complex mental functions, impulses travel along several pathways to different integration centers.

Developmental Aspects of Neurons (pp. 423–424)

1. Neuron development involves proliferation, migration, and the formation of interconnections. The formation of interconnections involves axons finding their targets and forming synapses, and the synthesis of specific neurotransmitters.

2. Axon outgrowth and synapse formation are guided by other neurons, glial cells, and chemicals (such as N-CAM and nerve growth factor). Neurons that do not make appropriate synapses die, and approximately two-thirds of neurons formed in the embryo undergo programmed cell death.

Review Questions

Multiple Choice/Matching

(Some questions have more than one correct answer. Select the best answer or answers from the choices given.)

1. Which of the following structures is not part of the central nervous system? (**a**) the brain, (**b**) a nerve, (**c**) the spinal cord, (**d**) a tract.

2. Match the names of the supporting cells found in column B with the appropriate descriptions in column A.

Column A	Column B
____ (1) myelinates nerve fibers in the CNS	(**a**) astrocyte
____ (2) lines brain cavities	(**b**) ependymal cell
____ (3) myelinates nerve fibers in the PNS	(**c**) microglial cell
	(**d**) oligodendrocyte
____ (4) CNS phagocyte	(**e**) satellite cell
____ (5) helps regulate the ionic composition of CNS extracellular fluid	(**f**) Schwann cell

3. What type of current flows through the axolemma during the steep phase of repolarization? (**a**) chiefly a sodium current, (**b**) chiefly a potassium current, (**c**) sodium and potassium currents of approximately the same magnitude.

4. Assume that an EPSP is being generated on the dendritic membrane. Which will occur? (**a**) specific Na^+ channels will open, (**b**) specific K^+ channels will open, (**c**) a single type of channel will open, permitting simultaneous flow of Na^+ and K^+, (**d**) Na^+ channels will open first and then close as K^+ channels open.

5. The velocity of nerve impulse conduction is greatest in (**a**) heavily myelinated, large-diameter fibers, (**b**) myelinated, small-diameter fibers, (**c**) nonmyelinated, small-diameter fibers, (**d**) nonmyelinated, large-diameter fibers.

6. Chemical synapses are characterized by all of the following except (**a**) the release of neurotransmitter by the presynaptic membranes, (**b**) postsynaptic membranes bearing receptors that bind neurotransmitter, (**c**) ions flowing through protein channels from the presynaptic to the postsynaptic neuron, (**d**) a fluid-filled gap separating the neurons.

7. Biogenic amine neurotransmitters include all but (**a**) norepinephrine, (**b**) acetylcholine, (**c**) dopamine, (**d**) serotonin.

8. The neuropeptides that act as natural opiates are (**a**) substance P, (**b**) somatostatin and cholecystokinin, (**c**) tachykinins, (**d**) enkephalins.

9. Inhibition of acetylcholinesterase by poisoning blocks neurotransmission at the neuromuscular junction because (**a**) ACh is no longer released by the presynaptic terminal, (**b**) ACh synthesis in the presynaptic terminal is blocked, (**c**) ACh is not degraded, hence prolonged depolarization is enforced on the postsynaptic cell, (**d**) ACh is blocked from attaching to the postsynaptic ACh receptors.

10. The anatomical region of a multipolar neuron that has the lowest threshold for generating an AP is the (**a**) soma, (**b**) dendrites, (**c**) axon hillock, (**d**) distal axon.

11. An IPSP is inhibitory because (**a**) it hyperpolarizes the postsynaptic membrane, (**b**) it reduces the amount of neurotransmitter released by the presynaptic terminal, (**c**) it prevents calcium ion entry into the presynaptic terminal, (**d**) it changes the threshold of the neuron.

12. Identify the neuronal circuits described by choosing the correct response from the key.

Key: (**a**) converging   (**c**) parallel after-discharge
      (**b**) diverging   (**d**) reverberating

____ (1) Impulses continue around and around the circuit until one neuron stops firing.

____ (2) One or a few inputs ultimately influence large numbers of neurons.

____ (3) Many neurons influence a few neurons.

____ (4) May be involved in exacting types of mental activity.

Short Answer Essay Questions

13. Explain both the anatomical and functional divisions of the nervous system. Include the subdivisions of each.

14. (**a**) Describe the composition and function of the cell body. (**b**) How are axons and dendrites alike? In what ways (structurally and functionally) do they differ?

15. (**a**) What is myelin? (**b**) How does the myelination process differ in the CNS and PNS?

16. (**a**) Contrast unipolar, bipolar, and multipolar neurons structurally. (**b**) Indicate where each is most likely to be found.

17. What is the polarized membrane state? How is it maintained? (Note the relative roles of both passive and active mechanisms.)

18. Describe the events that must occur to generate an AP. Relate the sequence of changes in permeability to changes in the ion channels, and explain why the AP is an all-or-none phenomenon.

19. Since all APs generated by a given nerve fiber have the same magnitude, how does the CNS "know" whether a stimulus is strong or weak?

20. (**a**) Explain the difference between an EPSP and an IPSP. (**b**) What specifically determines whether an EPSP or IPSP will be generated at the postsynaptic membrane?

21. Since at any moment a neuron is likely to have thousands of neurons releasing neurotransmitters at its surface, how is neuronal activity (to fire or not to fire) determined?

22. The effects of neurotransmitter binding are very brief. Explain.

23. During a neurobiology lecture, a professor repeatedly refers to group A and group B fibers, absolute refractory period, and myelin sheath gaps. Define these terms.

24. Distinguish between serial and parallel processing.

25. Briefly describe the three stages of neuron development.

26. What factors appear to guide the outgrowth of an axon and its ability to make the "correct" synaptic contacts?

Critical Thinking and Clinical Application Questions

1. Mr. Miller is hospitalized for cardiac problems. Somehow, medical orders are mixed up and Mr. Miller is infused with a K^+-enhanced intravenous solution meant for another patient who is taking potassium-wasting diuretics (i.e., drugs that cause excessive loss of potassium from the body in urine). Mr. Miller's potassium levels are normal before the IV is administered. What do you think will happen to Mr. Miller's resting membrane potentials? To his neurons' ability to generate APs?

2. Local anesthetics block voltage-gated Na^+ channels. General anesthetics are thought to activate chemically gated Cl^- channels,

thereby rendering the nervous system quiescent while surgery is performed. What specific process do anesthetics impair, and how does this interfere with nerve impulse transmission?

3. When admitted to the emergency room, John was holding his right hand, which had a deep puncture hole in its palm. He explained that he had fallen on a nail while exploring a barn. John was given an antitetanus shot to prevent neural complications. Tetanus bacteria fester in deep, dark wounds, but how do their toxins travel in neural tissue?

4. Rochelle developed multiple sclerosis when she was 27. After eight years she had lost a good portion of her ability to control her skeletal muscles. How did this happen?

5. In the Netherlands a young man named Jan was admitted to the emergency room. He and his friends had been to a rave. His friends say he started twitching and having muscle spasms which progressed until he was "stiff as a board." On examination, staff found a marked increase in muscle tone and hyperreflexia involving facial and limb muscles. In his pocket, he had unmarked dark yellow tablets with dark flecks. Analysis of the tablets showed them to contain a mixture of ecstasy and strychnine. Ecstasy would not cause this clinical picture, but strychnine, which blocks glycine receptors, could. Explain how.

AT THE CLINIC

Related Clinical Terms

Neuroblastoma (nu″ro-blas-to′mah; *oma* = tumor) A malignant tumor in children; arises from cells that retain a neuroblast-like structure. These tumors sometimes arise in the brain, but most occur in the peripheral nervous system.

Neurologist (nu-rol′o-jist) A medical specialist in the study of the nervous system and its functions and disorders.

Neuropathy (nu-rop′ah-the) Any disease of nervous tissue, but particularly degenerative diseases of nerves.

Neuropharmacology (nu″ro-far″mah-kol′o-je) Scientific study of the effects of drugs on the nervous system.

Neurotoxin Substance that is poisonous or destructive to nervous tissue, e.g., botulinum and tetanus toxins.

Rabies (*rabies* = madness) A viral infection of the nervous system transmitted by the bite of an infected mammal (such as a dog, bat, or skunk). After entry, the virus travels via axonal transport in peripheral nerve axons to the CNS, where it causes brain inflammation, delirium, and death. A vaccine- and antibody-based treatment is effective if given before symptoms appear. Rabies in humans is very rare in the United States.

Shingles (herpes zoster) Inflammation of virally infected sensory neurons serving the skin. Caused by the varicella-zoster virus, which causes chicken pox (generally during childhood); during the initial infection the virus is transported from the skin lesions to the sensory cell bodies in the sensory ganglia. Typically, the immune system holds the virus in check. It remains dormant until the immune system is weakened, often by stress. Then viral particles multiply, causing nerve pain (neuralgia), and travel back to the skin, producing characteristic scaly blisters. This rash is usually confined to one side of the body trunk. Attacks last several weeks, alternating between periods of healing and relapse. Seen mostly in those over 50 years old. Vaccination can prevent occurrence and minimize pain.

Case Study — Nervous System

Elaine Sawyer, 35, was on her way to the local elementary school with her three children when the accident on Route 91 occurred. As Mrs. Sawyer swerved to avoid the bus, the right rear corner of her minivan struck the side of the bus, causing the minivan to tip over and slide on its side. Her children were shaken but unhurt. Mrs. Sawyer, however, suffered a severe head injury that caused post-traumatic seizures.

The drugs initially prescribed for her treatment were insufficient to control these seizures. Her doctor additionally prescribed Valium (diazepam), but suggested that she use it only for a month because Valium induces tolerance (loses its effectiveness). After a month of Valium treatment, Mrs. Sawyer no longer had seizures and gradually reduced and eliminated her use of Valium. After being seizure-free for another year, restrictions on her driver's license were lifted.

1. Seizures reflect uncontrolled electrical activity of groups of neurons in the brain. Valium is described as a drug that can "quiet the nerves," which means that it inhibits the ability of neurons to generate electrical signals. What are these electrical signals called, and what is happening at the level of the cell when they are generated?

2. Valium enhances inhibitory postsynaptic potentials (IPSPs). What is an IPSP? How does it affect action potential generation?

3. Valium enhances the natural effects of the neurotransmitter GABA [gamma (γ)-aminobutyric acid]. What chemical class of neurotransmitters does GABA belong to? What are some of the other neurotransmitters that fall into this same class?

4. Theoretically, there are a number of possible ways that a drug such as Valium could act to enhance the action of GABA. What are three such possibilities?

5. Valium actually works postsynaptically to promote binding of GABA to its receptor, thereby enhancing the influx of Cl⁻ ions into the postsynaptic cell (the natural effect produced by GABA). Why would this effect reduce the likelihood that this cell would be able to produce an electrical signal?

(Answers in Appendix H)

12

The Central Nervous System

nterconnecting and directing a dizzying number of incoming and outgoing calls, the central switchboard of a telephone system historically seemed an apt comparison for the **central nervous system (CNS)**—brain and spinal cord. Nowadays, many people compare the CNS to a "cloud" of networked computers. These analogies may explain some workings of the spinal cord, but neither does justice to the fantastic complexity of the human brain. Whether we view the brain as an evolved biological organ, an impressive network of computers, or simply a miracle, it is one of the most amazing things known.

During the course of animal evolution, **cephalization** (se"fah-lĭ-za'shun) has occurred. That is, there has been an elaboration of the *rostral* ("toward the snout"), or anterior, portion of the CNS, along with an increase in the number of neurons in the head. This phenomenon reaches its highest level in the human brain.

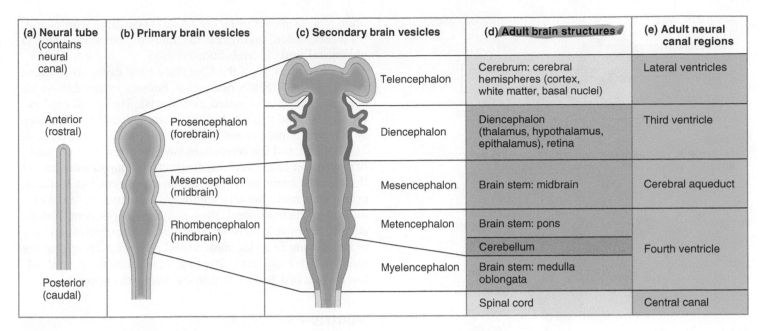

(a) Neural tube (contains neural canal)	(b) Primary brain vesicles	(c) Secondary brain vesicles	(d) Adult brain structures	(e) Adult neural canal regions
Anterior (rostral)	Prosencephalon (forebrain)	Telencephalon	Cerebrum: cerebral hemispheres (cortex, white matter, basal nuclei)	Lateral ventricles
		Diencephalon	Diencephalon (thalamus, hypothalamus, epithalamus), retina	Third ventricle
	Mesencephalon (midbrain)	Mesencephalon	Brain stem: midbrain	Cerebral aqueduct
	Rhombencephalon (hindbrain)	Metencephalon	Brain stem: pons	Fourth ventricle
			Cerebellum	
Posterior (caudal)		Myelencephalon	Brain stem: medulla oblongata	
			Spinal cord	Central canal

Figure 12.1 Embryonic development of the human brain. (a) Formed by week 4, the neural tube quickly subdivides into **(b)** the primary brain vesicles, which subsequently form **(c)** the secondary brain vesicles by week 5. These five vesicles differentiate into **(d)** the adult brain structures. **(e)** The adult structures derived from the neural canal.

In this chapter, we examine the structure of the CNS and the functions associated with its various regions. We also touch on complex integrative functions, such as sleep-wake cycles and memory.

The Brain

The unimpressive appearance of the human **brain** gives few hints of its remarkable abilities. It is about two good fistfuls of quivering pinkish gray tissue, wrinkled like a walnut, with a consistency somewhat like cold oatmeal. The average adult human brain has a mass of about 1500 g (3.3 lb).

Embryonic Development

✓ Describe how space constraints affect brain development.

✓ Name the major regions of the adult brain.

✓ Name and locate the ventricles of the brain.

We begin with an introduction to brain embryology, as the terminology used for the structural divisions of the adult brain is easier to follow when you understand brain development.

The brain and spinal cord begin as an embryonic structure called the **neural tube (Figure 12.1a)**. As soon as the neural tube forms, its anterior (rostral) end begins to expand and constrictions appear that mark off the three **primary brain vesicles** (Figure 12.1b):

- **Prosencephalon** (pros″en-sef′ah-lon), or **forebrain**
- **Mesencephalon** (mes″en-sef′ah-lon), or **midbrain**
- **Rhombencephalon** (romb″en-sef′ah-lon), or **hindbrain**

(Note that *encephalo* means "brain.") The remaining *caudal* ("toward the tail"), or posterior, portion of the neural tube becomes the spinal cord, which we will discuss later in the chapter.

The primary vesicles give rise to the **secondary brain vesicles** (Figure 12.1c). The forebrain divides into the **telencephalon** ("endbrain") and **diencephalon** ("interbrain"), and the hindbrain constricts, forming the **metencephalon** ("afterbrain") and **myelencephalon** ("spinal brain"). The midbrain remains undivided.

Each of the five secondary vesicles then develops rapidly to produce the major structures of the adult brain (Figure 12.1d). The greatest change occurs in the telencephalon, which sprouts two lateral swellings that look like Mickey Mouse's ears. These become the two *cerebral hemispheres*, referred to collectively as the **cerebrum** (ser′ĕ-brum). The diencephalon specializes to form the *hypothalamus* (hi″po-thal′ah-mus), *thalamus*, *epithalamus*, and *retina* of the eye. Less dramatic changes occur in the mesencephalon, metencephalon, and myelencephalon as these regions transform into the *midbrain*, the *pons* and *cerebellum*, and the *medulla oblongata*, respectively. All these midbrain and hindbrain structures, except the cerebellum, form the **brain stem**.

The central cavity of the neural tube remains continuous and enlarges in four areas to form the fluid-filled *ventricles* (*ventr* = little belly) of the brain (Figure 12.1e). We will describe the ventricles shortly.

Because the brain grows more rapidly than the membranous skull that contains it, it folds up to occupy the available space. The *midbrain* and *cervical flexures* move the forebrain toward the brain stem **(Figure 12.2a)**. The cerebral hemispheres are forced to take a horseshoe-shaped course and grow posteriorly and laterally (indicated by black arrows in Figure 12.2b). As a result, they grow back over and almost completely envelop the diencephalon and midbrain. By week 26, the continued growth

Anterior (rostral)   Posterior (caudal)

- Metencephalon
- Mesencephalon
- Diencephalon
- Midbrain
- Cervical ⎤ **Flexures**
- Telencephalon
- Myelencephalon
- Spinal cord

(a) Week 5: Two major flexures form, causing the telencephalon and diencephalon to angle toward the brain stem.

↓

- Cerebral hemisphere
- Outline of diencephalon
- Midbrain
- Cerebellum
- Pons
- Medulla oblongata
- Spinal cord

(b) Week 13: Cerebral hemispheres develop and grow posterolaterally to enclose the diencephalon and the rostral brain stem.

↓

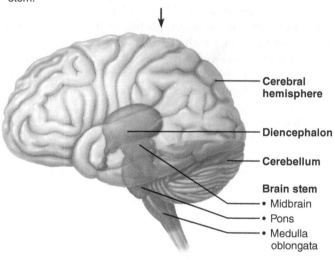

- **Cerebral hemisphere**
- **Diencephalon**
- **Cerebellum**
- **Brain stem**
  - Midbrain
  - Pons
  - Medulla oblongata

(c) Birth: Shows adult pattern of structures and convolutions.

Figure 12.2 Brain development. Initially, the cerebral surface is smooth. Folding begins in month 6, and convolutions become more obvious as development continues. See-through view in (b) and (c).

of the cerebral hemispheres causes their surfaces to crease and fold into *convolutions* (Figure 12.2c), which increases their surface area and allows more neurons to occupy the limited space.

Regions and Organization

Some textbooks discuss brain anatomy in terms of the *embryonic scheme* (see Figure 12.1c), but in this text, we will consider the brain in terms of the medical scheme and the four adult

brain regions shown in Figure 12.2c: (1) cerebral hemispheres, (2) diencephalon, (3) brain stem (midbrain, pons, and medulla oblongata), and (4) cerebellum.

The basic pattern of the CNS is a central cavity surrounded by gray matter (mostly neuron cell bodies), external to which is white matter (myelinated fiber tracts). The spinal cord exhibits this basic pattern, but the brain has additional regions of gray matter not present in the spinal cord. Both the cerebral hemispheres and the cerebellum have an outer layer or "bark" of gray matter called a cortex. This pattern changes with descent through the brain stem—the cortex disappears, but scattered gray matter nuclei are seen within the white matter. At the caudal end of the brain stem, the basic pattern is evident. Knowledge of the basic pattern of the CNS will help you explore the brain, moving from the most rostral region (cerebrum) to the most caudal (brain stem). But first, let's explore the central hollow cavities that lie deep within the brain—the ventricles.

Ventricles

The brain **ventricles** are continuous with one another and with the central canal of the spinal cord **(Figure 12.3)**. The hollow ventricular chambers are filled with cerebrospinal fluid and lined by *ependymal cells*, a type of neuroglia (see Figure 11.3c on p. 389).

The paired **lateral ventricles**, one deep within each cerebral hemisphere, are large C-shaped chambers that reflect the pattern of cerebral growth. Anteriorly, the lateral ventricles lie close together, separated only by a thin median membrane called the **septum pellucidum** (pě-lu′sid-um; "transparent wall"). (See Figure 12.10, p. 440.)

Each lateral ventricle communicates with the narrow **third ventricle** in the diencephalon via a channel called an **interventricular foramen**.

The third ventricle is continuous with the **fourth ventricle** via the canal-like **cerebral aqueduct** that runs through the midbrain. The fourth ventricle lies in the hindbrain dorsal to the pons and superior medulla. It is continuous with the central canal of the spinal cord inferiorly. Three openings mark the walls of the fourth ventricle: the paired **lateral apertures** in its side walls and the **median aperture** in its roof. These apertures connect the ventricles to the *subarachnoid space* (sub″ah-rak′noid), a fluid-filled space surrounding the brain.

☑ Check Your Understanding

1. Which ventricle is surrounded by the diencephalon?
2. Which two areas of the adult brain have an outside layer of gray matter in addition to central gray matter and surrounding white matter?
3. What is the function of convolutions of the brain?

For answers, see Appendix H.

Cerebral Hemispheres

✓ List the major lobes, fissures, and functional areas of the cerebral cortex.

✓ Explain lateralization of hemisphere function.

(a) Anterior view

(b) Left lateral view

Figure 12.3 Ventricles of the brain. Different regions of the large lateral ventricles are labeled anterior horn, posterior horn, and inferior horn.

✓ Differentiate between commissures, association fibers, and projection fibers.

✓ Describe the general function of the basal nuclei (basal ganglia).

The **cerebral hemispheres** form the superior part of the brain **(Figure 12.4)**. The most conspicuous parts of an intact brain, together they account for about 83% of total brain mass. Picture how a mushroom cap covers the top of its stalk, and you have a good idea of how the paired cerebral hemispheres cover and obscure the diencephalon and the top of the brain stem (see Figure 12.2c).

Elevated ridges of tissue called **gyri** (ji'ri; singular: *gyrus*; "twisters")—separated by shallow grooves called **sulci** (sul'ki; singular: *sulcus*; "furrows")—mark nearly the entire surface of the cerebral hemispheres. Deeper grooves, called **fissures**, separate large regions of the brain (Figure 12.4c).

The more prominent gyri and sulci are important anatomical landmarks that are similar in all humans. The median **longitudinal fissure** separates the cerebral hemispheres (Figure 12.4a). Another large fissure, the **transverse cerebral fissure**, separates the cerebral hemispheres from the cerebellum below (Figure 12.4b, c).

Several sulci divide each hemisphere into five lobes—frontal, parietal, temporal, occipital, and insula (Figure 12.4c, d). All but the last are named for the cranial bones that overlie them (see Figure 7.5, pp. 204–205). The **central sulcus**, which lies in the frontal plane, separates the **frontal lobe** from the **parietal lobe**. Bordering the central sulcus are the **precentral gyrus** anteriorly and the **postcentral gyrus** posteriorly. The **parieto-occipital sulcus** (pah-ri"ĕ-to-ok-sip'ĭ-tal), located more posteriorly on the medial surface of the hemisphere, separates the **occipital lobe** from the parietal lobe.

The deep **lateral sulcus** outlines the flaplike **temporal lobe** and separates it from the parietal and frontal lobes. A fifth lobe

of the cerebral hemisphere, the **insula** (in'su-lah; "island"), is buried deep within the lateral sulcus and forms part of its floor (Figure 12.4d). The insula is covered by portions of the temporal, parietal, and frontal lobes.

The cerebral hemispheres fit snugly in the skull. The frontal lobes lie in the anterior cranial fossa, and the anterior parts of the temporal lobes fill the middle cranial fossa (see Figure 7.2b, c, p. 201). The posterior cranial fossa, however, houses the brain stem and cerebellum. The occipital lobes are located well superior to that cranial fossa.

Each cerebral hemisphere has three basic regions:

- A superficial *cerebral cortex* of gray matter, which looks gray in fresh brain tissue

- Internal *white matter*

- *Basal nuclei*, islands of gray matter situated deep within the white matter

We consider these regions next.

Cerebral Cortex

The **cerebral cortex** is the "executive suite" of the nervous system, where our *conscious mind* is found. It enables us to be aware of ourselves and our sensations, to communicate, remember, understand, and initiate voluntary movements.

The cerebral cortex is composed of gray matter: neuron cell bodies, dendrites, associated glia and blood vessels, but no fiber tracts. It contains billions of neurons arranged in six layers. Although only 2–4 mm (about 1/8 inch) thick, it accounts for roughly 40% of total brain mass. Its many convolutions effectively triple its surface area.

Modern imaging techniques allow us to see the brain in action—PET scans show maximal metabolic activity in the brain,

12

(a) Superior view

(b) Left lateral view

(c) Lobes and sulci of the cerebrum

(d) Location of the insula lobe

Figure 12.4 Lobes, sulci, and fissures of the cerebral hemispheres.

and functional MRI scans reveal blood flow **(Figure 12.5)**. They show that specific motor and sensory functions are localized in discrete cortical areas called *domains*. However, many higher mental functions, such as memory and language, appear to be spread over large areas of the cortex in overlapping domains.

Before we examine the functional regions of the cerebral cortex, let's consider four generalizations:

- The cerebral cortex contains three kinds of functional areas: *motor areas*, *sensory areas*, and *association areas*. As you read about these areas, do not confuse the sensory and motor areas of the cortex with sensory and motor neurons. All neurons in the cortex are interneurons.

- Each hemisphere is chiefly concerned with the sensory and motor functions of the **contralateral** (literally, "opposite") side of the body.

- Although largely symmetrical in structure, the two hemispheres are not entirely equal in function. Instead, there is lateralization (specialization) of cortical functions.

- And finally, keep in mind that our approach is a gross oversimplification. No functional area of the cortex acts alone, and conscious behavior involves the entire cortex in one way or another.

Motor Areas   The following **motor areas** of the cortex, which control voluntary movement, lie in the posterior part of the frontal lobes: primary motor cortex, premotor cortex, Broca's area, and the frontal eye field (**Figure 12.6a**, dark and light red areas).

1. **Primary motor cortex.** The **primary (somatic) motor cortex** is located in the precentral gyrus of the frontal lobe of each hemisphere (Figure 12.6, dark red area). Large neurons, called **pyramidal cells,** in these gyri allow us to consciously control the precise or skilled voluntary movements of our skeletal muscles. Their long axons, which project to the spinal cord, form the massive voluntary motor tracts called *pyramidal tracts* or *corticospinal tracts* (kor″tĭ-ko-spi′nal). All other descending motor tracts issue from brain stem nuclei and consist of chains of two or more neurons.

   The entire body is represented spatially in the primary motor cortex of each hemisphere. For example, the pyramidal cells that control foot movements are in one place and those that control hand movements are in another. Such mapping of the body in CNS structures is called **somatotopy** (so″mah-to-to′pe).

   As illustrated in **Figure 12.7** (p. 435), in somatotopy the body is represented upside down—with the head at the inferolateral part of the precentral gyrus, and the toes at the superomedial end. Most of the neurons in these gyri control muscles in body areas having the most precise motor control—that is, the face, tongue, and hands. Consequently, these regions are disproportionately large in the caricature-like **motor homunculus** (ho-mung′ku-lus; "little man") drawn in Figure 12.7. The motor innervation of the body is contralateral: In other words, the left primary motor gyrus controls muscles on the right side of the body, and vice versa.

   The motor homunculus view of the primary motor cortex, shown at the left in Figure 12.7, implies a one-to-one correspondence between cortical neurons and the muscles they control, but this is somewhat misleading. In fact, a given muscle is controlled by multiple spots on the cortex, and individual cortical neurons actually send impulses to more than one muscle. In other words, individual pyramidal motor neurons control muscles that work together in a synergistic way to perform a given movement.

   For example, reaching forward with one arm involves some muscles acting at the shoulder and some acting at the elbow. Instead of the discrete map offered by the motor

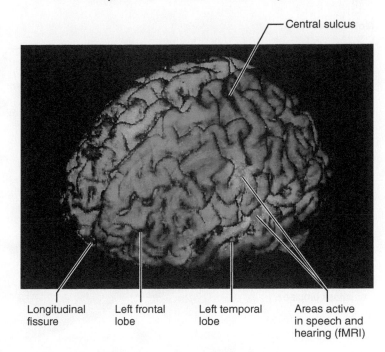

Figure 12.5 Functional neuroimaging (fMRI) of the cerebral cortex. Speaking and hearing increase activity (blood flow, shown by yellow and orange areas) in the posterior frontal and superior temporal lobes, respectively.

homunculus, the primary motor cortex map is an orderly but fuzzy map with neurons arranged in useful ways to control and coordinate sets of muscles. Neurons controlling the arm, for instance, intermingle and overlap with those controlling the hand and shoulder. However, neurons controlling unrelated movements, such as those controlling the arm and those controlling body trunk muscles, do not cooperate in motor activity.

   Thus, the motor homunculus is useful to show that broad areas of the primary cortex are devoted to the leg, arm, torso, and head, but neuron organization within those broad areas is much more diffuse than initially imagined.

2. **Premotor cortex.** Just anterior to the precentral gyrus in the frontal lobe is the **premotor cortex** (see Figure 12.6, light red area). The premotor cortex helps plan movements. This region selects and sequences basic motor movements into more complex tasks, such as playing a musical instrument or typing. Using highly processed sensory information received from other cortical areas, it can control voluntary actions that depend on sensory feedback, such as moving an arm through a maze to grasp a hidden object.

   The premotor cortex coordinates the movement of several muscle groups either simultaneously or sequentially, mainly by sending activating impulses to the primary motor cortex. However, the premotor cortex also influences motor activity more directly by supplying about 15% of pyramidal tract fibers. Think of this region as the staging area for skilled motor activities.

3. **Broca's area.** **Broca's area** (bro′kahz) lies anterior to the inferior region of the premotor area. It has long been

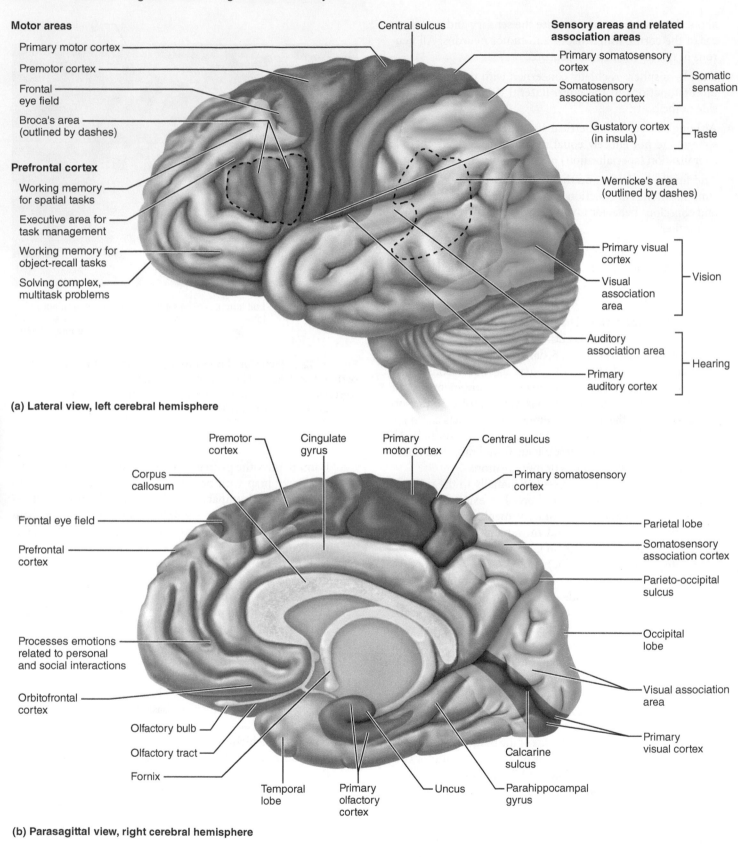

Motor areas

Primary motor cortex

Premotor cortex

Frontal eye field

Broca's area (outlined by dashes)

Prefrontal cortex

Working memory for spatial tasks

Executive area for task management

Working memory for object-recall tasks

Solving complex, multitask problems

Central sulcus

Sensory areas and related association areas

Primary somatosensory cortex

Somatosensory association cortex

Somatic sensation

Gustatory cortex (in insula) — Taste

Wernicke's area (outlined by dashes)

Primary visual cortex

Visual association area

Vision

Auditory association area

Primary auditory cortex

Hearing

(a) Lateral view, left cerebral hemisphere

Premotor cortex

Cingulate gyrus

Primary motor cortex

Central sulcus

Corpus callosum

Frontal eye field

Prefrontal cortex

Primary somatosensory cortex

Parietal lobe

Somatosensory association cortex

Parieto-occipital sulcus

Processes emotions related to personal and social interactions

Orbitofrontal cortex

Occipital lobe

Visual association area

Olfactory bulb

Olfactory tract

Fornix

Primary visual cortex

Calcarine sulcus

Temporal lobe

Primary olfactory cortex

Uncus

Parahippocampal gyrus

(b) Parasagittal view, right cerebral hemisphere

◼ Primary motor cortex   ◼ Motor association cortex   ◼ Primary sensory cortex   ◼ Sensory association cortex   ◼ Multimodal association cortex

Figure 12.6 Functional and structural areas of the cerebral cortex.

12

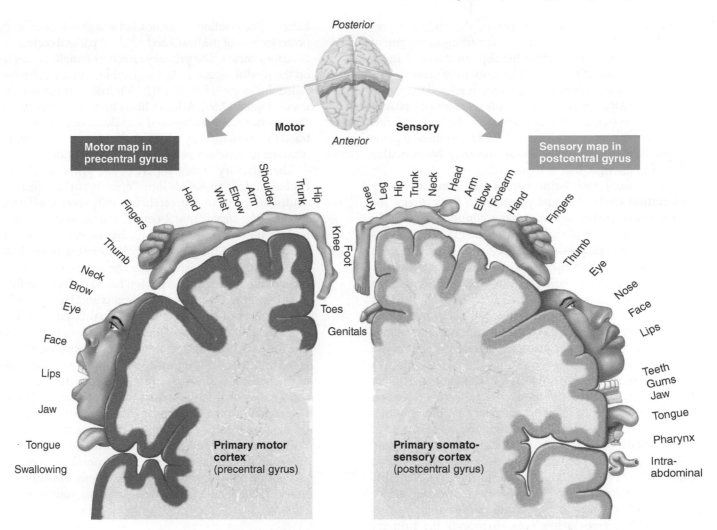

Figure 12.7 Body maps in the primary motor cortex and somatosensory cortex of the cerebrum. The relative amount and location of cortical tissue devoted to each function is proportional to the distorted body diagrams (homunculi).

considered to be (1) present in one hemisphere only (usually the left) and (2) a special *motor speech area* that directs the muscles involved in speech production. However, imaging studies indicate that Broca's area also becomes active as we prepare to speak and even as we think about (plan) many voluntary motor activities other than speech.

4. **Frontal eye field.** The **frontal eye field** is located partially in and anterior to the premotor cortex and superior to Broca's area. This cortical region controls voluntary movement of the eyes.

Homeostatic Imbalance 12.1

Damage to localized areas of the *primary motor cortex* (as from a stroke) paralyzes the body muscles controlled by those areas. If the lesion is in the right hemisphere, the left side of the body will be paralyzed. Only *voluntary* control is lost, however, as the muscles can still contract reflexively.

Destruction of the *premotor cortex*, or part of it, results in loss of the motor skill(s) programmed by that region, but does not impair muscle strength and the ability to perform the discrete individual movements. For example, if the premotor area controlling the flight of your fingers over a computer keyboard were damaged, you couldn't type with your usual speed, but you could still make the same movements with your fingers. Reprogramming the skill into another set of premotor neurons would require practice, just as the initial learning process did. +

Sensory Areas Areas concerned with conscious awareness of sensation, the sensory areas of the cortex, occur in the parietal, insular, temporal, and occipital lobes (see Figure 12.6, dark and light blue areas).

1. **Primary somatosensory cortex.** The **primary somatosensory cortex** resides in the postcentral gyrus of the parietal lobe, just posterior to the primary motor cortex. Neurons in this gyrus receive information from the general (somatic) sensory receptors in the skin and from proprioceptors (position sense receptors) in skeletal muscles, joints, and tendons. The neurons then identify the body region being stimulated, an ability called **spatial discrimination**.

As with the primary motor cortex, the body is represented spatially and upside down according to the site of stimulus input, and the right hemisphere receives input from the left side of the body. The amount of sensory cortex devoted to a particular body region is related to that region's sensitivity (that is, to how many receptors it has), not its size. In humans, the face (especially the lips) and fingertips are the most sensitive body areas, so these regions are the largest parts of the **somatosensory homunculus** (shown in the right half of Figure 12.7).

2. **Somatosensory association cortex.** The **somatosensory association cortex** lies just posterior to the primary somatosensory cortex and has many connections with it. The major function of this area is to integrate sensory inputs (temperature, pressure, and so forth) relayed to it via the primary somatosensory cortex to produce an understanding of an object being felt: its size, texture, and the relationship of its parts.

   For example, when you reach into your pocket, your somatosensory association cortex draws upon stored memories of past sensory experiences to perceive the objects you feel as coins or keys. Someone with damage to this area could not recognize these objects without looking at them.

3. **Visual areas.** The **primary visual (striate) cortex** is seen on the extreme posterior tip of the occipital lobe, but most of it is buried deep in the *calcarine sulcus* in the medial aspect of the occipital lobe (Figure 12.6b). The largest cortical sensory area, the primary visual cortex receives visual information that originates on the retina of the eye. There is a contralateral map of visual space on the primary visual cortex, analogous to the body map on the somatosensory cortex.

   The **visual association area** surrounds the primary visual cortex and covers much of the occipital lobe. Communicating with the primary visual cortex, the visual association area uses past visual experiences to interpret visual stimuli (color, form, and movement), enabling us to recognize a flower or a person's face and to appreciate what we are seeing. We do our "seeing" with these cortical neurons. However, complex visual processing involves the entire posterior half of the cerebral hemispheres. Particularly important are two visual "streams"—one running along the top of the brain and handling spatial relationships and object location, the other taking the lower road and focusing on recognizing faces, words, and objects.

4. **Auditory areas.** Each **primary auditory cortex** is located in the superior margin of the temporal lobe abutting the lateral sulcus. Sound energy exciting the hearing receptors of the inner ear causes impulses to be transmitted to the primary auditory cortex, where they are interpreted as pitch, loudness, and location.

   The more posterior **auditory association area** then permits the perception of the sound stimulus, which we "hear" as speech, a scream, music, thunder, noise, and so on. Memories of sounds heard in the past appear to be stored here for reference. Wernicke's area, which we describe later, includes parts of the auditory cortex.

5. **Vestibular (equilibrium) cortex.** Imaging studies show that the part of the cortex responsible for conscious awareness of balance (the position of the head in space) is located in the posterior part of the insula and adjacent parietal cortex.

6. **Olfactory cortex.** The **primary olfactory (smell) cortex** lies on the medial aspect of the temporal lobe in a small region called the *piriform lobe* which is dominated by the hooklike *uncus* (Figure 12.6b). Afferent fibers from smell receptors in the superior nasal cavities send impulses along the olfactory tracts that are ultimately relayed to the olfactory cortices. The outcome is conscious awareness of different odors.

   The olfactory cortex is part of the primitive **rhinencephalon** (ri"nen-sef'ah-lon; "nose brain"), which includes all parts of the cerebrum that receive olfactory signals—the orbitofrontal cortex, uncus, and associated regions located on or in the medial aspects of the temporal lobes, and the protruding olfactory tracts and bulbs that extend to the nose. During the course of evolution, most of the "old" rhinencephalon has taken on new functions concerned chiefly with emotions and memory. It has become part of the "newer" emotional brain, called the *limbic system*, which we will consider later in this chapter. The only portions of the human rhinencephalon still devoted to smell are the olfactory bulbs and tracts (described in Chapter 13) and the greatly reduced olfactory cortices.

7. **Gustatory cortex.** The **gustatory (taste) cortex** (gus'tah-tor-e), a region involved in perceiving taste stimuli, is located in the insula just deep to the temporal lobe (Figure 12.6a).

8. **Visceral sensory area.** The cortex of the insula just posterior to the gustatory cortex is involved in conscious perception of visceral sensations. These include upset stomach, full bladder, and the feeling that your lungs will burst when you hold your breath too long.

Homeostatic Imbalance 12.2

Damage to the *primary visual cortex* (Figure 12.6) results in functional blindness. By contrast, individuals with a damaged visual association area can see, but they do not comprehend what they are looking at. ✚

Multimodal Association Areas The association areas that we have considered so far (colored light red or light blue in Figure 12.6) have all been tightly tied to one kind of primary motor or sensory cortex (colored dark red or dark blue). Most of the cortex, though, consists of complexly connected **multimodal association areas** (colored light violet in Figure 12.6) that receive inputs from multiple senses and send outputs to multiple areas.

In general, information flows from sensory receptors to the appropriate primary sensory cortex, then to a sensory association cortex and then on to the multimodal association cortex. Multimodal association cortex allows us to give meaning to the information that we receive, store it in memory, tie it to previous experience and knowledge, and decide what action to take. Those decisions are relayed to the premotor cortex, which in turn communicates with the motor cortex. The multimodal association cortex seems to be where sensations, thoughts, and emotions become conscious. It is what makes us who we are.

Suppose, for example, you drop a bottle of acid in the chem lab and it splashes on you. You see the bottle shatter, hear the crash, feel your skin burning, and smell the acid fumes. These individual perceptions come together in the multimodal association areas. Along with feelings of panic, these perceptions are woven into a seamless whole, which (hopefully) recalls instructions about what to do in this situation. As a result your premotor and primary motor cortices direct your legs to propel you to the safety shower.

The multimodal association areas can be broadly divided into three parts: the anterior association, posterior association, and limbic association areas.

1. **Anterior association area.** The **anterior association area** in the frontal lobe, also called the **prefrontal cortex**, is the most complicated cortical region of all (Figure 12.6). It is involved with intellect, complex learning abilities (called cognition), recall, and personality. It contains working memory, which is necessary for abstract ideas, judgment, reasoning, persistence, and planning. These abilities develop slowly in children, which implies that the prefrontal cortex matures slowly and depends heavily on positive and negative feedback from our social environment.

2. **Posterior association area.** The **posterior association area** is a large region encompassing parts of the temporal, parietal, and occipital lobes. This area plays a role in recognizing patterns and faces, localizing us and our surroundings in space, and binding different sensory inputs into a coherent whole. In the spilled acid example above, your awareness of the entire scene originates from this area. Attention to an area of space or an area of one's own body is also a function of this part of the brain. Many parts of the posterior association area (including Wernicke's area, Figure 12.6a) are also involved in understanding written and spoken language.

3. **Limbic association area.** The **limbic association area** includes the cingulate gyrus, parahippocampal gyrus, and hippocampus (see Figures 12.6b and 12.16). Part of the limbic system (which we describe later), the limbic association area provides the emotional impact that makes a scene important to us. In our example above, it provides the sense of "danger" when the acid splashes on our legs. The hippocampus establishes memories that allow us to remember this incident. More on this later.

Homeostatic Imbalance 12.3

Tumors or other lesions of the *anterior association area* may cause mental and personality disorders including loss of judgment, attentiveness, and inhibitions. The affected individual may be oblivious to social restraints, perhaps becoming careless about personal appearance, or rashly attacking a 7-foot opponent rather than running.

Different problems arise for individuals with lesions in the part of the *posterior association area* that provides awareness of self in space. They may refuse to wash or dress the side of their body opposite to the lesion because "that doesn't belong to me." ✚

Lateralization of Cortical Functioning We use both cerebral hemispheres for almost every activity, and the hemispheres appear nearly identical. Nonetheless, there is a division of labor, and each hemisphere has abilities not completely shared by its partner. This phenomenon is called **lateralization**.

Although one cerebral hemisphere or the other "dominates" each task, the term **cerebral dominance** designates the hemisphere that is *dominant for language*. In most people (about 90%), the left hemisphere has greater control over language abilities, math, and logic. This so-called dominant hemisphere is working when we compose a sentence, balance a checkbook, and memorize a list. The other hemisphere (usually the right) is more free-spirited, more involved in visual-spatial skills, intuition, emotion, and artistic and musical skills. It is the poetic, creative, and the "Ah-ha!" (insightful) side of our nature, and in males it is better at recognizing faces.

Most individuals with left cerebral dominance are right-handed. In the remaining 10% of people, the roles of the hemispheres are reversed or the hemispheres share their functions equally. Typically, right-cerebral-dominant people are left-handed and male. Some "lefties" who have a cerebral cortex that functions bilaterally are ambidextrous.

The two cerebral hemispheres have almost instantaneous communication with each other via connecting fiber tracts, as well as complete functional integration. Furthermore, although lateralization means that each hemisphere is better than the other at certain functions, neither hemisphere is better at everything.

Cerebral White Matter

The second of the three basic regions of each cerebral hemisphere is the internal **cerebral white matter**. From what we have already described, you know that communication within the brain is extensive. The white matter deep to the cortical gray matter is responsible for communication between cerebral areas and between the cerebral cortex and lower CNS centers.

White matter consists largely of myelinated fibers bundled into large tracts. These fibers and tracts are classified according to the direction in which they run as *association*, *commissural*, or *projection* (**Figure 12.8**).

- **Association fibers** connect different parts of the same hemisphere. Short association fibers connect adjacent gyri. Long association fibers are bundled into tracts and connect different cortical lobes.

- **Commissural fibers** connect corresponding gray areas of the two hemispheres. These **commissures** (kom′ĭ-shūrz) allow the two hemispheres to function as a coordinated whole. The largest commissure is the **corpus callosum** (kah-lo′sum; "thickened body"), which lies superior to the lateral ventricles, deep within the longitudinal fissure. Less prominent examples are the **anterior** and **posterior commissures** (see Figure 12.10, p. 440).

- **Projection fibers** either enter the cerebral cortex from lower brain or cord centers or descend from the cortex to lower areas. Sensory information reaches the cerebral cortex and motor output leaves it through these projection fibers. They tie the cortex to the rest of the nervous system and to the body's receptors and effectors. In contrast to commissural and association fibers, which run horizontally, projection fibers run vertically (Figure 12.8a).

At the top of the brain stem, the projection fibers on each side form a compact band, the **internal capsule**, that passes between the thalamus and some of the basal nuclei. Beyond that point, the fibers radiate fanlike through the cerebral white matter to the cortex. This distinctive arrangement is called the **corona radiata** ("radiating crown").

Longitudinal fissure

Superior

Association fibers
(within hemisphere)

Lateral
ventricle

Commissural fibers
(between hemispheres)

• Corpus callosum

Basal nuclei
• Caudate
• Putamen
• Globus
  pallidus

Projection fibers
(cerebral cortex
to lower area)

• Corona
  radiata

Thalamus

• Internal
  capsule

Third
ventricle

Gray matter

White matter

Pons

Medulla oblongata

Decussation
(cross-over)
of pyramids

(a) Frontal section

*— fiber tract
that come up
from spinal cord*

Association fibers

Commissural fibers
• Corpus callosum

Gray
matter

Projection fibers
• Corona radiata
• Internal capsule

(b) Parasagittal section and dissection

Figure 12.8 White fiber tracts of the cerebral hemispheres. Commissural, association, and projection fibers run within the cerebrum, and between the cerebrum and lower CNS centers. In all views, notice the tight band of projection fibers, called the internal capsule, that passes between the thalamus and the basal nuclei, and then fans out as the corona radiata.

12

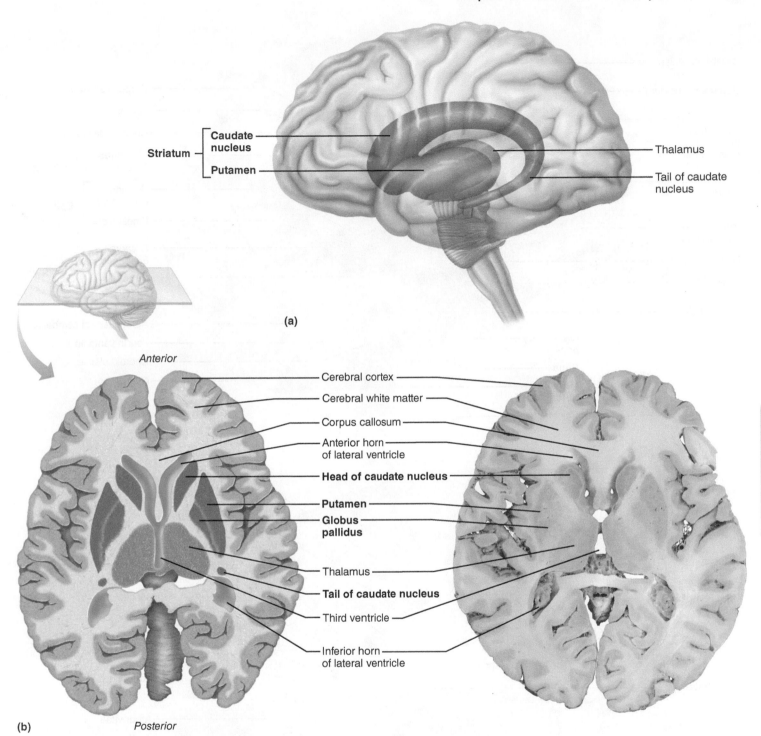

Figure 12.9 Basal nuclei. (a) Three-dimensional view of the basal nuclei (basal ganglia), showing their position in the cerebrum. **(b)** Transverse section of cerebrum and diencephalon showing the relationship of the basal nuclei to the thalamus and the lateral and third ventricles.

Basal Nuclei

Deep within the cerebral white matter is the third basic region of each hemisphere, a group of subcortical nuclei called the **basal nuclei** or **basal ganglia**.* Although the definition of the precise

*Because a nucleus is a collection of nerve cell bodies within the CNS, the term *basal nuclei* is technically correct. The more frequently used but misleading historical term *basal ganglia* is a misnomer and should be abandoned, because ganglia are PNS structures.

structures forming the basal nuclei is controversial, most anatomists agree each hemisphere's basal nuclei include the **caudate nucleus** (kaw'dāt), **putamen** (pu-ta'men), and **globus pallidus** (glo'bis pal'ĭ-dus) **(Figure 12.9)**.

The comma-shaped caudate nucleus arches superiorly over the diencephalon. Together with the putamen, it forms the **striatum** (stri-a'tum), so called because the fibers of the internal capsule passing through them create a striped appearance. Although

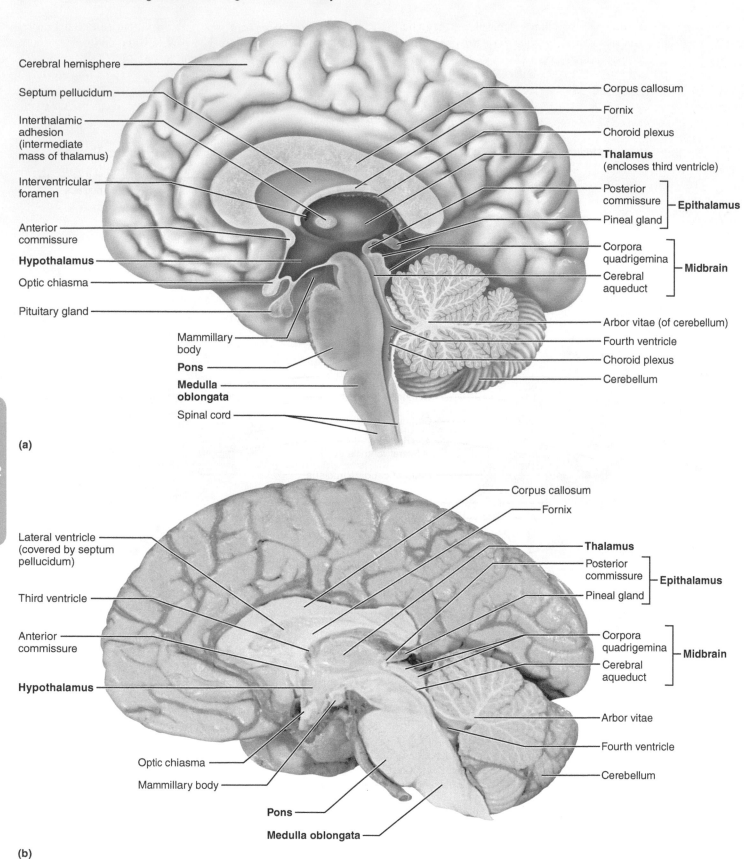

Cerebral hemisphere

Septum pellucidum

Interthalamic
adhesion
(intermediate
mass of thalamus)

Interventricular
foramen

Anterior
commissure

Hypothalamus

Optic chiasma

Pituitary gland

Mammillary
body

Pons

**Medulla
oblongata**

Spinal cord

Corpus callosum

Fornix

Choroid plexus

Thalamus
(encloses third ventricle)

Posterior
commissure ⎤
⎥ **Epithalamus**
Pineal gland ⎦

Corpora
quadrigemina ⎤
⎥ **Midbrain**
Cerebral ⎦
aqueduct

Arbor vitae (of cerebellum)

Fourth ventricle

Choroid plexus

Cerebellum

(a)

12

Lateral ventricle
(covered by septum
pellucidum)

Third ventricle

Anterior
commissure

Hypothalamus

Optic chiasma

Mammillary body

Pons

Medulla oblongata

Corpus callosum

Fornix

Thalamus

Posterior
commissure ⎤
⎥ **Epithalamus**
Pineal gland ⎦

Corpora
quadrigemina ⎤
⎥ **Midbrain**
Cerebral ⎦
aqueduct

Arbor vitae

Fourth ventricle

Cerebellum

(b)

Figure 12.10 Midsagittal section of the brain. (a) Illustration highlighting the
diencephalon (purple) and brain stem (green). **(b)** Photo of same view.

the putamen ("pod") and globus pallidus ("pale globe") together form a lens-shaped mass, sometimes called the *lentiform nucleus*, these two nuclei are functionally separate.

The basal nuclei are functionally associated with the *subthalamic nuclei* (located in the lateral "floor" of the diencephalon) and the *substantia nigra* of the midbrain (see Figure 12.14a).

The basal nuclei receive input from the entire cerebral cortex, as well as from other subcortical nuclei and each other. Via relays through the thalamus, the output nucleus of the basal nuclei (globus pallidus) and the substantia nigra project to the premotor and prefrontal cortices and so influence muscle movements directed by the primary motor cortex. The basal nuclei have no direct access to motor pathways.

The precise role of the basal nuclei has been elusive because of their inaccessible location and because their motor functions overlap with those of the cerebellum. In addition to their motor functions, the basal nuclei play a role in cognition and emotion. In all of these cases, the basal nuclei seem to filter out incorrect or inappropriate responses, passing only the best response on to the cortex.

For example, in motor activity, the basal nuclei are particularly important in starting, stopping, and monitoring the intensity of movements executed by the cortex, especially those that are relatively slow or stereotyped, such as arm-swinging during walking. Additionally, they inhibit antagonistic or unnecessary movements. Disorders of the basal nuclei result in either too much movement (as in Huntington's disease) or too little movement (Parkinson's disease); see p. 464.

☑ Check Your Understanding

4. What anatomical landmark of the cerebral cortex separates primary motor areas from somatosensory areas?
5. Mike, who is left-handed, decided to wear his favorite T-shirt to his anatomy class. On his T-shirt were the words "Only left-handed people are in their right minds." What does this statement mean?
6. Which type of fiber allows the two cerebral hemispheres to "talk to each other"?
7. Name the components of the basal nuclei.

For answers, see Appendix H.

Diencephalon

✓ Describe the location of the diencephalon, and name its subdivisions and functions.

Forming the central core of the forebrain and surrounded by the cerebral hemispheres, the **diencephalon** consists largely of three paired structures—the thalamus, hypothalamus, and epithalamus. These gray matter areas collectively enclose the third ventricle **(Figure 12.10)**.

Thalamus

The **thalamus** consists of bilateral egg-shaped nuclei, which form the superolateral walls of the third ventricle (Figures 12.8 and 12.10). In most people, an **interthalamic adhesion** (**intermediate mass**) connects the nuclei. *Thalamus* is a Greek word mean-

ing "inner room," which well describes this deep, well-hidden brain region that makes up 80% of the diencephalon.

The thalamus is *the* relay station for information coming into the cerebral cortex. Within the thalamus are a large number of nuclei, most named according to their location **(Figure 12.11a)**. Each nucleus has a functional specialty, and each projects fibers to and receives fibers from a specific region of the cerebral cortex.

Afferent impulses from all senses and all parts of the body converge on the thalamus and synapse with at least one of its nuclei. For example, the ventral posterolateral nuclei receive impulses from the general somatic sensory receptors (touch, pressure, pain, etc.), and the *lateral* and *medial geniculate bodies* (jĕ-nik′u-lāt; "knee shaped") are important visual and auditory relay centers, respectively.

Within the thalamus, information is sorted out and "edited." Impulses having to do with similar functions are relayed as a group via the internal capsule to the appropriate area of the sensory cortex as well as to specific cortical association areas. As the afferent impulses reach the thalamus, we have a crude recognition of the sensation as pleasant or unpleasant. However, specific stimulus localization and discrimination occur in the cerebral cortex.

In addition to sensory inputs, virtually *all* other inputs ascending to the cerebral cortex funnel through thalamic nuclei. These include:

- Inputs that help regulate emotion and visceral function from the hypothalamus (via the anterior nuclei)
- Instructions that help direct the activity of the motor cortices from the cerebellum and basal nuclei (via the ventral lateral and ventral anterior nuclei, respectively)
- Inputs for memory or sensory integration that are projected to specific association cortices (via pulvinar, lateral dorsal, and lateral posterior nuclei)

In summary, the thalamus plays a key role in mediating sensation, motor activities, cortical arousal, learning, and memory. It is truly the gateway to the cerebral cortex.

Hypothalamus

Named for its position below (*hypo*) the thalamus, the **hypothalamus** caps the brain stem and forms the inferolateral walls of the third ventricle (Figure 12.10). Merging into the midbrain inferiorly, the hypothalamus extends from the optic chiasma (crossover point of the optic nerves) to the posterior margin of the mammillary bodies.

The **mammillary bodies** (mam′mil-er-e; "little breast"), paired pealike nuclei that bulge anteriorly from the hypothalamus, are relay stations in the olfactory pathways. Between the optic chiasma and mammillary bodies is the **infundibulum** (in″fun-dib′u-lum), a stalk of hypothalamic tissue that connects the **pituitary gland** to the base of the hypothalamus. Like the thalamus, the hypothalamus contains many functionally important nuclei (Figure 12.11b).

Despite its small size, the hypothalamus is the main visceral control center of the body and is vitally important to overall

Medial dorsal nucleus

Lateral dorsal nucleus

Lateral posterior nucleus

Anterior nuclei

Reticular nucleus

Pulvinar

Medial geniculate body

Lateral geniculate body

Ventral anterior

Ventral lateral

Ventral postero-lateral

Ventral nuclei

(a) **The main thalamic nuclei.** (The reticular nuclei that "cap" the thalamus laterally are depicted as curving translucent structures.)

Paraventricular nucleus

Anterior commissure

Preoptic nucleus

Anterior hypothalamic nucleus

Supraoptic nucleus

Suprachiasmatic nucleus

Optic chiasma

Infundibulum (stalk of the pituitary gland)

Fornix

Dorsomedial nucleus

Posterior hypothalamic nucleus

Lateral hypothalamic area

Ventromedial nucleus

Arcuate nucleus

Mammillary body

Pituitary gland

(b) **The main hypothalamic nuclei.**

Figure 12.11 **Selected structures of the diencephalon.**

body homeostasis. Few tissues in the body escape its influence. Its chief homeostatic roles are to:

- **Control the autonomic nervous system.** Recall that the autonomic nervous system (ANS) is a system of peripheral nerves that regulates cardiac and smooth muscle and secretion by the glands. The hypothalamus regulates ANS activity by controlling the activity of centers in the brain stem and spinal cord. In this role, the hypothalamus influences blood pressure, rate and force of heartbeat, digestive tract motility, eye pupil size, and many other visceral activities.

- **Initiate physical responses to emotions.** The hypothalamus lies at the "heart" of the limbic system (the emotional part of the brain). It contains nuclei involved in perceiving pleasure, fear, and rage, as well as those involved in biological rhythms and drives (such as the sex drive).

  The hypothalamus acts through ANS pathways to initiate most physical expressions of emotion. For example, a fearful person has a pounding heart, high blood pressure, pallor, sweating, and a dry mouth.

- **Regulate body temperature.** The body's thermostat is in the hypothalamus. Hypothalamic neurons monitor blood temperature and receive input from other thermoreceptors in the brain and body periphery. Accordingly, the hypothalamus initiates cooling (sweating) or heat-generating actions (shivering) as needed to maintain a relatively constant body temperature (see Figure 24.26, p. 946).

- **Regulate food intake.** In response to changing blood levels of certain nutrients (glucose and amino acids) or hormones (cholecystokinin, ghrelin, and others), the hypothalamus regulates feelings of hunger and satiety.

- **Regulate water balance and thirst.** When body fluids become too concentrated, hypothalamic neurons called *osmoreceptors* are activated. Osmoreceptors excite hypothalamic nuclei that trigger the release of antidiuretic hormone (ADH) from the posterior pituitary. ADH causes the kidneys to retain water. The same conditions also stimulate hypothalamic neurons in the *thirst center*, causing us to feel thirsty and drink more fluids.

- **Regulate sleep-wake cycles.** Acting with other brain regions, the hypothalamus helps regulate sleep. Its *suprachiasmatic nucleus* (our biological clock) sets the timing of the sleep cycle in response to daylight-darkness cues received from the visual pathways.

- **Control endocrine system function.** The hypothalamus acts as the helmsman of the endocrine system in two important ways. First, its *releasing* and *inhibiting hormones* control the secretion of hormones by the anterior pituitary gland. Second, its *supraoptic* and *paraventricular nuclei* produce the hormones ADH and oxytocin.

Homeostatic Imbalance 12.4

Hypothalamic disturbances cause a number of disorders including severe body wasting, obesity, sleep disturbances, dehydration, and emotional imbalances. For example, the hypothalamus is implicated in *failure to thrive*, a condition characterized by delay in growth or development that occurs when a child is deprived of a warm, nurturing relationship. ✚

Epithalamus

The most dorsal portion of the diencephalon, the **epithalamus** forms the roof of the third ventricle. Extending from its posterior border and visible externally is the **pineal gland** or **body** (pin′e-al; "pine cone shaped") (see Figures 12.10 and 12.13c). The pineal gland secretes the hormone *melatonin* (a sleep-inducing signal and antioxidant; see Chapter 16) and, along with hypothalamic nuclei, helps regulate the sleep-wake cycle. The *posterior commissure* forms the caudal border of the epithalamus.

☑ **Check Your Understanding**

8. Why is the thalamus called the "gateway to the cerebral cortex"?
9. The hypothalamus oversees a branch of the peripheral nervous system. Which branch?

For answers, see Appendix H.

Brain Stem

✓ Identify the three major regions of the brain stem, and note the functions of each area.

From superior to inferior, the brain stem regions are midbrain, pons, and medulla oblongata (Figures 12.10, 12.12, and 12.13). Each roughly an inch long, collectively they account for only 2.5% of total brain mass. Histologically, the organization of the brain stem is similar (but not identical) to that of the spinal cord—deep gray matter surrounded by white matter fiber tracts. However, the brain stem has nuclei of gray matter embedded in the white matter, a feature not found in the spinal cord.

Brain stem centers produce the rigidly programmed, automatic behaviors necessary for survival. Positioned between the cerebrum and the spinal cord, the brain stem also provides a pathway for fiber tracts running between higher and lower neural centers. Additionally, brain stem nuclei are associated with 10 of the 12 pairs of cranial nerves (which we will describe in Chapter 13), so it is heavily involved with innervating the head.

Midbrain

The **midbrain** is located between the diencephalon and pons (**Figure 12.12** and **Figure 12.13**). On its ventral aspect two bulging **cerebral peduncles** (pĕ-dung′klz) form vertical pillars that seem to hold up the cerebrum, hence their name meaning "little feet of the cerebrum" (Figure 12.13a, b, and **Figure 12.14a**). The *crus cerebri* ("leg of the cerebrum") of each peduncle contains a large pyramidal (corticospinal) motor tract descending toward the spinal cord. The *superior*

Frontal lobe

Olfactory bulb (synapse point of cranial nerve I)

Optic chiasma

Optic nerve (II)

Optic tract

Mammillary body

Midbrain

Pons

Temporal lobe

Medulla oblongata

Cerebellum

Spinal cord

Figure 12.12 Inferior view of the brain, showing the three parts of the brain stem: midbrain, pons, and medulla oblongata. Only a small portion of the midbrain is visible in this view. (For a related image, see *A Brief Atlas of the Human Body*, Figure 49.)

12

Thalamus ⎤
Hypothalamus ⎦ Diencephalon

Midbrain ⎤
Pons ⎥ Brain stem
Medulla oblongata ⎦

View (a) → ← View (c)

View (b)

Diencephalon
• Thalamus
• Hypothalamus

Mammillary body

Oculomotor nerve (III)

Trochlear nerve (IV)

Middle cerebellar peduncle

Abducens nerve (VI)

Vestibulocochlear nerve (VIII)

Pyramid

Ventral root of first cervical nerve

Decussation of pyramids

Spinal cord

Optic chiasma
Optic nerve (II)
Optic tract

Infundibulum
Pituitary gland

Crus cerebri of cerebral peduncles (midbrain)
Trigeminal nerve (V)
Pons
Facial nerve (VII)
Abducens nerve (VI)
Glossopharyngeal nerve (IX)
Hypoglossal nerve (XII)
Vagus nerve (X)
Accessory nerve (XI)

Thalamus

Superior colliculus
Inferior colliculus
Trochlear nerve (IV)
Superior cerebellar peduncle
Middle cerebellar peduncle
Inferior cerebellar peduncle
Vestibulocochlear nerve (VIII)
Olive

(a) Ventral view

(b) Left lateral view

Figure 12.13 Three views of the brain stem (green) and the diencephalon (purple).

cerebellar peduncles, also fiber tracts, connect the midbrain to the cerebellum dorsally (Figure 12.13b, c).

Running through the midbrain is the hollow *cerebral aqueduct*, which connects the third and fourth ventricles (Figures 12.10 and 12.14a). It delineates the cerebral peduncles ventrally from the *tectum*, the midbrain's roof. Surrounding the aqueduct is the *periaqueductal gray matter*, which is involved in pain suppression and links the fear-perceiving amygdaloid body and ANS pathways that control the "fight-or-flight" response. The periaqueductal gray matter also includes nuclei that control two cranial nerves, the *oculomotor* and the *trochlear nuclei* (trok′le-ar).

Nuclei are also scattered in the surrounding white matter of the midbrain. The **corpora quadrigemina** (kor′por-ah kwod″rĭ-jem′ĭ-nah; "quadruplets"), the largest midbrain nuclei, raise four domelike protrusions on the dorsal midbrain surface (Figures 12.10 and 12.13c). The superior pair, the **superior colliculi** (kŏ-lik′u-li), are visual reflex centers that coordinate head

and eye movements when we visually follow a moving object, even if we are not consciously looking at it. The **inferior colliculi** are part of the auditory relay from the hearing receptors of the ear to the sensory cortex. They also act in reflexive responses to sound, such as the *startle reflex* which causes you to turn your head toward an unexpected noise.

Also embedded in each side of the midbrain white matter are two pigmented nuclei, the substantia nigra and red nucleus. The bandlike **substantia nigra** (sub-stan′she-ah ni′grah) is located deep to the cerebral peduncle (Figure 12.14a). Its dark (*nigr* = black) color reflects a high content of melanin pigment, a precursor of the neurotransmitter (dopamine) released by these neurons. The substantia nigra is functionally linked to the basal nuclei (its axons project to the putamen), and many authorities consider it part of the basal nuclear complex. Degeneration of the dopamine-releasing neurons of the substantia nigra is the ultimate cause of Parkinson's disease.

12

Diencephalon

Pineal gland

Floor of
fourth ventricle

Facial nerve (VII)

Choroid plexus
(fourth ventricle)

Dorsal median sulcus

Dorsal root of
first cervical nerve

(c) Dorsal view

Thalamus

Midbrain
• Superior colliculus
• Inferior colliculus
— Corpora quadrigemina of tectum
• Trochlear nerve (IV)
• Superior cerebellar peduncle

Pons
• Middle cerebellar peduncle

Medulla oblongata
• Inferior cerebellar peduncle
• Vestibulocochlear nerve (VIII)
• Glossopharyngeal nerve (IX)
• Vagus nerve (X)
• Accessory nerve (XI)

Figure 12.13 (*continued*)

The oval **red nucleus** lies deep to the substantia nigra (Figure 12.14a). Its reddish hue is due to its rich blood supply and to the presence of iron pigment in its neurons. The red nuclei are relay nuclei in some descending motor pathways that effect limb flexion, and they are embedded in the *reticular formation*, a system of small nuclei scattered through the core of the brain stem (see pp. 450–451).

Pons

The **pons** is the bulging brain stem region wedged between the midbrain and the medulla oblongata (see Figures 12.10, 12.12, and 12.13). Dorsally, the fourth ventricle separates it from the cerebellum.

As its name suggests (*pons* = bridge), the pons is chiefly composed of conduction tracts. They are oriented in two different directions:

- The deep projection fibers run longitudinally as part of the pathway between higher brain centers and the spinal cord.
- The more superficial ventral fibers are oriented transversely and dorsally. They form the *middle cerebellar peduncles* and connect the pons bilaterally with the two sides of the cerebellum dorsally (Figure 12.13). These fibers issue from numerous *pontine nuclei*, which relay "conversations" between the motor cortex and cerebellum.

Several cranial nerve pairs issue from pontine nuclei. They include the *trigeminal* (tri-jem′ĭ-nal), *abducens* (ab-du′senz), and *facial nerves* (Figures 12.13a, b and 12.14b). We discuss the cranial nerves and their functions in Chapter 13.

Other important pontine nuclei are part of the reticular formation and some help the medulla oblongata maintain the normal rhythm of breathing.

Medulla Oblongata

The conical **medulla oblongata** (mĕ-dul′ah ob″long-gah′tah), or simply **medulla**, is the most inferior part of the brain stem. It blends imperceptibly into the spinal cord at the level of the foramen magnum of the skull (Figures 12.10 and 12.12; see Figure 7.6, p. 206).

The central canal of the spinal cord continues upward into the medulla, where it broadens out to form the cavity of the fourth ventricle. Together, the medulla and the pons form the ventral wall of the fourth ventricle. [The dorsal ventricular wall is formed by a thin capillary-rich membrane called a choroid plexus which abuts the cerebellum dorsally (Figure 12.10).]

Structures of the Medulla Oblongata Flanking the midline on the medulla's ventral aspect are two longitudinal ridges called **pyramids**, formed by the large pyramidal (corticospinal) tracts descending from the motor cortex (Figure 12.14c). Just above the medulla–spinal cord junction, most of these fibers cross over to the opposite side before continuing into the spinal cord. This crossover point is called the **decussation of the pyramids** (de″kus-sa′shun; "a crossing"). As a result of this crossover, each cerebral hemisphere chiefly controls the voluntary movements of muscles on the opposite side of the body.

Several other structures are visible externally. The *inferior cerebellar peduncles* are fiber tracts that connect the medulla to the cerebellum dorsally. Situated lateral to the pyramids,

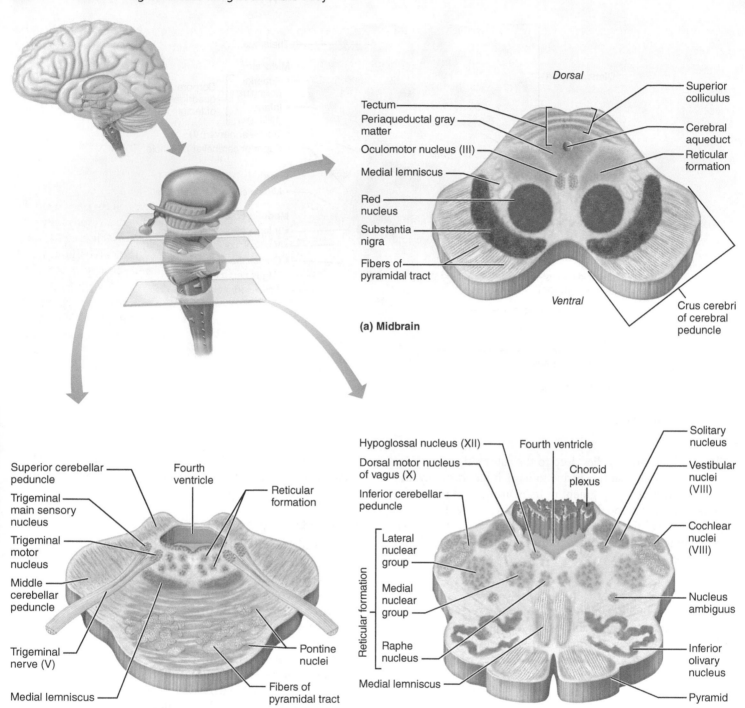

Tectum
Periaqueductal gray matter
Oculomotor nucleus (III)
Medial lemniscus
Red nucleus
Substantia nigra
Fibers of pyramidal tract

Dorsal
Superior colliculus
Cerebral aqueduct
Reticular formation
Ventral
Crus cerebri of cerebral peduncle

(a) Midbrain

Superior cerebellar peduncle
Trigeminal main sensory nucleus
Trigeminal motor nucleus
Middle cerebellar peduncle
Trigeminal nerve (V)
Medial lemniscus

Fourth ventricle
Reticular formation
Pontine nuclei
Fibers of pyramidal tract

(b) Pons

Hypoglossal nucleus (XII)
Dorsal motor nucleus of vagus (X)
Inferior cerebellar peduncle
Fourth ventricle
Choroid plexus

Reticular formation
Lateral nuclear group
Medial nuclear group
Raphe nucleus
Medial lemniscus

Solitary nucleus
Vestibular nuclei (VIII)
Cochlear nuclei (VIII)
Nucleus ambiguus
Inferior olivary nucleus
Pyramid

(c) Medulla oblongata

Figure 12.14 Cross sections through different regions of the brain stem.

the **olives** are oval swellings (which *do* resemble olives) (Figure 12.13b). These swellings are caused mainly by the wavy folds of gray matter of the underlying **inferior olivary nuclei** (Figure 12.14c). These nuclei relay sensory information on the degree of stretch in muscles and joints to the cerebellum. The rootlets of the *hypoglossal nerves* emerge from the groove between the pyramid and olive on each side of the brain stem. Other cranial nerves associated with the medulla are the *glossopharyngeal nerves* and *vagus nerves*. Additionally, the fibers

of the *vestibulocochlear nerves* (ves-tib″u-lo-kok′le-ar) synapse with the **cochlear nuclei** (auditory relays), and with numerous **vestibular nuclei** in both the pons and medulla. The vestibular nuclei mediate responses that maintain equilibrium.

Also housed in the medulla are several nuclei associated with ascending sensory tracts. The most prominent are the dorsally located **nucleus gracilis** (grah-sĭ′lis) and **nucleus cuneatus** (ku′ne-āt-us), associated with a tract called the *medial lemniscus* (Figure 12.14). These serve as relay nuclei in a pathway by which general somatic sensory information ascends from the spinal cord to the somatosensory cortex.

Functions of the Medulla Oblongata The small size of the medulla belies its crucial role as an autonomic reflex center involved in maintaining body homeostasis. The medulla contains these important functional groups of visceral motor nuclei:

- **Cardiovascular center.** This includes the *cardiac center*, which adjusts the force and rate of heart contraction to meet the body's needs, and the *vasomotor center*, which changes blood vessel diameter to regulate blood pressure.

- **Respiratory centers.** These generate the respiratory rhythm and (in concert with pontine centers) control the rate and depth of breathing.

- **Various other centers.** Additional centers regulate such activities as vomiting, hiccuping, swallowing, coughing, and sneezing.

Notice that many functions listed above are also attributed to the hypothalamus (pp. 441–442). The overlap is easily explained. The hypothalamus controls many visceral functions by relaying its instructions through medullary reticular centers, which carry them out.

☑ **Check Your Understanding**

10. What are the pyramids of the medulla? What is the result of decussation of the pyramids?
11. Which region of the brain stem is associated with the cerebral peduncles and the superior and inferior colliculi?

For answers, see Appendix H.

Cerebellum

✓ Describe the structure and function of the cerebellum.

The cauliflower-like **cerebellum** (ser″ĕ-bel′um; "small brain"), exceeded in size only by the cerebrum, accounts for about 11% of total brain mass. The cerebellum is located dorsal to the pons and medulla (and to the intervening fourth ventricle). It protrudes under the occipital lobes of the cerebral hemispheres, from which it is separated by the transverse cerebral fissure (see Figure 12.4b).

By processing inputs received from the cerebral motor cortex, various brain stem nuclei, and sensory receptors, the cerebellum provides the precise timing and appropriate patterns of skeletal muscle contraction for smooth, coordinated movements and agility needed for our daily living—driving, typing, and for some of us, playing the tuba. Cerebellar activity occurs subconsciously—we have no awareness of it.

Cerebellar Anatomy

The cerebellum is bilaterally symmetrical. The wormlike **vermis** connects its two apple-sized **cerebellar hemispheres** medially **(Figure 12.15)**. Its surface is heavily convoluted, with fine, transversely oriented pleatlike gyri known as **folia** ("leaves"). Deep

fissures subdivide each hemisphere into **anterior**, **posterior**, and **flocculonodular lobes** (flok″u-lo-nod′u-lar). The small propeller-shaped flocculonodular lobes, situated deep to the vermis and posterior lobe, cannot be seen in a surface view.

Like the cerebrum, the cerebellum has a thin outer cortex of gray matter, internal white matter, and small, deeply situated, paired masses of gray matter, the most familiar of which are the *dentate nuclei*. Several types of neurons populate the cerebellar cortex, including **Purkinje cells** (see Table 11.1 on p. 394). These large cells, with their extensively branched dendrites, are the only cortical neurons that send axons through the white matter to synapse with the central nuclei of the cerebellum. The distinctive pattern of white matter in the cerebellum resembles a branching tree, a pattern fancifully called the **arbor vitae** (ar′bor vi′te; "tree of life") (Figure 12.15a, b).

The anterior and posterior lobes of the cerebellum, which coordinate body movements, have three sensory maps of the entire body as indicated by the homunculi in Figure 12.15d. The part of the cerebellar cortex that receives sensory input from a body region influences motor output to that region. The medial portions influence the motor activities of the trunk and girdle muscles. The intermediate parts of each hemisphere influence the distal parts of the limbs and skilled movements. The lateral-most parts of each hemisphere integrate information from the association areas of the cerebral cortex and appear to play a role in planning movements rather than executing them. The flocculonodular lobes receive inputs from the equilibrium apparatus of the inner ears, and adjust posture to maintain balance.

Cerebellar Peduncles

As noted earlier, three paired fiber tracts—the cerebellar peduncles—connect the cerebellum to the brain stem (see Figures 12.13 and 12.15b). Unlike the contralateral fiber distribution to and from the cerebral cortex, virtually all fibers entering and leaving the cerebellum are **ipsilateral** (*ipsi* = same)—from and to the same side of the body.

- The **superior cerebellar peduncles** connecting cerebellum and midbrain carry instructions from neurons in the deep cerebellar nuclei to the cerebral motor cortex via thalamic relays. Like the basal nuclei, the cerebellum has no *direct* connections to the cerebral cortex.

- The **middle cerebellar peduncles** carry one-way communications from the pons to the cerebellum, advising the cerebellum of voluntary motor activities initiated by the motor cortex (via relays in the pontine nuclei).

- The **inferior cerebellar peduncles** connect medulla and cerebellum. These peduncles convey sensory information to the cerebellum from (1) muscle proprioceptors throughout the body, and (2) the vestibular nuclei of the brain stem, which are concerned with equilibrium and balance.

Cerebellar Processing

Cerebellar processing fine-tunes motor activity as follows:

1. The motor areas of the cerebral cortex, via relay nuclei in the brain stem, notify the cerebellum of their intent to initiate voluntary muscle contractions.

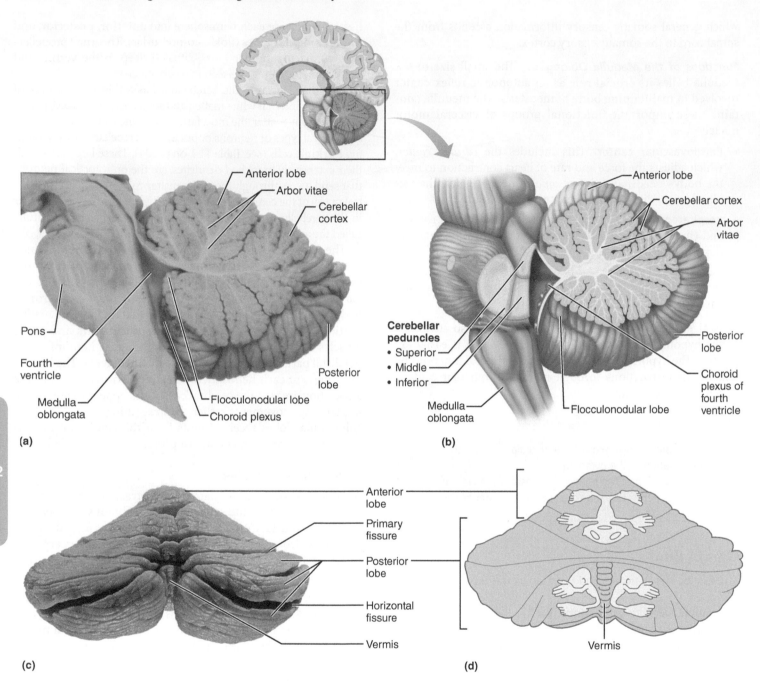

Figure 12.15 Cerebellum. (a) Photo of midsagittal section. **(b)** Drawing of parasagittal section. **(c)** Photograph of the posterior aspect of the cerebellum. **(d)** Three body maps of the cerebellar cortex (in the form of homunculi).

2. At the same time, the cerebellum receives information from proprioceptors throughout the body (regarding tension in the muscles and tendons, and joint position) and from visual and equilibrium pathways. This information enables the cerebellum to evaluate body position and momentum—where the body is and where it is going.

3. The cerebellar cortex calculates the best way to coordinate the force, direction, and extent of muscle contraction to prevent overshoot, maintain posture, and ensure smooth, coordinated movements.

4. Then, via the superior peduncles, the cerebellum dispatches to the cerebral motor cortex its "blueprint" for coordinating movement. Cerebellar fibers also send information to brain stem nuclei, which in turn influence motor neurons of the spinal cord.

Just as an automatic pilot compares a plane's instrument readings with the planned course, the cerebellum continually compares the body's performance with the higher brain's intention and sends out messages to initiate appropriate corrective measures. Cerebellar injury results in loss of muscle tone and clumsy, unsure movements.

Septum pellucidum

Corpus callosum

Fiber tracts connecting limbic system structures
• Fornix
• Anterior commissure

Diencephalic structures of the limbic system
• Anterior thalamic nuclei (flanking 3rd ventricle)
• Hypothalamus
• Mammillary body

Cerebral structures of the limbic system
• Cingulate gyrus
• Septal nuclei
• Amygdaloid body
• Hippocampus
• Dentate gyrus
• Parahippocampal gyrus

Olfactory bulb

Figure 12.16 The limbic system. Lateral view of the brain, showing some of the structures of the limbic system, the emotional-visceral brain. The brain stem is not illustrated.

Cognitive Functions of the Cerebellum

Neuroanatomy, imaging studies, and observations of patients with cerebellar injuries suggest that the cerebellum also plays a role in thinking, language, and emotion. As in the motor system, the cerebellum may compare the actual output of these systems with the expected output and adjust accordingly. Much still remains to be discovered about the precise role of the cerebellum in nonmotor functions.

☑ Check Your Understanding

12. In what ways are the cerebellum and the cerebrum similar? In what ways are they different?

For answers, see Appendix H.

Functional Brain Systems

✓ Locate the limbic system and the reticular formation, and explain the role of each functional system.

Functional brain systems are networks of neurons that work together but span relatively large distances in the brain, so they cannot be localized to specific regions. The *limbic system* and the *reticular formation* are excellent examples. **Table 12.1** summarizes their functions, as well as those of the cerebral hemispheres, diencephalon, brain stem, and cerebellum.

The Limbic System

The **limbic system** is a group of structures located on the medial aspect of each cerebral hemisphere and diencephalon. Its cerebral structures encircle (*limbus* = ring) the upper part of the brain stem **(Figure 12.16)**. The limbic system includes the **amygdaloid body**

(ah-mig′dah-loid), an almond-shaped nucleus that sits on the tail of the caudate nucleus, and other parts of the rhinencephalon (*cingulate gyrus, septal nuclei*, the C-shaped *hippocampus, dentate gyrus,* and *parahippocampal gyrus*). In the diencephalon, the main limbic structures are the *hypothalamus* and the *anterior thalamic nuclei*. The **fornix** ("arch") and other fiber tracts link these limbic system regions together.

The limbic system is our *emotional*, or *affective* (feelings), *brain*. The amygdaloid body and the anterior part of the **cingulate gyrus** seem especially important in emotions. The amygdaloid body is critical for responding to perceived threats (such as angry or fearful facial expressions) with fear or aggression. The cingulate gyrus plays a role in expressing our emotions through gestures and in resolving mental conflicts when we are frustrated.

Odors often trigger emotional reactions and memories. These responses reflect the origin of much of the limbic system in the primitive "smell brain" (rhinencephalon). Our reactions to odors are rarely neutral (a skunk smells *bad* and repulses us), and odors often recall memories of emotion-laden events.

Extensive connections between the limbic system and lower and higher brain regions allow the system to integrate and respond to a variety of environmental stimuli. Most limbic system output is relayed through the hypothalamus. Because the hypothalamus is the neural clearinghouse for both autonomic (visceral) function and emotional response, it is not surprising that some people under acute or unrelenting emotional stress fall prey to visceral illnesses, such as high blood pressure and heartburn. Such emotion-induced illnesses are called **psychosomatic illnesses**.

Because the limbic system interacts with the prefrontal lobes, there is an intimate relationship between our feelings (mediated

Table 12.1	Functions of Major Brain Regions
REGION	**FUNCTION**

Cerebral Hemispheres (pp. 430–441)

■ **Cortical gray matter:**
  ▪ Localizes and interprets sensory inputs
  ▪ Controls voluntary and skilled skeletal muscle activity
  ▪ Functions in intellectual and emotional processing

Basal nuclei (ganglia):
  ▪ Subcortical motor centers
  ▪ Help control skeletal muscle movements

Diencephalon (pp. 441–443)

■ **Thalamus:**
  ▪ Relays sensory impulses to cerebral cortex for interpretation
  ▪ Relays impulses between cerebral motor cortex and lower (subcortical) motor centers, including cerebellum
  ▪ Involved in memory processing

■ **Hypothalamus:**
  ▪ Chief integration center of autonomic (involuntary) nervous system
  ▪ Regulates body temperature, food intake, water balance, thirst, and biological rhythms and drives
  ▪ Regulates hormonal output of anterior pituitary gland
  ▪ Acts as an endocrine organ, producing posterior pituitary hormones ADH and oxytocin

■ **Limbic System** (pp. 449–450)—A functional system:
  ▪ Includes cerebral and diencephalon structures (e.g., hypothalamus and anterior thalamic nuclei)
  ▪ Mediates emotional response
  ▪ Involved in memory processing

by the emotional brain) and our thoughts (mediated by the cognitive brain). As a result, we (1) react emotionally to things we consciously understand to be happening, and (2) are consciously aware of the emotional richness of our lives. Communication between the cerebral cortex and limbic system explains why emotions sometimes override logic and, conversely, why reason can stop us from expressing our emotions in inappropriate situations. Particular limbic system structures—the **hippocampus** and amygdaloid body—also play a role in memory.

The Reticular Formation

The **reticular formation** extends through the central core of the medulla oblongata, pons, and midbrain **(Figure 12.17)**. It is composed of loosely clustered neurons in what is otherwise white matter. These neurons form three broad columns along the length of the brain stem (Figure 12.14c): (1) the midline **raphe nuclei** (ra′fe; *raphe* = seam or crease), which are flanked laterally by (2) the **medial (large cell) group of nuclei** and (3) the **lateral (small cell) group of nuclei**.

The outstanding feature of the reticular neurons is their far-flung axonal connections. Individual reticular neurons project to the hypothalamus, thalamus, cerebral cortex, cerebellum, and spinal cord, making reticular neurons ideal for governing the arousal of the brain as a whole.

For example, unless inhibited by other brain areas, the neurons of the part of the reticular formation known as the **reticular activating system (RAS)** send a continuous stream of impulses to the cerebral cortex, keeping the cortex alert and conscious and enhancing its excitability. Impulses from all the great ascending sensory tracts synapse with RAS neurons, keeping them active and enhancing their arousing effect on the cerebrum. (This may explain why many students, stimulated by a bustling environment, like to study in a crowded cafeteria.)

The RAS also filters this flood of sensory inputs. Repetitive, familiar, or weak signals are filtered out, but unusual, significant, or strong impulses do reach consciousness. For example, you are probably unaware of your watch encircling your wrist, but would immediately notice it if the clasp broke. Between them, the RAS and the cerebral cortex disregard perhaps 99% of all sensory stimuli as unimportant. If this filtering did not occur, the sensory overload would drive us crazy. The drug LSD interferes with these sensory dampers, promoting an often overwhelming sensory overload.

Table 12.1 (continued)	
REGION	**FUNCTION**

Brain Stem (pp. 443–447)

- **Midbrain:**
  - Contains visual (superior colliculi) and auditory (inferior colliculi) reflex centers
  - Contains subcortical motor centers (substantia nigra and red nuclei)
  - Contains nuclei for cranial nerves III and IV
  - Contains projection fibers (e.g., fibers of the pyramidal tracts)

- **Pons:**
  - Relays information from the cerebrum to the cerebellum
  - Cooperates with the medullary respiratory centers to control respiratory rate and depth
  - Contains nuclei of cranial nerves V–VII
  - Contains projection fibers

- **Medulla oblongata:**
  - Relays ascending sensory pathway impulses from skin and proprioceptors through nuclei cuneatus and gracilis
  - Contains visceral nuclei controlling heart rate, blood vessel diameter, respiratory rate, vomiting, coughing, etc.
  - Relays sensory information to the cerebellum through inferior olivary nuclei
  - Contains nuclei of cranial nerves VIII–XII
  - Contains projection fibers
  - Site of decussation of pyramids

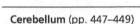

- **Reticular formation** (pp. 450–451)—A functional system:
  - Maintains cerebral cortical alertness (reticular activating system)
  - Filters out repetitive stimuli
  - Helps regulate skeletal and visceral muscle activity

Cerebellum (pp. 447–449)

- **Cerebellum:**
  - Processes information from cerebral motor cortex, proprioceptors, and visual and equilibrium pathways
  - Provides "instructions" to cerebral motor cortex and subcortical motor centers, resulting in smooth, coordinated skeletal muscle movements
  - Responsible for proper balance and posture

- Take a moment to become aware of all the stimuli in your environment. Notice all the colors, shapes, odors, sounds, and so on. How many of these sensory stimuli are you usually aware of?

The RAS is inhibited by sleep centers located in the hypothalamus and other neural regions, and is depressed by alcohol, sleep-inducing drugs, and tranquilizers. Severe injury to this system, as might follow a knockout punch that twists the brain stem, results in permanent unconsciousness (irreversible *coma*). Although the RAS is central to wakefulness, some of its nuclei are also involved in sleep, which we will discuss later in this chapter.

The reticular formation also has a *motor* arm. Some of its motor nuclei project to motor neurons in the spinal cord via the *reticulospinal tracts*, and help control skeletal muscles during coarse limb movements. Other reticular motor nuclei, such as the vasomotor, cardiac, and respiratory centers of the medulla, are autonomic centers that regulate visceral motor functions.

☑ **Check Your Understanding**

13. The limbic system is sometimes called the emotional-visceral brain. Which part of the limbic system is responsible for the visceral connection?
14. When Taylor begins to feel drowsy while driving, she opens her window, turns up the volume of the car stereo, and sips ice-cold water. How do these actions keep her awake?

For answers, see Appendix H.

Radiations to cerebral cortex

Visual impulses

Auditory impulses

Reticular formation

Ascending general sensory tracts (touch, pain, temperature)

Descending motor projections to spinal cord

Figure 12.17 The reticular formation. This functional brain system extends the length of the brain stem. Part of this formation, the reticular activating system (RAS), maintains alert wakefulness of the cerebral cortex. Ascending blue arrows indicate sensory input to the RAS. Purple arrows indicate reticular output (some via thalamic relays) to the cerebral cortex. Descending red arrow represents motor output involved in regulating muscle tone.

Higher Mental Functions

During the last four decades, an exciting exploration of our "inner space," or what we commonly call the *mind*, has been going on. But researchers in the field of cognition are still struggling to understand how the mind's qualities spring from living tissue and electrical impulses. Souls and synapses are hard to reconcile!

Because brain waves reflect the electrical activity on which higher mental functions are based, we will consider them first, along with the related topics of consciousness and sleep. We will then examine language and memory, an area of ongoing research that is of particular interest to our aging population.

Brain Wave Patterns and the EEG

✓ Define EEG and distinguish between alpha, beta, theta, and delta brain waves.

Normal brain function involves continuous electrical activity of neurons. An **electroencephalogram** (e-lek″tro-en-sef′ah-lo-gram), or **EEG**, records some aspects of this activity. An EEG is made by placing electrodes on the scalp and connecting the electrodes to an apparatus that measures voltage differences between various cortical areas **(Figure 12.18a)**. The patterns of neuronal electrical activity recorded, called **brain waves**, are generated by

synaptic activity at the surface of the cortex, rather than by action potentials in the white matter.

Each of us has a brain wave pattern that is as unique as our fingerprints. For simplicity, however, we can group brain waves into the four frequency classes shown in Figure 12.18b. Each wave is a continuous train of peaks and troughs, and the wave frequency, expressed in hertz (Hz), is the number of peaks in one second. A frequency of 1 Hz means that one peak occurs each second.

The amplitude or intensity of any wave is represented by how high the wave peaks rise and how low the troughs dip. The amplitude of brain waves reflects the synchronous activity of many neurons and not the degree of electrical activity of individual neurons. Usually, brain waves are complex and low amplitude. During some stages of sleep, neurons tend to fire synchronously, producing similar, high-amplitude brain waves.

- **Alpha waves** (8–13 Hz) are relatively regular and rhythmic, low-amplitude, synchronous waves. In most cases, they indicate a brain that is "idling"—a calm, relaxed state of wakefulness.

- **Beta waves** (14–30 Hz) are also rhythmic, but less regular than alpha waves and with a higher frequency. Beta waves occur when we are mentally alert, as when concentrating on some problem or visual stimulus.

- **Theta waves** (4–7 Hz) are still more irregular. Though common in children, theta waves are uncommon in awake adults but may appear when concentrating.

- **Delta waves** (4 Hz or less) are high-amplitude waves seen during deep sleep and when the reticular activating system is damped, such as during anesthesia. In awake adults, they indicate brain damage.

Brain waves change with age, sensory stimuli, brain disease, and the chemical state of the body. EEGs are used for diagnosing epilepsy and sleep disorders, and in research on brain function. Brain waves whose frequency is too high or too low suggest problems with cerebral cortical functions, and unconsciousness occurs at both extremes. Because spontaneous brain waves are always present, even during unconsciousness and coma, their absence—a "flat EEG"—is clinical evidence of brain death.

Homeostatic Imbalance 12.5

Almost without warning, a person with epilepsy may lose consciousness and fall stiffly to the ground, wracked by uncontrollable jerking. These **epileptic seizures** reflect a torrent of electrical discharges by groups of brain neurons, and during their uncontrolled activity no other messages can get through.

Epilepsy, manifested by one out of 100 of us, is not associated with, nor does it cause, intellectual impairment. Genetic factors induce some cases, but epilepsy can also result from brain injuries caused by blows to the head, stroke, infections, or tumors.

Epileptic seizures vary tremendously in their expression and severity.

- *Absence seizures,* formerly known as *petit mal,* are mild forms in which the expression goes blank for a few seconds as

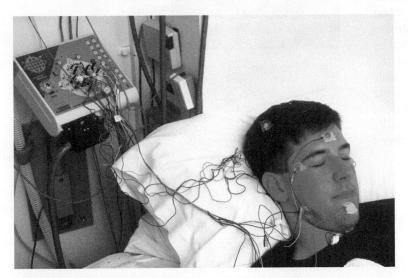

(a) Scalp electrodes are used to record brain wave activity.

(b) Brain waves shown in EEGs fall into four general classes.

Figure 12.18 Electroencephalography (EEG) and brain waves.

consciousness disappears. These are typically seen in young children and usually disappear by age 10.

- *Tonic-clonic seizures*, formerly called *grand mal*, are the most severe, convulsive form of epileptic seizures. The person loses consciousness, often breaking bones during the intense convulsions, showing the incredible strength of these muscle contractions. Loss of bowel and bladder control and severe biting of the tongue are common. The seizure lasts for a few minutes, then the muscles relax and the person awakens but remains disoriented for several minutes.

Many seizure sufferers experience a sensory hallucination, such as a taste, smell, or flashes of light, just before the seizure begins. This phenomenon, called an **aura**, is helpful because it gives the person time to lie down and avoid falling to the floor.

Epilepsy can usually be controlled by anticonvulsive drugs. If drugs fail to control the seizures, a *vagus nerve stimulator* or *deep brain stimulator* can be implanted. These devices deliver pulses to the vagus nerve or directly to the brain at predetermined intervals to stabilize the brain's electrical activity. A current line of research seeks to implant electrodes in the brain to detect and prevent oncoming seizures. +

Consciousness

✓ Describe consciousness clinically.

Consciousness encompasses conscious perception of sensations, voluntary initiation and control of movement, and capabilities associated with higher mental processing (memory, logic, judgment, perseverance, and so on). Clinically, consciousness is defined on a continuum that grades behavior in response to stimuli as (1) *alertness*, (2) *drowsiness* or *lethargy* (which proceeds to sleep), (3) *stupor*, and (4) *coma*. Alertness is the highest state of consciousness and cortical activity, and coma the most depressed.

Consciousness is difficult to define. And to be frank, reducing our response to a Key West sunset to a series of interactions between dendrites, axons, and neurotransmitters does not capture what makes that event so special. A sleeping person obviously lacks something that he or she has when awake, and we call this "something" consciousness.

Current suppositions about consciousness are as follows:

- **Consciousness involves simultaneous activity of large areas of the cerebral cortex.**

- **It is superimposed on other types of neural activity.** At any time, specific neurons and neuronal pools are involved both in localized activities (such as motor control) and in cognition.

- **It is holistic and totally interconnected.** Information for "thought" can be claimed from many locations in the cerebrum simultaneously. For example, retrieval of a specific memory can be triggered by several routes—a smell, a place, a particular person, and so on.

Homeostatic Imbalance 12.6

Except during sleep, unconsciousness is always a signal that brain function is impaired. A brief loss of consciousness is called **fainting** or **syncope** (sing'ko-pe; "cut short"). Most often, syncope indicates inadequate cerebral blood flow due to low blood pressure, as might follow hemorrhage or sudden emotional stress.

Significant unresponsiveness to sensory stimuli for an extended period is called **coma**. Coma is *not* deep sleep. During sleep, the brain remains active and oxygen consumption resembles that of the waking state. In coma patients, oxygen use is always below normal resting levels.

Factors that can induce coma include: (1) blows to the head that cause widespread cerebral or brain stem trauma, (2) tumors or infections that invade the brain stem, (3) metabolic disturbances such as hypoglycemia (abnormally low blood sugar levels), (4) drug overdose, (5) liver or kidney failure. Strokes rarely cause coma unless they are massive and accompanied by extreme swelling of the brain, or are located in the brain stem.

When the brain has suffered irreparable damage, irreversible coma occurs, even though life-support measures may restore vitality to other body organs. The result is **brain death**, a dead brain in an otherwise living body. Because life support can be removed only after death, physicians must determine whether a patient in an irreversible coma is legally alive or dead. ✚

Sleep and Sleep-Wake Cycles

✓ Compare and contrast the events and importance of slow-wave and REM sleep, and indicate how their patterns change through life.

Sleep is defined as a state of partial unconsciousness from which a person can be aroused by stimulation. This distinguishes sleep from coma, a state of unconsciousness from which a person *cannot* be aroused by even the most vigorous stimuli.

For the most part, cortical activity is depressed during sleep, but brain stem functions continue, such as control of respiration, heart rate, and blood pressure. Even environmental monitoring continues to some extent, as illustrated by the fact that strong stimuli ("things that go bump in the night") immediately arouse us. In fact, people who sleepwalk can avoid objects and navigate stairs while truly asleep.

Types of Sleep

The two major types of sleep, which alternate through most of the sleep cycle, are **non–rapid eye movement (NREM) sleep** and **rapid eye movement (REM) sleep**, defined in terms of their EEG patterns **(Figure 12.19)**. During the first 30 to 45 minutes of the sleep cycle, we pass through the first two stages of NREM sleep and into NREM stages 3 and 4, also called **slow-wave sleep**. As we pass through these stages and slip into deeper and deeper sleep, the frequency of the EEG waves declines, but their amplitude increases. Blood pressure and heart rate also decrease.

About 90 minutes after sleep begins, after reaching NREM stage 4, the EEG pattern changes abruptly. It becomes very irregular and appears to backtrack quickly through the stages until alpha waves (more typical of the awake state) reappear, indicating the onset of REM sleep. This brain wave change is coupled with increases in heart rate, respiratory rate, and blood pressure and a decrease in gastrointestinal motility. Oxygen use by the brain is tremendous during REM—greater than during the awake state.

Although the eyes move rapidly under the lids during REM, most of the body's skeletal muscles are actively inhibited and go limp. This temporary paralysis prevents us from acting out our dreams. Most dreaming occurs during REM sleep, and some suggest that the flitting eye movements are following the visual imagery of our dreams. (Note, however, that most nightmares and night terrors occur during NREM stages 3 and 4.) In adolescents and adults, REM episodes are frequently associated with erection of the penis or engorgement of the clitoris.

Awake

REM: Skeletal muscles (except ocular muscles and diaphragm) are actively inhibited; most dreaming occurs.

NREM stage 1: Relaxation begins; EEG shows alpha waves; arousal is easy.

NREM stage 2: Irregular EEG with sleep spindles (short high-amplitude bursts); arousal is more difficult.

NREM stage 3: Sleep deepens; theta and delta waves appear; vital signs decline.

NREM stage 4: EEG is dominated by delta waves; arousal is difficult; bed-wetting, night terrors, and sleepwalking may occur.

(a) Typical EEG patterns

(b) Typical progression of an adult through one night's sleep stages

Figure 12.19 Types and stages of sleep. The four stages of non–rapid eye movement (NREM) sleep and rapid eye movement (REM) sleep are shown.

Sleep Patterns

The alternating cycles of sleep and wakefulness reflect a natural *circadian*, or 24-hour, *rhythm*. The hypothalamus is responsible for the timing of the sleep cycle. Its *suprachiasmatic nucleus* (a biological clock) regulates its *preoptic nucleus* (a sleep-inducing center). By inhibiting the brain stem's reticular activating system (RAS; see Figure 12.17), the preoptic nucleus puts the cerebral cortex to sleep. However, sleep is much more than simply turning off the arousal system. RAS centers not only help maintain the awake state but also mediate some sleep stages, especially dreaming sleep.

In young and middle-aged adults, a typical night's sleep starts with the four stages of NREM sleep and then alternates between REM and NREM sleep with occasional partial arousals. Following each REM episode, the sleeper descends toward stage 4 again. REM recurs about every 90 minutes, with each REM period getting longer. The first REM of the night lasts 5–10 minutes and the final one 20 to 50 minutes (Figure 12.19b). Consequently, our longest dreams occur at the end of the sleep period. Just before we wake, hypothalamic neurons release peptides called *orexins*, which in this situation act as "wake-up" chemicals. As a result, certain neurons of the brain stem reticular formation fire at maximal rates, arousing the sleepy cortex.

The slow theta and delta waves of deep sleep are the result of synchronized firing of thalamic neurons that is normally inhibited during wakefulness by the RAS of the pons. Some pontine neurons of the reticular formation control the transition from NREM sleep to REM sleep, and others suppress motor activity, inducing paralysis. A large number of chemical substances in the body cause sleepiness, but the relative importance of these various sleep-inducing substances is not known.

Importance of Sleep

Why do we sleep? Slow-wave (NREM stages 3 and 4) and REM sleep seem to be important in different ways. Slow-wave sleep is presumed to be restorative—the time when most neural activity can wind down to basal levels. When deprived of sleep, we spend more time than usual in slow-wave sleep during the next sleep episode.

A person persistently deprived of REM sleep becomes moody and depressed, and exhibits various personality disorders. REM sleep may give the brain an opportunity to analyze the day's events and work through emotional problems in dream imagery.

Another idea is that REM sleep is reverse learning. According to this hypothesis, accidental, repetitious, and meaningless communications continually occur. Dreaming eliminates them from our neural networks so the cortex remains a well-behaved and efficient thinking system. In other words, we dream to forget.

Alcohol and some sleep medications (barbiturates and others) suppress REM sleep but not slow-wave sleep. On the other hand, certain tranquilizers, such as diazepam (Valium) reduce slow-wave sleep much more than REM sleep.

Whatever its importance, a person's daily sleep requirement declines steadily from 16 hours or so in infants to approximately 7½ to 8½ hours in early adulthood. It then levels off before declining again in old age. Sleep patterns also change throughout life. REM sleep occupies about half the total sleeping time in infants and then declines until age 10, when it stabilizes at about 25%. In contrast, stage 4 sleep declines steadily from birth and often disappears completely in those over 60.

Homeostatic Imbalance 12.7

People with **narcolepsy** lapse abruptly into REM sleep from the awake state. These sleep episodes last about 15 minutes, can occur without warning, and are often triggered by a pleasurable event—a good joke, a game of poker.

In most patients with narcolepsy, an emotionally intense experience can also trigger *cataplexy*, a sudden loss of voluntary muscle control similar to that seen during REM sleep. During cataplectic attacks, lasting seconds to minutes, the patient remains fully conscious but unable to move. Obviously this can be extremely hazardous if the person is driving a car or swimming!

Cells in the hypothalamus that secrete peptides called orexins (the peptides mentioned above as a wake-up chemical; also called hypocretins) are selectively destroyed in patients with narcolepsy, probably by the patient's own immune system. Replacing the orexins may be a key to future treatments.

Conversely, drugs that block the actions of orexin and promote sleep may treat **insomnia**, a chronic inability to obtain the *amount* or *quality* of sleep needed to function adequately during the day. Sleep requirements vary from four to nine hours a day in healthy people, so there is no way to determine the "right" amount. Insomniacs tend to overestimate the extent of their sleeplessness, and some come to rely on hypnotics (sleep medications), which can exacerbate the problem.

True insomnia often reflects normal age-related changes, but perhaps the most common cause is psychological disturbance. We have difficulty falling asleep when we are anxious or upset, and depression is often accompanied by early awakening.

Sleep apnea, a temporary cessation of breathing during sleep, is scary. The victim awakes abruptly due to hypoxia (lack of oxygen)—a condition that may occur several hundred times per night.

Obstructive sleep apnea, the most common form, occurs when the loss of muscle tone during sleep allows excess fatty tissue or other structural abnormalities to block the upper airway. It is associated with obesity and made worse by alcohol and other depressants. Aside from weight loss, effective treatments are either a mask that blows air in through the nose, keeping the airway open, or surgery to correct the problem. ✚

☑ Check Your Understanding

15. When would you see delta waves in an EEG?
16. Which two states of consciousness are between alertness and coma?
17. During which sleep stage are most skeletal muscles actively inhibited?

For answers, see Appendix H.

Language

Language is such an important function of the brain that it involves practically all of the association cortex on the left side in one way or another. Pioneering studies of patients with *aphasias* (the loss of language abilities due to damage to specific areas of the brain) pointed to two critically important regions, Broca's area and Wernicke's area (see areas outlined by dashes in Figure 12.6a).

Patients with lesions involving **Broca's area** can understand language but have difficulty speaking (and sometimes cannot write or type or use sign language). On the other hand, patients with lesions involving **Wernicke's area** are able to speak but

Figure 12.20 Memory processing.

produce a type of nonsense often referred to as "word salad." They also have great difficulty understanding language.

Recent imaging studies of the brain indicate that this picture is clinically useful, but oversimplified. In fact, Broca's and Wernicke's areas together with the basal nuclei form a single language implementation system that analyzes incoming and produces outgoing word sounds and grammatical structures. A surrounding set of cortical areas forms a bridge between this system and the regions of cortex that hold concepts and ideas, which are distributed throughout the remainder of the association cortices.

The corresponding areas in the right or non-language-dominant hemisphere are involved in "body language"—the nonverbal emotional (affective) components of language. These areas allow the lilt or tone of our voice and our gestures to express our emotions when we speak, and permit us to comprehend the emotional content of what we hear. For example, a soft, melodious response to your question conveys quite a different meaning than a sharp reply.

Memory

✓ Compare and contrast the stages and categories of memory.

✓ Describe the roles of the major brain structures believed to be involved in declarative and procedural memories.

Memory is the storage and retrieval of information. Memories are essential for learning and incorporating our experiences into behavior and are part and parcel of our consciousness. Stored somewhere in your 3 pounds of wrinkled brain are zip codes, the face of your grandfather, and the taste of yesterday's pizza. Your memories reflect your lifetime.

Stages of Memory

Memory storage involves two distinct stages: short-term memory and long-term memory **(Figure 12.20)**.

Short-term memory (STM), also called *working memory*, is the preliminary step, as well as the power that lets you look up a telephone number, dial it, and then never think of it again. STM is limited to seven or eight chunks of information, such as the digits of a telephone number or the sequence of words in an elaborate sentence.

In contrast, **long-term memory (LTM)** seems to have a limitless capacity. Although our STM cannot recall numbers much longer than a telephone number, we can remember scores of telephone numbers by committing them to LTM. However, long-term memories can be forgotten, and so our memory bank continually changes with time. Furthermore, our ability to store and retrieve information declines with aging.

We do not remember or even consciously notice much of what is going on around us. As sensory inputs flood into our cerebral cortex, they are processed (yellow box in Figure 12.20). Some 5% of this information is selected for transfer to STM (light green box in Figure 12.20). STM serves as a temporary holding bin for data that we may or may not want to retain.

Information is then transferred from STM to LTM (dark green box in Figure 12.20). Many factors can influence this transfer, including:

■ **Emotional state.** We learn best when we are alert, motivated, surprised, and aroused. For example, when we witness shocking events, transferral is almost immediate. Norepinephrine, a neurotransmitter involved in memory processing of emotionally charged events, is released when we are excited or "stressed out," which helps to explain this phenomenon.

■ **Rehearsal.** Rehearsing or repeating the material enhances memory.

■ **Association.** Tying "new" information to "old" information already stored in LTM appears to be important in remembering facts.

■ **Automatic memory.** Not all impressions that become part of LTM are consciously formed. A student concentrating on a lecturer's speech may record an automatic memory of the pattern of the lecturer's tie.

Memories transferred to LTM take time to become permanent. The process of **memory consolidation** apparently involves fitting new facts into the categories of knowledge already stored in the cerebral cortex.

Categories of Memory

The brain distinguishes between factual knowledge and skills, and we process and store these two kinds of information in different ways.

(a) Declarative memory circuits

(b) Procedural (skills) memory circuits

Figure 12.21 Proposed memory circuits. **(a)** Information from association cortices flows to the medial temporal lobe (including the hippocampus), which communicates with the thalamus and prefrontal cortex. The association cortices receive feedback from these structures. Acetylcholine from the basal forebrain is necessary for this circuit to function. **(b)** Sensory and motor inputs flow through the association cortices and are relayed to the premotor cortex. Dopamine from the substantia nigra is necessary for this circuit to function.

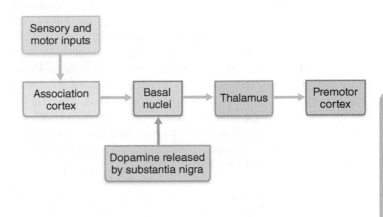

Declarative (fact) memory entails learning explicit information, such as names, faces, words, and dates. It is related to our conscious thoughts and our ability to manipulate symbols and language. When fact memories are committed to LTM, they are usually filed with the context in which they were learned. For instance, when you think of your new acquaintance Joe, you probably picture him at the basketball game where you met him.

Nondeclarative memory is less conscious or even unconscious learning. Categories of nondeclarative memory are **procedural (skills) memory** (piano playing), **motor memory** (riding a bike), and **emotional memory** (your pounding heart when you hear a rattlesnake nearby). We acquire nondeclarative memories through experience and usually repetition. They do not preserve the circumstances of learning, and in fact, they are best remembered in the doing. You do not have to think through how to tie your shoes. Once learned, nondeclarative memories are hard to unlearn.

Brain Structures Involved in Memory

Specific pieces of each memory are thought to be stored near regions of the brain that need them so new inputs can be quickly associated with the old. Accordingly, visual memories are stored in the occipital cortex, memories of music in the temporal cortex, and so on.

But how do we create new memories? It seems that different types of memory are created in different parts of the brain. **Figure 12.21a** shows a proposed scheme of information flow for declarative memory.

12

When sensory input is processed in the association cortices, the cortical neurons dispatch impulses to the medial temporal lobe, which includes the hippocampus and surrounding temporal cortical areas. These temporal lobe areas play a major role in memory consolidation and memory access by communicating with the thalamus and the prefrontal cortex. The prefrontal cortex and medial temporal lobe receive input from acetylcholine-releasing neurons in the basal forebrain. The sprinkling of acetylcholine (ACh) onto these structures is thought to prime them to allow the formation of memories. The loss of this ACh input, for example in Alzheimer's disease, seems to disrupt both the formation of new memories and the retrieval of old ones. Memories are retrieved when the same sets of neurons that were initially involved in forming the memories are stimulated.

Homeostatic Imbalance 12.8

Damage to the hippocampus and surrounding medial temporal lobe structures on either side results in only slight memory loss, but bilateral destruction causes widespread amnesia. Consolidated memories are not lost, but new sensory inputs cannot be associated with old, and the person lives in the here and now from that point on. This condition is called *anterograde amnesia* (an'ter-o-grād"), in contrast to *retrograde amnesia*, which is the loss of memories formed in the distant past. You could carry on an animated conversation with a person with anterograde amnesia, excuse yourself, return five minutes later, and that person would not remember you. +

Individuals suffering from anterograde amnesia can still learn skills such as drawing, so procedural memory must involve a different learning circuit. As Figure 12.21b shows, the basal nuclei (pink) are key players for procedural memory. Sensory and motor inputs pass through the association cortex to the basal nuclei. These inputs are then relayed via the thalamus to the premotor cortex. Note that the basal nuclei receive input from dopamine-releasing neurons in the substantia nigra of the midbrain. Just as acetylcholine is necessary for declarative memory, dopamine appears to be necessary for this procedural memory circuit to function. The loss of this dopamine input, as in Parkinson's disease, interferes with procedural memory.

The two other kinds of nondeclarative memory involve yet other brain regions. The cerebellum is involved in motor memory, while the amygdaloid body is crucial for emotional memory (see Figure 12.16). We will not describe these pathways here.

Molecular Basis of Memory

What happens at the molecular level when we form memories? Human memory is notoriously difficult to study. Animal experimental studies reveal that during learning:

- Neuronal RNA content is altered and newly synthesized mRNAs are delivered to axons and dendrites.
- Dendritic spines change shape.
- Unique extracellular proteins are deposited at synapses involved in long-term memory.

- The number and size of presynaptic terminals may increase.
- Presynaptic neurons release more neurotransmitter.

Each of these changes is an aspect of **long-term potentiation (LTP)**, a persistent increase in synaptic strength that has been shown to be crucial for memory formation. LTP was first identified in hippocampal neurons that use the amino acid glutamate as a neurotransmitter. One kind of glutamate receptor, the *NMDA receptor*, can act as a calcium channel and initiate the cellular changes that bring about LTP.

Normally, NMDA receptors are blocked, preventing calcium entry. When glutamate binds to different receptors and depolarizes the postsynaptic terminal, as would happen upon the rapid arrival of action potentials at the synapse, this NMDA block is removed and calcium flows into the postsynaptic cell.

Calcium influx activates enzymes that carry out two main tasks:

- The enzymes modify the proteins in the postsynaptic terminal, and also in the presynaptic terminal via retrograde messengers such as nitric oxide and endocannabinoids. These changes strengthen the response to subsequent stimuli.
- They activate genes in the postsynaptic neuron's nucleus, which leads to synthesis of synaptic proteins. The molecular messenger that alerts the nucleus that more protein is needed is a molecule called CREB (cAMP response-element binding protein). A neurotrophic factor called BDNF (brain-derived neurotrophic factor) is required for the protein synthesis phase of LTP.

Together, these changes create long-lasting increases in synaptic strength that are believed to underlie memory.

The events underlying memory at a cellular level suggest several approaches to enhancing memory formation. Currently several drugs to improve memory are undergoing clinical trials. Among these are drugs that enhance CREB production—the more CREB, the more protein synthesis and the stronger the synapse becomes.

☑ Check Your Understanding

18. Name three factors that can enhance transfer of information from STM to LTM.
19. Which functional areas of the cerebrum are involved in the formation of procedural (skills) memory, but not involved in declarative memory?

For answers, see Appendix H.

Protection of the Brain

✓ Describe how meninges, cerebrospinal fluid, and the blood brain barrier protect the CNS.

✓ Explain how cerebrospinal fluid is formed and describe its circulatory pathway.

Nervous tissue is soft and delicate, and even slight pressure can injure neurons. However, the brain is protected by bone (the skull), membranes (the meninges), and a watery cushion

Figure 12.22 Meninges: dura mater, arachnoid mater, and pia mater. The meningeal dura forms the falx cerebri fold. A dural sinus, the superior sagittal sinus, is enclosed by the dural membranes superiorly. Arachnoid villi return cerebrospinal fluid to the dural sinus. (Frontal section.)

(cerebrospinal fluid). Furthermore, the blood brain barrier protects the brain from harmful substances in the blood. We described the cranium, the brain's bony encasement, in Chapter 7. Here we will consider the other protective elements.

Meninges

The **meninges** (mĕ-nin′jēz; *mening* = membrane) are three connective tissue membranes that lie just external to the CNS organs. The meninges:

- Cover and protect the CNS
- Protect blood vessels and enclose venous sinuses
- Contain cerebrospinal fluid
- Form partitions in the skull

From external to internal, the meninges (singular: **meninx**) are the dura mater, arachnoid mater, and pia mater **(Figure 12.22)**.

Dura Mater

The leathery **dura mater** (du′rah ma′ter), meaning "tough mother," is the strongest meninx. Where it surrounds the brain, it is a two-layered sheet of fibrous connective tissue. The more superficial *periosteal layer* attaches to the inner surface of the skull (the periosteum). (There is no dural periosteal layer surrounding the spinal cord.) The deeper *meningeal layer* forms the true external covering of the brain and continues caudally in the vertebral canal as the spinal dura mater. The brain's two dural layers are fused together except in certain areas, where they separate to enclose **dural venous sinuses** that collect venous blood from the brain and direct it into the internal jugular veins of the neck **(Figure 12.23)**.

In several places, the meningeal dura mater extends inward to form flat partitions that subdivide the cranial cavity. These **dural septa**, which limit excessive movement of the brain within the cranium, include the following (Figure 12.23a):

- **Falx cerebri** (falks ser′ĕ-bri). A large sickle-shaped (*falx* = sickle) fold that dips into the longitudinal fissure between the cerebral hemispheres. Anteriorly, it attaches to the crista galli of the ethmoid bone.
- **Falx cerebelli** (ser″ĕ-bel′i). Continuing inferiorly from the posterior falx cerebri, this small midline partition runs along the vermis of the cerebellum.
- **Tentorium cerebelli** (ten-to′re-um; "tent"). Resembling a tent over the cerebellum, this nearly horizontal dural fold extends into the transverse fissure between the cerebral hemispheres (which it helps to support) and the cerebellum.

Arachnoid Mater

The middle meninx, the **arachnoid mater** (ah-rak′noid), forms a loose brain covering, never dipping into the sulci at the cerebral surface. It is separated from the dura mater by a narrow serous cavity, the **subdural space**, which contains a film of fluid. Beneath the arachnoid membrane is the wide **subarachnoid space**. Spider-web-like extensions span this space and secure the arachnoid mater to the underlying pia mater (*arachnida* means "spider"). The subarachnoid space is filled with cerebrospinal fluid and also contains the largest blood vessels serving the brain. Because the arachnoid mater is fine and elastic, these blood vessels are poorly protected.

Knoblike projections of the arachnoid mater called **arachnoid villi** (vil′i) protrude superiorly through the dura mater and into the superior sagittal sinus (see Figure 12.22). These villi absorb cerebrospinal fluid into the venous blood of the sinus.

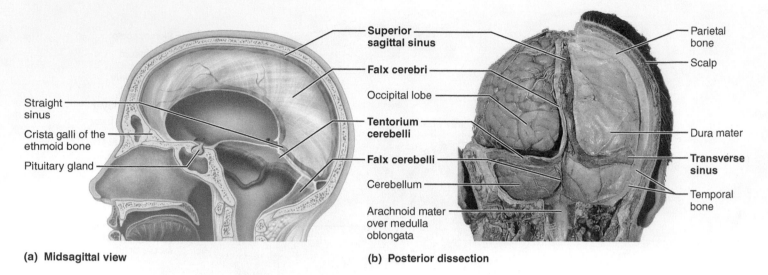

(a) Midsagittal view

(b) Posterior dissection

Figure 12.23 Dural septa and dural venous sinuses. (a) Dural septa are partitioning folds of dura mater in the cranial cavity. **(b)** Dural venous sinuses (injected with blue latex) are spaces between the periosteal and meningeal dura containing venous blood.

Pia Mater

The **pia mater** (pi′ah), meaning "gentle mother," is composed of delicate connective tissue and richly invested with tiny blood vessels. It is the only meninx that clings tightly to the brain like cellophane wrap, following its every convolution. Small arteries entering the brain tissue carry ragged sheaths of pia mater inward with them for short distances.

Homeostatic Imbalance 12.9

Meningitis, inflammation of the meninges, is a serious threat to the brain because a bacterial or viral meningitis may spread to the CNS. Brain inflammation is called *encephalitis* (en-sef′ah-li′tis). Meningitis is usually diagnosed by obtaining a sample of cerebrospinal fluid via a lumbar tap (see Figure 12.27, p. 466) and examining it for microbes. **+**

Cerebrospinal Fluid (CSF)

Cerebrospinal fluid, found in and around the brain and spinal cord, forms a liquid cushion that gives buoyancy to CNS structures. By floating the jellylike brain, the CSF effectively reduces brain weight by 97% and prevents the delicate brain from crushing under its own weight. CSF also protects the brain and spinal cord from blows and other trauma. Additionally, although the brain has a rich blood supply, CSF helps nourish the brain, and there is some evidence that it carries chemical signals (such as hormones and sleep- and appetite-inducing molecules) from one part of the brain to another.

CSF is a watery "broth" similar in composition to blood plasma, from which it is formed. However, it contains less protein than plasma and its ion concentrations are different. For example, CSF contains more Na^+, Cl^-, and H^+ than does blood plasma, and less Ca^{2+} and K^+.

The **choroid plexuses** that hang from the roof of each ventricle form CSF. These plexuses are frond-shaped clusters of broad, thin-walled capillaries (*plex* = interwoven) enclosed first by pia mater and then by a layer of ependymal cells lining the ventricles **(Figure 12.24b)**. These capillaries are fairly permeable, and tissue fluid filters continuously from the bloodstream. However, the choroid plexus ependymal cells are joined by tight junctions, and they have ion pumps that allow them to modify this filtrate by actively transporting only certain ions across their membranes into the CSF pool. This careful regulation of CSF composition is important because CSF mixes with the extracellular fluid bathing neurons and influences the composition of this fluid. Ion pumping also sets up ionic gradients that cause water to diffuse into the ventricles.

In adults, the total CSF volume of about 150 ml (about half a cup) is replaced every 8 hours or so. About 500 ml of CSF is formed daily. The choroid plexuses also help cleanse the CSF by removing waste products and unnecessary solutes.

Once produced, CSF moves freely through the ventricles. CSF enters the subarachnoid space via the lateral and median apertures in the walls of the fourth ventricle (Figure 12.24a). The long cilia of the ependymal cells lining the ventricles help keep the CSF in constant motion. In the subarachnoid space, CSF bathes the outer surfaces of the brain and spinal cord and then returns to the blood in the dural sinuses via the arachnoid villi.

Homeostatic Imbalance 12.10

Ordinarily, CSF is produced and drained at a constant rate. However, if something (such as a tumor) obstructs its circulation or drainage, CSF accumulates and exerts pressure on the brain. This condition is called *hydrocephalus* ("water on the brain").

Superior sagittal sinus

Choroid plexus

Interventricular foramen

Third ventricle

Cerebral aqueduct

Lateral aperture

Fourth ventricle

Median aperture

Central canal of spinal cord

Arachnoid villus

Subarachnoid space

Arachnoid mater

Meningeal dura mater

Periosteal dura mater

Right lateral ventricle (deep to cut)

Choroid plexus of fourth ventricle

① The choroid plexus of each ventricle produces CSF.

② CSF flows through the ventricles and into the subarachnoid space via the median and lateral apertures.

③ CSF flows through the subarachnoid space.

④ CSF is absorbed into the dural venous sinuses via the arachnoid villi.

Ependymal cells

Capillary

Connective tissue of pia mater

Section of choroid plexus

Wastes and unnecessary solutes absorbed

Cavity of ventricle

CSF forms as a filtrate containing glucose, oxygen, vitamins, and ions (Na^+, Cl^-, Mg^{2+}, etc.)

(a) CSF circulation

(b) CSF formation by choroid plexuses

Figure 12.24 Formation, location, and circulation of CSF. (a) Location and circulatory pattern of cerebrospinal fluid (CSF). Arrows indicate the direction of flow. **(b)** Each choroid plexus consists of a knot of porous capillaries surrounded by a single layer of ependymal cells joined by tight junctions and bearing long cilia. Fluid leaking from porous capillaries is processed by the ependymal cells to form the CSF in the ventricles.

12

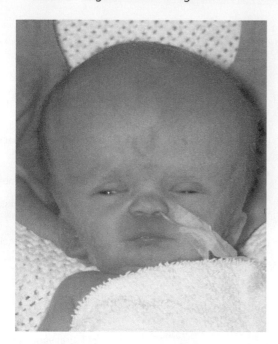

Figure 12.25 Hydrocephalus in a newborn.

Hydrocephalus enlarges the head of a newborn baby because the skull bones have not yet fused **(Figure 12.25)**. In adults, however, the skull is rigid and hard, and hydrocephalus is likely to damage the brain because accumulating fluid compresses blood vessels and crushes the soft nervous tissue. Hydrocephalus is treated by inserting a shunt into the ventricles to drain excess fluid into the abdominal cavity. ✚

Blood Brain Barrier

The **blood brain barrier** is a protective mechanism that helps maintain a stable environment for the brain. No other body tissue is so absolutely dependent on a constant internal environment as is the brain. In other body regions, the extracellular concentrations of hormones, amino acids, and ions are in constant flux, particularly after eating or exercise. If the brain were exposed to such chemical variations, its neurons would fire uncontrollably, because some hormones and amino acids serve as neurotransmitters and certain ions (particularly K^+) modify the threshold for neuronal firing.

Bloodborne substances in the brain's capillaries must pass through three layers before they reach the neurons: (1) the endothelium of the capillary wall, (2) a relatively thick basal lamina surrounding the external face of each capillary, and (3) the bulbous "feet" of the astrocytes clinging to the capillaries.

Which of these layers constitutes the blood brain barrier? As you might expect, the astrocyte "feet" play a role but they are not themselves the barrier. Instead, they supply required signals to the endothelial cells, causing them to make *tight junctions*. These tight junctions seamlessly join together the endothelial cells, forming the blood brain barrier and making these the least permeable capillaries in the body.

The blood brain barrier is selective, not absolute. Nutrients such as glucose, essential amino acids, and some electrolytes move passively by facilitated diffusion through the endothelial cell membranes. Bloodborne metabolic wastes, proteins, certain toxins, and most drugs are denied entry. Small nonessential amino acids and potassium ions not only are prevented from entering the brain, but also are actively pumped from the brain across the capillary endothelium.

The barrier is ineffective against fats, fatty acids, oxygen, carbon dioxide, and other fat-soluble molecules that diffuse easily through all plasma membranes. This explains why bloodborne alcohol, nicotine, and anesthetics can affect the brain.

The structure of the blood brain barrier is not completely uniform. In some brain areas surrounding the third and fourth ventricles, the barrier is entirely absent and the capillary endothelium is quite permeable, allowing bloodborne molecules easy access to the neural tissue. One such region is the vomiting center of the brain stem, which monitors the blood for poisonous substances. Another is in the hypothalamus, which regulates water balance, body temperature, and many other metabolic activities. Lack of a blood brain barrier here is essential to allow the hypothalamus to sample the chemical composition of the blood. The barrier is incomplete in newborn and premature infants, and potentially toxic substances can enter the CNS and cause problems not seen in adults.

Injury to the brain, whatever the cause, may result in a localized breakdown of the blood brain barrier. Most likely, this breakdown reflects some change in the capillary endothelial cells or their tight junctions.

Homeostatic Imbalances of the Brain

✓ Describe the cause (if known) and major signs and symptoms of cerebrovascular accidents, Alzheimer's disease, Parkinson's disease, and Huntington's disease.

Brain dysfunctions are unbelievably varied and extensive. We have mentioned some of them already, but here we will focus on traumatic brain injuries, cerebrovascular accidents, and degenerative brain disorders.

Traumatic Brain Injuries

Head injuries are a leading cause of accidental death in North America. Consider, for example, what happens if you forget to fasten your seat belt and then rear-end another car. Your head is moving and then stops suddenly as it hits the windshield. Brain damage is caused not only by localized injury at the site of the blow (the *coup* injury), but also by the ricocheting effect as the brain hits the opposite end of the skull (the *contrecoup* injury).

A **concussion** is an alteration in brain function, usually temporary, following a blow to the head. The victim may be dizzy or lose consciousness. Although typically mild and short-lived, even a seemingly mild concussion can be damaging, and multiple concussions over time produce cumulative damage.

More serious concussions can bruise the brain and cause permanent neurological damage, a condition called a **contusion**. In cortical contusions, the individual may remain conscious. Severe

12

brain stem contusions always cause coma, lasting from hours to a lifetime because of injury to the reticular activating system.

Following a head blow, death may result from **subdural** or **subarachnoid hemorrhage** (bleeding from ruptured vessels into those spaces). Individuals who are initially lucid and then begin to deteriorate neurologically are, in all probability, hemorrhaging intracranially. Blood accumulating in the skull increases intracranial pressure and compresses brain tissue. If the pressure forces the brain stem inferiorly through the foramen magnum, control of blood pressure, heart rate, and respiration is lost. Intracranial hemorrhages are treated by surgically removing the hematoma (localized blood mass) and repairing the ruptured vessels.

Another consequence of traumatic head injury is **cerebral edema**, swelling of the brain. At best, cerebral edema aggravates the injury. At worst, it can be fatal in and of itself.

Cerebrovascular Accidents (CVAs) *strokes*

The single most common nervous system disorder and the third leading cause of death in North America are **cerebrovascular accidents (CVAs)** (ser″ĕ-bro-vas′ku-lar), also called *strokes* or "brain attacks." CVAs occur when blood circulation to a brain area is blocked and brain tissue dies. [**Ischemia** (is-ke′me-ah; "to hold back blood"), deprivation of blood supply to any tissue, impairs the delivery of oxygen and nutrients to cells.]

The most common cause of CVA is a blood clot that blocks a cerebral artery. A clot can originate outside the brain (from the heart, for example) or form on the roughened interior wall of a brain artery narrowed by atherosclerosis. Less frequently, strokes are caused by bleeding, which compresses brain tissue.

Those who survive a CVA are typically paralyzed on one side of the body (*hemiplegia*). Many exhibit sensory deficits or have difficulty understanding or vocalizing speech. Even so, the picture is not hopeless. Some patients recover at least part of their lost faculties, because undamaged neurons sprout new branches that spread into the injured area and take over some lost functions. Physical therapy should start as soon as possible to prevent muscle contractures (abnormally shortened muscles due to differences in strength between opposing muscle groups).

Not all strokes are "completed." Temporary episodes of reversible cerebral ischemia, called **transient ischemic attacks (TIAs)**, are common. TIAs last from 5 to 50 minutes and are characterized by temporary numbness, paralysis, or impaired speech. These deficits are not permanent, but TIAs do constitute "red flags" that warn of impending, more serious CVAs.

A CVA is like an undersea earthquake. It's not the initial temblor that does most of the damage, it's the tsunami that floods the coast later. Similarly, the initial vascular blockage during a stroke is not usually disastrous because there are many blood vessels in the brain that can pick up the slack. Rather, it's the neuron-killing events outside the initial ischemic zone that wreak the most havoc.

Experimental evidence indicates that the main culprit is *glutamate*, an excitatory neurotransmitter also involved in learning and memory. Normally, glutamate binding to NMDA receptors opens NMDA channels that allow Ca^{2+} to enter the stimulated neuron. After brain injury, neurons totally deprived of oxygen begin to disintegrate, unleashing the cellular equivalent of "buckets" of glutamate. Under these conditions, glutamate acts as an *excitotoxin*, literally exciting surrounding cells to death.

The initial events in excitotoxicity are identical to those in LTP: Ca^{2+} flows in through NMDA receptor channels (see p. 458). In excitotoxicity, however, the amount of Ca^{2+} swamps the cell's ability to cope and Ca^{2+} homeostasis breaks down. High levels of Ca^{2+} kill cells in two ways:

- Ca^{2+} damages mitochondria, causing them to produce the free radical superoxide, which damages cells directly and can also cause programmed cell death (apoptosis).

- Ca^{2+} turns on the synthesis of certain proteins. Some of these promote apoptosis while others are enzymes that produce the free radical NO and other powerful inflammatory agents.

Although the NMDA receptor and the enzyme that makes NO are attractive targets for drug therapies to decrease damage around the stroke epicenter, clinical trials so far have all failed. At present, the most successful treatment for stroke is tissue plasminogen activator (tPA), which dissolves blood clots in the brain. Alternatively, a mechanical device can drill into a blood clot and pull it from a blood vessel like a cork from a bottle.

Other approaches currently under study focus on recovering function after a stroke. One method implants immature neurons into stroke-damaged brain regions in the hope that they will take on properties of nearby mature neurons. Another tries to coax adult brain stem cells to replace damaged neurons. Mice with strokes can generate new tissue and recover motor function when treated with a combination of growth factors during a critical time following injury. Hopefully, this will be true for humans, too.

Degenerative Brain Disorders

Alzheimer's Disease

Alzheimer's disease (AD) (altz′hi-merz), a progressive degenerative disease of the brain, ultimately results in **dementia** (mental deterioration). Alzheimer's patients represent nearly half of the people living in nursing homes. Between 5 and 15% of people over 65 develop this condition, and for up to half of those over 85 it is a major contributing cause in their deaths.

Its victims exhibit memory loss (particularly for recent events), shortened attention span, disorientation, and eventual language loss. Over a period of several years, formerly good-natured people may become irritable, moody, and confused. Hallucinations may ultimately occur.

Examinations of brain tissue reveal senile plaques littering the brain like shrapnel between the neurons. The plaques consist of extracellular aggregations of *beta-amyloid peptide*, which is cut from a normal membrane precursor protein (APP) by enzymes. One form of Alzheimer's disease is caused by an inherited mutation in the gene for APP, which suggests that too much beta-amyloid may be toxic. New evidence suggests that the beta-amyloid peptide may exert its toxic effect through the prion protein, the same protein that (in an altered form) causes mad cow disease. Current clinical trials focus on using the immune system to clear away beta-amyloid peptide.

Another hallmark of Alzheimer's disease is the presence of *neurofibrillary tangles* inside neurons. These tangles involve a protein called tau, which functions like railroad ties to bind microtubule "tracks" together. In the brains of AD victims, tau abandons its microtubule-stabilizing role and grabs onto other tau molecules, forming spaghetti-like neurofibrillary tangles, which kill the neurons by disrupting their transport mechanisms.

As the brain cells die, the brain shrinks. Particularly vulnerable brain areas include the hippocampus and the basal forebrain, regions involved in thinking and memory (see Figure 12.21). Loss of neurons in the basal forebrain is associated with a shortage of the neurotransmitter acetylcholine, and drugs that inhibit breakdown of acetylcholine slightly enhance cognitive function in AD patients. Interestingly, a drug that blocks NMDA receptors, memantine, also slightly improves thinking in more advanced stages of AD, suggesting that glutamate excitotoxicity is also involved in this disease.

Parkinson's Disease

Typically striking people in their 50s and 60s, **Parkinson's disease** results from a degeneration of the dopamine-releasing neurons of the substantia nigra. As those neurons deteriorate, the dopamine-deprived basal nuclei they target become overactive. Afflicted individuals have a persistent tremor at rest (exhibited by "pill-rolling" movements of the fingers and wrist), a forward-bent walking posture and shuffling gait, and a stiff facial expression. They are slow initiating and executing movement.

The cause of Parkinson's disease is still unknown, but multiple factors may interact to destroy dopamine-releasing neurons. Recent evidence points to abnormalities in certain mitochondrial proteins and protein degradation pathways. The drug L-*dopa* helps to alleviate some symptoms. It passes through the blood brain barrier and is then converted into dopamine.

However, as more and more neurons die off, L-dopa becomes ineffective. Mixing L-dopa with drugs that inhibit the breakdown of dopamine (for example, deprenyl) can prolong its effectiveness. In addition, deprenyl by itself, early in the disease, slows the neurological deterioration to some extent and delays the need to administer L-dopa for up to 18 months.

Deep brain stimulation via implanted electrodes shuts down abnormal brain activity and can alleviate tremors. This treatment (for patients who no longer respond to drug therapy) is expensive and risky, but it works. Another possibility is to use gene therapy to insert genes into adult brain cells, causing them to secrete the inhibitory neurotransmitter GABA. GABA then inhibits the abnormal brain activity just as the electrical stimulation does. Replacing dead or damaged cells by implanting stem cells is promising, but results to date are no better than more conventional treatments.

Huntington's Disease

Huntington's disease, a fatal hereditary disorder, strikes during middle age. Mutant *huntingtin* protein accumulates in brain cells and the tissue dies, leading to massive degeneration of the basal nuclei and later of the cerebral cortex. Its initial symptoms in many are wild, jerky, almost continuous "flapping" movements called *chorea* (Greek for "dance"). Although the movements appear to be voluntary, they are not. Late in the disease, marked mental deterioration occurs. Huntington's disease is progressive and usually fatal within 15 years of onset of symptoms.

The hyperkinetic manifestations of Huntington's disease are essentially the opposite of those of Parkinson's disease (overstimulation rather than inhibition of the motor drive). Huntington's is usually treated with drugs that block, rather than enhance, dopamine's effects. As with Parkinson's disease, stem cell implants may be a promising treatment in the future.

☑ Check Your Understanding

20. What is CSF? Where is it produced? What are its functions?
21. What is a transient ischemic attack (TIA) and how is it different from a stroke?
22. Mrs. Lee, a neurology patient, seldom smiles, has a shuffling, stooped gait, and often spills her coffee. What degenerative brain disorder might she have?

For answers, see Appendix H.

The Spinal Cord

✓ Describe the gross and microscopic structure of the spinal cord.

✓ List the major spinal cord tracts, and classify each as a motor or sensory tract.

Gross Anatomy and Protection

The spinal cord, enclosed in the vertebral column, extends from the foramen magnum of the skull to the first or second lumbar vertebra, just inferior to the ribs **(Figure 12.26)**. About 42 cm (17 inches) long and 1.8 cm (3/4 of an inch) thick, the glistening-white **spinal cord** provides a two-way conduction pathway to and from the brain. It is a major reflex center: Spinal reflexes are initiated and completed at the spinal cord level. We discuss reflex functions and motor activity of the cord in subsequent chapters. In this section we focus on the anatomy of the spinal cord and its ascending and descending tracts.

Like the brain, the spinal cord is protected by bone, meninges, and cerebrospinal fluid. The single-layered **spinal dura mater** (Figure 12.26c) is not attached to the bony walls of the vertebral column. Between the bony vertebrae and the spinal dura mater is an **epidural space** filled with a soft padding of fat and a network of veins (see Figure 12.28a). Cerebrospinal fluid fills the subarachnoid space between the *arachnoid* and *pia mater* meninges.

Inferiorly, the dural and arachnoid membranes extend to the level of S_2, well beyond the end of the spinal cord. The spinal cord typically ends between L_1 and L_2 (Figure 12.26a). For this reason, the subarachnoid space within the meningeal sac inferior to that point provides a nearly ideal spot for removing cerebrospinal fluid for testing, a procedure called a **lumbar**

(b) **Cervical spinal cord.**

(c) **Thoracic spinal cord, showing denticulate ligaments.**

(d) **Inferior end of spinal cord, showing conus medullaris, cauda equina, and filum terminale.**

(a) **The spinal cord and its nerve roots, with the bony vertebral arches removed. The dura mater and arachnoid mater are cut open and reflected laterally.**

Figure 12.26 Gross structure of the spinal cord, dorsal view. (For related images, see *A Brief Atlas of the Human Body*, Figures 52, 53, and 55.)

12

Figure 12.27 Diagram of a lumbar tap. This procedure removes CSF for testing.

puncture or **tap** (Figure 12.27). Because the spinal cord is absent there and the delicate nerve roots drift away from the point of needle insertion, there is little or no danger of damaging the cord (or spinal roots) beyond L_3.

Inferiorly, the spinal cord terminates in a tapering cone-shaped structure called the **conus medullaris** (ko′nus mĕ″dul-ar′is). The **filum terminale** (fi′lum ter″mĭ-nah′le; "terminal filament"), a fibrous extension of the conus covered by pia mater, extends inferiorly from the conus medullaris to the coccyx, where it anchors the spinal cord so it is not jostled by body movements (Figure 12.26a, d). Furthermore, saw-toothed shelves of pia mater called **denticulate ligaments** (den-tik′u-lāt; "toothed") secure the spinal cord to the tough dura mater meninx throughout its length (Figure 12.26c).

In humans, 31 pairs of *spinal nerves*—part of the peripheral nervous system—attach to the cord by paired roots. Each nerve exits from the vertebral column by passing superior to its corresponding vertebra via the intervertebral foramen, and travels to the body region it serves. While each nerve pair defines a segment of the cord, the spinal cord is, in fact, continuous throughout its length and its internal structure changes gradually.

The spinal cord is about the width of a thumb for most of its length, but it has obvious enlargements in the cervical and lumbosacral regions, where the nerves serving the upper and lower limbs arise. These enlargements are the **cervical** and **lumbar enlargements**, respectively (Figure 12.26a).

Because the cord does not reach the end of the vertebral column, the lumbar and sacral spinal nerve roots angle sharply downward and travel inferiorly through the vertebral canal for some distance before reaching their intervertebral foramina.

The collection of nerve roots at the inferior end of the vertebral canal is named the **cauda equina** (kaw′da e-kwi′nuh) because it resembles a horse's tail (Figure 12.26a, d). This strange arrangement reflects the fact that during fetal development, the vertebral column grows faster than the spinal cord, forcing the lower spinal nerve roots to "chase" their exit points inferiorly through the vertebral canal.

We will discuss the spinal nerves in more detail in Chapter 13.

Spinal Cord Cross-Sectional Anatomy

The spinal cord is somewhat flattened from front to back and two grooves mark its surface: the **ventral (anterior) median fissure** and the shallower **dorsal (posterior) median sulcus** (Figure 12.28b). These grooves run the length of the cord and partially divide it into right and left halves. The gray matter of the cord is located in its core, the white matter outside.

Gray Matter and Spinal Roots

In cross section the gray matter of the cord looks like the letter H or like a butterfly (Figure 12.28b). It consists of mirror-image lateral gray masses connected by a crossbar of gray matter, the **gray commissure**, that encloses the central canal. The two dorsal projections of the gray matter are the **dorsal (posterior) horns**, and the ventral pair are the **ventral (anterior) horns**. In 3-D, these horns form columns of gray matter that run the entire length of the spinal cord. The thoracic and superior lumbar segments of the cord have an additional pair of gray matter columns, the small **lateral horns**.

All neurons whose cell bodies are in the spinal cord gray matter are multipolar. The dorsal horns consist entirely of interneurons. The ventral horns have some interneurons but mainly house cell bodies of somatic motor neurons. These motor neurons send their axons out to the skeletal muscles (their effector organs) via the *ventral rootlets* that fuse together to become the **ventral roots** of the spinal cord (Figure 12.28b).

The amount of ventral gray matter present at a given level of the spinal cord reflects the amount of skeletal muscle innervated at that level. As a result, the ventral horns are largest in the limb-innervating cervical and lumbar regions of the cord and are responsible for the cord enlargements seen in those regions.

The lateral horns consist mostly of the cell bodies of autonomic (sympathetic division) motor neurons that serve visceral organs. Their axons leave the cord via the ventral root along with those of the somatic motor neurons. Because the ventral roots contain both somatic and autonomic efferent fibers, they serve both motor divisions of the peripheral nervous system (Figure 12.29).

Afferent fibers carrying impulses from peripheral sensory receptors form the **dorsal roots** of the spinal cord that fan out as the *dorsal rootlets* before they enter the spinal cord (Figure 12.28). The cell bodies of the associated sensory neurons are found in an enlarged region of the dorsal root called the **dorsal root ganglion** or **spinal ganglion**. After entering the cord, the axons of these neurons may take a number of routes. Some enter the dorsal white matter of the cord directly and travel to synapse at higher cord or brain levels. Others synapse with interneurons in the dorsal horns of the spinal cord gray matter at their entry level. The

(a) Cross section of spinal cord and vertebra

(b) The spinal cord and its meningeal coverings

Figure 12.28 Anatomy of the spinal cord. (a) Cross section through the spinal cord illustrating its relationship to the surrounding vertebral column. **(b)** Anterior view of the spinal cord and its meningeal coverings.

Figure 12.29 Organization of the gray matter of the spinal cord. The gray matter of the spinal cord is divided into a sensory half dorsally and a motor half ventrally. Note that the dorsal and ventral roots are part of the PNS, not of the spinal cord.

SS Interneurons receiving input from somatic sensory neurons

VS Interneurons receiving input from visceral sensory neurons

VM Visceral motor (autonomic) neurons

SM Somatic motor neurons

dorsal and ventral roots are very short and fuse laterally to form the **spinal nerves** (see Chapter 13).

The spinal gray matter can be divided further according to its neurons' relative involvement in innervating the somatic and visceral regions of the body. Spinal gray matter has the following four zones (Figure 12.29): **somatic sensory (SS), visceral sensory (VS), visceral (autonomic) motor (VM), somatic motor (SM).**

White Matter

The white matter of the spinal cord is composed of myelinated and nonmyelinated nerve fibers that allow communication between different parts of the spinal cord and between the cord and brain. These fibers run in three directions:

- *Ascending*—up to higher centers (sensory inputs)
- *Descending*—down to the cord from the brain or within the cord to lower levels (motor outputs)
- *Transverse*—across from one side of the cord to the other (commissural fibers)

Ascending and descending tracts make up most of the white matter.

The white matter on each side of the cord is divided into three **white columns**, or **funiculi** (fu-nik′u-li; "long ropes"), named according to their position as **dorsal (posterior), lateral**, and **ventral (anterior) funiculi** (Figure 12.28b). Each funiculus contains several fiber tracts, and each tract is made up of axons with similar destinations and functions. With a few exceptions, the names of the spinal tracts reveal both their origin and destination. **Figure 12.30** schematically illustrates the principal ascending and descending tracts of the spinal cord in cross-sectional view.

Neuronal Pathways

All major spinal tracts are part of *multineuron pathways* that connect the brain to the body periphery. These great ascending and descending pathways contain not only spinal cord neurons but also parts of peripheral neurons and neurons in the brain. Before we get specific about the individual tracts, we will note four key generalizations about them and the pathways to which they contribute:

- **Decussation.** Most pathways cross from one side of the CNS to the other (decussate) at some point along their journey.
- **Relay.** Most pathways consist of a chain of two or three neurons (a relay) that contribute to successive tracts of the pathway.
- **Somatotopy.** Most pathways exhibit *somatotopy*, a precise spatial relationship among the tract fibers that reflects the orderly mapping of the body. For example, in an ascending sensory tract, fibers transmitting inputs from sensory receptors in superior body regions lie lateral to those conveying sensory information from inferior body regions.
- **Symmetry.** All pathways and tracts are paired symmetrically (right and left), with a member of the pair present on each side of the spinal cord or brain.

Ascending Pathways to the Brain

The ascending pathways conduct sensory impulses upward, typically through chains of three successive neurons (first-, second-, and third-order neurons) to various areas of the brain. Note that both second- and third-order neurons are interneurons.

- **First-order neurons**, whose cell bodies reside in a ganglion (dorsal root or cranial), conduct impulses from the cutaneous receptors of the skin and from proprioceptors to the spinal cord or brain stem, where they synapse with second-order neurons. Impulses from the facial area are transmitted by cranial nerves,

Figure 12.30 Major ascending (sensory) and descending (motor) tracts of the spinal cord, cross-sectional view.

and spinal nerves conduct somatic sensory impulses from the rest of the body to the CNS. First-order neurons entering the spinal cord are shown at the bottom of Figure 12.31.

- The cell bodies of **second-order neurons** (Figure 12.31, middle) reside in the dorsal horn of the spinal cord or in medullary nuclei. They transmit impulses to the thalamus or to the cerebellum where they synapse.

- **Third-order neurons** have cell bodies in the thalamus (Figure 12.31, top). They relay impulses to the somatosensory cortex of the cerebrum. (There are no third-order neurons in the cerebellum.)

In general, somatosensory information travels along three main pathways on each side of the spinal cord. Two of these pathways (the *dorsal column–medial lemniscal* and *spinothalamic pathways*) transmit impulses via the thalamus to the sensory cortex for conscious interpretation. Collectively the inputs of these sister tracts provide *discriminative touch* and *conscious proprioception*. Both pathways decussate—the first in the medulla and the second in the spinal cord.

The third pathway, the *spinocerebellar pathway*, terminates in the cerebellum, and does not contribute to sensory perception. Let's examine these pathways more closely.

1. **Dorsal column–medial lemniscal pathways.** The **dorsal column–medial lemniscal pathways** (lem-nis′kul; "ribbon") mediate precise, straight-through transmission of inputs from a single type (or a few related types) of sensory receptor that can be localized precisely on the body surface, such as discriminative touch and vibrations. These pathways are formed by the paired tracts of the **dorsal white column** of the spinal cord—**fasciculus cuneatus** and **fasciculus gracilis**—and the **medial lemniscus**.

   The medial lemniscus arises in the medulla and terminates in the thalamus (Figure 12.31a and Table 12.2).

From the thalamus, impulses are forwarded to specific areas of the somatosensory cortex.

2. **Spinothalamic pathways.** The **spinothalamic pathways** receive input from many different types of sensory receptors and make multiple synapses in the brain stem. These pathways consist of the **lateral** and **ventral (anterior) spinothalamic tracts** (see Figure 12.31b and Table 12.2). Their fibers cross over in the spinal cord.

   The fibers in these pathways primarily transmit impulses for pain and temperature, but also for coarse touch and pressure. All are sensations that we are aware of but have difficulty localizing precisely on the body surface.

3. **Spinocerebellar pathways.** The third ascending pathway consists of the **ventral** and **dorsal spinocerebellar tracts**. They convey information about muscle or tendon stretch to the cerebellum, which uses this information to coordinate skeletal muscle activity (see Figure 12.31a and Table 12.2). As noted earlier, these pathways do not contribute to conscious sensation. The fibers of the spinocerebellar pathways either do not decussate or else cross over twice (thus "undoing" the decussation).

Descending Pathways and Tracts

The descending pathways that deliver efferent impulses from the brain to the spinal cord are divided into two groups: (1) the *direct pathways,* equivalent to the pyramidal tracts, and (2) the *indirect pathways,* essentially all others. Motor pathways involve two neurons, referred to as the upper and lower motor neurons:

- *Upper motor neurons* are the pyramidal cells of the motor cortex (see p. 433) and the neurons of subcortical motor nuclei.

- *Lower motor neurons* are the ventral horn motor neurons. These directly innervate the skeletal muscles (their effectors).

We give a brief overview of these pathways on p. 471. See Table 12.3 on p. 473 for more information.

12

Primary somatosensory cortex

Axons of third-order neurons

Thalamus

Cerebrum

Midbrain

Cerebellum

Pons

Dorsal spinocerebellar tract (axons of second-order neurons)

Medial lemniscus (tract) (axons of second-order neurons)

Nucleus gracilis

Nucleus cuneatus

Medulla oblongata

Fasciculus cuneatus (axon of first-order sensory neuron)

Joint stretch receptor (proprioceptor)

Axon of first-order neuron

Muscle spindle (proprioceptor)

Cervical spinal cord

Fasciculus gracilis (axon of first-order sensory neuron)

Lumbar spinal cord

Touch receptor

Lateral spinothalamic tract (axons of second-order neurons)

Pain receptors

Axons of first-order neurons

Temperature receptors

(a) Spinocerebellar pathway   Dorsal column–medial lemniscal pathway

(b) Spinothalamic pathway

Figure 12.31 Pathways of selected ascending spinal cord tracts. Cross sections up to the cerebrum, which is shown in frontal section. **(a)** The spinocerebellar pathway (left) transmits proprioceptive information only to the cerebellum, and so is subconscious. The dorsal column–medial lemniscal pathway transmits discriminative touch and conscious proprioception signals to the cerebral cortex. **(b)** The lateral spinothalamic pathway transmits pain and temperature.

Table 12.2   Major Ascending (Sensory) Pathways and Spinal Cord Tracts

SPINAL CORD TRACT	LOCATION (FUNICULUS)	ORIGIN	TERMINATION	FUNCTION
Dorsal Column–Medial Lemniscal Pathways				
Fasciculus cuneatus and fasciculus gracilis (dorsal white column)	Dorsal	Central axons of sensory (first-order) neurons enter dorsal root of the spinal cord and branch. Branches enter dorsal white column on same side without synapsing.	By synapse with second-order neurons in nucleus cuneatus and nucleus gracilis in medulla. Fibers of medullary neurons cross over and ascend in medial lemniscus to thalamus, where they synapse with third-order neurons. Thalamic neurons then transmit impulses to somatosensory cortex.	Both tracts transmit sensory impulses from general sensory receptors of skin and proprioceptors, which are interpreted as discriminative touch, pressure, and "body sense" (limb and joint position) in opposite somatosensory cortex. Cuneatus transmits afferent impulses from upper limbs, upper trunk, and neck. Gracilis carries impulses from lower limbs and inferior body trunk.
Spinothalamic Pathways				
Lateral spinothalamic	Lateral	Interneurons (second-order neurons) in dorsal horns. Fibers cross to opposite side before ascending.	By synapse with third-order neurons in thalamus. Thalamic neurons then convey impulses to somatosensory cortex.	Transmits impulses concerned with pain and temperature to opposite side of brain for interpretation by somatosensory cortex.
Ventral spinothalamic	Ventral	Interneurons (second-order neurons) in dorsal horns. Fibers cross to opposite side before ascending.	By synapse with third-order neurons in thalamus. Thalamic neurons eventually convey impulses to somatosensory cortex.	Transmits impulses concerned with crude touch and pressure to opposite side of brain for interpretation by somatosensory cortex.
Spinocerebellar Pathways				
Dorsal spinocerebellar*	Lateral (dorsal part)	Interneurons (second-order neurons) in dorsal horn on same side of cord. Fibers ascend without crossing.	By synapse in cerebellum	Transmits impulses from trunk and lower limb proprioceptors on one side of body to same side of cerebellum for subconscious proprioception.
Ventral spinocerebellar*	Lateral (ventral part)	Interneurons (second-order neurons) of dorsal horn. Contains crossed fibers that cross back to the opposite side in the pons.	By synapse in cerebellum	Transmits impulses from the trunk and lower limb on the same side of body to cerebellum for subconscious proprioception.

*These spinocerebellar tracts carry information from the lower limbs and trunk only. The corresponding tracts for the upper limb and neck (rostral spinocerebellar and others) are beyond the scope of this book.

Direct (Pyramidal) Pathways The direct pathways originate mainly with the pyramidal neurons located in the precentral gyri. These neurons send impulses through the brain stem via the large **pyramidal (corticospinal) tracts** (Figure 12.32a). The direct pathways are so called because their axons descend without synapsing from the pyramidal neurons to the spinal cord. There they synapse either with interneurons or with ventral horn motor neurons.

Stimulation of the ventral horn neurons activates the skeletal muscles with which they are associated. The direct pathway primarily regulates fast and fine (or skilled) movements such as doing needlework and writing.

Indirect Pathways The indirect pathways include brain stem motor nuclei and *all motor pathways except* the pyramidal pathways. These pathways were formerly lumped together as

(a) Pyramidal (lateral and ventral corticospinal) pathways

(b) Rubrospinal tract

Figure 12.32 Three descending pathways by which the brain influences movement.
Cross sections up to the cerebrum, which is shown in frontal section. **(a)** Pyramidal (lateral and ventral corticospinal pathways) are direct pathways that control skilled voluntary movements. **(b)** The rubrospinal tract, one of the indirect pathways, helps regulate muscle tone.

Table 12.3 Major Descending (Motor) Pathways and Spinal Cord Tracts

SPINAL CORD TRACT	LOCATION (FUNICULUS)	ORIGIN	TERMINATION	FUNCTION
Direct (Pyramidal) Pathways				
Lateral corticospinal	Lateral	Pyramidal neurons of motor cortex of the cerebrum. Cross over in pyramids of medulla.	By synapse with ventral horn interneurons that influence motor neurons and occasionally with ventral horn motor neurons directly.	Transmits motor impulses from cerebrum to spinal cord motor neurons (which activate skeletal muscles on opposite side of body). A voluntary motor tract.
Ventral corticospinal	Ventral	Pyramidal neurons of motor cortex. Fibers cross over at the spinal cord level.	Ventral horn (as above).	Same as lateral corticospinal tract.
Indirect Pathways				
Tectospinal	Ventral	Superior colliculus of midbrain of brain stem (fibers cross to opposite side of cord).	Ventral horn (as above).	Turns neck so eyes can follow a moving object.
Vestibulospinal	Ventral	Vestibular nuclei in medulla of brain stem (fibers descend without crossing).	Ventral horn (as above).	Transmits motor impulses that maintain muscle tone and activate ipsilateral limb and trunk extensor muscles and muscles that move head. Helps maintain balance during standing and moving.
Rubrospinal	Lateral	Red nucleus of midbrain of brain stem (fibers cross to opposite side just inferior to the red nucleus).	Ventral horn (as above).	In experimental animals, transmits motor impulses concerned with muscle tone of distal limb muscles (mostly flexors) on opposite side of body. In humans, functions are largely assumed by corticospinal tracts.
Reticulospinal (ventral, medial, and lateral)	Ventral and lateral	Reticular formation of brain stem (medial nuclear group of pons and medulla). Both crossed and uncrossed fibers.	Ventral horn (as above).	Transmits impulses concerned with muscle tone and many visceral motor functions. May control most unskilled movements.

the *extrapyramidal system* because their nuclei of origin were presumed to be independent of ("extra to") the pyramidal tracts. This term is still widely used clinically. However, pyramidal tract neurons are now known to project to and influence the activity of most "extrapyramidal" nuclei, so modern anatomists prefer the term **indirect**, or **multineuronal**, **pathways**, or even just the names of the individual motor pathways.

Indirect motor pathways are complex and multisynaptic. They are most involved in regulating:

- Axial muscles that maintain balance and posture
- Muscles controlling coarse limb movements
- Head, neck, and eye movements that follow objects in the visual field

Many of the activities controlled by subcortical motor nuclei depend heavily on reflex activity. Figure 12.32b illustrates one of these tracts, the rubrospinal tract.

Overall, the **reticulospinal** and **vestibulospinal tracts** maintain balance by varying the tone of postural muscles (Table 12.3). The **rubrospinal tracts** control flexor muscles, whereas the **tectospinal tracts** and the *superior colliculi* mediate head movements in response to visual stimuli.

☑ **Check Your Understanding**

23. What is the explanation for the cervical and lumbar enlargements of the spinal cord?
24. Where are the cell bodies of the first-, second-, and third-order sensory neurons in the spinothalamic pathway located?

_____ *For answers, see Appendix H.*

12

Spinal Cord Trauma and Disorders

✓ Distinguish between flaccid and spastic paralysis, and between paralysis and paresthesia.

Spinal Cord Trauma

The spinal cord is elastic, stretching with every turn of the head or bend of the trunk, but it is exquisitely sensitive to direct pressure. Any localized damage to the spinal cord or its roots leads to some functional loss, either **paralysis** (loss of motor function) or **paresthesias** (par″es-the′ze-ahz) (abnormal sensations).

Severe damage to ventral root or ventral horn cells results in **flaccid paralysis** (flak′sid) of the skeletal muscles served. Nerve impulses do not reach these muscles, which consequently cannot move either voluntarily or involuntarily. Without stimulation, the muscles atrophy.

When only the upper motor neurons of the primary motor cortex are damaged, **spastic paralysis** occurs. In this case, the spinal motor neurons remain intact and spinal reflex activity continues to stimulate the muscles irregularly. As a result, the muscles remain healthy longer, but their movements are no longer subject to voluntary control. In many cases, the muscles shorten permanently.

Transection (cross sectioning) of the spinal cord at any level results in total motor and sensory loss in body regions inferior to the site of damage.

- If the transection occurs between T_1 and L_1, both lower limbs are affected, resulting in **paraplegia** (par″ah-ple′je-ah; *para* = beside, *plegia* = a blow).
- If the injury occurs in the cervical region, all four limbs are affected and the result is **quadriplegia**.

Hemiplegia, paralysis of one side of the body, usually reflects brain injury rather than spinal cord injury.

Anyone with a spinal cord transection must be watched for symptoms of **spinal shock**, a transient period of functional loss that follows the injury. Spinal shock immediately depresses all reflex activity caudal to the lesion site. Bowel and bladder reflexes stop, blood pressure falls, and all muscles (somatic and visceral alike) below the injury are paralyzed and insensitive. Neural function usually returns within a few hours following injury. If function does not resume within 48 hours, paralysis is permanent in most cases.

Poliomyelitis

Poliomyelitis (po″le-o-mi″ĕ-li′tis; *polio* = gray matter; *myelitis* = inflammation of the spinal cord) results from the poliovirus, which typically enters the body in feces-contaminated water and destroys ventral horn motor neurons. Early symptoms include fever, headache, muscle pain and weakness, and loss of certain somatic reflexes. Later, paralysis develops and the muscles served atrophy. The victim may die from paralyzed respiratory muscles or from cardiac arrest. Fortunately, vaccines have nearly eliminated this disease and a global effort is ongoing to eradicate it completely.

However, many survivors of the great polio epidemic of the late 1940s and 1950s have begun to experience extreme lethargy, sharp burning pains in their muscles, and progressive muscle weakness and atrophy. These disturbing symptoms are referred to as **postpolio syndrome**. The cause of postpolio syndrome is not known, but a likely explanation is that its victims, like the rest of us, continue to lose neurons throughout life. While a healthy nervous system can recruit nearby neurons to compensate, polio survivors have already drawn on that "pool" and have few neurons left to take over. Ironically, those who worked hardest to overcome their disease are its newest victims.

Amyotrophic Lateral Sclerosis (ALS)

Amyotrophic lateral sclerosis (ALS) (ah-mi″o-trof′ik), also called Lou Gehrig's disease, is a devastating neuromuscular condition that progressively destroys ventral horn motor neurons and fibers of the pyramidal tracts. As the disease progresses, the sufferer loses the ability to speak, swallow, and breathe. Death typically occurs within five years.

Environmental and genetic factors interact to cause ALS. In 10% of cases mutations are inherited; spontaneous mutations are probably involved in the rest. Recently, the mutations have been localized to genes that are involved in RNA processing. While the exact mechanism is not clear, the presence of excess extracellular glutamate suggests that excitotoxic cell death is involved. Riluzole, a drug that interferes with glutamate signaling, is the only available life-prolonging treatment.

Diagnostic Procedures for Assessing CNS Dysfunction

✓ List and explain several techniques used to diagnose brain disorders.

If you have had a routine physical examination, you are familiar with the reflex tests done to assess neural function. A tap with a reflex hammer stretches your quadriceps tendon and your anterior thigh muscles contract. This produces the knee-jerk response, which shows that your spinal cord and upper brain centers are functioning normally.

Abnormal responses to a reflex test may indicate such serious disorders as intracranial hemorrhage, multiple sclerosis, or hydrocephalus. They indicate that more sophisticated neurological tests are needed to identify the problem.

New imaging techniques have revolutionized the diagnosis of brain lesions (see *A Closer Look*, pp. 18–19). Together, various *CT* and *MRI scanning techniques* allow quick identification of most tumors, intracranial lesions, multiple sclerosis plaques, and areas of dead brain tissue (infarcts). PET scans can localize brain lesions that generate seizures (epileptic tissue), and new radiotracer dyes that bind to beta-amyloid promise earlier, more reliable diagnosis of Alzheimer's disease.

Take, for example, a patient arriving in the emergency room with a stroke. A race against time begins to save the affected area of the patient's brain. The first step is to determine if the stroke is due to a clot or a bleed by imaging the brain, most often with CT. If the stroke is due to a clot, the clot-busting drug tPA can be used, but only within the first hours. tPA is usually given intravenously, but a longer time window is possible if tPA is applied directly to the clot using a catheter guided into position.

To visualize the location of the clot and the catheter, dye is injected to make arteries stand out in an X ray, a procedure called *cerebral angiography*. Cerebral angiography can also help patients who have had a warning stroke, or TIA.

Another test to assess risk of a CVA uses ultrasound. The carotid arteries of the neck, which feed most of the cerebral vessels, often narrow with age, which can lead to strokes. Cheaper and less invasive than angiography, ultrasound can be used to quickly examine the carotid arteries and even measure blood flow through them.

☑ Check Your Understanding

25. Roy was tackled while playing football. After hitting the ground, he was unable to move his lower limbs. What is a loss of motor function called? What level of his spinal cord do you think was injured (cervical, thoracic, lumbar, or sacral)? Is this a permanent injury? What diagnostic procedures might be helpful?

For answers, see Appendix H.

Developmental Aspects of the Central Nervous System

✓ Describe the development of the brain and spinal cord.

✓ Indicate several maternal factors that can impair development of the nervous system in an embryo.

✓ Explain the effects of aging on the brain.

Figure 12.33 shows the earliest phase of CNS development. Starting in the three-week-old embryo:

①	The ectoderm (cell layer at the dorsal surface) thickens along the dorsal midline axis of the embryo to form the **neural plate**. The neural plate invaginates, forming a **neural groove** flanked by **neural folds**.

②	Small groups of neural fold cells migrate laterally from between the surface ectoderm and the neural groove, forming the **neural crest**. Neural crest cells give rise (among other things) to some neurons destined to reside in ganglia.

③	As the neural groove deepens, the superior edges of the neural folds fuse, forming the **neural tube**, which soon detaches from the surface ectoderm and sinks to a deeper position.

The neural tube, formed by the fourth week of pregnancy, differentiates rapidly into the CNS. The brain forms rostrally, as we described on p. 429, and the spinal cord develops from the caudal portion of the neural tube.

By the sixth week, each side of the developing spinal cord has two recognizable clusters of neuroblasts that have migrated outward from the original neural tube: a dorsal **alar plate** (a'lar) and a ventral **basal plate** (Figure 12.34). Alar plate neuroblasts become interneurons. Basal plate neuroblasts develop into motor neurons and sprout axons that grow out to the effector organs. Axons that emerge from alar plate cells (and some basal plate cells) form the white matter of the cord. As development progresses, these plates

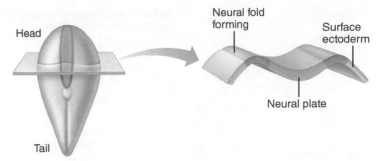

① The neural plate forms from surface ectoderm. It then invaginates, forming the neural groove flanked by neural folds.

② Neural fold cells migrate to form the neural crest, which will form much of the PNS and many other structures.

③ The neural groove becomes the neural tube, which will form CNS structures.

Figure 12.33 Development of the neural tube from embryonic ectoderm. Left: Dorsal surface views of the embryo. Right: Transverse sections at days 17, 20, and 22.

expand dorsally and ventrally to produce the H-shaped central mass of gray matter in the adult spinal cord.

Neural crest cells that come to lie alongside the cord form the *dorsal root ganglia* containing sensory neuron cell bodies. These sensory neurons send their axons into the dorsal aspect of the cord.

As the brain and spinal cord grow and mature throughout the prenatal period, gender-specific areas appear. For example, certain hypothalamic nuclei concerned with regulating typical male sexual behavior and clusters of neurons in the spinal cord that serve the external genitals are much larger in males. Females have a larger corpus callosum, and gender differences are seen in the language and auditory areas of the cerebral cortex. The key to CNS gender-specific development is whether or not the fetus is secreting testosterone. If it is, the male pattern develops.

Figure 12.34 Structure of the embryonic spinal cord. At six weeks of development, aggregations of gray matter called the alar plates (future interneurons) and basal plates (future motor neurons) have formed. Dorsal root ganglia (future sensory neurons) have arisen from neural crest cells.

Maternal exposure to radiation, various drugs (alcohol, opiates, and others), and infections can harm a developing infant's nervous system, particularly during the initial formative stages. For example, rubella (German measles) often leads to deafness and other types of CNS damage in the newborn. Smoking decreases the amount of oxygen in the blood, and lack of oxygen for even a few minutes destroys neurons. A mother who smokes may sentence her infant to some degree of brain damage.

Homeostatic Imbalance 12.11

Cerebral palsy is a neuromuscular disability in which the voluntary muscles are poorly controlled or paralyzed as a result of brain damage. It may be caused by temporary lack of oxygen during a difficult delivery, or by any of the factors listed above.

In addition to spasticity, speech difficulties, and other motor impairments, about half of cerebral palsy victims have seizures, half are mentally retarded, and about a third have some degree of deafness. Visual impairments are also common. Cerebral palsy does not get worse over time, but its deficits are irreversible. It is the largest single cause of physical disability in children, affecting three out of every 1000 births.

The CNS is plagued by a number of other congenital malformations triggered by genetic or environmental factors during early development. The most serious are congenital hydrocephalus (discussed previously), anencephaly, and spina bifida.

In **anencephaly** (an″en-sef′ah-le; "without brain"), the cerebrum and part of the brain stem never develop because the neural folds fail to fuse rostrally. The child is totally vegetative, unable to see, hear, or process sensory inputs. Muscles are flaccid, and no voluntary movement is possible. Mental life as we know it does not exist. Mercifully, death occurs soon after birth.

Figure 12.35 Newborn with a lumbar myelomeningocele.

Spina bifida (spi′nah bif′ĭ-dah; "forked spine") results from incomplete formation of the vertebral arches and typically involves the lumbosacral region. The technical definition is that laminae and spinous processes are missing on at least one vertebra. If the condition is severe, neural deficits occur as well.

Spina bifida occulta, the least serious type, involves one or only a few vertebrae and causes no neural problems. Other than a small dimple or tuft of hair over the site of nonfusion, it has no external manifestations.

In *spina bifida cystica*, the more common and severe form, a saclike cyst protrudes dorsally from the child's spine. The cyst may contain meninges and cerebrospinal fluid [a *meningocele* (mĕ-ning′go-sēl)], or even portions of the spinal cord and spinal nerve roots (a *myelomeningocele*, "spinal cord in a meningeal sac," **Figure 12.35**). The larger the cyst and the more neural structures it contains, the greater the neurological impairment. In the worst case, where the inferior spinal cord is functionless, the infant experiences bowel incontinence, bladder muscle paralysis (which promotes urinary tract infection and kidney failure), and lower limb paralysis. Infections occur continually because the cyst wall is thin and porous and tends to rupture or leak. Hydrocephalus accompanies spina bifida cystica in 90% of cases.

In the past, up to 70% of cases of spina bifida were caused by inadequate amounts of the B vitamin folic acid in the maternal diet. The incidence of spina bifida has dropped significantly in countries (such as the U.S.) that have introduced mandatory supplementation of folic acid in bread, flour, and pasta products. ✚

One of the last CNS areas to mature is the hypothalamus. Since the hypothalamus contains body temperature regulatory centers, premature babies have problems controlling their loss of body heat and must be kept in temperature-controlled environments. PET scans reveal that the thalamus and somatosensory cortex are active in a 5-day-old baby, but the visual cortex is not. This explains why infants of this age respond to touch but have poor vision. By 11 weeks, more of the cortex is active, and the baby can reach for a rattle. By 8 months, the cortex is very active and the child can think about what he or she sees.

Growth and maturation of the nervous system continue throughout childhood and largely reflect progressive myelination. As described in Chapter 9, neuromuscular coordination progresses in a superior-to-inferior direction and in a proximal-to-distal direction, and we know that myelination also occurs in this sequence.

The brain reaches its maximum weight in the young adult. Over the next 60 years or so, neurons are damaged and die, and brain weight and volume steadily decline. However, the number of neurons lost over the decades is normally only a small percentage of the total, and the remaining neurons can change their synaptic connections, providing for continued learning throughout life.

Although age brings some cognitive declines in spatial ability, speed of perception, decision making, reaction time, and working memory, these losses are not significant in the healthy individual until after the seventh decade. Then the brain becomes increasingly fragile, presumably due to less efficient calcium clearance in aging neurons (as we have seen, elevated Ca^{2+} levels are neurotoxic). A fairly rapid decline occurs in some, but not all, of these abilities.

However, mathematical skills, verbal fluency, and the ability to build on experience do not decline with age, and many people continue to enjoy intellectual lives and work at mentally demanding tasks their entire life. Fewer people over 65 than you might think demonstrate true dementia. Sadly, many cases of "reversible dementia" are caused by prescription drug side effects, low blood pressure, poor nutrition, hormone imbalances, depression, and/or dehydration that go undiagnosed. The best way to maintain your mental abilities in old age may be to seek regular medical checkups throughout life.

Although eventual shrinking of the brain is normal and accelerates in old age, alcoholics and professional boxers hasten the process. Whether a boxer wins the match or not, the likelihood of brain damage and atrophy increases with every blow. And everyone recognizes that alcohol profoundly affects both the mind and the body. CT scans of alcoholics reveal reduced brain size and density starting at a fairly early age. Both boxers and alcoholics exhibit signs of mental deterioration unrelated to the aging process.

☑ Check Your Understanding

26. What functional type of neuron is derived from the alar plate? From the basal plate?
27. Premature babies have problems controlling their body temperature. Why?
28. List several causes of reversible dementia in the elderly.

For answers, see Appendix H.

The human cerebral hemispheres—our "thinking caps"—are awesome in their complexity. But no less amazing are the brain regions that oversee our subconscious, autonomic body functions—the diencephalon and brain stem—particularly when you consider their relatively insignificant size. The spinal cord, which acts as a reflex center and a communication link between the brain and body periphery, is equally important to body homeostasis.

We have introduced a good deal of new terminology in this chapter, and much of it will come up again in the remaining nervous system chapters. Chapter 13, your next challenge, considers the structures of the peripheral nervous system that work hand in hand with the CNS to keep it informed and deliver its orders to the effectors of the body.

Chapter Summary

(MAP)™ For more chapter study tools, go to the Study Area of Mastering A&P at **www.masteringaandp.com**. There you will find:

- Interactive Physiology **iP**
- A&PFlix **A&PFlix**
- Practice Anatomy Lab **PAL**
- PhysioEx **PEx**
- Videos, Practice Quizzes and Tests, MP3 Tutor Sessions, Case Studies, and much more!

The Brain   (pp. 429–452)

1. The brain provides for voluntary movements, interpretation and integration of sensation, consciousness, and cognitive function.

Embryonic Development   (pp. 429–430)

2. Early brain development yields the three primary brain vesicles: the prosencephalon (cerebral hemispheres and diencephalon), mesencephalon (midbrain), and rhombencephalon (pons, medulla oblongata, and cerebellum).

3. As a result of cephalization, the diencephalon and superior brain stem are enveloped by the cerebral hemispheres.

Regions and Organization   (p. 430)

4. In a widely used system, the adult brain is divided into the cerebral hemispheres, diencephalon, brain stem, and cerebellum.
5. The cerebral hemispheres and cerebellum have gray matter nuclei surrounded by white matter and an outer cortex of gray matter. The diencephalon and brain stem lack a cortex.

Ventricles   (p. 430)

6. The brain contains four ventricles filled with cerebrospinal fluid. The lateral ventricles are in the cerebral hemispheres; the third ventricle is in the diencephalon; the fourth ventricle is between the brain stem and the cerebellum and connects with the central canal of the spinal cord.

Cerebral Hemispheres   (pp. 430–441)

7. The two cerebral hemispheres exhibit gyri, sulci, and fissures. The longitudinal fissure partially separates the hemispheres; other fissures or sulci subdivide each hemisphere into lobes.
8. Each cerebral hemisphere consists of the cerebral cortex, the cerebral white matter, and basal nuclei (ganglia).

9. Each cerebral hemisphere receives sensory impulses from, and dispatches motor impulses to, the opposite side of the body. The body is represented in an upside-down fashion in the sensory and motor cortices.

10. Functional areas of the cerebral cortex include (1) motor areas: primary motor and premotor cortices of the frontal lobe, the frontal eye field, and Broca's area in the frontal lobe of one hemisphere (usually the left); (2) sensory areas: primary somatosensory cortex and somatosensory association cortex in the parietal lobe; visual areas in the occipital lobe; olfactory and auditory areas in the temporal lobe; gustatory, visceral, and vestibular areas in the insula; (3) association areas: anterior association area in the frontal lobe, and posterior and limbic association areas spanning several lobes.

11. The cerebral hemispheres show lateralization of cortical function. In most people, the left hemisphere is dominant (i.e., specialized for language and mathematical skills); the right hemisphere is more concerned with visual-spatial skills and creative endeavors.

12. Fiber tracts of the cerebral white matter include commissures, association fibers, and projection fibers.

13. The paired basal nuclei (also called basal ganglia) include the globus pallidus, putamen, and caudate nucleus. The basal nuclei are subcortical nuclei that help control movements. Functionally they are closely associated with the substantia nigra of the midbrain.

Diencephalon (pp. 441–443)

14. The diencephalon includes the thalamus, hypothalamus, and epithalamus and encloses the third ventricle.

15. The thalamus is the major relay station for (1) sensory impulses ascending to the sensory cortex, (2) inputs from subcortical motor nuclei and the cerebellum traveling to the cerebral motor cortex, and (3) impulses traveling to association cortices from lower centers.

16. The hypothalamus is an important control center of the autonomic nervous system and a pivotal part of the limbic system. It maintains water balance and regulates thirst, eating behavior, gastrointestinal activity, body temperature, and the activity of the anterior pituitary gland.

17. The epithalamus includes the pineal gland, which secretes the hormone melatonin.

Brain Stem (pp. 443–447)

18. The brain stem includes the midbrain, pons, and medulla oblongata.

19. The midbrain contains the corpora quadrigemina (visual and auditory reflex centers), the red nucleus (subcortical motor centers), and the substantia nigra. The periaqueductal gray matter is involved in pain suppression and contains the motor nuclei of cranial nerves III and IV. The cerebral peduncles on its ventral face house the pyramidal fiber tracts. The midbrain surrounds the cerebral aqueduct.

20. The pons is mainly a conduction area. Its nuclei contribute to regulating respiration and cranial nerves V–VII.

21. The pyramids (descending corticospinal tracts) form the ventral face of the medulla oblongata. These fibers cross over (decussation of the pyramids) before entering the spinal cord. Important nuclei in the medulla regulate respiratory rhythm, heart rate, and blood pressure and serve cranial nerves VIII–XII. The olivary nuclei and cough, sneezing, swallowing, and vomiting centers are also in the medulla.

Cerebellum (pp. 447–449)

22. The cerebellum consists of two hemispheres, marked by convolutions and separated by the vermis. It is connected to the brain stem by superior, middle, and inferior peduncles.

23. The cerebellum processes and interprets impulses from the motor cortex and sensory pathways and coordinates motor activity so that smooth, well-timed movements occur. It also plays a poorly understood role in cognition.

Functional Brain Systems (pp. 449–452)

24. The limbic system consists of numerous structures that encircle the brain stem. It is the "emotional-visceral brain." It also plays a role in memory.

25. The reticular formation is a diffuse network of neurons and nuclei spanning the length of the brain stem. It maintains the alert state of the cerebral cortex (RAS), and its motor nuclei serve both somatic and visceral motor activities.

Higher Mental Functions (pp. 452–458)

Brain Wave Patterns and the EEG (pp. 452–453)

1. Patterns of electrical activity of the brain are called brain waves; a record of this activity is an electroencephalogram (EEG). Brain wave patterns, identified by their frequencies, include alpha, beta, theta, and delta waves.

2. Epilepsy results from abnormal electrical activity of brain neurons. Involuntary muscle contractions and sensory auras are typical during some epileptic seizures.

Consciousness (pp. 453–454)

3. Consciousness is described clinically on a continuum from alertness to drowsiness to stupor and finally to coma.

4. Human consciousness is thought to involve holistic information processing, which is (1) not localizable, (2) superimposed on other types of neural activity, and (3) totally interconnected.

5. Fainting (syncope) is a temporary loss of consciousness that usually reflects inadequate blood delivery to the brain. Coma is loss of consciousness in which the victim is unresponsive to stimuli.

Sleep and Sleep-Wake Cycles (pp. 454–455)

6. Sleep is a state of partial consciousness from which a person can be aroused by stimulation. The two major types of sleep are non–rapid eye movement (NREM) sleep and rapid eye movement (REM) sleep.

7. During stages 1–4 of NREM sleep, brain wave frequency decreases and amplitude increases until delta wave sleep (stage 4) is achieved. REM sleep is indicated by a return to alpha waves on the EEG. During REM, the eyes move rapidly under the lids. NREM and REM sleep alternate throughout the night.

8. Slow-wave sleep (stages 3 and 4 of NREM) appears to be restorative. REM sleep is important for emotional stability.

9. REM occupies half of an infant's sleep time and then declines to about 25% of sleep time by age 10. Time spent in slow-wave sleep declines steadily throughout life.

10. Narcolepsy is involuntary lapses into REM sleep that occur without warning during waking periods. Insomnia is a chronic inability to obtain the amount or quality of sleep needed to function adequately. A person with sleep apnea stops breathing temporarily during sleep, causing hypoxia.

Language   (pp. 455–456)

11. In most people the left hemisphere controls language. The language implementation system, which includes Broca's and Wernicke's areas and the basal nuclei, analyzes incoming and produces outgoing language. The opposite hemisphere deals with the emotional content of language.

Memory   (pp. 456–458)

12. Memory is the storage and retrieval of information. It is essential for learning and is part of consciousness.

13. Memory storage has two stages: short-term memory (STM) and long-term memory (LTM). Transfer of information from STM to LTM takes minutes to hours, but more time is required for LTM consolidation.

14. Declarative memory is the ability to learn and consciously remember information. Procedural memory is the learning of motor skills, which are then performed without conscious thought.

15. Declarative memory appears to involve the medial temporal lobe (hippocampus and surrounding temporal cortical areas), thalamus, basal forebrain, and prefrontal cortex. Procedural memory (a type of nondeclarative memory) relies on the basal nuclei.

16. The nature of memory formation at the molecular level is not fully known, but NMDA receptors (essentially calcium channels), activated by depolarization and glutamate binding, play a major role in long-term potentiation (LTP). The calcium influx that follows NMDA receptor activation mobilizes enzymes that mediate events necessary for memory formation.

Protection of the Brain   (pp. 458–462)

1. The delicate brain is protected by bone, meninges, cerebrospinal fluid, and the blood brain barrier.

Meninges   (pp. 459–460)

2. The meninges from superficial to deep are the dura mater, arachnoid mater, and pia mater. They enclose the brain and spinal cord and their blood vessels. Inward folds of the inner layer of the dura mater secure the brain to the skull.

Cerebrospinal Fluid   (pp. 460–462)

3. Cerebrospinal fluid (CSF), formed by the choroid plexuses from blood plasma, circulates through the ventricles and into the subarachnoid space. It returns to the dural venous sinuses via the arachnoid villi. CSF supports and cushions the brain and cord and helps to nourish them.

Blood Brain Barrier   (p. 462)

4. The blood brain barrier reflects the relative impermeability of the epithelium of capillaries of the brain. It allows water, respiratory gases, essential nutrients, and fat-soluble molecules to enter the neural tissue, but blocks other, water-soluble, potentially harmful substances.

Homeostatic Imbalances of the Brain   (pp. 462–464)

Traumatic Brain Injuries   (pp. 462–463)

1. Head trauma may cause brain injuries called concussions or, in severe cases, contusions (bruising). When the brain stem is affected, unconsciousness (temporary or permanent) occurs. Trauma-induced brain injuries may be aggravated by intracranial hemorrhage or cerebral edema, both of which compress brain tissue.

Cerebrovascular Accidents (CVAs)   (p. 463)

2. Cerebrovascular accidents (strokes) result when blood circulation to brain neurons is impaired and brain tissue dies. The result may be hemiplegia, sensory deficits, or speech impairment.

Degenerative Brain Disorders   (pp. 463–464)

3. Alzheimer's disease is a degenerative brain disease in which beta-amyloid peptide deposits and neurofibrillary tangles appear. Marked by a deficit of ACh, it results in slow, progressive loss of memory and motor control and increasing dementia.

4. Parkinson's disease and Huntington's disease are neurodegenerative disorders of the basal nuclei. Both involve abnormalities of the neurotransmitter dopamine (too little or too much secreted) and are characterized by abnormal movements.

The Spinal Cord   (pp. 464–474)

Gross Anatomy and Protection   (pp. 464–466)

1. The spinal cord, a two-way impulse conduction pathway and a reflex center, resides within the vertebral column and is protected by meninges and cerebrospinal fluid. It extends from the foramen magnum to the end of the first lumbar vertebra.

2. Thirty-one pairs of spinal nerves issue from the cord. The cord is enlarged in the cervical and lumbar regions, where spinal nerves serving the limbs arise.

Spinal Cord Cross-Sectional Anatomy   (pp. 466–468)

3. The central gray matter of the cord is H shaped. Ventral horns mainly contain somatic motor neurons. Lateral horns contain visceral (autonomic) motor neurons. Dorsal horns contain interneurons.

4. Axons of neurons of the lateral and ventral horns emerge in common from the cord via the ventral roots. Axons of sensory neurons (with cell bodies located in the dorsal root ganglion) form the dorsal roots and enter the dorsal aspect of the cord. The ventral and dorsal roots combine to form the spinal nerves.

5. Each side of the white matter of the cord has dorsal, lateral, and ventral columns (funiculi), and each funiculus contains a number of ascending and descending tracts. All tracts are paired and most decussate.

Neuronal Pathways   (pp. 468–473)

6. Ascending (sensory) tracts include the fasciculi gracilis and cuneatus, spinothalamic tracts, and spinocerebellar tracts.

7. The dorsal column–medial lemniscal pathway consists of the dorsal white column (fasciculus cuneatus, fasciculus gracilis) and the medial lemniscus, which are concerned with straight-through, precise transmission of one or a few related types of sensory input. The spinothalamic pathways transmit pain, temperature, and coarse touch, and permit brain stem processing of ascending impulses. The spinocerebellar tracts, which terminate in the cerebellum, serve muscle sense, not conscious sensory perception.

8. Descending tracts include the pyramidal tracts (ventral and lateral corticospinal tracts) and a number of motor tracts originating from subcortical motor nuclei. These descending fibers issue from the brain stem motor areas [indirect system] and cortical motor areas [direct (pyramidal) system].

Spinal Cord Trauma and Disorders   (p. 474)

9. Injury to the ventral horn neurons or the ventral roots results in flaccid paralysis. (Injury to the upper motor neurons in the brain results in spastic paralysis.) If the dorsal roots or sensory tracts are damaged, paresthesias occur.

12

10. Poliomyelitis results from inflammation and destruction of the ventral horn neurons by the poliovirus. Paralysis and muscle atrophy ensue.
11. Amyotrophic lateral sclerosis (ALS) results from destruction of the ventral horn neurons and the pyramidal tracts. The victim eventually loses the ability to swallow, speak, and breathe. Death generally occurs within five years.

Diagnostic Procedures for Assessing CNS Dysfunction (pp. 474–475)

1. Diagnostic procedures used to assess neurological condition and function range from routine reflex testing to sophisticated techniques such as cerebral angiography, CT scans, MRI scans, and PET scans.

Developmental Aspects of the Central Nervous System (pp. 475–477)

1. The CNS develops from the embryonic neural tube—the brain from the rostral part and the spinal cord from the caudal part.

2. The gray matter of the spinal cord forms from the alar and basal plates. Fiber tracts form the outer white matter. The neural crest forms the sensory (dorsal root) ganglia.
3. Maternal and environmental factors may impair embryonic brain development, and oxygen deprivation destroys brain cells. Severe congenital brain disorders include cerebral palsy, anencephaly, hydrocephalus, and spina bifida.
4. Premature babies have trouble regulating body temperature because the hypothalamus is one of the last brain areas to mature prenatally.
5. Development of motor control indicates progressive myelination and maturation of a child's nervous system.
6. Brain growth ends in young adulthood. Neurons die throughout life and most are not replaced; brain weight and volume decline with age.
7. Healthy elders maintain nearly optimal intellectual function. Disease—particularly cardiovascular disease—is the major cause of declining mental function with age.

Review Questions

Multiple Choice/Matching

(Some questions have more than one correct answer. Select the best answer or answers from the choices given.)

1. The primary motor cortex, Broca's area, and the premotor cortex are located in which lobe? **(a)** frontal, **(b)** parietal, **(c)** temporal, **(d)** occipital.
2. The innermost layer of the meninges, delicate and closely apposed to the brain tissue, is the **(a)** dura mater, **(b)** corpus callosum, **(c)** arachnoid mater, **(d)** pia mater.
3. Cerebrospinal fluid is formed by **(a)** arachnoid villi, **(b)** dura mater, **(c)** choroid plexuses, **(d)** all of these.
4. A patient has suffered a cerebral hemorrhage that has caused dysfunction of the precentral gyrus of his right cerebral cortex. As a result, **(a)** he cannot voluntarily move his left arm or leg, **(b)** he feels no sensation on the left side of his body, **(c)** he feels no sensation on his right side.
5. Choose the correct term from the key to respond to the statements describing various brain areas.

Key:

(a) cerebellum	**(d)** striatum	**(g)** midbrain
(b) corpora quadrigemina	**(e)** hypothalamus	**(h)** pons
(c) corpus callosum	**(f)** medulla	**(i)** thalamus

____ **(1)** basal nuclei involved in fine control of motor activities
____ **(2)** region where there is a gross crossover of fibers of descending pyramidal tracts
____ **(3)** control of temperature, autonomic nervous system reflexes, hunger, and water balance
____ **(4)** houses the substantia nigra and cerebral aqueduct
____ **(5)** relay stations for visual and auditory stimuli input; found in midbrain
____ **(6)** houses vital centers for control of the heart, respiration, and blood pressure
____ **(7)** brain area through which all the sensory input is relayed to get to the cerebral cortex
____ **(8)** brain area most concerned with equilibrium, body posture, and coordination of motor activity

6. Which of the following tracts convey vibration and other specific sensations that can be precisely localized? **(a)** pyramidal tract, **(b)** medial lemniscus, **(c)** lateral spinothalamic tract, **(d)** reticulospinal tract.
7. Destruction of the ventral horn cells of the spinal cord results in loss of **(a)** integrating impulses, **(b)** sensory impulses, **(c)** voluntary motor impulses, **(d)** all of these.
8. Fiber tracts that allow neurons within the same cerebral hemisphere to communicate are **(a)** association fibers, **(b)** commissures, **(c)** projection fibers.
9. A number of brain structures are listed below. If an area is primarily gray matter, write **a** in the answer blank; if mostly white matter, respond with **b**.

____ **(1)** cerebral cortex
____ **(2)** corpus callosum and corona radiata
____ **(3)** red nucleus
____ **(4)** medial and lateral nuclear groups
____ **(5)** medial lemniscus
____ **(6)** cranial nerve nuclei
____ **(7)** spinothalamic tract
____ **(8)** fornix
____ **(9)** cingulate and precentral gyri

10. A professor unexpectedly blew a loud horn in his anatomy and physiology class. The students looked up, startled. The reflexive movements of their eyes were mediated by the **(a)** cerebral cortex, **(b)** inferior olives, **(c)** raphe nuclei, **(d)** superior colliculi, **(e)** nucleus gracilis.
11. Identify the stage of sleep described by using choices from the key. (Note that responses a–d refer to NREM sleep.)

Key: **(a)** stage 1 **(b)** stage 2 **(c)** stage 3 **(d)** stage 4 **(e)** REM

____ **(1)** the stage when blood pressure and heart rate reach their lowest levels
____ **(2)** indicated by movement of the eyes under the lids; dreaming occurs
____ **(3)** when nightmares are likely to occur
____ **(4)** when the sleeper is very easily awakened; EEG shows alpha waves

12

12. All of the following descriptions refer to dorsal column–medial lemniscal ascending pathways except one: **(a)** they include the fasciculus gracilis and fasciculus cuneatus; **(b)** they include a chain of three neurons; **(c)** their connections are diffuse and poorly localized; **(d)** they are concerned with precise transmission of one or a few related types of sensory input.

Short Answer Essay Questions

13. Make a diagram showing the three primary (embryonic) brain vesicles. Name each and then use clinical terminology to name the resulting adult brain regions.

14. (a) What is the advantage of having a cerebrum that is highly convoluted? (b) What term is used to indicate its grooves? Its outward folds? (c) Which groove divides the cerebrum into two hemispheres? (d) What divides the parietal from the frontal lobe? The parietal from the temporal lobe?

15. (a) Make a rough drawing of the lateral aspect of the left cerebral hemisphere. (b) You may be thinking, "But I just can't draw!" So, name the hemisphere involved with most people's ability to draw. (c) On your drawing, locate the following areas and provide the major function of each: primary motor cortex, premotor cortex, somatosensory association cortex, primary somatosensory cortex, visual and auditory areas, prefrontal cortex, Wernicke's and Broca's areas.

16. (a) What does lateralization of cortical functioning mean? (b) Why is the term cerebral dominance a misnomer?

17. (a) What is the function of the basal nuclei? (b) Which basal nuclei form the striatum? (c) Which arches over the diencephalon?

18. Explain how the cerebellum is physically connected to the brain stem.

19. Describe the role of the cerebellum in maintaining smooth, coordinated skeletal muscle activity.

20. (a) Where is the limbic system located? (b) Which structures make up this system? (c) How is the limbic system important in behavior?

21. (a) Localize the reticular formation in the brain. (b) What does RAS mean, and what is its function?

22. What is an aura?

23. How do sleep patterns, extent of sleeping time, and amount of time spent in REM and NREM sleep change through life?

24. Compare and contrast short-term memory (STM) and long-term memory (LTM) relative to storage capacity and duration of the memory.

25. Define memory consolidation.

26. Compare and contrast declarative and procedural memory relative to the types of things remembered and the importance of conscious retrieval.

27. List four ways in which the CNS is protected.

28. (a) How is cerebrospinal fluid formed and drained? Describe its pathway within and around the brain. (b) What happens if CSF does not drain properly? Why is this consequence more harmful in adults?

29. What constitutes the blood brain barrier?

30. A brain surgeon is about to make an incision. Name all the tissue layers that she cuts through from the skin to the brain.

31. (a) Define concussion and contusion. (b) Why does severe brain stem injury result in unconsciousness?

32. Describe the spinal cord, depicting its extent, its composition of gray and white matter, and its spinal roots.

33. How do the types of motor activity controlled by the direct (pyramidal) and indirect systems differ?

34. Describe the functional problems that would be experienced by a person in which these fiber tracts have been cut: (a) lateral spinothalamic, (b) ventral and dorsal spinocerebellar, (c) tectospinal.

35. Differentiate between spastic and flaccid paralysis.

36. How do the conditions paraplegia, hemiplegia, and quadriplegia differ?

37. (a) Define cerebrovascular accident or CVA. (b) Describe its possible causes and consequences.

38. (a) What factors account for brain growth after birth? (b) List some structural brain changes observed with aging.

Critical Thinking and Clinical Application Questions

1. A 10-month-old infant has an enlarging head circumference and delayed overall development. She has a bulging anterior fontanelle and her CSF pressure is elevated. Based on these findings, answer the following questions: (a) What are the possible cause(s) of an enlarged head? (b) Which tests might be helpful in obtaining information about this infant's problem? (c) Assuming the tests conducted showed the cerebral aqueduct to be constricted, which ventricles or CSF-containing areas would you expect to be enlarged? Which would likely not be visible? Respond to the same questions based on a finding of obstructed arachnoid villi.

2. Mrs. Jones has had a progressive decline in her mental capabilities in the last five or six years. At first her family attributed her occasional memory lapses, confusion, and agitation to grief over her husband's death six years earlier. When examined, Mrs. Jones was aware of her cognitive problems and was shown to have an IQ score approximately 30 points less than would be predicted by her work history. A CT scan showed diffuse cerebral atrophy. The physician prescribed an acetylcholinesterase inhibitor and Mrs. Jones showed slight improvement. What is Mrs. Jones's problem? Why did the acetylcholinesterase inhibitor help?

3. Robert, a brilliant computer analyst, suffered a blow to his anterior skull from a falling rock while mountain climbing. Shortly thereafter, it was obvious to his coworkers that his behavior had undergone a dramatic change. Although previously a smart dresser, he was now unkempt. One morning, he was observed defecating into the wastebasket. His supervisor ordered Robert to report to the company's doctor immediately. Which region of Robert's brain was affected by the cranial blow?

4. Mrs. Adams is ready to deliver her first baby. Unfortunately, the baby appears to have a myelomeningocele. Would a vaginal or surgical (C-section) delivery be more appropriate and why?

5. The medical chart of a 68-year-old man includes the following notes: "Slight tremor of right hand at rest; stony facial expression; difficulty in initiating movements." (a) Based on your present knowledge, what is the diagnosis? (b) What brain areas are most likely involved in this man's disorder, and what is the deficiency? (c) How is this condition currently treated?

6. Cynthia, a 16-year-old girl, was rushed to the hospital after taking a bad spill off the parallel bars. After she had a complete neurological workup, her family was told that she would be permanently paralyzed from the waist down. The neurologist then outlined for Cynthia's parents the importance of preventing complications in such cases. Common complications include urinary infection, bed sores, and muscular spasms. Using your knowledge of neuroanatomy, explain the underlying reasons for these complications.

7. Five-year-old Amy wakes her parents up at 3 AM crying and complaining of a sore neck, severe headache, and feeling sick to her stomach. She has a temperature of 40°C (104°F) and hides her eyes, saying that the lights are too bright. The emergency physician suspects meningitis and performs a lumbar tap. Using your knowledge of neuroanatomy, explain into which space and at what level of the vertebral column the needle will be inserted to perform this test. Which fluid is being obtained and why?

AT THE CLINIC

Related Clinical Terms

Autism A complex developmental neurological disorder, typically appearing in the first three years of life, characterized by difficulty in communicating, forming relationships with others, and responding appropriately to the environment. A wide variety of mutations in functionally related genes can give rise to autism and its related disorders. Occurs in about two per 1000 people, and early behavioral intervention is beneficial.

Cordotomy (kor-dot′o-me) A procedure in which a tract in the spinal cord is severed surgically; usually done to relieve unremitting pain.

Dyslexia A learning disability in 5 to 15% of the population that specifically affects the ability of otherwise intelligent people to read. This deficit in visual symbol and language processing is thought to result from errors arising in one hemisphere. Several genes that predispose children to dyslexia have been identified, but dyslexia can also be acquired by brain injury or degeneration.

Encephalopathy (en-sef′ah-lop′ah-the; *enceph* = brain; *path* = disease) Any disease or disorder of the brain.

Hypersomnia (*hyper* = excess; *somnus* = sleep) A condition in which affected individuals sleep as much as 15 hours daily.

Microcephaly (mi″kro-sef′ah-le; *micro* = small) Congenital condition involving the formation of a small brain, as evidenced by reduced skull size; most microcephalic children are mentally retarded.

Myelitis (mi″ĕ-li′tis; *myel* = spinal cord; *itis* = inflammation) Inflammation of the spinal cord.

Myelogram (*gram* = recording) X ray of the spinal cord after injection of a contrast medium.

Myoclonus (mi″o-klo′nus; *myo* = muscle; *clon* = violent motion, tumult) Sudden contraction of a muscle or muscle part, usually involving muscles of the limbs. Myoclonal jerks can occur in normal individuals as they are falling asleep; others may be due to diseases of the reticular formation or cerebellum.

Neuroses (nu-ro′sēs) A less debilitating class of mental illness; examples include severe anxiety (panic attacks), phobias (irrational fears), and obsessive-compulsive behaviors (e.g., washing one's hands every few minutes). However, the affected individual retains contact with reality.

Psychoses (si-ko′sēs) A class of severe mental illness in which affected individuals lose touch with reality and exhibit bizarre behaviors; the legal word for psychotic behavior is insanity. Psychoses include schizophrenia (skit-so-fre′ne-ah), bipolar disorder, and some forms of depression.

Case Study **Central Nervous System**

Margaret Bryans, a 39-year-old female, was a passenger on the bus that crashed on Route 91. When paramedics arrived on the scene, she was unconscious, with cuts on her arms, face, and scalp. She regained consciousness en route to the hospital and appeared agitated and combative. Paramedics observed that she had a right hemiparesis (muscle weakness), with a near complete paresis of her right upper extremity and a partial paresis of the right lower extremity. A head CT scan revealed an acute subdural hematoma and an extensive subarachnoid hemorrhage. Doctors noted that she was able to follow commands from medical personnel. With difficulty, she could speak haltingly, using only simple words.

Surgery to remove large clots from the subarachnoid space was performed immediately. Two weeks after the surgery, she showed significant improvement in her speech and motor function.

1. The adult brain can be broken down into four functional regions (see Table 12.1). Based on the observed signs in this case, which of these four brain regions is involved? What evidence did you use to determine this?

2. Which side of the brain is involved in Mrs. Bryans's injury? What evidence did you use to determine this?

3. What specific parts of the region of the brain you identified in question 1 are being affected by the injury to cause the muscle weakness and language problems?

4. What are the three membranes that make up the meninges? Describe their positions relative to the brain.

5. Relative to the meninges, describe the location of the bleeding revealed on the CT scan.

(Answers in Appendix H)

The Peripheral Nervous System and Reflex Activity

✓ Define peripheral nervous system and list its components.

The human brain, for all its sophistication, would be useless without its links to the outside world. Consider one experiment that illustrates this point. Volunteers who were deprived of sensory input by being blindfolded and suspended in warm water in a sensory deprivation tank hallucinated. One saw charging pink and purple elephants. Another heard a chorus, still others had taste hallucinations. Our very sanity depends on a continuous flow of information from the outside.

Equally important to our well-being are the orders sent from the CNS to voluntary muscles and other effectors of the body, which allow us to move and take care of our own

Figure 13.1 Place of the PNS in the structural organization of the nervous system.

needs. The **peripheral nervous system (PNS)** provides these links from and to the world outside our bodies. Ghostly white nerves thread through virtually every part of the body, enabling the CNS to receive information and carry out its decisions.

The PNS includes all neural structures outside the brain and spinal cord, that is, the *sensory receptors*, peripheral *nerves* and their associated *ganglia*, and efferent *motor endings*. **Figure 13.1** diagrams its basic components.

In the first portion of this chapter we deal with the functional anatomy of each PNS element. Then we consider the components of reflex arcs and some important somatic reflexes, played out almost entirely in PNS structures, that help maintain homeostasis.

PART 1
Sensory Receptors and Sensation

Sensory Receptors

✓ Classify general sensory receptors by structure, stimulus detected, and body location.

Sensory receptors are specialized to respond to changes in their environment, which are called **stimuli**. Typically, activation of a sensory receptor by an adequate stimulus results in graded potentials that in turn trigger nerve impulses along the afferent PNS fibers coursing to the CNS. *Sensation* (awareness of the stimulus) and *perception* (interpretation of the meaning of the stimulus) occur in the brain. But we are getting ahead of ourselves here.

For now, let's just examine how sensory receptors are classified. Basically, there are three ways to classify sensory receptors: (1) by the type of stimulus they detect; (2) by their body location; and (3) by their structural complexity.

Classification by Stimulus Type

These categories are easy to remember because the name usually indicates the stimulus that activates the receptor.

■ **Mechanoreceptors** respond to mechanical force such as touch, pressure (including blood pressure), vibration, and stretch.

■ **Thermoreceptors** respond to temperature changes.

■ **Photoreceptors**, such as those of the retina of the eye, respond to light.

■ **Chemoreceptors** respond to chemicals in solution (molecules smelled or tasted, or changes in blood or interstitial fluid chemistry).

■ **Nociceptors** (no″se-sep′torz; *noci* = harm) respond to potentially damaging stimuli that result in pain. For example, searing heat, extreme cold, excessive pressure, and inflammatory chemicals are all interpreted as painful. These signals stimulate subtypes of thermoreceptors, mechanoreceptors, and chemoreceptors.

Classification by Location

Receptors can be grouped into three receptor classes according to either their location or the location of the activating stimulus: exteroceptors, interoceptors, and proprioceptors.

■ **Exteroceptors** (ek″ster-o-sep′torz) are sensitive to stimuli arising outside the body (*extero* = outside), so most exteroceptors are near or at the body surface. They include touch, pressure, pain, and temperature receptors in the skin and most receptors of the special senses (vision, hearing, equilibrium, taste, smell).

■ **Interoceptors** (in″ter-o-sep′torz), also called *visceroceptors*, respond to stimuli within the body (*intero* = inside), such as from the internal viscera and blood vessels. Interoceptors monitor a variety of stimuli, including chemical changes,

Table 13.1	**General Sensory Receptors Classified by Structure and Function**		
STRUCTURAL CLASS	**ILLUSTRATION**	**FUNCTIONAL CLASSES ACCORDING TO LOCATION (L) AND STIMULUS TYPE (S)**	**BODY LOCATION**
Nonencapsulated			
Free nerve endings of sensory neurons		L: Exteroceptors, interoceptors, and proprioceptors S: Thermoreceptors (warm and cool), chemoreceptors (itch, pH, etc.), mechanoreceptors (pressure), nociceptors (pain, hot, cold, pinch, and chemicals)	Most body tissues; most dense in connective tissues (ligaments, tendons, dermis, joint capsules, periostea) and epithelia (epidermis, cornea, mucosae, and glands)
Modified free nerve endings: Tactile (Merkel) discs		L: Exteroceptors S: Mechanoreceptors (light pressure); slowly adapting	Basal layer of epidermis
Hair follicle receptors		L: Exteroceptors S: Mechanoreceptors (hair deflection); rapidly adapting	In and surrounding hair follicles

tissue stretch, and temperature. Sometimes their activity causes us to feel pain, discomfort, hunger, or thirst. However, we are usually unaware of their workings.

- **Proprioceptors** (pro″pre-o-sep′torz), like interoceptors, respond to internal stimuli. However, their location is much more restricted. Proprioceptors occur in skeletal muscles, tendons, joints, and ligaments and in connective tissue coverings of bones and muscles. (Some authorities include the equilibrium receptors of the inner ear in this class.) Proprioceptors constantly advise the brain of our body movements (*propria* = one's own) by monitoring how much the organs containing these receptors are stretched.

Classification by Receptor Structure

The overwhelming majority of sensory receptors belong to the **general senses** and are simply the modified dendritic endings of sensory neurons. They are found throughout the body and monitor most types of general sensory information.

Receptors for the **special senses** (vision, hearing, equilibrium, smell, and taste) are housed in complex **sense organs**. For example, the sense organ we know as the eye is composed not only of sensory neurons but also of nonneural cells that form its supporting wall, lens, and other associated structures.

Though the special senses are most familiar to us, the simple sensory receptors associated with the general senses are no less

important, and we will concentrate on their structure and function in this chapter. The special senses are the topic of Chapter 15.

Simple Receptors of the General Senses

The widely distributed general sensory receptors are involved in tactile sensation (a mix of touch, pressure, stretch, and vibration), temperature monitoring, and pain, as well as the "muscle sense" provided by proprioceptors. As you read about these receptors, notice that there is no perfect "one-receptor–one-function" relationship. Instead, one type of receptor can respond to several different kinds of stimuli. Likewise, different types of receptors can respond to similar stimuli. Anatomically, general sensory receptors are nerve endings that are either *nonencapsulated* (*free*) or *encapsulated*. Table 13.1 illustrates the general sensory receptors. You may find it helpful to refer to this table throughout the discussion that follows.

Nonencapsulated (Free) Nerve Endings   Present nearly everywhere in the body, **nonencapsulated (free) nerve endings** of sensory neurons are particularly abundant in epithelia and connective tissues. Most of these sensory fibers are nonmyelinated, small-diameter group C fibers, and their distal endings (the sensory terminals) usually have small knoblike swellings.

Free nerve endings respond chiefly to temperature and painful stimuli, but some respond to tissue movements caused by pressure as well. Nerve endings that respond to

Table 13.1	General Sensory Receptors Classified by Structure and Function (continued)		
STRUCTURAL CLASS	**ILLUSTRATION**	**FUNCTIONAL CLASSES ACCORDING TO LOCATION (L) AND STIMULUS TYPE (S)**	**BODY LOCATION**
Encapsulated			
Tactile (Meissner's) corpuscles		L: Exteroceptors S: Mechanoreceptors (light pressure, discriminative touch, vibration of low frequency); rapidly adapting	Dermal papillae of hairless skin, particularly nipples, external genitalia, fingertips, soles of feet, eyelids
Lamellar (Pacinian) corpuscles		L: Exteroceptors, interoceptors, and some proprioceptors S: Mechanoreceptors (deep pressure, stretch, vibration of high frequency); rapidly adapting	Dermis and hypodermis; periostea, mesentery, tendons, ligaments, joint capsules; most abundant on fingers, soles of feet, external genitalia, nipples
Bulbous corpuscles (Ruffini endings)		L: Exteroceptors and proprioceptors S: Mechanoreceptors (deep pressure and stretch); slowly or nonadapting	Deep in dermis, hypodermis, and joint capsules
Muscle spindles	Intrafusal fibers	L: Proprioceptors S: Mechanoreceptors (muscle stretch, length)	Skeletal muscles, particularly in the extremities
Tendon organs		L: Proprioceptors S: Mechanoreceptors (tendon stretch, tension)	Tendons
Joint kinesthetic receptors		L: Proprioceptors S: Mechanoreceptors and nociceptors	Joint capsules of synovial joints

cold (10–40°C, or 50–104°F) are located in the superficial dermis. Those responding to heat (32–48°C, or 90–120°F) are deeper in the dermis.

Heat or cold outside the range of thermoreceptors activates nociceptors and is perceived as painful. Nociceptors also respond to pinch and chemicals released from damaged tissue. A key player in detecting painful stimuli is a plasma membrane protein called the *vanilloid receptor*. This protein is an ion channel that is opened by heat, low pH, and various chemicals including capsaicin, the substance found in red peppers.

Another sensation mediated by free nerve endings is itch. Located in the dermis, the *itch receptor* escaped detection for years because of its thin diameter. A number of chemicals—notably histamine—present at inflamed sites activate these nerve endings.

Other nonencapsulated nerve endings include:

- **Tactile (Merkel) discs**, which lie in the deepest layer of the epidermis, function as light touch receptors. Certain free nerve endings associate with enlarged, disc-shaped epidermal cells (*tactile* or *Merkel cells*) to form tactile discs.

- **Hair follicle receptors**, free nerve endings that wrap basket-like around hair follicles, are light touch receptors that detect bending of hairs. The tickle of a mosquito landing on your skin is mediated by hair follicle receptors.

Encapsulated Nerve Endings All **encapsulated nerve endings** consist of one or more fiber terminals of sensory neurons enclosed in a connective tissue capsule. Virtually all encapsulated receptors are mechanoreceptors, but they vary greatly in shape, size, and distribution in the body. They include tactile corpuscles, lamellar corpuscles, bulbous corpuscles, muscle spindles, tendon organs, and joint kinesthetic receptors.

- **Tactile corpuscles** or *Meissner's corpuscles* are small receptors in which a few spiraling sensory terminals are surrounded by Schwann cells and then by a thin egg-shaped connective tissue capsule. Tactile corpuscles are found just beneath the epidermis in the dermal papillae and are especially numerous in sensitive and hairless skin areas such as the nipples, fingertips, and soles of the feet. They are receptors for discriminative touch, and apparently play the same role in sensing light touch in hairless skin that hair follicle receptors do in hairy skin.

- **Lamellar corpuscles**, also called *Pacinian corpuscles*, are scattered deep in the dermis, and in subcutaneous tissue underlying the skin. Although they are mechanoreceptors stimulated by deep pressure, they respond only when the pressure is first applied, and thus are best suited to monitoring vibration (an "on/off" pressure stimulus). They are the largest corpuscular receptors. Some are over 3 mm long and half as wide and are visible to the naked eye as white, egg-shaped bodies. In section, a lamellar corpuscle resembles a cut onion. Its single dendrite is surrounded by a capsule containing up to 60 layers of collagen fibers and flattened supporting cells.

- **Bulbous corpuscles** or *Ruffini endings*, which lie in the dermis, subcutaneous tissue, and joint capsules, contain a spray of receptor endings enclosed by a flattened capsule. They bear a striking resemblance to tendon organs (which monitor tendon stretch) and probably play a similar role in other dense connective tissues where they respond to deep and *continuous* pressure.

- **Muscle spindles** are fusiform (spindle-shaped) proprioceptors found throughout the perimysium of a skeletal muscle. Each muscle spindle consists of a bundle of modified skeletal muscle fibers, called *intrafusal fibers* (in″trah-fu′zal), enclosed in a connective tissue capsule (Table 13.1). Muscle spindles detect muscle stretch and initiate a reflex that resists the stretch. We will consider the details of their innervation later when we describe the stretch reflex (see p. 515).

- **Tendon organs** are proprioceptors located in tendons, close to the skeletal muscle insertion. They consist of small bundles of tendon (collagen) fibers enclosed in a layered capsule, with sensory terminals coiling between and around the fibers. When muscle contraction stretches the tendon fibers, the resulting compression of the nerve fibers activates the tendon organs. This initiates a reflex that causes the contracting muscle to relax.

- **Joint kinesthetic receptors** (kin″es-thet′ik) are proprioceptors that monitor stretch in the articular capsules that enclose synovial joints. This receptor category contains at least four receptor types: lamellar corpuscles, bulbous corpuscles, free nerve endings, and receptors resembling tendon organs. Together these receptors provide information on joint position and motion (*kines* = movement), a sensation of which we are highly conscious.

Close your eyes and flex and extend your fingers—you can feel exactly which joints are moving.

☑ **Check Your Understanding**

1. Your PNS mostly consists of nerves. What else belongs to your PNS?
2. You've cut your finger on a broken beaker in your A&P lab. Using stimulus type, location, and receptor structure, classify the sensory receptors that allow you to feel the pain.

For answers, see Appendix H.

Sensory Integration: From Sensation to Perception

✓ Outline the events that lead to sensation and perception.

✓ Describe receptor and generator potentials and sensory adaptation.

✓ Describe the main aspects of sensory perception.

Our survival depends not only on **sensation** (awareness of changes in the internal and external environments) but also on **perception** (conscious interpretation of those stimuli). For example, a pebble in your shoe causes the *sensation* of localized deep pressure, but your *perception* of it is an awareness of discomfort. Perception in turn determines how we will respond: In this case, you take off your shoe to get rid of the pesky pebble.

General Organization of the Somatosensory System

The **somatosensory system**—the part of the sensory system serving the body wall and limbs—receives inputs from exteroceptors, proprioceptors, and interoceptors. Consequently, it transmits information about several different sensory modalities, or types of sensation.

Three main levels of neural integration operate in the somatosensory (or any sensory) system (**Figure 13.2**):

① **Receptor level:** sensory receptors
② **Circuit level:** processing in ascending pathways
③ **Perceptual level:** processing in cortical sensory areas

Sensory input is generally relayed toward the head, but note that it is also processed along the way.

Let's examine the events that must occur at each level along the pathway.

Processing at the Receptor Level

For sensation to occur, a stimulus must excite a receptor and action potentials must reach the CNS (Figure 13.2, ①). For this to happen:

- The stimulus energy must match the *specificity* of the receptor. For example, a touch receptor may be sensitive to mechanical pressure, stretch, and vibration, but not to light

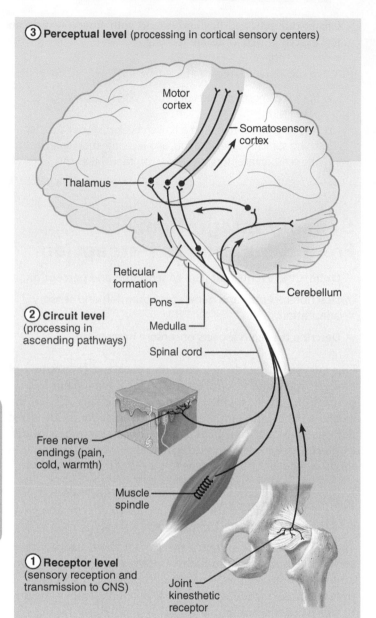

③ **Perceptual level** (processing in cortical sensory centers)

Motor cortex

Somatosensory cortex

Thalamus

Reticular formation

Pons

Cerebellum

② **Circuit level**
(processing in ascending pathways)

Medulla

Spinal cord

Free nerve endings (pain, cold, warmth)

Muscle spindle

① **Receptor level**
(sensory reception and transmission to CNS)

Joint kinesthetic receptor

Figure 13.2 Three basic levels of neural integration in sensory systems.

(as with free dendrites or the encapsulated receptors of most general sense receptors), the graded potential is called a **generator potential** because it generates action potentials in a sensory neuron.

When the receptor is a separate cell (as in most special senses), the graded potential is called a **receptor potential** because it occurs in a separate receptor cell. The receptor potential changes the amount of neurotransmitter released by the receptor cell onto the sensory neuron. The neurotransmitters then generate graded potentials in the sensory neuron.

■ Graded potentials in the first-order sensory neuron must reach *threshold* so that voltage-gated sodium channels on the axon are opened and nerve impulses are generated and propagated to the CNS.

Adaptation Information about a stimulus—its strength, duration, and pattern—is encoded in the frequency of nerve impulses: the greater the frequency, the stronger the stimulus. Many but not all sensory receptors exhibit **adaptation**, a change in sensitivity (and nerve impulse generation) in the presence of a constant stimulus. For example, when you step into bright sunlight from a darkened room, your eyes are initially dazzled, but your photoreceptors rapidly adapt, allowing you to see both bright areas and dark areas in the scene.

Phasic receptors are *fast adapting*, often giving bursts of impulses at the beginning and the end of the stimulus. Phasic receptors report changes in the internal or external environment. Examples are lamellar and tactile corpuscles.

Tonic receptors provide a sustained response with little or no adaptation. Nociceptors and most proprioceptors are tonic receptors because of the protective importance of their information.

Processing at the Circuit Level

At the second level of integration, the circuit level, the task is to deliver impulses to the appropriate region of the cerebral cortex for localization and perception of the stimulus (Figure 13.2, ②).

Recall from Chapter 12 that ascending sensory pathways typically consist of a chain of three neurons called first-, second-, and third-order sensory neurons. The axons of first-order sensory neurons, whose cell bodies are in the dorsal root or cranial ganglia, link the receptor and circuit levels of processing. Central processes of first-order neurons branch diffusely when they enter the spinal cord. Some branches take part in local spinal cord reflexes. Others synapse with second-order sensory neurons, which then synapse with the third-order sensory neurons that take the message to the cortex of the cerebrum.

As we saw in Chapter 12, the different ascending pathways (spinothalamic, dorsal column–medial lemniscal, and spinocerebellar) carry various types of information to different destinations in the brain. You may wish to review this information on p. 469.

Processing at the Perceptual Level

Sensory input is interpreted in the cerebral cortex (Figure 13.2, ③). The ability to identify and appreciate sensations depends on the location of the target neurons in the sensory cortex, not

energy (which is the province of receptors in the eye). The more complex the sensory receptor, the more specific it is.

■ The stimulus must be applied within a sensory receptor's *receptive field*—the area the receptor monitors. Typically, the smaller the receptive field, the greater the ability of the brain to accurately localize the stimulus site.

■ The stimulus energy must be converted into the energy of a *graded potential*, a process called **transduction**. This graded potential may be depolarizing or hyperpolarizing, similar to the EPSPs or IPSPs generated at postsynaptic membranes in response to neurotransmitter binding (see Chapter 11, p. 411).

Receptors can produce one of two types of graded potentials. When the receptor region is part of a sensory neuron on the nature of the message (which is, after all, just an action potential). Each sensory fiber is analogous to a "labeled line" that tells the brain "who" is calling—a taste bud or a pressure receptor—and from "where." The brain always interprets the activity of a specific sensory receptor ("who") as a specific sensation, no matter how it is activated.

For example, pressing on your eyeball activates photoreceptors, but what you "see" is light. The exact point in the cortex that is activated always refers to the same "where," regardless of how it is activated, a phenomenon called **projection**. Electrically stimulating a particular spot in the visual cortex causes you to "see" light in a particular place.

Let's examine the major features of sensory perception.

- **Perceptual detection** is the ability to detect that a stimulus has occurred. This is the simplest level of perception. As a general rule, inputs from several receptors must be summed for perceptual detection to occur.

- **Magnitude estimation** is the ability to detect how *intense* the stimulus is. Perceived intensity increases as stimulus intensity increases because of frequency coding (see Figure 11.13).

- **Spatial discrimination** allows us to identify the site or pattern of stimulation. A common tool for studying this quality in the laboratory is the **two-point discrimination** test. The test determines how close together two points on the skin can be and still be perceived as two points rather than as one. This test provides a crude map of the density of tactile receptors in the various regions of the skin. The distance between perceived points varies from less than 5 mm on highly sensitive body areas (tip of the tongue) to more than 50 mm on less sensitive areas (the back).

- **Feature abstraction** is the mechanism by which a neuron or circuit is tuned to one feature, or property, of a stimulus in preference to others. Sensation usually involves an interplay of several stimulus features.

  For example, one touch tells us that velvet is warm, compressible, and smooth but not completely continuous, each a feature that contributes to our perception of "velvet." Feature abstraction enables us to identify more complex aspects of a sensation.

- **Quality discrimination** is the ability to differentiate the submodalities of a particular sensation. Each sensory modality has several **qualities**, or submodalities. For example, taste is a sensory modality and its submodalities include sweet and bitter.

- **Pattern recognition** is the ability to take in the scene around us and recognize a familiar pattern, an unfamiliar one, or one that has special significance for us. For example, we can look at an image made of dots and recognize it as the portrait of a familiar face. We can listen to music and hear a melody, not just a string of notes.

Perception of Pain

Everyone has suffered pain—the cruel persistence of a headache, the smart of a bee sting or a cut finger. Although we may not appreciate it at the time, pain is invaluable because it warns us of actual or impending tissue damage and strongly motivates us to take protective action. Managing a patient's pain can be difficult because pain is an intensely personal experience that cannot be measured objectively.

Pain receptors are activated by extremes of pressure and temperature as well as a veritable soup of chemicals released from injured tissue. Histamine, K^+, ATP, acids, and bradykinin are among the most potent pain-producing chemicals. All of these chemicals act on small-diameter fibers.

When you cut your finger, you may have noticed that you first felt a sharp pain followed some time later by burning or aching. Sharp pain is carried by the smallest of the myelinated sensory fibers, the A delta fibers, while burning pain is carried more slowly by small nonmyelinated C fibers. Both types of fibers release the neurotransmitters *glutamate* and *substance P*, which activate second-order sensory neurons. Axons from these second-order neurons ascend to the brain via the spinothalamic tract and other pathways.

If you cut your finger while fighting off an attacker, you might not notice the cut at all. How can that be? The brain has its own pain-suppressing analgesic systems in which the endogenous opioids such as *endorphins* and *enkephalins* (p. 417) play a key role. Various nuclei in the brain stem, including the periaqueductal gray matter of the midbrain, relay descending cortical and hypothalamic pain-suppressing signals. Descending fibers activate interneurons in the spinal cord, which release enkephalins. Enkephalins are inhibitory neurotransmitters that quash the pain signals generated by nociceptors.

Pain Tolerance

We all have the same *pain threshold*—that is, we begin to perceive pain at roughly the same stimulus intensity. However, our tolerance to pain varies widely. When we say that someone is "sensitive" to pain, we mean that the person has a low *pain tolerance* rather than a low pain threshold.

A number of genes help determine a person's pain tolerance and response to pain medications. The genetics of pain is currently an area of intense research, aimed at allowing an individual's genes to determine the best pain treatment.

Homeostatic Imbalance 13.1

Normally the body maintains a steady state that correlates injury and pain. Long-lasting or very intense pain inputs, such as limb amputation, can disrupt this system, leading to **hyperalgesia** (pain amplification), chronic pain, and **phantom limb pain**. Intense or long-lasting pain activates *NMDA receptors*, the same receptors that strengthen neural connections during certain kinds of learning. Essentially, the spinal cord *learns* hyperalgesia. In light of this, it is crucial that health professionals effectively manage pain early to prevent chronic pain from becoming established.

Phantom limb pain (pain perceived in tissue that is no longer present) is a curious example of hyperalgesia. Until recently, surgical limb amputations were conducted under general anesthesia only and the spinal cord still experienced the pain of amputation. Epidural anesthetics block neurotransmission in the spinal cord, and using them during surgery greatly reduces the incidence of phantom limb pain. ✚

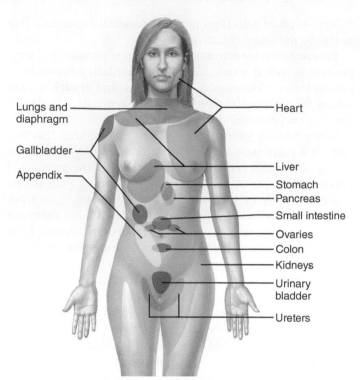

Lungs and diaphragm

Heart

Gallbladder

Liver

Appendix

Stomach

Pancreas

Small intestine

Ovaries

Colon

Kidneys

Urinary bladder

Ureters

Figure 13.3 Map of referred pain. This map shows the anterior skin areas to which pain is referred from certain visceral organs.

Visceral and Referred Pain

Visceral pain results from noxious stimulation of receptors in the organs of the thorax and abdominal cavity. Like deep somatic pain, it is usually a vague sensation of dull aching, gnawing, or burning. Important stimuli for visceral pain are extreme stretching of tissue, ischemia (low blood flow), irritating chemicals, and muscle spasms.

The fact that visceral pain afferents travel along the same pathways as somatic pain fibers helps explain the phenomenon of **referred pain**, in which pain stimuli arising in one part of the body are perceived as coming from another part. For example, a person experiencing a heart attack may feel pain that radiates along the medial aspect of the left arm. Because the same spinal segments (T_1–T_5) innervate both the heart and arm, the brain interprets these inputs as coming from the more common somatic pathway. **Figure 13.3** shows cutaneous areas to which visceral pain is commonly referred.

☑ Check Your Understanding

3. What are the three levels of sensory integration?
4. What is the key difference between tonic and phasic receptors? Why are pain receptors tonic?
5. Your cortex decodes incoming action potentials from sensory pathways. How does it tell the difference between hot and cold? Between cool and cold? Between ice on your finger and ice on your foot?

For answers, see Appendix H.

PART 2

Transmission Lines: Nerves and Their Structure and Repair

Nerves and Associated Ganglia

✓ Define ganglion and indicate the general body location of ganglia.

✓ Describe the general structure of a nerve.

✓ Follow the process of nerve regeneration.

Structure and Classification

A **nerve** is a cordlike organ that is part of the peripheral nervous system. Nerves vary in size, but every nerve consists of parallel bundles of peripheral axons (some myelinated and some not) enclosed by successive wrappings of connective tissue (**Figure 13.4**):

■ Each axon is surrounded by **endoneurium** (en″do-nu′re-um), a delicate layer of loose connective tissue that also encloses the fiber's associated Schwann cells.

■ A coarser connective tissue wrapping, the **perineurium,** binds groups of fibers into bundles called **fascicles**.

■ A tough fibrous sheath, the **epineurium,** encloses all the fascicles to form the nerve.

Axons constitute only a small fraction of a nerve's bulk. The balance consists chiefly of myelin, the protective connective tissue wrappings, blood vessels, and lymphatic vessels.

Recall that the PNS is divided into *sensory* (afferent) and *motor* (efferent) divisions. Nerves are also classified according to the direction in which they transmit impulses:

■ **Mixed nerves** contain both sensory and motor fibers and transmit impulses both to and from the central nervous system.

■ **Sensory (afferent) nerves** carry impulses only toward the CNS.

■ **Motor (efferent) nerves** carry impulses only away from the CNS.

Most nerves are mixed. Pure sensory or motor nerves are rare.

Because mixed nerves often carry both somatic and autonomic (visceral) nervous system fibers, the fibers in them may be classified according to the region they innervate as *somatic afferent, somatic efferent, visceral afferent,* and *visceral efferent.*

For convenience, the peripheral nerves are classified as *cranial* or *spinal* depending on whether they arise from the brain or spinal cord. Although we mention autonomic efferents of cranial nerves, in this chapter we will focus on somatic functions. We will defer the discussion of the autonomic nervous system and its visceral functions to Chapter 14.

Recall from Chapter 11 that **ganglia** are collections of neuron cell bodies associated with nerves in the PNS, whereas *nuclei* are collections of neuron cell bodies in the CNS. Ganglia associated with *afferent* nerve fibers contain cell bodies of sensory neurons.

(a)

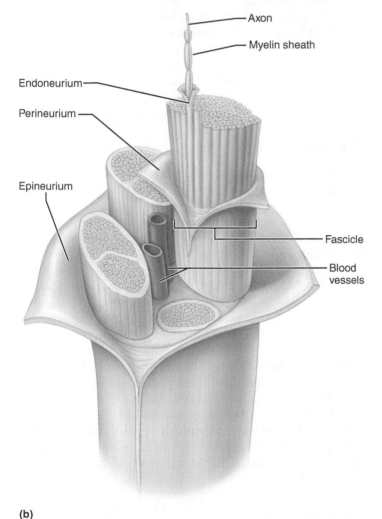

(b)

Figure 13.4 Structure of a nerve. (a) Scanning electron micrograph of a cross section of a portion of a nerve (90×). **(b)** Three-dimensional view of a portion of a nerve, showing connective tissue wrappings.

(These are the *dorsal root ganglia* described in Chapter 12.) Ganglia associated with *efferent* nerve fibers mostly contain cell bodies of autonomic motor neurons. We will describe these more complicated ganglia in Chapter 14.

Regeneration of Nerve Fibers

Damage to nervous tissue is serious because, as a rule, mature neurons do not divide. If the damage is severe or close to the cell body, the entire neuron may die, and other neurons that are normally stimulated by its axon may die as well. However, if the cell body remains intact, cut or compressed axons of peripheral nerves can regenerate successfully.

PNS Fibers

What happens if a peripheral axon is severed or crushed? As shown in **Figure 13.5**:

1. **The axon fragments.** Almost immediately, the separated ends seal themselves off and then swell as substances being transported along the axon accumulate in the sealed ends. Within a few hours, the axon and its myelin sheath distal to the injury site begin to disintegrate because they cannot receive nutrients from the cell body. This process, **Wallerian degeneration**, spreads distally from the injury site, fragmenting the distal part of the axon.

2. **Macrophages clean out the dead axon.** Within a week, macrophages generally degrade the entire axon distal to the injury, disposing of the debris. However, the myelin sheath remains intact within the endoneurium. The macrophages also release chemicals that stimulate the Schwann cells to divide.

3. **Axon filaments grow through a regeneration tube.** Surviving Schwann cells proliferate in response to the mitosis-stimulating chemicals, and migrate into the injury site. Once there, they release growth factors and begin to express cell adhesion molecules (CAMs) that encourage axonal growth. Additionally, they form a *regeneration tube*, a system of cellular cords that guide the regenerating axon "sprouts" across the gap to their original contacts.

4. **The axon regenerates and a new myelin sheath forms.** The same Schwann cells protect, support, and remyelinate the regenerating axons.

Changes also occur in the neuronal cell body after the axon has been destroyed. Within two days, its rough endoplasmic reticulum breaks apart, and then the cell body swells as protein synthesis revs up to support regeneration of its axon.

Axons regenerate at the approximate rate of 1.5 mm a day. The greater the distance between the severed ends, the less the chance of recovery because adjacent tissues block growth by protruding into the gaps, and axonal sprouts fail to find the regeneration tube. Neurosurgeons align cut nerve ends surgically to promote successful regeneration, and scaffolding devices can help guide the axons.

Whatever the measures taken, post-trauma axon regrowth never exactly matches what existed before the injury. Patients must often "retrain" the nervous system to respond appropriately so that stimulus and response are coordinated.

13

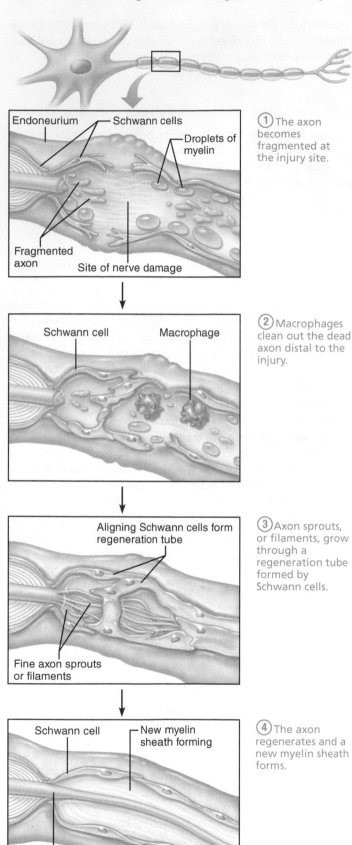

Endoneurium — Schwann cells — Droplets of myelin

Fragmented axon

Site of nerve damage

① The axon becomes fragmented at the injury site.

Schwann cell   Macrophage

② Macrophages clean out the dead axon distal to the injury.

Aligning Schwann cells form regeneration tube

Fine axon sprouts or filaments

③ Axon sprouts, or filaments, grow through a regeneration tube formed by Schwann cells.

Schwann cell — New myelin sheath forming

Single enlarging axon filament

④ The axon regenerates and a new myelin sheath forms.

Figure 13.5 Regeneration of a nerve fiber in a peripheral nerve.

13

CNS Fibers

Unlike peripheral nerve fibers, most CNS fibers never regenerate. Consequently, damage to the brain or spinal cord has been viewed as irreversible. This difference in regenerative capacity seems to have less to do with the neurons themselves than with the "company they keep"—oligodendrocytes, their supporting cells.

Oligodendrocytes are studded with growth-inhibiting proteins. Consequently, the neuronal growth cone collapses and the fiber fails to regrow. Moreover, astrocytes at the site of injury form scar tissue rich in chondroitin sulfate (see p. 127) that blocks axonal regrowth.

For the clinician treating spinal cord injury, this means that multiple inhibitory processes need to be blocked simultaneously to promote axon regrowth. To date, experimentally neutralizing the myelin-bound growth inhibitors, blocking the receptors for the inhibitory proteins, or enzymatically destroying chondroitin sulfate have yielded promising results.

☑ **Check Your Understanding**

6. What are ganglia?
7. What is in a nerve besides axons?
8. Bill's femoral nerve was crushed while clinicians tried to control bleeding from his femoral artery. This resulted in loss of function and sensation in his leg, which gradually returned over the course of a year. Which cells were important in his recovery?

_____

For answers, see Appendix H.

Cranial Nerves

✓ Name the 12 pairs of cranial nerves; indicate the body region and structures innervated by each.

Twelve pairs of **cranial nerves** are associated with the brain **(Figure 13.6)**. The first two pairs attach to the forebrain, and the rest are associated with the brain stem. Other than the vagus nerves, which extend into the abdomen, cranial nerves serve only head and neck structures.

In most cases, the names of the cranial nerves reveal either the structures they serve or their functions. The nerves are also numbered (using Roman numerals) from the most rostral to the most caudal.

We will begin with a brief overview of each cranial nerve and then describe the composition of all cranial nerves (p. 501). After that, you will be ready to tackle **Table 13.2** (p. 494), which provides detailed descriptions of the cranial nerves. Notice that it describes the pathways of the purely or mostly sensory nerves (I, II, and VIII) from the receptors to the brain, and the pathways of the other nerves in the oppositive direction (from the brain distally).

An Overview

I. Olfactory. These are the tiny sensory nerves (filaments) of smell, which run from the nasal mucosa to synapse with the olfactory bulbs. Note that the olfactory bulbs and tracts, shown in

Filaments of olfactory nerve (I)
Olfactory bulb
Olfactory tract
Optic nerve (II)   PNS
Optic chiasma
CNS
Optic tract
Oculomotor nerve (III)
Trochlear nerve (IV)
Trigeminal nerve (V)
Abducens nerve (VI)
Cerebellum
Medulla oblongata

Frontal lobe
Temporal lobe
Infundibulum
Facial nerve (VII)
Vestibulocochlear nerve (VIII)
Glossopharyngeal nerve (IX)
Vagus nerve (X)
Accessory nerve (XI)
Hypoglossal nerve (XII)

(a)

(b)

Cranial nerves I – VI	Sensory function	Motor function	PS* fibers
I Olfactory	Yes (smell)	No	No
II Optic	Yes (vision)	No	No
III Oculomotor	No	Yes	Yes
IV Trochlear	No	Yes	No
V Trigeminal	Yes (general sensation)	Yes	No
VI Abducens	No	Yes	No

Cranial nerves VII – XII	Sensory function	Motor function	PS* fibers
VII Facial	Yes (taste)	Yes	Yes
VIII Vestibulocochlear	Yes (hearing and balance)	Some	No
IX Glossopharyngeal	Yes (taste)	Yes	Yes
X Vagus	Yes (taste)	Yes	Yes
XI Accessory	No	Yes	No
XII Hypoglossal	No	Yes	No

*PS = parasympathetic

Figure 13.6 Location and function of cranial nerves. (a) Ventral view of the human brain, showing the cranial nerves. **(b)** Summary of cranial nerves by function.

Two cranial nerves (I and II) have sensory function only, no motor function. Four nerves (III, VII, IX, and X) carry parasympathetic fibers that serve visceral muscles and glands.

All cranial nerves that innervate muscles also carry afferent fibers from proprioceptors in the muscles served. Only sensory functions other than proprioception are indicated.

Figure 13.6a, are brain structures and not part of cranial nerve I. (See Table 13.2 art for the olfactory nerve filaments.)

II. Optic. Because this sensory nerve of vision develops as an outgrowth of the brain, it is really a brain tract.

III. Oculomotor. The name *oculomotor* means "eye mover." This nerve supplies four of the six extrinsic muscles that move the eyeball in the orbit.

IV. Trochlear. The term *trochlear* means "pulley" and it innervates an extrinsic eye muscle that loops through a pulley-shaped ligament in the orbit.

V. Trigeminal. Three (*tri*) branches spring from this, the largest cranial nerve. It supplies sensory fibers to the face and motor fibers to the chewing muscles.

VI. Abducens. This nerve controls the extrinsic eye muscle that *abducts* the eyeball (turns it laterally).

VII. Facial. A large nerve that innervates muscles of *facial* expression (among other things).

VIII. Vestibulocochlear. This mostly sensory nerve for hearing and balance was formerly called the *auditory nerve*.

(Text continues on p. 500.)

Table 13.2 Cranial Nerves

I Olfactory Nerves (ol-fak'to-re)

Origin and course: Olfactory nerve fibers arise from olfactory sensory neurons located in olfactory epithelium of nasal cavity and pass through cribriform plate of ethmoid bone to synapse in olfactory bulb. Fibers of olfactory bulb neurons extend posteriorly as olfactory tract, which runs beneath frontal lobe to enter cerebral hemispheres and terminates in primary olfactory cortex. See also Figure 15.20.

Function: Purely sensory; carry afferent impulses for sense of smell.

Clinical testing: Ask subject to sniff and identify aromatic substances, such as oil of cloves and vanilla.

Homeostatic Imbalance Fracture of ethmoid bone or lesions of olfactory fibers may result in partial or total loss of smell, a condition known as *anosmia* (an-oz'me-ah). +

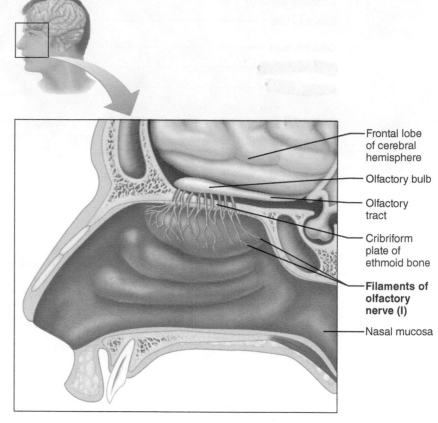

- Frontal lobe of cerebral hemisphere
- Olfactory bulb
- Olfactory tract
- Cribriform plate of ethmoid bone
- **Filaments of olfactory nerve (I)**
- Nasal mucosa

II Optic Nerves

Origin and course: Fibers arise from retina of eye to form optic nerve, which passes through optic canal of orbit. The optic nerves converge to form the optic chiasma (ki-az'mah) where fibers partially cross over, continue on as optic tracts, enter thalamus, and synapse there. Thalamic fibers run (as the optic radiation) to occipital (visual) cortex, where visual interpretation occurs. See also Figure 15.19.

Function: Purely sensory; carry afferent impulses for vision.

Clinical testing: Assess vision and visual field with eye chart and by testing the point at which the person first sees an object (finger) moving into the visual field. View fundus of eye with ophthalmoscope to detect papilledema (swelling of optic disc, the site where the optic nerve leaves the eyeball) and examine optic disc and retinal blood vessels.

Homeostatic Imbalance Damage to optic nerve results in blindness in eye served by nerve. Damage to visual pathway beyond the optic chiasma results in partial visual losses. Visual defects are called *anopsias* (ah-nop'se-ahz). +

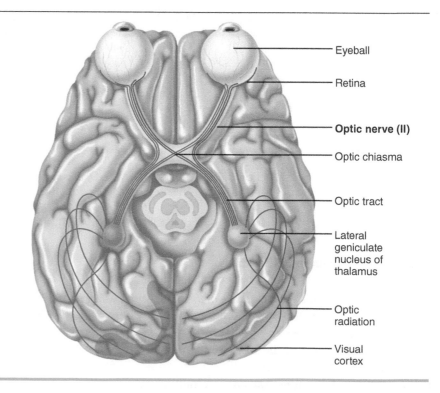

- Eyeball
- Retina
- **Optic nerve (II)**
- Optic chiasma
- Optic tract
- Lateral geniculate nucleus of thalamus
- Optic radiation
- Visual cortex

Table 13.2 *(continued)*

III Oculomotor Nerves (ok″u-lo-mo′tor)

Origin and course: Fibers extend from ventral midbrain (near its junction with pons) and pass through bony orbit, via superior orbital fissure, to eye.

Function: Chiefly motor nerves (*oculomotor* = motor to the eye); contain a few proprioceptive afferents. Each nerve includes the following:

- Somatic motor fibers to four of the six extrinsic eye muscles (inferior oblique and superior, inferior, and medial rectus muscles) that help direct eyeball, and to levator palpebrae superioris muscle, which raises upper eyelid.

- Parasympathetic (autonomic) motor fibers to sphincter pupillae (circular muscles of iris), which cause pupil to constrict, and to ciliary muscle, controlling lens shape for visual focusing. Some parasympathetic cell bodies are in the ciliary ganglia.

- Sensory (proprioceptor) afferents, which run from same four extrinsic eye muscles to midbrain.

Clinical testing: Examine pupils for size, shape, and equality. Test pupillary reflex with penlight (pupils should constrict when illuminated). Test convergence for near vision and subject's ability to follow objects with the eyes.

Homeostatic Imbalance In oculomotor nerve paralysis, eye cannot be moved up, down, or inward. At rest, eye rotates laterally [*external strabismus* (strah-biz′mus)] because the actions of the two extrinsic eye muscles not served by cranial nerves III are unopposed. Upper eyelid droops (*ptosis*), and the person has double vision and trouble focusing on close objects. ✛

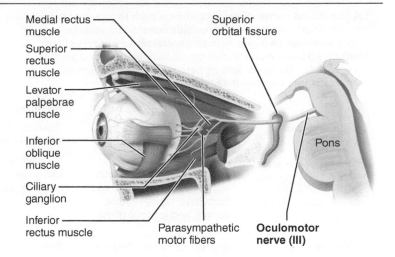

IV Trochlear Nerves (trok′le-ar)

Origin and course: Fibers emerge from dorsal midbrain and course ventrally around midbrain to enter orbit through superior orbital fissure along with oculomotor nerves.

Function: Primarily motor nerves; supply somatic motor fibers to (and carry proprioceptor fibers from) one of the extrinsic eye muscles, the superior oblique muscle, which passes through the pulley-shaped trochlea.

Clinical testing: Test with cranial nerve III (oculomotor).

Homeostatic Imbalance Damage to a trochlear nerve results in double vision and impairs ability to rotate eye inferolaterally. ✛

13

Table 13.2	Cranial Nerves (continued)

V Trigeminal Nerves

Largest cranial nerves; fibers extend from pons to face, and form three divisions (*trigemina* = threefold): ophthalmic, maxillary, and mandibular divisions. As main general sensory nerves of face, transmit afferent impulses from touch, temperature, and pain receptors. Cell bodies of sensory neurons of all three divisions are located in large *trigeminal ganglion*.

The mandibular division also contains motor fibers that innervate chewing muscles.

Dentists desensitize upper and lower jaws by injecting local anesthetic (such as Novocain) into alveolar branches of maxillary and mandibular divisions, respectively. Since this blocks pain-transmitting fibers of teeth, the surrounding tissues become numb.

	Ophthalmic division (V$_1$)	Maxillary division (V$_2$)	Mandibular division (V$_3$)
Origin and course	Fibers run from face to pons via superior orbital fissure.	Fibers run from face to pons via foramen rotundum.	Fibers pass through skull via foramen ovale.
Function	Conveys sensory impulses from skin of anterior scalp, upper eyelid, and nose, and from nasal cavity mucosa, cornea, and lacrimal gland.	Conveys sensory impulses from nasal cavity mucosa, palate, upper teeth, skin of cheek, upper lip, lower eyelid.	Conveys sensory impulses from anterior tongue (except taste buds), lower teeth, skin of chin, temporal region of scalp. Supplies motor fibers to, and carries proprioceptor fibers from, muscles of mastication.
Clinical testing	Corneal reflex test: Touching cornea with wisp of cotton should elicit blinking.	Test sensations of pain, touch, and temperature with safety pin and hot and cold objects.	Assess motor branch by asking person to clench his teeth, open mouth against resistance, and move jaw side to side.

Homeostatic Imbalance *Trigeminal neuralgia* (nu-ral'je-ah), or *tic douloureux* (tik doo"loo-roo'; *tic* = twitch, *douloureux* = painful), caused by inflammation of trigeminal nerve, is widely considered to produce most excruciating pain known. The stabbing pain lasts for a few seconds to a minute, but it can be relentless, occurring a hundred times a day. Usually provoked by some sensory stimulus, such as brushing teeth or even a passing breeze hitting the face. Thought to be caused by a loop of artery or vein that compresses the trigeminal nerve near its exit from the brain stem. Analgesics and carbamazepine (an anticonvulsant) are only partially effective. In severe cases, surgery relieves the agony—either by moving the compressing vessel or by destroying the nerve. Nerve destruction results in loss of sensation on that side of face. +

(b) Distribution of sensory fibers of each division

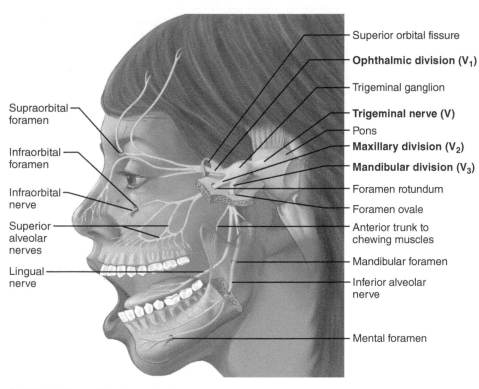

- Supraorbital foramen
- Infraorbital foramen
- Infraorbital nerve
- Superior alveolar nerves
- Lingual nerve

- Superior orbital fissure
- **Ophthalmic division (V$_1$)**
- Trigeminal ganglion
- **Trigeminal nerve (V)**
- Pons
- **Maxillary division (V$_2$)**
- **Mandibular division (V$_3$)**
- Foramen rotundum
- Foramen ovale
- Anterior trunk to chewing muscles
- Mandibular foramen
- Inferior alveolar nerve
- Mental foramen

(a) Distribution of the trigeminal nerve

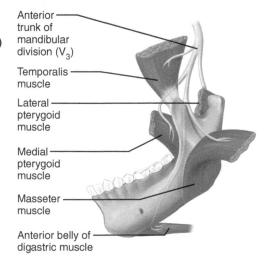

- Anterior trunk of mandibular division (V$_3$)
- Temporalis muscle
- Lateral pterygoid muscle
- Medial pterygoid muscle
- Masseter muscle
- Anterior belly of digastric muscle

(c) Motor branches of the mandibular division (V$_3$)

Table 13.2 *(continued)*

VI Abducens Nerves (ab-du'senz)

Origin and course: Fibers leave inferior pons and enter orbit via superior orbital fissure to run to eye.

Function: Primarily motor; supply somatic motor fibers to lateral rectus muscle, an extrinsic muscle of the eye. Convey proprioceptor impulses from same muscle to brain.

Clinical testing: Test in common with cranial nerve III (oculomotor).

Homeostatic Imbalance In abducens nerve paralysis, eye cannot be moved laterally. At rest, eyeball rotates medially *(internal strabismus).* ✚

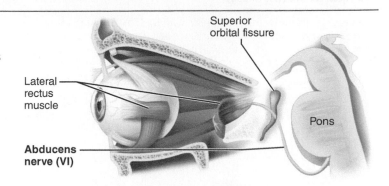

VII Facial Nerves

Origin and course: Fibers issue from pons, just lateral to abducens nerves (see Figure 13.6), enter temporal bone via *internal acoustic meatus*, and run within bone (and through inner ear cavity) before emerging through *stylomastoid foramen*. Nerve then courses to lateral aspect of face.

Function: Mixed nerves that are the chief motor nerves of face. Five major branches: temporal, zygomatic, buccal, mandibular, and cervical (see **c** on next page).

■ Convey motor impulses to skeletal muscles of face (muscles of facial expression), except for chewing muscles served by trigeminal nerves, and transmit proprioceptor impulses from same muscles to pons (see **b**).

■ Transmit parasympathetic (autonomic) motor impulses to lacrimal (tear) glands, nasal and palatine glands, and submandibular and sublingual salivary glands. Some of the cell bodies of these parasympathetic motor neurons are in

pterygopalatine (ter"eh-go-pal'ah-tīn) and *submandibular ganglia* on the trigeminal nerve (see **a**).

■ Convey sensory impulses from taste buds of anterior two-thirds of tongue; cell bodies of these sensory neurons are in *geniculate ganglion* (see **a**).

Clinical testing: Test anterior two-thirds of tongue for ability to taste sweet (sugar), salty, sour (vinegar), and bitter (quinine) substances. Check symmetry of face. Ask subject to close eyes, smile, whistle, and so on. Assess tearing with ammonia fumes.

Homeostatic Imbalance *Bell's palsy* is characterized by paralysis of facial muscles on affected side and partial loss of taste sensation. May develop rapidly (often overnight). Caused by inflamed and swollen facial nerve, possibly due to herpes simplex 1 viral infection. Lower eyelid droops, corner of mouth sags (making it difficult to eat or speak normally), tears drip continuously from eye and eye cannot be completely closed (conversely, dry-eye syndrome may occur). Treated with corticosteroids. Recovery is complete in 70% of cases. ✚

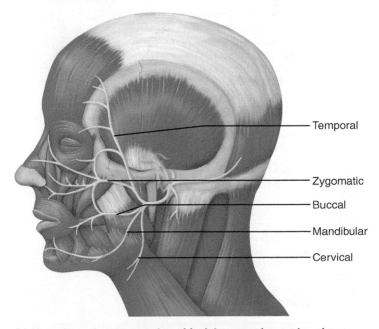

(a) Parasympathetic efferents and sensory afferents

(b) Motor branches to muscles of facial expression and scalp muscles (see pp. 329–331)

Table 13.2 **Cranial Nerves** (continued)

VII Facial Nerves (continued)

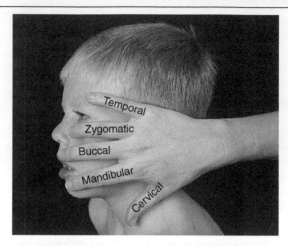

(c) A simple way to remember the courses of the five major branches of the facial nerve

---

VIII Vestibulocochlear Nerves (ves-tib"u-lo-kok'le-ar)

Origin and course: Fibers arise from hearing and equilibrium apparatus located within inner ear of temporal bone and pass through internal acoustic meatus to enter brain stem at pons-medulla border. Afferent fibers from hearing receptors in cochlea form the *cochlear division*; those from equilibrium receptors in semicircular canals and vestibule form the *vestibular division* (vestibular nerve). The two divisions merge to form vestibulocochlear nerve. See also Figure 15.26.

Function: Mostly sensory. Vestibular branch transmits afferent impulses for sense of equilibrium, and sensory nerve cell bodies are located in *vestibular ganglia*. Cochlear branch transmits afferent impulses for sense of hearing, and sensory nerve cell bodies are located in *spiral ganglion* within cochlea. Small motor component adjusts the sensitivity of sensory receptors. See also Figure 15.27.

Clinical testing: Check hearing by air and bone conduction using tuning fork.

Homeostatic Imbalance Lesions of cochlear nerve or cochlear receptors result in *central*, or *nerve*, *deafness*. Damage to vestibular division produces dizziness, rapid involuntary eye movements, loss of balance, nausea, and vomiting. ✚

Semicircular canals

Vestibular ganglia

Vestibular nerve

Internal acoustic meatus

Cochlear nerve

Vestibule

Pons

Cochlea (containing spiral ganglion)

Vestibulocochlear nerve (VIII)

13

Table 13.2   *(continued)*

IX Glossopharyngeal Nerves (glos"o-fah-rin'je-al)

Origin and course: Fibers emerge from medulla and leave skull via *jugular foramen* to run to throat.

Function: Mixed nerves that innervate part of tongue and pharynx. Provide somatic motor fibers to, and carry proprioceptor fibers from, a superior pharyngeal muscle called the *stylopharyngeus*, which elevates the pharynx in swallowing. Provide parasympathetic motor fibers to parotid salivary glands (some of the nerve cell bodies of these parasympathetic motor neurons are located in *otic ganglion*).

Sensory fibers conduct taste and general sensory (touch, pressure, pain) impulses from pharynx and posterior tongue, from chemoreceptors in the carotid body (which monitor O_2 and CO_2 levels in the blood and help regulate respiratory rate and depth), and from baroreceptors of carotid sinus (which monitor blood pressure). Sensory neuron cell bodies are located in *superior* and *inferior ganglia*.

Clinical testing: Check position of uvula; check gag and swallowing reflexes. Ask subject to speak and cough. Test posterior third of tongue for taste.

Homeostatic Imbalance Injured or inflamed glossopharyngeal nerves impair swallowing and taste. ✚

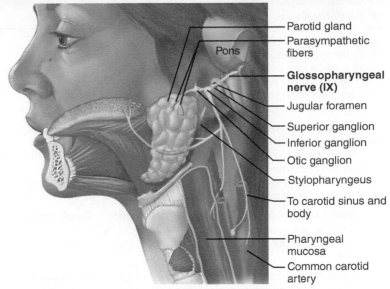

Parotid gland

Parasympathetic fibers

Pons

Glossopharyngeal nerve (IX)

Jugular foramen

Superior ganglion

Inferior ganglion

Otic ganglion

Stylopharyngeus

To carotid sinus and body

Pharyngeal mucosa

Common carotid artery

X Vagus Nerves (va'gus)

Origin and course: The only cranial nerves to extend beyond head and neck region. Fibers emerge from medulla, pass through skull via jugular foramen, and descend through neck region into thorax and abdomen. See also Figure 14.4.

Function: Mixed nerves. Nearly all motor fibers are parasympathetic efferents, except those serving skeletal muscles of pharynx and larynx (involved in swallowing). Parasympathetic motor fibers supply heart, lungs, and abdominal viscera and are involved in regulating heart rate, breathing, and digestive system activity. Transmit sensory impulses from thoracic and abdominal viscera, from the aortic arch baroreceptors (for blood pressure) and the carotid and aortic bodies (chemoreceptors for respiration), and taste buds on the epiglottis. Carry proprioceptor fibers from muscles of larynx and pharynx.

Clinical testing: As for cranial nerve IX (glossopharyngeal; IX and X are tested in common, since they both innervate muscles of throat and mouth).

Homeostatic Imbalance Since laryngeal branches of the vagus innervate nearly all muscles of the larynx ("voice box"), vagal nerve paralysis can lead to hoarseness or loss of voice. Other symptoms are difficulty swallowing and impaired digestive system motility. These parasympathetic nerves are important for maintaining the normal state of visceral organ activity. Without their influence, the sympathetic nerves, which mobilize and accelerate vital body processes (and shut down digestion), would dominate. ✚

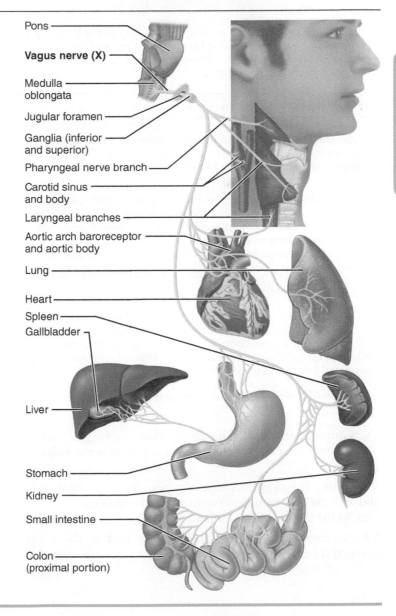

Pons

Vagus nerve (X)

Medulla oblongata

Jugular foramen

Ganglia (inferior and superior)

Pharyngeal nerve branch

Carotid sinus and body

Laryngeal branches

Aortic arch baroreceptor and aortic body

Lung

Heart

Spleen

Gallbladder

Liver

Stomach

Kidney

Small intestine

Colon (proximal portion)

13

Table 13.2	Cranial Nerves *(continued)*

XI Accessory Nerves

Origin and course: Unique in that they form from rootlets that emerge from the spinal cord, not the brain stem. These rootlets arise laterally from superior region (C_1–C_5) of spinal cord, pass upward along spinal cord, and enter the skull as the accessory nerves via foramen magnum. The accessory nerves exit from skull through *jugular foramen* together with the vagus nerves, and supply two large neck muscles.

Until recently, was considered to have both a cranial and spinal portion, but the cranial rootlets are actually part of the vagus nerves. This raises an interesting question: Should the accessory nerves still be considered cranial nerves? Some anatomists say "no" because they don't arise from the brain. Others say "yes" because their origin is different from a typical spinal nerve and they pass through the skull. Stay tuned!

Function: Mixed nerves, but primarily motor in function. Supply motor fibers to trapezius and sternocleidomastoid muscles, which together move head and neck, and convey proprioceptor impulses from same muscles.

Clinical testing: Check strength of sternocleidomastoid and trapezius muscles by asking person to rotate head and shrug shoulders against resistance.

Homeostatic Imbalance Injury to one accessory nerve causes head to turn toward injury side as result of sterno-cleidomastoid muscle paralysis. Shrugging that shoulder (role of trapezius muscle) becomes difficult. +

- Jugular foramen
- Foramen magnum
- **Accessory nerve (XI)**
- Sternocleidomastoid muscle
- Rootlets of accessory nerve emerging from spinal cord (C_1–C_5)
- Trapezius muscle

XII Hypoglossal Nerves (hi"po-glos'al)

Origin and course: As their name implies (*hypo* = below; *glossal* = tongue), hypoglossal nerves mainly serve the tongue. Fibers arise by a series of roots from medulla and exit from skull via *hypoglossal canal* to travel to tongue. See also Figure 13.6.

Function: Mixed nerves, but primarily motor in function. Carry somatic motor fibers to intrinsic and extrinsic muscles of tongue, and proprioceptor fibers from same muscles to brain stem. Hypoglossal nerve control allows tongue movements that mix and manipulate food during chewing, and contribute to swallowing and speech.

Clinical testing: Ask subject to protrude and retract tongue. Note any deviations in position.

Homeostatic Imbalance Damage to hypoglossal nerves causes difficulties in speech and swallowing. If both nerves are impaired, the person cannot protrude tongue. If only one side is affected, tongue deviates (points) toward affected side; eventually paralyzed side begins to atrophy. +

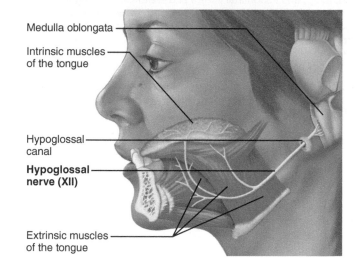

- Medulla oblongata
- Intrinsic muscles of the tongue
- Hypoglossal canal
- **Hypoglossal nerve (XII)**
- Extrinsic muscles of the tongue

IX. Glossopharyngeal. The name *glossopharyngeal* means "tongue and pharynx," the structures that this nerve helps to innervate.

X. Vagus. This nerve's name means "wanderer" or "vagabond," and it is the only cranial nerve to extend beyond the head and neck to the thorax and abdomen.

XI. Accessory. Considered an *accessory* part of the vagus nerve, this nerve was formerly called the *spinal accessory nerve*.

XII. Hypoglossal. The name *hypoglossal* means under the tongue. This nerve runs inferior to the tongue and innervates the tongue muscles.

You might make up your own saying to remember the first letters of the cranial nerves in order, or use the following memory jog sent by a student: "**O**n **o**ccasion, **o**ur **t**rusty **t**ruck **a**cts **f**unny—**v**ery **g**ood **v**ehicle **a**ny**h**ow."

Composition of Cranial Nerves

In the last chapter, we described how ventral (motor) and dorsal (sensory) roots fuse to form spinal nerves. Cranial nerves, on the other hand, vary markedly in their composition.

Most cranial nerves are mixed nerves, as shown in Figure 13.6b. However, two nerve pairs (the olfactory and optic) associated with special sense organs are generally considered purely sensory. The cell bodies of the sensory neurons in the olfactory and optic nerves are located *within* their respective special sense organs. In other sensory neurons contributing to cranial nerves (V, VII, IX, and X), the cell bodies are located in **cranial sensory ganglia** just outside the brain. Some cranial nerves have a single sensory ganglion, others have several, and still others have none.

Several of the mixed cranial nerves contain both somatic and autonomic motor fibers and hence serve both skeletal muscles and visceral organs. Except for some autonomic motor neurons located in ganglia, the cell bodies of motor neurons contributing to the cranial nerves are located in the ventral gray matter regions (nuclei) of the brain stem.

Remembering the primary functions of the cranial nerves (as **s**ensory, **m**otor, or **b**oth) can be a challenge. This sentence might help: "**S**ome **s**ay **m**arry **m**oney, **b**ut **m**y **b**rother **b**elieves (it's) **b**ad **b**usiness (to) **m**arry **m**oney."

☑ Check Your Understanding

9. Name the cranial nerve(s) most involved in each of the following: moving your eyeball; sticking out your tongue; controlling your heart rate and digestive activity; shrugging your shoulders.

For answers, see Appendix H.

Spinal Nerves

✓ Describe the general structure of a spinal nerve and the general distribution of its rami.

✓ Define plexus. Name the major plexuses and describe the distribution and function of the peripheral nerves arising from each plexus.

Thirty-one pairs of **spinal nerves**, each containing thousands of nerve fibers, arise from the spinal cord and supply all parts of the body except the head and some areas of the neck. All are mixed nerves.

Spinal nerves are named according to where they issue from the spinal cord (**Figure 13.7**). The spinal nerves include:

- 8 pairs of cervical spinal nerves (C_1–C_8)
- 12 pairs of thoracic nerves (T_1–T_{12})
- 5 pairs of lumbar nerves (L_1–L_5)
- 5 pairs of sacral nerves (S_1–S_5)
- 1 pair of tiny coccygeal nerves (Co_1)

Notice that there are eight pairs of cervical nerves but only seven cervical vertebrae. This "discrepancy" is easily explained. The first seven pairs exit the vertebral canal *superior* to the vertebrae for which they are named, but C_8 emerges *inferior* to the seventh cervical vertebra (between C_7 and T_1). Below the cervical

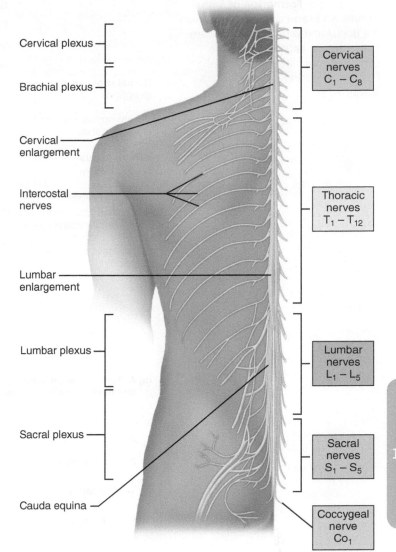

Figure 13.7 Spinal nerves. (Posterior view.) The spinal nerves are shown at right; their ventral rami are shown at left. Most ventral rami form nerve plexuses (cervical, brachial, lumbar, and sacral).

level, each spinal nerve leaves the vertebral column *inferior* to the same-numbered vertebra.

As we mentioned in Chapter 12, each spinal nerve connects to the spinal cord by a dorsal root and a ventral root (**Figure 13.8**). Each root forms from a series of **rootlets** that attach along the length of the corresponding spinal cord segment (Figure 13.8a).

- **Ventral roots** contain *motor* (efferent) fibers that arise from ventral horn motor neurons and extend to and innervate the skeletal muscles. (In Chapter 14, we describe autonomic nervous system efferents that are also contained in the ventral roots.)

- **Dorsal roots** contain *sensory* (afferent) fibers that arise from sensory neurons in the dorsal root ganglia and conduct impulses from peripheral receptors to the spinal cord.

The spinal roots pass laterally from the cord and unite just distal to the dorsal root ganglion to form a spinal nerve before emerging from the vertebral column via their respective

Figure 13.8 Formation of spinal nerves and rami distribution. Notice the dorsal and ventral roots and rami. In the thorax, each ventral ramus continues as an intercostal nerve. (The small meningeal branch is not illustrated.)

Gray matter
White matter
Ventral root
Dorsal root
Dorsal and ventral rootlets of spinal nerve
Dorsal root ganglion
Dorsal ramus of spinal nerve
Ventral ramus of spinal nerve
Spinal nerve
Rami communicantes
Sympathetic trunk ganglion

(a) Anterior view showing spinal cord, associated nerves, and vertebrae. The dorsal and ventral roots arise medially as rootlets and join laterally to form the spinal nerve.

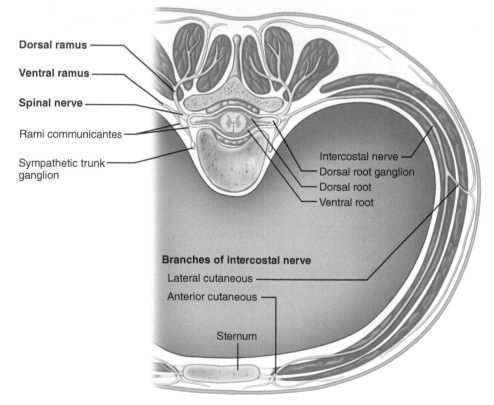

Dorsal ramus
Ventral ramus
Spinal nerve
Rami communicantes
Sympathetic trunk ganglion
Intercostal nerve
Dorsal root ganglion
Dorsal root
Ventral root
Branches of intercostal nerve
Lateral cutaneous
Anterior cutaneous
Sternum

(b) Cross section of thorax showing the main roots and branches of a spinal nerve.

intervertebral foramina. Because motor and sensory fibers mingle in a spinal nerve, it contains both efferent and afferent fibers.

The spinal roots become progressively longer from the superior to the inferior aspect of the cord. In the cervical region, the roots are short and run horizontally, but the roots of the lumbar and sacral nerves extend inferiorly for some distance through the lower vertebral canal as the *cauda equina* before exiting the vertebral column (Figure 13.7).

A spinal nerve is quite short (only 1–2 cm). Almost immediately after emerging from its foramen, it divides into a small **dorsal ramus** (ra'mus; "branch"), a larger **ventral ramus**, and a tiny **meningeal branch** (mĕ-nin'je-al) that reenters the vertebral canal to innervate the meninges and blood vessels within. Each ramus, like the spinal nerve itself, is mixed.

Special rami called **rami communicantes**, which contain autonomic (visceral) nerve fibers, attach to the base of the ventral rami of the thoracic spinal nerves (Figure 13.8).

Innervation of Specific Body Regions

The spinal nerve rami and their main branches supply the entire somatic region of the body (skeletal muscles and skin) from the neck down. The dorsal rami supply the posterior body trunk. The thicker ventral rami supply the rest of the trunk and the limbs.

To be clear, let's review the difference between roots and rami:

- Roots lie medial to and form the spinal nerves. Each root is strictly sensory or motor.
- Rami lie distal to and are lateral branches of the spinal nerves. Like spinal nerves, rami carry both sensory and motor fibers.

Before we get into the specifics of how the body is innervated, it is important for you to understand some points about the ventral rami of the spinal nerves. Except for T_2–T_{12}, all ventral rami branch and join one another lateral to the vertebral column, forming complicated interlacing nerve networks called **nerve plexuses** (Figure 13.7). Nerve plexuses occur in the cervical, brachial, lumbar, and sacral regions and primarily serve the limbs. Notice that *only ventral rami form plexuses*.

Within a plexus, fibers from the various ventral rami crisscross one another and become redistributed so that (1) each resulting branch of the plexus contains fibers from several spinal nerves and (2) fibers from each ventral ramus travel to the body periphery via several routes. As a result, each muscle in a limb receives its nerve supply from more than one spinal nerve. An advantage of this fiber regrouping is that damage to one spinal segment or root cannot completely paralyze any limb muscle.

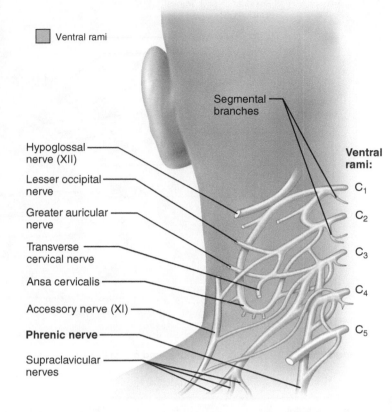

Ventral rami

Segmental branches

Hypoglossal nerve (XII)

Lesser occipital nerve

Greater auricular nerve

Transverse cervical nerve

Ansa cervicalis

Accessory nerve (XI)

Phrenic nerve

Supraclavicular nerves

Ventral rami:

C_1

C_2

C_3

C_4

C_5

Figure 13.9 The cervical plexus. The nerves colored gray connect to the plexus but do not belong to it. See Table 13.3 for structures served. (Posterior view.)

In the rest of this section, we summarize the major groups of skeletal muscles served. For more specific information on muscle innervations, see Tables 10.1–10.17.

Cervical Plexus and the Neck

Buried deep in the neck under the sternocleidomastoid muscle, the ventral rami of the first four cervical nerves form the looping **cervical plexus** (Figure 13.9). Most of its branches are **cutaneous nerves** that supply only the skin (Table 13.3).

Table 13.3	Branches of the Cervical Plexus (See Figure 13.9)	
NERVES	**VENTRAL RAMI**	**STRUCTURES SERVED**
Cutaneous Branches (Superficial)		
Lesser occipital	C_2 (C_3)	Skin on posterolateral aspect of head and neck
Greater auricular	C_2, C_3	Skin of ear, skin over parotid gland
Transverse cervical	C_2, C_3	Skin on anterior and lateral aspect of neck
Supraclavicular (medial, intermediate, and lateral)	C_3, C_4	Skin of shoulder and clavicular region
Motor Branches (Deep)		
Ansa cervicalis (superior and inferior roots)	C_1–C_3	Infrahyoid muscles of neck (omohyoid, sternohyoid, and sternothyroid)
Segmental and other muscular branches	C_1–C_5	Deep muscles of neck (geniohyoid and thyrohyoid) and portions of scalenes, levator scapulae, trapezius, and sternocleidomastoid muscles
Phrenic	C_3–C_5	Diaphragm (sole motor nerve supply)

13

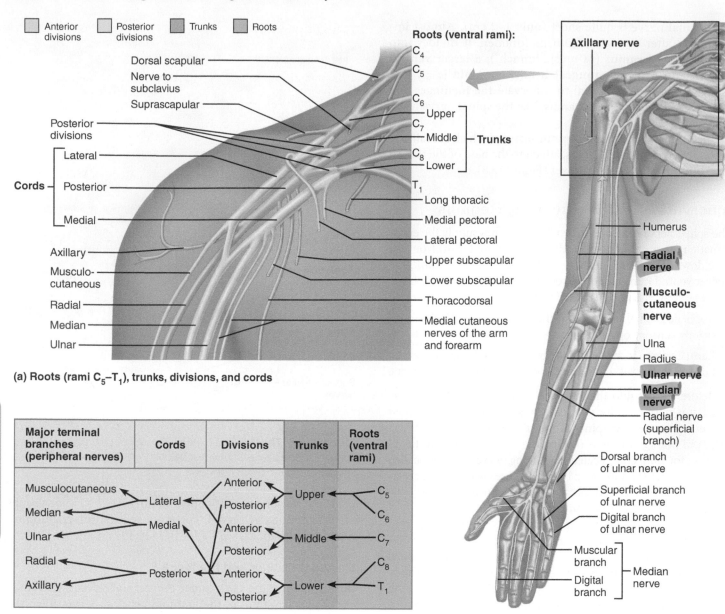

Anterior divisions   Posterior divisions   Trunks   Roots

(a) Roots (rami C₅–T₁), trunks, divisions, and cords

(b) Flowchart summarizing relationships within the brachial plexus

(c) The major nerves of the upper limb

(d) Cadaver photo

Figure 13.10 **The brachial plexus.** (Anterior view.)

Table 13.4	Branches of the Brachial Plexus (See Figure 13.10 and Appendix G)	
NERVES	**CORD AND VENTRAL RAMI**	**STRUCTURES SERVED**
Musculocutaneous	Lateral cord (C_5–C_7)	Muscular branches: flexor muscles in anterior arm (biceps brachii, brachialis, coracobrachialis) Cutaneous branches: skin on lateral forearm (extremely variable)
Median	By two branches, one from medial cord (C_8, T_1) and one from the lateral cord (C_5–C_7)	Muscular branches to flexor group of anterior forearm (palmaris longus, flexor carpi radialis, flexor digitorum superficialis, flexor pollicis longus, lateral half of flexor digitorum profundus, and pronator muscles); intrinsic muscles of lateral palm and digital branches to the fingers Cutaneous branches: skin of lateral two-thirds of hand on ventral side and dorsum of fingers 2 and 3
Ulnar	Medial cord (C_8, T_1)	Muscular branches: flexor muscles in anterior forearm (flexor carpi ulnaris and medial half of flexor digitorum profundus); most intrinsic muscles of hand Cutaneous branches: skin of medial third of hand, both anterior and posterior aspects
Radial	Posterior cord (C_5–C_8, T_1)	Muscular branches: posterior muscles of arm and forearm (triceps brachii, anconeus, supinator, brachioradialis, extensors carpi radialis longus and brevis, extensor carpi ulnaris, and several muscles that extend the fingers) Cutaneous branches: skin of posterolateral surface of entire limb (except dorsum of fingers 2 and 3)
Axillary	Posterior cord (C_5, C_6)	Muscular branches: deltoid and teres minor muscles Cutaneous branches: some skin of shoulder region
Dorsal scapular	Branches of C_5 rami	Rhomboid muscles and levator scapulae
Long thoracic	Branches of C_5–C_7 rami	Serratus anterior muscle
Subscapular	Posterior cord; branches of C_5 and C_6 rami	Teres major and subscapularis muscles
Suprascapular	Upper trunk (C_5, C_6)	Shoulder joint; supraspinatus and infraspinatus muscles
Pectoral (lateral and medial)	Branches of lateral and medial cords (C_5–T_1)	Pectoralis major and minor muscles

They transmit sensory impulses from the skin of the neck, the ear area, the back of the head, and the shoulder. Other branches innervate muscles of the anterior neck.

The single most important nerve from this plexus is the **phrenic nerve** (fren'ik), which receives fibers from C_3, C_4, and C_5. The phrenic nerve runs inferiorly through the thorax and supplies both motor and sensory fibers to the diaphragm (*phren* = diaphragm), which is the chief muscle causing breathing movements.

Homeostatic Imbalance 13.2

Irritation of the phrenic nerve causes spasms of the diaphragm, or hiccups. If both phrenic nerves are severed, or if the C_3–C_5 region of the spinal cord is crushed or destroyed, the diaphragm is paralyzed and respiratory arrest occurs. Mechanical respirators keep victims alive by forcing air into their lungs—literally breathing for them. ✚

Brachial Plexus and Upper Limb

The large, important **brachial plexus**, situated partly in the neck and partly in the axilla, gives rise to virtually all the nerves that innervate the upper limb (Table 13.4). It can be palpated (felt) in a living person just superior to the clavicle at the lateral border of the sternocleidomastoid muscle. Ventral rami of C_5–C_8

and most of the T_1 ramus intermix to form the brachial plexus. Additionally, it often receives fibers from C_4 or T_2 or both.

The brachial plexus is very complex (some consider it the anatomy student's nightmare). Perhaps the simplest approach is to master the terms used for its four major groups of branches (Figure 13.10a, b). From medial to lateral, these are (1) the ventral rami, misleadingly called *roots*, which form (2) *trunks*, which form (3) *divisions*, which form (4) *cords*. You might want to use the saying "Really tired? Drink coffee" to help you remember this branching sequence.

The five **roots** (ventral rami C_5–T_1) of the brachial plexus lie deep to the sternocleidomastoid muscle. At the lateral border of that muscle, these roots unite to form **upper**, **middle**, and **lower trunks**, each of which divides almost immediately into an **anterior division** and a **posterior division**.

The anterior and posterior divisions, which generally indicate which fibers serve the front or back of the limb, pass deep to the clavicle and enter the axilla. There they give rise to three large fiber bundles called the **lateral**, **medial**, and **posterior cords**. (The cords are named for their relationship to the axillary artery, which runs through the axilla; see Figure 19.23.) All along the plexus, small nerves branch off. These supply the muscles and skin of the shoulder and superior thorax.

Homeostatic Imbalance 13.3

Injuries to the brachial plexus are common. When severe, they weaken or paralyze the entire upper limb. Such injuries may occur when the upper limb is pulled hard, stretching the plexus (as when a football tackler yanks the arm of the running back), or by blows to the top of the shoulder that force the humerus inferiorly (as when a cyclist pitches headfirst off a motorcycle and his shoulder grinds into the pavement). ✚

The brachial plexus ends in the axilla, where its three cords wind along the axillary artery and give rise to the main nerves of the upper limb (Figure 13.10c, d). Five of these nerves are especially important: the axillary, musculocutaneous, median, ulnar, and radial nerves. We describe their distribution and targets briefly here. For more detail, see Table 13.4 and Appendix G.

Axillary Nerve   The **axillary nerve** branches off the posterior cord and runs posterior to the surgical neck of the humerus. It innervates the deltoid and teres minor muscles and the skin and joint capsule of the shoulder.

Musculocutaneous Nerve   The **musculocutaneous nerve**, the major end branch of the lateral cord, courses inferiorly in the anterior arm, supplying motor fibers to the biceps brachii, brachialis, and coracobrachialis muscles. Distal to the elbow, it provides cutaneous sensation in the lateral forearm.

Median Nerve   The **median nerve** descends through the arm to the anterior forearm, where it gives off branches to the skin and to most flexor muscles. On reaching the hand, it innervates five intrinsic muscles of the lateral palm. The median nerve activates muscles that pronate the forearm, flex the wrist and fingers, and oppose the thumb.

 Homeostatic Imbalance 13.4

Median nerve injury makes it difficult to use the pincer grasp (opposed thumb and index finger) to pick up small objects. Because this nerve runs down the midline of the forearm and wrist, it is a frequent casualty of wrist-slashing suicide attempts. In carpal tunnel syndrome (see p. 234), the median nerve is compressed. ✚

Ulnar Nerve   The **ulnar nerve** branches off the medial cord of the plexus. It descends along the medial aspect of the arm toward the elbow, swings behind the medial epicondyle, and then follows the ulna along the medial forearm. There it supplies the flexor carpi ulnaris and the medial part of the flexor digitorum profundus (the flexors not supplied by the median nerve).

The ulnar nerve continues into the hand, where it innervates most intrinsic hand muscles and the skin of the medial aspect of the hand. It causes the wrist and fingers to flex, and (with the median nerve) adducts and abducts the medial fingers.

 Homeostatic Imbalance 13.5

Where it takes a superficial course, the ulnar nerve is very vulnerable to injury. Striking the "funny bone"—the spot where this nerve rests against the medial epicondyle—makes the little finger tingle. Severe or chronic damage can lead to sensory loss,

paralysis, and muscle atrophy. Affected individuals have trouble making a fist and gripping objects. As the little and ring fingers become hyperextended at the knuckles and flexed at the distal interphalangeal joints, the hand contorts into a *clawhand*. ✚

Radial Nerve   The **radial nerve**, the largest branch of the brachial plexus, is a continuation of the posterior cord. This nerve wraps around the humerus (in the radial groove), and then runs anteriorly around the lateral epicondyle at the elbow. There it divides into a superficial branch that follows the lateral edge of the radius to the hand and a deep branch (not illustrated) that runs posteriorly. It supplies the posterior skin of the limb along its entire course. Its motor branches innervate essentially all the extensor muscles of the upper limb. Muscles controlled by the radial nerve extend the elbow, supinate the forearm, extend the wrist and fingers, and abduct the thumb.

 Homeostatic Imbalance 13.6

Trauma to the radial nerve results in *wrist drop*, inability to extend the hand at the wrist. Improper use of a crutch or "Saturday night paralysis," in which an intoxicated person falls asleep with an arm draped over the back of a chair or sofa edge, can compress the radial nerve and impair its blood supply. ✚

Lumbosacral Plexus and Lower Limb

The sacral and lumbar plexuses overlap substantially. Because many fibers of the lumbar plexus contribute to the sacral plexus via the **lumbosacral trunk**, the two plexuses are often referred to as the **lumbosacral plexus**. Although the lumbosacral plexus serves mainly the lower limb, it also sends some branches to the abdomen, pelvis, and buttock.

Lumbar Plexus   The **lumbar plexus** arises from spinal nerves L_1–L_4 and lies within the psoas major muscle **(Figure 13.11)**. Its proximal branches innervate parts of the abdominal wall muscles and the psoas muscle, but its major branches descend to innervate the anterior and medial thigh. Appendix G shows the distribution and targets of the major lumbosacral nerves.

The **femoral nerve**, the largest terminal nerve of this plexus, runs deep to the inguinal ligament to enter the thigh and then divides into several large branches. The motor branches innervate anterior thigh muscles (quadriceps), which are the principal thigh flexors and knee extensors. The cutaneous branches serve the skin of the anterior thigh and the medial surface of the leg from knee to foot.

The **obturator nerve** (ob"tu-ra′tor) enters the medial thigh via the obturator foramen and innervates the adductor muscles. Table 13.5 summarizes the branches of the lumbar plexus.

 Homeostatic Imbalance 13.7

When the spinal roots of the lumbar plexus are compressed, as by a herniated disc, gait problems occur because the femoral nerve serves the prime movers that flex the hip and extend the knee. Other symptoms are pain or numbness of the anterior thigh and (if the obturator nerve is impaired) of the medial thigh. ✚

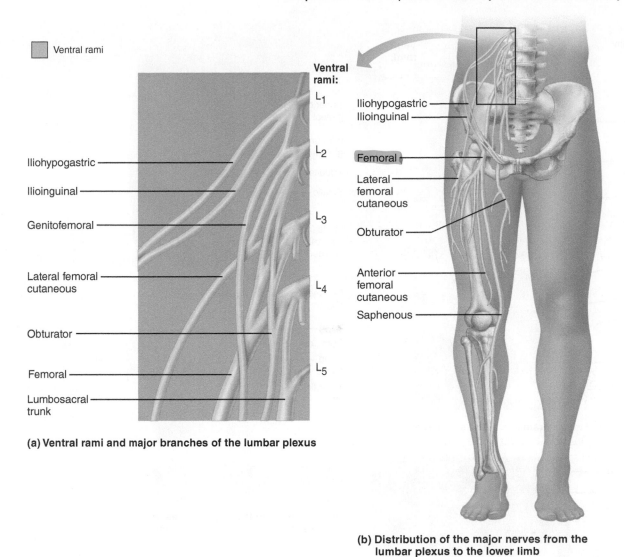

(a) Ventral rami and major branches of the lumbar plexus

(b) Distribution of the major nerves from the lumbar plexus to the lower limb

Figure 13.11 The lumbar plexus. (Anterior view.)

Table 13.5	Branches of the Lumbar Plexus (See Figure 13.11 and Appendix G)	
NERVES	**VENTRAL RAMI**	**STRUCTURES SERVED**
Femoral	L_2–L_4	Skin of anterior and medial thigh via *anterior femoral cutaneous* branch; skin of medial leg and foot, hip and knee joints via *saphenous* branch; motor to anterior muscles (quadriceps and sartorius) of thigh and to pectineus, iliacus
Obturator	L_2–L_4	Motor to adductor magnus (part), longus, and brevis muscles, gracilis muscle of medial thigh, obturator externus; sensory for skin of medial thigh and for hip and knee joints
Lateral femoral cutaneous	L_2, L_3	Skin of lateral thigh; some sensory branches to peritoneum
Iliohypogastric	L_1	Skin of lower abdomen and hip; muscles of anterolateral abdominal wall (internal obliques and transversus abdominis)
Ilioinguinal	L_1	Skin of external genitalia and proximal medial aspect of the thigh; inferior abdominal muscles
Genitofemoral	L_1, L_2	Skin of scrotum in males, of labia majora in females, and of anterior thigh inferior to middle portion of inguinal region; cremaster muscle in males

(a) Ventral rami and major branches of the sacral plexus

(b) Distribution of the major nerves from the sacral plexus to the lower limb

(c) Cadaver photo

Figure 13.12 The sacral plexus. (Posterior view.)

Sacral Plexus   The **sacral plexus** arises from spinal nerves L_4–S_4 and lies immediately caudal to the lumbar plexus **(Figure 13.12)**. Some fibers of the lumbar plexus contribute to the sacral plexus via the *lumbosacral trunk*, as mentioned earlier.

The sacral plexus has about a dozen named branches. About half of these serve the buttock and lower limb; the others innervate pelvic structures and the perineum. Here we describe the most important branches. **Table 13.6** summarizes all but the smallest ones.

The largest branch of the sacral plexus is the **sciatic nerve** (si-at′ik), the thickest and longest nerve in the body. It supplies the entire lower limb, except the anteromedial thigh.

The sciatic nerve is actually two nerves—the *tibial* and *common fibular*—wrapped in a common sheath. The sciatic nerve leaves the pelvis via the greater sciatic notch. It courses deep to the gluteus maximus muscle and enters the posterior thigh just medial to the hip joint (*sciatic* = of the hip). There it gives off motor branches to the hamstring muscles

Table 13.6	Branches of the Sacral Plexus (See Figure 13.12 and Appendix G)	
NERVES	**VENTRAL RAMI**	**STRUCTURES SERVED**
Sciatic nerve	L_4, L_5, S_1–S_3	Composed of two nerves (tibial and common fibular) in a common sheath; they diverge just proximal to the knee
▪ Tibial (including sural, medial and lateral plantar, and medial calcaneal branches)	L_4–S_3	Cutaneous branches: to skin of posterior surface of leg and sole of foot Motor branches: to muscles of back of thigh, leg, and foot [hamstrings (except short head of biceps femoris), posterior part of adductor magnus, triceps surae, tibialis posterior, popliteus, flexor digitorum longus, flexor hallucis longus, and intrinsic muscles of foot]
▪ Common fibular (superficial and deep branches)	L_4–S_2	Cutaneous branches: to skin of anterior and lateral surface of leg and dorsum of foot Motor branches: to short head of biceps femoris of thigh, fibular muscles of lateral compartment of leg, tibialis anterior, and extensor muscles of toes (extensor hallucis longus, extensors digitorum longus and brevis)
Superior gluteal	L_4, L_5, S_1	Motor branches: to gluteus medius and minimus and tensor fasciae latae
Inferior gluteal	L_5–S_2	Motor branches: to gluteus maximus
Posterior femoral cutaneous	S_1–S_3	Skin of buttock, posterior thigh, and popliteal region; length varies; may also innervate part of skin of calf and heel
Pudendal	S_2–S_4	Supplies most of skin and muscles of perineum (region encompassing external genitalia and anus and including clitoris, labia, and vaginal mucosa in females, and scrotum and penis in males); external anal sphincter

(all thigh extensors and knee flexors) and to the adductor magnus. Immediately above the knee, the two divisions of the sciatic nerve diverge.

The **tibial nerve** continues through the popliteal fossa (the region just posterior to the knee joint) and supplies the posterior compartment muscles of the leg and the skin of the posterior calf and sole of the foot.

- In the vicinity of the knee, the tibial nerve gives off the **sural nerve**, which serves the skin of the posterolateral leg.
- At the ankle the tibial nerve divides into the **medial** and **lateral plantar nerves**, which serve most of the foot.

The **common fibular nerve**, or *common peroneal nerve* (*perone* = fibula), descends from its point of origin, wraps around the neck of the fibula, and then divides into superficial and deep branches. These branches innervate the knee joint, skin of the anterior and lateral leg and dorsum of the foot, and muscles of the anterolateral leg (the extensors that dorsiflex the foot).

The next largest sacral plexus branches are the **superior** and **inferior gluteal nerves**. Together, they innervate the buttock (gluteal) and tensor fasciae latae muscles. The **pudendal nerve** (pu-den′dal; "shameful") innervates the muscles and skin of the perineum, and helps stimulate erection and control urination (see Table 10.7). Other branches of the sacral plexus supply the thigh rotators and muscles of the pelvic floor.

Homeostatic Imbalance 13.8

Injury to the proximal part of the sciatic nerve—as might follow a fall, disc herniation, or badly placed injection into the buttock—can impair the lower limbs in a variety of ways depending on the nerve roots injured.

Sciatica (si-at′ĭ-kah), characterized by stabbing pain radiating over the course of the sciatic nerve, is common. When the nerve is transected, the leg is nearly useless. The leg cannot be flexed (because the hamstrings are paralyzed), and the foot and ankle cannot move at all. The foot drops into plantar flexion (it dangles), a condition called *footdrop*. Recovery from sciatic nerve injury is usually slow and incomplete.

If the lesion occurs below the knee, thigh muscles are spared. When the tibial nerve is injured, the paralyzed calf muscles cannot plantar flex the foot and a shuffling gait develops. The common fibular nerve is susceptible to injury largely because of its superficial location at the head and neck of the fibula. Even a tight leg cast, or lying too long on your side on a firm mattress, can compress this nerve and cause footdrop. ✚

Anterolateral Thorax and Abdominal Wall

Only in the thorax are the ventral rami arranged in a simple segmental pattern corresponding to that of the dorsal rami. The ventral rami of T_1–T_{12} mostly course anteriorly, deep to each rib, as the **intercostal nerves**. These nerves supply the intercostal muscles, the muscle and skin of the anterolateral thorax, and most of the abdominal wall. Along their course, these nerves give off *cutaneous branches* to the skin (Figure 13.8b).

Two thoracic nerves are unusual: the tiny T_1 (most fibers enter the brachial plexus) and T_{12}, which lies inferior to the twelfth rib, making it a **subcostal nerve**.

Back

The dorsal rami innervate the posterior body trunk in a neat, segmented pattern. Via its several branches, each dorsal ramus innervates the narrow strip of muscle (and skin) in line with where it emerges from the spinal column (Figure 13.8b).

Innervation of Skin: Dermatomes

A **dermatome** (der′mah-tōm; "skin segment") is an area of skin innervated by the cutaneous branches of a single spinal nerve. Every spinal nerve except C_1 innervates dermatomes. In patients

13

(a) Anterior view

(b) Posterior view

Figure 13.13 Map of dermatomes. Each dermatome is the skin segment innervated by the cutaneous sensory branches of a single spinal nerve. All spinal nerves except C$_1$ participate in the innervation of the dermatomes.

with spinal cord injuries, you can pinpoint the damaged nerves and the injured region of the spinal cord by determining which dermatomes are affected.

Adjacent dermatomes on the body trunk are fairly uniform in width, almost horizontal, and in direct line with their spinal nerves (Figure 13.13). The dermatome arrangement in the limbs is less obvious. (It is also more variable—different clinicians have mapped a variety of areas for the same dermatomes.) The skin of the upper limbs is supplied by ventral rami of C$_5$–T$_1$ (or T$_2$). The lumbar nerves supply most of the anterior surfaces of the thighs and legs, and the sacral nerves serve most of the posterior surfaces of the lower limbs. (This distribution

basically reflects the areas supplied by the lumbar and sacral plexuses, respectively.)

Adjacent dermatomes are not as cleanly separated as a typical dermatome map indicates. On the trunk, neighboring dermatomes overlap considerably (about 50%). As a result, destruction of a single spinal nerve will not cause complete numbness anywhere. In the limbs, the overlap is less complete and some skin regions are innervated by just one spinal nerve.

Innervation of Joints

The easiest way to remember which nerves serve which synovial joint is to use **Hilton's law:** *Any nerve serving a muscle that produces movement at a joint also innervates the joint and the skin over* *the joint.* Hence, once you learn which nerves serve the various major muscles and muscle groups, no new learning is necessary.

For example, the quadriceps, gracilis, and hamstring muscles all cross the knee. The nerves to these muscles are the femoral nerve anteriorly and branches of the sciatic and obturator nerves posteriorly. Consequently, these nerves innervate the knee joint as well.

☑ **Check Your Understanding**

10. Spinal nerves have both *dorsal roots* and *dorsal rami*. How are these different from each other in location and composition?

11. After his horse-riding accident, the actor Christopher Reeve was unable to breathe on his own. Which spinal nerve roots, spinal nerve, and spinal nerve plexus were involved?

—————————————————— *For answers, see Appendix H.*

PART 3
Motor Endings and Motor Activity

Peripheral Motor Endings

✓ Compare and contrast the motor endings of somatic and autonomic nerve fibers.

So far we have covered the sensory receptors that detect stimuli and the nerves containing the afferent and efferent fibers that deliver impulses to and from the CNS. We now turn to **motor endings**, the PNS elements that activate effectors by releasing neurotransmitters. Because we discussed that topic in Chapter 9 with the innervation of body muscles, all we need to do here is recap. We will follow the recap with a brief overview of motor integration.

Innervation of Skeletal Muscle

Recall that the terminals of somatic motor fibers that innervate voluntary muscles form elaborate **neuromuscular junctions** with their effector cells (Figure 9.8, p. 287). As each axon branch reaches its target, a single muscle fiber, the ending splits into a cluster of *axon terminals* that branch treelike over the junctional folds of the sarcolemma of the muscle fiber. The axon terminals contain mitochondria and synaptic vesicles filled with the neurotransmitter acetylcholine (ACh).

When a nerve impulse reaches an axon terminal, ACh is released by exocytosis, diffuses across the fluid-filled synaptic cleft (about 50 nm wide), and attaches to ACh receptors on the sarcolemma at the junction. ACh binding opens ligand-gated channels that allow both Na^+ and K^+ to pass. Because more Na^+ enters the cell than K^+ leaves, the muscle cell interior at that point depolarizes. The resulting graded potential is called an *end plate potential.*

The end plate potential spreads to adjacent areas of the membrane where it triggers the opening of voltage-gated sodium channels. This event causes an action potential to propagate along the sarcolemma, which stimulates the muscle fiber to contract. The synaptic cleft at somatic neuromuscular junctions is filled with a glycoprotein-rich basal lamina, a structure not seen at other synapses. The basal lamina contains *acetylcholinesterase*, the enzyme that breaks down ACh.

Innervation of Visceral Muscle and Glands

The junctions between autonomic motor endings and their effectors (smooth and cardiac muscle and glands) are much simpler than the junctions formed between somatic fibers and skeletal muscle cells. The autonomic motor axons branch repeatedly, each branch forming *synapses en passant* ("synapses in passing") with its effector cells. Instead of a cluster of bulblike terminals, an axon ending serving smooth muscle or a gland (but not cardiac muscle) has a series of **varicosities**, knoblike swellings containing mitochondria and synaptic vesicles, that make it look like a string of beads (see Figure 9.26, p. 306).

The autonomic synaptic vesicles typically contain either acetylcholine or norepinephrine, both of which act indirectly on their targets via second messengers. Consequently, visceral motor responses tend to be slower than those induced by somatic motor fibers, which directly open ion channels.

Motor Integration: From Intention to Effect

✓ Outline the three levels of the motor hierarchy.

✓ Compare the roles of the cerebellum and basal nuclei in controlling motor activity.

How does integration in the motor system compare with integration in sensory systems? In the motor system, we have motor endings serving effectors (muscle fibers) instead of sensory receptors, descending efferent circuits instead of ascending afferent circuits, and motor behavior instead of perception. However, as in sensory systems, the basic mechanisms of motor systems operate at three levels.

Levels of Motor Control

The cerebral cortex is at the highest level of our conscious motor pathways, but it is *not* the ultimate planner and coordinator of complex motor activities. The cerebellum and basal nuclei (ganglia) play this role and are therefore at the top of the motor control hierarchy. Motor control exerted by lower levels is mediated by *reflex arcs* in some cases, but complex motor behavior, such as walking and swimming, depends on more complex patterns. Currently, we define three levels of motor control: the *segmental level*, *projection level*, and *precommand level* (**Figure 13.14**).

The Segmental Level

The lowest level of the motor hierarchy, the **segmental level**, consists of reflexes and spinal cord circuits that control automatic movements. A segmental circuit activates a network of ventral horn neurons in a group of cord segments, causing them to stimulate specific groups of muscles.

Circuits that control locomotion and other specific and oft-repeated motor activities are called **central pattern generators**

(a) Levels of motor control and their interactions

Figure 13.14 Hierarchy of motor control. Dashed lines in (a) indicate feedback.

(CPGs). CPGs consist of networks of oscillating inhibitory and excitatory neurons, which set crude rhythms and alternating patterns of movement.

The Projection Level

The spinal cord is under the direct control of the **projection level** of motor control. The projection level consists of neurons acting through the direct and indirect motor pathways (see Table 12.3 and pp. 469–473):

- *Upper motor neurons* of the motor cortex initiate the *direct (pyramidal) pathways*. Axons of direct pathway neurons produce discrete voluntary movements of the skeletal muscles.

- Brain stem motor nuclei oversee the *indirect pathways*. Axons of these pathways help control reflex and CPG-controlled motor actions, modifying and controlling the activity of the segmental apparatus.

Projection motor pathways convey information to lower motor neurons, and send a copy of that information as *internal feedback* to higher command levels, continually informing them of what is supposed to happen. The direct (pyramidal) and indirect pathways provide separate and parallel pathways for controlling the spinal cord, but these systems are interrelated at all levels.

The Precommand Level

Two other systems of brain neurons, located in the cerebellum and basal nuclei, regulate motor activity. They precisely start or stop movements, coordinate movements with posture, block unwanted movements, and monitor muscle tone. Collectively called **precommand areas**, these systems *control the outputs* of the cortex and brain stem motor centers and stand at the highest level of the motor hierarchy.

The key center for "online" sensorimotor integration and control is the **cerebellum**. Remember the cerebellum is a target of ascending proprioceptor, tactile, equilibrium, and visual inputs—feedback that it needs to rapidly correct "errors" in motor activity. It also receives information via branches from descending pyramidal tracts, and from various brain stem nuclei.

The cerebellum lacks direct connections to the spinal cord. It acts on motor pathways through the projection areas of the brain stem and on the motor cortex via the thalamus to fine-tune motor activity.

The **basal nuclei** receive inputs from *all* cortical areas and send their output back mainly to premotor and prefrontal cortical areas via the thalamus. Compared to the cerebellum, the basal nuclei appear to be involved in more complex aspects of motor control. Under resting conditions, the basal nuclei inhibit various motor centers of the brain. When the motor centers are released from inhibition, coordinated motions can begin.

Cells in both the basal nuclei and the cerebellum are involved in this unconscious planning and discharge *in advance* of willed movements. When you actually move your fingers, both the precommand areas and the primary motor cortex are active. At the risk of oversimplifying, it appears that the cortex says, "I want to do this," and then lets the precommand areas take over to provide the proper timing and patterns to execute the desired movements. The precommand areas control the motor cortex and provide its readiness to initiate a voluntary act. The conscious cortex then chooses to act or not act, but the groundwork has already been laid.

☑ Check Your Understanding

12. What are varicosities and where would you find them?

13. Which parts of the nervous system ultimately plan and coordinate complex motor activities?

For answers, see Appendix H.

PART 4
Reflex Activity

The Reflex Arc

✓ Name the components of a reflex arc and distinguish between autonomic and somatic reflexes.

Many of the body's control systems are reflexes, which can be either inborn or learned.

An *inborn (intrinsic) reflex* is a rapid, predictable motor response to a stimulus. It is unlearned, unpremeditated, and involuntary, and is built into our neural anatomy. Reflexes prevent us from having to *think* about all the little details of staying upright, intact, and alive—helping us maintain posture, avoid pain, and control visceral activities.

For instance, what happens when you splash a pot of boiling water on your arm? You are likely to drop the pot instantly and involuntarily even before you feel any pain. Your response is triggered by an inborn spinal reflex without any help from the brain. In many cases we are aware of the final response of a basic reflex (you know you've dropped the pot of boiling water). In other cases, reflex activities go on without any awareness on our part. This is typical of many visceral reflexes, which are regulated by the subconscious lower regions of the CNS, specifically the brain stem and spinal cord.

The second type of reflex, a *learned (acquired) reflex,* results from practice or repetition. Take, for instance, the complex sequence of reactions that occurs when an experienced driver drives a car. The process is largely automatic, but only because substantial time and effort were expended to acquire driving skills.

In reality, the distinction between inborn and learned reflexes is not clear-cut and most inborn reflex actions can be modified by learning and conscious effort. For instance, if a 3-year-old child was standing by your side when you scalded your arm, you most likely would set the pot down (rather than just letting go) because you consciously recognized the danger to the child.

Recall the discussion in Chapter 11 about serial and parallel processing of sensory input. What happens when you scald your arm is a good example of how these two processing modes work together. You drop the pot before feeling any pain, but the pain signals picked up by the interneurons of the spinal cord are quickly transmitted to the brain, so that within the next few seconds you do become aware of pain, and you also know what happened to cause it. The withdrawal reflex is serial processing mediated by the spinal cord, and pain awareness reflects simultaneous parallel processing of the sensory input.

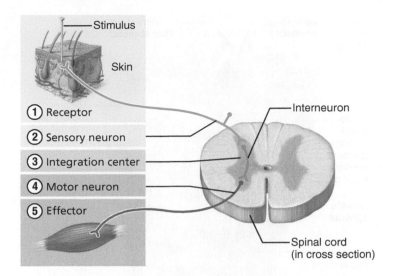

Figure 13.15 The five basic components of all reflex arcs. The reflex arc illustrated is polysynaptic.

Components of a Reflex Arc

As you learned in Chapter 11, reflexes occur over highly specific neural paths called reflex arcs. All reflex arcs have five essential components (**Figure 13.15**):

① **Receptor:** Site of the stimulus action.

② **Sensory neuron:** Transmits afferent impulses to the CNS.

③ **Integration center:** In simple reflex arcs, the integration center may be a single synapse between a sensory neuron and a motor neuron (**monosynaptic reflex**). More complex reflex arcs involve multiple synapses with chains of interneurons (**polysynaptic reflex**). The integration center for the reflexes we will describe in this chapter is within the CNS.

④ **Motor neuron:** Conducts efferent impulses from the integration center to an effector organ.

⑤ **Effector:** Muscle fiber or gland cell that responds to the efferent impulses (by contracting or secreting).

Reflexes are classified functionally as **somatic reflexes** if they activate skeletal muscle, or as **autonomic (visceral) reflexes** if they activate visceral effectors (smooth or cardiac muscle or glands). Here we describe some common somatic reflexes mediated by the spinal cord. We will consider autonomic reflexes in later chapters along with the visceral processes they help to regulate.

Spinal Reflexes

✓ Compare and contrast stretch, flexor, crossed-extensor, and tendon reflexes.

Spinal reflexes are somatic reflexes that are mediated by the spinal cord. Many spinal reflexes occur without the direct involvement of higher brain centers. Generally, these reflexes are even present in animals whose brains have been destroyed as long as the spinal cord is still functional.

13

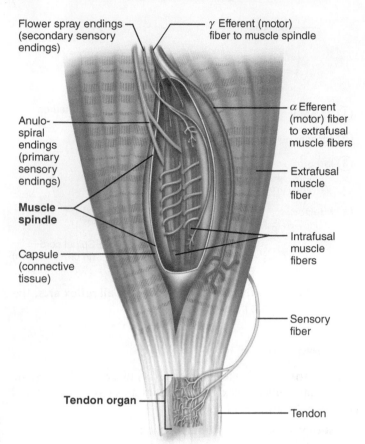

Flower spray endings (secondary sensory endings)

γ Efferent (motor) fiber to muscle spindle

Anulo-spiral endings (primary sensory endings)

α Efferent (motor) fiber to extrafusal muscle fibers

Extrafusal muscle fiber

Muscle spindle

Intrafusal muscle fibers

Capsule (connective tissue)

Sensory fiber

Tendon organ

Tendon

Figure 13.16 Anatomy of the muscle spindle and tendon organ. Notice the afferent fibers from and efferent fibers to the muscle spindle. Myelin has been omitted from all nerve fibers for clarity.

However, the brain is "advised" of most spinal reflex activity and can facilitate, inhibit, or adapt it, depending on the circumstances (as we described in the example of the hot water–filled pot). Moreover, continuous facilitating signals from the brain are required for normal spinal reflex activity. As we saw in Chapter 12, *spinal shock* occurs when the spinal cord is transected, immediately depressing all functions controlled by the cord.

Tests of somatic reflexes are important clinically to assess the condition of the nervous system. Exaggerated, distorted, or absent reflexes indicate degeneration or pathology of specific nervous system regions, often before other signs appear.

Stretch and Tendon Reflexes

What information does your nervous system need to smoothly coordinate the activity of your skeletal muscles? Two types of information about the current state of a muscle are key. First, the nervous system needs to know the length of the muscle. This information comes from the *muscle spindles*, found in skeletal muscles. Second, it needs to know the amount of tension in the muscle and its associated tendons. *Tendon organs* provide this information.

These two types of proprioceptors play an important role in spinal reflexes and also provide essential feedback to the cerebral cortex and cerebellum. Just remember, muscle spindles measure **l**ength and **t**endon organs measure **t**ension. Let's take

a closer look at the functional anatomy of these proprioceptors and their roles in certain spinal reflexes.

Functional Anatomy of Muscle Spindles

Each muscle spindle consists of three to ten modified skeletal muscle fibers called **intrafusal muscle fibers** (*intra* = within; *fusal* = the spindle) enclosed in a connective tissue capsule **(Figure 13.16)**. These fibers are less than one-quarter the size of the effector fibers of the muscle, called **extrafusal muscle fibers**.

The central regions of the intrafusal fibers lack myofilaments and are noncontractile. These regions are the receptive surfaces of the spindle. Two types of afferent endings send sensory inputs to the CNS:

- **Anulospiral endings** (also called *primary sensory endings*) are the endings of large axons that wrap around the spindle center. They are stimulated by both the rate and degree of stretch.

- **Flower spray endings** (also called *secondary sensory endings*) are formed by smaller axons that supply the spindle ends. They are stimulated only by degree of stretch.

The intrafusal muscle fibers have contractile regions at their ends, which are the only areas containing actin and myosin myofilaments. These regions are innervated by **gamma (γ) efferent fibers** that arise from small motor neurons in the ventral horn of the spinal cord. These γ motor fibers, which maintain spindle sensitivity (as described shortly), are distinct from the **alpha (α) efferent fibers** of the large **alpha (α) motor neurons** that stimulate the extrafusal muscle fibers to contract.

The muscle spindle is stretched (and excited) in one of two ways:

- By applying an external force that lengthens the entire muscle, such as when we carry a heavy weight or when antagonistic muscles contract (external stretch)

- By activating the γ motor neurons that stimulate the distal ends of the intrafusal fibers to contract, thereby stretching the middle of the spindle (internal stretch).

Whenever the muscle spindle is stretched, its associated sensory neurons transmit impulses at higher frequency to the spinal cord **(Figure 13.17a)**.

During voluntary skeletal muscle contraction, the muscle shortens. If the intrafusal muscle fibers didn't contract along with the extrafusal fibers, the muscle spindle would go slack and cease generating action potentials (Figure 13.17b). At this point it would be unable to signal further changes in muscle length, so it would be useless.

Fortunately, **α-γ coactivation** prevents this from happening. Descending fibers of motor pathways synapse with both α and γ motor neurons, and motor impulses are simultaneously sent to the large extrafusal fibers and to muscle spindle intrafusal fibers. Stimulating the intrafusal fibers maintains the spindle's tension (and sensitivity) during muscle contraction, so that the brain continues to be notified of changes in the muscle length (Figure 13.17b). Without such a system, information on changes in muscle length would cease to flow from contracting muscles.

Figure 13.17 Operation of the muscle spindle. The action potentials generated in the sensory fibers are shown for each case as black lines in yellow bars.

The Stretch Reflex

By sending commands to the motor neurons, the brain essentially sets a muscle's length. The **stretch reflex** makes sure that the muscle stays at that length. For example, the **patellar** (pah-tel′ar) or **knee-jerk reflex** is a stretch reflex that helps keep your knees from buckling when you are standing upright. As your knees begin to buckle and the quadriceps lengthens, the stretch reflex causes the quadriceps to contract without your having to think about it. *Focus on the Stretch Reflex* **(Figure 13.18)** shows the stretch reflex and a specific example—the knee-jerk reflex.

The stretch reflex is important for maintaining muscle tone and adjusting it reflexively. It is most important in the large extensor muscles that sustain upright posture and in postural muscles of the trunk. For example, stretch reflexes initiated first on one side of the spine and then on the other regulate contractions of the postural muscles of the spine almost continuously.

Let's look at how the stretch reflex works. As we've just seen in Figure 13.17, when stretch activates sensory neurons of muscle spindles, they transmit impulses at a higher frequency to the spinal cord. There the sensory neurons synapse directly with α motor neurons, which rapidly excite the extrafusal muscle fibers of the stretched muscle (Figure 13.18). The reflexive muscle contraction that follows (an example of serial processing) resists further muscle stretching.

Branches of the afferent fibers also synapse with interneurons that inhibit motor neurons controlling antagonistic muscles (parallel processing), and the resulting inhibition is called **reciprocal inhibition**. Consequently, the stretch stimulus causes the antagonists to relax so that they cannot resist the shortening of the "stretched" muscle caused by the main reflex arc. While this spinal reflex is occurring, information on muscle length and the speed of muscle shortening is being relayed (mainly via the dorsal white columns) to higher brain centers (more parallel processing).

The most familiar clinical example of a stretch reflex is the knee-jerk reflex we have just described. Stretch reflexes can be elicited in any skeletal muscle by a sudden jolt to the tendon or the muscle itself. All stretch reflexes are **monosynaptic** and **ipsilateral**. In other words, they involve a single synapse and motor activity on the same side of the body. Stretch reflexes are the only monosynaptic reflexes in the body. However, even in these reflexes, the part of the reflex arc that inhibits the motor neurons serving the antagonistic muscles is polysynaptic.

A positive knee jerk (or a positive result for any other stretch reflex test) provides two important pieces of information. First, it proves that the sensory and motor connections between that muscle and the spinal cord are intact. Second, the vigor of the response indicates the degree of excitability of the spinal cord. When the spinal motor neurons are highly facilitated by impulses

Figure 13.18 Stretched muscle spindles initiate a stretch reflex, causing contraction of the stretched muscle and inhibition of its antagonist.

The events by which muscle stretch is damped

① When stretch activates muscle spindles, the associated sensory neurons (blue) transmit afferent impulses at higher frequency to the spinal cord.

② The sensory neurons synapse directly with alpha motor neurons (red), which excite extrafusal fibers of the stretched muscle. Sensory fibers also synapse with interneurons (green) that inhibit motor neurons (purple) controlling antagonistic muscles.

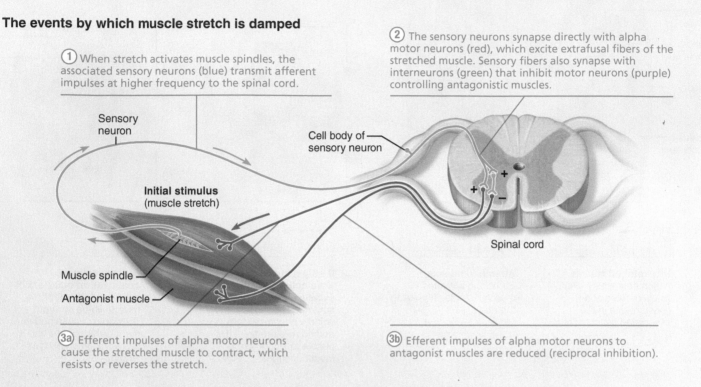

Sensory neuron

Cell body of sensory neuron

Initial stimulus (muscle stretch)

Spinal cord

Muscle spindle

Antagonist muscle

③a Efferent impulses of alpha motor neurons cause the stretched muscle to contract, which resists or reverses the stretch.

③b Efferent impulses of alpha motor neurons to antagonist muscles are reduced (reciprocal inhibition).

The patellar (knee-jerk) reflex—an example of a stretch reflex

Quadriceps (extensors)

Muscle spindle

Patella

Hamstrings (flexors)

Patellar ligament

Spinal cord (L₂–L₄)

① Tapping the patellar ligament stretches the quadriceps and excites its muscle spindles.

② Afferent impulses (blue) travel to the spinal cord, where synapses occur with motor neurons and interneurons.

③a The motor neurons (red) send activating impulses to the quadriceps causing it to contract, extending the knee.

③b The interneurons (green) make inhibitory synapses with ventral horn neurons (purple) that prevent the antagonist muscles (hamstrings) from resisting the contraction of the quadriceps.

+ Excitatory synapse

− Inhibitory synapse

① Quadriceps strongly contracts. Tendon organs are activated.

② Afferent fibers synapse with interneurons in the spinal cord.

Quadriceps (extensors)

Tendon organ

Hamstrings (flexors)

Interneurons

Spinal cord

+ Excitatory synapse

− Inhibitory synapse

③a Efferent impulses to muscle with stretched tendon are damped. Muscle relaxes, reducing tension.

③b Efferent impulses to antagonist muscle cause it to contract.

Figure 13.19 The tendon reflex.

descending from higher centers, just touching the muscle tendon produces a vigorous reflex response. On the other hand, when inhibitory signals bombard the lower motor neurons, even pounding on the tendon may fail to trigger the reflex response.

Homeostatic Imbalance 13.9

Stretch reflexes tend to be hypoactive or absent in cases of peripheral nerve damage or ventral horn injury involving the tested area. These reflexes are absent in those with chronic diabetes mellitus or neurosyphilis and during coma. However, they are hyperactive when lesions of the corticospinal tract reduce the inhibitory effect of the brain on the spinal cord (as in stroke patients). ✚

Adjusting Muscle Spindle Sensitivity

The motor supply to the muscle spindle allows the brain to voluntarily modify the stretch reflex response and the firing rate of α motor neurons. When the γ neurons are vigorously stimulated by impulses from the brain, the spindle is stretched and highly sensitive, and muscle contraction force is maintained or increased. When the γ motor neurons are inhibited, the spindle resembles a loose rubber band and is nonresponsive, and the extrafusal muscles relax.

The ability to modify the stretch reflex is important in many situations. As the speed and difficulty of a movement increase, the brain increases γ motor output to make the muscle spindles more sensitive. This sensitivity is highest when balance reflexes must be razor sharp, as for a gymnast on a balance beam. On the other hand, if you want to wind up to pitch a baseball, it is essential to suppress the stretch reflex so that your muscles can

produce a large degree of motion (i.e., circumduct your pitching arm). Other athletes who require movements of maximum force learn to stretch muscles as much and as quickly as possible just before the movement. This advantage is demonstrated by the crouch that athletes assume just before jumping or running.

As we have seen, muscle tone and smooth coordination of movement depend upon intact stretch reflex pathways. Both afferent and efferent fibers to the muscle spindle are vitally important. If either afferent or efferent fibers are cut, the muscle immediately loses its tone and becomes flaccid.

The Tendon Reflex

Stretch reflexes cause muscle contraction in response to increased muscle length (stretch). The polysynaptic **tendon reflexes**, on the other hand, produce exactly the opposite effect: Muscles relax and lengthen in response to tension.

When muscle tension increases substantially during contraction or passive stretching, high-threshold *tendon organs* may be activated. Afferent impulses are transmitted to the spinal cord, and then to the cerebellum, where the information is used to adjust muscle tension. Simultaneously, motor neurons in spinal cord circuits supplying the contracting muscle are inhibited and antagonist muscles are activated, a phenomenon called **reciprocal activation**. As a result, the contracting muscle relaxes as its antagonist is activated **(Figure 13.19)**.

Tendon organs help to prevent muscles and tendons from tearing when they are subjected to possibly damaging stretching force. Tendon organs also function at normal muscle tensions. In the normal range, tendon organs help to ensure smooth onset and termination of muscle contraction.

13

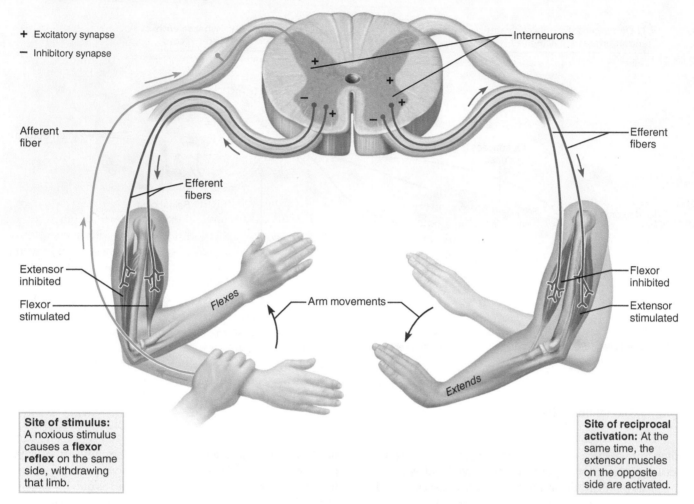

+ Excitatory synapse
− Inhibitory synapse

Interneurons

Afferent fiber

Efferent fibers

Efferent fibers

Extensor inhibited

Flexor stimulated

Flexes

Arm movements

Flexor inhibited

Extensor stimulated

Extends

Site of stimulus: A noxious stimulus causes a **flexor reflex** on the same side, withdrawing that limb.

Site of reciprocal activation: At the same time, the extensor muscles on the opposite side are activated.

Figure 13.20 The crossed-extensor reflex. In this example, a stranger suddenly grasps the right arm, which is withdrawn reflexively while the opposite (left) arm reflexively extends and pushes the stranger away.

The Flexor and Crossed-Extensor Reflexes

A painful stimulus initiates the **flexor**, or **withdrawal**, **reflex**, which causes automatic withdrawal of the threatened body part from the stimulus (**Figure 13.20**, left). Think of the response that occurs when you prick your finger. Flexor reflexes are ipsilateral and polysynaptic, the latter a necessity when several muscles must be recruited to withdraw the injured body part.

Because flexor reflexes are protective and important to our survival, they override the spinal pathways and prevent any other reflexes from using them at the same time. However, like other spinal reflexes, descending signals from the brain can override flexor reflexes. This happens when you are expecting a painful stimulus, for example a skin prick as a lab technician prepares to draw blood from a vein.

The **crossed-extensor reflex** often accompanies the flexor reflex in weight-bearing limbs and is particularly important in maintaining balance. It is a complex spinal reflex consisting of an ipsilateral withdrawal reflex and a contralateral extensor reflex. Incoming afferent fibers synapse with interneurons that control the flexor withdrawal response on the same side of the body and with other interneurons that control the extensor muscles on the opposite side.

The crossed-extensor reflex is obvious when you step barefoot on broken glass. The ipsilateral response causes you to quickly lift your cut foot, while the contralateral response activates the extensor muscles of your opposite leg to support the weight suddenly shifted to it. The crossed-extensor reflex also occurs when someone unexpectedly grabs your arm. The grasped arm is withdrawn as the opposite arm pushes you away from the attacker (Figure 13.20).

Superficial Reflexes

Superficial reflexes are elicited by gentle cutaneous stimulation, such as that produced by stroking the skin with a tongue depressor. These clinically important reflexes depend both on functional upper motor pathways and on cord-level reflex arcs. The best known are the plantar and abdominal reflexes.

Plantar Reflex

The **plantar reflex** tests the integrity of the spinal cord from L_4 to S_2 and indirectly determines if the corticospinal tracts are functioning properly. To elicit the plantar reflex, draw a blunt object downward along the lateral aspect of the plantar surface (sole) of the foot. The normal response is for the toes to flex downward (curl). However, if the primary motor cortex or corticospinal tract is damaged, the plantar reflex is replaced by an abnormal reflex called **Babinski's sign**, in which the great toe dorsiflexes and the smaller toes fan laterally.

Infants exhibit Babinski's sign until they are about a year old because their nervous systems are incompletely myelinated. Despite its clinical significance, the physiological mechanism of Babinski's sign is not understood.

Abdominal Reflexes

Stroking the skin of the lateral abdomen above, to the side, or below the umbilicus induces a reflex contraction of the abdominal muscles in which the umbilicus moves toward the stimulated site. These reflexes, called **abdominal reflexes**, check the integrity of the spinal cord and ventral rami from T_8 to T_{12}.

Abdominal reflexes vary in intensity from one person to another. However, their absence indicates lesions in the corticospinal tract.

☑ Check Your Understanding

14. Name the five components of a reflex arc.
15. What is the role of the stretch reflex? The flexor reflex?
16. Juan injured his back in a fall. When his ER physician stroked the bottom of Juan's foot, she noted that his big toe pointed up and his other toes fanned out. What is this response called and what does it indicate?

For answers, see Appendix H.

Developmental Aspects of the Peripheral Nervous System

✓ Describe the developmental relationship between the segmented arrangement of peripheral nerves, skeletal muscles, and skin dermatomes.

✓ List changes that occur in the peripheral nervous system with aging.

Most skeletal muscles derive from paired blocks of mesoderm (somites) distributed segmentally down the posteromedial aspect of the embryo. The spinal nerves branch from the developing spinal cord and adjacent neural crest and exit between the forming vertebrae, and each nerve becomes associated with the adjacent muscle mass. The spinal nerves supply both sensory and motor fibers to the developing muscles and help direct their maturation. Cranial nerves innervate muscles of the head in a comparable manner.

The distribution of cutaneous nerves to the skin follows a similar pattern. The trigeminal nerves innervate most of the scalp and facial skin. Spinal nerves supply cutaneous branches to specific (adjacent) dermatomes that eventually become dermal segments. As a result, the distribution and growth of the spinal nerves correlate with the segmented body plan, which is established by the fourth week of embryonic development.

Growth of the limbs and unequal growth of other body areas result in an adult pattern of dermatomes with unequal sizes and shapes and varying degrees of overlap. Because embryonic muscle cells migrate extensively, much of the early segmental pattern is lost.

It's crucial that physicians understand the general pattern of sensory nerve distribution. For example, in areas where several dermatomes overlap, two or three spinal nerves must be blocked (anesthetized) to perform local surgery.

Sensory receptors atrophy to some degree with age, and muscle tone decreases in the face and neck. Reflexes occur a bit more slowly during old age. This deterioration seems to reflect a general loss of neurons, fewer synapses per neuron, and a slowdown in central processing rather than any major changes in the peripheral nerve fibers. In fact, peripheral nerves remain viable and normally functional throughout life unless subjected to traumatic injury or ischemia. The most common symptoms of ischemia are sensations of tingling or numbness in the affected region.

☑ Check Your Understanding

17. Segmentation in the embryo gives rise to segmentation in the adult. Name two examples of segmentation in the adult body.

For answers, see Appendix H.

The PNS is an essential part of any functional nervous system. Without it, the CNS would lack its rich bank of information about events of the external and internal environments. Now that we have connected the CNS to both of these environments, we are ready to consider the autonomic nervous system, the topic of Chapter 14.

Chapter Summary

 For more chapter study tools, go to the Study Area of MasteringA&P at **www.masteringaandp.com**.
There you will find:

- Interactive Physiology **iP**
- A&PFlix **A&PFlix**
- Practice Anatomy Lab **PAL**
- PhysioEx **PEx**
- Videos, Practice Quizzes and Tests, MP3 Tutor Sessions, Case Studies, and much more!

1. The peripheral nervous system consists of sensory receptors, nerves conducting impulses to and from the CNS, their associated ganglia, and motor endings.

PART 1 Sensory Receptors and Sensation

Sensory Receptors (pp. 484–487)

1. Sensory receptors are specialized to respond to environmental changes (stimuli).
2. Sensory receptors include the receptors for the general senses—pain, touch, pressure, and temperature receptors in the skin—as

well as receptors in skeletal muscles and tendons and in the visceral organs. Sense organs contain sensory receptors and other cells that serve the special senses (vision, hearing, equilibrium, smell, and taste).

3. Receptors are classified according to stimulus detected as mechanoreceptors, thermoreceptors, photoreceptors, chemoreceptors, and nociceptors, and according to location as exteroceptors, interoceptors, and proprioceptors.

4. The general sensory receptors are classified structurally as free or encapsulated nerve endings of sensory neurons. The free endings are mainly receptors for temperature and pain, although two are for light touch (tactile discs and hair follicle receptors). The encapsulated endings, which are mechanoreceptors, include tactile corpuscles, lamellar corpuscles, bulbous corpuscles, muscle spindles, tendon organs, and joint kinesthetic receptors.

Sensory Integration: From Sensation to Perception (pp. 487–490)

1. Sensation is awareness of internal and external stimuli. Perception is conscious interpretation of those stimuli.

2. The three levels of sensory integration are the receptor, circuit, and perceptual levels. These levels are functions of the sensory receptors, the ascending pathways, and the cerebral cortex, respectively.

3. Sensory receptors transduce (convert) stimulus energy via receptor or generator potentials into action potentials. Stimulus strength is frequency coded. Adaptation (decreased response to a continuous or unchanging stimulus) occurs in all general receptors except pain and proprioceptors.

4. The circuit level consists of the ascending pathways—the axons of the first-, second-, and third-order sensory neurons. These were discussed in Chapter 12.

5. Perception—the internal, conscious image of the stimulus that serves as the basis for response—is the result of cortical processing.

6. The main features of sensory perception are perceptual detection, magnitude estimation, spatial discrimination, feature abstraction, quality discrimination, and pattern recognition.

PART 2 Transmission Lines: Nerves and Their Structure and Repair

Nerves and Associated Ganglia   (pp. 490–492)

1. A nerve is a bundle of axons in the PNS. Each fiber is enclosed by an endoneurium, fascicles of fibers are wrapped by a perineurium, and the whole nerve is bundled by the epineurium.

2. Nerves are classified according to the direction of impulse conduction as sensory, motor, or mixed; most nerves are mixed. Efferent fibers may be somatic or autonomic.

3. Ganglia are collections of neuron cell bodies associated with nerves in the PNS. Examples are the dorsal root (sensory) ganglia and autonomic (motor) ganglia.

4. Injured PNS fibers may regenerate if macrophages enter the area, phagocytize the debris, and promote the proliferation of Schwann cells. Schwann cells then form a channel and secrete chemicals to guide axon sprouts to their original contacts. Fibers in the CNS do not normally regenerate because the oligodendrocytes inhibit axonal sprouting and regrowth.

Cranial Nerves   (pp. 492–501)

1. Twelve pairs of cranial nerves issue through the skull to innervate the head and neck. Only the vagus nerves extend into the thoracic and abdominal cavities. All but the accessory nerve originate from the brain.

2. Cranial nerves are (generally) numbered from rostral to caudal in order of emergence from the brain. Their names reflect structures served or function or both. The cranial nerves and their numbers are

   I. Olfactory nerves: purely sensory. Concerned with the sense of smell.

   II. Optic nerves: purely sensory. Transmit visual impulses from the retina to the thalamus.

   III. Oculomotor nerves: primarily motor. Emerge from the midbrain and serve four extrinsic eye muscles, the levator palpebrae superioris of the eyelid, and the intrinsic ciliary muscle of the eye and constrictor fibers of the iris. Also carry proprioceptive impulses from the skeletal muscles served.

   IV. Trochlear nerves: primarily motor. Issue from the dorsal midbrain and carry motor and proprioceptor impulses to and from superior oblique muscles of the eyeballs.

   V. Trigeminal nerves: mixed nerves. Emerge from the lateral pons as the main general sensory nerves of the face. Each has three sensory divisions: ophthalmic, maxillary, and mandibular. The mandibular branch also contains motor fibers that innervate the chewing muscles.

   VI. Abducens nerves: primarily motor. Emerge from the pons and serve the motor and proprioceptive functions of the lateral rectus muscles of the eyeballs.

   VII. Facial nerves: mixed nerves. Emerge from the pons as the major motor nerves of the face. Also carry sensory impulses from the taste buds of anterior two-thirds of the tongue.

   VIII. Vestibulocochlear nerves: mostly sensory. Transmit impulses from the hearing and equilibrium receptors of the inner ears.

   IX. Glossopharyngeal nerves: mixed nerves. Issue from the medulla. Transmit sensory impulses from the taste buds of the posterior tongue, the pharynx, and chemo- and baroreceptors of the carotid bodies and sinuses. Innervate some pharyngeal muscles and parotid glands.

   X. Vagus nerves: mixed nerves. Arise from the medulla. Almost all motor fibers are autonomic parasympathetic fibers; motor efferents to, and sensory fibers from, the pharynx, larynx, and visceral organs of the thoracic and abdominal cavities.

   XI. Accessory nerves: primarily motor. Arise as spinal rootlets from the cervical spinal cord and enter the foramen magnum. Supply somatic efferents to the trapezius and sternocleidomastoid muscles of the neck and carry proprioceptor afferents from the same muscles.

   XII. Hypoglossal nerves: primarily motor. Issue from the medulla and carry somatic motor efferents to, and proprioceptive fibers from, the tongue muscles.

Spinal Nerves   (pp. 501–511)

1. The 31 pairs of spinal nerves (all mixed nerves) are numbered successively according to the region of the spinal cord from which they issue.

2. Dorsal and ventral roots of the spinal cord fuse to form spinal nerves. Spinal nerves are short, confined to the intervertebral foramina.

3. Branches of each spinal nerve include dorsal and ventral rami, a meningeal branch, and in the thoracic region, rami communicantes (ANS branches).

4. Ventral rami, except T_2–T_{12}, form plexuses that serve the limbs.

5. The cervical plexus (C_1–C_4) innervates the muscles and skin of the neck and shoulder. Its phrenic nerve serves the diaphragm.

6. The brachial plexus serves the shoulder, some thorax muscles, and the upper limb. It arises primarily from C_5–T_1. Proximal to distal, the brachial plexus has roots, trunks, divisions, and cords. The main nerves arising from the cords are the axillary, musculocutaneous, median, radial, and ulnar nerves.

7. The lumbar plexus (L_1–L_4) provides the motor supply to the anterior and medial thigh muscles and the cutaneous supply to the anterior thigh and part of the leg. Its chief nerves are the femoral and obturator.

8. The sacral plexus (L_4–S_4) supplies the posterior muscles and skin of the lower limb. Its principal nerve is the large sciatic nerve composed of the tibial and common fibular nerves.

9. Dorsal rami serve the muscles and skin of the posterior body trunk. T_1–T_{12} ventral rami give rise to intercostal nerves that serve the thorax wall and abdominal surface.

10. Joints are innervated by the same nerves that serve the muscles acting at the joint. All spinal nerves except C_1 innervate specific segments of the skin called dermatomes.

PART 3 **Motor Endings and Motor Activity**

Peripheral Motor Endings   (p. 511)

1. Motor endings of somatic nerve fibers (axon terminals) form neuromuscular junctions with skeletal muscle cells. Axon terminals contain synaptic vesicles filled with acetylcholine, which (when released) signals the muscle cell to contract. An elaborate basal lamina fills the synaptic cleft.

2. Autonomic motor endings, called varicosities, are functionally similar, but structurally simpler, beaded terminals that innervate smooth muscle and glands. They do not form specialized neuromuscular junctions and the motor responses elicited are generally slower.

Motor Integration: From Intention to Effect (pp. 511–513)

1. Motor mechanisms operate at the level of the effectors (muscle fibers), descending circuits, and control levels of motor behavior.

2. The motor control hierarchy consists of the segmental level, the projection level, and the precommand level.

3. The segmental level is the spinal cord circuitry that activates ventral horn motor neurons to stimulate the muscles. It consists of reflexes and central pattern generators (CPGs), segmental circuits controlling locomotion.

4. The projection level consists of descending fibers that project to and control the segmental level. These fibers issue from the brain stem motor areas (indirect system) and cortical motor areas [direct (pyramidal) system]. Neurons in the brain stem appear to turn CPGs on and off, or to modulate them.

5. The cerebellum and basal nuclei constitute the precommand areas that subconsciously integrate mechanisms mediated by the projection level.

PART 4 **Reflex Activity**

The Reflex Arc   (p. 513)

1. A reflex is a rapid, involuntary motor response to a stimulus. The reflex arc has five elements: receptor, sensory neuron, integration center, motor neuron, and effector.

Spinal Reflexes   (pp. 513–519)

1. Testing of somatic spinal reflexes provides information on the integrity of the reflex pathway and the degree of excitability of the spinal cord.

2. Somatic spinal reflexes include stretch, tendon, flexor, crossed-extensor, and superficial reflexes.

3. A stretch reflex, initiated by stretching of muscle spindles, causes contraction of the stimulated muscle and inhibits its antagonist. It is monosynaptic and ipsilateral. Stretch reflexes maintain muscle tone and body posture.

4. Tendon reflexes, initiated by stimulation of tendon organs by excessive muscle tension, are polysynaptic reflexes. They cause relaxation of the stimulated muscle and contraction of its antagonist to prevent muscle and tendon damage.

5. Flexor reflexes are initiated by painful stimuli. They are polysynaptic, ipsilateral reflexes that are protective in nature.

6. Crossed-extensor reflexes consist of an ipsilateral flexor reflex and a contralateral extensor reflex.

7. Superficial reflexes (plantar and abdominal reflexes) are elicited by cutaneous stimulation. They require functional cord reflex arcs and corticospinal pathways.

Developmental Aspects of the Peripheral Nervous System   (p. 519)

1. Each spinal nerve provides the sensory and motor supply of an adjacent muscle mass (destined to become skeletal muscles) and the cutaneous supply of a dermatome (skin segment).

2. Reflexes slow down with age; this probably reflects neuronal loss or sluggish CNS integration circuits.

Review Questions

Multiple Choice/Matching

(Some questions have more than one correct answer. Select the best answer or answers from the choices given.)

1. The large onion-shaped receptors that are found deep in the dermis and in subcutaneous tissue and that respond to deep pressure are (a) tactile discs, (b) lamellar corpuscles, (c) free nerve endings, (d) muscle spindles.

2. Proprioceptors include all of the following except (a) muscle spindles, (b) tendon organs, (c) tactile discs, (d) joint kinesthetic receptors.

3. The aspect of sensory perception by which the cerebral cortex identifies the site or pattern of stimulation is (a) perceptual detection, (b) feature abstraction, (c) pattern recognition, (d) spatial discrimination.

4. The neural machinery of the spinal cord is at the (a) precommand level, (b) projection level, (c) segmental level.

5. Dorsal root ganglia contain (a) cell bodies of somatic motor neurons, (b) axon terminals of somatic motor neurons, (c) cell bodies of autonomic motor neurons, (d) axon terminals of sensory neurons, (e) cell bodies of sensory neurons.

6. The connective tissue sheath that surrounds a fascicle of nerve fibers is the (a) epineurium, (b) endoneurium, (c) perineurium, (d) epimysium.

7. Match the receptor type in column B to the correct description in column A.

Column A	Column B
____ **(1)** pain, itch, and temperature receptors	**(a)** bulbous corpuscles
____ **(2)** contains intrafusal fibers and anulospiral and flower spray endings	**(b)** tendon organ
____ **(3)** discriminative touch receptor in hairless skin (fingertips)	**(c)** muscle spindle
	(d) free nerve endings
	(e) lamellar corpuscle
	(f) tactile corpuscle
____ **(4)** contains receptor endings wrapped around thick collagen bundles	
____ **(5)** rapidly adapting deep-pressure receptor	
____ **(6)** slowly adapting deep-pressure receptor	

8. Match the names of the cranial nerves in column B to the appropriate description in column A.

Column A	Column B
____ **(1)** causes pupillary constriction	**(a)** abducens
____ **(2)** the major sensory nerve of the face	**(b)** accessory
	(c) facial
____ **(3)** serves the sternocleidomastoid and trapezius muscles	**(d)** glossopharyngeal
	(e) hypoglossal
	(f) oculomotor
____ **(4)** purely sensory (two nerves)	**(g)** olfactory
____ **(5)** serves the tongue muscles	**(h)** optic
____ **(6)** allows you to chew your food	**(i)** trigeminal
	(j) trochlear
____ **(7)** impaired in Bell's palsy	**(k)** vagus
____ **(8)** helps regulate heart activity	**(l)** vestibulocochlear
____ **(9)** helps you hear and maintain your balance	

____, ____, ____, ____, **(10)** contain parasympathetic motor fibers (four nerves)

9. For each of the following muscles or body regions, identify the plexus and the peripheral nerve(s) (or branch of one) involved. Use choices from keys A and B.

____; ____ **(1)** the diaphragm
____; ____ **(2)** muscles of the posterior leg
____; ____ **(3)** anterior thigh muscles
____; ____ **(4)** medial thigh muscles
____; ____ **(5)** anterior arm muscles that flex the forearm
____; ____ **(6)** muscles that flex the wrist and digits (two nerves)
____; ____ **(7)** muscles that extend the wrist and digits
____; ____ **(8)** skin and extensor muscles of the posterior arm
____; ____ **(9)** fibularis muscles, tibialis anterior, and toe extensors
____; ____, ____, ____, **(10)** elbow joint

Key A: Plexuses

(a) brachial
(b) cervical
(c) lumbar
(d) sacral

Key B: Nerves

(1) common fibular
(2) femoral
(3) median
(4) musculocutaneous
(5) obturator
(6) phrenic
(7) radial
(8) tibial
(9) ulnar

10. Characterize each receptor activity described below by choosing the appropriate letter and number(s) from keys A and B.

____, ____ **(1)** You are enjoying an ice cream cone.
____, ____ **(2)** You have just scalded yourself with hot coffee.
____, ____ **(3)** The retinas of your eyes are stimulated.
____, ____ **(4)** You bump (lightly) into someone.
____, ____ **(5)** You are in a completely dark room and reaching toward the light switch.
____, ____ **(6)** You feel uncomfortable after a large meal.

Key A:

(a) exteroceptor
(b) interoceptor
(c) proprioceptor

Key B:

(1) chemoreceptor
(2) mechanoreceptor
(3) nociceptor
(4) photoreceptor
(5) thermoreceptor

11. A reflex that causes reciprocal activation of the antagonist muscle is the **(a)** crossed-extensor, **(b)** flexor, **(c)** tendon, **(d)** muscle stretch.

Short Answer Essay Questions

12. What is the functional relationship of the peripheral nervous system to the central nervous system?

13. List the structural components of the peripheral nervous system, and describe the function of each component.

14. Differentiate clearly between sensation and perception.

15. Central pattern generators (CPGs) are found at the segmental level of motor control. (a) What is the job of the CPGs? (b) What controls them, and where is this control localized?

16. Make a diagram of the hierarchy of motor control. Position the CPGs, motor cortex, brain stem nuclei, cerebellum, and basal nuclei in this scheme.

17. Why are the cerebellum and basal nuclei called precommand areas?

18. Explain why damage to peripheral nerve fibers is often reversible, whereas damage to CNS fibers rarely is.

19. (a) Describe the formation and composition of a spinal nerve. (b) Name the branches of a spinal nerve (other than the rami communicantes), and indicate their distribution.

20. (a) Define plexus. (b) Indicate the spinal roots of origin of the four major nerve plexuses, and name the general body regions served by each.

21. Differentiate between ipsilateral and contralateral reflexes.

22. What is the homeostatic value of flexor reflexes?

23. Compare and contrast flexor and crossed-extensor reflexes.

24. Explain how a crossed-extensor reflex exemplifies both serial and parallel processing.

25. What clinical information can be gained by conducting somatic reflex tests?

26. What is the structural and functional relationship between spinal nerves, skeletal muscles, and dermatomes?

Critical Thinking and Clinical Application Questions

1. In 1962 a boy playing in a train yard fell under a train. The train wheel cleanly cut off his right arm. Surgeons reattached the arm, sewing nerves and vessels back together. The boy was told he should eventually regain the use of his arm but that it would never be strong enough to pitch a baseball. Explain why full recovery of strength was unlikely.

2. Jefferson, a football quarterback, suffered torn menisci in his right knee joint when tackled from the side. The same injury crushed his common fibular nerve against the head of the fibula. What locomotor problems did Jefferson have after this?

3. As Harry fell off a ladder, he grabbed a tree branch with his right hand, but unfortunately lost his grip and fell heavily to the ground. Days later, Harry complained that his upper limb was numb. What was damaged in his fall?

4. Mr. Frank, a former stroke victim who had made a remarkable recovery, suddenly began to have problems reading. He complained of seeing double and also had problems navigating steps. He was unable to move his left eye downward and laterally. Which cranial nerve was the site of lesion? (Right or left?)

5. One of a group of rabbit hunters was accidentally sprayed with buckshot in both of his gluteal prominences. When his companions saw that he would survive, they laughed and joked about where he had been shot. They were horrified and ashamed a week later when they learned their friend would be

permanently paralyzed and without sensation in both legs from the knee down, as well as on the back of his thighs. What had happened?

6. You are at a party at Mary's house. After you are blindfolded, an object (a key or a rabbit's foot) is placed in your hand. Which spinal tracts carry the signals to the cortex that will allow you to differentiate between these objects, and what aspects of sensory perception are operating?

7. Mr. Jake was admitted to the hospital with excruciating pain in his left shoulder and arm. He was found to have suffered a heart attack. Explain the phenomenon of referred pain as exhibited by Mr. Jake.

AT THE CLINIC

Related Clinical Terms

Analgesia (an"al-je'zeah; *an* = without; *algos* = pain) Reduced ability to feel pain, but without losing consciousness. An analgesic is a pain-relieving drug.

Dysarthria (dis-ar'thre-ah) Difficulty in articulating speech due to motor pathway disorders that result in weakness, uncoordinated motion, or altered respiration or rhythm. For example, lesions of cranial nerves IX, X, and XII result in nasal, breathy speech, and lesions in upper motor pathways produce a hoarse, strained voice. Not to be confused with *dysphasia* or *aphasia*, which are disorders of language processing.

Dystonia (dis-to'ne-ah) Impaired muscle tone.

Nerve conduction studies Diagnostic tests that assess nerve integrity as indicated by their conduction velocities. The nerve is stimulated at one point, activity is recorded at a second point a known distance away, and the time required for the response to reach the recording electrode is measured. Used to assess suspected *peripheral neuropathies* (see entry in this list).

Neuralgia (nu-ral'je-ah; *neuro* = nerve) Sharp spasmlike pain along the course of one or more nerves. May be caused by inflammation or injury to the nerve(s) (for example, trigeminal neuralgia).

Paresthesia (par"es-the'ze-ah) An abnormal sensation (burning, numbness, tingling) in the absence of stimuli. Caused by a sensory nerve disorder.

Peripheral neuropathy (nu-rop'ah-the) Disease of the peripheral nerves characterized by muscle weakness and atrophy, pain, and numbness. Diabetes is a common cause. Other causes are genetic, other metabolic disorders, infections or inflammation, and toxins.

Tabes dorsalis (ta'bēz dor-sa'lis) A slowly progressive condition caused by deteriorating dorsal tracts (gracilis and cuneatus) and associated dorsal roots. A late sign of the neurological damage caused by the syphilis bacterium. Because joint proprioceptor tracts are destroyed, affected individuals have poor muscle coordination and an unstable gait. Bacterial invasion of the sensory (dorsal) roots results in pain, which ends when dorsal roots have been completely destroyed.

Case Study   Peripheral Nervous System

William Hancock, a 44-year-old male, was a passenger on the bus involved in the accident on Route 91. When emergency personnel arrived on the scene, they found Mr. Hancock unconscious, but with stable vital signs. As paramedics placed him on a backboard to stabilize his head, neck, and back, they noted watery blood leaking from his right ear. In the hospital, Mr. Hancock regained consciousness and was treated for deep lacerations on his scalp and face. Head CT scans revealed both longitudinal and transverse fractures of the right petrous temporal and sphenoid bones that extended through the foramen rotundum and foramen ovale.

The following observations were recorded on Mr. Hancock's chart on admission:

- Complete loss of hearing in the right ear.
- Paresthesia (sensation of "pins and needles") at the right corner of the mouth, extending to the lower lip and chin.
- Numbness of the right upper lip, lower eyelid, and cheek.
- Right eye turned slightly inward when looking straight ahead. Diplopia (double vision), particularly when looking to the right.

Mr. Hancock was given a course of antibiotics, the head of his bed was elevated by 30°, and he was placed under close observation. After 24 hours, doctors noted that the right side of Mr. Hancock's face showed signs of drooping, with incomplete eye closure and asymmetric facial expressions. Mr. Hancock's right eye showed minimal tear production. The weakness and asymmetry on the right side of his face began to subside after a few days, and the leak of fluid from his ear stopped, but he continued to complain of paresthesia, diplopia, and an inability to hear with his right ear.

1. In addition to blood, which fluid was leaking from Mr. Hancock's right ear? Which structures must have been damaged to allow this to happen? Why would this lead Mr. Hancock's doctors to give him antibiotics? Why was the head of his bed elevated?

2. Each of the four observations on Mr. Hancock's chart indicates damage to a cranial nerve. Identify each cranial nerve involved. If applicable, identify which specific branch of that nerve is involved.

3. The observations after 24 hours suggest that yet another cranial nerve has been damaged. Which one? How can you explain the lack of tear production in the right eye?

(Answers in Appendix H)

14

The Autonomic Nervous System

The human body is exquisitely sensitive to changes in its internal environment, and engages in a lifelong struggle to balance competing demands for resources under ever-changing conditions. Although all body systems contribute, the stability of our internal environment depends largely on the **autonomic nervous system (ANS)**, the system of motor neurons that innervates smooth and cardiac muscle and glands (**Figure 14.1**).

At every moment, signals stream from visceral organs into the CNS, and autonomic nerves make adjustments as necessary to ensure optimal support for body activities. In response to changing conditions, the ANS shunts blood to "needy" areas, speeds or slows heart rate, adjusts blood pressure and body temperature, and increases or decreases stomach secretions.

Most of this fine-tuning occurs without our awareness or attention. Can you tell when your arteries are constricting or your pupils are dilating? Probably not—but if you've ever been stuck in a checkout line, and your full bladder was contracting as if it had a mind of its own, you've been very aware of visceral activity. The ANS controls all these functions, both those we're aware of and those we're not. Indeed, as the term *autonomic* (*auto* = self; *nom* = govern) implies, this motor subdivision of the peripheral nervous system has a certain amount of functional independence. The ANS is also called the **involuntary nervous system**, which reflects its subconscious control, or the **general visceral motor system**, which indicates the location of most of its effectors.

Overview

✓ Define autonomic nervous system and explain its relationship to the peripheral nervous system.

✓ Compare the somatic and autonomic nervous systems relative to effectors, efferent pathways, and neurotransmitters released.

✓ Compare and contrast the functions of the parasympathetic and sympathetic divisions.

Figure 14.1 Place of the ANS in the structural organization of the nervous system.

Comparison of the Somatic and Autonomic Nervous Systems

In our previous discussions of motor nerves, we have focused largely on the somatic nervous system. So, before describing autonomic nervous system anatomy, let's point out key differences between the somatic and autonomic systems as well as areas of functional overlap.

Both systems have motor fibers, but the somatic and autonomic nervous systems differ in: (1) their effectors, (2) their efferent pathways and ganglia, and (3) target organ responses to their neurotransmitters. Consult **Figure 14.2** for a summary of the differences as we discuss them next.

Effectors

The somatic nervous system stimulates skeletal muscles, whereas the ANS innervates cardiac and smooth muscle and glands. Differences in the physiology of the effector organs account for most of the remaining differences between somatic and autonomic effects on their target organs.

Efferent Pathways and Ganglia

In the somatic nervous system, the motor neuron cell bodies are in the CNS, and their axons extend in spinal or cranial nerves all the way to the skeletal muscles they activate. Somatic motor fibers are typically thick, heavily myelinated group A fibers that conduct nerve impulses rapidly.

In contrast, the ANS uses a *two-neuron chain* to reach its effectors:

1. The cell body of the first neuron, the **preganglionic neuron**, resides in the brain or spinal cord. Its axon, the **preganglionic axon**, synapses with the second motor neuron.
2. The **postganglionic neuron** (sometimes called the *ganglionic neuron*), is the second motor neuron. Its cell body is in an **autonomic ganglion** outside the CNS. Its axon, the **postganglionic axon,** extends to the effector organ.

If you think about the meanings of all these terms while referring to Figure 14.2, understanding the rest of the chapter will be much easier.

Preganglionic axons are thin, lightly myelinated fibers, and postganglionic axons are even thinner and nonmyelinated. Consequently, conduction through the autonomic efferent chain is slower than conduction in the somatic motor system. For most of their course, many pre- and postganglionic fibers are incorporated into spinal or cranial nerves.

Keep in mind that autonomic ganglia are *motor* ganglia, containing the cell bodies of motor neurons. Technically, they are sites of synapse and information transmission from preganglionic to postganglionic neurons. Also, remember that the somatic motor division *lacks* ganglia entirely. The dorsal root ganglia are part of the sensory, not the motor, division of the PNS.

Neurotransmitter Effects

All somatic motor neurons release **acetylcholine (ACh)** at their synapses with skeletal muscle fibers. The effect is always *excitatory*, and if stimulation reaches threshold, the muscle fibers contract.

Autonomic postganglionic fibers release two neurotransmitters: **norepinephrine (NE)** secreted by most sympathetic fibers, and ACh secreted by parasympathetic fibers. Depending on the type of receptors on the target organ, the effect may be excitatory or inhibitory (Figure 14.2; see Table 14.2 on p. 534).

Overlap of Somatic and Autonomic Function

Higher brain centers regulate and coordinate both somatic and autonomic motor activities, and most spinal nerves (and many cranial nerves) contain both somatic and autonomic fibers. Moreover, most of the body's adaptations to changing internal and external conditions involve both skeletal muscles and visceral organs. For example, when skeletal muscles are working hard, they need more oxygen and glucose, so autonomic

Cell bodies in central nervous system	Peripheral nervous system		Neurotransmitter at effector	Effector organs	Effect

Acetylcholine (ACh) Norepinephrine (NE)

Figure 14.2 Comparison of motor neurons in the somatic and autonomic nervous systems.

control mechanisms speed up heart rate and dilate airways to meet these needs and maintain homeostasis.

Next, we will describe the role of the ANS. But as you read, remember that the ANS does not act in isolation—it is only one part of our highly integrated nervous system.

ANS Divisions

The ANS has two arms, parasympathetic and sympathetic. The *parasympathetic division* promotes maintenance functions and conserves body energy, whereas the *sympathetic division* mobilizes the body during activity.

Both divisions generally serve the same visceral organs but cause opposite effects: While one division stimulates certain smooth muscles to contract or a gland to secrete, the other division inhibits that action. Through this **dual innervation**, the two divisions counterbalance each other to keep body systems running smoothly. Let's elaborate on these functional differences by focusing briefly on extreme situations in which each division exerts primary control.

Role of the Parasympathetic Division

The **parasympathetic division**, sometimes called the "rest and digest" system, keeps body energy use as low as possible, even as it directs vital "housekeeping" activities like digesting food

and eliminating feces and urine. (This explains why it is a good idea to relax after a heavy meal: so sympathetic activity does not interfere with digestion.)

Parasympathetic activity is best illustrated in a person who relaxes after a meal and reads a magazine. Blood pressure and heart rate are regulated at low normal levels, and the gastrointestinal tract is actively digesting food. In the eyes, the pupils are constricted and the lenses are accommodated for close vision to improve the clarity of the close-up image (such as your magazine).

Role of the Sympathetic Division

The activity of the **sympathetic division** (often called the "fight-or-flight" system) is evident when we are excited or find ourselves in emergency or threatening situations, such as being frightened by street toughs late at night. A rapidly pounding heart; deep breathing; dry mouth; cold, sweaty skin; and dilated eye pupils are sure signs of sympathetic nervous system mobilization.

During any type of vigorous physical activity, the sympathetic division also promotes a number of other adjustments. It:

■ Constricts visceral (and sometimes cutaneous) blood vessels, shunting blood to active skeletal muscles and the vigorously working heart

- Dilates the bronchioles in the lungs, increasing ventilation (and thus increasing oxygen delivery to body cells)
- Causes the liver to release more glucose into the blood to accommodate the increased energy needs of body cells

At the same time, the sympathetic division temporarily damps nonessential activities, such as gastrointestinal tract motility. If you are running from a mugger, digesting lunch can wait! It is far more important to give your muscles everything they need to get you out of danger. In such active situations, the sympathetic division generates a head of steam that enables the body to cope with situations that threaten homeostasis. It provides the optimal conditions for an appropriate response to some threat, whether that response is to run, see distant objects better, or think more clearly.

We have just looked at two extreme situations in which one or the other branch of the ANS dominates. Think of the parasympathetic division as the **D** division [digestion, defecation, and diuresis (urination)], and the sympathetic division as the **E** division (exercise, excitement, emergency, embarrassment). Table 14.4 (p. 536) presents a more detailed summary of how each division affects various organs.

Remember, however, that the two ANS divisions rarely work in an all-or-none fashion as described above. A dynamic antagonism exists between the divisions, and both make continuous fine adjustments to maintain homeostasis.

☑ Check Your Understanding

1. Name the three types of effectors of the autonomic nervous system.
2. Which relays instructions from the CNS to muscles more quickly, the somatic nervous system or the ANS? Explain why.
3. Which branch of the ANS would predominate if you were lying on the beach enjoying the sun and the sound of the waves? Which branch would predominate if you were on a surfboard and a shark appeared within a few feet of you?

For answers, see Appendix H.

ANS Anatomy

✓ For the parasympathetic and sympathetic divisions, describe the site of CNS origin, locations of ganglia, and general fiber pathways.

Anatomically, the sympathetic and parasympathetic divisions differ in

- **Sites of origin.** Parasympathetic fibers are craniosacral—they originate in the brain (cranium) and sacral spinal cord. Sympathetic fibers are thoracolumbar—they originate in the thoracic and lumbar regions of the spinal cord.
- **Relative lengths of their fibers.** The parasympathetic division has long preganglionic and short postganglionic fibers. The sympathetic division has the opposite condition—the preganglionic fibers are short and the postganglionic fibers are long.

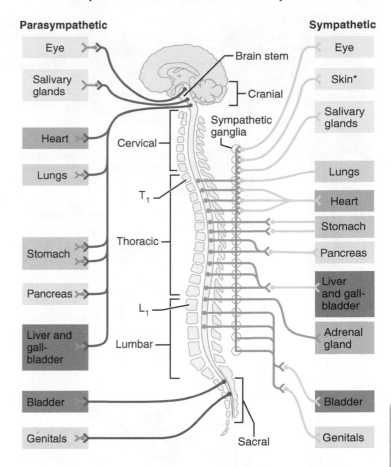

Figure 14.3 The subdivisions of the ANS. The parasympathetic and sympathetic divisions differ anatomically in the (1) sites where their nerves originate, (2) relative lengths of their preganglionic and postganglionic fibers, and (3) locations of their ganglia (indicated here by synapse sites).

*Although sympathetic innervation to the skin is mapped to the cervical region here, all nerves to the periphery carry postganglionic sympathetic fibers.

- **Location of their ganglia.** Most parasympathetic ganglia are located in the visceral effector organs. Sympathetic ganglia lie close to the spinal cord.

Figure 14.3 illustrates these and other key differences, which are summarized in Table 14.1.

We begin our detailed exploration of the ANS with the anatomically simpler parasympathetic division.

Parasympathetic (Craniosacral) Division

The parasympathetic division is also called the **craniosacral division** because its preganglionic fibers spring from opposite ends of the CNS—the brain stem and the sacral region of the spinal cord (Figure 14.4). The preganglionic axons extend from the CNS nearly all the way to the structures they innervate. There the axons synapse with postganglionic neurons located in **terminal ganglia** that lie close to or within the target organs. Very short postganglionic axons issue from the terminal ganglia and synapse with effector cells in their immediate area.

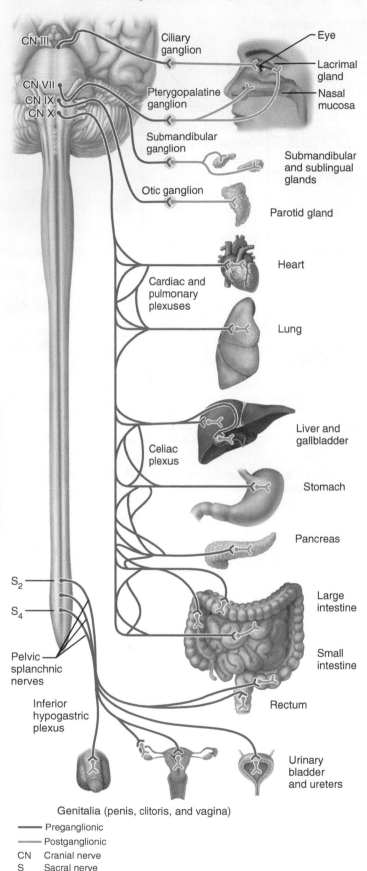

Preganglionic
Postganglionic
CN   Cranial nerve
S   Sacral nerve

Figure 14.4 Parasympathetic division of the ANS.

Cranial Part

Preganglionic fibers run in the oculomotor, facial, glossopharyngeal, and vagus cranial nerves. Their cell bodies lie in associated motor cranial-nerve nuclei in the brain stem (see Figures 12.13 and 12.14). Next, let's look at where the neurons of the cranial parasympathetics are located.

Oculomotor Nerves The parasympathetic fibers of the **oculomotor nerves (III)** innervate smooth muscles in the eyes that cause the pupils to constrict and the lenses to bulge—actions needed to focus on close objects. The preganglionic axons found in the oculomotor nerves issue from the *accessory oculomotor (Edinger-Westphal) nuclei* in the midbrain. The cell bodies of the postganglionic neurons are in the **ciliary ganglia** within the eye orbits (see Table 13.2, p. 495).

Facial Nerves The parasympathetic fibers of the **facial nerves (VII)** stimulate many large glands in the head.

Fibers that activate the nasal glands and the lacrimal glands of the eyes originate in the *lacrimal nuclei* of the pons. The preganglionic fibers synapse with postganglionic neurons in the **pterygopalatine ganglia** (ter″eh-go-pal′ah-tīn) just posterior to the maxillae.

The preganglionic neurons that stimulate the submandibular and sublingual salivary glands originate in the *superior salivatory nuclei* of the pons. They synapse with postganglionic neurons in the **submandibular ganglia**, deep to the mandibular angles (see Table 13.2, p. 497).

Glossopharyngeal Nerves The parasympathetics in the **glossopharyngeal nerves (IX)** originate in the *inferior salivatory nuclei* of the medulla and synapse in the **otic ganglia**, located just inferior to the foramen ovale of the skull. The postganglionic fibers course to and activate the parotid salivary glands anterior to the ears (see Table 13.2, p. 499).

Cranial nerves III, VII, and IX supply the entire parasympathetic innervation of the head. Note that only the *preganglionic* fibers lie within these three pairs of cranial nerves—*postganglionic* fibers do not. Many of the postganglionic fibers "hitch a ride" with branches of the *trigeminal nerve* (*V*), taking advantage of its wide distribution.

Vagus Nerves Between them, the two **vagus nerves (X)** account for about 90% of all preganglionic parasympathetic fibers in the body. They provide fibers to the neck and to nerve plexuses (interweaving networks of nerves) that serve virtually every organ in the thoracic and abdominal cavities.

The vagal nerve fibers (preganglionic axons) arise mostly from the *dorsal motor nuclei* of the medulla and synapse in terminal ganglia usually located in the walls of the target organ. Rather than having individual names, most of the terminal ganglia are collectively called *intramural ganglia*, literally, "ganglia within the walls."

As the vagus nerves pass into the thorax, they send branches to the **cardiac plexuses** supplying fibers to the heart that slow heart rate, the **pulmonary plexuses** serving the lungs and bronchi, and the **esophageal plexuses** (ĕ-sof″ah-je′al) supplying the esophagus.

Table 14.1 Anatomical and Physiological Differences Between the Parasympathetic and Sympathetic Divisions

CHARACTERISTIC	PARASYMPATHETIC	SYMPATHETIC
Origin	Craniosacral part: brain stem nuclei of cranial nerves III, VII, IX, and X; spinal cord segments S_2–S_4.	Thoracolumbar part: lateral horns of gray matter of spinal cord segments T_1–L_2.
Location of ganglia	Ganglia (terminal ganglia) are within the visceral organ (intramural) or close to the organ served.	Ganglia are within a few centimeters of CNS: alongside vertebral column (sympathetic trunk ganglia) and anterior to vertebral column (collateral, or prevertebral, ganglia).
Relative length of pre- and postganglionic fibers	Long preganglionic; short postganglionic.	Short preganglionic; long postganglionic.
Rami communicantes	None.	Gray and white rami communicantes. White rami contain myelinated preganglionic fibers. Gray contain nonmyelinated postganglionic fibers.
Degree of branching of preganglionic fibers	Minimal.	Extensive.
Functional role	Maintenance functions; conserves and stores energy; "rest and digest."	Prepares body for activity; "fight or flight."
Neurotransmitters	All preganglionic and postganglionic fibers release ACh (cholinergic fibers).	All preganglionic fibers release ACh. Most postganglionic fibers release norepinephrine (adrenergic fibers). Postganglionic fibers serving sweat glands release ACh. Neurotransmitter activity is augmented by release of adrenal medullary hormones (norepinephrine and epinephrine).

When the main trunks of the vagus nerves reach the esophagus, their fibers intermingle, forming the **anterior** and **posterior vagal trunks**, each containing fibers from both vagus nerves. These vagal trunks then "ride" the esophagus down to the abdominal cavity. There they send fibers *through* the large **abdominal aortic plexus** [formed by a number of smaller plexuses (e.g., *celiac, superior mesenteric,* and *hypogastric*) that run along the aorta] before giving off branches to the abdominal viscera. The vagus nerves innervate the liver, gallbladder, stomach, small intestine, kidneys, pancreas, and the proximal half of the large intestine.

Sacral Part

The sacral part of the parasympathetic division serves the pelvic organs and the distal half of the large intestine. The sacral part arises from neurons located in the lateral gray matter of spinal cord segments S_2–S_4. Axons of these neurons run in the ventral roots of the spinal nerves to the ventral rami and then branch off to form the **pelvic splanchnic nerves** (splank'nik; *splanchni* = viscera), which pass through the **inferior hypogastric (pelvic) plexus** in the pelvic floor (Figure 14.4). Some preganglionic fibers synapse with ganglia in this plexus, but most synapse in intramural ganglia in the walls of the following organs: distal half of the large intestine, urinary bladder, ureters, and reproductive organs.

Sympathetic (Thoracolumbar) Division

The sympathetic division is anatomically more complex than the parasympathetic division, partly because it innervates more organs. It supplies not only the visceral organs in the internal body cavities but also all visceral structures in the superficial (somatic) part of the body. This sounds impossible, but there is an explanation—some glands and smooth muscle structures in

the soma (sweat glands and the hair-raising arrector pili muscles of the skin) require autonomic innervation and are served only by sympathetic fibers. In addition, sympathetic fibers innervate smooth muscle in the walls of all arteries and veins, both deep and superficial. But we will explain these matters later—let's get on with the anatomy of the sympathetic division.

All preganglionic fibers of the sympathetic division arise from cell bodies of preganglionic neurons in spinal cord segments T_1 through L_2 (Figure 14.3). For this reason, the sympathetic division is also referred to as the **thoracolumbar division** (tho-rah″ko-lum′bar).

The numerous preganglionic sympathetic neurons in the gray matter of the spinal cord form the **lateral horns** (see Figures 12.28b, p. 467, and 12.29, p. 468). The lateral horns are just posterolateral to the ventral horns that house somatic motor neurons. (Parasympathetic preganglionic neurons in the sacral cord are far less abundant than the comparable sympathetic neurons in the thoracolumbar regions, so there are no lateral horns in the sacral region of the spinal cord. This is a major anatomical difference between the two divisions.)

After leaving the cord via the ventral root, preganglionic sympathetic fibers pass through a **white ramus communicans** [plural: **rami communicantes** (kom-mu″nĭ-kan′tēz)] to enter an adjoining **sympathetic trunk ganglion** forming part of the **sympathetic trunk** (or *sympathetic chain*, Figure 14.5). Looking like strands of glistening white beads, the sympathetic trunks flank each side of the vertebral column. They consist of the sympathetic ganglia and fibers running from one ganglion to another. The sympathetic trunk ganglia are also called *chain ganglia* or *paravertebral* ("near the vertebrae") *ganglia*.

Although the sympathetic *trunks* extend from neck to pelvis, sympathetic *fibers* arise only from the thoracic and lumbar

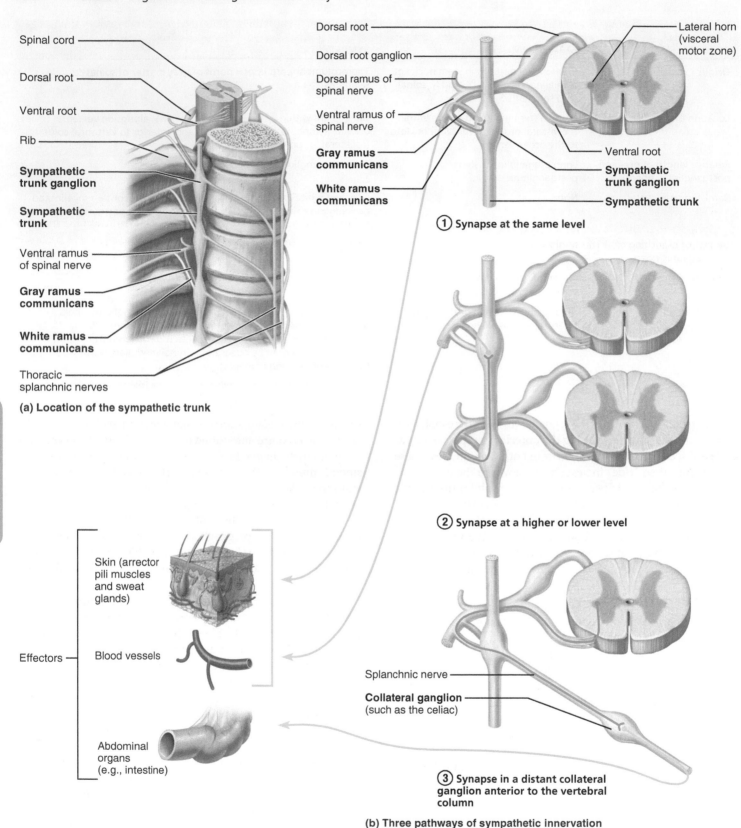

Spinal cord

Dorsal root

Ventral root

Rib

Sympathetic trunk ganglion

Sympathetic trunk

Ventral ramus of spinal nerve

Gray ramus communicans

White ramus communicans

Thoracic splanchnic nerves

(a) Location of the sympathetic trunk

Dorsal root

Dorsal root ganglion

Dorsal ramus of spinal nerve

Ventral ramus of spinal nerve

Gray ramus communicans

White ramus communicans

Lateral horn (visceral motor zone)

Ventral root

Sympathetic trunk ganglion

Sympathetic trunk

① **Synapse at the same level**

② **Synapse at a higher or lower level**

Skin (arrector pili muscles and sweat glands)

Effectors

Blood vessels

Abdominal organs (e.g., intestine)

Splanchnic nerve

Collateral ganglion (such as the celiac)

③ **Synapse in a distant collateral ganglion anterior to the vertebral column**

(b) Three pathways of sympathetic innervation

Figure 14.5 Sympathetic trunks and pathways. (a) Diagram of the right sympathetic trunk in the posterior thorax. **(b)** Synapses between preganglionic and postganglionic sympathetic neurons can occur at three different locations—in a sympathetic trunk ganglion at the same level, in a sympathetic trunk ganglion at a different level, or in a collateral ganglion.

14

cord segments, as shown in Figure 14.3. The ganglia vary in size, position, and number, but typically there are 23 in each sympathetic trunk—3 cervical, 11 thoracic, 4 lumbar, 4 sacral, and 1 coccygeal.

Once a preganglionic axon reaches a trunk ganglion, one of three things can happen to the axon (see the three pathways in Figure 14.5b). The preganglionic and postganglionic neurons can:

1. **Synapse at the same level.** In this case, the synapse is in the same trunk ganglion.

2. **Synapse at a higher or lower level.** The preganglionic axon ascends or descends the sympathetic trunk to another trunk ganglion.

3. **Synapse in a distant collateral ganglion.** The preganglionic axon passes through the trunk ganglion and emerges from the sympathetic trunk without synapsing. These preganglionic fibers help form several *splanchnic nerves* and synapse in **collateral**, or *prevertebral*, **ganglia** located anterior to the vertebral column. Unlike sympathetic trunk ganglia, the collateral ganglia are neither paired nor segmentally arranged. They occur only in the abdomen and pelvis.

Regardless of where the synapse occurs, all sympathetic ganglia are close to the spinal cord, and their postganglionic fibers are typically much longer than their preganglionic fibers. Recall that the opposite condition exists in the parasympathetic division, an important anatomical distinction.

Pathways with Synapses in Trunk Ganglia

When synapses are made in sympathetic trunk ganglia, the postganglionic axons enter the ventral (or dorsal) ramus of the adjoining spinal nerves by way of communicating branches called **gray rami communicantes** (Figure 14.5). From there they travel via branches of the rami to their effectors, including sweat glands and arrector pili muscles of the skin. Anywhere along their path, the postganglionic axons may transfer over to nearby blood vessels and innervate the vascular smooth muscle all the way to the final branches of the blood vessels.

Notice that the names of the rami communicantes—*white* or *gray*—reflect their appearance, revealing whether or not their fibers are myelinated. Preganglionic fibers composing the white rami are myelinated. Postganglionic axons forming the gray rami are not. (This has no relationship to the white and gray matter of the CNS.)

The white rami, which carry preganglionic axons to the sympathetic trunks, are found only in the T_1–L_2 cord segments, regions of sympathetic outflow. However, gray rami carrying postganglionic fibers headed for the periphery issue from every trunk ganglion from the cervical to the sacral region, allowing sympathetic output to reach all parts of the body.

Note that *rami communicantes are associated only with the sympathetic division*. They never carry parasympathetic fibers.

Pathways to the Head Sympathetic preganglionic fibers serving the head emerge from spinal cord segments T_1–T_4 and ascend the sympathetic trunk to synapse with postganglionic neurons in the **superior cervical ganglion** (Figure 14.6). This ganglion contributes sympathetic fibers that run in several cranial nerves and in the upper three or four cervical spinal nerves.

Besides serving the skin and blood vessels of the head, fibers from the superior cervical ganglion stimulate the dilator muscles of the irises of the eyes, inhibit the nasal and salivary glands (the reason your mouth goes dry when you are scared), and innervate the smooth (tarsal) muscle that lifts the upper eyelid. The superior cervical ganglion also sends direct branches to the heart.

Pathways to the Thorax Sympathetic preganglionic fibers innervating the thoracic organs originate at T_1–T_6. From there the preganglionic fibers run to synapse in the cervical trunk ganglia. Postganglionic fibers emerging from the **middle** and **inferior cervical ganglia** enter cervical nerves C_4–C_8 (Figure 14.6). Some of these fibers innervate the heart via the cardiac plexus, and some innervate the thyroid gland, but most serve the skin. Additionally, some T_1–T_6 preganglionic fibers synapse in the nearest trunk ganglion, and the postganglionic fibers pass directly to the organ served. Fibers to the heart, aorta, lungs, and esophagus take this direct route. Along the way, they run through the plexuses associated with those organs.

Pathways with Synapses in Collateral Ganglia

Most of the preganglionic fibers from T_5 down synapse in collateral ganglia, and so most of these fibers enter and leave the sympathetic trunks without synapsing. They form several nerves called **splanchnic nerves**, including the thoracic splanchnic nerves (greater, lesser, and least) and the **lumbar** and **sacral splanchnic nerves**.

The splanchnic nerves contribute to a number of interweaving nerve plexuses known collectively as the *abdominal aortic plexus*, which clings to the surface of the abdominal aorta. This complex plexus contains several ganglia that together serve the abdominopelvic viscera. From superior to inferior, the most important of these ganglia (and related subplexuses) are the **celiac, superior mesenteric**, and **inferior mesenteric**, named for the arteries with which they most closely associate (Figure 14.6). Postganglionic fibers issuing from these ganglia generally travel to their target organs in the company of the arteries serving these organs.

Pathways to the Abdomen Sympathetic preganglionic fibers from T_5 to L_2 innervate the abdomen. They travel in the thoracic splanchnic nerves to synapse mainly at the celiac and superior mesenteric ganglia. Postganglionic fibers issuing from these ganglia serve the stomach, intestines (except the distal half of the large intestine), liver, spleen, and kidneys.

Pathways to the Pelvis Preganglionic fibers innervating the pelvis originate from T_{10} to L_2 and then descend in the sympathetic trunk to the lumbar and sacral trunk ganglia. Some fibers synapse there and the postganglionic fibers run in lumbar and sacral splanchnic nerves to plexuses on the lower aorta and in the pelvis. Other preganglionic fibers pass directly to these autonomic plexuses and synapse in collateral ganglia, such as the inferior mesenteric ganglion.

Postganglionic fibers proceed from these plexuses to the pelvic organs (the urinary bladder and reproductive organs) and

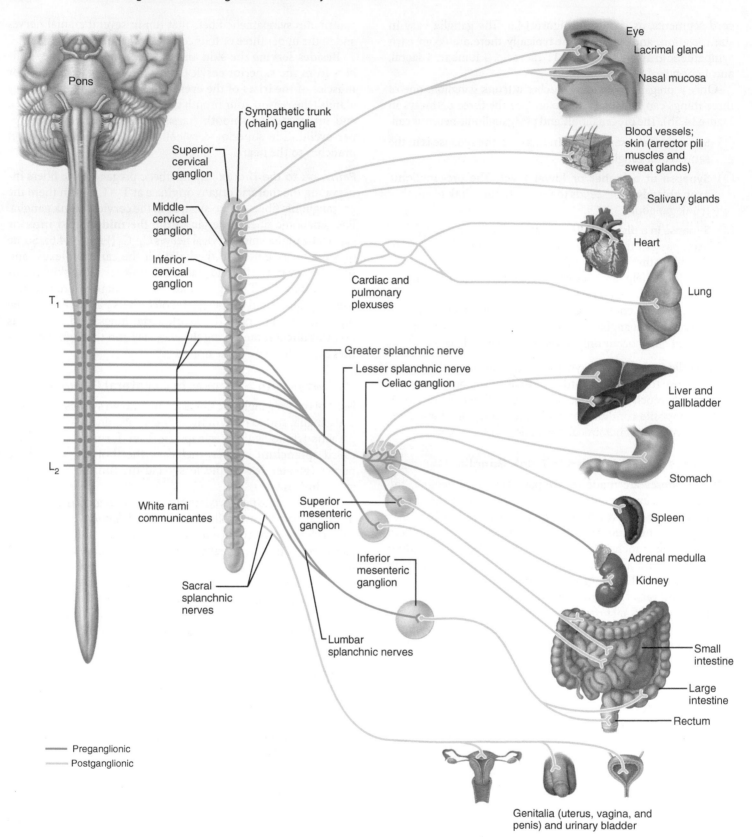

Pons

Sympathetic trunk (chain) ganglia

Superior cervical ganglion

Middle cervical ganglion

Inferior cervical ganglion

T₁

L₂

White rami communicantes

Sacral splanchnic nerves

Greater splanchnic nerve

Lesser splanchnic nerve

Celiac ganglion

Superior mesenteric ganglion

Inferior mesenteric ganglion

Lumbar splanchnic nerves

Cardiac and pulmonary plexuses

Eye
Lacrimal gland
Nasal mucosa
Blood vessels; skin (arrector pili muscles and sweat glands)
Salivary glands
Heart
Lung
Liver and gallbladder
Stomach
Spleen
Adrenal medulla
Kidney
Small intestine
Large intestine
Rectum
Genitalia (uterus, vagina, and penis) and urinary bladder

— Preganglionic
— Postganglionic

Figure 14.6 Sympathetic division of the ANS. Sympathetic innervation to peripheral structures (blood vessels, glands, and arrector pili muscles) occurs in all areas but is shown only in the cervical area.

also the distal half of the large intestine. For the most part, sympathetic fibers *inhibit* the activity of muscles and glands in the abdominopelvic visceral organs.

Pathways with Synapses in the Adrenal Medulla

Some fibers traveling in the thoracic splanchnic nerves pass through the celiac ganglion without synapsing and terminate by synapsing with the hormone-producing medullary cells of the adrenal gland. When stimulated by preganglionic fibers, the medullary cells secrete *norepinephrine* and *epinephrine* (also called *noradrenaline* and *adrenaline*, respectively) into the blood, producing the excitatory effects we have all felt as a "surge of adrenaline."

Embryologically, sympathetic ganglia and the adrenal medulla arise from the same tissue. For this reason, the adrenal medulla is sometimes viewed as a "misplaced" sympathetic ganglion, and its hormone-releasing cells, although lacking nerve processes, are considered equivalent to postganglionic sympathetic neurons.

Visceral Reflexes

Because most anatomists consider the ANS to be a visceral motor system, the presence of sensory fibers (mostly visceral pain afferents) is often overlooked. However, **visceral sensory neurons**, which send information concerning chemical changes, stretch, and irritation of the viscera, are the first link in autonomic reflexes.

Visceral reflex arcs have essentially the same components as somatic reflex arcs—receptor, sensory neuron, integration center, motor neuron, and effector. However, a key difference is that a visceral reflex arc has *two* neurons in its motor component (**Figure 14.7**; compare with Figure 13.15). Two examples of visceral reflexes are the reflexes that empty the rectum and bladder, which we discuss in Chapters 23 and 25.

Nearly all the sympathetic and parasympathetic fibers we have described so far are accompanied by afferent fibers conducting sensory impulses from glands or muscles. This means that peripheral processes of visceral sensory neurons are found in cranial nerves VII, IX, and X, splanchnic nerves, and the sympathetic trunk, as well as in spinal nerves.

Like sensory neurons serving somatic structures (skeletal muscles and skin), the cell bodies of visceral sensory neurons are located either in sensory ganglia of cranial nerves or in dorsal root ganglia of the spinal cord. Visceral sensory neurons are also found in sympathetic ganglia where preganglionic neurons synapse.

Furthermore, complete three-neuron reflex arcs (with sensory neurons, interneurons, and motor neurons) exist entirely within the walls of the gastrointestinal tract. Neurons composing these reflex arcs make up the *enteric nervous system*, which plays an important role in controlling gastrointestinal tract activity. We will discuss the enteric nervous system in more detail in Chapter 23.

Visceral sensory neurons are also involved in the phenomenon of referred pain that we described in Chapter 13 (p. 490).

☑ Check Your Understanding

4. State whether each of the following is a characteristic of the sympathetic or parasympathetic nervous system: short preganglionic fibers; origin from thoracolumbar region of

Stimulus

1. Receptor in viscera
2. Visceral sensory neuron
3. Integration center
   • May be preganglionic neuron (as shown)
   • May be a dorsal horn interneuron
   • May be within walls of gastrointestinal tract
4. Motor neuron (two-neuron chain)
   • Preganglionic neuron
   • Postganglionic neuron
5. Visceral effector

Response

Dorsal root ganglion
Spinal cord
Autonomic ganglion

Figure 14.7 Visceral reflexes. Visceral reflex arcs have the same five elements as somatic reflex arcs. The visceral afferent (sensory) fibers are found both in spinal nerves (as depicted here) and in autonomic nerves.

spinal cord; terminal ganglia; collateral ganglia; innervates adrenal medulla.

5. How does a visceral reflex differ from a somatic reflex?

For answers, see Appendix H.

ANS Physiology

✓ Define cholinergic and adrenergic fibers, and list the different types of their receptors.

✓ Describe the clinical importance of drugs that mimic or inhibit adrenergic or cholinergic effects.

✓ State the effects of the parasympathetic and sympathetic divisions on the following organs: heart, blood vessels, gastrointestinal tract, lungs, adrenal medulla, and external genitalia.

✓ Describe autonomic nervous system controls.

Neurotransmitters and Receptors

The major neurotransmitters released by ANS neurons are *acetylcholine* (*ACh*) and *norepinephrine* (*NE*). ACh, the same neurotransmitter secreted by somatic motor neurons, is released by (1) all ANS preganglionic axons and (2) all parasympathetic postganglionic axons at synapses with their effectors. Fibers that release ACh are called **cholinergic fibers** (ko"lin-er'jik).

Table 14.2 Cholinergic and Adrenergic Receptors

NEUROTRANSMITTER	RECEPTOR TYPE	MAJOR LOCATIONS*	EFFECT OF BINDING
Acetylcholine (ACh)	**Cholinergic**		
	Nicotinic	All postganglionic neurons; adrenal medullary cells (also neuromuscular junctions of skeletal muscle)	Excitation
	Muscarinic	All parasympathetic target organs	Excitation in most cases; inhibition of cardiac muscle
		Limited sympathetic targets (e.g., eccrine sweat glands†)	Activation
Norepinephrine (NE) (and epinephrine released by adrenal medulla)	**Adrenergic**		
	β_1	Heart predominantly, but also kidneys and adipose tissue	Increases heart rate and force of contraction; stimulates kidneys to release renin
	β_2	Lungs and most other sympathetic target organs; abundant on blood vessels serving the heart, liver, and skeletal muscle	Effects mostly inhibitory; dilates blood vessels and bronchioles; relaxes smooth muscle walls of digestive and urinary visceral organs; relaxes uterus
	β_3	Adipose tissue	Stimulates lipolysis by fat cells
	α_1	Most importantly blood vessels serving the skin, mucosae, abdominal viscera, kidneys, and salivary glands; also, virtually all sympathetic target organs except heart	Constricts blood vessels and visceral organ sphincters; dilates pupils of the eyes
	α_2	Membrane of adrenergic axon terminals; pancreas; blood platelets	Inhibits NE release from adrenergic terminals; inhibits insulin secretion by pancreas; promotes blood clotting

* Note that all of these receptor subtypes are also found in the CNS.
† Sympathetic cholinergic vasodilator fibers are found in other animals, but do not appear to be present in humans.

In contrast, most sympathetic postganglionic axons release NE and are called **adrenergic fibers** (ad"ren-er'jik). An exception is sympathetic postganglionic fibers that secrete ACh onto sweat glands.

Unfortunately for memorization purposes, the effects of ACh and NE on their effectors are not consistently excitatory or inhibitory. Why not? Because the action of any neurotransmitter depends on the receptor to which it binds. Each autonomic neurotransmitter binds with two or more kinds of receptors, allowing it to exert different effects (activation or inhibition) at different body targets. Table 14.2 summarizes the receptor types that we introduce next.

Cholinergic Receptors

The two types of cholinergic (ACh-binding) receptors are named for drugs that bind to them and mimic acetylcholine's effects. **Nicotinic receptors** (nik"o-tin'ik) respond to nicotine. **Muscarinic receptors**, the other set of ACh receptors, can be activated by the mushroom poison *muscarine* (mus'kah-rin). All ACh receptors are either nicotinic or muscarinic.

Nicotinic Receptors Nicotinic receptors are found on:

- The sarcolemma of skeletal muscle cells at neuromuscular junctions (which, as you will recall, are somatic and not autonomic targets)

- *All* postganglionic neurons, both sympathetic and parasympathetic

- The hormone-producing cells of the adrenal medulla

When ACh binds to nicotinic receptors anywhere, the effect is *always* stimulatory. Just as at the sarcolemma of skeletal muscle (examined in Chapter 9), ACh binding to any nicotinic receptor directly opens ion channels, depolarizing the postsynaptic cell.

Muscarinic Receptors Muscarinic receptors occur on all effector cells stimulated by postganglionic cholinergic fibers— that is, all parasympathetic target organs and a few sympathetic targets, such as eccrine sweat glands. When ACh binds to muscarinic receptors, the effect can be either inhibitory or stimulatory, depending on the subclass of muscarinic receptor on the target organ. For example, ACh binding to cardiac muscle receptors slows heart activity, whereas ACh binding to receptors on smooth muscle of the gastrointestinal tract increases its motility.

Adrenergic Receptors

There are also two major classes of adrenergic (NE-binding) receptors: **alpha** (**α**) and **beta** (**β**). These receptors are further divided into subclasses (α_1 and α_2; β_1, β_2, and β_3). Organs that

Table 14.3	Selected Drug Classes That Influence the Autonomic Nervous System			
DRUG CLASS	RECEPTOR BOUND	EFFECTS	EXAMPLE	CLINICAL APPLICATION
Nicotinic agents (little therapeutic value, but important for public health because tobacco contains nicotine)	Nicotinic ACh receptors on all postganglionic neurons and in CNS	Typically stimulates sympathetic effects; blood pressure rises	Nicotine	Smoking cessation products
Parasympathomimetic agents (muscarinic agents)	Muscarinic ACh receptors	Enhance parasympathetic activity by mimicking effects of ACh	Pilocarpine	Glaucoma (opens aqueous humor drainage pores)
			Bethanechol	Difficulty urinating (increases bladder contraction)
Acetylcholinesterase inhibitors	None; bind to the enzyme (AChE) that degrades ACh	Indirect effect at all ACh receptors; prolong the effect of ACh	Neostigmine	Myasthenia gravis (increases availability of ACh)
			Sarin	Used as chemical warfare agent (similar to widely used insecticides)
Sympathomimetic agents	Adrenergic receptors	Enhance sympathetic activity by binding to adrenergic receptors or increasing NE release	Albuterol (Ventolin)	Asthma (dilates bronchioles by binding to β_2 receptors)
			Phenylephrine	Colds (nasal decongestant, binds to α_1 receptors)
Sympatholytic agents	Adrenergic receptors	Decrease sympathetic activity by blocking adrenergic receptors or inhibiting NE release	Propranolol	Hypertension (member of a class of drugs called *beta-blockers* that block β receptors, decreasing blood pressure)

respond to NE (or to epinephrine) have one or more of these receptor subtypes.

NE or epinephrine can be either excitatory or inhibitory depending on which subclass of receptor predominates in the target organ. For example, NE binding to the β_1 receptors of cardiac muscle prods the heart into more vigorous activity, whereas epinephrine binding to β_2 receptors in bronchiole smooth muscle causes it to relax, dilating the bronchiole.

The Effects of Drugs

Knowing the locations of the cholinergic and adrenergic receptor subtypes allows clinicians to prescribe specific drugs to stimulate or inhibit selected target organs.

For example, *atropine* is an anticholinergic drug that blocks muscarinic ACh receptors. It is routinely administered before surgery to prevent salivation and dry up respiratory system secretions. Ophthalmologists also administer atropine to dilate the pupils for eye examination.

The anticholinesterase drug *neostigmine* inhibits the enzyme acetylcholinesterase that breaks down ACh. This allows ACh to accumulate in synapses. Neostigmine is used to treat myasthenia gravis, a condition in which inadequate ACh stimulation impairs skeletal muscle activity.

As we described in Chapter 11, NE is one of our "feel good" neurotransmitters, and drugs that prolong the activity of NE on

postsynaptic membranes in the brain help to relieve depression. Hundreds of over-the-counter drugs used to treat colds, coughs, allergies, and nasal congestion contain *sympathomimetics*—sympathetic-mimicking drugs such as phenylephrine that stimulate α-adrenergic receptors. This constricts the blood vessels in the nasal mucosa, inhibiting secretions.

Much pharmaceutical research is directed toward finding medications that affect only one subclass of receptor without upsetting the whole adrenergic or cholinergic system. An important breakthrough was finding drugs that mainly activate β_2 receptors. People with asthma use such β_2 activators to dilate their lung bronchioles without activating β_1 receptors, which would increase their heart rate. Table 14.3 summarizes selected drug classes that influence ANS activity.

Interactions of the Autonomic Divisions

As we mentioned earlier, most visceral organs receive *dual innervation* from both the parasympathetic and sympathetic divisions. Normally, both ANS divisions are partially active. Action potentials continually fire down both sympathetic and parasympathetic axons, producing a dynamic antagonism that precisely controls visceral activity. However, one division or the other usually predominates in given circumstances, and in a few cases, the two divisions actually cooperate with each other. Table 14.4 contains an organ-by-organ summary of how their effects differ.

Table 14.4	Effects of the Parasympathetic and Sympathetic Divisions on Various Organs	
TARGET ORGAN OR SYSTEM	**PARASYMPATHETIC EFFECTS**	**SYMPATHETIC EFFECTS**
Eye (iris)	Stimulates sphincter pupillae muscles; constricts pupils	Stimulates dilator pupillae muscles; dilates pupils
Eye (ciliary muscle)	Stimulates muscle, which makes lens bulge for close vision	Weakly inhibits muscle, which flattens lens for far vision
Glands (nasal, lacrimal, gastric, pancreas)	Stimulates secretory activity	Inhibits secretory activity; constricts blood vessels supplying the glands
Salivary glands	Stimulates secretion of watery saliva	Stimulates secretion of thick, viscous saliva
Sweat glands	No effect (no innervation)	Stimulates copious sweating (cholinergic fibers)
Adrenal medulla	No effect (no innervation)	Stimulates medulla cells to secrete epinephrine and norepinephrine
Arrector pili muscles attached to hair follicles	No effect (no innervation)	Stimulates contraction (erects hairs and produces "goosebumps")
Heart (muscle)	Decreases rate; slows heart	Increases rate and force of heartbeat
Heart (coronary blood vessels)	No effect (no innervation)	Dilates blood vessels (vasodilation)*
Urinary bladder/urethra	Contracts smooth muscle of bladder wall; relaxes urethral sphincter; promotes voiding	Relaxes smooth muscle of bladder wall; constricts urethral sphincter; inhibits voiding
Lungs	Constricts bronchioles	Dilates bronchioles*
Digestive tract organs	Increases motility (peristalsis) and amount of secretion by digestive organs; relaxes sphincters to allow foodstuffs to move through tract	Decreases activity of glands and muscles of digestive system; constricts sphincters (e.g., anal sphincter)
Liver	Increases glucose uptake from blood	Stimulates release of glucose to blood*
Gallbladder	Excites (gallbladder contracts to expel bile)	Inhibits (gallbladder is relaxed)
Kidney	No effect (no innervation)	Promotes renin release; causes vasoconstriction; decreases urine output
Penis	Causes erection (vasodilation)	Causes ejaculation
Vagina/clitoris	Causes erection (vasodilation) of clitoris; increases vaginal lubrication	Causes vagina to contract
Blood vessels	Little or no effect	Constricts most vessels and increases blood pressure; constricts vessels of abdominal viscera and skin to divert blood to muscles, brain, and heart when necessary; epinephrine weakly dilates vessels of skeletal muscles during exercise*
Blood coagulation	No effect (no innervation)	Increases coagulation*
Cellular metabolism	No effect (no innervation)	Increases metabolic rate*
Adipose tissue	No effect (no innervation)	Stimulates lipolysis (fat breakdown)

*Effects are mediated by epinephrine release into the bloodstream from the adrenal medulla.

Antagonistic Interactions

Antagonistic effects, described earlier, are most clearly seen on the activity of the heart, respiratory system, and gastrointestinal organs. In a fight-or-flight situation, the sympathetic division increases heart rate, dilates airways, and inhibits digestion and elimination. When the emergency is over, the parasympathetic division restores heart rate and airway diameter to resting levels and then attends to processes that refuel your body cells and discard wastes.

Sympathetic and Parasympathetic Tone

We have described the parasympathetic division as the "rest and digest" division, but the sympathetic division is the major actor in controlling blood pressure, even at rest. With few exceptions, the vascular system is entirely innervated by sympathetic fibers that keep the blood vessels in a continual state of partial constriction called **sympathetic**, or **vasomotor**, **tone**.

When blood pressure is too low to maintain blood flow, the sympathetic fibers fire more rapidly, causing blood vessels to constrict and raising blood pressure. When blood pressure becomes too high, sympathetic fibers fire less rapidly and the vessels dilate. *Alpha-blockers*, drugs that block the responses in these **vasomotor fibers**, are sometimes used to treat hypertension (high blood pressure).

During circulatory shock (inadequate blood flow to body tissues), or when more blood is needed to meet the soaring needs of working skeletal muscles, blood vessels serving the skin and abdominal viscera strongly constrict. This blood "shunting" helps maintain circulation to vital organs and skeletal muscles.

In contrast to the sympathetic division's dominance of blood vessels, parasympathetic effects normally dominate the heart and the smooth muscle of digestive and urinary tract organs. These organs exhibit **parasympathetic tone**. The parasympathetic division slows the heart and dictates the normal activity levels of the digestive and urinary tracts. However, the sympathetic division can override these parasympathetic effects during times of stress. Drugs that block parasympathetic responses increase heart rate and cause fecal and urinary retention. Parasympathetic fibers activate most glands, except for the adrenal glands and sweat glands of the skin.

Cooperative Effects

The best example of cooperative ANS effects occurs in the external genitalia. Parasympathetic stimulation dilates blood vessels in the external genitalia, producing the erection of the male penis or female clitoris during sexual excitement. (This may explain why anxiety can impair sexual performance—the sympathetic division is in charge.) Sympathetic stimulation then causes ejaculation of semen by the penis or reflex contractions of the vagina.

Homeostatic Imbalance 14.1

Autonomic neuropathy (damage to autonomic nerves) is a common complication of diabetes mellitus. One of the earliest and most troubling symptoms is sexual dysfunction. Up to 75% of male diabetics experience erectile dysfunction, and female diabetics often experience reduced vaginal lubrication. Other frequent manifestations of autonomic neuropathy include dizziness after standing suddenly (poor blood pressure control), urinary incontinence, sluggish eye pupil reactions, and impaired sweating. Maintaining tight control of blood glucose levels is the best way to prevent diabetic neuropathy. ✚

Unique Roles of the Sympathetic Division

The adrenal medulla, sweat glands and arrector pili muscles of the skin, the kidneys, and most blood vessels receive only sympathetic fibers. It is easy to remember that the sympathetic system innervates these structures because most of us sweat under stress, our scalp "prickles" during fear, and our blood pressure skyrockets (from widespread constriction of blood vessels) when we get excited.

We have already described how sympathetic control of blood vessels regulates blood pressure and shunting of blood in the vascular system. We will now consider several other uniquely sympathetic functions.

Thermoregulatory Responses to Heat The sympathetic division mediates reflexes that regulate body temperature. For example, applying heat to the skin causes blood vessels in that area to dilate reflexively. When systemic body temperature rises, sympathetic nerves (1) dilate the skin's blood vessels, allowing heat to escape from skin flushed with warm blood, and (2) activate the sweat glands to help cool the body. When body temperature falls, skin blood vessels constrict, preventing heat loss from the skin.

Release of Renin from the Kidneys Sympathetic impulses stimulate the kidneys to release *renin*, an enzyme that causes the formation of blood pressure–increasing hormones. We describe this renin-triggered mechanism in Chapter 25.

Metabolic Effects Through both direct neural stimulation and release of adrenal medullary hormones, the sympathetic division promotes a number of metabolic effects not reversed by parasympathetic activity. It (1) increases the metabolic rate of body cells; (2) raises blood glucose levels; and (3) mobilizes fats for use as fuels.

The medullary hormones also cause skeletal muscle to contract more strongly and quickly. As a side effect, this stimulates muscle spindles more often and, consequently, nerve impulses traveling to the muscles occur more synchronously. These neural bursts, which put muscle contractions on a "hair trigger," are great if you have to make a quick jump or run, but they can be embarrassing or even disabling to the nervous musician or surgeon.

Localized Versus Diffuse Effects

In the parasympathetic division, one preganglionic neuron synapses with one (or at most a few) postganglionic neurons. Additionally, all parasympathetic fibers release ACh, which is quickly destroyed (hydrolyzed) by acetylcholinesterase. Consequently, the parasympathetic division exerts short-lived, highly localized control over its effectors.

In contrast, in the sympathetic division, preganglionic axons branch profusely as they enter the sympathetic trunk, and they synapse with postganglionic neurons at several levels. As a result, when the sympathetic division is activated, it responds in a diffuse and highly interconnected way. Indeed, the literal translation of sympathetic (*sym* = together; *pathos* = feeling) relates to the bodywide mobilization this division provokes. Nevertheless, parts of the sympathetic nervous system can be activated individually. For example, just because your eye pupils dilate in dim light doesn't necessarily mean that your heart rate also speeds up.

Sympathetic activation produces much longer-lasting effects than parasympathetic activation. The sympathetic system's neurotransmitter, NE, is inactivated more slowly than the parasympathetic system's ACh, because NE must be taken back up into the presynaptic ending before being hydrolyzed or stored. More importantly, adrenal medullary cells secrete NE and epinephrine into the blood when the sympathetic division is mobilized. These hormones reinforce and prolong the effects of the sympathetic nervous system. Although epinephrine is more potent at increasing heart rate and raising blood glucose levels and metabolic rate, these hormones have essentially the same effects as NE released by sympathetic neurons. In fact, circulating adrenal medullary hormones produce 25–50% of all the sympathetic effects acting on the body at a given time. These effects continue for several minutes until the liver destroys the hormones.

In short, sympathetic nerve impulses act only briefly, but the hormonal effects they provoke linger. The widespread and prolonged effect of sympathetic activation explains why we need time to "come down" after an extremely stressful experience.

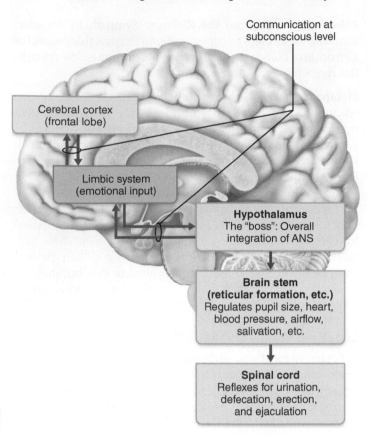

Communication at subconscious level

Cerebral cortex (frontal lobe)

Limbic system (emotional input)

Hypothalamus
The "boss": Overall integration of ANS

Brain stem (reticular formation, etc.)
Regulates pupil size, heart, blood pressure, airflow, salivation, etc.

Spinal cord
Reflexes for urination, defecation, erection, and ejaculation

Figure 14.8 Levels of ANS control. The hypothalamus stands at the top of the control hierarchy as the integrator of ANS activity, but it is influenced by subconscious cerebral inputs via limbic system connections.

Control of Autonomic Function

Although the ANS is not usually considered to be under voluntary control, its activity is regulated by CNS controls in the spinal cord, brain stem, hypothalamus, and cerebral cortex (Figure 14.8). In general, the hypothalamus is the integrative center at the top of the ANS control hierarchy. From there, orders flow to lower and lower CNS centers for execution. Although the cerebral cortex may modify the workings of the ANS, it does so at the subconscious level and by acting through limbic system structures on hypothalamic centers.

Brain Stem and Spinal Cord Controls

The hypothalamus is the "boss," but the brain stem reticular formation appears to exert the most *direct* influence over autonomic functions (see Figure 12.14 on p. 446). For example, certain motor centers in the ventrolateral medulla (*cardiac* and *vasomotor centers*) reflexively regulate heart rate and blood vessel diameter. Other medullary regions oversee gastrointestinal activities. Most sensory impulses involved in these autonomic reflexes reach the brain stem via vagus nerve afferents. Midbrain centers (*oculomotor nuclei*) control the muscles concerned with pupil diameter and lens focus.

Defecation and micturition (urination) reflexes that empty the rectum and urinary bladder are integrated at the spinal cord level but are subject to conscious inhibition. We will describe all of these autonomic reflexes in later chapters in relation to the organ systems they serve.

Hypothalamic Controls

As we noted, the hypothalamus is the main integration center of the autonomic nervous system. In general, anterior hypothalamic regions direct parasympathetic functions, and posterior areas direct sympathetic functions. Hypothalamic centers exert their effects both directly and via relays through the *reticular formation*, which in turn influences the preganglionic motor neurons in the brain stem and spinal cord (Figure 14.8). The hypothalamus, acting through the ANS, coordinates heart activity, blood pressure, body temperature, water balance, and endocrine activity.

The hypothalamus also mediates our reactions to fear via its associations with the amygdala and the periaqueductal gray matter. Emotional responses of the limbic system of the cerebrum to danger and stress signal the hypothalamus to activate the sympathetic system to fight-or-flight status. In this way, the hypothalamus serves as the keystone of the emotional and visceral brain. Through its centers, emotions influence ANS function and behavior.

Cortical Controls

Originally, scientists believed the ANS was not subject to voluntary controls. However, we have all had occasions when just remembering a frightening event made our heart race (sympathetic response) or the thought of a favorite food, pecan pie for example, made our mouth water (parasympathetic response). These inputs converge on the hypothalamus through its connections to the limbic lobe.

Additionally, studies have shown that voluntary cortical control of visceral activities is possible—a capability untapped by most people.

Influence of Biofeedback on Autonomic Function **Biofeedback** is a way of becoming aware of physiological conditions (such as heart rate and blood pressure), with the goal of being able to influence them consciously. During **biofeedback training**, subjects are connected to monitoring devices that detect and amplify changes in these physiological processes. The feedback comes in the form of flashing lights or audible tones.

Subjects try to alter or control some "involuntary" function by concentrating on calming, pleasant thoughts. The monitor allows them to identify changes in the desired direction, so they can recognize the feelings associated with these changes and learn to produce the changes at will.

Biofeedback techniques have been successful in helping individuals plagued by migraine headaches. Some cardiac patients also use them to manage stress and reduce their risk of heart attack. However, biofeedback training is time-consuming and often frustrating, and the training equipment is expensive and difficult to use.

☑ Check Your Understanding

6. Name the division of the ANS that does each of the following: increases digestive activity; increases blood pressure; dilates bronchioles; decreases heart rate; stimulates the adrenal medulla to release its hormones; causes ejaculation.

7. Would you find nicotinic receptors on skeletal muscle? Smooth muscle? Eccrine sweat glands? The adrenal medulla? CNS neurons?

8. Which part of the brain is the main integration center of the ANS? Which part exerts the most direct influence over autonomic functions?

For answers, see Appendix H.

Homeostatic Imbalances of the ANS

✓ Explain the relationship of some types of hypertension, Raynaud's disease, and autonomic dysreflexia to disorders of autonomic function.

The ANS is involved in nearly every important process that goes on in the body, so it is not surprising that abnormalities of autonomic function can have far-reaching effects. Most autonomic disorders reflect exaggerated or deficient controls of smooth muscle activity. The most devastating involve blood vessels and include conditions such as hypertension, Raynaud's disease, and autonomic dysreflexia.

■ *Hypertension*, or high blood pressure, may result from an overactive sympathetic vasoconstrictor response promoted by continuous high levels of stress. Hypertension is always serious because it forces the heart to work harder, which may precipitate heart disease, and increases the wear and tear on artery walls. Hypertension is sometimes treated with adrenergic receptor–blocking drugs that counteract the effects of the sympathetic nervous system on the cardiovascular system. We will discuss hypertension in more detail in Chapter 19.

■ *Raynaud's disease* is characterized by intermittent attacks causing the skin of the fingers and toes to become pale, then cyanotic (bluish) and painful. Commonly provoked by exposure to cold or emotional stress, it is an exaggerated vasoconstriction response. The severity of Raynaud's disease ranges from merely uncomfortable to severe blood vessel constriction that causes ischemia and gangrene (tissue death).

Vasodilators (for example, adrenergic blockers) usually suffice. To treat very severe cases, preganglionic sympathetic fibers serving the affected regions are severed (a procedure called *sympathectomy*). The involved vessels then dilate, reestablishing adequate blood flow to the region.

■ *Autonomic dysreflexia* is a life-threatening condition involving uncontrolled activation of autonomic neurons. It occurs in a majority of individuals with quadriplegia and in others with spinal cord injuries above the T_6 level, usually in the first year after injury. The usual trigger is a painful stimulus to the skin or an overfilled visceral organ, such as the urinary bladder. Arterial blood pressure skyrockets to life-threatening levels, which may rupture a blood vessel in the brain, precipitating stroke. Symptoms include headache, flushed face, sweating above the level of the injury, and cold, clammy skin below. The precise mechanism of autonomic dysreflexia is not yet clear.

☑ **Check Your Understanding**

9. Jackson works long, stress-filled shifts as an air traffic controller at a busy airport. His doctor has prescribed a beta-blocker. Why might his doctor have done this? What does a beta-blocker do?

For answers, see Appendix H.

Developmental Aspects of the ANS

✓ Describe several effects of aging on the autonomic nervous system.

ANS preganglionic neurons derive from the embryonic *neural tube*, as do somatic motor neurons. ANS structures in the PNS—postganglionic neurons, the adrenal medulla, and all autonomic ganglia—derive from the **neural crest** (along with all sensory neurons) (see Figure 12.33, ②).

Neural crest cells reach their ultimate destinations by migrating along growing axons. Forming ganglia receive axons from preganglionic neurons in the spinal cord or brain and send their axons to synapse with their effector cells in the body periphery. This process depends on the presence of **nerve growth factor**, and is guided by a number of signaling chemicals similar to those acting in the CNS.

During youth, impairments of ANS function are usually due to injuries to the spinal cord or autonomic nerves. In old age, the efficiency of the ANS declines. At least part of the problem is due to structural changes in some preganglionic axon terminals, which become congested with neurofilaments.

Many elderly people complain of constipation (a result of reduced gastrointestinal tract motility), and of dry eyes and frequent eye infections (both a result of a diminished ability to form tears). Additionally, when they stand up they may have fainting episodes due to **orthostatic hypotension** (*ortho* = straight; *stat* = standing), low blood pressure following changes in position. Orthostatic hypotension occurs because aging pressure receptors become less responsive to changes in blood pressure, and aging cardiovascular centers fail to maintain healthy blood pressure.

These problems are distressing, but not usually life threatening, and most can be managed by lifestyle changes or artificial aids. For example, changing position slowly gives the sympathetic nervous system time to adjust blood pressure, and eye drops (artificial tears) can alleviate the dry-eye problem.

☑ **Check Your Understanding**

10. Which embryonic structure gives rise to both the autonomic ganglia and the adrenal medulla?

For answers, see Appendix H.

In this chapter, we have described the structure and function of the ANS, one arm of the motor division of the peripheral nervous system. Because virtually every organ system still to be considered depends on autonomic controls, you will be hearing more about the ANS in chapters that follow. Now that we have explored most of the nervous system, this is a good time to examine how it interacts with the rest of the body as summarized in *System Connections*, p. 540.

Homeostatic Interrelationships Between the Nervous System and Other Body Systems

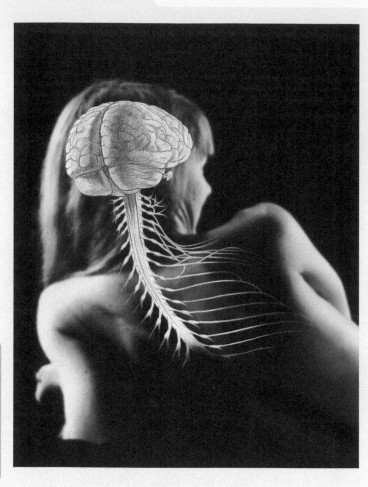

Endocrine System Chapter 16

- Sympathetic division of the ANS activates the adrenal medulla; hypothalamus helps regulate the activity of the anterior pituitary gland and produces the two posterior pituitary hormones
- Hormones influence neuronal metabolism

Cardiovascular System Chapters 17–19

- ANS helps regulate heart rate and blood pressure
- Cardiovascular system provides blood containing oxygen and nutrients to the nervous system and carries away wastes

Lymphatic System/Immunity Chapters 20–21

- Nerves innervate lymphoid organs; the brain plays a role in regulating immune function
- Lymphatic vessels carry away leaked tissue fluids from tissues surrounding nervous system structures; immune elements protect all body organs from pathogens (CNS has additional mechanisms as well)

Respiratory System Chapter 22

- Nervous system initiates and regulates respiratory rhythm and depth
- Respiratory system provides life-sustaining oxygen; disposes of carbon dioxide

Digestive System Chapter 23

- ANS (particularly the parasympathetic division) regulates digestive motility and glandular activity
- Digestive system provides nutrients needed for neuronal health

Urinary System Chapters 25–26

- ANS regulates bladder emptying and renal blood pressure
- Kidneys help dispose of metabolic wastes and maintain proper electrolyte composition and pH of blood for neural functioning

Reproductive System Chapter 27

- ANS regulates sexual erection and ejaculation in males; erection of the clitoris in females
- Testosterone causes masculinization of the brain and underlies sex drive and aggressive behavior

Integumentary System Chapter 5

- Sympathetic division of the ANS regulates sweat glands and blood vessels of skin (therefore heat loss/retention)
- Skin serves as heat loss surface

Skeletal System Chapters 6–8

- Nerves innervate bones and joints, providing for pain and joint sense
- Bones serve as depot for calcium needed for neural function; skeletal system protects CNS structures

Muscular System Chapters 9–10

- Somatic division of nervous system activates skeletal muscles; maintains muscle health
- Skeletal muscles are the effectors of the somatic division

14

 Access more System Connections in the Study Area at **www.masteringaandp.com**.

Chapter Summary

 For more chapter study tools, go to the Study Area of MasteringA&P at **www.masteringaandp.com**. There you will find:

- Interactive Physiology **iP**
- A&PFlix **A&PFlix**
- Practice Anatomy Lab **PAL**
- PhysioEx **PEx**
- Videos, Practice Quizzes and Tests, MP3 Tutor Sessions, Case Studies, and much more!

1. The autonomic nervous system (ANS) is the motor division of the PNS that controls visceral activities, with the goal of maintaining internal homeostasis.

Overview   (pp. 524–527)

Comparison of the Somatic and Autonomic Nervous Systems   (pp. 525–526)

1. The somatic (voluntary) nervous system provides motor fibers to skeletal muscles. The autonomic (involuntary or visceral motor) nervous system provides motor fibers to smooth and cardiac muscles and glands.

2. In the somatic division, a single motor neuron forms the efferent pathway from the CNS to the effectors. The efferent pathway of the autonomic division consists of a two-neuron chain: the preganglionic neuron in the CNS and the postganglionic neuron in a ganglion.

3. Acetylcholine, the neurotransmitter of somatic motor neurons, is stimulatory to skeletal muscle fibers. Neurotransmitters released by autonomic motor neurons (acetylcholine and norepinephrine) may excite or inhibit target cells.

iP Nervous System II; Topic: Synaptic Transmission, pp. 8–11.

ANS Divisions   (pp. 526–527)

4. The ANS consists of two divisions, parasympathetic and sympathetic, which normally exert antagonistic effects on many of the same target organs.

5. The parasympathetic division (the rest-digest system) conserves body energy and maintains body activities at basal levels.

6. Parasympathetic effects include constricted pupils, glandular secretion, increased digestive tract motility, and smooth muscle activity leading to elimination of feces and urine.

7. The sympathetic division prepares the body for activity (the fight-or-flight system).

8. Sympathetic responses include dilated pupils, increased heart rate, increased blood pressure, dilated bronchioles of the lungs, increased blood glucose levels, and sweating. During exercise, sympathetic vasoconstriction shunts blood from the skin and digestive viscera to the heart, brain, and skeletal muscles.

ANS Anatomy   (pp. 527–533)

Parasympathetic (Craniosacral) Division   (pp. 527–529)

1. Parasympathetic preganglionic neurons arise from the brain stem and from the sacral (S_2–S_4) region of the spinal cord.

2. Preganglionic fibers synapse with postganglionic neurons in terminal ganglia located in (intramural ganglia) or close to their effector organs. Preganglionic fibers are long; postganglionic fibers are short.

3. Cranial fibers arise in the brain stem nuclei of cranial nerves III, VII, IX, and X and synapse in ganglia of the head, thorax, and abdomen. The vagus nerves serve virtually all organs of the thoracic and abdominal cavities.

4. Sacral fibers (S_2–S_4) issue from the lateral region of the cord and form pelvic splanchnic nerves that innervate the pelvic viscera. The preganglionic axons do not travel within rami communicantes.

Sympathetic (Thoracolumbar) Division   (pp. 529–533)

5. Preganglionic sympathetic neurons arise from the lateral horns of the spinal cord from the level of T_1 through L_2.

6. Preganglionic axons leave the cord via white rami communicantes and enter the sympathetic trunk ganglia in the sympathetic trunk. An axon may synapse in a trunk ganglion at the same or at a different level, or it may issue from the sympathetic trunk without synapsing. Preganglionic fibers are short; postganglionic fibers are long.

7. When the synapse occurs in a trunk ganglion, the postganglionic fiber may enter the spinal nerve ramus via the gray ramus communicans to travel to the body periphery. Postganglionic fibers issuing from the cervical ganglia also serve visceral organs and blood vessels of the head, neck, and thorax.

8. When synapses do not occur in the trunk ganglia, the preganglionic fibers form splanchnic nerves (thoracic, lumbar, and sacral). Most splanchnic nerve fibers synapse in collateral ganglia, and the postganglionic fibers serve the abdominal viscera. Exceptions are that (1) some splanchnic nerve fibers synapse with cells of the adrenal medulla, and (2) some lumbar and sacral splanchnic nerve fibers *do* synapse in trunk ganglia.

Visceral Reflexes   (p. 533)

9. Visceral reflex arcs have the same components as somatic reflexes: receptor, sensory neuron, integration center, motor neurons, effector.

10. Cell bodies of visceral sensory neurons are located in dorsal root ganglia, sensory ganglia of cranial nerves, or autonomic ganglia. Visceral afferents are located in spinal nerves and in virtually all autonomic nerves.

ANS Physiology   (pp. 533–539)

Neurotransmitters and Receptors   (pp. 533–535)

1. Autonomic motor neurons release two major neurotransmitters, acetylcholine (ACh) and norepinephrine (NE). Based on the neurotransmitter they release, fibers are classified as cholinergic (ACh) or adrenergic (NE).

2. ACh is released by all preganglionic fibers and all parasympathetic postganglionic fibers. NE is released by all sympathetic postganglionic fibers except those serving the sweat glands of the skin.

3. Neurotransmitter effects depend on the receptors to which the neurotransmitter binds. Cholinergic (ACh) receptors are classified as nicotinic or muscarinic. Adrenergic (NE) receptors are classified as α_1 or α_2, or β_1, β_2, or β_3.

iP Nervous System II; Topic: Synaptic Transmission, pp. 8–11, 14.

The Effects of Drugs (p. 535)

4. Drugs that mimic, enhance, or inhibit the action of ANS neurotransmitters are used to treat conditions caused by excessive, inadequate, or inappropriate ANS function. Some drugs bind with only one receptor subtype, blocking or enhancing specific ANS-mediated activities.

Interactions of the Autonomic Divisions (pp. 535–537)

5. Most visceral organs are innervated by both parasympathetic and sympathetic divisions. The divisions interact in various ways but usually exert a dynamic antagonism. Antagonistic interactions mainly involve the heart, respiratory system, and gastrointestinal organs. Sympathetic activity increases heart activity, dilates bronchioles, and depresses gastrointestinal activity. Parasympathetic activity reverses these effects.

6. Most blood vessels are innervated only by sympathetic fibers and exhibit vasomotor tone. Parasympathetic activity dominates the heart and muscles of the gastrointestinal tract (which normally exhibit parasympathetic tone) and glands.

7. The two ANS divisions exert cooperative effects on the external genitalia.

8. Roles unique to the sympathetic division are regulating blood pressure, shunting blood in the vascular system, regulating body temperature, stimulating the kidneys to release renin, and metabolic effects.

9. Activation of the sympathetic division can cause widespread, long-lasting mobilization of the fight-or-flight response.

Parasympathetic effects are highly localized and short-lived.

Control of Autonomic Function (pp. 538–539)

10. Autonomic function is controlled at several levels: (1) The spinal cord and brain stem (particularly medullary) centers mediate reflex activity. (2) Hypothalamic integration centers interact with both higher and lower centers to orchestrate autonomic, somatic, and endocrine responses. (3) Cortical centers influence autonomic function via connections with the limbic system. Conscious control of autonomic function is rare but possible, as illustrated by biofeedback training.

Homeostatic Imbalances of the ANS (p. 539)

1. Most autonomic disorders reflect problems with smooth muscle control. Abnormalities in vascular control, such as hypertension, Raynaud's disease, and autonomic dysreflexia, are most devastating.

Developmental Aspects of the ANS (p. 539)

1. Preganglionic neurons develop from the neural tube; postganglionic neurons develop from the embryonic neural crest.

2. The efficiency of the autonomic nervous system declines in old age, as reflected by decreased gland secretion, reduced gastrointestinal motility, and slower sympathetic vasomotor responses to changes in position.

Review Questions

Multiple Choice/Matching

(Some questions have more than one correct answer. Select the best answer or answers from the choices given.)

1. All of the following characterize the ANS except (a) a two-neuron efferent chain, (b) presence of nerve cell bodies in the CNS, (c) presence of nerve cell bodies in the ganglia, (d) innervation of skeletal muscles.

2. Relate each of the following terms or phrases to either the sympathetic (S) or parasympathetic (P) division of the autonomic nervous system:

   ____ (1) short preganglionic, long postganglionic fibers
   ____ (2) intramural ganglia
   ____ (3) craniosacral part
   ____ (4) adrenergic fibers
   ____ (5) cervical ganglia
   ____ (6) otic and ciliary ganglia
   ____ (7) generally short-duration action
   ____ (8) increases heart rate and blood pressure
   ____ (9) increases gastric motility and secretion of lacrimal, salivary, and digestive juices
   ____ (10) innervates blood vessels
   ____ (11) most active when you are relaxing in a hammock
   ____ (12) active when you are running in the Boston Marathon

3. Preganglionic neurons develop from (a) neural crest cells, (b) neural tube cells, (c) alar plate cells, (d) endoderm.

4. The white rami communicantes contain what kind of fibers? (a) preganglionic parasympathetic, (b) postganglionic parasympathetic, (c) preganglionic sympathetic, (d) postganglionic sympathetic.

5. Collateral sympathetic ganglia are involved with innervating (a) abdominal organs, (b) thoracic organs, (c) head, (d) arrector pili, (e) all of these.

Short Answer Essay Questions

6. Briefly explain why the following terms are sometimes used to refer to the autonomic nervous system: involuntary nervous system and emotional-visceral system.

7. Describe the anatomical relationship of the white and gray rami communicantes to the spinal nerve, and indicate the kind of fibers found in each ramus type.

8. Indicate the results of sympathetic activation of the following structures: sweat glands, eye pupils, adrenal medullae, heart, bronchioles of the lungs, liver, blood vessels of vigorously working skeletal muscles, blood vessels of digestive viscera, salivary glands.

9. Which of the effects listed in response to question 8 would be reversed by parasympathetic activity?

10. Which ANS fibers release acetylcholine? Which release norepinephrine?

11. Describe the meaning and importance of sympathetic tone and parasympathetic tone.

12. List the receptor subtypes for ACh and NE, and indicate the major sites where each type is found.

13. Which area of the brain is most directly involved in mediating autonomic reflexes?

14. Describe the importance of the hypothalamus in controlling the autonomic nervous system.

15. Describe the basis and uses of biofeedback training.

16. What manifestations of decreased autonomic nervous system efficiency are seen in elderly individuals?

17. Postganglionic neurons are also called ganglionic neurons. Why is the latter term more accurate?

Critical Thinking and Clinical Application Questions

1. Mr. Johnson suffers from urinary retention and a hypoactive urinary bladder. Bethanechol, a drug that mimics acetylcholine's autonomic effects, is prescribed to manage his problem. First explain the rationale for prescribing bethanechol, and then predict which of the following adverse effects Mr. Johnson might experience while taking this drug (select all that apply): dizziness, low blood pressure, deficient tear formation, wheezing, increased mucus production in bronchi, deficient salivation, diarrhea, cramping, excessive sweating, undesirable erection of penis.

2. A 32-year-old woman complains of intermittent aching pains in the medial two fingers of both hands. During such episodes, the fingers become blanched and then blue. Her history is taken, and it is noted that she is a heavy smoker. The physician advises her that she must stop smoking and states that she will not prescribe any medication until the patient has discontinued smoking for a month. What is this patient's condition, and why was she told to stop smoking?

3. Tiffany, a 21-year-old college student, is having trouble sleeping, crying frequently, and having recurrent thoughts of suicide. An antidepressant is prescribed. Like many such drugs, this antidepressant has anticholinergic side effects. What side effects might Tiffany experience in the first week of treatment?

4. As the aroma of freshly brewed coffee drifted by dozing Henry's nose, his mouth started to water and his stomach began to rumble. Explain his reactions in terms of ANS activity.

AT THE CLINIC

Related Clinical Terms

Atonic bladder (ah-ton′ik; *a* = without; *ton* = tone, tension) A condition in which the urinary bladder becomes flaccid and overfills, allowing urine to dribble through the sphincters. Results from temporary loss of the micturition reflex following spinal cord injury.

Horner's syndrome A condition due to damage to the superior sympathetic trunk on one side of the body. On the affected side, the upper eyelid droops (ptosis) and the pupil constricts, and the person does not sweat on that side of the head.

Vagotomy (va-got′o-me) Cutting or severing the vagus nerve to decrease secretion of gastric juice. Treatment for peptic ulcers that do not respond to medication.

Vasovagal syncope Vasovagal syncope, also called *neurocardiogenic syncope*, is the most common cause of fainting. Although it may be provoked by emotional stress, pain, or dehydration, it typically occurs during prolonged standing. Fainting is due to a drop in blood pressure, which decreases blood flow to the brain.

Case Study   Autonomic Nervous System

On arrival at Holyoke Hospital, Jimmy Chin, a 10-year-old boy, is immobilized on a rigid stretcher so that he is unable to move his head or trunk. The paramedics report that when they found him some 50 feet from the bus, he was awake and alert, but crying and complaining that he couldn't "get up to find his mom" and he had a "wicked headache." He has severe bruises on his upper back and head, and lacerations of his back and scalp. His blood pressure is low, body temperature is below normal, lower limbs are paralyzed, and he is insensitive to painful stimuli below the nipples. Although still alert on arrival, Jimmy soon begins to drift in and out of unconsciousness.

Jimmy is immediately scheduled for a CT scan, and an operating room is reserved.

Relative to Jimmy's condition:

1. Why were his head and torso immobilized for transport to the hospital?

2. What do his worsening neurological signs (drowsiness, incoherence, etc.) probably indicate? Relate this to the type of surgery that will be performed.

3. Assuming that Jimmy's sensory and motor deficits are due to a spinal cord injury, at what level do you expect to find a spinal cord lesion?

4. Two days after his surgery, Jimmy is alert and his MRI scan shows no residual brain injury, but pronounced swelling and damage to the spinal cord at T4. On physical examination, Jimmy shows no reflex activity below the level of the spinal cord injury. His blood pressure is still low. Why are there no reflexes in his lower limbs and abdomen?

5. Over the next few days, his reflexes return in his lower limbs and become exaggerated. He is incontinent. Why is Jimmy hyperreflexive and incontinent?

On one occasion, Jimmy complains of a massive headache and his blood pressure is way above normal. On examination, he is sweating intensely above the nipples but has cold, clammy skin below the nipples and his heart rate is very slow.

6. What is this condition called and what precipitates it?

7. How does Jimmy's excessively high blood pressure put him at risk?

(Answers in Appendix H)

15

The Special Senses

People are responsive creatures. The aroma of freshly baked bread makes our mouths water. A sudden clap of thunder makes us jump. These stimuli and many others continually greet us and are interpreted by our nervous systems.

When people are asked to list the senses, they usually come up with five: vision, taste, smell, hearing, and touch. Actually, touch reflects the combined activity of the general senses that we considered in Chapter 13. The remaining senses—*vision, taste, smell, hearing,* and *equilibrium*—are called **special senses**. Most of us tend to forget the sense of equilibrium, whose receptors are housed in the ear along with the organ of hearing.

In contrast to the widely distributed general receptors (most of which are modified nerve endings of sensory neurons), the **special sensory receptors** are distinct *receptor cells.* These receptor cells are confined to the head region and are highly localized, either housed within complex sensory organs (eyes and ears) or in distinct epithelial structures (taste buds and olfactory epithelium).

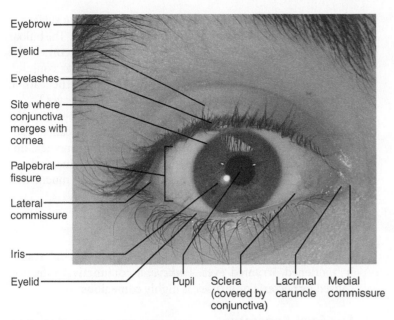

Eyebrow

Eyelid

Eyelashes

Site where conjunctiva merges with cornea

Palpebral fissure

Lateral commissure

Iris

Eyelid

Pupil   Sclera (covered by conjunctiva)   Lacrimal caruncle   Medial commissure

(a) Surface anatomy of the right eye

Figure 15.1 The eye and accessory structures.

Levator palpebrae superioris muscle

Orbicularis oculi muscle

Eyebrow

Tarsal plate

Palpebral conjunctiva

Tarsal glands

Cornea

Palpebral fissure

Eyelashes

Bulbar conjunctiva

Conjunctival sac

Orbicularis oculi muscle

(b) Lateral view; some structures shown in sagittal section

In this chapter we consider each of the five special senses in turn. But keep in mind that our perceptions of sensory inputs overlap. What we finally experience—our "feel" of the world—is a blending of stimulus effects.

The Eye and Vision

✓ Describe the structure and function of accessory eye structures, eye layers, the lens, and humors of the eye.

✓ Outline the causes and consequences of cataracts and glaucoma.

Vision is our dominant sense: Some 70% of all the sensory receptors in the body are in the eyes, and nearly half of the cerebral cortex is involved in some aspect of visual processing.

The adult **eye** is a sphere with a diameter of about 2.5 cm (1 inch). Only the anterior one-sixth of the eye's surface is visible **(Figure 15.1a)**. The rest is enclosed and protected by a cushion of fat and the walls of the bony orbit. The fat pad occupies nearly all of the orbit not occupied by the eye itself. The eye is a complex structure and only a small portion of its tissues are actually involved in photoreception. Before turning our attention to the eye itself, let us consider the accessory structures that protect it or aid its function.

Accessory Structures of the Eye

The **accessory structures** of the eye include the eyebrows, eyelids, conjunctiva, lacrimal apparatus, and extrinsic eye muscles.

Eyebrows

The **eyebrows** are short, coarse hairs that overlie the supraorbital margins of the skull (Figure 15.1). They help shade the eyes from sunlight and prevent perspiration trickling down the forehead from reaching the eyes.

Eyelids

Anteriorly, the eyes are protected by the mobile **eyelids** or **palpebrae** (pal'pĕ-bre). The eyelids are separated by the **palpebral fissure** ("eyelid slit") and meet at the medial and lateral angles of the eye—the **medial** and **lateral commissures** (*canthi*), respectively (Figure 15.1a).

The medial commissure sports a fleshy elevation called the **lacrimal caruncle** (kar'ung-kl; "a bit of flesh"). The caruncle contains sebaceous and sweat glands and produces the whitish, oily secretion (fancifully called the Sandman's eye-sand) that sometimes collects at the medial commissure, especially during sleep. In most Asian peoples, a vertical fold of skin called the *epicanthic fold* commonly appears on both sides of the nose and sometimes covers the medial commissure.

The eyelids are thin, skin-covered folds supported internally by connective tissue sheets called **tarsal plates** (Figure 15.1b). The tarsal plates also anchor the **orbicularis oculi** and **levator palpebrae superioris** muscles that run within the eyelid. The orbicularis muscle encircles the eye, and the eye closes when it contracts. Of the two eyelids, the larger, upper one is much more mobile, mainly because of the levator palpebrae superioris muscle, which raises that eyelid to open the eye.

Lacrimal sac

Lacrimal gland

Excretory ducts
of lacrimal glands

Lacrimal punctum

Lacrimal canaliculus

Nasolacrimal duct

Inferior meatus
of nasal cavity

Nostril

Figure 15.2 The lacrimal apparatus. Arrows indicate the flow of lacrimal fluid (tears) from the lacrimal gland to the nasal cavity.

The eyelid muscles are activated reflexively to cause blinking every 3–7 seconds and to protect the eye when it is threatened by foreign objects. Each time we blink, accessory structure secretions (oil, mucus, and saline solution) spread across the eyeball surface, keeping the eyes moist.

Projecting from the free margin of each eyelid are the **eyelashes**. The follicles of the eyelash hairs are richly innervated by nerve endings (hair follicle receptors), and anything that touches the eyelashes (even a puff of air) triggers reflex blinking.

Several types of glands are associated with the eyelids. The **tarsal glands** are embedded in the tarsal plates (Figure 15.1b), and their ducts open at the eyelid edge just posterior to the eyelashes. These modified sebaceous glands produce an oily secretion that lubricates the eyelid and the eye and prevents the eyelids from sticking together. Associated with the eyelash follicles are a number of smaller, more typical sebaceous glands, and modified sweat glands called ciliary glands lie between the hair follicles (*cilium* = eyelash).

Homeostatic Imbalance 15.1

An infected tarsal gland results in an unsightly cyst called a *chalazion* (kah-la′ze-on; "swelling"). Inflammation of any of the smaller glands is called a sty. ✚

Conjunctiva

The **conjunctiva** (kon″junk-ti′vah; "joined together") is a transparent mucous membrane. It lines the eyelids as the **palpebral**

conjunctiva and reflects (folds back) over the anterior surface of the eyeball as the **bulbar conjunctiva** (Figure 15.1b). The bulbar conjunctiva covers only the white of the eye, not the cornea (the clear "window" over the iris and pupil). The bulbar conjunctiva is very thin, and blood vessels are clearly visible beneath it. (They are even more visible in irritated "bloodshot" eyes.)

When the eye is closed, a slitlike space occurs between the conjunctiva-covered eyeball and eyelids. This so-called **conjunctival sac** is where a contact lens lies, and eye medications are often administered into its inferior recess. The major function of the conjunctiva is to produce a lubricating mucus that prevents the eyes from drying out.

Homeostatic Imbalance 15.2

Inflammation of the conjunctiva, called *conjunctivitis*, results in reddened, irritated eyes. *Pinkeye*, a conjunctival infection caused by bacteria or viruses, is highly contagious. ✚

Lacrimal Apparatus

The **lacrimal apparatus** (lak′rĭ-mal; "tear") consists of the lacrimal gland and the ducts that drain lacrimal secretions into the nasal cavity (Figure 15.2). The **lacrimal gland** lies in the orbit above the lateral end of the eye and is visible through the conjunctiva when the lid is everted. It continually releases a dilute saline solution called **lacrimal secretion**—or, more commonly, **tears**—into the superior part of the conjunctival sac through several small excretory ducts.

Blinking spreads the tears downward and across the eyeball to the medial commissure, where they enter the paired **lacrimal canaliculi** via two tiny openings called **lacrimal puncta** (literally, "prick points"), visible as tiny red dots on the medial margin of each eyelid. From the lacrimal canaliculi, the tears drain into the **lacrimal sac** and then into the **nasolacrimal duct**, which empties into the nasal cavity at the inferior nasal meatus.

Lacrimal fluid contains mucus, antibodies, and **lysozyme**, an enzyme that destroys bacteria. Thus, it cleanses and protects the eye surface as it moistens and lubricates it. When lacrimal secretion increases substantially, tears spill over the eyelids and fill the nasal cavities, causing congestion and the "sniffles." This spillover (tearing) happens when the eyes are irritated or when we are emotionally upset. In the case of eye irritation, enhanced tearing washes away or dilutes the irritating substance. The importance of emotionally induced tears is poorly understood.

Homeostatic Imbalance 15.3

Because the nasal cavity mucosa is continuous with that of the lacrimal duct system, a cold or nasal inflammation often causes the lacrimal mucosa to swell. This swelling constricts the ducts and prevents tears from draining, causing "watery" eyes. ✚

Extrinsic Eye Muscles

How do our eyes move? Six straplike **extrinsic eye muscles** control the movement of each eyeball. These muscles originate from the walls of the orbit and insert into the outer surface of

Trochlea

Superior oblique muscle

Superior oblique tendon

Superior rectus muscle

Lateral rectus muscle

Inferior rectus muscle

Inferior oblique muscle

(a) Lateral view of the right eye

Axis of rotation of eye

Inferior rectus muscle

Medial rectus muscle

Lateral rectus muscle

Common tendinous ring

(b) Superior view of the right eye

Muscle	Action	Controlling cranial nerve
Lateral rectus	Moves eye laterally	VI (abducens)
Medial rectus	Moves eye medially	III (oculomotor)
Superior rectus	Elevates eye and turns it medially	III (oculomotor)
Inferior rectus	Depresses eye and turns it medially	III (oculomotor)
Inferior oblique	Elevates eye and turns it laterally	III (oculomotor)
Superior oblique	Depresses eye and turns it laterally	IV (trochlear)

(c) Summary of muscle actions and innervating cranial nerves

Figure 15.3 Extrinsic eye muscles.

the eyeball **(Figure 15.3)**. They allow the eyes to follow a moving object, and provide external "guy-wires" that help maintain the shape of the eyeball and hold it in the orbit.

The four *rectus muscles* originate from the **common tendinous ring** (or annular ring) at the back of the orbit and run straight to their insertion on the eyeball. Their locations and the movements that they promote are clearly indicated by their names: **superior, inferior, lateral**, and **medial rectus muscles**.

The actions of the two *oblique muscles* are less easy to deduce because they take rather strange paths through the orbit. They move the eye in the vertical plane when the eyeball is already turned medially by the rectus muscles. The **superior oblique muscle** originates in common with the rectus muscles, runs along the medial wall of the orbit, and then makes a right-angle turn and passes through a fibrocartilaginous loop called the **trochlea** (trok′le-ah; "pulley") suspended from the frontal bone before inserting on the superolateral aspect of the eyeball. It rotates the eye downward and somewhat laterally.

The **inferior oblique muscle** originates from the medial orbit surface and runs laterally and obliquely to insert on the inferolateral eye surface. It rotates the eye up and laterally.

The four rectus muscles would seem to provide all the eye movements we require—medial, lateral, superior, and inferior—so why the two oblique muscles? The simplest way to answer this question is to point out that the superior and inferior recti cannot elevate or depress the eye *without also turning it medially* because they approach the eye from a posteromedial direction. For an eye to be *directly* elevated or depressed, the lateral pull of the oblique muscles is necessary to cancel the medial pull of the superior and inferior recti.

Except for the lateral rectus and superior oblique muscles, which are innervated respectively by the *abducens* and *trochlear nerves*, the *oculomotor nerves* serve all extrinsic eye muscles. Figure 15.3c summarizes the actions and nerve supply of these muscles. Table 13.2 (pp. 495–497) illustrates the courses of the associated cranial nerves.

15

Ora serrata

Ciliary body

Ciliary zonule (suspensory ligament)

Cornea

Iris

Pupil

Anterior pole

Anterior segment (contains aqueous humor)

Lens

Scleral venous sinus

Posterior segment (contains vitreous humor)

Sclera

Choroid

Retina

Macula lutea

Fovea centralis

Posterior pole

Optic nerve

Central artery and vein of the retina

Optic disc (blind spot)

(a) Diagrammatic view. The vitreous humor is illustrated only in the bottom part of the eyeball.

Ciliary body

Ciliary processes

Iris

Margin of pupil

Anterior segment

Lens

Cornea

Ciliary zonule (suspensory ligament)

Vitreous humor in posterior segment

Retina

Choroid

Sclera

Fovea centralis

Optic disc

Optic nerve

(b) Photograph of the human eye.

Figure 15.4 Internal structure of the eye (sagittal section).

The extrinsic eye muscles are among the most precisely and rapidly controlled skeletal muscles in the entire body. This precision reflects their high axon-to-muscle-fiber ratio: The motor units of these muscles contain only 8 to 12 muscle cells and in some cases as few as two or three.

⚖ Homeostatic Imbalance 15.4

When movements of the external muscles of the two eyes are not perfectly coordinated, a person cannot properly focus the images of the same area of the visual field from each eye and so sees two images instead of one. This condition is called **diplopia** (dĭ-plo′pe-ah), or *double vision*. It can result from paralysis or weakness of certain extrinsic muscles, neurological disorders, or it may be a temporary consequence of acute alcohol intoxication.

Congenital weakness of the external eye muscles may cause **strabismus** (strah-biz′mus; "cross-eyed"), in which the affected eye rotates medially or laterally. To compensate, the eyes may alternate in focusing on objects. In other cases, only the controllable eye is used, and the brain begins to disregard inputs from the deviant eye, which then becomes functionally blind. Strabismus is treated either with eye exercises to strengthen the weak muscles or by temporarily placing a patch on the stronger eye, which forces the child to use the weaker eye. Surgery is needed for unyielding conditions.✚

Structure of the Eyeball

The eye itself, commonly called the **eyeball**, is a slightly irregular hollow sphere **(Figure 15.4)**. Because the eyeball is shaped roughly like the globe of the earth, it is said to have poles. Its most anterior point is the **anterior pole**, and its most posterior point is the **posterior pole**. Its wall is composed of three layers: the fibrous, vascular, and inner layers. Its internal cavity is filled with fluids called *humors* that help to maintain its shape. The lens, the adjustable focusing apparatus of the eye, is supported vertically within the eyeball, dividing it into *anterior* and *posterior segments*.

Fibrous Layer

The outermost coat of the eyeball, the **fibrous layer**, is composed of dense avascular connective tissue. It has two obviously different regions: the sclera and the cornea.

Sclera The **sclera** (skle´rah), forming the posterior portion and the bulk of the fibrous layer, is glistening white and opaque. Seen anteriorly as the "white of the eye," the tough, tendon-like sclera (*sclera* = hard) protects and shapes the eyeball and provides a sturdy anchoring site for the extrinsic eye muscles. Posteriorly, where the sclera is pierced by the optic nerve, it is continuous with the dura mater of the brain.

Cornea The anterior sixth of the fibrous layer is modified to form the transparent **cornea**, which bulges anteriorly from its junction with the sclera. The crystal-clear cornea forms a window that lets light enter the eye, and is a major part of the light-bending apparatus of the eye.

Epithelial sheets cover both faces of the cornea. The external sheet, a stratified squamous epithelium that protects the cornea from abrasion, merges with the bulbar conjunctiva at the corneoscleral junction. Epithelial cells that continually renew the cornea are located here. The deep *corneal endothelium*, composed of simple squamous epithelium, lines the inner face of the cornea. Its cells have active sodium pumps that maintain the clarity of the cornea by keeping its water content low.

The cornea is well supplied with nerve endings, most of which are pain receptors. (For this reason, some people can never adjust to wearing contact lenses.) When the cornea is touched, blinking and increased tearing occur reflexively. Even so, the cornea is the most exposed part of the eye and is vulnerable to damage from dust, slivers, and the like. Luckily, its capacity for regeneration and repair is extraordinary.

The cornea has no blood vessels and so it is beyond the reach of the immune system. As a result, the cornea is the only tissue in the body that can be transplanted from one person to another with little risk of rejection.

Sphincter pupillae muscle contracts: Pupil size decreases.

Iris (two muscles)
• Sphincter pupillae
• Dilator pupillae

Dilator pupillae muscle contracts: Pupil size increases.

Figure 15.5 Pupil constriction and dilation, anterior view. (+ means activation.)

Vascular Layer

The **vascular layer** forms the middle coat of the eyeball. Also called the *uvea* (u´ve-ah; "grape"), this pigmented layer has three regions: choroid, ciliary body, and iris (Figure 15.4).

Choroid The **choroid** is a blood vessel–rich, dark brown membrane (*choroid* = membrane) that forms the posterior five-sixths of the vascular layer. Its blood vessels nourish all eye layers. Its brown pigment, produced by melanocytes, helps absorb light, preventing it from scattering and reflecting within the eye (which would cause visual confusion). The choroid is incomplete posteriorly where the optic nerve leaves the eye.

Ciliary Body Anteriorly, the choroid becomes the **ciliary body**, a thickened ring of tissue that encircles the lens. The ciliary body consists chiefly of interlacing smooth muscle bundles called **ciliary muscles**, which act to control lens shape. Near the lens, its posterior surface is thrown into radiating folds called **ciliary processes**, which secrete the fluid that fills the cavity of the anterior segment of the eyeball. The **ciliary zonule** (*suspensory ligament*) extends from the ciliary processes to the lens. This halo of fine fibers encircles and helps hold the lens in its upright position.

Iris The **iris**, the visible colored part of the eye, is the most anterior portion of the vascular layer. Shaped like a flattened doughnut, it lies between the cornea and the lens and is continuous with the ciliary body posteriorly. Its round central opening, the **pupil**, allows light to enter the eye. The iris is made up of two smooth muscle layers with bunches of sticky elastic fibers that congeal into a random pattern before birth. Its muscle fibers allow it to act as a reflexively activated diaphragm to vary pupil size **(Figure 15.5)**. In close vision and bright light, the *sphincter pupillae* (circular muscles) contract and the pupil constricts. In distant vision and dim light, the *dilator pupillae* (radial muscles) contract and the pupil dilates, allowing more light to enter. Sympathetic fibers control pupillary dilation and parasympathetic fibers control constriction.

Changes in pupil size may also reflect our interests and emotional reactions. Our pupils often dilate when the subject matter

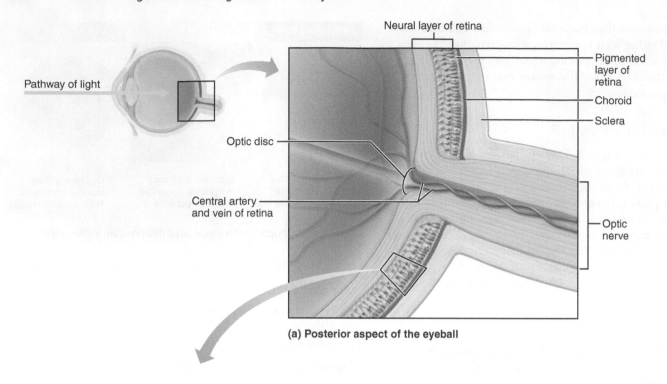

(a) Posterior aspect of the eyeball

(b) Cells of the neural layer of the retina

(c) Photomicrograph of retina

Figure 15.6 Microscopic anatomy of the retina. (a) The axons of the ganglion cells form the optic nerve, which leaves the back of the eyeball at the optic disc. **(b)** Light (indicated by the yellow arrow) passes through the retina to excite the photoreceptor cells (rods and cones). Information (output signals; gray arrow) flows in the opposite direction via bipolar and ganglion cells. **(c)** Photomicrograph (145×).

is appealing, in response to fear, and during problem solving. (Computing your taxes should make your pupils get bigger and bigger.) On the other hand, boredom or repulsive subject matter causes pupils to constrict.

Although irises come in different colors (*iris* = rainbow), they contain only brown pigment. When they have a lot of pigment, the eyes appear brown or black. If the amount of pigment is small and restricted to the posterior surface of the iris, the unpigmented parts simply scatter the shorter wavelengths of light and the eyes appear blue, green, or gray. Most newborn babies' eyes are slate gray or blue because their iris pigment is not yet developed.

Inner Layer (Retina)

The innermost layer of the eyeball is the delicate **retina** (ret′ĭ-nah), which originates as an outpocketing of the brain. It contains millions of photoreceptors that transduce (convert) light energy, other neurons involved in processing light responses, and glia. The retina consists of two layers: an outer *pigmented layer* and an inner *neural layer* **(Figure 15.6)**. Although the pigmented and neural layers are very close together, they are not fused. Only the neural layer of the retina plays a direct role in vision.

Pigmented Layer of the Retina The outer **pigmented layer**, a single-cell-thick lining, abuts the choroid, and extends anteriorly to cover the ciliary body and the posterior face of the iris. These pigment cells, like those of the choroid, absorb light and prevent it from scattering in the eye. They also act as phagocytes participating in photoreceptor cell renewal (described on p. 559), and store vitamin A needed by the photoreceptor cells.

Neural Layer of the Retina The transparent inner **neural layer** extends anteriorly to the posterior margin of the ciliary body. This junction is called the **ora serrata**, literally, the saw-toothed margin (see Figure 15.4).

From posterior to anterior, the neural layer is composed of three main types of neurons: **photoreceptors**, **bipolar cells**, and **ganglion cells** (Figure 15.6). Signals are produced in response to light and spread from the photoreceptors (abutting the pigmented layer) to the bipolar cells and then to the innermost ganglion cells, where action potentials are generated. The ganglion cell axons make a right-angle turn at the inner face of the retina, then leave the posterior aspect of the eye as the thick optic nerve. The retina also contains other types of neurons—horizontal cells and amacrine cells—which play a role in visual processing.

The **optic disc**, where the optic nerve exits the eye, is a weak spot in the **fundus** (posterior wall) of the eye because it is not reinforced by the sclera. The optic disc is also called the **blind spot** because it lacks photoreceptors, so light focused on it cannot be seen. Nonetheless, we do not usually notice these gaps in our vision because the brain uses a sophisticated process called *filling in* to deal with absence of input.

The quarter-billion photoreceptors found in the neural layer are of two types: rods and cones.

- **Rods** are our dim-light and peripheral vision receptors. They are more numerous and far more sensitive to light than cones

Figure 15.7 Part of the posterior wall (fundus) of the right eye as seen with an ophthalmoscope.

Central artery and vein emerging from the optic disc

Optic disc

Macula lutea

Retina

are, but they do not provide sharp images or color vision. This is why colors disappear and the edges of objects appear fuzzy in dim light and at the edges of our visual field.

- **Cones**, by contrast, are our vision receptors for bright light and provide high-resolution color vision.

Lateral to the blind spot of each eye, and located precisely at the eye's posterior pole, is an oval region called the **macula lutea** (mak′u-lah lu′te-ah; "yellow spot") with a minute (0.4 mm) pit in its center called the **fovea centralis** (see Figure 15.4). In this region, the retinal structures abutting the vitreous humor are displaced to the sides. This allows light to pass almost directly to the photoreceptors rather than through several retinal layers, greatly enhancing visual acuity (the ability to resolve detail). The fovea contains only cones, the macula contains mostly cones, and from the edge of the macula toward the retina periphery, cone density declines gradually. The retina periphery contains mostly rods, which continuously decrease in density from there to the macula.

Only the foveae (plural of fovea) have a sufficient cone density to provide detailed color vision, so anything we wish to view critically is focused on the foveae. Because each fovea is only about the size of the head of a pin, only a thousandth of the entire visual field is in *hard focus* (foveal focus) at a given moment. Consequently, for us to visually comprehend a scene that is rapidly changing (as when we drive in traffic), our eyes must flick rapidly back and forth to provide the foveae with images of different parts of the visual field.

The neural layer of the retina receives its blood supply from two sources. Vessels in the choroid supply the outer third (containing photoreceptors). The inner two-thirds is served by the **central artery** and **central vein of the retina**, which enter and leave the eye through the center of the optic nerve (see Figure 15.4a). Radiating outward from the optic disc, these vessels give rise to a rich vascular network. This is the only place where small blood vessels are visible in a living person **(Figure 15.7)**. Physicians may observe these tiny vessels with an ophthalmoscope for signs of hypertension, diabetes, and other vascular diseases.

15

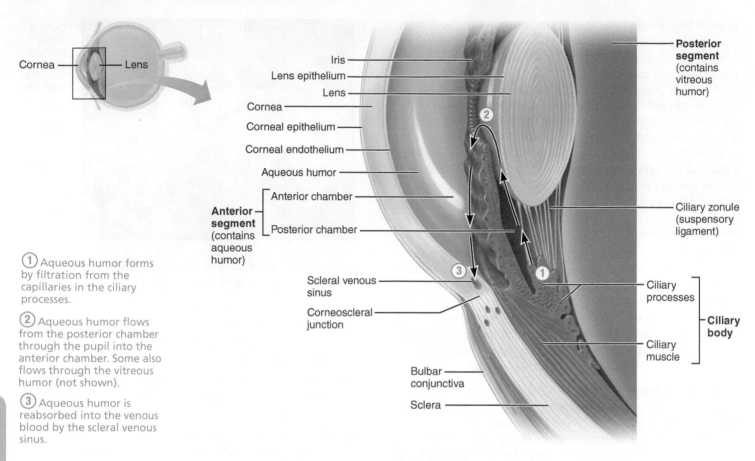

Cornea — Lens

Iris
Lens epithelium
Lens
Cornea
Corneal epithelium
Corneal endothelium
Aqueous humor

Anterior chamber
Anterior segment (contains aqueous humor)
Posterior chamber

Scleral venous sinus
Corneoscleral junction

Bulbar conjunctiva

Sclera

Posterior segment (contains vitreous humor)

Ciliary zonule (suspensory ligament)

Ciliary processes
Ciliary body
Ciliary muscle

① Aqueous humor forms by filtration from the capillaries in the ciliary processes.

② Aqueous humor flows from the posterior chamber through the pupil into the anterior chamber. Some also flows through the vitreous humor (not shown).

③ Aqueous humor is reabsorbed into the venous blood by the scleral venous sinus.

Figure 15.8 Circulation of aqueous humor. The arrows indicate the circulation pathway.

15

Homeostatic Imbalance 15.5

The pattern of vascularization of the retina makes it susceptible to *retinal detachment*. This condition, in which the pigmented and neural layers separate (detach) and allow the jellylike vitreous humor to seep between them, can cause permanent blindness because it deprives the photoreceptors of nutrients.

Retinal detachment usually happens when the retina is torn during a traumatic blow to the head or when the head stops moving suddenly and then jerks in the opposite direction (as in bungee jumping). The symptom that victims most often describe is "a curtain being drawn across the eye," but some people see sootlike spots or light flashes. If diagnosed early, it is often possible to reattach the retina with a laser before photoreceptors are permanently damaged. ✚

Internal Chambers and Fluids

As we noted earlier, the lens and its halolike ciliary zonule divide the eye into two segments, the anterior segment in front of the lens and the larger posterior segment behind it (see Figure 15.4a). The **posterior segment** is filled with a clear gel called **vitreous humor** (*vitre* = glassy) that binds tremendous amounts of water. Vitreous humor

- Transmits light
- Supports the posterior surface of the lens and holds the neural layer of the retina firmly against the pigmented layer

- Contributes to intraocular pressure, helping to counteract the pulling force of the extrinsic eye muscles

Vitreous humor forms in the embryo and lasts for a lifetime.

The iris divides the **anterior segment** into the **anterior chamber** (between the cornea and the iris) and the **posterior chamber** (between the iris and the lens) (Figure 15.8). The *entire* anterior segment is filled with **aqueous humor**, a clear fluid similar in composition to blood plasma. Unlike the vitreous humor, aqueous humor forms and drains continually and is in constant motion.

① The capillaries of the ciliary processes form the aqueous humor by filtering plasma into the posterior chamber.

② A portion of the fluid freely diffuses through the vitreous humor in the posterior segment while the remainder flows into the anterior chamber.

③ After flowing through the pupil into the anterior chamber, aqueous humor drains into the venous blood via the **scleral venous sinus**, an unusual venous channel that encircles the eye in the angle at the corneoscleral junction.

Normally, aqueous humor forms and drains at the same rate, maintaining a constant intraocular pressure of about 16 mm Hg, which helps to support the eyeball internally. Aqueous humor supplies nutrients and oxygen to the lens and cornea and to some cells of the retina, and it carries away their metabolic wastes.

Homeostatic Imbalance 15.6

If the drainage of aqueous humor is blocked, fluid backs up as in a clogged sink. Pressure within the eye may increase to dangerous levels and compress the retina and optic nerve—a condition called **glaucoma** (glaw-ko'mah). The eventual result is blindness (*glaucoma* = vision growing gray) unless the condition is detected early. Unfortunately, many forms of glaucoma steal sight so slowly and painlessly that people do not realize they have a problem until the damage is done. Late signs include seeing halos around lights and blurred vision.

The glaucoma examination is simple. The intraocular pressure is determined by directing a puff of air at the cornea and measuring the amount of corneal deformation it causes. This exam should be done yearly after age 40. The most common treatment is eye drops that increase the rate of aqueous humor drainage or decrease its production. Laser therapy or surgery can also help. +

Lens

The **lens** is a biconvex, transparent, flexible structure that can change shape to precisely focus light on the retina. It is enclosed in a thin, elastic capsule and held in place just posterior to the iris by the ciliary zonule (Figure 15.8). Like the cornea, the lens is avascular; blood vessels interfere with transparency.

The lens has two regions: the **lens epithelium** and the lens fibers. The lens epithelium, confined to the anterior lens surface, consists of cuboidal cells that eventually differentiate into the **lens fibers** that form the bulk of the lens. The lens fibers, which are packed tightly together like the layers in an onion, contain no nuclei and few organelles. They do, however, contain transparent, precisely folded proteins called **crystallins** that form the body of the lens. Since new lens fibers are continually added, the lens enlarges throughout life, becoming denser, more convex, and less elastic, all of which gradually impair its ability to focus light properly.

Homeostatic Imbalance 15.7

A **cataract** ("waterfall") is a clouding of the lens that causes the world to appear distorted, as if seen through frosted glass (Figure 15.9). Some cataracts are congenital, but most result from age-related hardening and thickening of the lens or are a secondary consequence of diabetes mellitus. Heavy smoking and frequent exposure to intense sunlight increase the risk for cataracts.

Oxidative stress and metabolic changes in the deeper lens fibers promote clumping of the crystallin proteins. A recent study unexpectedly showed that supplementation with the antioxidant vitamin C actually increases cataract formation. Fortunately, the offending lens can be surgically removed and an artificial lens implanted to save the patient's sight. +

☑ Check Your Understanding

1. What are tears and what structure secretes them?
2. What is the blind spot and why is it blind?

Figure 15.9 Photograph of a cataract. The lens, not the cornea, is milky and opaque.

3. Sam's optometrist tells him that his intraocular pressure is high. What is this condition called and which fluid does it involve?

For answers, see Appendix H.

Optics and the Eye

✓ Trace the pathway of light through the eye to the retina, and explain how light is focused for distant and close vision.

✓ Outline the causes and consequences of astigmatism, myopia, hyperopia, and presbyopia.

Overview: Light and Optics

To comprehend the function of the eye as a photoreceptor organ, we need to understand the properties of light.

Wavelength and Color **Electromagnetic radiation** includes all energy waves, from long radio waves (with wavelengths measured in meters) to very short gamma (γ) waves and X rays with wavelengths of 1 nm and less. Our eyes respond to the part of the spectrum called **visible light**, which has a wavelength range of approximately 400–700 nm (Figure 15.10a). (1 nm = 10^{-9} m, or one-billionth of a meter.)

Visible light travels in the form of waves, and its wavelengths can be measured very accurately. However, light can also be envisioned as small particles or packets of energy called **photons** or **quanta**. Attempts to reconcile these two findings have led to the present concept of light as packets of energy (photons) traveling in a wavelike fashion at very high speeds (300,000 km/s or about 186,000 mi/s). We can think of light as a vibration of pure energy ("a bright wiggle") rather than a material substance.

When visible light passes through a prism, each of its component waves bends to a different degree, dispersing the beam of

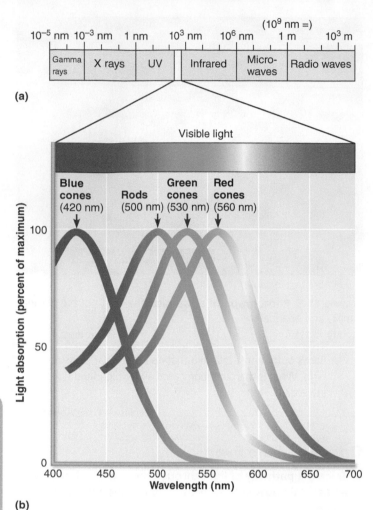

(a)

(b)

Figure 15.10 The electromagnetic spectrum and photoreceptor sensitivities. (a) The electromagnetic spectrum, of which visible light constitutes only a small portion. (nm = nanometers.) **(b)** Sensitivities of rods and the three cone types to the different wavelengths of the visible spectrum.

light into a **visible spectrum**, or band of colors (Figure 15.10b). (A rainbow that appears during a summer shower represents the collective prismatic effects of all the tiny water droplets suspended in air.) Red wavelengths are the longest and have the lowest energy, while violet wavelengths are the shortest and most energetic.

Like sound, light can reflect, or bounce, off a surface. This *reflection* of light by objects in our environment accounts for most of the light reaching our eyes. Objects have color because they absorb some wavelengths and reflect others. A red apple reflects mostly red light, while grass reflects more of the green. Things that look white reflect all wavelengths of light, whereas black objects absorb them all.

Refraction and Lenses Light travels in straight lines (rays) and is blocked by any nontransparent object. When light travels in a given medium, its speed is constant. But when it passes from

Figure 15.11 Refraction. A straw standing in a glass of water appears to be broken at the water-air interface. This occurs because light bends toward the perpendicular when it travels from a less dense medium (such as air) to a more dense medium (such as water).

one transparent medium into another with a different density, its speed changes. Light speeds up as it passes into a less dense medium and slows as it passes into a denser medium. Because of these changes in speed, bending or **refraction** of a light ray occurs when it meets the surface of a different medium at an oblique angle rather than at a right angle (perpendicular). The greater this angle, the greater the amount of bending. **Figure 15.11** shows refraction: A straw in a glass of water appears to break at the air-water interface.

A lens is a transparent object curved on one or both surfaces. Since light hits the curve at an angle, it is refracted. If the lens surface is convex, that is, thickest in the center like a camera lens, the light rays bend so that they converge or intersect at a single point called the **focal point** (Figure 15.12a). In general, the thicker (more convex) the lens, the more the light bends and the shorter the focal distance (distance between the lens and focal point). The image formed by a convex lens, called a **real image**, is inverted—upside down and reversed from left to right (Figure 15.12b).

Concave lenses, which are thicker at the edges than at the center, diverge the light (bend it outward) so that the light rays move away from each other. Consequently, concave lenses prevent light from focusing and extend the focal distance.

Focusing Light on the Retina

As light passes from air into the eye, it moves sequentially through the cornea, aqueous humor, lens, and vitreous humor, and then passes *through the entire neural layer of the retina* to excite the photoreceptors that abut the pigmented layer (see

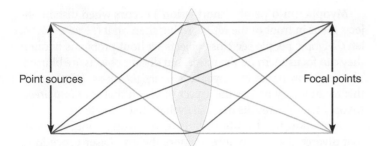

(a) Focusing of two points of light.

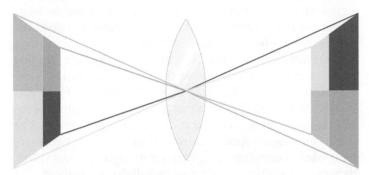

(b) The image is inverted—upside down and reversed.

Figure 15.12 Light is focused by a convex lens. The lens bends, or refracts, light rays so they converge on a focal point.

Figures 15.4 and 15.6). During its passage, light is bent three times: (1) entering the cornea, (2) entering the lens, and (3) leaving the lens.

The cornea accounts for the majority of the refractory power of the eye. However, the refractory power of the cornea is constant. On the other hand, the lens is highly elastic, and its curvature and light-bending power can actively change to allow fine focusing.

Focusing for Distant Vision Our eyes are best adapted ("preset to focus") for distant vision. To look at distant objects, we need only aim our eyeballs so that they are both fixated on the same spot. The **far point of vision** is that distance beyond which no change in lens shape (accommodation) is needed for focusing. For the normal or **emmetropic** (em″ĕ-tro′pik) eye, the far point is 6 m (20 feet).

Any object being viewed can be said to consist of many small points, with light radiating outward in all directions from each point. However, because distant objects appear smaller, light from an object at or beyond the far point of vision approaches the eyes as nearly parallel rays. The cornea and the at-rest lens focus the light from these distant objects precisely on the retina (Figure 15.13a).

During distant vision, the sphincterlike ciliary muscles are completely relaxed, and tension in the ciliary zonule stretches the lens flat. Consequently, the lens is as thin as it gets and is at its lowest refractory power when at rest. The ciliary muscles relax when sympathetic input to them increases and parasympathetic input decreases.

(a) Lens flattens for distant vision. Sympathetic input relaxes the ciliary muscle, tightening the ciliary zonule, and flattening the lens.

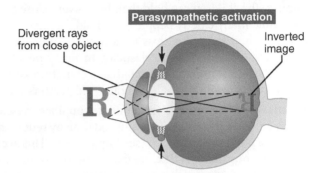

(b) Lens bulges for close vision. Parasympathetic input contracts the ciliary muscle, loosening the ciliary zonule, allowing the lens to bulge.

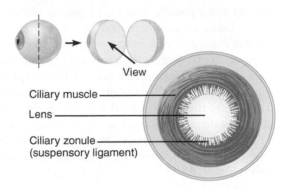

(c) The ciliary muscle and ciliary zonule are arranged sphincterlike around the lens. As a result, contraction loosens the ciliary zonule fibers and relaxation tightens them.

Figure 15.13 Focusing for distant and close vision.

Focusing for Close Vision Light from close objects (less than 6 m away) diverges as it approaches the eyes and comes to a focal point farther from the lens. For this reason, close vision demands that the eye make active adjustments. To restore focus, three processes must occur simultaneously: accommodation of the lenses, constriction of the pupils, and convergence of the eyeballs. The signal that induces this trio of reflex responses is blurring of the retinal image.

- **Accommodation of the lenses. Accommodation** is the process that increases the refractory power of the lens. The ciliary muscles contract, pulling the ciliary body anteriorly toward the pupil and inward, releasing tension in the ciliary zonule. No longer stretched, the elastic lens recoils and bulges, providing the shorter focal length needed to focus the image of a close object on the retina (Figure 15.13b). Parasympathetic fibers of the oculomotor nerves control the contraction of the ciliary muscles.

   The closest point on which we can focus clearly is called the **near point of vision**, and it represents the maximum bulge the lens can achieve. In young adults with emmetropic vision, the near point is 10 cm (4 inches) from the eye. However, it is closer in children and gradually recedes with age, explaining why children can hold their books very close to their faces while many elderly people must hold the newspaper at arm's length. The gradual loss of accommodation with age reflects the lens's decreasing elasticity. In many people over age 50, the lens is nonaccommodating, a condition known as **presbyopia** (pres″be-o′pe-ah), literally "old person's vision."

- **Constriction of the pupils.** The sphincter pupillae muscles of the iris enhance the effect of accommodation by reducing the size of the pupil toward 2 mm (see Figure 15.5). This **accommodation pupillary reflex**, mediated by parasympathetic fibers of the oculomotor nerves, prevents the most divergent light rays from entering the eye. Such rays would pass through the extreme edge of the lens and would not focus properly, causing blurred vision.

- **Convergence of the eyeballs.** The visual goal is always to keep the object being viewed focused on the retinal foveae. When we look at distant objects, both eyes are directed either straight ahead or to one side to the same degree, but when we fixate on a close object, our eyes converge. **Convergence**, controlled by somatic motor fibers of the oculomotor nerves, is medial rotation of the eyeballs by the medial rectus muscles so that each is directed toward the object being viewed. The closer that object, the greater the degree of convergence required. For example, when you focus on the tip of your nose, you "go cross-eyed."

Reading or other close work requires almost continuous accommodation, pupillary constriction, and convergence. This is why prolonged periods of reading tire the eye muscles and can result in eyestrain. When you read for an extended time, it helps to look up and stare into the distance occasionally to relax your intrinsic eye muscles.

Homeostatic Imbalance 15.8

Theoretically, visual problems related to refraction could result from a hyperrefractive (overconverging) or hyporefractive (underconverging) lens or from structural abnormalities of the eyeball. In practice, 99% of refractive problems are related to eyeball shape—either too long or too short.

Myopia (mi-o′pe-ah; "short vision") occurs when distant objects focus in front of the retina, rather than on it (**Figure 15.14**, left). Myopic people see close objects without problems because they can focus them on the retina, but distant objects are blurred. The common name for myopia is *nearsightedness*. (Notice that this terminology names the aspect of vision that is *unimpaired*.) Myopia typically results from an eyeball that is too long.

Correction has traditionally involved using concave lenses that diverge the light before it enters the eye. Laser procedures to flatten the cornea slightly offer other treatment options.

Hyperopia (hy′per-o″pe-ah; "far vision"), or *farsightedness*, occurs when the parallel light rays from distant objects focus *behind* the retina (Figure 15.14, right). Hyperopic individuals can see distant objects perfectly well because their ciliary muscles contract almost continuously to increase the light-bending power of the lens, which moves the focal point forward onto the retina. However, diverging light rays from *nearby* objects focus so far behind the retina that the lens cannot bring the focal point onto the retina even at its full refractory power. As a result, close objects appear blurry, and convex corrective lenses are needed to converge the light more strongly for close vision. Hyperopia usually results from an eyeball that is too short.

Unequal curvatures in different parts of the cornea or lens also lead to blurry images. This refractory problem is **astigmatism** (*astigma* = not a point). Special cylindrically ground lenses or laser procedures are used to correct this problem.✦

☑ Check Your Understanding

4. Arrange the following in the order that light passes through them to reach the photoreceptors (rods and cones) in the retina: lens, bipolar cells, vitreous humor, cornea, aqueous humor, ganglion cells. (Hint: See Figure 15.6 if you need a reminder of where ganglion cells and bipolar cells are.)
5. You have been reading this book for a while now and your eyes are beginning to tire. Which intrinsic eye muscles are relaxing as you stare thoughtfully into the distance?
6. Why does your near point of vision move farther away as you age?

For answers, see Appendix H.

Photoreceptors and Phototransduction

✓ Describe the events that convert light into a neural signal.

✓ Compare and contrast the roles of rods and cones in vision.

✓ Compare and contrast light and dark adaptation.

Once light is focused on the retina, the photoreceptors come into play. First, we will describe the functional anatomy of the rod and cone photoreceptor cells, then the chemistry and response of their visual pigments to light, and finally, photoreceptor activation, phototransduction, and information processing in the retina. **Phototransduction** is the process by which light energy is converted into a graded receptor potential.

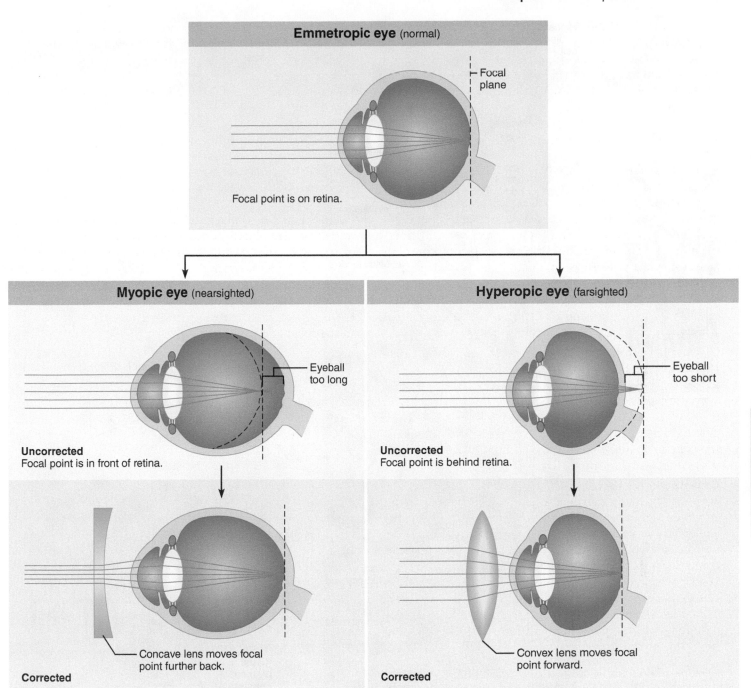

Figure 15.14 Problems of refraction. The refractive power of the cornea, which normally supplies about two-thirds of the light-bending power of the eye, is ignored here.

Functional Anatomy of the Photoreceptors

Photoreceptors are modified neurons, but structurally they resemble tall epithelial cells turned upside down with their "tips" immersed in the pigmented layer of the retina (Figure 15.15a). These "tips" are the receptive regions of rods and cones and are called the **outer segments**. Moving from the pigmented layer into the neural layer, a connecting cilium joins the outer segment of a rod or cone to the **inner segment**. The inner segment then connects to the *cell body*, which is continuous with an *inner fiber* bearing *synaptic terminals*.

In rods, the outer segment is slender and rod shaped (hence their name) and the inner segment connects to the cell body by the *outer fiber*. By contrast, the cones have a short conical outer segment and the inner segment directly joins the cell body.

(a) **The outer segments of rods and cones are embedded in the pigmented layer of the retina.**

(b) **Rhodopsin, the visual pigment in rods, is embedded in the membrane that forms discs in the outer segment.**

Figure 15.15 Photoreceptors of the retina.

The outer segments contain an elaborate array of **visual pigments (photopigments)** that change shape as they absorb light. These pigments are embedded in areas of the plasma membrane that form discs (Figure 15.15b). Folding the plasma membrane into discs increases the surface area available for trapping light.

In rods, the discs are discontinuous—stacked inside a cylinder of plasma membrane like pennies in a coin wrapper. In cones, the disc membranes are continuous with the plasma membrane, so the interiors of the cone discs are continuous with the extracellular space.

Photoreceptor cells are highly vulnerable to damage and immediately begin to degenerate if the retina becomes detached. They are also destroyed by intense light, the very energy they detect. How is it, then, that we do not all gradually go blind? The answer lies in the photoreceptors' unique system for renewing their light-trapping outer segment. Every 24 hours, new components are synthesized in the cell body and added to the base of the outer segment. As new discs are made, the discs at the tip of the outer segment continually fragment off and pigment cells phagocytize them.

Comparing Rod and Cone Vision

Rods and cones have different thresholds for activation. Rods, for example, are very sensitive (they respond to very dim light—a single photon), making them best suited for night vision and peripheral vision. Cones, on the other hand, need bright light for activation (have low sensitivity), but react more rapidly. Cones have one of three different pigments that furnish a vividly colored view of the world, but rods contain a single kind of visual pigment so their inputs are perceived only in gray tones.

Rods and cones are also "wired" differently to other retinal neurons. Rods participate in converging pathways, and as many as 100 rods may ultimately feed into each ganglion cell. As a result, rod effects are summated and considered collectively, resulting in vision that is fuzzy and indistinct. (The visual cortex has no way of knowing exactly *which* rods of the large number influencing a particular ganglion cell are actually activated.)

In contrast, each cone in the fovea (or at most a few) has a straight-through pathway via its "own personal bipolar cell" to a ganglion cell (see Figure 15.6b). Essentially, each foveal cone has its own "labeled line" to the higher visual centers—permitting detailed, high-acuity (high-resolution) views of very small areas of the visual field.

Because rods are absent from the foveae and cones do not respond to low-intensity light, we see dimly lit objects best when we do not look at them directly, and we recognize them best when they move. If you doubt this, go out into your backyard on a moonlit evening and see how much you can actually discriminate.

Table 15.1 summarizes the differences between rods and cones.

The Chemistry of Visual Pigments

How do photoreceptors translate incoming light into electrical signals? The key is a light-absorbing molecule called **retinal** that combines with proteins called **opsins** to form four types of visual pigments. Depending on the type of opsin to which it is bound, retinal absorbs different wavelengths of the visible spectrum.

The cone opsins differ both from the opsin of the rods and from one another. The naming of cones reflects the colors (that is, wavelengths) of light that each cone variety absorbs best. Blue cones respond maximally to wavelengths around 420 nm, green cones to wavelengths of 530 nm, and red cones to wavelengths at or close to 560 nm (see Figure 15.10b).

Table 15.1	Comparison of Rods and Cones
RODS	**CONES**
Noncolor vision (one visual pigment)	Color vision (three visual pigments)
High sensitivity; function in dim light	Low sensitivity; function in bright light
Low acuity (many rods converge onto one ganglion cell)	High acuity (one cone per ganglion cell in fovea)
More numerous (20 rods for every cone)	Less numerous
Mostly in peripheral retina	Mostly in central retina

How do we see other colors besides blue, green, and red? Cones' absorption spectra overlap, and our perception of intermediate hues, such as yellow, orange, and purple, results from differential activation of more than one type of cone at the same time. For example, yellow light stimulates both red and green cone receptors, but if the red cones are stimulated more than the green cones, we see orange instead of yellow. When all cones are stimulated equally, we see white.

Homeostatic Imbalance 15.9

Color blindness is due to a congenital lack of one or more cone pigments. Inherited as an X-linked condition, it is far more common in males than in females. As many as 8–10% of males have some form of color blindness.

The most common type is red-green color blindness, resulting from a deficit or absolute absence of either red or green cone pigments. Red and green are seen as the same color—either red or green, depending on the cone pigment present. Many color-blind people are unaware of their condition because they have learned to rely on other cues—such as different intensities of the same color—to distinguish something green from something red, such as traffic signals. ✛

Retinal is chemically related to vitamin A and is made from it. The cells of the pigmented layer of the retina absorb vitamin A from the blood and serve as the local vitamin A depot for rods and cones.

Retinal can assume a variety of distinct three-dimensional forms, each form called an isomer. When bound to opsin, retinal has a bent, or kinked, shape called **11-*cis*-retinal**, as shown at the top of Figure 15.16. However, when the pigment is struck by light and absorbs a photon, retinal twists and snaps into a new configuration, **all-*trans*-retinal**, shown at the bottom of Figure 15.16. This change, in turn, causes opsin to change shape and assume its activated form.

The capture of light by visual pigments is the *only* light-dependent stage, and this simple photochemical event initiates a whole chain of chemical and electrical reactions in rods and cones that ultimately causes electrical impulses to be transmitted

Figure 15.16 The formation and breakdown of rhodopsin. 11-*cis*-retinal can either be regenerated from all-*trans*-retinal or made from vitamin A.

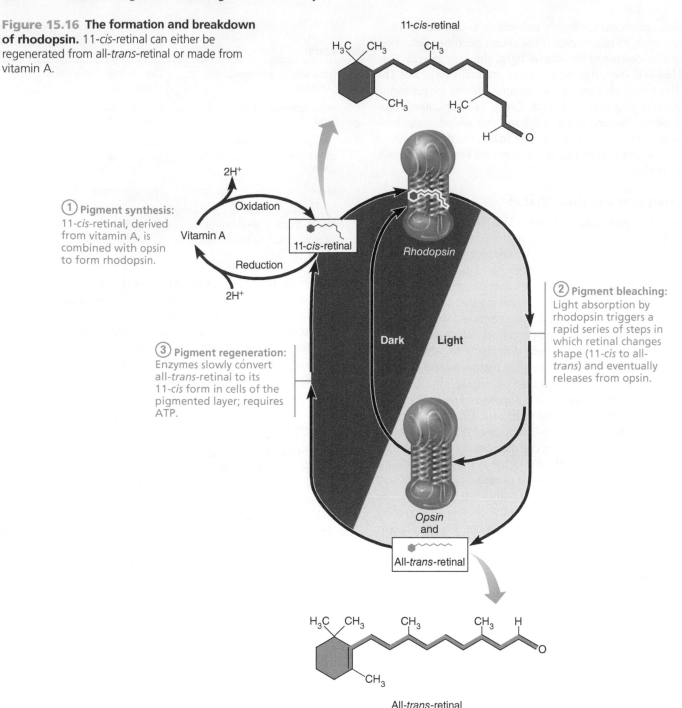

① **Pigment synthesis:** 11-*cis*-retinal, derived from vitamin A, is combined with opsin to form rhodopsin.

③ **Pigment regeneration:** Enzymes slowly convert all-*trans*-retinal to its 11-*cis* form in cells of the pigmented layer; requires ATP.

② **Pigment bleaching:** Light absorption by rhodopsin triggers a rapid series of steps in which retinal changes shape (11-*cis* to all-*trans*) and eventually releases from opsin.

along the optic nerve. Let's look more closely at these events in rods and in cones.

Phototransduction

Phototransduction begins when a visual pigment captures a photon of light.

Capturing Light The visual pigment of rods is a deep purple pigment called **rhodopsin** (ro-dop′sin; *rhodo* = rose, *opsis* = vision). (Do you suppose the person who coined the expression "looking at the world through rose-colored glasses" knew the meaning of "rhodopsin"?) Rhodopsin molecules are arranged in

a single layer in the membranes of each of the thousands of discs in the rods' outer segments. The formation and breakdown of rhodopsin is shown in Figure 15.16.

① **Pigment synthesis:** Rhodopsin forms and accumulates in the dark. Vitamin A is oxidized (and isomerized) to the 11-*cis*-retinal form and then combined with opsin to form rhodopsin.

② **Pigment bleaching:** When rhodopsin absorbs light, retinal changes shape to its all-*trans* isomer, allowing the surrounding protein to quickly relax like an uncoiling spring into its light-activated form. Eventually, the retinal-opsin

Recall from Chapter 3 that G protein signaling mechanisms are like a molecular relay race.

Light (1st messenger)   Receptor   G protein   Enzyme   2nd messenger

① Retinal absorbs light and changes shape. Visual pigment activates.

Visual pigment

Light

All-*trans*-retinal

Phosphodiesterase (PDE)

Ca^{2+} Ca^{2+}

Na^+ Na^+

cGMP

cGMP

GMP

cGMP-gated cation channel open in dark

cGMP-gated cation channel closed in light

11-*cis*-retinal

Transducin (a G protein)

② Visual pigment activates transducin (G protein).

③ Transducin activates phosphodiesterase (PDE).

④ PDE converts cGMP into GMP, causing cGMP levels to fall.

⑤ As cGMP levels fall, cGMP-gated cation channels close, resulting in hyperpolarization.

Figure 15.17 Events of phototransduction. A portion of photoreceptor disc membrane is shown. The G protein conversion of GTP to GDP has been omitted for clarity. For simplicity, the channels gated by cyclic GMP (cGMP) are shown on the same membrane as the visual pigment instead of in the plasma membrane.

combination breaks down, allowing retinal and opsin to separate. The breakdown of rhodopsin to retinal and opsin is known as the **bleaching of the pigment**.

③ **Pigment regeneration:** Once the light-struck all-*trans*-retinal detaches from opsin, enzymes within the pigmented epithelium reconvert it to its 11-*cis* isomer. Then, retinal heads "homeward" again to the photoreceptor cells' outer segments. Rhodopsin is regenerated when 11-*cis*-retinal is rejoined to opsin.

The breakdown and regeneration of visual pigments in cones is essentially the same as for rhodopsin. However, cones are about a hundred times less sensitive than rods, which means that it takes higher-intensity (brighter) light to activate cones.

Light Transduction Reactions What happens when light changes opsin's shape? An enzymatic cascade occurs that ultimately results in closing cation channels that are normally kept open in the dark. **Figure 15.17** illustrates this process in more detail, but in short, light-activated rhodopsin activates a G protein called **transducin**. Transducin, in turn, activates *PDE* (*phosphodiesterase*), the enzyme that breaks down **cyclic GMP** (**cGMP**). In the dark, cGMP binds to cation channels in the outer segments of photoreceptor cells, holding them open. This

allows Na^+ and Ca^{2+} to enter, depolarizing the cell to its *dark potential* of about −40 mV. In the light, cGMP breaks down, the cation channels close, Na^+ and Ca^{2+} stop entering the cell, and the cell hyperpolarizes to about −70 mV.

This arrangement can seem bewildering, to say the least. Here we have receptors built to detect light that depolarize in the dark and hyperpolarize when exposed to light! However, all that is required is a signal and hyperpolarization is just as good a signal as depolarization.

Information Processing in the Retina

How is the hyperpolarization of the photoreceptors transmitted through the retina and on to the brain? **Figure 15.18** illustrates this process. As you study this sequence, notice that the photoreceptors do not generate action potentials (APs), and neither do the bipolar cells that lie between them and the ganglion cells. Photoreceptors and bipolar cells only generate graded potentials—excitatory postsynaptic potentials (EPSPs) and inhibitory postsynaptic potentials (IPSPs).

This is not surprising if you remember that the primary function of APs is to carry information rapidly over long distances. Retinal cells are small cells that are very close together. Graded potentials can serve quite adequately as signals that directly

15

Below, we look at a tiny column of retina. The outer segment of the rod, closest to the back of the eye and farthest from the incoming light, is at the top.

In the dark

In the light

Light

Light

① cGMP-gated channels open, allowing cation influx. Photoreceptor depolarizes.

Na⁺
Ca²⁺

① cGMP-gated channels close, so cation influx stops. Photoreceptor hyperpolarizes.

Photoreceptor cell (rod)

② Voltage-gated Ca²⁺ channels open in synaptic terminals.

−40 mV

−70 mV

② Voltage-gated Ca²⁺ channels close in synaptic terminals.

Ca²⁺

③ Neurotransmitter is released continuously.

③ No neurotransmitter is released.

④ Neurotransmitter causes IPSPs in bipolar cell. Hyperpolarization results.

④ Lack of IPSPs in bipolar cell results in depolarization.

Bipolar cell

⑤ Depolarization opens voltage-gated Ca²⁺ channels; neurotransmitter is released.

⑤ Hyperpolarization closes voltage-gated Ca²⁺ channels, inhibiting neurotransmitter release.

Ca²⁺

⑥ No EPSPs occur in ganglion cell.

⑥ EPSPs occur in ganglion cell.

Ganglion cell

⑦ Action potentials propagate along the optic nerve.

⑦ No action potentials occur along the optic nerve.

Figure 15.18 Signal transmission in the retina. EPSP = excitatory postsynaptic potential; IPSP = inhibitory postsynaptic potential.

regulate neurotransmitter release at the synapse by opening or closing voltage-gated Ca²⁺ channels.

As shown in the right panel of Figure 15.18, for example, light hyperpolarizes photoreceptors, which then stop releasing their inhibitory neurotransmitter (glutamate). No longer inhibited, bipolar cells depolarize and release neurotransmitter onto ganglion cells. Once the signal reaches the ganglion cells, it is converted into an AP. This AP is transmitted to the brain along the ganglion cell axons that make up the optic nerve.

Light and Dark Adaptation

Rhodopsin is amazingly sensitive. Even starlight bleaches some of its molecules. As long as the light is low intensity, relatively little rhodopsin bleaches and the retina continues to respond to light stimuli. However, in high-intensity light, there is wholesale bleaching of the pigment, and rhodopsin bleaches as fast as it is re-formed. At this point, the rods are nonfunctional, but cones still respond. Hence, retinal sensitivity automatically adjusts to the amount of light present.

Light Adaptation   **Light adaptation** occurs when we move from darkness into bright light, as when leaving a movie matinee. We are momentarily dazzled—all we see is white light—because the sensitivity of the retina is still "set" for dim light. Both rods and cones are strongly stimulated, and large amounts of the visual pigments break down almost instantaneously, producing a flood of signals that accounts for the glare.

Under such conditions, compensations occur. The rod system turns off—all of the transducins "pack up and move" to the inner segment, uncoupling rhodopsin from the rest of the transduction cascade. Without transducin in the outer segment, light hitting rhodopsin cannot produce a signal. At the same time, the less sensitive cone system and other retinal neurons rapidly adapt, and retinal sensitivity decreases dramatically. Within about 60 seconds, the cones, initially overexcited by the bright light, are sufficiently desensitized to take over. Visual acuity and color vision continue to improve over the next 5–10 minutes. Thus, during light adaptation, we lose retinal sensitivity (rod function) but gain visual acuity.

Dark Adaptation   **Dark adaptation**, essentially the reverse of light adaptation, occurs when we go from a well-lit area into a dark one. Initially, we see nothing but velvety blackness because (1) our cones stop functioning in low-intensity light, and (2) the bright light bleached our rod pigments, and the rods are still turned off.

But once we are in the dark, rhodopsin accumulates, transducin returns to the outer segment, and retinal sensitivity increases. Dark adaptation is much slower than light adaptation and can go on for hours. However, there is usually enough rhodopsin within 20–30 minutes to allow adequate dim-light vision.

During both light and dark adaptation, reflexive changes occur in pupil size. Bright light shining in one or both eyes constricts both pupils (elicits the *pupillary* and *consensual light reflexes*). These pupillary reflexes are mediated by the pretectal nucleus of the midbrain and by parasympathetic fibers. In dim light, the pupils dilate, allowing more light to enter the eye.

Homeostatic Imbalance 15.10

Night blindness, or *nyctalopia* (nic″tă-lo′pe-uh), is a condition in which rod function is seriously hampered, impairing one's ability to drive safely at night. In countries where malnutrition is common, the most common cause of night blindness is prolonged vitamin A deficiency, which leads to rod degeneration.

Vitamin A supplements restore function if they are administered early.

In countries where nutrition isn't a problem, *retinitis pigmentosa*—a group of degenerative retinal diseases that destroy rods—are the most common causes of night blindness. Retinitis pigmentosa results from pigment epithelial cells that are unable to recycle the tips of the rods as they get sloughed off. ✚

☑ Check Your Understanding

7. For each of the following, indicate whether it applies to rods or cones: vision in bright light; only one type of visual pigment; most abundant in the periphery of the retina; many feed into one ganglion cell; color vision; higher sensitivity; higher acuity.
8. What does bleaching of the pigment mean and when does it happen?

For answers, see Appendix H.

Visual Pathways and Processing

✓ Trace the visual pathway to the visual cortex, and briefly describe the steps in visual processing.

The Visual Pathway to the Brain

As we described earlier, the axons of the retinal ganglion cells exit the eye in the **optic nerves** **(Figure 15.19)**. At the X-shaped **optic chiasma** (*chiasm* = cross), fibers from the medial aspect of each eye cross over to the opposite side and then continue on via the **optic tracts**. As a result, each optic tract

- Contains fibers from the lateral (temporal) aspect of the eye on the same side and fibers from the medial (nasal) aspect of the opposite eye
- Carries all the information from the same half of the visual field

Notice that, because the lens system of each eye reverses all images, the medial half of each retina receives light rays from the *temporal* (lateralmost) part of the visual field (that is, from the far left or far right rather than from straight ahead), and the lateral half of each retina receives an image of the nasal (central) part of the visual field. Consequently, the left optic tract carries (and sends on) a complete representation of the right half of the visual field, and the opposite is true for the right optic tract.

The paired optic tracts sweep posteriorly around the hypothalamus and send most of their axons to synapse with neurons in the **lateral geniculate nuclei** (contained within the lateral geniculate bodies) of the thalamus. The lateral geniculate nuclei maintain the fiber separation established at the chiasma, but they balance and combine the retinal input for delivery to the visual cortex. Axons of these thalamic neurons project through the internal capsule to form the **optic radiation** of fibers in the cerebral white matter (Figure 15.19). These fibers project to the **primary visual cortex** in the occipital lobes, where conscious perception of visual images (seeing) occurs.

Some nerve fibers in the optic tracts send branches to the midbrain. One set of these fibers ends in the **superior colliculi**,

(a) The visual fields of the two eyes overlap considerably.
Note that fibers from the lateral portion of each retinal field do not cross at the optic chiasma.

(b) Photograph of human brain, with the right side dissected to reveal internal structures.

Figure 15.19 Visual pathway to the brain and visual fields, inferior view.

visual reflex centers controlling the extrinsic muscles of the eyes. Another set comes from a small subset of ganglion cells in the retina that contain the visual pigment *melanopsin*, dubbed the circadian pigment. These ganglion cells respond directly to light stimuli and their fibers project to the **pretectal nuclei**, which mediate pupillary light reflexes, and to the **suprachiasmatic nucleus** of the hypothalamus, which functions as the "timer" to set our daily biorhythms.

Depth Perception

Notice that both eyes are set anteriorly and look in approximately the same direction. Their visual fields, each about 170 degrees, overlap to a considerable extent, and each eye sees a

slightly different view (Figure 15.19a). The visual cortex fuses the slightly different images delivered by the two eyes, providing us with **depth perception** (or **three-dimensional vision**), an accurate means of locating objects in space.

In contrast, many animals (pigeons, rabbits, and others) have *panoramic vision*. Their eyes are placed more laterally on the head, so that the visual fields overlap very little, and crossover of the optic nerve fibers is almost complete. Consequently, each visual cortex receives input principally from a single eye and a totally different visual field.

Depth perception depends on the two eyes working together. If only one eye is used, depth perception is lost, and the person must learn to judge an object's position based on learned cues (for example, nearer objects appear larger, and parallel lines converge with distance).

Homeostatic Imbalance 15.11

The visual system's pathways explain patterns of blindness that follow damage to different visual structures. Loss of an eye or destruction of one optic nerve eliminates true depth perception entirely, and peripheral vision on the damaged side. For example, if the "left eye" in Figure 15.19 was lost in a hunting accident, nothing would be seen in the visual field area that is stippled yellow in that figure.

If neural destruction occurs beyond the optic chiasma—in an optic tract, the thalamus, or visual cortex—then part or all of the opposite half of the visual field is lost. For example, a stroke affecting the left visual cortex leads to blindness in the right half of the visual field. However, since the right (undamaged) visual cortex still receives inputs from both eyes, depth perception in the remaining half of the visual field is retained.✚

Visual Processing

How does information received by rods and cones become vision? Visual processing begins in the retina.

Retinal cells simplify and condense the information from rods and cones, splitting it into a number of different "channels," each with its own type of ganglion cell. These "channels" include information about color and brightness, but also about more complex aspects of what we see—the angle, direction and speed of movement of *edges* (sudden changes in brightness or color). Extracting information about edges depends on a type of processing called *lateral inhibition*, a kind of contrast enhancement, which is the job of the amacrine and horizontal cells mentioned on p. 551.

The ganglion cells pass the processed information to the lateral geniculate nuclei of the thalamus. There, the retinal axons from each visual field of the two eyes are combined in preparation for depth perception, input from cones is emphasized, and contrast is further sharpened.

The *primary visual cortex*, also called the **striate cortex**, receives the thick bundle of fibers coming in from the lateral geniculate nucleus. This area contains an accurate topographical map of the retina, with the left visual cortex receiving input from the right visual field and vice versa. Visual processing here occurs at a relatively basic level, with the processing neurons responding to dark and bright edges (contrast information) and object orientation.

The striate cortex also provides form, color, and motion inputs to *visual association areas* collectively called the **prestriate cortices**. The more anterior prestriate cortices are occipital lobe centers that continue processing visual information concerned with form, color, and movement.

Functional neuroimaging of humans has revealed that complex visual processing extends well forward into the temporal, parietal, and frontal lobes via two parallel streams:

- The "what" processing stream extends through the ventral part of the temporal lobe and specializes in identifying objects in the visual field.

- The "where" processing stream takes a dorsal path through the parietal cortex all the way to the postcentral gyrus and uses information from the primary visual cortex to assess the location of objects in space.

Output from both these regions then passes to the frontal cortex, which uses that information to direct activities that, among other things, can guide movements such as reaching for a juicy peach.

☑ Check Your Understanding

9. Which part of the visual field would be affected by a tumor in the right visual cortex? By a tumor compressing the right optic nerve?

For answers, see Appendix H.

The Chemical Senses: Smell and Taste

✓ Describe the location, structure, and afferent pathways of smell and taste receptors, and explain how these receptors are activated.

Smell and taste are gritty, primitive senses that alert us to whether that "stuff" nearby (or in our mouth) is to be savored or avoided. The receptors for smell (olfaction) and taste (gustation) are **chemoreceptors** (they respond to chemicals in an aqueous solution). They complement each other and respond to different classes of chemicals. Smell receptors are excited by airborne chemicals that dissolve in fluids coating nasal membranes, and taste receptors are excited by food chemicals dissolved in saliva.

Olfactory Epithelium and the Sense of Smell

Although our olfactory sense (*olfact* = to smell) is far less acute than that of many other animals, the human nose is still no slouch in picking up small differences in odors. Some people capitalize on this ability by becoming wine tasters.

Location and Structure of Olfactory Receptors

Olfaction detects chemicals (*odorants*) in solution. The organ of smell is a yellow-tinged patch (about 5 cm^2) of pseudostratified epithelium, called the **olfactory epithelium**, located in the roof of the nasal cavity **(Figure 15.20a)**. Air entering the nasal cavity must make a hairpin turn to stimulate olfactory receptors before entering the respiratory passageway below, so the human olfactory epithelium is in a poor position for doing its job. (This is why sniffing, which draws more air superiorly across the olfactory epithelium, intensifies the sense of smell.)

The olfactory epithelium covers the superior nasal concha on each side of the nasal septum, and contains millions of bowling pin–shaped receptor cells—the **olfactory sensory neurons**. These are surrounded and cushioned by columnar **supporting cells**, which make up the bulk of the penny-thin epithelial

Figure 15.20 Olfactory receptors. (a) Site of olfactory epithelium in the superior nasal cavity. **(b)** An enlarged view of the olfactory epithelium showing the course of the fibers [filaments of the olfactory nerve (I)] through the ethmoid bone. These synapse in the glomeruli of the overlying olfactory bulb. The mitral cells are the output cells of the olfactory bulb.

membrane (Figure 15.20b). The supporting cells contain a yellow-brown pigment similar to lipofuscin, which gives the olfactory epithelium its yellow hue. At the base of the epithelium lie the short **olfactory stem cells**.

The olfactory sensory neurons are unusual bipolar neurons. Each has a thin apical dendrite that terminates in a knob from which several long cilia radiate. These **olfactory cilia**, which substantially increase the receptive surface area, typically lie flat on the nasal epithelium and are covered by a coat of thin mucus produced by the supporting cells and by olfactory glands in the underlying connective tissue. This mucus is a solvent that "captures" and dissolves airborne odorants. Unlike other cilia in the body, which beat rapidly in a coordinated manner, olfactory cilia are largely nonmotile.

The slender, nonmyelinated axons of the olfactory sensory neurons are gathered into small fascicles that collectively form the **filaments of the olfactory nerve** (cranial nerve I). They project superiorly through the openings in the cribriform plate of the ethmoid bone, where they synapse in the overlying olfactory bulbs.

Olfactory sensory neurons are also unusual because they are one of the few types of *neurons* that undergo noticeable turnover throughout adult life. Their superficial location puts them

at risk for damage, and their typical life span is 30–60 days. Olfactory stem cells in the olfactory epithelium differentiate to replace them.

Specificity of Olfactory Receptors

Smell is difficult to research because any given odor (say, tobacco smoke) may be made up of hundreds of different chemicals. Taste has been neatly packaged into five taste qualities as you will see, but science has yet to discover any similar means for classifying smell. Humans can distinguish 10,000 or so odors, but research suggests that our olfactory sensory neurons are stimulated by different combinations of a more limited number of olfactory qualities.

There are about 400 "smell genes" in humans that are active only in the nose. Each gene encodes a unique receptor protein. It appears that each protein responds to one or more odors and each odor binds to several different receptor types. However, each receptor cell has only one type of receptor protein.

Olfactory neurons are exquisitely sensitive—in some cases, just a few molecules activate them. Some of what we call smell is really pain. The nasal cavities contain pain and temperature receptors that respond to irritants such as the sharpness of

Figure 15.21 Olfactory transduction process. A portion of olfactory cilium membrane is shown.

ammonia, the hotness of chili peppers, and the "chill" of menthol. Impulses from these receptors reach the central nervous system via afferent fibers of the trigeminal nerves.

Physiology of Smell

For us to smell a particular odorant, it must be *volatile*—that is, it must be in the gaseous state as it enters the nasal cavity. Additionally, it must dissolve in the fluid coating the olfactory epithelium.

Activation of Olfactory Sensory Neurons Dissolved odorants stimulate olfactory sensory neurons by binding to receptor proteins in the olfactory cilium membranes, opening cation channels and generating a receptor potential. Ultimately (assuming threshold stimulation) an action potential is conducted to the first relay station in the olfactory bulb.

Smell Transduction Transduction of odorants uses a receptor linked to a G protein. The events that follow odorant binding will be easy for you to remember if you compare them to what you already know: general mechanisms of receptors and G proteins (see Figure 11.21) and phototransduction (see Figure 15.17).

As **Figure 15.21** shows, olfactory transduction begins when an odorant binds to a receptor. This event activates G proteins (G_{olf}), which activate enzymes (adenylate cyclases) that synthesize cyclic AMP as a second messenger. Cyclic AMP then acts directly on a plasma membrane cation channel, causing it to open, allowing Na^+ and Ca^{2+} to enter.

Na^+ influx leads to depolarization and impulse transmission. Ca^{2+} influx causes the transduction process to adapt, decreasing its response to a sustained stimulus. This *olfactory adaptation* helps explain how a person working in a paper mill or sewage treatment plant can still enjoy lunch!

The Olfactory Pathway

As we have already noted, axons of the olfactory sensory neurons form the olfactory nerves that synapse in the overlying **olfactory bulbs**, the distal ends of the olfactory tracts (see Table 13.2 on p. 494). There, the filaments of the olfactory nerves synapse with **mitral cells** (mi'tral), which are second-order sensory neurons, in complex structures called **glomeruli** (glo-mer'u-li; "little balls") (see Figure 15.20).

Axons from neurons bearing the same kind of receptor converge on a given type of glomerulus. That is, each glomerulus represents a single aspect of an odor (like one note in a chord) but each odor activates a unique set of glomeruli (the chord itself). Different odors activate different subsets of glomeruli (making different chords which may have some of the same notes). The mitral cells refine the signal, amplify it, and then relay it. The olfactory bulbs also house *amacrine granule cells*, GABA-releasing cells that inhibit mitral cells, so that only highly excitatory olfactory impulses are transmitted.

When the mitral cells are activated, impulses flow from the olfactory bulbs via the **olfactory tracts** (composed mainly of mitral cell axons) to the piriform lobe of the olfactory cortex. From there, two major pathways take information to various parts of the brain. One pathway brings information to part of the frontal lobe just above the orbit, where smells are consciously interpreted and identified. Only some of this information passes through the thalamus.

The other pathway flows to the hypothalamus, amygdala, and other regions of the limbic system. There, emotional responses to odors are elicited. Smells associated with danger—smoke, cooking gas, or skunk scent—trigger the sympathetic fight-or-flight response. Appetizing odors stimulate salivation and the digestive tract, and unpleasant odors can trigger protective reflexes such as sneezing and choking.

(a) Taste buds are associated with fungiform, foliate, and vallate papillae.

(b) Enlarged section of a vallate papilla.

(c) Enlarged view of a taste bud (210×).

Figure 15.22 Location and structure of taste buds on the tongue. (For a related image, see *A Brief Atlas of the Human Body*, Figure 62.)

Taste Buds and the Sense of Taste

The word *taste* comes from the Latin *taxare*, meaning "to touch, estimate, or judge." When we taste things, we are in fact intimately testing or judging our environment, and the sense of taste is considered by many to be the most pleasurable of the special senses.

Location and Structure of Taste Buds

Most of our 10,000 or so **taste buds**—the sensory organs for taste—are located on the tongue. A few taste buds are scattered on the soft palate, inner surface of the cheeks, pharynx, and epiglottis of the larynx, but most are found in **papillae** (pah-pil′e), peglike projections of the tongue mucosa that make the tongue surface slightly abrasive. Taste buds are located mainly on the tops of the mushroom-shaped **fungiform papillae** (fun′jĭ-form) (which are scattered over the entire tongue surface) and in the epithelium of the side walls of the **foliate papillae** and of the large round **vallate papillae** (val′āt). The vallate papillae are the largest and least numerous papillae, and 7 to 12 of them form an inverted V at the back of the tongue **(Figure 15.22a, b)**.

Each flask-shaped taste bud consists of 50 to 100 *epithelial cells* of two major types: *gustatory epithelial cells* and *basal epithelial cells* (Figure 15.22c).

Gustatory Epithelial Cells The **gustatory epithelial cells** are the receptor cells for taste—the *taste cells*. Long microvilli called **gustatory hairs** project from the tips of all gustatory epithelial cells and extend through a **taste pore** to the surface of the epithelium, where they are bathed by saliva. The gustatory hairs are the sensitive portions (*receptor membranes*) of the gustatory epithelial cells. Coiling intimately around the gustatory epithelial cells are sensory dendrites that represent the initial part of the gustatory pathway to the brain. Each afferent fiber receives signals from several gustatory epithelial cells within the taste bud.

There are at least three kinds of gustatory epithelial cells. One kind forms traditional synapses with the sensory dendrites and releases the neurotransmitter serotonin. The other two kinds lack synaptic vesicles, but at least one releases ATP that acts as a neurotransmitter.

Basal Epithelial Cells Because of their location, taste bud cells are subjected to friction and are routinely burned by hot foods. Luckily, they are among the most dynamic cells in the body, and they are replaced every seven to ten days. **Basal epithelial cells** act as stem cells, dividing and differentiating into new gustatory epithelial cells.

Basic Taste Sensations

Normally, our taste sensations are complicated mixtures of qualities. However, when taste is tested with pure chemical compounds, all taste sensations can be grouped into one of five basic modalities: sweet, sour, salty, bitter, and umami.

- *Sweet* taste is elicited by many organic substances including sugars, saccharin, alcohols, some amino acids, and some lead salts (such as those found in lead paint).

- *Sour* taste is produced by acids, specifically their hydrogen ions (H^+) in solution.

- *Salty* taste is produced by metal ions (inorganic salts); table salt (sodium chloride) tastes the "saltiest."

- *Bitter* taste is elicited by alkaloids (such as quinine, nicotine, caffeine, morphine, and strychnine) as well as a number of nonalkaloid substances, such as aspirin.

- *Umami* (u-mam′e; "delicious"), a subtle taste discovered by the Japanese, is elicited by the amino acids glutamate and aspartate, which appear to be responsible for the "beef taste" of steak, the characteristic tang of aging cheese, and the flavor of the food additive monosodium glutamate.

In addition, there is growing evidence for our ability to taste long-chain fatty acids from lipids. This possible sixth modality may help explain our liking for fatty foods.

Keep in mind that many substances produce a mixture of these basic taste sensations, and taste buds generally respond to all five. However, it appears that a single taste cell has receptors for only one taste modality.

Although taste maps that assign specific tastes to various areas of the tongue are common, researchers have known for years that these maps are dubious. All areas that contain taste buds can detect all modalities of taste.

Taste likes and dislikes have homeostatic value. Umami guides the intake of proteins, and a liking for sugar and salt helps satisfy the body's need for carbohydrates and minerals (as well as some amino acids). Many sour, naturally acidic foods (such as oranges, lemons, and tomatoes) are rich sources of vitamin C, an essential vitamin. On the other hand, intensely sour tastes warn us of spoilage. Likewise, many natural poisons and spoiled foods are bitter. Consequently, our dislike for sourness and bitterness is protective.

Physiology of Taste

For a chemical to be tasted it must dissolve in saliva, diffuse into a taste pore, and contact the gustatory hairs.

Activation of Taste Receptors Gustatory epithelial cells contain neurotransmitters. When a food chemical, or *tastant*, binds to receptors in the gustatory epithelial cell membrane, it induces a graded depolarizing potential that causes neurotransmitter release. Binding of the neurotransmitter to the associated sensory dendrites triggers generator potentials that elicit action potentials in these fibers.

The different gustatory epithelial cells have different thresholds for activation. In line with their protective nature, the bitter

receptors detect substances present in minute amounts. The other receptors are less sensitive. Taste receptors adapt rapidly, with partial adaptation in 3–5 seconds and complete adaptation in 1–5 minutes.

Taste Transduction The mechanisms of taste transduction are only now beginning to become clear. Three different mechanisms underlie how we taste.

- Salty taste is due to Na^+ influx through Na^+ channels, which directly depolarizes gustatory epithelial cells.

- Sour is mediated by H^+, which acts intracellularly to open channels that allow other cations to enter.

- Bitter, sweet, and umami responses share a common mechanism, but each occurs in a different cell. Each taste's unique set of receptors is coupled to a common G protein called *gustducin*. Activation leads to the release of Ca^{2+} from intracellular stores, which causes cation channels in the plasma membrane to open, thereby depolarizing the cell and releasing the neurotransmitter ATP.

The Gustatory Pathway

Afferent fibers carrying taste information from the tongue are found primarily in two cranial nerve pairs. A branch of the **facial nerve** (VII), the *chorda tympani*, transmits impulses from taste receptors in the anterior two-thirds of the tongue **(Figure 15.23)**. The lingual branch of the **glossopharyngeal nerve** (IX) services the posterior third and the pharynx just behind. Taste impulses from the few taste buds in the epiglottis and the lower pharynx are conducted primarily by the **vagus nerve** (X).

These afferent fibers synapse in the **solitary nucleus** of the medulla, and from there impulses stream to the thalamus and ultimately to the *gustatory cortex* in the insula. Fibers also project to the hypothalamus and limbic system structures, regions that determine our appreciation of what we are tasting.

An important role of taste is to trigger reflexes involved in digestion. As taste impulses pass through the solitary nucleus, they initiate reflexes (via synapses with parasympathetic nuclei) that increase secretion of saliva into the mouth and of gastric juice into the stomach. Saliva contains mucus that moistens food and digestive enzymes that begin digesting starch. Acidic foods are particularly strong stimulants of the salivary reflex. On the other hand, when we eat revolting or foul-tasting substances, the taste may initiate protective reactions such as gagging or reflexive vomiting.

Influence of Other Sensations on Taste

Taste is 80% smell. When nasal congestion (or just pinching your nostrils) blocks access to your olfactory receptors, food tastes bland. Without smell, our morning coffee would lack its richness and simply taste bitter.

The mouth also contains thermoreceptors, mechanoreceptors, and nociceptors, and the temperature and texture of foods can enhance or detract from their taste. "Hot" foods such as chili peppers actually bring about their pleasurable effects by exciting pain receptors in the mouth.

Figure 15.23 The gustatory pathway. Taste signals are relayed from the taste buds to the gustatory area of the cerebral cortex.

Homeostatic Imbalances of the Chemical Senses

Most olfactory disorders, or *anosmias* (an-oz′me-ahz; "without smells"), result from head injuries that tear the olfactory nerves, the aftereffects of nasal cavity inflammation, and neurological disorders such as Parkinson's disease. Some people have *uncinate fits* (un′sih-nāt), olfactory hallucinations during which they experience a particular (usually unpleasant) odor, such as rotting meat. *Olfactory auras* experienced by some epileptics just before they have a seizure are transient uncinate fits. These hallucinations can result from irritation of the olfactory pathway by brain surgery or head trauma.

Taste disorders are less common than disorders of smell, in part because the taste receptors are served by three different nerves and thus are less likely to be "put out of business" completely. Causes of taste disorders include upper respiratory tract infections, head injuries, chemicals or medications, or head and neck radiation for cancer treatment. Zinc supplements may help some cases of radiation-induced taste disorders.

☑ **Check Your Understanding**

10. Name the five taste modalities. Name the three types of papillae that have taste buds.
11. Olfactory sensory neurons have cilia and gustatory epithelial cells have hairs. How do these structures help the cells perform their functions?

For answers, see Appendix H.

The Ear: Hearing and Balance

✓ Describe the structure and general function of the outer, middle, and internal ears.

✓ Describe the sound conduction pathway to the fluids of the internal ear, and follow the auditory pathway from the spiral organ to the temporal cortex.

✓ Explain how we are able to differentiate pitch and loudness, and localize the source of sounds.

✓ List possible causes and symptoms of otitis media, deafness, and Ménière's syndrome.

At first glance, the machinery for hearing and balance appears very crude—fluids must be stirred to stimulate the mechanoreceptors of the internal ear. Nevertheless, our hearing apparatus allows us to hear an extraordinary range of sound, and our equilibrium (balance) receptors continually inform the nervous system of head movements and position. Although the organs serving these two senses are structurally interconnected within the ear, their receptors respond to different stimuli and are activated independently of one another.

Structure of the Ear

The ear is divided into three major areas: external ear, middle ear, and internal ear **(Figure 15.24a)**. The external and middle ear structures are involved with hearing only and are rather simply engineered. The internal ear functions in both equilibrium and hearing and is extremely complex.

External Ear

The **external (outer) ear** consists of the auricle and the external acoustic meatus. The **auricle**, or **pinna**, is what most people call the ear—the shell-shaped projection surrounding the opening of the external acoustic meatus. The auricle is composed of elastic cartilage covered with thin skin and an occasional hair. Its rim, the **helix**, is somewhat thicker, and its fleshy, dangling **lobule** ("earlobe") lacks supporting cartilage. The function of the auricle is to funnel sound waves into the external acoustic meatus.

The **external acoustic meatus** (auditory canal) is a short, curved tube (about 2.5 cm long by 0.6 cm wide) that extends from the auricle to the eardrum. Near the auricle, its framework is elastic cartilage; the remainder of the canal is carved into the

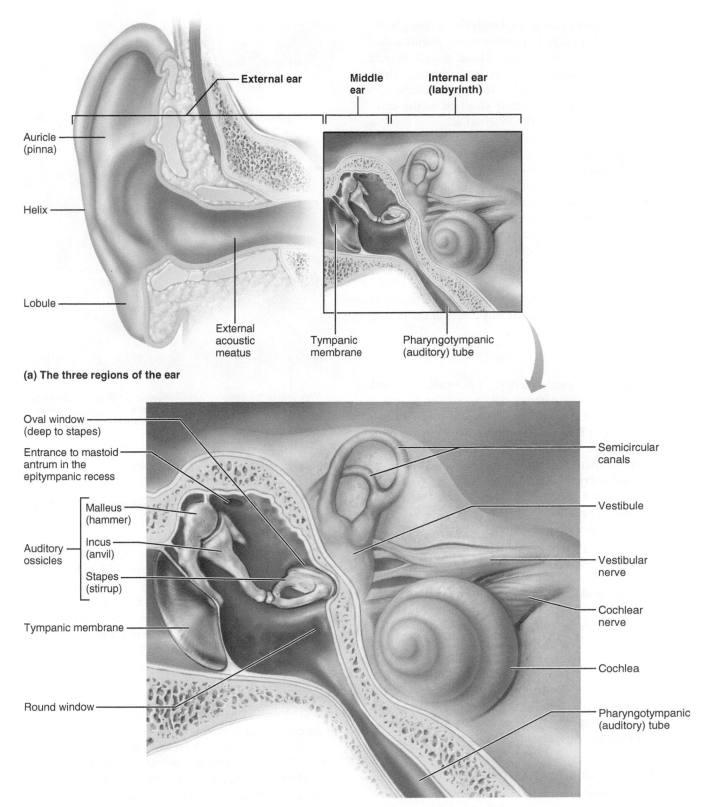

(a) The three regions of the ear

Auricle (pinna)

Helix

Lobule

External ear

Middle ear

Internal ear (labyrinth)

External acoustic meatus

Tympanic membrane

Pharyngotympanic (auditory) tube

(b) Middle and internal ear

Oval window (deep to stapes)

Entrance to mastoid antrum in the epitympanic recess

Malleus (hammer)

Incus (anvil)

Auditory ossicles

Stapes (stirrup)

Tympanic membrane

Round window

Semicircular canals

Vestibule

Vestibular nerve

Cochlear nerve

Cochlea

Pharyngotympanic (auditory) tube

Figure 15.24 Structure of the ear. The inner ear structures in (b) appear as though they are veiled because they are cavities within the temporal bone.

15

temporal bone. The entire canal is lined with skin bearing hairs, sebaceous glands, and modified apocrine sweat glands called **ceruminous glands** (sĕ-roo′mĭ-nus). These glands secrete yellow-brown waxy **cerumen**, or earwax (*cere* = wax), which provides a sticky trap for foreign bodies and repels insects.

In many people, the ear is naturally cleansed as the cerumen dries and then falls out of the external acoustic meatus. Jaw movements as a person eats, talks, and so on, create an unnoticeable conveyor-belt effect that moves the wax out. In other people, cerumen builds up and becomes compacted.

Sound waves entering the external acoustic meatus eventually hit the **tympanic membrane**, or *eardrum* (*tympanum* = drum), the boundary between the outer and middle ears. The eardrum is a thin, translucent, connective tissue membrane, covered by skin on its external face and by mucosa internally. Shaped like a flattened cone, its apex protrudes medially into the middle ear.

Sound waves make the eardrum vibrate. The eardrum, in turn, transfers the sound energy to the tiny bones of the middle ear and sets them vibrating.

Middle Ear

The **middle ear**, or **tympanic cavity**, is a small, air-filled, mucosa-lined cavity in the petrous portion of the temporal bone. It is flanked laterally by the eardrum and medially by a bony wall with two openings, the superior **oval window** and the inferior **round window**. Superiorly the tympanic cavity arches upward as the **epitympanic recess**, the "roof" of the middle ear cavity. The **mastoid antrum**, a canal in the posterior wall of the tympanic cavity, allows it to communicate with *mastoid air cells* housed in the mastoid process.

The anterior wall of the middle ear abuts the internal carotid artery (the main artery supplying the brain) and contains the opening of the **pharyngotympanic (auditory) tube** (formerly called the eustachian tube). The pharyngotympanic tube runs obliquely downward to link the middle ear cavity with the nasopharynx (the superiormost part of the throat), and the mucosa of the middle ear is continuous with that lining the pharynx (throat).

Normally, the pharyngotympanic tube is flattened and closed, but swallowing or yawning opens it briefly to equalize pressure in the middle ear cavity with external air pressure. This is important because the eardrum vibrates freely only if the pressure on both of its surfaces is the same; otherwise sounds are distorted. The ear-popping sensation of the pressures equalizing is familiar to anyone who has flown in an airplane.

Homeostatic Imbalance 15.12

Otitis media (me′de-ah), or middle ear inflammation, is a fairly common result of a sore throat, especially in children, whose pharyngotympanic tubes are shorter and run more horizontally. Otitis media is the most frequent cause of hearing loss in children. In acute infectious forms, the eardrum bulges and becomes inflamed and red. Most cases of otitis media are treated with antibiotics. When large amounts of fluid or pus accumulate in the cavity, an emergency *myringotomy* (lancing of the eardrum) may be required to relieve the pressure, and a tiny tube

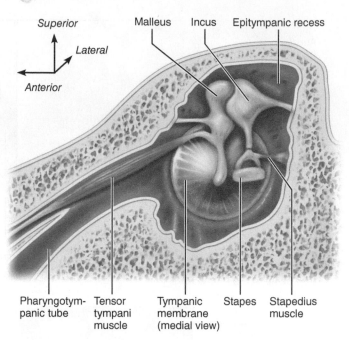

Superior
Lateral
Anterior

Malleus Incus Epitympanic recess

Pharyngotym- Tensor Tympanic Stapes Stapedius
panic tube tympani membrane muscle
  muscle (medial view)

View

Figure 15.25 The three auditory ossicles and associated skeletal muscles. Right middle ear, medial view.

implanted in the eardrum permits pus to drain into the external ear. The tube falls out by itself within a year. ✚

The tympanic cavity is spanned by the three smallest bones in the body: the **auditory ossicles** (Figure 15.24 and Figure 15.25). These bones, named for their shape, are the **malleus** (mal′e-us; "hammer"); the **incus** (ing′kus; "anvil"); and the **stapes** (sta′pēz; "stirrup"). The "handle" of the malleus is secured to the eardrum, and the base of the stapes fits into the oval window.

Tiny ligaments suspend the ossicles, and mini synovial joints link them into a chain that spans the middle ear cavity. The incus articulates with the malleus laterally and the stapes medially. The ossicles transmit the vibratory motion of the eardrum to the oval window, which in turn sets the fluids of the internal ear into motion, eventually exciting the hearing receptors.

Two tiny skeletal muscles are associated with the ossicles (Figure 15.25). The **tensor tympani** (ten′sor tim′pah-ni) arises from the wall of the pharyngotympanic tube and inserts on the malleus. The **stapedius** (stah-pe′de-us) runs from the posterior wall of the middle ear to the stapes. When loud sounds assault the ears, these muscles contract reflexively to limit the ossicles' vibration and minimize damage to the hearing receptors.

Internal Ear

The **internal ear** is also called the **labyrinth** ("maze") because of its complicated shape (see Figure 15.24). It lies deep in the temporal bone behind the eye socket and provides a secure site for all of the delicate receptor machinery.

Figure 15.26 Membranous labyrinth of the internal ear. The membranous labyrinth (blue) lies within the chambers of the bony labyrinth (tan). The locations of the sensory organs for hearing (spiral organ) and equilibrium (maculae and cristae ampullares) are shown in purple.

The internal ear has two major divisions: the bony labyrinth and the membranous labyrinth.

- The **bony labyrinth** is a system of tortuous channels worming through the bone. The views of the bony labyrinth typically seen in textbooks, including this one, are somewhat misleading because we are talking about a *cavity* here. The representation in Figure 15.24 can be compared to a plaster of paris cast of the cavity or hollow space inside the bony labyrinth.

- The **membranous labyrinth** is a continuous series of membranous sacs and ducts contained within the bony labyrinth and (more or less) following its contours **(Figure 15.26)**.

The bony labyrinth is filled with **perilymph**, a fluid similar to cerebrospinal fluid and continuous with it. The membranous labyrinth is suspended in the surrounding perilymph, and its interior contains **endolymph**, which is chemically similar to K+-rich intracellular fluid. These two fluids conduct the sound vibrations involved in hearing and respond to the mechanical forces occurring during changes in body position and acceleration.

The bony labyrinth has three regions: the *vestibule*, the *semicircular canals*, and the *cochlea*.

Vestibule The **vestibule** is the central egg-shaped cavity of the bony labyrinth. It lies posterior to the cochlea, anterior to the semicircular canals, and flanks the middle ear medially. In its lateral wall is the oval window.

Suspended in the vestibular perilymph and united by a small duct are two membranous labyrinth sacs, the **saccule** and **utricle** (u'trĭ-kl) (Figure 15.26). The smaller saccule is continuous with the membranous labyrinth extending anteriorly into the cochlea (the *cochlear duct*), whereas the utricle is continuous with the semicircular ducts extending into the semicircular

canals posteriorly. The saccule and utricle house equilibrium receptor regions called *maculae* that respond to the pull of gravity and report on changes of head position.

Semicircular Canals The **semicircular canals** lie posterior and lateral to the vestibule, and each of these canals defines about two-thirds of a circle. The cavities of the bony semicircular canals project from the posterior aspect of the vestibule, each oriented in one of the three planes of space. Accordingly, there is an *anterior*, a *posterior*, and a *lateral* semicircular canal in each internal ear. The anterior and posterior canals are oriented at right angles to each other in the vertical plane, whereas the lateral canal lies horizontally (Figure 15.26).

Snaking through each semicircular canal is a corresponding membranous **semicircular duct**, which communicates with the utricle anteriorly. Each of these ducts has an enlarged swelling at one end called an **ampulla**, which houses an equilibrium receptor region called a *crista ampullaris* (literally, crest of the ampulla). These receptors respond to angular (rotational) movements of the head.

Cochlea The **cochlea** (kok'le-ah), from the Latin "snail," is a spiral, conical, bony chamber about the size of a split pea. It extends from the anterior part of the vestibule and coils for about 2½ turns around a bony pillar called the **modiolus** (mo-di'o-lus) **(Figure 15.27a)**. Running through its center like a wedge-shaped worm is the membranous **cochlear duct**, which ends blindly at the cochlear apex. The cochlear duct houses the receptor organ of hearing, called the **spiral organ** or the *organ of Corti* (Figures 15.26 and 15.27b).

The cochlear duct and the **osseous spiral lamina**, a thin shelflike extension of bone that spirals up the modiolus like the thread on a screw, together divide the cavity of the bony cochlea into three separate chambers or **scalae** (*scala* = ladder).

Helicotrema
at apex

Modiolus

Cochlear nerve,
division of the
vestibulocochlear
nerve (VIII)

Spiral ganglion

Osseous spiral lamina

Vestibular membrane

Cochlear duct
(scala media)

(a)

Vestibular membrane

Tectorial membrane

Cochlear duct
(**scala media**;
contains
endolymph)

Stria
vascularis

Spiral organ

Basilar
membrane

Osseous spiral lamina

*Scala
vestibuli*
(contains
perilymph)

Spiral
ganglion

*Scala
tympani*
(contains
perilymph)

(b)

Tectorial membrane

Hairs (stereocilia)

Outer hair cells

Supporting cells

Inner hair cell

Afferent nerve
fibers

Fibers of
cochlear
nerve

**Basilar
membrane**

(c)

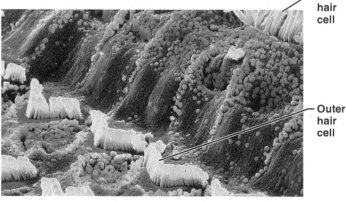

Inner
hair
cell

Outer
hair
cell

(d)

Figure 15.27 Anatomy of the cochlea. (a) Lateral view of part
of the internal ear with a wedge-shaped section removed from the
cochlea. **(b)** Magnified cross section of one turn of the cochlea,
showing the relationship of the three scalae. This cross section has
been rotated from its position in (a). **(c)** Detailed structure of the
spiral organ. **(d)** Electron micrograph of cochlear hair cells (550×).

(a) A struck tuning fork alternately compresses and rarefies the air molecules around it, creating alternate zones of high and low pressure.

(b) Sound waves radiate outward in all directions.

Figure 15.28 Sound: Source and propagation. The graph in (a) shows that plotting the oscillating air pressures yields a sine wave. The height (amplitude) of the crests is proportional to the energy, or intensity, of the sound wave. The distance between two corresponding points on the wave (crests or troughs) is the wavelength.

The **scala vestibuli** (ska′lah věs-tĭ′bu-li), which lies superior to the cochlear duct, is continuous with the vestibule and abuts the oval window. The middle **scala media** is the cochlear duct itself. The **scala tympani**, which terminates at the membrane-covered round window, is inferior to the cochlear duct.

Since the scala media is part of the membranous labyrinth, it is filled with endolymph. The scala vestibuli and the scala tympani, both part of the bony labyrinth, contain perilymph. The perilymph-containing chambers are continuous with each other at the cochlear apex, a region called the **helicotrema** (hel″ĭ-ko-tre′mah; "the hole in the spiral").

The "roof" of the cochlear duct, separating the scala media from the scala vestibuli, is the **vestibular membrane** (Figure 15.27b). The duct's external wall, the **stria vascularis**, is composed of an unusual richly vascularized mucosa that secretes endolymph. The "floor" of the cochlear duct is composed of the osseous spiral lamina and the flexible, fibrous basilar membrane, which supports the spiral organ. (We will describe the spiral organ when we discuss hearing.) The **basilar membrane**, which plays a critical role in sound reception, is narrow and thick near the oval window and gradually widens and thins as it approaches the cochlear apex. The *cochlear nerve*, a division of the *vestibulocochlear nerve* (VIII), runs from the spiral organ through the modiolus on its way to the brain.

Table 15.2 summarizes the structures of the internal ear and their functions.

Physiology of Hearing

We can summarize human hearing in a single sprawling sentence: Sounds set up vibrations in air that beat against the eardrum that pushes a chain of tiny bones that press fluid in the internal ear against membranes that set up shearing forces that pull on the tiny hair cells that stimulate nearby neurons that give rise to impulses that travel to the brain, which interprets them—and you hear. Before we unravel this intriguing sequence, let us describe sound, the stimulus for hearing.

Overview: Properties of Sound

Light can be transmitted through a vacuum (for instance, outer space), but sound depends on an *elastic* medium for its transmission. Sound also travels much more slowly than light. Its speed in dry air is only about 331 m/s (0.2 mi/s), as opposed to about 300,000 km/s (186,000 mi/s) for light. A lightning flash is almost instantly visible, but the sound it creates (thunder) reaches our ears much more slowly. (For each second between the lightning bolt and the roll of thunder, the storm is 1/5 mile farther away.) The speed of sound is fastest in solids and slowest in gases, but it is constant in a given medium.

Sound is a pressure disturbance—alternating areas of high and low pressure—produced by a vibrating object and propagated by the molecules of the medium. Consider a vibrating tuning fork **(Figure 15.28a)**. If the tuning fork is struck on the left, its prongs will move first to the right, creating an area of high pressure by compressing the air molecules there. Then, as the prongs rebound to the left, the air on the left will be compressed, and the region on the right will be a *rarefied*, or low-pressure, area (since most of its air molecules have been pushed farther to the right).

As the fork vibrates alternately from right to left, it produces a series of compressions and rarefactions, collectively called a *sound wave*, which moves outward in all directions (Figure 15.28b). However, the individual air molecules just vibrate back and forth for short distances as they bump other molecules and rebound. Because the outward-moving molecules give up kinetic energy

Table 15.2	Summary of the Internal Ear		
BONY LABYRINTH	**MEMBRANOUS LABYRINTH**	**FUNCTION**	**RECEPTOR REGION**
Semicircular canals	Semicircular ducts	Equilibrium: rotational (angular) acceleration	Crista ampullaris
Vestibule	Utricle and saccule	Equilibrium: head position relative to gravity, linear acceleration	Macula
Cochlea	Cochlear duct (scala media)	Hearing	Spiral organ

to the molecules they bump, energy is always transferred in the direction the sound wave is traveling. For this reason, the energy of the wave declines with time and distance, and the sound dies a natural death.

We can illustrate a sound wave as an S-shaped curve, or *sine wave*, in which the compressed areas are crests and the rarefied areas are troughs (Figure 15.28a). Sound can be described in terms of two physical properties that you can see in this sine wave graph: frequency and amplitude.

Frequency **Frequency** is defined as the number of waves that pass a given point in a given time. The sine wave of a pure tone has crests and troughs that repeat at definite distances. The distance between two consecutive crests (or troughs) is the

- High frequency (short wavelength) = high pitch
- Low frequency (long wavelength) = low pitch

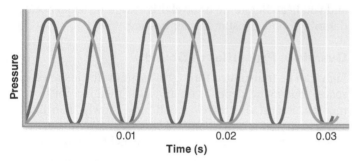

(a) Frequency is perceived as pitch.

- High amplitude = loud
- Low amplitude = soft

(b) Amplitude (size or intensity) is perceived as loudness.

Figure 15.29 Frequency and amplitude of sound waves.

wavelength of the sound and is constant for a particular tone. The shorter the wavelength, the higher the frequency of the sound (Figure 15.29a).

The frequency range of human hearing is from 20 to 20,000 waves per second, or *hertz* (*Hz*). Our ears are most sensitive to frequencies between 1500 and 4000 Hz and, in that range, we can distinguish frequencies differing by only 2–3 Hz. We perceive different sound frequencies as differences in **pitch**: the higher the frequency, the higher the pitch.

A tuning fork produces a *tone*—a pure (but bland) sound with a single frequency—but most sounds are mixtures of several frequencies. This characteristic of sound, called **quality**, enables us to distinguish between the same musical note—say, high C—sung by a soprano or played on a piano or clarinet. Sound quality also provides the richness and complexity of sounds (and music) that we hear.

Amplitude The **amplitude**, or height, of the sine wave crests reveals a sound's intensity, which is related to its energy, or the pressure differences between its compressed and rarefied areas (Figure 15.29b).

Loudness refers to our subjective interpretation of sound intensity. Because we can hear such an enormous range of intensities, from the proverbial pin drop to a jet engine 10 million times more intense, sound intensity (and loudness) is measured in logarithmic units called **decibels (dB)** (des′ĭ-belz).

On a clinical audiometer, the decibel scale is arbitrarily set to begin at 0 dB, which is the threshold of hearing (barely audible sound) for normal ears. Each 10-dB increase represents a tenfold increase in sound intensity. A sound of 10 dB has 10 times more energy than one of 0 dB, and a 20-dB sound has 100 times (10 × 10) more energy. However, the same 10-dB increase represents only a twofold increase in loudness. In other words, most people would report that a 20-dB sound seems about twice as loud as a 10-dB sound. The normal range of hearing (from barely audible to the loudest sound we can process without excruciating pain) extends over a range of 120 dB. (The threshold of pain is 120 dB.)

Severe hearing loss occurs with frequent or prolonged exposure to sounds with intensities greater than 90 dB, and in the U.S., employees exposed to occupational noise over that range must wear ear (hearing) protection. That number becomes more meaningful when you realize that a normal conversation is in the 50-dB range, a noisy restaurant has 70-dB levels, and amplified rock music is 120 dB or more, far above the 90-dB danger zone.

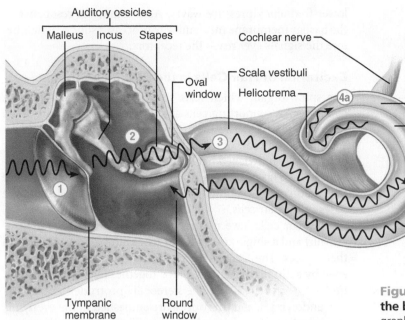

Auditory ossicles

Malleus Incus Stapes

Cochlear nerve

Oval window

Scala vestibuli

Helicotrema

Scala tympani

Cochlear duct

Basilar membrane

Tympanic membrane

Round window

(a) Route of sound waves through the ear

① Sound waves vibrate the tympanic membrane.

② Auditory ossicles vibrate. Pressure is amplified.

③ Pressure waves created by the stapes pushing on the oval window move through fluid in the scala vestibuli.

④a Sounds with frequencies below hearing travel through the helicotrema and do not excite hair cells.

④b Sounds in the hearing range go through the cochlear duct, vibrating the basilar membrane and deflecting hairs on inner hair cells.

Figure 15.30 Pathway of sound waves and resonance of the basilar membrane. The cochlea is depicted as if uncoiled. The graph in the bottom panel of (b) represents fibers that span the width of the basilar membrane. The stiffness of these fibers "tunes" specific regions of the basilar membrane to vibrate at specific frequencies.

Basilar membrane

High-frequency sounds displace the basilar membrane near the base.

Medium-frequency sounds displace the basilar membrane near the middle.

Low-frequency sounds displace the basilar membrane near the apex.

Fibers of basilar membrane

Base (short, stiff fibers)

Apex (long, floppy fibers)

20,000   2000   200   20

Frequency (Hz)

(b) Different sound frequencies cross the basilar membrane at different locations.

Transmission of Sound to the Internal Ear

Hearing occurs when the auditory area of the temporal lobe cortex is stimulated. However, before this can happen, sound waves must be propagated through air, membranes, bones, and fluids to stimulate receptor cells in the spiral organ (**Figure 15.30a**).

Airborne sound entering the external acoustic meatus strikes the tympanic membrane and sets it vibrating at the same frequency. The greater the intensity, the farther the membrane is displaced in its vibratory motion. The motion of the tympanic membrane is amplified and transferred to the oval window by the ossicle lever system, which acts much like a hydraulic press or piston to transfer the same total force hitting the eardrum to the oval window.

Because the tympanic membrane is 17–20 times larger than the oval window, the pressure (force per unit area) actually exerted on the oval window is about 20 times that on the tympanic membrane. This increased pressure overcomes the stiffness and inertia of cochlear fluid and sets it into wave motion. This situation can be roughly compared to the difference in pressure relayed to the floor by the broad rubber heels of a man's shoes versus a woman's tiny spike heels. The man's weight—say, 70 kg (about 150 pounds)—is spread over several square inches, and his heels will not make dents in a pliable vinyl floor. But spike heels concentrate the same 70-kg force in an area of about 2.5 cm^2 (1 square inch) and *will* dent the floor.

15

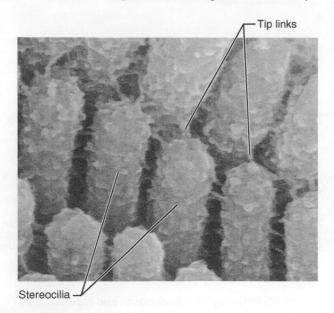

Tip links

Stereocilia

Figure 15.31 Photo of stereocilia on a hair cell. Note the precise order of the stereocilia.

Resonance of the Basilar Membrane

As the stapes rocks back and forth against the oval window, it sets the perilymph in the scala vestibuli into a similar back-and-forth motion. A pressure wave travels through the perilymph from the basal end toward the helicotrema, much as a piece of rope held horizontally can be set into wave motion by movements initiated at one end.

Fluids cannot be compressed. Think of what happens when you sit on a water bed—you sit "here" and it bulges over "there." In a similar way, each time the stapes forces the fluid adjacent to the oval window medially, the membrane of the round window bulges laterally into the middle ear cavity and acts as a pressure valve.

Sounds of very low frequency (below 20 Hz) create pressure waves that take the complete route through the cochlea—up the scala vestibuli, around the helicotrema, and back toward the round window through the scala tympani (Figure 15.30a). These low-frequency sounds do not activate the spiral organ and so are below the range of hearing.

In contrast, sounds with frequencies high enough to hear create pressure waves that take a "shortcut" and are transmitted through the cochlear duct into the perilymph of the scala tympani. As a pressure wave descends through the flexible cochlear duct, it vibrates the entire basilar membrane.

Maximal displacement of the membrane occurs where the fibers of the basilar membranes are "tuned" to a particular sound frequency (Figure 15.30b). This characteristic of maximum movement at a particular frequency is called *resonance*. The fibers of the basilar membrane span its width like the strings of a harp. The fibers near the oval window (cochlear base) are short and stiff, and they resonate in response to high-frequency pressure waves (Figure 15.30b). The longer, more floppy basilar membrane fibers near the cochlear apex resonate in time with lower-frequency pressure waves. As a result, the resonance of the basilar membrane mechanically processes sound signals before the signals ever reach the receptors.

Excitation of Hair Cells in the Spiral Organ

The spiral organ, which rests atop the basilar membrane, is composed of supporting cells and hearing receptor cells called *cochlear hair cells*. The hair cells are arranged functionally—specifically, one row of **inner hair cells** and three rows of **outer hair cells**—sandwiched between the tectorial and basilar membranes (see Figure 15.27c). Afferent fibers of the **cochlear nerve** [a division of the vestibulocochlear nerve (VIII)] coil about the bases of the hair cells.

The hair cells have numerous *stereocilia* (actually long microvilli) and a single *kinocilium* (a true cilium) protruding from their apices. The "hairs" (stereocilia) of the hair cells are stiffened by actin filaments and linked together by fine fibers called *tip links* **(Figure 15.31)**. The stereocilia protrude into the K^+-rich endolymph, and the longest are enmeshed in the overlying, stiff gel-like **tectorial membrane** (see Figure 15.27c).

Transduction of sound stimuli occurs after localized movements of the basilar membrane "tweak" or deflect the trapped stereocilia of the hair cells. Bending the stereocilia toward the kinocilium puts tension on the tip links, which in turn opens cation channels in the adjacent shorter stereocilia like a rope pulling on a trap door. This results in an inward K^+ (and Ca^{2+}) current and a graded depolarization (receptor potential). Bending the cilia away from the kinocilium relaxes the tip links, closes the mechanically gated ion channels, and allows repolarization and even a graded hyperpolarization.

Depolarization increases intracellular Ca^{2+} and so increases the hair cells' release of neurotransmitter (glutamate), which causes the afferent cochlear fibers to transmit a faster stream of impulses to the brain for auditory interpretation. Hyperpolarization produces the exact opposite effect. As you might guess, activation of the hair cells occurs at points of vigorous basilar membrane vibration.

The vast majority of the sensory fibers of the spiral ganglia (90–95%) service the inner hair cells, which shoulder nearly the entire responsibility for sending auditory messages to the brain. By contrast, most fibers coiling around the more numerous outer hair cells are *efferent* fibers that convey messages from brain to ear. So what do the outer hair cells do?

The outer hair cells act on the basilar membrane itself. When outer hair cells depolarize and hyperpolarize as the basilar membrane moves, they contract and stretch in a type of cellular boogie called *fast motility*. Their strange behavior changes the stiffness of the basilar membrane.

Outer hair cell motility serves two functions:

- It increases the responsiveness of the inner hair cells by amplifying the motion of the basilar membrane—a kind of cochlear tuning.

- It may help protect the inner hair cells from damage. Loud sounds activate a negative feedback loop from the brain stem to the outer hair cells via the efferent fibers, which release neurotransmitters that cause the outer hair cells to stiffen. This dampens the motion of the basilar membrane and spreads the sound energy over a wider area.

The Auditory Pathway to the Brain

The ascending auditory pathway transmits auditory information primarily from the cochlear receptors (the inner hair cells) to the cerebral cortex. Impulses generated in the cochlea pass through the **spiral ganglion**, where the auditory bipolar cells reside, and along the afferent fibers of the cochlear nerve to the **cochlear nuclei** of the medulla **(Figure 15.32)**.

From there, neurons project to the **superior olivary nucleus**, which lies at the junction of the medulla and pons. Beyond this, axons ascend in the **lateral lemniscus** (a fiber tract) to the **inferior colliculus** (auditory reflex center in the midbrain), which projects to the **medial geniculate nucleus** of the thalamus. Axons of the thalamic neurons then project to the **primary auditory cortex**, which provides conscious awareness of sound.

The auditory pathway is unusual because not all of the fibers from each ear cross over to the other side of the brain. For this reason, each auditory cortex receives impulses from both ears.

Auditory Processing

If you are at a Broadway musical, the sound of the instruments, the actors' voices, rustling of clothing, and closing of doors are all intermingled in your awareness. Yet, your auditory cortex can distinguish the separate parts of this auditory jumble. Whenever the difference between sound wavelengths is sufficient for discrimination, you hear two separate and distinct tones. In fact, the analytic powers of the auditory cortex are so great that we are able to pick single instruments out of a whole orchestra.

Cortical processing of sound stimuli is complex. For example, certain cortical cells depolarize at the beginning of a particular tone, and others depolarize when the tone ends. Some cortical cells depolarize continuously, and others appear to have high thresholds (low sensitivity), and so on. Here we will concentrate on the more straightforward aspects of cortical perception of pitch, loudness, and sound location.

Perception of Pitch   As we explained, sound waves of different frequencies activate hair cells in different positions along the length of the basilar membrane, and impulses from specific hair cells are interpreted as specific pitches. When a sound is composed of tones of many frequencies, it activates several populations of cochlear hair cells and cortical cells simultaneously, and we perceive multiple tones.

Detection of Loudness   Louder sounds cause larger movements of the tympanic membrane, auditory ossicles, and oval window, and pressure waves of greater amplitude in the fluids of the cochlea. These larger waves in turn cause larger movements of the basilar membrane, larger deflections of the hairs on the hair cells, and larger graded potentials in the hair cells. As a result, they release more neurotransmitter and generate more frequent action potentials. The brain interprets more

Figure 15.32 The auditory pathway. This simplified diagram shows only the pathway from the right ear.

frequent action potentials as greater loudness. In addition, as more neurotransmitter is released, more of the 10 or so bipolar cells connected to a given hair cell are recruited to fire action potentials.

Localization of Sound   Several brain stem nuclei (most importantly the superior olivary nuclei) help us localize a sound's source in space by means of two cues: the *relative intensity* and the *relative timing* of sound waves reaching the two ears. If the sound source is directly in front, in back, or overhead, the intensity and timing cues are the same for both ears. However, when sound comes from one side, it activates the receptors of the nearer ear slightly earlier and also more vigorously (because of the greater intensity of the sound waves entering that ear).

☑ Check Your Understanding

12. Apart from the bony boundaries, which structure separates the external from the middle ear? Which two (nonbone) structures separate the middle from the inner ear?
13. Which structure inside the spiral organ allows us to differentiate sounds of different pitch?
14. If the brain stem did not receive input from both ears, what would you not be able to do?

For answers, see Appendix H.

Figure 15.33 Structure of a macula. The "hairs" of the receptor cells of a macula project into the gelatinous otolith membrane. Vestibular nerve fibers surround the base of the hair cells.

Equilibrium and Orientation

✓ Explain how the balance organs of the semicircular canals and the vestibule help maintain equilibrium.

The equilibrium sense is not easy to describe because it does not "see," "hear," or "feel," but responds (frequently without our awareness) to various head movements. Furthermore, this sense depends not only on inputs from the internal ear but also on vision and information from stretch receptors of muscles and tendons.

The equilibrium receptors in the semicircular canals and vestibule are collectively called the **vestibular apparatus**. Under normal conditions, they send signals to the brain that initiate reflexes needed to make the simplest changes in position as well as more complex moves such as serving a tennis ball precisely to the right spot (your opponent's backhand).

The equilibrium receptors of the vestibular apparatus can be divided into two functional arms. The receptors in the vestibule monitor linear acceleration and the position of the head with respect to gravity. Because gravity is constant, this is sometimes called our sense of *static equilibrium*. The semicircular canals monitor changes in head rotation, sometimes called our sense of *dynamic equilibrium*.

The Maculae

The **maculae** (mak'u-le; "spots"), one in each saccule wall and one in each utricle wall (Figure 15.33), are sensory receptor organs that monitor the position of the head in space. In so doing, they play a key role in controlling posture. They respond to *linear* acceleration, that is, changes in straight-line speed and direction, but not rotation.

Anatomy of a Macula Each macula is a flat epithelial patch containing **hair cells**. These hair cells, like all those of the internal ear, have stereocilia plus one kinocilium that project into a gel-like mass. **Supporting cells** surround the macula's scattered hair cells (Figure 15.33). The "hairs" of the hair cells are embedded in the overlying **otolith membrane** (o'to-lith), a jelly-like mass studded with tiny stones (calcium carbonate crystals) called **otoliths** ("ear stones"). The otoliths, though small, are dense and they increase the membrane's weight and its inertia (resistance to changes in motion).

In the utricle, the macula is horizontal, and the hairs are vertically oriented when the head is upright (Figure 15.33). For this reason, the utricular maculae respond best to acceleration in the horizontal plane and tilting the head to the side, because vertical (up-down) movements do not displace their horizontal otolith membrane.

In the saccule, on the other hand, the macula is nearly vertical, and the hairs protrude horizontally into the otolith membrane. The saccular maculae respond best to vertical movements, such as the sudden acceleration of an elevator.

The hair cells synapse with fibers of the **vestibular nerve**, whose endings coil around their bases. Like the cochlear nerve, the vestibular nerve is a subdivision of the vestibulocochlear nerve (VIII). The cell bodies of the sensory neurons are located in the nearby **superior** and **inferior vestibular ganglia** (see Figure 15.26).

Activating Macula Receptors What happens in the maculae that leads to sensory transduction? When your head starts or stops moving in a linear direction, inertia causes the otolith membrane to slide backward or forward like a greased plate over the hair cells, bending the hairs. For example, when you start to run, the otolith membranes of the utricle maculae lag behind, bending the hairs backward. When you suddenly stop, the otolith membrane slides abruptly forward (just as you slide forward in your car when you brake), bending the hair cells forward. Likewise, when you nod your head or fall, the otoliths roll inferiorly, bending the hairs of the maculae in the saccules.

The hair cells release neurotransmitter continuously but movement of their hairs modifies the amount they release (Figure 15.34).

■ When the hairs bend toward the kinocilium, the hair cells depolarize, stepping up their pace of neurotransmitter release, and more impulses travels up the vestibular nerve to the brain.

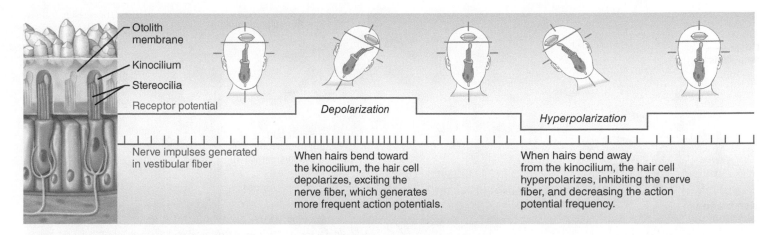

Otolith membrane
Kinocilium
Stereocilia
Receptor potential

Depolarization

Hyperpolarization

Nerve impulses generated in vestibular fiber

When hairs bend toward the kinocilium, the hair cell depolarizes, exciting the nerve fiber, which generates more frequent action potentials.

When hairs bend away from the kinocilium, the hair cell hyperpolarizes, inhibiting the nerve fiber, and decreasing the action potential frequency.

Figure 15.34 The effect of gravitational pull on a macula receptor cell in the utricle.

■ When the hairs bend away from the kinocilium, the receptors hyperpolarize and release less neurotransmitter, generating fewer impulses.

In either case, the brain is informed of the changing position of the head in space.

It is important to understand that the maculae respond to *changes* in the velocity of head movement (linear acceleration or deceleration). Because most hair cells adapt quickly (resuming their basal level of neurotransmitter release), they do not report on unchanging head positions. In this way, the maculae help us to maintain normal head position with respect to gravity.

The Cristae Ampullares

The receptor for rotational acceleration, called the **crista ampullaris** or simply *crista*, is a minute elevation in the ampulla of each semicircular canal (see Figure 15.26). Like the maculae, the cristae are excited by head movement (acceleration and deceleration), but in this case the major stimuli are rotational (angular) movements. When you twirl on the dance floor or suffer through a rough boat ride, these gyroscope-like receptors are working overtime. Since the semicircular canals are located in all three planes of space, all rotational movements of the head disturb one or another *pair* of cristae (one in each ear).

Anatomy of a Crista Ampullaris Each crista is composed of supporting cells and hair cells whose structure and function are basically the same as the hair cells of the cochlea and maculae. In this case, the gelled mass is an **ampullary cupula** (ku'pu-lah), which resembles a pointed cap (**Figure 15.35**). The cupula is a delicate, loosely organized network of gelatinous strands that radiate outward to contact the "hairs" of each hair cell. Dendrites of vestibular nerve fibers encircle the base of the hair cells.

Activating Crista Ampullaris Receptors The cristae respond to *changes* in the velocity of rotational movements of the head. Because of its inertia, the endolymph in the semicircular ducts moves briefly in the direction *opposite* the body's rotation, deforming the crista in the duct. As the hairs bend, the hair cells depolarize and impulses reach the brain at a faster rate (Figure 15.35c, middle panel). Bending the cilia in the opposite

direction causes hyperpolarization and generates fewer impulses. Because the axes of the hair cells in the complementary semicircular ducts are opposite, rotation in a given direction depolarizes the receptors in one ampulla of the pair, and hyperpolarizes the receptors in the other.

If the body continues to rotate at a constant rate, the endolymph eventually comes to rest—it moves along at the same speed as the body and the hair cells are no longer stimulated. Consequently, if we are blindfolded, we cannot tell whether we are moving at a constant speed or not moving at all after the first few seconds of rotation. However, when we suddenly stop moving, the endolymph keeps on going, in effect reversing its direction within the canal. This sudden reversal in the direction of hair bending alters membrane voltage in the receptor cells and modifies the rate of impulse transmission, which tells the brain that we have slowed or stopped (Figure 15.35c, right panel).

The key point to remember when considering both types of equilibrium receptors is that the rigid bony labyrinth moves with the body, while the fluids (and gels) within the membranous labyrinth are free to move at various rates, depending on the forces (such as gravity, acceleration, and so on) acting on them.

Vestibular Nystagmus Impulses transmitted from the semicircular canals are particularly important to reflex movements of the eyes. **Vestibular nystagmus** is a complex of rather strange eye movements that occurs during and immediately after rotation.

As you rotate, your eyes slowly drift in the opposite direction, as though fixed on some object in the environment. This reaction relates to the backflow of endolymph in the semicircular canals. Then, because of CNS compensating mechanisms, the eyes jump rapidly toward the direction of rotation to establish a new fixation point. These alternating eye movements continue until the endolymph comes to rest.

When you stop rotating, at first your eyes continue to move in the direction of the previous spin, and then they jerk rapidly in the opposite direction. This sudden change is caused by the change in the direction in which the cristae bend after you stop. Nystagmus is often accompanied by vertigo.

(a) Anatomy of a crista ampullaris in a semicircular canal

Crista ampullaris

Membranous labyrinth

Ampullary cupula

Endolymph

Hair bundle (kinocilium plus stereocilia)

Crista ampullaris

Hair cell

Fibers of vestibular nerve

Supporting cell

(b) Scanning electron micrograph of a crista ampullaris (200×)

Section of ampulla, filled with endolymph

Cupula

Fibers of vestibular nerve

Flow of endolymph

At rest, the cupula stands upright.

During rotational acceleration, endolymph moves inside the semicircular canals in the direction opposite the rotation (it lags behind due to inertia). Endolymph flow bends the cupula and excites the hair cells.

As rotational movement slows, endolymph keeps moving in the direction of rotation. Endolymph flow bends the cupula in the opposite direction from acceleration and inhibits the hair cells.

(c) Movement of the ampullary cupula during rotational acceleration and deceleration

Figure 15.35 Location, structure, and function of a crista ampullaris in the internal ear.

The Equilibrium Pathway to the Brain

Our responses to body imbalance, such as when we stumble, must be fast and reflexive. By the time we "thought about" correcting our fall, we would already be on the ground! Accordingly, information from equilibrium receptors goes directly to reflex centers in the brain stem, rather than to the cerebral cortex as with the other special senses.

The nerve pathways connecting the vestibular apparatus with the brain are complex. The transmission sequence begins when the hair cells in the vestibular apparatus are activated. As

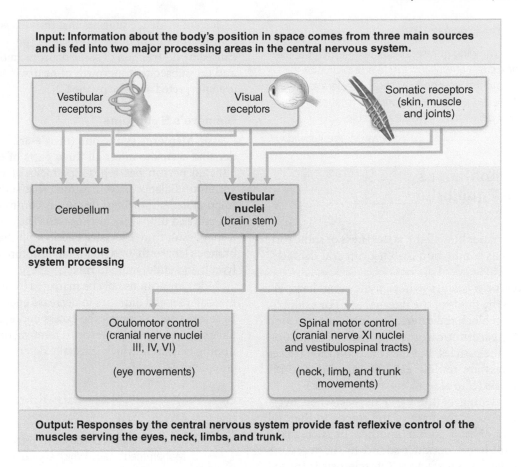

Figure 15.36 **Neural pathways of the balance and orientation system.**

depicted in **Figure 15.36**, impulses travel initially to one of two destinations: the **vestibular nuclei** in the brain stem or the **cerebellum**. The vestibular nuclei, the major integrative center for balance, also receive inputs from the visual and somatic receptors, particularly from proprioceptors in neck muscles that report on the position of the head. These nuclei integrate this information and then send commands to brain stem motor centers that control the extrinsic eye muscles (cranial nerve nuclei III, IV, and VI) and reflex movements of the neck, limb, and trunk muscles (via the vestibulospinal tracts). The ensuing reflex movements of the eyes and body allow us to remain focused on the visual field and quickly adjust our body position to maintain or regain balance.

The cerebellum also integrates inputs from the eyes and somatic receptors (as well as from the cerebrum). It coordinates skeletal muscle activity and regulates muscle tone to maintain head position, posture, and balance, often in the face of rapidly changing inputs. Its "specialty" is fine control of delicate postural movements and timing.

Notice that the vestibular apparatus *does not automatically compensate* for forces acting on the body. Its job is to send warning signals to the central nervous system, which initiates the appropriate compensations (righting) to keep your body balanced, your weight evenly distributed, and your eyes focused on what you were looking at when the disturbance occurred.

Homeostatic Imbalance 15.13

Responses to equilibrium signals are totally reflexive, and usually we are aware of vestibular apparatus activity only when its function is impaired. Equilibrium problems are usually obvious and unpleasant. Nausea, dizziness, and loss of balance are common and there may be nystagmus in the absence of rotational stimuli.

Motion sickness has been difficult to explain, but it appears to be due to sensory input mismatches. For example, if you are inside a ship during a storm, visual inputs indicate that your body is fixed with reference to a stationary environment (your cabin). But as rough seas toss the ship about, your vestibular apparatus detects movement and sends impulses that disagree with the visual information. The brain thus receives conflicting signals, and its "confusion" somehow leads to motion sickness.

Warning signals, which precede nausea and vomiting, include excessive salivation, pallor, rapid deep breathing, and profuse sweating. Removal of the stimulus usually ends the symptoms. Over-the-counter antimotion drugs, such as meclizine (Bonine), depress vestibular inputs and help alleviate the symptoms. They are most effective when taken "before the fact." Scopolamine-containing timed-release skin patches may also head off motion sickness. ✚

15. For each of the following phrases, indicate whether it applies to a macula or a crista ampullaris: inside a semicircular canal; contains otoliths; responds to linear acceleration and deceleration; has a cupula; responds to rotational acceleration and deceleration; inside a saccule.

For answers, see Appendix H.

Homeostatic Imbalances of Hearing and Equilibrium

Deafness

Any hearing loss, no matter how slight, is **deafness** of some sort. Deafness is classified as conduction or sensorineural deafness, according to its cause.

Conduction deafness occurs when something hampers sound conduction to the fluids of the internal ear. For example, compacted earwax can block the external acoustic meatus, or a *perforated* (*ruptured*) eardrum can prevent sound conduction from the eardrum to the ossicles. But the most common causes of conduction deafness are middle ear inflammations (otitis media) and **otosclerosis** (o″to-sklĕ-ro′sis) of the ossicles.

Otosclerosis ("hardening of the ear") occurs when overgrowth of bony tissue fuses the base of the stapes to the oval window or welds the ossicles to one another. In such cases, vibrations of the skull bones conduct sound to the receptors of that ear, which is far less satisfactory. Otosclerosis is treated surgically.

Sensorineural deafness results from damage to neural structures at any point from the cochlear hair cells to and including the auditory cortical cells. This type of deafness typically results from the gradual loss of hair cells throughout life. Hair cells can also be destroyed at an earlier age by a single explosively loud noise or prolonged exposure to high-intensity sounds, such as rock bands or airport noise, which literally tear off their cilia. Other causes of sensorineural deafness are degeneration of the cochlear nerve, strokes, and tumors in the auditory cortex.

Hair cells don't normally regenerate in mammals, but researchers are seeking ways to prod supporting cells into differentiating into hair cells. For congenital defects or age- or noise-related cochlear damage, cochlear implants (devices that convert sound energy into electrical signals) can be inserted into a drilled recess in the temporal bone. The original cochlear implants made human voices sound tinny and robotlike, but modern versions are so effective that even children born deaf can hear well enough to learn to speak well.

Tinnitus

Tinnitus (tĭ-ni′tus) is a ringing or clicking sound in the ears in the absence of auditory stimuli. It is usually a symptom rather than a disease. For example, tinnitus is one of the first symptoms of cochlear nerve degeneration. It may also signal inflammation of the middle or internal ears and is a side effect of some medications, such as aspirin.

Recent evidence suggests that tinnitus is analogous to phantom limb pain. In other words, it is "phantom cochlear noise" caused by destruction of some neurons in the auditory pathway and the subsequent ingrowth of nearby neurons whose signals are interpreted as noise by the CNS.

Ménière's Syndrome

Classic **Ménière's syndrome** (men″ē-ārz′) is a labyrinth disorder that seems to affect all three parts of the internal ear. The afflicted person has repeated attacks of vertigo, nausea, and vomiting. Balance is so disturbed that standing erect is nearly impossible. A "howling" tinnitus is common, so hearing is impaired (and ultimately lost) as well. The cause is uncertain, but it may result from excessive endolymph that distorts the membranous labyrinth, or a membrane rupture that allows the perilymph and endolymph to mix.

Mild cases can usually be managed by antimotion drugs or a low-salt diet and diuretics to decrease endolymph fluid volume. In severe cases, draining the excess endolymph from the internal ear may help. A last resort is removal of the entire malfunctioning labyrinth, which is usually deferred until hearing loss is complete.

16. Six-year-old Mohammed has a cold and says his ears feel "full" and he "can't hear well." Explain what has happened in Mohammed's ears. Which type of deafness does Mohammed have—conduction or sensorineural?

For answers, see Appendix H.

Developmental Aspects of the Special Senses

✓ List changes that occur in the special sense organs with aging.

Taste and Smell

All the special senses are functional, to a greater or lesser degree, at birth. Smell and taste are sharp, and infants relish food that adults consider bland or tasteless. Some researchers claim that smell is just as important as touch in guiding newborn infants to their mother's breast. However, very young children seem indifferent to odors and can play happily with their own feces.

There are few problems with the chemical senses during childhood and young adulthood. Women generally have a more acute sense of smell than men, and nonsmokers have a sharper sense of smell than smokers.

Beginning in the fourth decade of life, our ability to taste and smell declines due to the gradual loss of receptors, which are replaced more slowly than in younger people. More than half of people over age 65 have serious problems detecting odors, which may explain why some tend to douse themselves with large amounts of cologne, or pay little attention to formerly disagreeable odors. Additionally, their sense of taste is poor. This along with the decline in the sense of smell makes food taste bland and contributes to loss of appetite.

Vision

By the fourth week of development, the eyes begin forming as the **optic vesicles** that protrude from the diencephalon (see Figure 12.1c on p. 429). Soon these hollow vesicles indent to form double-layered **optic cups**, and their stalks form the optic nerves and provide a pathway for blood vessels to reach the eye interior.

Once an optic vesicle reaches the overlying surface ectoderm, it induces the ectoderm to thicken and then form a **lens vesicle** that pinches off into the cavity of the optic cup, where it becomes the lens. The lining (internal layer) of the optic cup becomes the neural layer of the retina, and the outer layer forms the pigmented layer. The rest of the eye tissues and the vitreous humor are formed by mesenchymal cells derived from the mesoderm that surrounds the optic cup.

In the darkness of the uterus, the fetus cannot see. Nonetheless, even before the light-sensitive portions of the photoreceptors develop, the central nervous system connections have been made and are functional. During infancy, synaptic connections are fine-tuned, and the typical cortical fields that allow binocular vision are established.

Homeostatic Imbalance 15.14

Congenital problems of the eyes are relatively uncommon, but their incidence is dramatically increased by certain maternal infections, particularly rubella (German measles) during the critical first three months of pregnancy. Common rubella sequels include blindness and cataracts. ✚

As a rule, vision is the only special sense not fully functional at birth. Because the eyeballs are foreshortened, most babies are hyperopic. The newborn infant sees only in gray tones, eye movements are uncoordinated, and often only one eye at a time is used. The lacrimal glands are not completely developed until about two weeks after birth, so babies are tearless for this period, even though they may cry lustily. By 5 months, infants can follow moving objects with their eyes, but visual acuity is still poor (20/200).

By the age of 3 years, depth perception is present and color vision is well developed. Because the eyeball has grown, visual acuity has improved to about 20/30, providing a readiness to begin reading. By first grade, emmetropia has usually replaced the initial hyperopia, and the eye reaches its adult size at 8–9 years of age. Emmetropia usually continues until presbyopia begins to set in around age 40 owing to decreasing lens elasticity.

With age, the lens loses its crystal clarity and discolors. As a result, it begins to scatter light, causing a glare that is distressing when driving at night. The dilator pupillae muscles become less efficient, so the pupils stay partly constricted. These two changes together decrease the amount of light reaching the retina, and visual acuity is dramatically lower in people over 70. In addition, the lacrimal glands are less active and the eyes tend to be dry and more susceptible to infection. Elderly persons are also at risk for certain conditions that cause blindness, such as macular degeneration, glaucoma, cataracts, atherosclerosis, and diabetes mellitus.

Hearing and Balance

The ear begins to develop in the three-week embryo. The internal ears develop first, from thickenings of the surface ectoderm called the **otic placodes** (o′tik plak′ōds), which lie lateral to the hindbrain on each side. The otic placode invaginates, forming the **otic pit** and then the **otic vesicle**, which detaches from the surface epithelium. The otic vesicle develops into the membranous labyrinth. The surrounding mesenchyme forms the bony labyrinth.

The middle ear cavity and pharyngotympanic tube of the middle ear develop from **pharyngeal pouches**, lateral outpocketings of the endoderm lining the pharynx. The auditory ossicles develop from neural crest cells.

The external acoustic meatus and external face of the tympanic membrane of the external ear differentiate from the **pharyngeal cleft** (*branchial groove*), an indentation of the surface ectoderm, and the auricle develops from swellings of the surrounding tissue.

Newborn infants can hear, but early responses to sound are mostly reflexive—for example, crying and clenching the eyelids in response to a startling noise. By the fourth month, infants will turn to the voices of family members. Critical listening begins as toddlers increase their vocabulary, and good language skills are closely tied to the ability to hear well.

Homeostatic Imbalance 15.15

Congenital abnormalities of the ears are fairly common. Examples include partly or completely missing pinnae and closed or absent external acoustic meatuses. Maternal rubella during the first trimester commonly results in sensorineural deafness. ✚

Except for ear inflammations, mostly due to infections, few problems affect the ears during childhood and adult life. By the 60s, however, deterioration of the spiral organ becomes noticeable. We are born with approximately 30,000 hair cells, but their number declines as they are damaged or destroyed by loud noises, disease, or drugs (for example, the antibiotic streptomycin). The hair cells *are* replaced, but at such a slow rate that there really is no functional regeneration. It is estimated that if we were to live 140 years, we would lose all of our hearing receptors.

The ability to hear high-pitched sounds leaves us first. This condition, called **presbycusis** (pres″bĭ-ku′sis), is a type of sensorineural deafness. Although presbycusis is considered a disability of old age, it is becoming much more common in younger people as our world grows noisier.

☑ Check Your Understanding

17. What age-related changes make it more difficult for the elderly to see at night?

For answers, see Appendix H.

Our abilities to see, hear, taste, and smell—and some of our responses to the effects of gravity—are largely the work of our brain. However, as we have discovered in this final nervous system chapter, the large and often elaborate sensory receptor organs that serve the special senses are works of art in and of themselves.

The concluding chapter of this unit describes how the body's functions are controlled by chemicals called hormones in a manner quite different from what we have described for neural control.

Chapter Summary

 For more chapter study tools, go to the Study Area of MasteringA&P at **www.masteringaandp.com**. There you will find:

- Interactive Physiology **iP**
- A&PFlix **A&PFlix**
- Practice Anatomy Lab **PAL**
- PhysioEx **PEx**
- Videos, Practice Quizzes and Tests, MP3 Tutor Sessions, Case Studies, and much more!

The Eye and Vision   (pp. 545–565)

1. The eye is enclosed in the bony orbit and cushioned by fat.

Accessory Structures of the Eye   (pp. 545–549)

2. Eyebrows help to shade and protect the eyes.
3. Eyelids protect and lubricate the eyes by reflex blinking. Within the eyelids are the orbicularis oculi and levator palpebrae superioris muscles, and modified sebaceous and sweat glands.
4. The conjunctiva is a mucosa that lines the eyelids and covers the anterior eyeball surface. Its mucus lubricates the eyeball surface.
5. The lacrimal apparatus consists of the lacrimal gland (which produces a saline solution containing mucus, lysozyme, and antibodies), the lacrimal canaliculi, the lacrimal sac, and the nasolacrimal duct.
6. The extrinsic eye muscles (superior, inferior, lateral, and medial rectus and superior and inferior oblique) move the eyeballs.

Structure of the Eyeball   (pp. 549–553)

7. The wall of the eyeball is made up of three layers. The outermost fibrous layer consists of the sclera and the cornea. The sclera protects the eye and gives it shape; the cornea allows light to enter the eye.
8. The middle, pigmented vascular layer (uvea) consists of the choroid, the ciliary body, and the iris. The choroid provides nutrients to the eye and prevents light scattering within the eye. The ciliary muscles of the ciliary body control lens shape; the iris controls the size of the pupil.
9. The inner layer, or retina, consists of an outer pigmented layer and an inner neural layer. The neural layer contains photoreceptors (rods and cones), bipolar cells, and ganglion cells. Ganglion cell axons form the optic nerve, which exits via the optic disc ("blind spot").
10. The posterior segment of the eyeball, behind the lens, contains vitreous humor, which helps support the eyeball and keep the retina in place. The anterior segment, anterior to the lens, is filled with aqueous humor, formed by capillaries in the ciliary processes and drained into the scleral venous sinus. Aqueous humor is a major factor in maintaining intraocular pressure.
11. The biconvex lens is suspended within the eye by the ciliary zonule attached to the ciliary body. The lens is the only adjustable refractory structure of the eye.

Optics and the Eye   (pp. 553–556)

12. Visible light is made up of those wavelengths of the electromagnetic spectrum that excite the photoreceptors.
13. Light is refracted (bent) when passing from one transparent medium to another of different density. Concave lenses disperse light; convex lenses converge light and bring its rays to a focal point. The greater the lens curvature, the more light bends.
14. As light passes through the eye, the cornea and lens bend and focus it on the retina. The cornea accounts for most of the refraction, but the lens allows active focusing for different distances.
15. Focusing for distant vision requires no special movements of the eye structures. Focusing for close-up vision requires accommodation (bulging of the lens), pupillary constriction, and convergence of the eyeballs. Cranial nerve III controls all three reflexes.
16. Refractory problems include presbyopia, myopia, hyperopia, and astigmatism.

Photoreceptors and Phototransduction   (pp. 556–563)

17. The outer segments of the photoreceptors contain light-absorbing visual pigment in membrane-bounded discs.
18. The light-absorbing molecule retinal is combined with various opsins to form the visual pigments. Rod visual pigment, rhodopsin, is a combination of retinal and opsin. The three types of cones all contain retinal, but each has a different type of opsin. Each cone type responds maximally to one color of light: red, blue, or green. The chemistry of cone function is similar to that of rods.
19. Rods respond to low-intensity light and provide night and peripheral vision. Cones are bright-light, high-discrimination receptors that provide color vision. Anything that must be viewed precisely is focused on the cone-rich fovea centralis.
20. When struck by light, retinal changes shape (11-*cis* to all-*trans*) and activates opsin. Activated opsin activates transducin (a G protein) which in turn activates PDE, an enzyme that breaks down cGMP, allowing the cation channels to close. This hyperpolarizes the receptor cells and inhibits their release of neurotransmitter.
21. Photoreceptors and bipolar cells generate graded potentials only; ganglion cells generate action potentials.
22. During light adaptation, photopigments are bleached and rods are inactivated; then, as cones decrease their light sensitivity, high-acuity vision ensues. In dark adaptation, cones cease functioning, and visual acuity decreases; rod function begins when sufficient rhodopsin has accumulated.

Visual Pathways and Processing   (pp. 563–565)

23. The visual pathway to the brain begins with the optic nerve fibers (ganglion cell axons) from the retina. At the optic chiasma, fibers from the medial half of each retina cross over and continue in the optic tracts to the thalamus. Thalamic neurons project to the visual cortex via the optic radiation. Fibers also project from the retina to the midbrain pretectal nuclei and the superior colliculi, and to the suprachiasmatic nucleus of the hypothalamus.

24. Each eye receives a slightly different view of the visual field. The visual cortices fuse these views to provide depth perception.

25. Retinal processing involves the selective destruction of inputs so as to emphasize bright/dark or color contrasts (edges). Thalamic processing subserves high-acuity color vision and depth perception. Cortical processing involves neurons of the striate (primary) cortex, which receive inputs from the retinal ganglion cells, and neurons of the prestriate (association) cortices, which receive inputs from striate cortical cells and mostly integrate inputs concerned with color, form, and movement. Visual processing also proceeds anteriorly in the "what" and "where" processing streams via the temporal and parietal lobes, respectively.

The Chemical Senses: Smell and Taste (pp. 565–570)

The Olfactory Epithelium and the Sense of Smell (pp. 565–567)

1. The olfactory epithelium is located in the roof of the nasal cavity. The olfactory sensory neurons are ciliated bipolar neurons. Their axons are the filaments of the olfactory nerve (cranial nerve I).

2. Individual olfactory neurons show a range of responsiveness to different chemicals. Olfactory neurons bearing the same odorant receptors synapse in the same glomerulus type.

3. Olfactory neurons are excited by volatile chemicals that bind to receptors in the olfactory cilia.

4. Action potentials of the olfactory nerve filaments are transmitted to the olfactory bulb where the filaments synapse with mitral cells. The mitral cells send impulses via the olfactory tract to the olfactory cortex. Fibers carrying impulses from the olfactory bulb also project to the limbic system.

Taste Buds and the Sense of Taste (pp. 568–570)

5. The taste buds are scattered in the oral cavity and pharynx but are most abundant on the tongue papillae.

6. Gustatory epithelial cells, the receptor cells of the taste buds, have gustatory hairs (microvilli) that serve as the receptor regions. The gustatory epithelial cells are excited by the binding of tastants (food chemicals) to receptors on their microvilli.

7. The five basic taste qualities are sweet, sour, salty, bitter, and umami.

8. The taste sense is served by cranial nerves VII, IX, and X, which send impulses to the solitary nucleus of the medulla. From there, impulses are sent to the thalamus and the gustatory cortex.

Homeostatic Imbalances of the Chemical Senses (p. 570)

9. Most chemical sense dysfunctions are olfactory disorders (anosmias). Common causes are trauma, inflammation, or neurological disorders.

The Ear: Hearing and Balance (pp. 570–584)

Structure of the Ear (pp. 570–575)

1. The auricle and external acoustic meatus compose the external ear. The tympanic membrane, the boundary between the outer and middle ears, transmits sound waves to the middle ear.

2. The middle ear is a small chamber within the temporal bone, connected by the pharyngotympanic tube to the nasopharynx. The ossicles, which help amplify sound, span the middle ear cavity and transmit sound vibrations from the tympanic membrane to the oval window.

3. The internal ear consists of the bony labyrinth, within which the membranous labyrinth is suspended. The bony labyrinth chambers contain perilymph; the membranous labyrinth ducts and sacs contain endolymph.

4. The vestibule contains the saccule and utricle. The semicircular canals extend posteriorly from the vestibule in three planes. They contain the semicircular ducts.

5. The cochlea houses the cochlear duct (scala media), containing the spiral organ, the receptor organ for hearing. Within the cochlear duct, the hair (receptor) cells rest on the basilar membrane, and their hairs project into the gelatinous tectorial membrane.

Physiology of Hearing (pp. 575–579)

6. Sound originates from a vibrating object and travels in waves consisting of alternating areas of compression and rarefaction of the medium.

7. The distance from crest to crest on a sine wave is the sound's wavelength; the shorter the wavelength, the higher the frequency (measured in hertz). Frequency is perceived as pitch.

8. The amplitude of sound is the height of the peaks of the sine wave, which reflect the sound's intensity. Sound intensity is measured in decibels. Intensity is perceived as loudness.

9. Sound passing through the external acoustic meatus sets the tympanic membrane into vibration at the same frequency. The ossicles amplify and deliver the vibrations to the oval window.

10. Pressure waves in cochlear fluids set specific locations on the basilar membrane into resonance. At points of maximal membrane vibration, the vibratory motion alternately depolarizes and hyperpolarizes the hair cells of the spiral organ. Movements of the stereocilia toward the kinocilium depolarize the hair cells and increase the rate of impulse generation in the auditory nerve fibers. Movements away from the kinocilium have the opposite effect. High-frequency sounds stimulate hair cells near the oval window; low-frequency sounds stimulate hair cells near the apex. Inner hair cells send most auditory inputs to the brain. Outer hair cells amplify the inner hair cells' responsiveness.

11. Impulses generated along the cochlear nerve travel to the cochlear nuclei of the medulla and from there through several brain stem nuclei to the medial geniculate nucleus of the thalamus and then the auditory cortex. Each auditory cortex receives impulses from both ears.

12. Auditory processing is analytic; each tone is perceived separately. Perception of pitch is related to the position of the excited hair cells along the basilar membrane. Intensity perception reflects the fact that as sound intensity increases, basilar membrane motion increases, and the frequency of impulse transmission to the cortex increases. Cues for sound localization include the intensity and timing of sound arriving at each ear.

Equilibrium and Orientation (pp. 580–584)

13. The equilibrium receptor regions of the internal ear are called the vestibular apparatus.

14. The receptors for linear acceleration and gravity are the maculae of the saccule and utricle. A macula consists of hair cells with stereocilia and a kinocilium embedded in an overlying otolith membrane. Linear movements cause the otolith membrane to move, pulling on the hair cells and changing the rate of impulse generation in the vestibular nerve fibers.

15. The receptor within each semicircular duct, the crista ampullaris, responds to angular or rotational acceleration in one plane. It consists of a tuft of hair cells whose stereocilia are embedded in the gelatinous ampullary cupula. Rotational movements cause the endolymph to flow in the opposite direction, bending the cupula and either exciting or inhibiting the hair cells.

16. Impulses from the vestibular apparatus are sent via vestibular nerve fibers mainly to the vestibular nuclei of the brain stem and

the cerebellum. These centers initiate responses that fix the eyes on objects and activate muscles to maintain balance.

Homeostatic Imbalances of Hearing and Equilibrium (p. 584)

17. Conduction deafness results from interference with conduction of sound vibrations to the fluids of the internal ear. Sensorineural deafness reflects damage to neural structures.

18. Tinnitus is an early sign of sensorineural deafness; it may also result from inflammation or certain drugs.

19. Ménière's syndrome is a disorder of the membranous labyrinth. Symptoms include tinnitus, deafness, and vertigo. Excessive endolymph accumulation is the suspected cause.

Developmental Aspects of the Special Senses (pp. 584–585)

Taste and Smell   (pp. 548–585)

1. The chemical senses are sharpest at birth and gradually decline with age as receptor cells are replaced more slowly.

Vision   (p. 585)

2. Congenital eye problems are uncommon, but maternal rubella can cause blindness.

3. The eye starts as an optic vesicle, an outpocketing of the diencephalon that invaginates to form the optic cup, which becomes the retina. Overlying ectoderm folds to form the lens vesicle, which gives rise to the lens. The remaining eye tissues and the accessory structures are formed by mesenchyme.

4. The eye is foreshortened at birth and reaches adult size at the age of 8–9 years. Depth perception and color vision develop before age 3.

5. With age, the lens loses its elasticity and clarity, there is a decline in the ability of the iris to dilate, and visual acuity decreases. The elderly are at risk for eye problems resulting from dry eyes and disease.

Hearing and Balance   (p. 585)

6. The membranous labyrinth develops from the otic placode, an ectodermal thickening lateral to the hindbrain. Mesenchyme forms the surrounding bony structures. Pharyngeal pouch endoderm, in conjunction with mesenchyme, forms most middle ear structures; the external ear is formed largely by ectoderm.

7. Congenital ear problems are fairly common. Maternal rubella can cause deafness.

8. Response to sound in infants is reflexive. By the fourth month, an infant can locate sound. Critical listening develops in toddlers.

9. The spiral organ deteriorates throughout life as noise, disease, and drugs destroy cochlear hair cells. Age-related loss of hearing (presbycusis) occurs in the 60s and 70s.

Review Questions

Multiple Choice/Matching

(Some questions have more than one correct answer. Select the best answer or answers from the choices given.)

1. Accessory glands that produce an oily secretion are the (a) conjunctiva, (b) lacrimal glands, (c) tarsal glands.

2. The portion of the fibrous layer that is white and opaque is the (a) choroid, (b) cornea, (c) retina, (d) sclera.

3. Which sequence best describes a normal route for the flow of tears from the eyes into the nasal cavity? (a) lacrimal canaliculi, lacrimal sacs, nasolacrimal ducts; (b) lacrimal ducts, lacrimal canaliculi, nasolacrimal ducts; (c) nasolacrimal ducts, lacrimal canaliculi, lacrimal sacs.

4. Activation of the sympathetic nervous system causes (a) contraction of the sphincter pupillae muscles, (b) contraction of the dilator pupillae muscles, (c) contraction of the ciliary muscles, (d) a decrease in ciliary zonule tension.

5. Damage to the medial recti muscles would probably affect (a) accommodation, (b) refraction, (c) convergence, (d) pupil constriction.

6. The phenomenon of dark adaptation is best explained by the fact that (a) rhodopsin does not function in dim light, (b) rhodopsin breakdown occurs slowly, (c) rods exposed to intense light need time to generate rhodopsin, (d) cones are stimulated to function by bright light.

7. Blockage of the scleral venous sinus might result in (a) a sty, (b) glaucoma, (c) conjunctivitis, (d) a cataract.

8. Nearsightedness is more properly called (a) myopia, (b) hyperopia, (c) presbyopia, (d) emmetropia.

9. Of the neurons in the retina, the axons of which of these form the optic nerve? (a) bipolar cells, (b) ganglion cells, (c) cone cells, (d) horizontal cells.

10. Which sequence of reactions occurs when a person looks at a distant object? (a) pupils constrict, ciliary zonule (suspensory ligament) relaxes, lenses become less convex; (b) pupils dilate, ciliary zonule becomes taut, lenses become less convex; (c) pupils dilate, ciliary zonule becomes taut, lenses become more convex; (d) pupils constrict, ciliary zonule relaxes, lenses become more convex.

11. During embryonic development, the lens of the eye forms (a) as part of the choroid coat, (b) from the surface ectoderm overlying the optic cup, (c) as part of the sclera, (d) from mesodermal tissue.

12. The blind spot of the eye is (a) where more rods than cones are found, (b) where the macula lutea is located, (c) where only cones occur, (d) where the optic nerve leaves the eye.

13. Olfactory tract damage would probably affect your ability to (a) see, (b) hear, (c) feel pain, (d) smell.

14. Sensory impulses transmitted over the facial, glossopharyngeal, and vagus nerves are involved in the sensation of (a) taste, (b) touch, (c) equilibrium, (d) smell.

15. Taste buds are found on the (a) anterior part of the tongue, (b) posterior part of the tongue, (c) palate, (d) all of these.

16. Gustatory epithelial cells are stimulated by (a) movement of otoliths, (b) stretch, (c) substances in solution, (d) photons of light.

17. Cells in the olfactory bulb that act as local "integrators" of olfactory inputs are the (a) hair cells, (b) amacrine granule cells, (c) olfactory stem cells, (d) mitral cells, (e) supporting cells.

18. Olfactory nerve filaments are found (a) in the optic bulbs, (b) passing through the cribriform plate of the ethmoid bone, (c) in the optic tracts, (d) in the olfactory cortex.

19. Conduction of sound from the middle ear to the internal ear occurs via vibration of the (a) malleus against the tympanic

membrane, **(b)** stapes in the oval window, **(c)** incus in the round window, **(d)** stapes against the tympanic membrane.

20. The transmission of sound vibrations through the internal ear occurs chiefly through **(a)** nerve fibers, **(b)** air, **(c)** fluid, **(d)** bone.

21. Which of the following statements does not correctly describe the spiral organ? **(a)** Sounds of high frequency stimulate hair cells at the basal end, **(b)** the "hairs" of the receptor cells are embedded in the tectorial membrane, **(c)** the basilar membrane acts as a resonator, **(d)** the more numerous outer hair cells are largely responsible for our perception of sound.

22. Pitch is to frequency of sound as loudness is to **(a)** quality, **(b)** intensity, **(c)** overtones, **(d)** all of these.

23. The structure that allows pressure in the middle ear to be equalized with atmospheric pressure is the **(a)** pinna, **(b)** pharyngotympanic tube, **(c)** tympanic membrane, **(d)** oval window.

24. Which of the following is important in maintaining the balance of the body? **(a)** visual cues, **(b)** semicircular canals, **(c)** the saccule, **(d)** proprioceptors, **(e)** all of these.

25. Equilibrium receptors that report the position of the head in space relative to the pull of gravity are **(a)** spiral organs, **(b)** maculae, **(c)** cristae ampullares, **(d)** otoliths.

26. Which of the following is not a possible cause of conduction deafness? **(a)** impacted cerumen, **(b)** middle ear infection, **(c)** cochlear nerve degeneration, **(d)** otosclerosis.

27. Which of the following are intrinsic eye muscles? **(a)** superior rectus, **(b)** orbicularis oculi, **(c)** smooth muscles of the iris and ciliary body, **(d)** levator palpebrae superioris.

28. Which lies closest to the exact posterior pole of the eye? **(a)** optic nerve, **(b)** optic disc, **(c)** macula lutea, **(d)** point of entry of central artery into the eye.

29. Otoliths (ear stones) are **(a)** a cause of deafness, **(b)** a type of hearing aid, **(c)** important in equilibrium, **(d)** the rock-hard petrous temporal bones.

Short Answer Essay Questions

30. Why do you often have to blow your nose after crying?
31. How do rods and cones differ functionally?
32. Where is the fovea centralis, and why is it important?
33. Describe the response of rhodopsin to light stimuli. What is the outcome of this cascade of events?
34. Since there are only three types of cones, how can you explain the fact that we see many more colors?
35. Where are the olfactory sensory neurons, and why is that site poorly suited for their job?
36. Each olfactory sensory neuron responds to a single type of odorant molecule. True or false? Explain your choice.
37. Name the five primary taste qualities and the cranial nerves that serve the sense of taste.
38. Describe the effect of aging on the special sense organs.

Critical Thinking and Clinical Application Questions

1. During an ophthalmoscopic examination, Mrs. James was found to have bilateral papilledema. Further investigation indicated that this condition resulted from a rapidly growing intracranial tumor. First, define papilledema (see *Related Clinical Terms*). Then explain its presence in terms of Mrs. James's diagnosis.

2. Sally, a 9-year-old girl, told the clinic physician that her "ear lump hurt" and she kept "getting dizzy and falling down." As she told her story, she pointed to her mastoid process. An otoscopic examination of the external acoustic meatus revealed a red, swollen eardrum, and her throat was inflamed. Her condition was described as mastoiditis with secondary labyrinthitis (inflammation of the labyrinth). Describe the most likely route of infection and the infected structures in Sally's case. Also explain the cause of her dizziness and falling.

3. Mr. Gaspe appeared at the eye clinic complaining of a chip of wood in his eye. No foreign body was found, but the conjunctiva was obviously inflamed. What name is given to this inflammatory condition, and where would you look for a foreign body that has been floating around on the eye surface for a while?

4. Mrs. Orlando has been noticing flashes of light and tiny specks in her right visual field. When she begins to see a "veil" floating before her right eye, she makes an appointment to see the eye doctor. What is your diagnosis? Is the condition serious? Explain.

5. David Norris, an engineering student, has been working in a nightclub to earn money to pay for his education. After about eight months, he notices that he is having problems hearing high-pitched tones. What is the cause-and-effect relationship here?

6. Assume that a tumor in the pituitary gland or hypothalamus is protruding inferiorly and compressing the optic chiasma. What could be the visual outcome?

7. Four-year-old Gary Zammer is brought to the ophthalmologist for a routine checkup on his vision. Gary is an albino. How do you think albinism affects vision?

8. Right before Jan, a senior citizen, had a large plug of earwax cleaned from her ear, she developed a constant howling sound in her ear that would not stop. It was very annoying and stressful, and she had to go to counseling to learn how to live with this awful noise. What was her condition called?

9. During an anatomy and physiology lab exercise designed to teach the use of the ophthalmoscope, you notice that your lab partner has difficulty seeing objects in the darkened room. Upon examining her retina through the ophthalmoscope, you observe streaks and patches of dark pigmentation at the back of the eye. What might this condition be?

10. Henri, a chef in a five-star French restaurant, has been diagnosed with leukemia. He is about to undergo chemotherapy, which will kill rapidly dividing cells in his body. He needs to continue working between bouts of chemotherapy. What consequences of chemotherapy would you predict that might affect his job as a chef?

AT THE CLINIC

Related Clinical Terms

Ageusia (ah-gu′ze-ah) Loss or impairment of the taste sense.

Age-related macular degeneration (ARMD) Progressive deterioration of the macula lutea that destroys central vision; the main cause of vision loss in those over age 65. Buildup of pigments in the macula impairs functioning of the pigmented epithelium. Continued accumulation of pigment leads to the "dry" form of ARMD, in which many pigment cells and macular photoreceptors die. The dry form is largely untreatable, although a specific cocktail of vitamins and zinc slows its progression. Less common is the "wet" form in which new blood vessels from the choroid grow into the retina. Blood and fluids leak from these vessels, scarring and detaching the retina. The cause of wet ARMD is unknown, but several treatment options can slow its progression—laser treatments that destroy some of the invading vessels and drugs that prevent blood vessel growth. Clinical trials using RNA interference to inhibit vascular growth are underway.

Blepharitis (blef′ah-ri′tis; *blephar* = eyelash; *itis* = inflammation) Inflammation of the margins of the eyelids.

Enucleation (e-nu″kle-a′shun) Surgical removal of an eyeball.

Exophthalmos (ek″sof-thal′mos; *ex* = out; *ophthalmo* = the eye) Anteriorly bulging eyeballs. Seen in some cases of hyperthyroidism.

Labyrinthitis Inflammation of the labyrinth.

Ophthalmology (of′thal-mol′o-je) The science that studies the eye and eye diseases. An ophthalmologist is a medical doctor who specializes in treating eye disorders.

Optometrist A licensed nonphysician who measures vision and prescribes corrective lenses.

Otalgia (o-tal′je-ah; *algia* = pain) Earache.

Otitis externa Inflammation and infection of the external acoustic meatus, caused by bacteria or fungi that enter the canal from outside, especially when the canal is moist (e.g., after swimming).

Otoacoustic emissions Sounds generated by the movement of outer hair cells in the cochlea. Stimulated otoacoustic emissions are an inexpensive way to screen newborns for hearing defects.

Papilledema (pap″il-ě-de′mah; *papill* = nipple; *edema* = swelling) Protrusion of the optic disc into the eyeball, which can be observed by ophthalmoscopic examination; caused by conditions that increase intracranial pressure.

Scotoma (sko-to′mah; *scoto* = darkness) A blind spot other than the normal (optic disc) blind spot. Has many causes, including stroke or a brain tumor pressing on fibers of the visual pathway.

Trachoma (trah-ko′mah; *trach* = rough) A highly contagious bacterial (chlamydial) infection of the conjunctiva and cornea. Common worldwide, it blinds millions of people in poor countries of Africa and Asia. Treated with eye ointments containing antibiotic drugs.

Weber's test Hearing test during which a sounding tuning fork is held to the forehead. In those with normal hearing, the tone is heard equally in both ears. The tone will be heard best in the "good" ear if sensorineural deafness is present, and in the "bad" ear if conduction deafness is present.

Case Study Special Senses

When emergency personnel arrived on the scene of the bus crash, they found Brian Rhen, 42, sitting on the side of the road holding his head in his hands. He complained of a severe headache and nausea, and was evaluated and treated for a concussion. Several days later, Mr. Rhen began to experience recurring episodes of vertigo and was referred to a neurologist. (Vertigo is a sensation of motion or movement while the person is stationary, and can be accompanied by nausea and vomiting.)

Mr. Rhen was diagnosed with *benign paroxysmal positional vertigo* (BPPV). With this condition, which can be caused by head trauma, vertigo can be provoked by specific changes in head position. Mr. Rhen reported that his vertigo usually occurred when rolling over in bed, or when turning his head from side to side while sitting up, and that these movements provoked the sensation of a spinning room, which led to nausea. The neurologist confirmed the diagnosis of BPPV by using a test called the Dix-Hallpike maneuver. During this test, the neurologist looks for nystagmus (involuntary, jerking eye movements) as he makes specific rotational changes to Mr. Rhen's head position.

1. The ear is divided into three major areas (compartments). What are these three areas, and which of these areas is involved in Mr. Rhen's BPPV?

2. What are the three main sources of sensory input that the body uses in order to control balance and equilibrium?

3. Name the two functional divisions of the vestibular apparatus. Identify the sensory receptor associated with each division, and state which aspect of equilibrium each receptor senses.

4. BPPV can be caused by otoliths that have been dislodged from the otolithic membrane of the maculae. Based on Mr. Rhen's symptoms and the head movements that provoke these symptoms, what part of the vestibular apparatus are the displaced otoliths now affecting?

5. Explain why nystagmus is associated with the Dix-Hallpike maneuver.

(Answers in Appendix H)

MEASUREMENT	UNIT AND ABBREVIATION	METRIC EQUIVALENT	METRIC TO ENGLISH CONVERSION FACTOR	ENGLISH TO METRIC CONVERSION FACTOR
Length	1 kilometer (km)	= 1000 (10^3) meters	1 km = 0.62 mile	1 mile = 1.61 km
	1 meter (m)	= 100 (10^2) centimeters = 1000 millimeters	1 m = 1.09 yards 1 m = 3.28 feet 1 m = 39.37 inches	1 yard = 0.914 m 1 foot = 0.305 m
	1 centimeter (cm)	= 0.01 (10^{-2}) meter	1 cm = 0.394 inch	1 foot = 30.5 cm 1 inch = 2.54 cm
	1 millimeter (mm)	= 0.001 (10^{-3}) meter	1 mm = 0.039 inch	
	1 micrometer (μm) [formerly micron (μ)]	= 0.000001 (10^{-6}) meter		
	1 nanometer (nm)	= 0.000000001 (10^{-9}) meter		
	1 angstrom (Å)	= 0.0000000001 (10^{-10}) meter		
Area	1 square meter (m²)	= 10,000 square centimeters	1 m² = 1.1960 square yards 1 m² = 10.764 square feet	1 square yard = 0.8361 m² 1 square foot = 0.0929 m²
	1 square centimeter (cm²)	= 100 square millimeters	1 cm² = 0.155 square inch	1 square inch = 6.4516 cm²
Mass	1 metric ton (t)	= 1000 kilograms	1 t = 1.103 ton	1 ton = 0.907 t
	1 kilogram (kg)	= 1000 grams	1 kg = 2.205 pounds	1 pound = 0.4536 kg
	1 gram (g)	= 1000 milligrams	1 g = 0.0353 ounce 1 g = 15.432 grains	1 ounce = 28.35 g
	1 milligram (mg)	= 0.001 gram	1 mg = approx. 0.015 grain	
	1 microgram (μg)	= 0.000001 gram		
Volume (solids)	1 cubic meter (m³)	= 1,000,000 cubic centimeters	1 m³ = 1.3080 cubic yards 1 m³ = 35.315 cubic feet	1 cubic yard = 0.7646 m³ 1 cubic foot = 0.0283 m³
	1 cubic centimeter (cm³ or cc)	= 0.000001 cubic meter = 1 milliliter	1 cm³ = 0.0610 cubic inch	1 cubic inch = 16.387 cm³
	1 cubic millimeter (mm³)	= 0.000000001 cubic meter		
Volume (liquids and gases)	1 kiloliter (kl or kL)	= 1000 liters	1 kL = 264.17 gallons	1 gallon = 3.785 L
	1 liter (l or L)	= 1000 milliliters	1 L = 0.264 gallon 1 L = 1.057 quarts	1 quart = 0.946 L
	1 milliliter (ml or mL)	= 0.001 liter = 1 cubic centimeter	1 ml = 0.034 fluid ounce 1 ml = approx. $\frac{1}{5}$ teaspoon 1 ml = approx. 15–16 drops (gtt)	1 quart = 946 ml 1 pint = 473 ml 1 fluid ounce = 29.57 ml 1 teaspoon = approx. 5 ml
	1 microliter (μl or μL)	= 0.000001 liter		
Time	1 second (s)	= $\frac{1}{60}$ minute		
	1 millisecond (ms)	= 0.001 second		
Temperature	Degrees Celsius (°C)		$°F = \frac{9}{5}(°C) + 32$	$°C = \frac{5}{9}(°F - 32)$

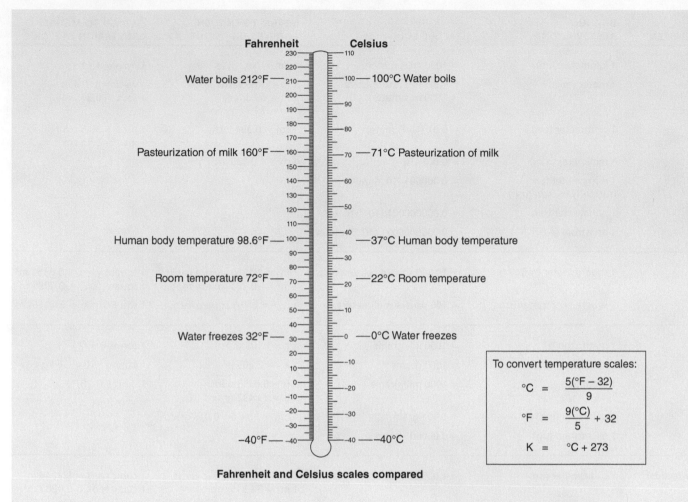

Fahrenheit and Celsius scales compared

To convert temperature scales:

$$°C = \frac{5(°F - 32)}{9}$$

$$°F = \frac{9(°C)}{5} + 32$$

$$K = °C + 273$$

Functional group	General formula	Name of compounds	Example	Where else found
Hydroxyl —OH (or HO—)	—O—H	Alcohols	Ethanol	Sugars; water-soluble vitamins
Carbonyl 〉CO	—C(=O)—H	Aldehydes	Propanal	Some sugars; formaldehyde (a preservative)
	—C(=O)—	Ketones	Acetone	Some sugars; "ketone bodies" in urine (from fat breakdown)
Carboxyl —COOH	—C(=O)—OH	Carboxylic acids	Acetic acid	Amino acids; proteins; some vitamins; fatty acids
Amino —NH$_2$ (or H$_2$N—)	—N—H,H	Amines	Methylamine	Amino acids; proteins; urea in urine (from protein breakdown)

Nonpolar

Glycine (Gly)   Alanine (Ala)   Valine (Val)   Leucine (Leu)   Isoleucine (Ile)

Methionine (Met)   Phenylalanine (Phe)   Tryptophan (Trp)   Proline (Pro)

Polar

Serine (Ser)   Threonine (Thr)   Cysteine (Cys)   Tyrosine (Tyr)   Asparagine (Asn)   Glutamine (Gln)

Electrically charged

Acidic   Basic

Aspartic acid (Asp)   Glutamic acid (Glu)   Lysine (Lys)   Arginine (Arg)   Histidine (His)

① Glucose enters the cell and is phosphorylated by the enzyme hexokinase, which catalyzes the transfer of a phosphate group, indicated as ⓟ, from ATP to the number six carbon of the sugar, producing glucose-6-phosphate. The electrical charge of the phosphate group traps the sugar in the cell because the plasma membrane is impermeable to ions. Phosphorylation of glucose also makes the molecule more chemically reactive. Although glycolysis is supposed to *produce* ATP, ATP is actually consumed in step 1—an energy investment that will be repaid with dividends later in glycolysis.

② Glucose-6-phosphate is rearranged and converted to its isomer, fructose-6-phosphate. Isomers, remember, have the same number and types of atoms but in different structural arrangements.

③ In this step, still another molecule of ATP is used to add a second phosphate group to the sugar, producing fructose-1,6-bisphosphate. So far, the ATP ledger shows a debit of –2. With phosphate groups on its opposite ends, the sugar is now ready to be split in half.

④ This is the reaction from which glycolysis gets its name. An enzyme cleaves the sugar molecule into two different 3-carbon sugars: glyceraldehyde 3-phosphate and dihydroxyacetone phosphate. These two sugars are isomers of one another.

⑤ An isomerase enzyme interconverts the 3-carbon sugars, and if left alone in a test tube, the reaction reaches equilibrium. This does not happen in the cell, however, because the next enzyme in glycolysis uses only glyceraldehyde phosphate as its substrate and not dihydroxyacetone phosphate. This pulls the equilibrium between the two 3-carbon sugars in the direction of glyceraldehyde phosphate, which is removed as fast as it forms. Thus, the net result of steps 4 and 5 is cleavage of a 6-carbon sugar into two molecules of glyceraldehyde phosphate; each will progress through the remaining steps of glycolysis.

⑥ An enzyme now catalyzes two sequential reactions while it holds glyceraldehyde phosphate in its active site. First, the sugar is oxidized by the transfer of H from the number one carbon of the sugar to NAD^+, forming $NADH + H^+$. Here we see in metabolic context the oxidation-reduction reaction described in Chapter 24. This reaction releases substantial amounts of energy, and the enzyme capitalizes on this by coupling the reaction to the creation of a high-energy phosphate bond at the number one carbon of the oxidized substrate. The source of the phosphate is inorganic phosphate (P_i) always present in the cytosol. The enzyme releases $NADH + H^+$ and 1,3-bisphosphoglyceric acid as products. Notice in the figure that the new phosphate bond is symbolized with a squiggle (~), which indicates that the bond is at least as energetic as the high-energy phosphate bonds of ATP.

THE TEN STEPS OF GLYCOLYSIS Each of the ten steps of glycolysis is catalyzed by a specific enzyme found dissolved in the cytoplasm. All steps are reversible. An abbreviated version of the three major phases of glycolysis appears in the lower right-hand corner of the next page.

7 Finally, glycolysis produces ATP. The phosphate group, with its high-energy bond, is transferred from 1,3-bisphosphoglyceric acid to ADP. For each glucose molecule that began glycolysis, step 7 produces two molecules of ATP, because every product after the sugar-splitting step (step 4) is doubled. Of course, two ATPs were invested to get sugar ready for splitting. The ATP ledger now stands at zero. By the end of step 7, glucose has been converted to two molecules of 3-phosphoglyceric acid. This compound is not a sugar. The sugar was oxidized to an organic acid back in step 6, and now the energy made available by that oxidation has been used to make ATP.

8 Next, an enzyme relocates the remaining phosphate group of 3-phosphoglyceric acid to form 2-phosphoglyceric acid. This prepares the substrate for the next reaction.

9 An enzyme forms a double bond in the substrate by removing a water molecule from 2-phosphoglyceric acid to form phosphoenolpyruvic acid, or PEP. This results in the electrons of the substrate being rearranged in such a way that the remaining phosphate bond becomes very unstable; it has been upgraded to high-energy status.

10 The last reaction of glycolysis produces another molecule of ATP by transferring the phosphate group from PEP to ADP. Because this step occurs twice for each glucose molecule, the ATP ledger now shows a net gain of two ATPs. Steps 7 and 10 each produce two ATPs for a total credit of four, but a debt of two ATPs was incurred from steps 1 and 3. Glycolysis has repaid the ATP investment with 100% interest. In the meantime, glucose has been broken down and oxidized to two molecules of pyruvic acid, the compound produced from PEP in step 10.

Summary

① Two-carbon acetyl CoA is combined with oxaloacetic acid, a 4-carbon compound. The unstable bond between the acetyl group and CoA is broken as oxaloacetic acid binds and CoA is freed to prime another 2-carbon fragment derived from pyruvic acid. The product is the 6-carbon citric acid, for which the cycle is named.

② A molecule of water is removed, and another is added back. The net result is the conversion of citric acid to its isomer, isocitric acid.

③ The substrate loses a CO_2 molecule, and the remaining 5-carbon compound is oxidized, forming an α-ketoglutaric acid and reducing NAD^+.

④ This step is catalyzed by a multienzyme complex very similar to the one that converts pyruvic acid to acetyl CoA. CO_2 is lost; the remaining 4-carbon compound is oxidized by the transfer of electrons to NAD^+ to form $NADH+H^+$ and is then attached to CoA by an unstable bond. The product is succinyl CoA.

⑤ Substrate-level phosphorylation occurs in this step. CoA is displaced by a phosphate group, which is then transferred to GDP to form guanosine triphosphate (GTP). GTP is similar to ATP, which is formed when GTP donates a phosphate group to ADP. The products of this step are succinic acid and ATP.

⑥ In another oxidative step, two hydrogens are removed from succinic acid (forming fumaric acid) and transferred to FAD to form $FADH_2$. The function of this coenzyme is similar to that of $NADH+H^+$, but $FADH_2$ stores less energy. The enzyme that catalyzes this oxidation-reduction reaction is the only enzyme of the cycle that is embedded in the mitochondrial membrane. All other enzymes of the citric acid cycle are dissolved in the mitochondrial matrix.

⑦ Bonds in the substrate are rearranged in this step by the addition of a water molecule. The product is malic acid.

⑧ The last oxidative step reduces another NAD^+ and regenerates oxaloacetic acid, which accepts a 2-carbon fragment from acetyl CoA for another turn of the cycle.

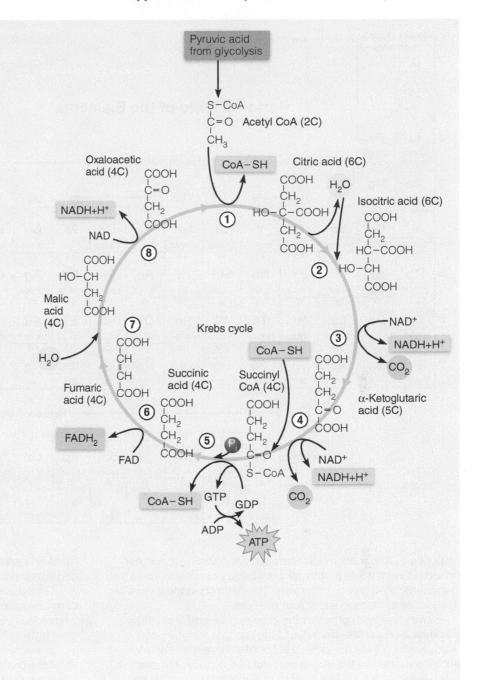

KREBS CYCLE (CITRIC ACID CYCLE) All but one of the steps (step 6) occur in the mitochondrial matrix. The preparation of pyruvic acid (by oxidation, decarboxylation, and reaction with coenzyme A) to enter the cycle as acetyl CoA is shown above the cycle. Acetyl CoA is picked up by oxaloacetic acid to form citric acid; and as it passes through the cycle, it is oxidized four more times [forming three molecules of reduced NAD ($NADH + H^+$) and one of reduced FAD ($FADH_2$)] and decarboxylated twice (releasing 2 CO_2). Energy is captured in the bonds of GTP, which then acts in a coupled reaction with ADP to generate one molecule of ATP by substrate-level phosphorylation.

Periodic Table of the Elements

Representative (main group) elements

Representative (main group) elements

Period	IA	IIA											IIIA	IVA	VA	VIA	VIIA	VIIIA
1	1 **H** 1.0079																	2 **He** 4.003
2	3 **Li** 6.941	4 **Be** 9.012											5 **B** 10.811	6 **C** 12.011	7 **N** 14.007	8 **O** 15.999	9 **F** 18.998	10 **Ne** 20.180
3	11 **Na** 22.990	12 **Mg** 24.305	IIIB	IVB	VB	VIB	VIIB		VIIIB		IB	IIB	13 **Al** 26.982	14 **Si** 28.086	15 **P** 30.974	16 **S** 32.065	17 **Cl** 35.453	18 **Ar** 39.948
4	19 **K** 39.098	20 **Ca** 40.078	21 **Sc** 44.956	22 **Ti** 47.867	23 **V** 50.942	24 **Cr** 51.996	25 **Mn** 54.938	26 **Fe** 55.845	27 **Co** 58.933	28 **Ni** 58.69	29 **Cu** 63.546	30 **Zn** 65.38	31 **Ga** 69.723	32 **Ge** 72.64	33 **As** 74.922	34 **Se** 78.96	35 **Br** 79.904	36 **Kr** 83.8
5	37 **Rb** 85.468	38 **Sr** 87.62	39 **Y** 88.906	40 **Zr** 91.224	41 **Nb** 92.906	42 **Mo** 95.96	43 **Tc** 98	44 **Ru** 101.07	45 **Rh** 102.906	46 **Pd** 106.42	47 **Ag** 107.868	48 **Cd** 112.411	49 **In** 114.82	50 **Sn** 118.71	51 **Sb** 121.76	52 **Te** 127.60	53 **I** 126.905	54 **Xe** 131.29
6	55 **Cs** 132.905	56 **Ba** 137.327	57 **La** 138.906	72 **Hf** 178.49	73 **Ta** 180.948	74 **W** 183.84	75 **Re** 186.207	76 **Os** 190.23	77 **Ir** 192.22	78 **Pt** 195.08	79 **Au** 196.967	80 **Hg** 200.59	81 **Tl** 204.383	82 **Pb** 207.2	83 **Bi** 208.980	84 **Po** 209	85 **At** 210	86 **Rn** 222
7	87 **Fr** 223	88 **Ra** 226	89 **Ac** 227	104 **Rf** 267	105 **Db** 268	106 **Sg** 271	107 **Bh** 272	108 **Hs** 270	109 **Mt** 276	110 **Ds** 281	111 **Rg** 280	112 **Cn** 285	113 **Uut** 284	114 **Uuq** 289	115 **Uup** 288	116 **Uuh** 293	117 **Uus** 292	118 **Uuo** 294

Transition metals

Rare earth elements

	58	59	60	61	62	63	64	65	66	67	68	69	70	71
Lanthanides	**Ce** 140.116	**Pr** 140.908	**Nd** 144.24	**Pm** 145	**Sm** 150.36	**Eu** 151.964	**Gd** 157.25	**Tb** 158.925	**Dy** 162.5	**Ho** 164.93	**Er** 167.26	**Tm** 168.934	**Yb** 173.054	**Lu** 174.967
	90	91	92	93	94	95	96	97	98	99	100	101	102	103
Actinides	**Th** 232.038	**Pa** 231.036	**U** 238.029	**Np** 237.048	**Pu** 244	**Am** 243	**Cm** 247	**Bk** 247	**Cf** 251	**Es** 252	**Fm** 257	**Md** 258	**No** 259	**Lr** 262

The periodic table arranges elements according to atomic number and atomic weight into horizontal rows called periods and 18 vertical columns called groups or families. The elements in the groups are classified as being in either A or B classes.

Elements of each group of the A series have similar chemical and physical properties. This reflects the fact that members of a particular group have the same number of valence shell electrons, which is indicated by the roman numeral of the group. For example, group IA elements have one valence shell electron, group IIA elements have two, and group VA elements have five. In contrast, as you progress across a period from left to right, the properties of the elements change in discrete steps, varying gradually from the very metallic properties of groups IA and IIA elements to the nonmetallic properties seen in group VIIA (chlorine and others), and finally to the inert elements (noble gases) in group VIIIA. This change reflects the continual increase in the number of valence shell electrons seen in elements (from left to right) within a period.

Class B elements are referred to as transition elements. All transition elements are metals, and in most cases they have one or two valence shell electrons. (In these elements, some electrons occupy more distant electron shells before the deeper shells are filled.)

In this periodic table, the colors are used to convey information about the phase (solid, liquid, or gas) in which a pure element exists under standard conditions (25 degrees Celsius and 1 atmosphere of pressure). If the element's symbol is solid black, then the element exists as a solid. If its symbol is red, then it exists as a gas. If its symbol is dark blue, then it is a liquid. If the element's symbol is green, the element does not exist in nature and must be created by some type of nuclear reaction.

*Atomic weights of the elements per IUPAC Commission on Isotopic Abundances and Atomic Weights, 2007.

The reference values listed for the selected blood and urine studies are common ranges for adults, but specific "normals" are established by the laboratory performing the analysis. The values may be affected by a wide range of circumstances, including testing methods and equipment used, client age, body mass, sex, diet, activity level, medications, and extent of disease processes.

Reference values are identified in both standard or conventional units and in the system of international (SI) units. SI units (given in parentheses) are measurements of amount per volume and are used in most countries and scientific journals. SI units are often given as moles or millimoles per liter. Most clinical laboratories and textbooks in the United States use conventional or standard units, which measure mass per volume. These values are given as grams, milligrams, or milliequivalents per deciliter or liter. It is anticipated that the United States will eventually use SI units exclusively.

For enzymes, 1 international unit (IU) represents an arbitrary but defined amount of activity, whereas 1 katal (kat) is the amount of enzyme required to consume 1 mol of substrate per second.

Sample types in column 1 are serum (S), plasma (P), arterial whole blood (A), and whole blood (WB).

TEST (SAMPLE)	REFERENCE VALUES: CONVENTIONAL (SI)	PHYSIOLOGICAL INDICATION AND CLINICAL IMPLICATIONS
Blood Chemistry Studies		
Ammonia (P)	15–120 µg/dl (9–70 µmol/L)	Liver and renal function. Increased values in liver disease, renal failure, newborn hemolytic disease, heart failure, cor pulmonale. Decreased values in hypertension.
Amylase (S)	56–190 IU/L (0.4–2.1 µkat/L)	Pancreatic function. Increased values in pancreatitis, mumps, obstruction of pancreatic duct, ketoacidosis. Decreased values in kidney disease, pancreatic damage or cancer, toxemia of pregnancy.
Aspartate aminotransferase (AST, or SGOT) (S)	≤40 IU/L (≤0.7 µkat/L)	Cellular damage. Increased after myocardial infarction, acute liver disease, drug toxicity, muscle trauma. Decreased in pyridoxine (vitamin B_6) deficiency.
Bilirubin (S)	Total: 0.1–1.0 mg/dl (1.7–17.1 µmol/L) Direct: <0.4 mg/dl (<6.8 µmol/L) Indirect: 0.1–1.0 mg/dl (1.7–17.1 µmol/L) Newborn: <13.0 mg/dl (<222 µmol/L)	Liver function and red cell breakdown. Increased levels of direct in liver disease and biliary obstruction. Increased levels of indirect in hemolysis of red blood cells.
Blood urea nitrogen (S)	7–26 mg/dl (2.5–9.3 mmol/L)	Kidney function. Increased values in renal disease, dehydration, urinary obstruction, congestive heart failure, myocardial infarction, burns. Decreased values in liver failure, overhydration, impaired protein absorption, pregnancy.
Cholesterol	<200 mg/dl (<5.2 mmol/L)	Metabolism—fat utilization. Increased values in diabetes mellitus, pregnancy, use of oral contraceptives or anabolic steroids.
High-density lipoprotein (HDL) cholesterol (S)	20–30% of total >40 mg/dl (>1.0 mmol/L)	Increased levels in liver disease, aerobic exercise. Decreased levels in atherosclerotic heart disease, malnutrition.
Low-density lipoprotein (LDL) cholesterol (S)	60–70% of total <130 mg/dl (<3.4 mmol/L)	Increased values in hyperlipidemia, atherosclerotic heart disease. Decreased values in fat malabsorption and malnutrition.
Very low density lipoprotein cholesterol (VLDL) (S)	10–15% of total	Same as LDL.
Creatine kinase (CK) (S)	Female: ≤190 U/L (≤3.2 µkat/L) Male: ≤235 U/L (≤3.9 µkat/L)	Cellular damage. Increased values in myocardial infarction, muscular dystrophy, hypothyroidism, pulmonary infarction, cerebrovascular accident (CVA), shock, tissue damage, and trauma.
Creatinine (S)	0.5–1.2 mg/dl (44–106 µmol/L)	Renal function. Increased values in renal disease and acromegaly. Decreased in muscular dystrophy.

TEST (SAMPLE)	REFERENCE VALUES: CONVENTIONAL (SI)	PHYSIOLOGICAL INDICATION AND CLINICAL IMPLICATIONS
Blood Chemistry Studies (*continued*)		
Gases (A)		
Bicarbonate	22–26 mEq/L (22–26 mmol/L)	Acid-base balance. Increased values in metabolic alkalosis and respiratory acidosis. Decreased values in metabolic acidosis and respiratory alkalosis.
Carbon dioxide content	Arterial: 19–24 mEq/L (19–24 mmol/L) Venous: 22–30 mEq/L (22–30 mmol/L)	
Carbon dioxide partial pressure (P_{CO_2})	Arterial: 35–45 mm Hg Venous: 45 mm Hg	
Oxygen (O_2) saturation	95–98% (same)	Values increased slightly in hyperventilation. Decreased values (hypoxia) in pulmonary disease, hypoventilation, high altitude.
Oxygen partial pressure (P_{O_2})	80–105 mm Hg	
pH	7.35–7.45 (same)	Increased values in metabolic and respiratory alkalosis. Decreased values in metabolic and respiratory acidosis.
Glucose (S)	70–120 mg/dl (3.9–6.7 mmol/L)	Metabolic function. Increased values in diabetes mellitus, Cushing's syndrome, liver disease, acute stress, and acromegaly. Decreased levels in Addison's disease, insulinomas.
Immunoglobulins (S)		
IgG	560–1800 mg/dl (5.6–18 g/L)	Immune response. Increased levels in chronic infections, rheumatic fever, liver disease, rheumatoid arthritis. Decreased levels in amyloidosis, leukemia, and preeclampsia.
IgE	<43.2 µg/dl (<432 µg/L)	Allergic responses. Increased values in allergic responses. Decreased values in agammaglobulinemia.
IgA	85–563 mg/dl (0.85–5.6 g/L)	Immune integrity. Increased values in liver disease, rheumatic fever, chronic infection, inflammatory bowel disease. Decreased values in immunodeficiency disorders and immunosuppression.
IgM	55–375 mg/dl (0.5–3.8 g/L)	Immune integrity. Increased in autoimmune disease (e.g., rheumatoid arthritis), acute infections. Decreased in amyloidosis and leukemia.
IgD	0.5–14 mg/dl (5–140 mg/L)	Immune integrity. Increased values in myelomas.
Ketone bodies (S or P)	Negative Toxic level >20 mg/dl (0.2 g/L)	Fatty acid catabolism. Increased values (ketosis, ketoacidosis) in starvation, low-carbohydrate diet, uncontrolled diabetes mellitus, aspirin overdose.
Lactate dehydrogenase (LDH) (S)	105–333 U/L (1.7–5.6 µkat/L)	Tissue damage of organs or striated muscle. Increased in myocardial infarction, pulmonary infarction, liver disease, cerebrovascular accident, infectious mononucleosis, muscular dystrophy, fractures.
Lactic acid (lactate) (P)	9–16 mg/dl (1.0–1.8 mmol/L)	Anaerobic tissue metabolism. Increased values in congestive heart failure, shock, hemorrhage, strenuous exercise.
Osmolality (S)	280–300 mOsm/kg H_2O (280–300 mmol/kg H_2O)	Fluid and electrolyte balance. Increased levels in hypernatremia, dehydration, kidney disease, alcohol ingestion. Decreased levels in hyponatremia, overhydration, and syndrome of inappropriate ADH secretion (SIADH).
Phosphate (S) (phosphorus)	2.5–4.5 mg/dl (0.8–1.5 mmol/L)	Parathyroid function; bone disease. Increased levels in hypoparathyroidism, renal failure, bone metastasis, hypocalcemia. Decreased values in hyperparathyroidism, hypercalcemia, alcoholism, vitamin D deficiency, ketoacidosis, osteomalacia.
Potassium (S)	3.5–5.5 mEq/L (3.5–5.5 mmol/L)	Fluid and electrolyte balance. Increased levels in renal disease, Addison's disease, ketoacidosis, burns, and crush injuries. Decreased levels in vomiting, diarrhea, Cushing's syndrome, alkalosis, diuretics.

TEST (SAMPLE)	REFERENCE VALUES: CONVENTIONAL (SI)	PHYSIOLOGICAL INDICATION AND CLINICAL IMPLICATIONS
Blood Chemistry Studies *(continued)*		
Protein (S)		
Total	6.0–8.5 g/dl (60–85 g/L)	Osmotic pressure; immune system integrity. Increased values in multiple myeloma, dehydration, myxedema. Decreased values in protein malnutrition, burns, diarrhea, renal failure, liver failure.
Albumin	3.2–5.0 g/dl (32–50 g/L)	Osmotic pressure. Increased levels in dehydration. Decreased levels in liver disease, malnutrition, Crohn's disease, nephrotic syndrome, systemic lupus erythematosus.
Sodium (S)	135–145 mEq/L (135–145 mmol/L)	Fluid and electrolyte balance. Increased values in dehydration, diabetes insipidus, Cushing's syndrome. Decreased values in vomiting, diarrhea, burns, Addison's disease, myxedema, congestive heart failure, overhydration, syndrome of inappropriate ADH secretion (SIADH).
Triglycerides	10–150 mg/dl (0.1–1.5 g/L)	Increased values in diabetes mellitus, liver disease, nephrotic syndrome, pregnancy.
Uric acid (S)	Female: 2.0–7.3 mg/dl (119–434 µmol/L) Male: 2.1–8.5 mg/dl (125–506 µmol/L)	Renal function. Increased in lead poisoning, impaired renal function, gout, alcoholism, hematologic cancers. Decreased in Wilson's disease.
Hematology Studies		
Hemoglobin (S)	Female: 12–16 g/dl (120–160 g/L) Male: 13–18 g/dl (130–180 g/L)	Oxygenation status. Increased values in dehydration, polycythemia, congestive heart failure, chronic obstructive pulmonary disease, high altitudes. Decreased levels in anemia, hemorrhage, bone marrow cancer, renal disease, systemic lupus erythematosus, nutritional deficiency.
Hematocrit (WB)	Female: 37–47% (same) Male: 42–52% (same)	Oxygenation status. Increased levels in polycythemia, dehydration, congestive heart failure, shock, surgery. Decreased levels in anemia, hemorrhage, bone marrow disease, malnutrition, cirrhosis, rheumatoid arthritis.
Partial thromboplastin time (activated) (PTT or aPTT)	20–36 s (same)	Clotting mechanisms. Increased values in clotting factor deficiencies, cirrhosis, vitamin K deficiency, disseminated intravascular coagulation (DIC). Decreased values in early DIC, extensive cancer.
Platelet count (WB)	150,000–400,000/µl (150–400 × 10⁹/L)	Clotting mechanisms. Increased values in polycythemia, cancers, rheumatoid arthritis, trauma. Decreased values in liver disease, hemolytic uremic syndrome, disseminated intravascular coagulation (DIC), idiopathic thrombocytopenic purpura (ITP), systemic lupus erythematosus (SLE).
Prothrombin time (PT) (WB)	11–12.5 s (same) 1.5–2 × control (evaluating anticoagulant treatment)	Clotting mechanisms. Increased values in liver disease, vitamin K deficiency, salicylate intoxication. Decreased values in disseminated intravascular coagulation (DIC).
Red blood cell count (RBC) (WB)	Female: 4.2–5.4 million/µl (4.2–5.4 × 10¹²/L) Male: 4.7–6.1 million/µl (4.7–6.1 × 10¹²/L)	Oxygenation status. Increased values in high altitudes, polycythemia, hemoconcentration, cor pulmonale. Decreased values in hemorrhage, hemolysis, anemias, chronic illness, nutritional deficiencies, leukemia, overhydration.
Reticulocyte count (WB)	0.5–2.0% (same)	Bone marrow function. Increased values in hemolytic anemia, sickle-cell anemia, leukemia, pregnancy. Decreased values in pernicious anemia, folic acid deficiency, cirrhosis, chronic infection, bone marrow depression or failure.
White blood cell count (WBC) (WB)		
Total (males)	4800–10,800/µl (4.8–10.8 × 10⁹/L)	Immune system integrity. Increased values in infection, trauma, stress, tissue necrosis, inflammation. Decreased values in bone marrow depression or failure, drug toxicity, overwhelming infection, malnutrition.

TEST (SAMPLE)	REFERENCE VALUES: CONVENTIONAL (SI)	PHYSIOLOGICAL INDICATION AND CLINICAL IMPLICATIONS
Hematology Studies (continued)		
White blood cell count, differential (WB)		
Neutrophils	50–70% (same)	Immune system integrity. Increased values in acute bacterial infections, stress, Cushing's syndrome, inflammatory disorders, ketoacidosis, gout. Decreased levels in aplastic anemia, bone marrow suppression, and overwhelming bacterial infections.
Lymphocytes	25–40% (same)	Immune system integrity. Increased values in viral infections (e.g., mumps, rubella, infectious mononucleosis, hepatitis), lymphocytic leukemia, certain bacterial infections. Decreased levels in leukemia, immunodeficiency, lupus erythematosus, bone marrow depressive drugs.
Eosinophils	1–4% (same)	Immune system integrity. Increased levels in allergic reactions, parasitic infections, leukemia. Decreased levels in excess adrenocorticosteroid production.
Monocytes	3–8% (same)	Immune system integrity. Increased levels in certain infections (e.g., tuberculosis, malaria), inflammatory disorders.
Basophils	0.5–1.0% (same)	Immune system integrity. Increased levels in myeloproliferative disorders, leukemia. Decreased levels in allergic reactions, hyperthyroidism, stress.
Urine Tests		
Amylase (24 h)	<6000 Somogyi units/24 h 0–500 U/24 h (0–8.3 μkat/24 h)	Pancreatic function. Increased values in pancreatic disease or obstruction, inflammation of the salivary glands, and cholecystitis.
Bilirubin (random)	Negative (same)	Liver function. Increased values in liver disease, extrahepatic obstruction (gallstones, tumor, inflammation).
Blood (hemoglobin) (random)	Negative (same)	Urinary system function. Increased values in cystitis, renal disease, hemolytic anemia, transfusion reaction, prostatitis, burns.
Osmolality (random or fasting)	Random: 50–1200 mOsm/kg H_2O (50–1200 mmol/kg H_2O) Fluid restriction: ≥850 mOsm/kg H_2O (≥850 mmol/kg H_2O)	Fluid and electrolyte balance, renal function, and endocrine function. Increased levels in hypernatremia, syndrome of inappropriate ADH secretion (SIADH), congestive heart failure, metabolic acidosis. Decreased levels in diabetes insipidus, water intoxication, pyelonephritis, renal tubular necrosis, aldosteronism.
Phosphate (24 h)	0.9–1.3g/24 hr (same)	Parathyroid function. Increased levels in hyperparathyroidism, osteomalacia, certain renal diseases, vitamin D deficiency. Decreased levels in hypoparathyroidism.
Potassium (24 h)	25–120 mEq/24 h (25–120 mmol/24 h)	Fluid and electrolyte balance. Increased values in renal tubular necrosis, metabolic acidosis, dehydration, aldosteronism, Cushing's syndrome. Decreased values in Addison's disease, malabsorption, acute renal failure.
Protein (random)	<8 mg/dl (<80 mg/L)	Renal function. Increased levels in nephrotic syndrome, renal trauma, hyperthyroidism, diabetic nephropathy, systemic lupus erythematosus.
Sodium (24 h)	40–220 mEq/24 h (40–220 mmol/24 h)	Fluid and electrolyte balance. Increased values in dehydration, ketoacidosis, syndrome of inappropriate ADH secretion (SIADH), adrenocortical insufficiency. Decreased levels in congestive heart failure, renal failure, diarrhea, aldosteronism.
Uric acid (24 h)	250–750 mg/24 h (1.5–4.5 mmol/24 h)	Renal function and metabolism. Increased in gout, leukemia, liver disease, ulcerative colitis. Decreased in renal disease, alcoholism, lead toxicity, folic acid deficiency.

TEST (SAMPLE)	REFERENCE VALUES: CONVENTIONAL (SI)	PHYSIOLOGICAL INDICATION AND CLINICAL IMPLICATIONS
Urine Tests (continued)		
Urinalysis (random)		
Color	Straw, yellow, amber	Fluid balance and renal function. Darker in dehydration. Lighter in overhydration, diabetes insipidus. Color varies with disease states, diet, and medications.
Odor	Aromatic	Metabolic function, infection. Abnormal odors in infection, ketonuria, rectal fistula, hepatic failure, phenylketonuria.
Specific gravity	1.001–1.035	An indirect measurement of urine concentration (osmolality). Same physiological indications and clinical implications as osmolality.
pH	4.5–8.0	A crude indicator of acid-base balance. Decreased by acidic diet (proteins). Increased by a vegetarian diet, prolonged vomiting, and bacterial infection of the urinary tract.
Urobilinogen (24 h)	0.2–1.0 mg/dl (2–10 mg/L)	Liver function. Increased in hemolytic anemias, hepatitis, cirrhosis, biliary disease. Decreased in common bile duct obstruction.
Volume (24 h)	800–2000 ml/24 h (0.8–2.0 L/24 h)	Fluid and electrolyte balance, renal function. Increased values in diabetes insipidus, diabetes mellitus, renal disease. Decreased values in dehydration, syndrome of inappropriate ADH secretion (SIADH), renal disease.

Figure G.1 Each upper limb is innervated by five major nerves arising from the brachial plexus.

The nerves from the **anterior division of the brachial plexus** innervate the muscles in the anterior compartments: the flexor muscles of the arm, forearm, and hand. These nerves continue distally to supply cutaneous innervation to the forearm and hand.

Muscular innervation

Cutaneous innervation

Musculocutaneous nerve

Median nerve

Ulnar nerve

C5
C6
C7

C5
C6
C7
C8
T1

C8
T1

Anterior view   Posterior view

Coraco-brachialis

Biceps brachii
Brachialis

Medial cutaneous nerves off medial cord

Pronator teres

Flexor carpi radialis

Palmaris longus

Flexor digitorum superficialis

Flexor carpi ulnaris

Flexor pollicis longus

Flexor digitorum profundus

Musculocutaneous nerve

Pronator quadratus

Adductor pollicis

3 Thenar muscles

7 Interossei

3 Hypothenar muscles

Ulnar nerve

Lumbricals to digits 2,3

Lumbricals to digits 4,5

Median nerve

▬▬▬▬ Indicates variable contribution

The nerves from the **posterior division of the brachial plexus** innervate the muscles in the posterior compartments: the extensor muscles of the upper limb. These nerves continue distally to supply cutaneous innervation to much of the posterior arm, forearm, and hand.

Muscular innervation

Cutaneous innervation

Radial nerve

Axillary nerve

C5
C6
C7
C8
T1

C5
C6

Anterior view *Posterior view*

Teres minor

Deltoid

Axillary nerve

Axillary nerve

Triceps brachii (long head)

Triceps brachii (lateral head)

Radial nerve

Radial nerve

Triceps brachii (medial head)

Brachioradialis*

Anconeus

Extensor carpi radialis longus

Extensor carpi radialis brevis

Extensor digitorum

Extensor digiti minimi

Supinator

Extensor carpi ulnaris

Abductor pollicis longus

Extensor pollicis brevis

Extensor pollicis longus

Extensor indicis

Radial nerve

*Functionally brachioradialis acts as a flexor of the forearm. It develops from the posterior compartment and thus is innervated by a posterior division nerve.

▰▰▰▰Indicates variable contribution

A-15

Figure G.2 Each lower limb is innervated by nerves arising from the lumbar and sacral plexuses, together called the lumbosacral plexus.

The nerves from the **lumbar plexus** innervate the muscles in the anterior and medial compartments of the thigh, and supply cutaneous innervation to anterior and medial portions of the thigh and leg.

Muscular innervation of anterior thigh

Femoral nerve

Muscular innervation of medial thigh

Obturator nerve

Cutaneous innervation

Anterior view   Posterior view

L2
L3
L4

L2
L3
L4

Iliacus

Sartorius

Rectus femoris

Pectineus

Adductor brevis

Obturator externus

Vastus lateralis
Vastus intermedius
Vastus medialis

Adductor longus

Adductor magnus

Gracilis

Lateral femoral cutaneous nerve

Obturator nerve

Femoral nerve

The nerves from the **sacral plexus** innervate the muscles in the posterior compartments of the thigh and all of the muscles in the leg, and supply cutaneous innervation to the lateral and posterior portions of the leg and to the foot.

Muscular innervation of posterior thigh and leg

Muscular innervation of lateral and anterior leg

Cutaneous innervation

Tibial nerve

Common fibular nerve

Anterior view

Posterior view

L4
L5
S1
S2
S3

Sciatic nerve*

Biceps femoris (long head)

Semitendinosus

Adductor magnus

Semimembranosus

Biceps femoris (short head)

Gastrocnemius

Plantaris
Gastrocnemius

Popliteus
Soleus

Tibialis posterior

Fibularis longus

Tibialis anterior

Flexor digitorum longus

Flexor hallucis longus

Fibularis brevis

Extensor digitorum longus

Extensor hallucis longus

Fibularis tertius

Abductor hallucis
Flexor digitorum brevis
Flexor hallucis brevis
Lumbricals

All other muscles of the sole

Extensor digitorum brevis

Posterior femoral cutaneous nerve

Common fibular nerve

Tibial nerve

*Sciatic nerve formed by tibial and common fibular nerves wrapped by common sheath.

A-17

Chapter 1

Check Your Understanding 1. The operation or function of a structure is promoted or prevented by its anatomy. For example, oxygen and carbon dioxide are exchanged across the very thin membranes of the lungs but not across the skin. **2.** Muscle shortening is a topic of physiology. The body location of the lungs is an anatomy topic. **3.** Cytologists study the cellular level of organization. **4.** The order in the structural hierarchy is cell, tissue, organ, and organism. **5.** Bones and cartilages are part of the skeletal system. The nasal cavity, lungs, and trachea are respiratory system organs. **6.** Living organisms can maintain their boundaries, move, respond to environmental changes, digest nutrients, carry out metabolism, dispose of wastes, reproduce, and grow. While inanimate objects may exhibit some of these properties, they do not exhibit all of them. **7.** Metabolism is the term that encompasses all the chemical reactions that occur in body cells. **8.** In flight, the cabin must be pressurized because the atmosphere is thinner at high altitudes and the amount of oxygen entering the blood under such conditions may be insufficient to maintain life. **9.** Negative feedback mechanisms allow us to adjust to conditions outside the normal temperature range by causing heat to be lost from the body (in hot conditions) and retained or generated by the body (in cold conditions). **10.** Thirst is part of a negative feedback control system because it prods us to drink, which ends the thirst stimulus and returns body fluid volume to the normal range. **11.** This is a positive feedback mechanism because it enhances the change (formation of a platelet plug) set into motion by the stimulus (damage to the blood vessel). The response ends when the platelet plug has plugged the hole in the blood vessel. **12.** The position in which a person is standing erect with feet slightly separated and palms facing anteriorly. Knowing the anatomical position is important because directional terms refer to the body as if it is in this position. **13.** Axillary region is the armpit. Acromial area is the tip of the shoulder. **14.** A frontal (coronal) section would separate the brain into anterior and posterior parts. **15.** He may have appendicitis if the pain is in the lower right quadrant of his abdomen. **16.** Of these organs, only the spinal cord is in the dorsal body cavity. **17.** As mobile organs (heart, lungs, digestive organs) work, friction is greatly reduced by the presence of serous fluid. Serous fluid allows the surrounding serous membranes to glide easily over one another.

Review Questions 1. c; **2.** a; **3.** e; **4.** a, d; **5.** (a) wrist (b) hip bone (c) nose (d) toes (e) scalp; **6.** neither c nor d would be visible in the median section; **7.** (a) dorsal (b) ventral (c) dorsal (d) ventral; **8.** b; **9.** b; **10.** c

Chapter 2

Check Your Understanding 1. Foods contain chemical energy. **2.** Electrical energy is the energy used by nerve cells to transmit messages in the body. **3.** Potential energy (PE) is available when we are still. PE is converted to kinetic (working) energy when we exercise. **4.** Besides hydrogen and nitrogen, carbon and oxygen help to make up the bulk of living matter. **5.** This element has 82 protons in its nucleus and 82 electrons in its orbitals (electron cloud). **6.** Atomic mass indicates the sum of the protons and neutrons in a given atom's nucleus. Atomic weight indicates the average mass of all the isotopes of a given element. **7.** A molecule is 2 or more atoms held together by chemical bonds. **8.** A compound is formed when two or more different kinds of atoms chemically bond together, as in NaCl. Oxygen gas is 2 oxygen atoms (the same kind of atom) bonded together. **9.** Blood is a mixture because its components are not changed by their combination and they can be separated by physical means. **10.** Hydrogen bonds (linking H of one water molecule to O of another) form between water molecules. **11.** Argon's valence shell is full:)2e)8e)8e. Hence it is nonreactive. **12.** Electrons would spend more time in the vicinity of the more electronegative atom in XY, whereas electrons in XX

would orbit both X atoms to an equal extent. **13.** Fats are digested in the small intestine by decomposition reactions. **14.** Biochemical reactions in the body tend to be irreversible because (a) one or more of the products is removed from the reaction site or (b) the product is needed more than the reactants, so the cell would not provide energy to reverse the reaction. **15.** Decomposition reactions in which foods are broken down for energy are oxidation-reduction (redox) reactions. **16.** Water is an excellent solvent because of its polarity. As a dipole, it can orient itself to the end of other molecules, causing them to dissociate or go into solution. **17.** Electrolytes are substances like salts that will conduct an electrical current in aqueous solution. **18.** H^+ is responsible for acidity. **19.** It is better to add a weak base, which will act to buffer the strong acid. **20.** Monomers of carbohydrates are called monosaccharides or simple sugars. Glucose is blood sugar. **21.** The animal form of stored carbohydrate is glycogen. **22.** Triglycerides, the major source of stored energy in the body, are composed of three fatty acid chains and a glycerol molecule and are found in fat tissue. Phospholipids consist of two fatty acid chains and a charged P-containing group. They are found in all cell membranes and form the basis of those membranes. **23.** Hydrolysis reactions break down polymers or macromolecules to their monomers by adding water to each bond joining monomers. **24.** An "amino acid" has an amine group (NH_2) and a COOH group that has acidic properties. **25.** The primary structure of proteins is the stringlike chain of amino acids. **26.** The secondary structures of proteins are the alpha helix and the beta-pleated sheet. **27.** Molecular chaperones prevent inaccurate or inappropriate folding in the 3-D structure of a protein. **28.** Enzymes hold the substrate(s) in a desirable position to interact. **29.** DNA contains deoxyribose sugar and the bases A, T, G, C. RNA contains ribose sugar and the bases A, U, G, C. **30.** DNA dictates protein structure by its base sequence and reproduces itself before a cell divides to ensure that the genetic information in the daughter cells is identical. **31.** ATP stores energy in smaller packets that are more readily released and transferred (during ATP hydrolysis) than the energy stored in glucose. Hence the use of ATP as an energy source keeps energy waste to a minimum. **32.** When ATP releases energy, it loses a phosphate group and becomes ADP (also energy rich).

Review Questions 1. d; **2.** d; **3.** b; **4.** a; **5.** b; **6.** a; **7.** a; **8.** b; **9.** d; **10.** a; **11.** b; **12.** a, c; **13.** (1)a, (2)c; **14.** c; **15.** d; **16.** e; **17.** d; **18.** d; **19.** a; **20.** b; **21.** b; **22.** c

Chapter 3

Check Your Understanding 1. The cell is the structural and functional unit of life. The activity of an organism depends on the activities of its cells. The activities of cells depend on their form and relative numbers of subcellular structures. Continuity of life has a cellular basis. **2.** It is the cell concept that includes structures and functions common to all cells. **3.** All cellular membranes consist of a double layer of phospholipids in which proteins are embedded. **4.** Hydrophobic regions (tails of phospholipid molecules) orient toward each other while the hydrophilic regions (phospholipid heads) orient to the aqueous fluid inside and outside the cell. **5.** The sugar residues of the glycocalyx provide recognizable biological markers for cells to recognize each other. **6.** The heart has desmosomes (anchoring junctions) that secure cardiac cells together as the heart works and gap junctions (communicating junctions) that allow ions to flow from cardiac cell to cardiac cell. **7.** Diffusion is driven by kinetic energy of the molecules. **8.** The relative concentration of the substance in different areas determines the direction of diffusion. Diffusion occurs from regions of high concentration to regions of low concentration. **9.** In channel-mediated diffusion, the diffusing substance moves through a membrane channel. In carrier-mediated diffusion, the diffusing substance attaches to a membrane (protein) carrier that moves it across the membrane. **10.** Phosphorylation of the Na⁺-K⁺ pump causes the pump protein to change shape so that it "pumps" Na⁺ across the membrane. K⁺ binding to the pump protein triggers the release of phosphate and the pump protein returns to its original shape. **11.** The plasma membrane expands as a result of exocytosis. **12.** Phagocytic cells engulf debris, and a smoker's lungs would be laden with carbon particles and other debris from smoke inhalation. **13.** Cholesterol is taken in by receptor-mediated endocytosis. **14.** Diffusion of ions, mainly the diffusion of K⁺ from the cell through leakage channels, establishes the resting membrane potential. **15.** In a polarized membrane, the inside is negative relative to its outside. **16.** Signaling chemicals that bind to membrane receptors are called ligands. G protein–linked receptors direct intracellular events by promoting formation of second messengers. **17.** Mitochondria are the major sites of ATP synthesis. **18.** Ribosomes are the sites of protein synthesis. The rough ER provides a site for ribosome attachment, and its cisterns package in vesicles the proteins made on the ribosomes for transport to the Golgi apparatus. The Golgi apparatus modifies and packages the proteins it receives for various destinations within or outside the cell. **19.** The lysosomal enzymes digest foreign substances engulfed by the cell, nonuseful or deteriorating organelles, or even the cell itself to prevent the buildup of cellular debris. The enzymes in peroxisomes detoxify harmful chemicals and neutralize free radicals. **20.** Both microfilaments and microtubules are involved in organelle movements within the cell and/or movements of the cell as a whole. **21.** Intermediate filaments are the most important cytoskeletal elements in maintaining cell shape. **22.** The major function of microvilli is to increase the cell's surface area for absorption of substances. **23.** If a cell loses its nucleus, it is doomed to die because it will be unable to make proteins, which include the enzymes needed for all metabolic reactions. **24.** Nucleoli are the site of synthesis of ribosomal subunits. **25.** Histone proteins provide the means to pack DNA in a compact, orderly way, and they play a role in gene regulation. **26.** The base sequence of the corresponding strand will be GCTTAC. **27.** DNA is synthesized during the S phase. **28.** Nuclear envelope breaks up, spindle forms, nucleoli disappear, and the chromosomes coil and condense. **29.** Codons are three-base sequences in mRNA, each of which specifies an amino acid. Anticodons are three-base sequences in tRNA that are complementary to the codons specifying the amino acid they transport to the ribosome during protein synthesis. **30.** The A site is the entry site for tRNA at the ribosome. The P site is where the tRNA carrying the growing polypeptide is located. The E site is the tRNA exit site from the ribosome. **31.** DNA provides the coded instructions (is the template) for protein synthesis via the mRNA synthesized on it. **32.** Ubiquitin attaches to misfolded, damaged, or unneeded proteins, tagging them for destruction by proteasomes. **33.** Blood plasma is extracellular fluid that transports nutrients, gases, hormones, and other substances throughout the body. Interstitial fluid is an important transport and dissolving medium. **34.** Apoptosis is a process of programmed cell death which rids the body of cells that are stressed, damaged, old, or no longer needed. **35.** The wear-and-tear theory of aging attributes aging to little chemical insults and free radicals, which have cumulative detrimental effects.

Review Questions 1. d; **2.** a, c; **3.** b; **4.** b; **5.** e; **6.** c; **7.** d; **8.** a; **9.** d; **10.** a; **11.** b; **12.** d; **13.** c; **14.** b; **15.** d; **16.** a; **17.** b; **18.** d; **19.** c

Chapter 4

Check Your Understanding 1. Fixing tissue preserves it and prevents it from deteriorating. **2.** Heavy metal salts are used to stain tissues viewed by electron microscopes. **3.** Epithelial tissue lines body cavities and covers the body's external surface; thus polarity with one free (apical) surface is a requirement. **4.** Epithelial tissue can regenerate and its cells are joined by lateral contacts. **5.** Simple epithelia are "built" to provide for efficient absorption and filtration across their thin epithelial barriers. **6.** Pseudo-

stratified epithelia appear to be stratified because their cells' nuclei lie at different distances from the basement membrane. However, all cells rest on the basement membrane. **7.** Transitional epithelium is found in the urinary bladder and other hollow urinary organs. The ability of this epithelium to thin allows the urinary organs to handle (store or transport) a larger urine volume when necessary. **8.** All unicellular exocrine glands secrete the protein mucin (which becomes mucus on mixing with water). **9.** These exocrine glands are classified by duct structure and secretory mode. **10.** Holocrine glands have the highest rate of cell division. The secretory cells fragment and are lost in the secretion; thus the secretory cells must be continuously replaced. **11.** Connective tissue functions to bind, support, protect, and insulate body organs. In addition, blood acts to transport substances throughout the body. **12.** Reticular, collagen, and elastic fibers are found in the various connective tissues. **13.** Areolar connective tissue, because of its loose weblike nature, is capable of serving as a fluid reservoir. **14.** Dense regular connective tissue is damaged when you lacerate a tendon. **15.** Hyaline cartilage forms the growth plates. **16.** Cardiac muscle cells have striations and are branching cells. **17.** Skeletal muscle tissue is voluntary and is the muscle tissue injured when you "pull a muscle" while exercising. **18.** With extended processes, a neuron can conduct electrical signals a great distance within the body. **19.** A mucous membrane consists of both connective tissue and epithelium. It lines body cavities open to the exterior. **20.** The serous membranes called pleurae line the thorax walls and cover the lungs. **21.** The three main steps of tissue repair are inflammation, organization, and regeneration and fibrosis (which is a permanent repair). **22.** More severe injuries damage and destroy more tissue, requiring greater replacement with scar tissue. **23.** The three embryonic germ layers are the ectoderm, mesoderm, and endoderm. **24.** Ectoderm gives rise to the nervous system. **25.** Epithelium and blood-forming tissue remain highly mitotic all through life.

Review Questions 1. (1)a, (2)c, (3)d, (4)b; **2.** c, e; **3.** (1)b, (2)f, (3)a, (4)d, (5)g, (6)d; **4.** b; **5.** c; **6.** b

Chapter 5

Check Your Understanding 1. Since the sole of the foot has thick skin, the layers from most superficial to deepest would be the stratum corneum, stratum lucidum, stratum granulosum, stratum spinosum, and stratum basale. **2.** The stratum basale undergoes almost continuous mitosis to replace cells lost by abrasion. **3.** The skin is subjected to a lot of abrasion and physical trauma. The desmosomes, which are connecting junctions, help to hold the cells together during such stress. **4.** The stratum basale, which abuts the dermis where the blood supply is, has the best nourished cells. **5.** The papillary layer of the dermis gives rise to fingerprint patterns. **6.** Fatty tissue in the hypodermis gives it insulating and shock-absorbing properties. **7.** Because there is no bleeding, the cut has penetrated into the avascular epidermis only. **8.** The third pigment contributing to skin color is hemoglobin, the pigment contained in red blood cells found in blood vessels of the dermis. **9.** Cyanosis is a bluish cast of the skin that indicates that hemoglobin in the red blood cells in the dermal capillaries is poorly oxygenated. **10.** Jaundice or a yellow cast to the skin due to the deposit of yellow bile pigments in body tissues may indicate a liver disorder. **11.** The regions of a hair from outside in are the cuticle, cortex, and medulla. **12.** There are no nerves in a hair, so cutting hair is painless. **13.** The arrector pili muscles pull the hair (normally slanted) to the upright position (when cold or scared). **14.** The hair papilla contains a knot of capillaries that supplies nutrients to cells of the hair bulb. **15.** The lunule of the nail is white because the thick nail matrix that underlies it blocks the rosy color of the dermal blood supply from showing through. **16.** Nails are hard because the keratin they contain is the hard keratin variety. **17.** Sebaceous (oil) glands and apocrine glands are associated with the hair follicles. **18.** His sympathetic nervous system activated his eccrine sweat glands and caused heat-induced sweating in order to cool the body. **19.** Heat-induced sweating occurs all over the body when we are overheated. A cold sweat is emotionally induced sweating that begins on the palms, soles, and armpits and then spreads to other body areas. Both types of sweating are produced by the eccrine sweat glands, but activity of apocrine sweat glands is also likely during a cold sweat. **20.** The palms of the hands and soles of the feet are thick skin areas. It would be dangerous to have oily soles, and oily palms would decrease the ability of the hands to hang onto things. **21.** The low pH of skin secretions (acid mantle) inhibits division of bacteria, and many bacteria are killed by bactericidal substances in sebum or by natural antibiotics called defensins. Damaged skin secretes cathelicidins that are effective against a certain strain of strep bacteria. **22.** The epidermal dendritic cells play a role in body immunity. **23.** Sunlight causes the skin to produce a precursor of vitamin D from cholesterol. Vitamin D is essential for bone synthesis. **24.** The skin carries out chemical conversions that supplement some of the protective conversions carried out by the liver, convert some chemicals into carcinogens, activate some steroid hormones, and synthesize the vitamin D precursor. **25.** Basal cell carcinoma develops from the youngest epidermal cells. **26.** The ABCD rule helps one to recognize signs of melanoma. **27.** First- and second-degree burns can heal uneventfully by regeneration of epidermal cells as long as infection does not occur. Third-degree burns destroy the entire depth of skin and regeneration is not possible. Infection and loss of body fluid and proteins are problematic. **28.** Burns to the face are serious because damage to the respiratory passageways can occur in such burns. **29.** Vernix caseosa is a product of the sebaceous glands. **30.** Loss of subcutaneous fat, common in the elderly, leads to cold intolerance seen in this group of people. **31.** UV radiation degrades collagen and leads to loss of skin elasticity and water-holding capacity.

Review Questions 1. a; **2.** c; **3.** d; **4.** d; **5.** b; **6.** b; **7.** c; **8.** c; **9.** b; **10.** a; **11.** d; **12.** b

Case Study 1. The skin separates and protects the internal environment of the body from potentially dangerous elements in the external environment. Mrs. DeStephano's chart indicates epidermal abrasions, which represent the loss of this barrier. Epidermal loss will also cost Mrs. DeStephano the acid mantle of her skin, protection against UV radiation, and dendritic cells, which protect against invasion by microorganisms. **2.** Macrophages found in the dermis can act as a backup system against bacterial and viral invasion when the epidermis is damaged. **3.** Suturing brings the edges of wounds close together and promotes faster healing because smaller amounts of granulation tissue need to be formed. This is termed healing by first intention. **4.** Cyanosis signals a decrease in the amount of oxygen carried by hemoglobin in the blood. Respiratory system and/or cardiovascular system impairments can lead to cyanosis.

Chapter 6

Check Your Understanding 1. Hyaline cartilage is the most plentiful in the adult body. **2.** The epiglottis and external ear cartilages are flexible elastic cartilage. **3.** Interstitial growth is growth from within. **4.** The components of the axial skeleton are the skull, the vertebral column, and the thoracic cage. **5.** The major function of the axial skeleton is to establish the long axis of the body and to protect structures that it encloses. The general function of the appendicular skeleton is to allow us mobility for propulsion and manipulation of our environment. **6.** The ribs and skull bones are flat bones. **7.** Skeletal muscles use bones as levers to cause movement of the body and its parts. **8.** Bone matrix stores minerals and growth factors. **9.** Bone marrow cavities serve as sites for blood cell formation and fat storage. **10.** Crests, tubercles, and spines are bony projections. **11.** Compact bone looks fairly solid and homogeneous whereas spongy bone has an open network of bone spicules. **12.** Endosteum lines the internal canals and covers the trabeculae. **13.** Bone's inorganic component (bone salts) makes it hard. **14.** The

osteoclast fits this description. **15.** Bones begin as fibrous membranes or hyaline cartilages. **16.** The cartilage model grows, then breaks down and is replaced by bone. **17.** The primary ossification center in a long bone is in the center of the shaft. The secondary ossification centers are in the epiphyses (bone ends). **18.** The chondrocytes are enlarging and their lacunae are breaking down and leaving holes in the cartilage matrix. **19.** If bone-destroying cells (osteoclasts) are more active than bone-forming cells (osteoblasts), bone mass will decrease. **20.** The hormonal stimulus maintains homeostatic blood calcium levels. **21.** In an open fracture, the bone ends are exposed to the external environment. In a closed fracture, the bone ends do not penetrate the external boundary of the skin. **22.** Bone growth increases bone mass, as during childhood or when exceptional stress is placed on the bones. Bone remodeling follows bone growth to maintain the proper proportions of the bone considering stresses placed upon it. **23.** Paget's disease is characterized by excessive deposit of weak, poorly mineralized bone. **24.** Sufficient vitamin D, calcium, and weight-bearing exercise all help to maintain healthy bone density. **25.** Adult rickets is called osteomalacia. **26.** At birth, most bones are well formed and ossified except for their epiphyses. **27.** The skull bones do not appear to lose mass with aging.

Review Questions 1. e; **2.** b; **3.** c; **4.** d; **5.** e; **6.** b; **7.** c; **8.** b; **9.** d, e; **10.** c; **11.** b; **12.** c; **13.** a; **14.** b

Case Study 1. Mrs. DeStephano's broken leg has a transverse fracture of the open variety because the broken ends of the bone are protruding through the skin. **2.** The laceration of the skin caused by the broken end of the bone creates a breach in the protective barrier created by the skin, providing an entry point for bacteria and other microorganisms. In addition, the protruding ends of the bone have now been exposed to the nonsterile external environment. This could result in the development of osteomyelitis, a bacterial infection, which can be treated with antibiotics. **3.** Reduction of a fracture is the clinical term for "setting the bone." Mrs. DeStephano's physician chose internal reduction, in which surgery is performed and the broken ends of the bone are secured together by pins or wires. A cast was applied to keep the aligned ends of the bone immobile until healing of the fracture has occurred. **4.** Healing of Mrs. DeStephano's fracture will begin as bony callus formation fills the break in the bone with bony tissue. This process begins 3–4 weeks after the break occurs and is completed within 2–3 months. **5.** Nutrient arteries supply blood to the bone tissue. In order for Mrs. DeStephano's break to heal normally, the bony tissue must be supplied with oxygen (to generate ATP for energy) and nutrients in order to rebuild the bone. Damage to a nutrient artery will decrease the delivery of these building materials and could slow the process of healing. **6.** For a fracture that is slow to heal, new techniques that promote healing include electrical stimulation, which promotes the deposition of new bone tissue; ultrasound treatments, known to speed healing; and possibly the addition of bone substitutes to the fractured area. **7.** At age 45, Mrs. DeStephano will most likely not regenerate her knee cartilage. (Cartilage growth typically ends during adolescence.) Cartilage damage that occurs during adulthood is slow to heal, due to the avascular nature of cartilage, and is usually irreparable. Surgical removal of cartilage fragments to allow improved movement of the joint is the usual treatment for this type of damage.

Chapter 7

Check Your Understanding 1. The three main parts of the axial skeleton are the skull, vertebral column, and thoracic cage. **2.** The axial skeleton is more important in protecting internal organs. **3.** The frontal, parietal, temporal, sphenoid, and ethmoid bones are all cranial bones. **4.** The ethmoid bone forms the crista galli. **5.** The temporal bones house the external ear canals. **6.** The parietal bones abut each other at the sagittal suture. The occipital bone abuts the parietal bones at the lambdoid suture. **7.** The zygomatic bones are the cheekbones. **8.** Eating or talking, because the only freely movable joints of the skull are the temporomandibular joints of the jaw. **9.** The maxillae are the keystone bones of the facial skeleton. **10.** The sphenoid, ethmoid, frontal, and maxillary bones contain paranasal sinuses. **11.** The cribriform plates of the ethmoid bone form the roof of the nasal cavity. **12.** The maxillae form the bulk of the orbit floor. The eye is housed in the orbit. **13.** The five major regions of the vertebral column are the cervical, thoracic, lumbar, sacral, and coccygeal regions. **14.** The cervical and lumbar regions are concave posteriorly. **15.** The fibrocartilage discs contribute to the flexibility of the vertebral column. **16.** There are 7 cervical and 12 thoracic vertebrae. **17.** The dens is the axis on which the atlas rotates. If it's broken, movements of the atlas would be less controllable. **18.** A lumbar vertebra is heavier and its massive body is kidney shaped. Its spinous processes are short and project directly back. A thoracic vertebral body is generally heart shaped, its spinous process is long, sharp, and points downward, and its transverse processes have facets for articulating with the ribs. **19.** A true rib connects to the sternum by its own costal cartilage. A false rib connects to the sternum via costal cartilages of other ribs or not at all. **20.** The sternal angle is a ridge across the front of the sternum where the manubrium joins the sternal body. It acts as a hinge allowing the sternum to swing anteriorly when we inhale. Because it is aligned with the second rib, it is a handy cue for finding that rib and then counting the ribs during a physical exam. **21.** The thoracic vertebrae also contribute to the thoracic cage. **22.** Each pectoral girdle is formed by a scapula and a clavicle. **23.** The pectoral girdle attaches to the sternal manubrium of the axial skeleton via the medial end of its clavicle. **24.** A consequence of its flexibility is that it is easily dislocated. **25.** Together the ulna and humerus form the elbow joint. **26.** The ulna and the radius each have a styloid process distally. **27.** Carpals are found in the proximal region of the palm. They are short bones. **28.** The third bone of the os coxae is the ischium. **29.** The pelvic girdle receives the weight of the upper body (trunk, head, and upper limbs) and transmits that weight to the lower limbs. **30.** The female pelvis is wider and has a shorter sacrum and a more movable coccyx. **31.** The tibia is the second largest bone in the body. **32.** The medial malleolus is located on the distalmost medial aspect of the tibia. **33.** The lateral condyles are not sites of muscle attachment, they are articular surfaces. **34.** Because of their springiness, the foot arches save energy during locomotion. **35.** The two largest tarsals are the talus and the calcaneus, which forms the heel. **36.** The enlargement of the facial skeleton between ages 6 and 13 is due to the enlargement of the nose and paranasal sinuses and the development of the permanent teeth. **37.** The lumbar curvature develops when the baby begins to walk.

Review Questions 1. (1)b, g; (2)h; (3)d; (4)d, f; (5)e; (6)c; (7)a, b, d, h; (8)i; **2.** (1)g, (2)f, (3)b, (4)a, (5)b, (6)c, (7)d, (8)e; **3.** (1)b, (2)c, (3)e, (4)a, (5)h, (6)e, (7)f

Case Study 1. The hemispherical socket at the point where her femur attaches is called the *acetabulum*. **2.** The structure on the femur that forms the "ball" that fits into the "socket" named in question 1 is called the *head* of the femur. **3.** The three bones in the pelvic girdle that fuse together at a point within the structure identified in question 1 are the *ilium, ischium*, and *pubis*. **4.** If you were asked to rest your hands on your hips, your hands would be resting on the *iliac crests*. **5.** The structures on the femur where the large muscles of the buttocks and thigh attach are the *greater trochanter* and *lesser trochanter*. **6.** The structure of the pelvis that the sciatic nerve passes through as it travels into the upper thigh is the *greater sciatic notch* of the *ilium*.

Chapter 8

Check Your Understanding 1. Joint and articulation are synonyms. **2.** The synarthroses are the least mobile of the joint types. **3.** Symphyses and synchondroses are cartilaginous joints. **4.** In general, the more stable a joint, the less mobile it is. **5.** The fibrous layer and the synovial membrane

make up the wall of the articular capsule. **6.** Bursae and tendon sheaths help to reduce friction during joint movement. **7.** The muscle tendons that cross the joint are typically the most important factor in stabilizing synovial joints. **8.** Weeping lubrication helps keep the joint cartilages nourished and "lubricates" the joint surfaces. **9.** John's hip joint was flexed and his knees extended and his thumb was in opposition (to his index finger). **10.** The hinge and pivot joints are uniaxial joints. **11.** The knee and temporomandibular joints have menisci. The elbow and knee act mainly as a uniaxial hinge. The shoulder depends largely on muscle tendons for stability. **12.** Arthritis means inflammation of the joint. **13.** RA typically produces pain, swelling, and joint deformations that tend to be bilateral and crippling. OA patients tend to have pain, particularly on arising, which is relieved by gentle exercise, and enlarged bone ends (due to spurs) in affected joints. Affected joints may exhibit crepitus. **14.** Lyme disease is caused by spirochete bacteria and transmitted by a tick bite. **15.** Regular exercise strengthens joints and keeps them well nourished.

Review Questions 1. (1)c, (2)a, (3)a, (4)b, (5)c, (6)b, (7)b, (8)a, (9)c; **2.** b; **3.** d; **4.** d; **5.** b; **6.** d; **7.** d

Case Study 1. The hip joint would be structurally classified as a *synovial joint* and functionally classified as a *diarthrotic* (freely movable) joint. **2.** The six distinguishing features that define a synovial joint are: (1) articular cartilage, (2) joint (synovial) cavity, (3) articular capsule, (4) synovial fluid, (5) reinforcing ligaments, (6) nerves and blood vessels. **3.** The joint space in a synovial joint is normally filled with *synovial fluid*. **4.** The acetabular labrum is a piece of fibrocartilage that attaches to and extends the rim of the acetabulum. The diameter of the labrum is less than the diameter of the head of the femur, and this helps stabilize the joint to prevent it from dislocating. **5.** Mrs. Tanner's hip was bent (flexed) and her thigh was pulled toward the midline of her body (adducted) and turned in toward this midline (medially rotated). **6.** Mrs. Tanner suffered a posterior dislocation of the hip. When the head of the femur comes away from the acetabulum and then turns posteriorly, it causes the femur to rotate counterclockwise. This can be determined from the fact that her thigh was adducted and medially rotated. **7.** The hip movements include flexion, extension, abduction, adduction, rotation, and circumduction of the thigh.

Chapter 9

Check Your Understanding 1. Striated means "with stripes." **2.** He should respond "smooth muscle," which fits the description. **3.** "Epimysium" literally translates to "outside the muscle" and this connective tissue sheath is the outermost muscle sheath, enclosing the entire muscle. **4.** The thin myofilaments have binding sites for calcium on the troponin molecules forming part of those filaments. **5.** In a resting muscle fiber, the SR would have the highest concentration of calcium ions. The mitochondrion provides the ATP needed for muscle activity. **6.** The components of the neuromuscular junction are the axon terminal, the synaptic cleft, and the junctional folds of the sarcolemma. **7.** The final trigger for contraction is a certain concentration of calcium ions in the cytosol. The initial trigger is depolarization of the sarcolemma. **8.** There are always some myosin cross bridges bound to the actin myofilament during the contraction phase. Thus, backward sliding of the actin filaments is prevented. **9.** Without ATP, rigor would occur because the myosin heads could not detach. **10.** A motor unit is an axon of a motor neuron and all the muscle fibers it innervates. **11.** During the latent period, events of excitation-contraction coupling are occurring. **12.** Immediately after Jay grabs the bar, his biceps muscles are contracting isometrically. As his body moves upward toward the bar, they are contracting isotonically and concentrically. As he lowers his body toward the mat, the biceps are contracting isotonically and eccentrically. **13.** Eric was breathing heavily because it takes some time for his heart rate and overall metabolism to return to the resting state after exercise. Moreover, he had likely incurred an oxygen debt that required he take in extra oxygen for the restorative process, the so-called EPOC. Although jogging is primarily an aerobic exercise, there is always some anaerobic respiration that occurs as well—the amount depends on exercise intensity. As fatigue occurs, potassium ions accumulate in the T tubules, and lactic acid and phosphate ions accumulate in the muscle cells. **14.** Factors that influence muscle contractile force include muscle fiber size, the number of muscle fibers stimulated, the frequency of stimulation, and the degree of muscle stretch. Factors that influence velocity of contraction include muscle fiber type, load, and the number of motor units contracting. **15.** Fast glycolytic fibers would provide for short periods of intense strength needed to lift and move furniture. **16.** To increase muscle size and strength, anaerobic exercise is best. Muscle endurance is enhanced by aerobic exercise. **17.** Both skeletal and smooth muscle fibers are elongated cells, but unlike smooth muscle cells, which are spindle shaped, uninucleate, and nonstriated, skeletal muscle cells are very large cigar-shaped, multinucleate, striated cells. **18.** Calcium binds to troponin on the thin filaments in skeletal muscle cells. In smooth muscle cells, it binds to a cytoplasmic protein called calmodulin. **19.** Hollow organs that have smooth muscle cells helping to form their walls often must temporarily store the organ's contents (urine, food residues, etc.), an ability ensured by the stress-relaxation response. **20.** During development of skeletal muscle fibers, the myoblast cells join together, forming multinucleate myotubes. **21.** The connective tissue in muscles increases with age, causing the muscles to get stringier. **22.** Regular exercise and strength training help to defer the loss in strength and muscle wasting that tends to occur with age, and improve neuromuscular function.

Review Questions 1. c; **2.** b; **3.** (1)b, (2)a, (3)b, (4)a, (5)b, (6)a; **4.** c; **5.** a; **6.** a; **7.** d; **8.** a; **9.** (1)a, (2)a, c, (3)b, (4)c, (5)b, (6)b; **10.** a; **11.** c; **12.** c; **13.** c; **14.** b

Case Study 1. The first reaction to tissue injury is the initiation of the inflammatory response. The inflammatory chemicals increase the permeability of the capillaries in the injured area, allowing white blood cells, fluid, and other substances to reach the injured area. The next step in healing involves the formation of granulation tissue, in which the vascular supply for the injured area is regenerated and collagen fibers that knit the torn edges of the tissue together are formed. Skeletal muscle does not regenerate well, so the damaged areas of Mrs. DeStephano's muscle tissue will probably be repaired primarily by the formation of fibrous tissue, creating scar tissue. **2.** Healing is aided by good circulation of blood within the injured area. Vascular damage compromises healing because the supply of oxygen and nutrients to the tissue is reduced. **3.** Under normal circumstances, skeletal muscles receive electrical signals from the nervous system continuously. These signals help to maintain muscle tone and readiness. Severing of the sciatic nerve removes this continuous nervous input to the muscles and will lead to muscle atrophy. Immobility of muscles will lead to a replacement of contractile muscle tissue with noncontractile fibrous connective tissue. Distal to the point of transection, the muscle will begin to decrease in size within 3–7 days of becoming immobile. This process can be delayed by electrically stimulating the tissues. Passive range-of-motion exercises also help prevent loss of muscle tone and joint range, and improve circulation in the injured areas. **4.** Mrs. DeStephano's physician wants to supply her damaged tissues with the necessary building materials to encourage healing. A high-protein diet will provide plenty of amino acids to rebuild or replace damaged proteins, carbohydrates will provide the fuel molecules needed to generate the required ATP, and vitamin C is important for the regeneration of connective tissue.

Chapter 10

Check Your Understanding 1. The term "prime mover" refers to the muscle that bears the most responsibility for causing a particular movement. **2.** The iliacus overlies the iliac bone; the adductor brevis is a small (size) mus-

cle that adducts (movement caused) the thigh; and the quadriceps (4 heads) femoris muscle follows the course of the femur. **3.** Of the muscles illustrated in Figure 10.2, the one with the parallel arrangement (sartorius) could shorten to the greatest degree. The stocky bipennate (rectus femoris) and multipennate (deltoid) muscles would be most powerful because they pack in the most fibers. **4.** Third-class levers are the fastest levers. **5.** A lever that operates at a mechanical advantage allows the muscle to exert less force than the load being moved. **6.** John was using the frontal belly of his epicranius to raise his eyebrows and the orbicularis oculi muscles to wink at Sarah. **7.** To make a sad clown's face you would contract your platysma, depressor anguli oris, and depressor labii inferioris muscles. **8.** The deltoid has a broad origin. When only its anterior fibers contract, it flexes and medially rotates the humerus. When only its posterior fibers contract, it extends and laterally rotates the humerus. **9.** The opponens pollicis does not have an insertion on the bones of the thumb.

Review Questions 1. c; **2.** c; **3.** (1)e, (2)c, (3)g, (4)f, (5)d; **4.** a; **5.** c; **6.** d; **7.** c; **8.** c; **9.** b; **10.** d; **11.** b; **12.** a; **13.** c; **14.** d; **15.** a, b; **16.** a

Case Study 1. A prime mover is a muscle that has primary or major responsibility for producing a specific movement. A synergist is a muscle that supports or helps the action of a prime mover by adding extra force, or providing stability so that the prime mover can perform its action. **2.** An antagonist is a muscle that opposes, resists, or reverses a particular movement. By mimicking the action of an antagonist, the therapist can test the strength of the agonist muscle and compare it with the same muscle in the other limb. **3.** Ideally, the therapist would assess each muscle individually. In reality, these assessments usually measure the function of a group of muscles because multiple muscles are often involved in similar actions. (a) This assessment focuses on the thigh adductors (magnus, longus, brevis), pectineus, and gracilis. Specifically, the adductor magnus is innervated by the damaged sciatic nerve. (b) This assessment addresses Mrs. Tanner's ability to dorsiflex her foot. Dorsiflexion involves all of the muscles in the anterior compartment of the lower leg: the tibialis anterior, extensor digitorum longus, fibularis (peroneus) tertius, and extensor hallucis longus. (c) This assessment addresses the function of the muscles of the posterior compartment of the thigh. The hamstrings (biceps femoris, semitendinosus, semimembranosus) are the prime movers involved in knee flexion. **4.** To assess these muscles, the therapist would apply resistance to the natural action of these muscles. (a) The extensor hallucis longus inserts on the distal phalanx of the great toe. The therapist can apply resistance to the top of the toe and ask Mrs. Tanner to extend the toe. (b) The fibularis longus is involved in eversion of the foot and plantar flexion. The therapist can apply resistance to the lateral aspect of the foot and ask Mrs. Tanner to evert (turn out) her ankle. In addition, resistance can be applied to the bottom of the foot and Mrs. Tanner asked to push against that resistance. (c) The gastrocnemius, along with the soleus, is a powerful plantar flexor. The therapist can (1) ask Mrs. Tanner to raise her body up on her toes using her right foot, or (2) apply pressure to the bottom of the foot and ask Mrs. Tanner to push against that resistance.

Chapter 11

Check Your Understanding 1. Integration involves processing and interpreting sensory information, and making a decision about motor output. Integration occurs primarily in the CNS. **2.** (a) This "full stomach" feeling would be relayed by the sensory (afferent) division of the PNS (via its visceral afferent fibers). (b) The somatic nervous system, which is part of the motor (efferent) division of the PNS, controls movement of skeletal muscle. (c) The autonomic nervous system, which is part of the motor (efferent) division of the PNS, controls the heart rate. **3.** Astrocytes control the extracellular environment around neuron cell bodies in the CNS, whereas satellite cells perform this function in the PNS. **4.** Oligodendrocytes and Schwann cells form myelin sheaths in the CNS and PNS, respectively.

5. A nerve fiber is a long axon, an extension of the cell. In connective tissue, fibers are extracellular proteins that provide support. In muscle tissue, a muscle fiber is a muscle cell. **6.** A nucleus within the brain is a cluster of cell bodies, whereas the nucleus within each neuron is a large organelle that acts as the control center of the cell. **7.** In the CNS, a myelin sheath is formed by oligodendrocytes that wrap their plasma membranes around the axon. The myelin sheath protects and electrically insulates axons and increases the speed of transmission of nerve impulses. **8.** Burning a finger will first activate unipolar (pseudounipolar) neurons that are sensory (afferent) neurons. The impulse to move your finger away from the heat will be carried by multipolar neurons that are motor (efferent) neurons. **9.** The concentration gradient and the electrical gradient—together called the electrochemical gradient—determine the direction in which ions flow through an open membrane channel. **10.** There is more leakage of K^+ than of any other cations. **11.** Action potentials are larger than graded potentials and travel further. Graded potentials generally initiate action potentials. **12.** An action potential is regenerated anew at each membrane patch. **13.** Conduction of action potentials is faster in myelinated axons because myelin allows the axon membrane between myelin sheath gaps to change its voltage rapidly, and allows current to flow only at the widely spaced gaps. **14.** If a second stimulus occurs before the end of the absolute refractory period, no AP can occur because sodium channels are still inactivated. **15.** At an electrical synapse, neurons are joined by gap junctions. **16.** Voltage-gated ion (Ca^{2+}) channels are found in the presynaptic axon terminal and open when an action potential reaches the axon terminal. Chemically gated ion channels are found in the postsynaptic membrane and open when neurotransmitter binds to the receptor protein. **17.** IPSPs result from the flow of either K^+ or Cl^- through chemically gated channels. EPSPs result from the flow of both Na^+ and K^+ through chemically gated channels. **18.** Temporal summation is summation in time of graded potentials occurring in quick succession at the postsynaptic membrane. It can result from EPSPs arising from just one synapse. Spatial summation is summation in space—a postsynaptic neuron is stimulated by a large number of terminals at the same time. **19.** ACh interacts with more than one specific receptor type, and this explains how it can excite at some synapses and inhibit at others. **20.** cAMP is called a second messenger because it relays the message between the first messenger (the original chemical messenger) outside of the cell and effector molecules that will ultimately bring about the desired response within the cell. **21.** Reverberating circuits and parallel after-discharge circuits both result in prolonged output. **22.** The pattern of neural processing is serial processing. The response is a reflex arc. **23.** The pattern of neural processing is parallel processing. **24.** The growing tip of an axon is called a growth cone. Neurotropins are chemicals that signal the growth cone.

Review Questions 1. b; **2.** (1)d, (2)b, (3)f, (4)c, (5)a; **3.** b; **4.** c; **5.** a; **6.** c; **7.** b; **8.** d; **9.** c; **10.** c; **11.** a; **12.** (1)d, (2)b, (3)a, (4)c

Case Study 1. The electrical signals generated by neurons are called *action potentials*. An action potential is a change in membrane potential that involves depolarization and repolarization phases. **2.** An inhibitory postsynaptic potential (IPSP) is a signal that makes it less likely that a postsynaptic neuron will be able to generate an action potential. This effect is usually produced when the signal causes the membrane potential of the postsynaptic neuron to become more negative, moving away from the axon's threshold potential. **3.** GABA falls into the amino acid class of neurotransmitters. This same class includes glycine, glutamate, and aspartate. **4.** To enhance the actions of GABA at a synapse, a drug could either (1) act presynaptically to increase the release of GABA at the synapse, (2) decrease the reuptake of GABA after it has been released, or (3) act postsynaptically to either increase the binding strength of GABA at its receptors, or increase the number of receptors. **5.** An influx of Cl^- into the postsynaptic cell causes the membrane potential to become more

negative (hyperpolarize). When hyperpolarized, the cell is farther from its threshold potential and so is less likely to produce an action potential.

Chapter 12

Check Your Understanding 1. The third ventricle is surrounded by the diencephalon. **2.** The cerebral hemispheres and the cerebellum have an outside layer of gray matter in addition to central gray matter and its surrounding white matter. **3.** Convolutions increase surface area of the cortex, which allows more neurons to occupy the limited space within the skull. **4.** The central sulcus separates primary motor areas from somatosensory areas. **5.** Motor functions on the left side of the body are controlled by the right hemisphere of the brain because motor tracts from the right hemisphere cross over (in the medulla oblongata) to the left side of the spinal cord to go to the left side of the body. **6.** Commissural fibers (which form commissures) allow the cerebral hemispheres to "talk to each other." **7.** The caudate nucleus, putamen, and globus pallidus together form the basal nuclei. **8.** Virtually all inputs ascending to the cerebral cortex synapse in the thalamus en route. **9.** The hypothalamus oversees the autonomic nervous system. **10.** The pyramids of the medulla are the corticospinal (pyramidal) tracts, the large voluntary motor tracts descending from the motor cortex. The result of decussation (crossing over) is that each side of the motor cortex controls the opposite side of the body. **11.** The cerebral peduncles and the colliculi are associated with the midbrain. **12.** There are many possible answers to this question—here are a few: Structurally, the cerebellum and cerebrum are similar in that they both have a thin outer cortex of gray matter, internal white matter, and deep gray matter nuclei. Also, both have body maps (homunculi) and large fiber tracts connecting them to the brain stem. Both receive sensory input and influence motor output. A major difference is that the cerebellum is almost entirely concerned with motor output, whereas the cerebrum has much broader responsibilities. Also, while a cerebral hemisphere controls the opposite side of the body, a cerebellar hemisphere controls the same side of the body. **13.** The hypothalamus is part of the limbic system and also an autonomic (visceral) control center. **14.** Taylor is increasing the amount of sensory stimuli she receives, which will be relayed to the reticular activating system, which, in turn, will increase activation of the cerebral cortex. **15.** Delta waves are typically seen in deep sleep in normal adults. **16.** Drowsiness (or lethargy) and stupor are stages of consciousness between alertness and coma. **17.** Most skeletal muscles are actively inhibited during REM sleep. **18.** Transfer of memory from STM to LTM is enhanced by (1) rehearsal, (2) association (tying "new" information to "old" information), and (3) a heightened emotional state (for example, alert, motivated, surprised, or aroused). **19.** The basal nuclei and premotor cortex are involved in procedural (skills) memory, but not in declarative memory. **20.** CSF, formed by the choroid plexuses as a filtrate of blood plasma, is a watery "broth" similar in composition to plasma. It protects the brain and spinal cord from blows and other trauma, helps nourish the brain, and carries chemical signals from one part of the brain to another. **21.** A TIA is a temporary loss of blood supply to brain tissue, and it differs from a stroke in that the resultant impairment is fully reversible. **22.** Mrs. Lee might have Parkinson's disease. **23.** The nerves serving the limbs arise in the cervical and lumbar enlargements of the spinal cord. **24.** In the spinothalamic pathway, the cell bodies of first-order sensory neurons are outside the spinal cord in a ganglion, cell bodies of second-order sensory neurons are in the dorsal horn of the spinal cord, and cell bodies of third-order sensory neurons are in the thalamus. (See also Figure 12.31b.) **25.** A loss of motor function is called paralysis. Lower limb paralysis could be caused by a spinal cord injury in the thoracic region (between T_1 and L_1). If the spinal cord is transected, the result is paraplegia. If the cord is only bruised, he may regain function in the limbs. An MRI scan (or CT scan) of the spinal cord would be helpful. **26.** Alar plate neuroblasts become interneurons, whereas basal plate neuroblasts become motor (efferent) neurons. **27.** Premature babies have trouble regulating body temperature because the hypothalamus is immature. **28.** Reversible causes of dementia include prescription drug effects, low blood pressure, poor nutrition, hormone imbalances, depression, and dehydration.

Review Questions 1. a; **2.** d; **3.** c; **4.** a; **5.** (1)d, (2)f, (3)e, (4)g, (5)b, (6)f, (7)i, (8)a; **6.** b; **7.** c; **8.** a; **9.** (1)a, (2)b, (3)a, (4)a, (5)b, (6)a, (7)b, (8)b, (9)a; **10.** d; **11.** (1)d, (2)e, (3)c and d, (4)a; **12.** c

Case Study 1. The four regions of the brain are the cerebral hemispheres, diencephalon, brain stem, and cerebellum. A cerebral hemisphere is involved in this case. Motor functions and language are both located in this cerebral hemisphere and have been affected by the injury. **2.** The left side of the brain has been affected in this case. The motor dysfunction on the right side of the body is the primary piece of evidence used to determine this. In addition, the brain areas serving speech are usually located in the left side. **3.** The motor dysfunction on the right side of the body suggests that the injury has affected the primary motor cortex and possibly the premotor cortex of the left cerebral hemisphere. In addition to the problems with motor function, Mrs. Bryans experienced difficulty with language. Two areas of the brain associated with language, Broca's and Wernicke's area, are usually located in the left cerebral cortex. The type of aphasia described suggests damage to Broca's area. **4.** From the surface of the brain to the skull, the three membranes that make up the meninges include the pia mater, arachnoid mater, and dura mater. **5.** The subarachnoid hemorrhage involves bleeding into the region below (*sub* = below) the arachnoid mater. The subdural hematoma involves blood collecting between the dura mater and the arachnoid mater.

Chapter 13

Check Your Understanding 1. In addition to nerves, the PNS also consists of sensory receptors, motor endings, and ganglia. **2.** Nociceptors respond to painful stimuli. They are exteroceptors that are nonencapsulated (free nerve endings). **3.** The three levels of sensory integration are receptor level, circuit level, and perceptual level. **4.** Phasic receptors adapt, whereas tonic receptors exhibit little or no adaptation. Pain receptors are tonic so that we are reminded to protect the injured body part. **5.** Hot and cold are conveyed by different sensory receptors that are parts of separate "labeled lines." Cool and cold are two different intensities of the same stimulus, detected by frequency coding—the frequency of APs would be higher for a cold than a cool stimulus. Action potentials arising in the fingers and foot arrive at different locations in the somatosensory cortex via their own "labeled lines" and in this way the cortex can determine their origin. **6.** Ganglia are collections of neuron cell bodies in the PNS. **7.** Nerves also contain connective tissue, blood vessels, lymphatic vessels, and the myelin surrounding the axons. **8.** Schwann cells, macrophages, and the neurons themselves were all important in healing the nerve. **9.** The oculomotor (III), trochlear (IV), and abducens (VI) nerves control eye movements. Sticking out your tongue involves the hypoglossal nerve (XII). The vagus nerve (X) influences heart rate and digestive activity. The accessory nerve (XI) innervates the trapezius muscle, which is involved in shoulder shrugging. **10.** Roots lie medial to spinal nerves, whereas rami lie lateral to spinal nerves. Dorsal roots are purely sensory, whereas dorsal rami carry both motor and sensory fibers. **11.** The spinal nerve roots were C_3–C_5, the spinal nerve was the phrenic nerve, the plexus was the cervical plexus. The phrenic nerve is the sole motor nerve supply to the diaphragm, the primary muscle for respiration. **12.** Varicosities are the series of knoblike swellings that are the axon endings of autonomic motor neurons. You would find them on axon endings serving smooth muscle or glands. **13.** The cerebellum and basal nuclei, which form the precommand level of motor control, plan and coordinate complex motor activities. **14.** The five components of a reflex arc are receptor,

sensory neuron, integration center, motor neuron, and effector. **15.** The stretch reflex is important for maintaining muscle tone and adjusting it reflexively by causing muscle contraction in response to increased muscle length (stretch). It maintains posture. The flexor or withdrawal reflex is initiated by a painful stimulus and causes automatic withdrawal of the painful body part from the stimulus. It is protective. **16.** This response is called Babinski's sign and it indicates damage to the corticospinal tract or primary motor cortex. **17.** The vertebral column, spinal nerves, and dermatomes are all examples of segmentation in the adult.

Review Questions 1. b; **2.** c; **3.** d; **4.** c; **5.** e; **6.** c; **7.** (1)d, (2)c, (3)f, (4)b, (5)e, (6)a; **8.** (1)f, (2)i, (3)b, (4)g, h, (5)e, (6)i, (7)c, (8)k, (9)l, (10)c, d, f, k; **9.** (1)b 2; (2)d 8; (3)c 2; (4)c 5; (5)a 4; (6)a 3, 9; (7)a 7; (8)a 7; (9)d 1; (10)a 3, 4, 7, 9; **10.** (1)a, 1 and 5; (2)a, 3 and 5; (3)a, 4; (4)a, 2; (5)c, 2; (6)b, 2; **11.** c

Case Study 1. Cerebrospinal fluid (CSF) is leaking out of Mr. Hancock's right ear. The fracture must have torn both the dura mater and arachnoid mater. In addition, the tympanic membrane must have ruptured. Antibiotics were administered to prevent infection by bacteria that might enter through the ruptured meninges, causing meningitis. Elevating the head of the bed decreases the CSF pressure in the skull. (This allows the torn meninges to heal spontaneously in the majority of cases.) **2.** The observations on Mr. Hancock's chart indicate: (a) Either damage to CN VIII (the vestibulocochlear nerve, which transmits afferent impulses for the sense of hearing) or destruction of the cochlea (the sensory organ for hearing). (b) Damage to CN V_3 (the mandibular division of the trigeminal nerve), which runs through the foramen ovale. This nerve conveys sensory information from the lower part of the face. (c) Damage to CN V_2 (the maxillary division of the trigeminal nerve), which runs through the foramen rotundum. This nerve conveys sensory information from the skin of the upper lip, lower eyelid, and cheek. (d) Damage to CN VI (the abducens nerve), which innervates the lateral rectus muscle of the eye. Because this muscle is responsible for pulling the eye laterally (abduction), loss of tone in this muscle at rest will cause the eye to turn inward. Diplopia will worsen when looking to the right because the eye cannot abduct. **3.** The facial nerve (cranial nerve VII) is the primary motor nerve associated with facial expression. The facial nerve also contains parasympathetic fibers that control secretion of tears from the lacrimal glands. Damage to this nerve explains both the motor symptoms and the dryness of his eye.

Chapter 14

Check Your Understanding 1. The effectors of the autonomic nervous system are cardiac muscle, smooth muscle, and glands. **2.** The somatic motor system relays instructions to muscles more quickly because it involves only one motor neuron, whereas the ANS uses a two-neuron chain. Moreover, axons of somatic motor neurons are typically heavily myelinated, whereas preganglionic autonomic axons are lightly myelinated and postganglionic axons are nonmyelinated. **3.** While you relax in the sun on the beach, the parasympathetic branch of the ANS would probably predominate. When you perceive danger (as in a shark), the sympathetic branch of the ANS predominates. **4.** "Short preganglionic fibers," "origin from thoracolumbar region of spinal cord," "collateral ganglia," and "innervates adrenal medulla" are all characteristic of the sympathetic nervous system. Terminal ganglia are found in the parasympathetic nervous system. **5.** The major differences are (1) the ANS has visceral afferents rather than somatic afferents, (2) the ANS has a two-neuron efferent chain, whereas the somatic nervous system (SNS) has one, and (3) the effectors of the ANS are smooth muscles, cardiac muscle, and glands, whereas the effectors of the SNS are skeletal muscles. **6.** The parasympathetic nervous system increases digestive activity and decreases heart rate. The sympathetic nervous system increases blood pressure, dilates bronchioles, stimulates the adrenal medulla to release its hormones, and causes ejaculation. **7.** You would find nicotinic receptors on skeletal muscle and the hormone-producing cells of the adrenal medulla, but not on smooth muscle or glands. Virtually all types of receptors (including nicotinic receptors) are also found in the CNS (see Table 11.3 on p. 415). **8.** The main integration center of the ANS is the hypothalamus, although the most direct influence is through the brain stem reticular formation and the reflex centers in the pons and medulla oblongata. **9.** Jackson's doctor may have prescribed a beta-blocker because Jackson has hypertension. (Chronic stress is a factor in causing hypertension.) The beta-blocker will decrease blood pressure by blocking beta-adrenergic receptors in the heart, thereby decreasing heart rate and force of contraction, and by decreasing renin release from the kidneys. **10.** The neural crest gives rise to both autonomic ganglia and the adrenal medulla.

Review Questions 1. d; **2.** (1)S, (2)P, (3)P, (4)S, (5)S, (6)P, (7)P, (8)S, (9)P, (10)S, (11)P, (12)S; **3.** b; **4.** c; **5.** a

Case Study 1. The location of Jimmy's lacerations and bruises and his inability to rise led the paramedics to suspect a head, neck, or back injury. They immobilized his head and torso to prevent any further damage to the brain and spinal cord. **2.** The worsening neurological signs indicate a probable intracranial hemorrhage. The blood escaping from the ruptured blood vessel(s) will begin to compress Jimmy's brain and increase his intracranial pressure. Jimmy's surgery will involve repair of the damaged vessel(s) and removal of the mass of clotted blood pressing on his brain. **3.** Loss of motor and sensory function below the level of the nipples indicates a lesion at T_4. See Figure 13.13. **4.** Jimmy is suffering from spinal shock, which occurs as a result of injury to the spinal cord. Spinal shock is a temporary condition in which all reflex and motor activities caudal to the level of spinal cord injury are lost, so Jimmy's muscles are paralyzed. His blood pressure is low due to the loss of sympathetic tone in his vasculature. **5.** Jimmy's exaggerated reflexes are caused by damaged upper motor neuron axons in the spinal cord. These upper motor neurons normally inhibit spinal reflexes. He is incontinent because there are no longer pathways to support voluntary control of bowel and bladder emptying. **6.** This condition is called autonomic dysreflexia (or autonomic hyperreflexia). This is a condition in which a normal stimulus triggers a massive activation of autonomic neurons. **7.** Extremely high arterial blood pressure can cause a rupture of the cerebral blood vessels (as well as other blood vessels in the body) and put Jimmy's life at risk.

Chapter 15

Check Your Understanding 1. Tears (lacrimal fluid) are a dilute saline secretion that contains mucus, antibodies, and lysozyme. They are secreted by the lacrimal glands. **2.** The blind spot of the eye is the optic disc. It is the part of the retina where the optic nerve exits the eye and it is "blind" because it is a region of the retina that lacks photoreceptors. **3.** An increase in intraocular pressure is called glaucoma and is due to an accumulation of aqueous humor, usually because of impaired drainage of the fluid. **4.** Light passes through the cornea, aqueous humor, lens, vitreous humor, ganglion cells and bipolar cells before it reaches the photoreceptors. **5.** The ciliary muscles and sphincter pupillae relax for distant vision. (If you said the medial rectus muscles also relax, this is

true, but remember that the rectus muscles are extrinsic eye muscles, not intrinsic.) **6.** The near point moves farther away as you age because the lens becomes less flexible (presbyopia), so that it is unable to assume the more rounded shape required for near vision. **7.** The following are characteristics of cones: "vision in bright light," "color vision," and "higher acuity." The following are characteristics of rods: "only one type of visual pigment," "most abundant in the periphery of the retina," "many feed into one ganglion cell," and "higher sensitivity." **8.** Breakdown of the retinal-opsin combination is called bleaching of the pigment. It occurs with exposure to light. **9.** A tumor in the right visual cortex would affect the left visual field. A tumor compressing the right optic nerve would affect both the left and right visual fields from the right eye only. **10.** The five taste modalities are sweet, sour, bitter, salty, and umami. The fungiform, vallate, and foliate papillae contain taste buds. **11.** The cilia and hairs of these receptor cells greatly increase the surface area for sensory receptors. **12.** The tympanic membrane separates the external from the middle ear. The oval and round windows separate the middle from the inner ear. **13.** The basilar membrane allows us to differentiate sounds of different pitch. **14.** You would not be able to locate the origin of a sound if the brain stem did not receive input from both ears. **15.** The following apply to a macula: "contains otoliths," "responds to linear acceleration or deceleration," and "inside a saccule." The following apply to a crista ampullaris: "inside a semicircular canal," "has a cupula," "responds to rotational acceleration and deceleration." **16.** The "fullness" in Mohammed's ears is likely due to an accumulation of fluid in the middle ear as a result of his upper respiratory infection ("cold") spreading into his ear. He has a form of conduction deafness. **17.** With age, the lens discolors and loses its clarity and the dilator pupillae muscles become less efficient, decreasing the amount of light that reaches the retinas at night.

Review Questions 1. c; **2.** d; **3.** a; **4.** b; **5.** c; **6.** c; **7.** b; **8.** a; **9.** b; **10.** b; **11.** b; **12.** d; **13.** d; **14.** a; **15.** d; **16.** c; **17.** d; **18.** b; **19.** b; **20.** c; **21.** d; **22.** b; **23.** b; **24.** e; **25.** b; **26.** c; **27.** c; **28.** c; **29.** c

Case Study 1. The ear is divided into three major areas: external ear, middle ear, and internal ear. The portion of the internal ear, or labyrinth, associated with balance and equilibrium is the part of the ear affected in Mr. Rhen's BPPV. **2.** Maintaining balance and equilibrium requires multiple sources of sensory input. The three main sources of sensory input are the vestibular apparatus of the ear, visual input, and input from the proprioceptors of the skin, muscles, and joints. **3.** The two functional divisions are the vestibule and semicircular canals. The vestibule's sensory receptors are the maculae, which sense linear (straight line) acceleration and deceleration. The semicircular canals' receptors are the cristae ampullares, which detect rotational acceleration and deceleration. **4.** Mr. Rhen's vertigo is brought on by rotational movements of the head, suggesting that the cristae ampullares of the semicircular canals are affected. **5.** The added mass of the displaced otoliths pushes on a cupula of a semicircular canal when the head is rotated during the Dix-Hallpike maneuver. The otoliths either stick to the gelatinous cupula, or swirl through the canals during head movement and drift against the cupula like snow. In both cases, the bending of the cupula is prolonged and vertigo persists. As a result, vestibular nystagmus is observed when it would ordinarily be absent.

Glossary

Pronunciation Key

′ = Primary accent

″ = Secondary accent

Pronounce:

a, fa, āt	as in	fate	o, no, ōt as in	note
ă, hă, at		hat	ŏ, frŏ, og	frog
ah		father	oo	soon
ar		tar	or	for
e, stre, ēt		street	ow	plow
ĕ, hĕ, en		hen	oy	boy
er		her	sh	she
ew		new	u, mu, ūt	mute
g		go	ŭ, sŭ, un	sun
i, bi, īt		bite	z	zebra
ĭ, hĭ, im		him	zh	measure
ng		ring		

Abduct (ab-dukt′) To move away from the midline of the body.

Absolute refractory period Period following stimulation during which no additional action potential can be evoked.

Absorption Process by which the products of digestion pass through the alimentary tube mucosa into the blood or lymph.

Accessory digestive organs Organs that contribute to the digestive process but are not part of the alimentary canal; include the tongue, teeth, salivary glands, pancreas, liver.

Accommodation The process of increasing the refractive power of the lens of the eye; focusing.

Acetabulum (as″ĕ-tab′u-lum) Cuplike cavity on lateral surface of the hip bone that receives the femur.

Acetylcholine (ACh) (as″ĕ-til-ko′lēn) Chemical transmitter substance released by some nerve endings.

Acetylcholinesterase (AChE) (as″ĕ-til-ko″lin-es′ter-ās) Enzyme present at the neuromuscular junction and synapses that degrades acetylcholine and terminates its action.

Achilles tendon *See* Calcaneal tendon.

Acid A substance that releases hydrogen ions when in solution (compare with Base); a proton donor.

Acid-base balance Situation in which the pH of the blood is maintained between 7.35 and 7.45.

Acidosis (as″ĭ-do′sis) State of abnormally high hydrogen ion concentration in the extracellular fluid.

Actin (ak′tin) A contractile protein of muscle.

Action potential A large transient depolarization event, including polarity reversal, that is conducted along the membrane of a muscle cell or a nerve fiber.

Activation energy The amount of energy required to push a reactant to the level necessary for action.

Active immunity Immunity produced by an encounter with an antigen; provides immunological memory.

Active site Region on the surface of a functional (globular) protein where it binds and interacts chemically with other molecules of complementary shape and charge.

Active (transport) processes (1) Membrane transport processes for which ATP is required, e.g., solute pumping and endocytosis. (2) "Active transport" also refers specifically to solute pumping.

Adaptation (1) Any change in structure or response to suit a new environment; (2) decline in the transmission of a sensory nerve when a receptor is stimulated continuously and without change in stimulus strength.

Adduct (a-dukt′) To move toward the midline of the body.

Adenine (A) (ad′ĕ-nēn) One of the two major purines found in both RNA and DNA; also found in various free nucleotides of importance to the body, such as ATP.

Adenohypophysis (ad″ĕ-no-hi-pof′ĭ-sis) Anterior pituitary; the glandular part of the pituitary gland.

Adenoids (ad′en-noids) Pharyngeal tonsil.

Adenosine triphosphate (ATP) (ah-den′o-sēn tri″fos′fāt) Organic molecule that stores and releases chemical energy for use in body cells.

Adipocyte (ad′ĭ-po-sīt) An adipose, or fat, cell.

Adipose tissue (ad′ĭ-pōs) Areolar connective tissue modified to store nutrients; a connective tissue consisting chiefly of fat cells.

Adrenal glands (uh-drē′nul) Hormone-producing glands located superior to the kidneys; each consists of medulla and cortex areas.

Adrenergic fibers (ad″ren-er′jik) Nerve fibers that release norepinephrine.

Adrenocorticotropic hormone (ACTH) (ah-dre″no-kor″tĭ-ko-trop′ik) Anterior pituitary hormone that influences the activity of the adrenal cortex.

Adventitia (ad″ven-tish′e-ah) Outermost layer or covering of some organs.

Aerobic (a′er-ōb″ik) Oxygen-requiring.

Aerobic endurance The length of time a muscle can continue to contract using aerobic pathways.

Aerobic respiration Respiration in which oxygen is consumed and glucose is broken down entirely; water, carbon dioxide, and large amounts of ATP are the final products.

Afferent (af′er-ent) Carrying to or toward a center.

Afferent (sensory) nerve Nerve that contains processes of sensory neurons and carries nerve impulses to the central nervous system.

Agglutination (ah-gloo″tĭ-na′shun) Clumping of (foreign) cells; induced by cross-linking of antigen-antibody complexes.

Agonist (ag′o-nist) Muscle that bears the major responsibility for effecting a particular movement; a prime mover.

AIDS Acquired immune deficiency syndrome; caused by human immunodeficiency virus (HIV); symptoms include severe weight loss, night sweats, swollen lymph nodes, opportunistic infections.

Albumin (al-bu′min) The most abundant plasma protein.

Aldosterone (al-dos′ter-ōn) Hormone produced by the adrenal cortex that regulates Na⁺ reabsorption and K⁺ secretion by the kidneys.

Alimentary canal (al″ĭ-men′tar-e) The continuous hollow tube extending from the mouth to the anus; its walls are constructed by the oral cavity, pharynx, esophagus, stomach, and small and large intestines.

Alkalosis (al″kah-lo′sis) State of abnormally low hydrogen ion concentration in the extracellular fluid.

Allantois (ah″lan′to-is) Embryonic membrane; its blood vessels develop into blood vessels of the umbilical cord.

Alleles Genes coding for the same trait and found at the same locus on homologous chromosomes.

Allergy A type of hypersensitivity (overzealous immune response to an otherwise harmless antigen) that involves IgE antibodies and histamine release.

Alopecia (al″o-pe′she-ah) Baldness.

Alpha (α)-helix The most common type of secondary structure of the amino acid chain in proteins; resembles the coils of a telephone cord.

Alveolar (acinar) gland (al-ve′o-lar) A gland whose secretory cells form small, flasklike sacs.

Alveolar ventilation rate (AVR) An index of respiratory efficiency; measures volume of fresh air that flows in and out of alveoli.

Alveolus (al-ve′o-lus) (1) One of the microscopic air sacs of the lungs; (2) tiny milk-producing glandular sac in the breast; (3) tooth socket.

Alzheimer's disease (AD) (altz′hi-merz) Degenerative brain disease resulting in progressive loss of memory and motor control, and increasing dementia.

Amino acid (ah-me′no) Organic compound containing nitrogen, carbon, hydrogen, and oxygen; building block of protein.

Ammonia (NH₃) Common waste product of protein breakdown in the body; a colorless volatile gas, very soluble in water and capable of forming a weak base; a proton acceptor.

Amniocentesis A common form of fetal testing in which a small sample of fluid is removed from the amniotic cavity.

Amnion (am′ne-on) Fetal membrane that forms a fluid-filled sac around the embryo.

Amoeboid motion (ah-me′boyd) The flowing movement of the cytoplasm of a phagocyte.

Amphiarthrosis (am″fe-ar-thro′sis) A slightly movable joint.

Ampulla (am-pul′lah) A localized dilation of a canal or duct.

Amylase Digestive system enzyme that breaks down starchy foods.

Anabolism (ah-nab′o-lizm) Energy-requiring building phase of metabolism in which simpler substances are combined to form more complex substances.

Anaerobic (an-a′er-ōb-ik) Not requiring oxygen.

Anaerobic glycolysis (gli-kol′ĭ-sis) Energy-yielding conversion of glucose to lactic acid in various tissues, notably muscle, when sufficient oxygen is not available.

Anaerobic threshold The point at which muscle metabolism converts to anaerobic glycolysis.

Anaphase Third stage of mitosis, meiosis I, and meiosis II in which daughter chromosomes move toward each pole of a cell.

Anastomosis (ah-nas″to-mo′sis) A union or joining of nerves, blood vessels, or lymphatics.

Anatomy Study of the structure of living organisms.

Androgen (an′dro-jen) A hormone such as testosterone that controls male secondary sex characteristics.

Anemia (ah-ne′me-ah) Reduced oxygen-carrying ability of blood resulting from too few erythrocytes or abnormal hemoglobin.

Aneurysm (an′u-rizm) Blood-filled sac in an artery wall caused by dilation or weakening of the wall.

Angina pectoris (an′jĭ-nah pek′tor-is) Severe suffocating chest pain caused by brief lack of oxygen supply to heart muscle.

Angiotensin II (an″je-o-ten′sin) A potent vasoconstrictor activated by renin; also triggers release of aldosterone.

Anion (an′i-on) An ion carrying one or more negative charges and therefore attracted to a positive pole.

Anoxia (an-nŏk′se-ah) Deficiency of oxygen.

Antagonist (an-tag′o-nist) (1) Muscle that reverses, or opposes, the action of another muscle. (2) Hormone that opposes the action of another hormone.

Anterior pituitary *See* Adenohypophysis.

Antibody A protein molecule that is released by a plasma cell (a daughter cell of an activated B lymphocyte) and that binds specifically to an antigen; an immunoglobulin.

Anticodon (an″ti-ko′don) The three-base sequence complementary to the messenger RNA (mRNA) codon.

Antidiuretic hormone (ADH, also called vasopressin) (an″ti-di″yer-eh′tik) Hormone produced by the hypothalamus and released by the posterior pituitary; stimulates the kidneys to reabsorb more water, reducing urine volume.

Antigen (Ag) (an′tĭ-jen) A substance or part of a substance (living or nonliving) that is recognized as foreign by the immune system, activates the immune system, and reacts with immune cells or their products.

Antigen-presenting cell (APC) A specialized cell (dendritic cell, macrophage, or B cell) that captures, processes, and presents antigens on its surface to T lymphocytes.

Anucleate cell (a-nu′kle-āt) A cell without a nucleus.

Anus (a′nus) Distal end of digestive tract; outlet of rectum.

Aorta (a-or′tah) Major systemic artery; arises from the left ventricle of the heart.

Aortic body Receptor in the aortic arch sensitive to changing oxygen, carbon dioxide, and pH levels of the blood.

Apgar score Evaluation of an infant's physical status at 1 and 5 minutes after birth by assessing five criteria: heart rate, respiration, color, muscle tone, and reflexes.

Apnea Breathing cessation.

Apocrine sweat gland (ap′o-krin) The less numerous type of sweat gland; produces a secretion containing water, salts, proteins, and fatty acids.

Apoenzyme (ap′ō-cn-zīm) The protein portion of an enzyme.

Aponeurosis (ap″o-nu-ro′sis) Fibrous or membranous sheet connecting a muscle and the part it moves.

Apoptosis A process of controlled cellular suicide; eliminates cells that are unneeded, stressed, or aged.

Appendicitis (ă-pen′dĭ-sī-′tis) Inflammation of the appendix (wormlike sac attached to the cecum of the large intestine).

Appendicular Relating to the limbs; one of the two major divisions of the body.

Appositional growth Growth accomplished by the addition of new layers onto those previously formed.

Aquaporins (ă″kwă-por′ins) Transmembrane proteins that form water channels.

Aqueous humor (a′kwe-us) Watery fluid in the anterior segment of the eye.

Arachnoid (ah-rak′noid) Weblike; specifically, the weblike arachnoid mater, the middle layer of the three meninges.

Areola (ah-re′o-lah) Circular, pigmented area surrounding the nipple; any small space in a tissue.

Areolar connective tissue A type of loose connective tissue.

Arrector pili (ah-rek′tor pi′li) Tiny, smooth muscles attached to hair follicles; contraction causes the hair to stand upright.

Arrhythmia (a-rith′me-ah) Irregular heart rhythm, often caused by defects in the intrinsic conduction system.

Arteries Blood vessels that conduct blood away from the heart and into the circulation.

Arteriole (ar-tĕr′e-ōl) A minute artery.

Arteriosclerosis (ar-tē-r′e-o-skler-o′sis) Any of a number of proliferative and degenerative changes in the arteries leading to their decreased elasticity.

Arthritis Inflammation of the joints.

Arthroscopic surgery (ar-thro-skop′ik) Procedure enabling a surgeon to repair the interior of a joint through a small incision.

Articular capsule Double-layered capsule composed of an outer fibrous layer lined by synovial membrane; encloses the joint cavity of a synovial joint.

Articular cartilage Hyaline cartilage covering bone ends at movable joints.

Articulation (joint) The junction of two or more bones.

Association areas Functional areas of the cerebral cortex that act mainly to integrate diverse information for purposeful action.

Astigmatism (ah-stig′mah-tizm) A condition in which unequal curvatures in different parts of the cornea or lens of the eye lead to blurred vision.

Astrocyte (as′tro-sīt) A type of CNS supporting cell; assists in exchanges between blood capillaries and neurons.

Atelectasis (at″ĕ-lik′tah-sis) Lung collapse.

Atherosclerosis (a″ther-o″skler-o′sis) Changes in the walls of large arteries consisting of lipid deposits on the artery walls; one form of arteriosclerosis.

Atmospheric pressure Force that air exerts on the surface of the body (760 mm Hg at sea level).

Atom Smallest particle of an elemental substance that exhibits the properties of that element; composed of protons, neutrons, and electrons.

Atomic number The number of protons in an atom.

Atomic symbol The one- or two-letter symbol used to indicate an element; usually the first letter(s) of the element's name.

Atomic weight The average of the mass numbers of all the isotopes of an element.

ATP (adenosine triphosphate) (ah-den′o-sēn tri″fos′fãt) Organic molecule that stores and releases chemical energy for use in body cells.

Atria (a′tre-ah) The two superior receiving chambers of the heart.

Atrial natriuretic peptide (ANP) (a′tre-al na″tre-u-ret′ik) A hormone released by certain cells of the heart atria that reduces blood pressure and blood volume by inhibiting nearly all events that promote vasoconstriction and Na^+ and water retention.

Atrioventricular (AV) bundle (a″tre-o-ven-tri′kyoo-ler) Bundle of specialized fibers that conduct impulses from the AV node to the right and left ventricles; also called bundle of His.

Atrioventricular (AV) node Specialized mass of conducting cells located at the atrioventricular junction in the heart.

Atrioventricular (AV) valve Valve that prevents backflow into the atrium when the connected ventricle is contracting.

Atrophy (at′ro-fe) Reduction in size or wasting away of an organ or cell resulting from disease or lack of use.

Auditory ossicles (ah′sih-kulz) The three tiny bones serving as transmitters of vibrations and located within the middle ear: the malleus, incus, and stapes.

Auditory tube *See* Pharyngotympanic tube.

Autoimmunity Production of antibodies or effector T cells that attack a person's own tissue.

Autolysis (aw″tol′ĭ-sis) Process of autodigestion (self-digestion) of cells, especially dead or degenerate cells.

Autonomic ganglion Collection of sympathetic or parasympathetic postganglionic neuronal cell bodies.

Autonomic nervous system (ANS) Efferent division of the peripheral nervous system that innervates cardiac and smooth muscles and glands; also called the involuntary or visceral motor system.

Autonomic (visceral) reflexes Reflexes that activate smooth or cardiac muscle and/or glands.

Autoregulation The automatic local adjustment of blood flow to a particular body area in response to its current requirements.

Autosomes Chromosomes number 1 to 22; do not include the sex chromosomes.

Avogadro's number (av″o-gad′rōz) The number of molecules in one mole of any substance, 6.02×10^{23}.

Axial Relating to the head, neck, and trunk; one of the two major divisions of the body.

Axolemma (ak″so-lem′ah) The plasma membrane of an axon.

Axon Neuron process that carries impulses away from the nerve cell body; efferent process; the conducting portion of a nerve cell.

Axon terminals (terminal boutons) The bulbous distal endings of the terminal branches of an axon.

B cells Also called B lymphocytes; oversee humoral immunity; their descendants differentiate into antibody-producing plasma cells.

Baroreceptor (bayr″o-re-sep′tor) A sensory nerve ending in the wall of the carotid sinus or aortic arch sensitive to vessel stretching.

Basal body (ba′sal) An organelle structurally identical to a centriole and forming the base of a cilium or flagellum.

Basal ganglia *See* Basal nuclei.

Basal lamina (lam'ĭ-nah) Noncellular, adhesive supporting sheet consisting largely of glycoproteins secreted by epithelial cells.

Basal metabolic rate (BMR) Rate at which energy is expended (heat produced) by the body per unit time under controlled (basal) conditions: 12 hours after a meal, at rest.

Basal nuclei (basal ganglia) Specific gray matter areas located deep within the white matter of the cerebral hemispheres.

Basal surface The surface near the base or interior of a structure; nearest the lower side or bottom of a structure.

Base A substance capable of binding with hydrogen ions; a proton acceptor.

Basement membrane Extracellular material consisting of a basal lamina secreted by epithelial cells and a reticular lamina secreted by underlying connective tissue cells.

Basophil (ba'zo-fil) White blood cell whose granules stain purplish-black and nucleus purple with basic dye.

Benign (be-nīn') Not malignant.

Bile Greenish-yellow or brownish fluid produced in and secreted by the liver, stored in the gallbladder, and released into the small intestine.

Bilirubin (bil"i-roo'bin) Yellow pigment of bile.

Bipolar neuron Neuron with axon and dendrite that extend from opposite sides of the cell body.

Blastocyst (blas'to-sist) Stage of early embryonic development; the product of cleavage.

Blood pressure (BP) Force exerted by blood against a unit area of the blood vessel walls; differences in blood pressure between different areas of the circulation provide the driving force for blood circulation.

Blood brain barrier Mechanism that inhibits passage of materials from the blood into brain tissues; reflects relative impermeability of brain capillaries.

Bolus (bo'lus) A rounded mass of food prepared by the mouth for swallowing; any soft round mass.

Bone marrow Fat- or blood-forming tissue found within bone cavities; called yellow and red bone marrow, respectively.

Bone (osseous tissue) (os'e-us) A connective tissue that forms the bony skeleton.

Bone remodeling Process involving bone formation and destruction in response to hormonal and mechanical factors.

Bone resorption The removal of osseous tissue; part of the continuous bone remodeling process.

Bowman's capsule (bo-manz) *See* Glomerular capsule.

Boyle's law States that when the temperature is constant, the pressure of a gas varies inversely with its volume.

Bradycardia (brad"e-kar'de-ah) A heart rate below 60 beats per minute.

Brain death State of irreversible coma, even though life-support measures may have restored other body organs.

Brain stem Collectively the midbrain, pons, and medulla of the brain.

Brain ventricle Fluid-filled cavity of the brain.

Branchial groove (brang'ke-al) An indentation of the surface ectoderm in the embryo; the external acoustic meatus develops from it.

Bronchioles Smaller (<1 mm in diameter) branching air passageways inside the lungs.

Bronchus (brong'kus) One of the two large branches of the trachea that lead to the lungs.

Buffer Chemical substance or system that minimizes changes in pH by releasing or binding hydrogen ions.

Burn Tissue damage inflicted by intense heat, electricity, radiation, or certain chemicals, all of which denature cell proteins and kill cells in the affected areas.

Bursa (ber'sa) A fibrous sac lined with synovial membrane and containing synovial fluid; occurs between bones and muscle tendons (or other structures), where it acts to decrease friction during movement.

Bursitis Inflammation of a bursa.

Calcaneal tendon (kal-ka'ne-al) Tendon that attaches the calf muscles to the heelbone (calcaneus); also called the Achilles tendon.

Calcitonin (kal"sih-to'nin) Hormone released by the thyroid. Lowers blood calcium levels only when present at high (therapeutic) levels.

Calculus (kal'ku-lus) A stone formed within various body parts.

Callus (kal'lus) (1) Localized thickening of skin epidermis resulting from physical trauma; (2) repair tissue (fibrous or bony) formed at a fracture site.

Calorie (cal) Amount of energy needed to raise the temperature of 1 gram of water 1° Celsius. Energy exchanges associated with biochemical reactions are usually reported in kilocalories (1 kcal = 1000 cal), also called large calories (Cal).

Calyx (ka'liks) A cuplike extension of the pelvis of the kidney.

Canaliculus (kan"ah-lik'u-lus) Extremely small tubular passage or channel.

Cancer A malignant, invasive cellular neoplasm that has the capability of spreading throughout the body or body parts.

Capillaries (kap'il-layr"ēs) The smallest of the blood vessels and the sites of exchange between the blood and tissue cells.

Carbohydrate (kar"bo-hi'drāt) Organic compound composed of carbon, hydrogen, and oxygen; includes starches, sugars, cellulose.

Carbonic acid–bicarbonate buffer system Chemical system that helps maintain pH homeostasis of the blood.

Carbonic anhydrase (kar-bon'ik an-hi'drās) Enzyme that facilitates the combination of carbon dioxide with water to form carbonic acid.

Carcinogen (kar"sĭ'no-jin) Cancer-causing agent.

Cardiac cycle Sequence of events encompassing one complete contraction and relaxation of the atria and ventricles of the heart.

Cardiac muscle Specialized muscle of the heart.

Cardiac output (CO) Amount of blood pumped out of a ventricle in one minute.

Cardiac reserve The difference between resting and maximal cardiac output.

Cardiogenic shock Pump failure; the heart is so inefficient that it cannot sustain adequate circulation.

Cardiovascular system Organ system that distributes the blood to deliver nutrients and remove wastes.

Carotene (kar'o-tēn) Yellow to orange pigment that accumulates in the stratum corneum epidermal layer and in fatty tissue of the hypodermis.

Carotid body (kar-rot'id) A receptor in the common carotid artery sensitive to changing oxygen, carbon dioxide, and pH levels of the blood.

Carotid sinus (si'nus) A dilation of a common carotid artery; involved in regulation of systemic blood pressure.

Carrier A transmembrane protein that changes shape to envelop and transport a polar substance across the cell membrane.

Cartilage (kar'tĭ-lij) White, semiopaque connective tissue.

Cartilage bone (endochondral bone) Bone formed by using hyaline cartilage structures as models for ossification.

Cartilaginous joints (kar"ti-laj'ĭ-nus) Bones united by cartilage; no joint cavity is present.

Catabolism (ka-tab′o-lizm) Process in which living cells break down substances into simpler substances.

Catalyst (kat′ah-list) Substance that increases the rate of a chemical reaction without itself becoming chemically changed or part of the product.

Cataract Clouding of the eye's lens; often congenital or age-related.

Catecholamines (kat″ĕ-kol′ah-mēnz) Epinephrine, norepinephrine, and dopamine; a class of amines that act as chemical transmitters.

Cation (kat′i-on) An ion with a positive charge.

Caudal (kaw′dul) Literally, toward the tail; in humans, the inferior portion of the anatomy.

Cecum (se′kum) The blind-ended pouch at the beginning of the large intestine.

Cell Structural unit of all living things.

Cell differentiation The development of specific and distinctive features in cells, from a single cell (the fertilized egg) to all the specialized cells of adulthood.

Cell cycle Series of changes a cell goes through from the time it is formed until it reproduces itself.

Cell membrane *See* Plasma membrane.

Cellular immunity Immunity conferred by activated T cells, which directly kill infected or cancerous body cells or cells of foreign grafts and release chemicals that regulate the immune response. Also called cell-mediated immunity.

Cellular respiration Metabolic processes in which ATP is produced.

Cellulose (sel′u-lōs) A fibrous carbohydrate that is the main structural component of plant tissues.

Central (Haversian) canal (hah-ver′zhan) The canal in the center of each osteon that contains minute blood vessels and nerve fibers that serve the needs of the osteocytes.

Central nervous system (CNS) Brain and spinal cord.

Centriole (sen′tre-ol) Minute body found near the nucleus of the cell; active in cell division.

Centrosome (cell center) A region near the nucleus which contains paired organelles called centrioles.

Cerebellum (ser″ĕ-bel′um) Brain region most involved in producing smooth, coordinated skeletal muscle activity.

Cerebral aqueduct (ser′ĕ-bral, sĕ-re′bral) The slender cavity of the midbrain that connects the third and fourth ventricles.

Cerebral arterial circle (*circle of Willis*) An arterial anastomosis at the base of the brain.

Cerebral cortex The outer gray matter region of the cerebral hemispheres.

Cerebral dominance Designates the hemisphere that is dominant for language.

Cerebral palsy Neuromuscular disability in which voluntary muscles are poorly controlled or paralyzed as a result of brain damage.

Cerebral white matter Consists largely of myelinated fibers bundled into large tracts; provides for communication between cerebral areas and lower CNS centers.

Cerebrospinal fluid (CSF) (ser″ĕ-bro-spi′nal) Plasmalike fluid that fills the cavities of the CNS and surrounds the CNS externally; protects the brain and spinal cord.

Cerebrovascular accident (CVA) (ser″ĕ-bro-vas′ku-lar) Condition in which brain tissue is deprived of a blood supply, as in blockage of a cerebral blood vessel; a stroke.

Cerebrum (ser′ĕ-brum) The cerebral hemispheres (including the cerebral cortex, white matter, and basal nuclei).

Cervical vertebrae The seven vertebrae of the vertebral column located in the neck.

Cervix Lower outlet of the uterus extending into the vagina.

Channel A transmembrane protein that forms an aqueous pore, allowing substances to move from one side of the membrane to the other.

Chemical bond An energy relationship holding atoms together; involves the interaction of electrons.

Chemical energy Energy stored in the bonds of chemical substances.

Chemical equilibrium A state of apparent repose created by two reactions proceeding in opposite directions at equal speed.

Chemical reaction Process in which molecules are formed, changed, or broken down.

Chemoreceptor (ke″mo-re-sep′ter) Receptor sensitive to various chemicals in solution.

Chemotaxis (ke″mo-tak′sis) Movement of a cell, organism, or part of an organism toward or away from a chemical substance.

Cholecystokinin (CCK) (ko″le-sis″to-ki′nin) An intestinal hormone that stimulates gallbladder contraction and pancreatic juice release.

Cholesterol (ko-les′ter-ol″) Steroid found in animal fats as well as in most body tissues; made by the liver.

Cholinergic fibers (ko″lin-er′jik) Nerve endings that, upon stimulation, release acetylcholine.

Chondroblast (kon′dro-blast) Actively mitotic cell of cartilage.

Chondrocyte (kon′dro-sīt) Mature cell of cartilage.

Chorion (kor′e-on) Outermost fetal membrane; helps form the placenta.

Chorionic villus sampling (ko″re-on′ik vil′us) Fetal testing procedure in which bits of the chorionic villi from the placenta are snipped off and the cells karyotyped. This procedure can be done as early as 8 weeks into the pregnancy.

Choroid (ko′roid) The vascular middle layer of the eye.

Choroid plexus (ko′roid plex′sus) A capillary knot that protrudes into a brain ventricle; produces cerebrospinal fluid.

Chromatin (kro′mah-tin) Structures in the nucleus that carry the hereditary factors (genes).

Chromosomes (kro′mo-somz) Barlike bodies of tightly coiled chromatin; visible during cell division.

Chronic obstructive pulmonary disease (COPD) Collective term for progressive, obstructive respiratory disorders; includes emphysema, chronic bronchitis.

Chyme (kīm) Semifluid, creamy mass consisting of partially digested food and gastric juice.

Cilia (sil′e-ah) Tiny, hairlike projections on cell surfaces that move in a wavelike manner.

Circumduction (ser″kum-duk′shun) Movement of a body part so that it outlines a cone in space.

Cirrhosis (sĭ-ro′sis) Chronic disease of the liver, characterized by an overgrowth of connective tissue, or fibrosis.

Cisterna chyli (sis-ter′nah ki′li) An enlarged sac at the base of the thoracic duct; the origin of the thoracic duct.

Cisternae (sis-ter′ne) Any cavity or enclosed space serving as a reservoir.

Cleavage An early embryonic phase consisting of rapid mitotic cell divisions without intervening growth periods; product is a blastocyst.

Clonal selection (klo′nul) Process during which a B cell or T cell becomes activated by binding with an antigen.

Clone Descendants of a single cell.

Coagulation Process in which blood is transformed from a liquid to a gel; blood clotting.

Cochlea (kok′le-ah) Snail-shaped chamber of the bony labyrinth that houses the receptor for hearing [the spiral organ (organ of Corti)].

Codon (ko′don) The three-base sequence on a messenger RNA molecule that provides the genetic information used in protein synthesis; code for a given amino acid.

Coenzyme (ko-en′zīm) Nonprotein substance associated with and activating an enzyme, typically a vitamin.

Cofactor Metal ion or organic molecule that is required for enzyme activity.

Collagen fiber The most abundant of the three fibers found in the matrix of connective tissue.

Colloid (kol′oid) (1) A mixture in which the solute particles (usually proteins) do not settle out readily. (2) Substance in the thyroid gland containing thyroglobulin protein.

Colloid osmotic pressure (kol′oid ahz-mah′tik) Pressure created in a fluid by large nondiffusible molecules, such as plasma proteins that are prevented from moving through a (capillary) membrane. Such substances tend to draw water to them.

Colon Regions of the large intestine; includes ascending, transverse, descending, and sigmoid portions.

Combination (synthesis) reaction Chemical reaction in which larger, more complex atoms or molecules are formed from simpler ones.

Complement A group of bloodborne proteins, which, when activated, enhance the inflammatory and immune responses and may lead to cell lysis.

Complementarity of structure and function The relationship between a structure and its function; i.e., structure determines function.

Complementary base Refers to how a given nitrogenous base of DNA or RNA bonds to another nitrogenous base. For example, adenine (A) is the complementary base of thymine (T). The result is base pairing.

Complete blood count (CBC) Clinical test that includes counts of all formed elements, a hematocrit, and measurements of erythrocyte size and hemoglobin content.

Compound Substance composed of two or more different elements, the atoms of which are chemically united.

Concentration gradient The difference in the concentration of a particular substance between two different areas.

Conducting zone Includes all respiratory passageways that provide conduits for air to reach the sites of gas exchange (the respiratory zone).

Conductivity Ability to transmit an electrical impulse.

Cones One of the two types of photoreceptor cells in the retina of the eye; provide for color vision.

Congenital (kun-jeh′nih-tul) Existing at birth.

Congestive heart failure (CHF) Condition in which the pumping efficiency of the heart is depressed so that circulation is inadequate to meet tissue needs.

Conjunctiva (kon″junk-ti′vah) Thin, protective mucous membrane lining the eyelids and covering the anterior surface of the eye itself.

Connective tissue A primary tissue; form and function vary extensively. Functions include support, storage, and protection.

Consciousness The ability to perceive, communicate, remember, understand, appreciate, and initiate voluntary movements.

Contraception The prevention of conception; birth control.

Contractility Muscle cell's ability to move by shortening.

Contraction To shorten or develop tension, an ability highly developed in muscle cells.

Contralateral Relating to the opposite side.

Cornea (kor′ne-ah) Transparent anterior portion of the eyeball; part of the fibrous layer.

Corona radiata (kor-o′nah ra-de-ah′tah) (1) Arrangement of elongated follicle cells around a mature ovum; (2) crownlike arrangement of nerve fibers radiating from the internal capsule of the brain to every part of the cerebral cortex.

Coronary circulation The functional blood supply of the heart; shortest circulation in the body.

Cortex (kor′teks) Outer surface layer of an organ.

Corticosteroids (kor″tĭ-ko-stě′roidz) Steroid hormones released by the adrenal cortex.

Cortisol (hydrocortisone) (kor′tih-sol) Glucocorticoid produced by the adrenal cortex.

Covalent bond (ko-va′lent) Chemical bond created by electron sharing between atoms.

Cranial nerves The 12 nerve pairs that arise from the brain.

Craniosacral division Another name for the parasympathetic division of the autonomic nervous system.

Cranium (cranial bones) (kra′ne-um) Bony protective encasement of the brain and organs of hearing and equilibrium.

Creatine kinase (kre′ah-tin) Enzyme that catalyzes the transfer of phosphate from creatine phosphate to ADP, forming creatine and ATP; important in muscle contraction.

Creatine phosphate (CP) (fos-fāt) Compound that serves as an alternative energy source for muscle tissue.

Creatinine (kre-at′ĭ-nin) A nitrogenous waste molecule which is not reabsorbed by the kidney; this characteristic makes it useful for measurement of the GFR and glomerular function.

Crista ampullaris Sensory receptor organ for rotational acceleration and deceleration housed within the ampulla of each semicircular canal of the inner ear.

Cross section A cut running horizontally from right to left, dividing the body or an organ into superior and inferior parts.

Cutaneous (ku-ta′ne-us) Pertaining to the skin.

Cutaneous sensory receptors Receptors located throughout the skin that respond to stimuli arising outside the body; part of the nervous system.

Cyclic AMP Intracellular second messenger that mediates the effects of the first (extracellular) messenger (hormone or neurotransmitter); formed from ATP by a plasma membrane enzyme (adenylate cyclase).

Cystic fibrosis (CF) Genetic disorder in which secretion of overly viscous mucus clogs the respiratory passages, predisposes to fatal respiratory infections.

Cytochromes (si′to-krōmz) Brightly colored iron-containing proteins that form part of the inner mitochondrial membrane and function as electron carriers in oxidative phosphorylation.

Cytokines Small proteins that act as chemical messengers between various parts of the immune system.

Cytokinesis (si″to-kĭ-ne′sis) The division of cytoplasm that occurs after the cell nucleus has divided.

Cytoplasm (si′to-plazm) The cellular material surrounding the nucleus and enclosed by the plasma membrane.

Cytosine (C) (si′to-sēn) Nitrogen-containing base that is part of a nucleotide structure.

Cytoskeleton Literally, cell skeleton. An elaborate series of rods running through the cystol, supporting cellular structures and providing the machinery to generate various cell movements.

Cytosol Viscous, semitransparent fluid substance of cytoplasm in which other elements are suspended.

Cytotoxic T cell (T$_C$ cell) Effector T cell that directly kills foreign cells, cancer cells, or virus-infected body cells by inducing apoptosis (cell suicide).

Deamination (de″am-ih-na′shun) Removal of an amine group from an organic compound.

Decomposition reaction Chemical reaction in which a molecule is broken down into smaller molecules or its constituent atoms.

Defecation (def″ih-ka′shun) Elimination of the contents of the bowels (feces).

Deglutition (deg″loo-tish′un) Swallowing.

Dehydration (de″hi-dra′shun) Condition of excessive water loss.

Dehydration synthesis Process by which a large molecule is synthesized by removing water and covalently bonding smaller molecules together.

Dendrite (den′drīt) Branching neuron process that serves as a receptive, or input, region; transmits an electrical signal toward the cell body.

Dendritic cells Protective cells that phagocytize antigens, migrate to lymph nodes, and present the antigen to T cells, causing them to activate and mount an immune response; those in the skin are sometimes called Langerhans cells.

Depolarization (de-po″ler-ah-za′shun) Loss of a state of polarity; loss or reduction of negative membrane potential.

Dermatome (der′mah-tōm) Portion of somite mesoderm that forms the dermis of the skin; also the area of skin innervated by the cutaneous branches of a single spinal nerve.

Dermis Layer of skin deep to the epidermis; composed mostly of dense irregular connective tissue.

Desmosome (dez′muh-sōm) Cell junction composed of thickened plasma membranes joined by filaments.

Diabetes insipidus (di″ah-be′tēz in-sih′pih-dus) Disease characterized by passage of a large quantity of dilute urine plus intense thirst and dehydration caused by inadequate release of antidiuretic hormone (ADH).

Diabetes mellitus (DM) (meh-li′tus) Disease caused by deficient insulin release or by insulin resistance, leading to inability of the body cells to use carbohydrates.

Dialysis (di-al′ah-sis) Diffusion of solute(s) through a semipermeable membrane.

Diapedesis (di″ah-pĕ-de′sis) Passage of white blood cells through intact vessel walls into tissue.

Diaphragm (di′ah-fram) (1) Any partition or wall separating one area from another; (2) a muscle that separates the thoracic cavity from the lower abdominopelvic cavity.

Diaphysis (di-af″ĭ-sis) Elongated shaft of a long bone.

Diarthrosis (di″ar-thro′sis) Freely movable joint.

Diastole (di-as′to-le) Period of the cardiac cycle when either the ventricles or the atria are relaxing.

Diastolic pressure (di-as-tah′lik) Arterial blood pressure reached during or as a result of diastole; lowest level of any given cardiac cycle.

Diencephalon (interbrain) (di″en-seh′fuh-lon) That part of the forebrain between the cerebral hemispheres and the midbrain including the thalamus, the epithalamus, and the hypothalamus.

Differential white blood cell count Diagnostic test to determine relative proportion of individual leukocyte types.

Diffusion (dĭ-fu′zhun) The spreading of particles in a gas or solution with a movement toward uniform distribution of particles; driven by kinetic energy.

Digestion A series of catabolic steps in which complex food molecules are broken down to their building blocks by enzymes.

Digestive system System that processes food into absorbable units and eliminates indigestible wastes.

Dipeptide A combination of two amino acids united by means of a peptide bond.

Diploë (dip′lo-e) The internal layer of spongy bone in flat bones.

Diploid chromosomal number The chromosomal number characteristic of an organism, symbolized as $2n$; twice the chromosomal number (n) of the gamete; in humans, $2n = 46$.

Diplopia (dĭ-plo′pe-ah) Double vision.

Dipole (polar molecule) Nonsymmetrical molecules that contain electrically unbalanced atoms.

Disaccharide (di-sak′ah-rīd″, di-sak′ah-rid) Literally, double sugar; e.g., sucrose, lactose.

Dislocation (luxation) Occurs when bones are forced out of their normal alignment at a joint.

Displacement (exchange) reaction Chemical reaction in which bonds are both made and broken; atoms become combined with different atoms.

Distal (dis′tul) Away from the attached end of a limb or the origin of a structure.

Diuretics (di″u-ret′iks) Chemicals that enhance urinary output.

Diverticulum (di″ver-tik′u-lum) A pouch or sac in the walls of a hollow organ or structure.

DNA (deoxyribonucleic acid) (de-ok″sĭ-ri″bo-nu-kla′ik) A nucleic acid found in all living cells; it carries the organism's hereditary information.

DNA replication Process that occurs before cell division; ensures that all daughter cells have identical genes.

Dominant traits Occurs when one allele masks or suppresses the expression of its partner.

Dominant-recessive inheritance Reflects the interaction of dominant and recessive alleles.

Dorsal (dor′sul) Pertaining to the back; posterior.

Dorsal root ganglion Peripheral collection of cell bodies of first-order afferent neurons whose central axons enter the spinal cord.

Double helix The secondary structure assumed by two strands of DNA, held together throughout their length by hydrogen bonds between bases on opposite strands.

Duct (dukt) A canal or passageway; a tubular structure that provides an exit for the secretions of a gland, or for conducting any fluid.

Ductus (vas) deferens Extends from the epididymis to the urethra; propels sperm into the urethra by peristalsis during ejaculation.

Duodenum (du″o-de′num) First part of the small intestine.

Dura mater (du′rah ma′ter) Outermost and toughest of the three membranes (meninges) covering the brain and spinal cord.

Dynamic equilibrium Sense that reports on angular (rotatory) acceleration or deceleration of the head in space.

Dyskinesia (dis-kĭ-ne′ze-ah) Disorders of muscle tone, posture, or involuntary movements.

Dyspnea (disp-ne′ah) Difficult or labored breathing; air hunger.

Eccrine glands (ek′rin) Sweat glands abundant on the palms, soles of feet, and the forehead.

Ectoderm (ek′to-derm) Embryonic germ layer; forms the epidermis of the skin and its derivatives, and nervous tissues.

Edema (ĕ-de′mah) Abnormal increase in the amount of interstitial fluid; causes swelling.

Effector (ef-ek′ter) Organ, gland, or muscle capable of being activated by nerve endings.

Efferent (ef′er-ent) Carrying away or away from, especially a nerve fiber that carries impulses away from the central nervous system.

Elastic cartilage Cartilage with abundant elastic fibers; more flexible than hyaline cartilage.

Elastic fiber Fiber formed from the protein elastin, which gives a rubbery and resilient quality to the matrix of connective tissue.

Electrical energy Energy formed by the movement of charged particles across cell membranes.

Electrocardiogram (ECG or EKG) (e-lek″tro-car′de-o-gram″) Graphic record of the electrical activity of the heart.

Electrochemical gradient The combined difference in concentration and charge; influences the distribution and direction of diffusion of ions.

Electroencephalogram (EEG) (e-lek″tro-en-sef′ah-lo-gram″) Graphic record of the electrical activity of nerve cells in the brain.

Electrolyte (e-lek′tro-līt) Chemical substances, such as salts, acids, and bases, that ionize and dissociate in water and are capable of conducting an electrical current.

Electrolyte balance Refers to the balance between input and output of salts (sodium, potassium, calcium, magnesium) in the body.

Electromagnetic radiation Emitted photons (wave packets) of energy, e.g., light, X ray, infrared.

Electron Negatively charged subatomic particle; orbits the atom's nucleus.

Electron shells (energy levels) Regions of space that consecutively surround the nucleus of an atom.

Element One of a limited number of unique varieties of matter that composes substances of all kinds; e.g., carbon, hydrogen, oxygen.

Embolism (em′bo-lizm) Obstruction of a blood vessel by an embolus (blood clot, fatty mass, bubble of air, or other debris) floating in the blood.

Embryo (em′bre-o) Developmental stage extending from fertilization to the end of the eighth week.

Emesis Reflexive emptying of the stomach through the esophagus and pharynx; also known as vomiting.

Encephalitis (en″seh-fuh-lī-′tis) Inflammation of the brain.

Endergonic reaction Chemical reaction that absorbs energy, e.g., an anabolic reaction.

Endocardium (en″do-kar′de-um) Endothelial membrane that lines the interior of the heart.

Endochondral ossification (en″do-kon′dral) Embryonic formation of bone by the replacement of calcified cartilage; most skeletal bones are formed by this process.

Endocrine glands (en′do-krin) Ductless glands that empty their hormonal products directly into the blood.

Endocrine system Body system that includes internal organs that secrete hormones.

Endocytosis (en″do-si-to′sis) Means by which fairly large extracellular molecules or particles enter cells, e.g., phagocytosis, pinocytosis, receptor-mediated endocytosis.

Endoderm (en′do-derm) Embryonic germ layer; forms the lining of the digestive tube and its associated structures.

Endogenous (en-doj′ĕ-nŭs) Originating or produced within the organism or one of its parts.

Endometrium (en″do-me′tre-um) Mucous membrane lining of the uterus.

Endomysium (en″do-mis′e-um) Thin connective tissue surrounding each muscle cell.

Endoplasmic reticulum (ER) (en″do-plaz′mik rĕ-tik′u-lum) Membranous network of tubular or saclike channels in the cytoplasm of a cell.

Endosteum (en-dos′te-um) Connective tissue membrane covering internal bone surfaces.

Endothelium (en″do-the′le-um) Single layer of simple squamous cells that line the walls of the heart, blood vessels, and lymphatic vessels.

Energy The capacity to do work; may be stored (potential energy) or in action (kinetic energy).

Energy intake Energy liberated during food oxidation.

Energy output Sum of energy lost as heat, as work, and as fat or glycogen storage.

Enzyme (en′zīm) A protein that acts as a biological catalyst to speed up a chemical reaction.

Eosinophil (e″o-sin′o-fil) Granular white blood cell whose granules readily take up an acid stain called eosin.

Ependymal cell (ĕ-pen′dĭ-mul) A type of CNS supporting cell; lines the central cavities of the brain and spinal cord.

Epidermis (ep″ĭ-der′mis) Superficial layer of the skin; composed of keratinized stratified squamous epithelium.

Epididymis (ep″ĭ-dĭ′dĭ-mis) That portion of the male duct system in which sperm mature. Empties into the ductus (or vas) deferens.

Epidural space Area between the bony vertebrae and the dura mater of the spinal cord.

Epiglottis (ep″ĭ-glot′is) Elastic cartilage at the back of the throat; covers the opening of the larynx during swallowing.

Epileptic seizures Abnormal electrical discharges of groups of brain neurons, during which no other messages can get through.

Epimysium (ep″ĭ-mis′e-um) Sheath of fibrous connective tissue surrounding a muscle.

Epinephrine (ep″ĭ-nef′rin) Chief hormone produced by the adrenal medulla. Also called adrenaline.

Epiphyseal plate (e″pĭ-fis′e-ul) Plate of hyaline cartilage at the junction of the diaphysis and epiphysis that provides for growth in length of a long bone.

Epiphysis (e-pif′ĭ-sis) The end of a long bone, attached to the shaft.

Epithalamus Most dorsal portion of the diencephalon; forms the roof of the third ventricle with the pineal gland extending from its posterior border.

Epithelium (epithelial tissue) (ep″ĭ-the′le-ul) Pertaining to a primary tissue that covers the body surface, lines its internal cavities, and forms glands.

Erythrocytes (e-rith′ro-sīts) Red blood cells.

Erythropoiesis (ĕ-rith″ro-poi-e′sis) Process of erythrocyte formation.

Erythropoietin (EPO) (ĕ-rith″ro-poi′ĕ-tin) Hormone that stimulates production of red blood cells.

Esophagus (ĕ-sof′ah-gus) Muscular tube extending from the laryngopharynx through the diaphragm to join the stomach; collapses when not involved in food propulsion.

Estrogens (es'tro-jenz) Hormones that stimulate female secondary sex characteristics; female sex hormones.

Eupnea (ūp-ne'ah) Normal respiratory rate and rhythm.

Excess postexercise oxygen consumption (EPOC) The volume of oxygen required after exercise to replenish stores of O_2, ATP, creatine phosphate, and glycogen and oxidize the lactic acid formed during exercise. Also called oxygen debt.

Exchange (displacement) reaction Chemical reaction in which bonds are both made and broken; atoms become combined with different atoms.

Excitability (responsiveness) Ability to respond to stimuli.

Excitation-contraction (E-C) coupling Sequence of events by which transmission of an action potential along the sarcolemma leads to the sliding of myofilaments.

Excitatory postsynaptic potential (EPSP) Depolarizing graded potential in a postsynaptic neuron.

Excretion (ek-skre'shun) Elimination of waste products from the body.

Exergonic reaction Chemical reaction that releases energy, e.g., a catabolic or oxidative reaction.

Exocrine glands (ek'so-krin) Glands that have ducts through which their secretions are carried to a particular site.

Exocytosis (ek″so-si-to'sis) Mechanism by which substances are moved from the cell interior to the extracellular space as a secretory vesicle fuses with the plasma membrane.

Exons Amino acid–specifying informational sequences (separated by introns) in the genes of higher organisms.

Extension Movement that increases the angle of a joint, e.g., straightening a flexed knee.

Exteroceptor (ek″ster-o-sep'tor) Sensory receptor that responds to stimuli from the external world.

Extracellular fluid (ECF) Internal fluid located outside cells; includes interstitial fluid, blood plasma, and cerebrospinal fluid.

Extracellular matrix Nonliving material in connective tissue consisting of ground substance and fibers that separates the living cells.

Extrasystole (ek″strah-sis'to-le) Premature heart contraction.

Extrinsic (ek-strin'sik) Of external origin.

Extrinsic eye muscles The six skeletal muscles that attach to and move each eye.

Facilitated diffusion Passive transport process used by certain large or charged molecules (e.g., glucose, Na^+) that are unable to pass through the plasma membrane unaided. Involves movement through channels or movement facilitated by a membrane carrier.

Fallopian tube (fah-lō'pe-un) *See* Uterine tube.

Fascia (fash'e-ah) Layers of fibrous tissue covering and separating muscle.

Fascicle (fas'ĭ-kl) Bundle of nerve or muscle fibers bound together by connective tissue.

Fatty acids Linear chains of carbon and hydrogen atoms (hydrocarbon chains) with an organic acid group at one end. A constituent of fat.

Feces (fe'sēz) Material discharged from the bowel; composed of food residue, secretions, bacteria.

Fenestrated (fen'es-tra-tid) Pierced with one or more small openings.

Fertilization Fusion of the sperm and egg nuclei.

Fetus Developmental stage extending from the ninth week of development to birth.

Fiber A slender threadlike structure or filament. *See also* Nerve fiber, Muscle fiber.

Fibrillation Condition of rapid and irregular or out-of-phase heart contractions.

Fibrin (fi'brin) Fibrous insoluble protein formed during blood clotting.

Fibrinogen (fi-brin'o-jin) A soluble blood protein that is converted to insoluble fibrin during blood clotting.

Fibrinolysis Process that removes unneeded blood clots when healing has occurred.

Fibroblast (fi'bro-blast) Young, actively mitotic cell that forms the fibers of connective tissue.

Fibrocartilage The most compressible type of cartilage; resistant to stretch. Forms vertebral discs and knee joint cartilages.

Fibrocyte (fi'bro-sīt) Mature fibroblast; maintains the matrix of fibrous types of connective tissue.

Fibrosis Proliferation of fibrous connective tissue called scar tissue.

Fibrous joints Bones joined by fibrous tissue; no joint cavity is present.

Filtrate A plasma-derived fluid that is processed by the renal tubules to form urine.

Filtration Passage of a solvent and dissolved substances through a membrane or filter.

First-degree burn A burn in which only the epidermis is damaged.

Fissure (fih'sher) (1) A groove or cleft; (2) the deepest depressions or inward folds on the brain.

Fixator (fix'a-ter) Muscle that immobilizes one or more bones, allowing other muscles to act from a stable base.

Flagellum (flah-jel'lum) Long, whiplike cellular extension containing microtubules; propels sperm and some single-celled eukaryotes.

Flexion (flek'shun) Movement that decreases the angle of the joint, e.g., bending the knee from a straight to an angled position.

Flexor (withdrawal) reflex Reflex initiated by a painful stimulus (actual or perceived); causes automatic withdrawal of the threatened body part from the stimulus.

Fluid mosaic model A depiction of the structure of the membranes of a cell as phospholipid bilayers in which proteins are dispersed.

Follicle (fah'lih-kul) (1) Ovarian structure consisting of a developing egg surrounded by one or more layers of follicle cells; (2) colloid-containing structure of the thyroid gland; (3) B cell–rich region in lymphoid tissue.

Follicle-stimulating hormone (FSH) Hormone produced by the anterior pituitary that stimulates ovarian follicle production in females and sperm production in males.

Fontanelles (fon″tah-nelz') Fibrous membranes at the angles of cranial bones that accommodate brain growth in the fetus and infant.

Foramen (fo-ra'men) Hole or opening in a bone or between body cavities.

Forebrain (prosencephalon) Anterior portion of the brain consisting of the telencephalon and the diencephalon.

Formed elements Cellular portion of blood.

Fossa (fos'ah) A depression, often an articular surface.

Fovea (fo've-ah) A pit.

Fracture A break in a bone.

Free radicals Highly reactive chemicals with unpaired electrons that can scramble the structure of proteins, lipids, and nucleic acids.

Frontal (coronal) plane Longitudinal (vertical) plane that divides the body or an organ into anterior and posterior parts.

Fulcrum The fixed point on which a lever moves when a force is applied.

Fundus (fun'dus) Base of an organ; part farthest from the opening of the organ. For example, the posterior wall of the eye.

G protein Protein that relays signals between extracellular first messengers (hormones or neurotransmitters) and intracellular second messengers (such as cyclic AMP) via an effector enzyme.

Gallbladder Sac beneath the right lobe of the liver used for bile storage.

Gallstones (biliary calculi) Crystallized cholesterol that obstructs the flow of bile from the gallbladder.

Gamete (gam′ēt) Sex or germ cell.

Gametogenesis (gam″eh-to-jen′eh-sis) Formation of *gametes*.

Ganglion (gang′gle-on) Collection of nerve cell bodies outside the CNS.

Gap junction A passageway between two adjacent cells; formed by transmembrane proteins called connexons.

Gastrin Hormone secreted in the stomach; regulates gastric juice secretion by stimulating HCl production.

Gastroenteritis Inflammation of the gastrointestinal tract.

Gastrulation (gas″troo-la′shun) Developmental process that produces the three primary germ layers (ectoderm, mesoderm, and endoderm).

Gene One of the biological units of heredity located in chromatin; transmits hereditary information.

Genetic code Refers to the rules by which the base sequence of a DNA gene is translated into protein structures (amino acid sequences).

Genitalia (jen″ĭ-ta′le-ă) The internal and external reproductive organs.

Genome The complete set of chromosomes derived from one parent (the haploid genome); or the two sets of chromosomes, i.e., one set from the egg, the other from the sperm (the diploid genome).

Genotype (jen′o-tīp) One's genetic makeup or genes.

Germ layers Three cellular layers (ectoderm, mesoderm, and endoderm) that represent the initial specialization of cells in the embryonic body and from which all body tissues arise.

Gestation period (jes-ta′shun) The period of pregnancy; about 280 days for humans.

Gland Organ specialized to secrete or excrete substances for further use in the body or for elimination.

Glaucoma (glaw-ko′mah) Condition in which intraocular pressure increases to levels that cause compression of the retina and optic nerve; results in blindness unless detected early.

Glial cells (gle′al) *See* Neuroglia.

Glomerular capsule (glo-mer′yoo-ler) Double-walled cup at end of a renal tubule; encloses a glomerulus. Also called Bowman's capsule.

Glomerular filtration rate (GFR) Rate of filtrate formation by the kidneys.

Glomerulus (glo-mer′u-lus) (1) Cluster of capillaries forming part of the nephron; forms filtrate; (2) odor-specific processing unit in olfactory bulb.

Glottis (glah′tis) Opening between the vocal cords in the larynx.

Glucagon (gloo′kah-gon) Hormone formed by alpha cells of pancreatic islets; raises the glucose level of blood.

Glucocorticoids (gloo″ko-kor′tĭ-koidz) Adrenal cortex hormones that increase blood glucose levels and aid the body in resisting long-term stressors.

Gluconeogenesis (gloo″ko-ne″o-jen′ĕ-sis) Formation of glucose from noncarbohydrate molecules.

Glucose (gloo′kōs) Principal blood sugar; a hexose.

Glycerol (glis′er-ol) A modified simple sugar (a sugar alcohol); a building block of fats.

Glycocalyx (cell coat) (gli″ko-kal′iks) A layer of externally facing glycoproteins on a cell's plasma membrane; its components determine blood type and are involved in the cellular interactions of fertilization, embryonic development, and immunity, and act as an adhesive between cells.

Glycogen (gli′ko-jin) Main carbohydrate stored in animal cells; a polysaccharide.

Glycogenesis (gli″ko-jen′ĕ-sis) Formation of glycogen from glucose.

Glycogenolysis (gli″ko-jĕ-nol′ĭ-sis) Breakdown of glycogen to glucose.

Glycolipid (gli″ko-lip′id) A lipid with one or more covalently attached sugars.

Glycolysis (gli-kol′ĭ-sis) Breakdown of glucose to pyruvic acid—an anaerobic process.

Goblet cells Individual cells (unicellular glands) that produce mucus.

Golgi apparatus (gol′je) Membranous system close to the cell nucleus that packages protein secretions for export, packages enzymes into lysosomes for cellular use, and modifies proteins destined to become part of cellular membranes.

Gonad (go′nad) Primary reproductive organ; i.e., the testis of the male or the ovary of the female.

Gonadocorticoids (gon″ah-do-kor′tĭ-koidz) Sex hormones, primarily androgens, secreted by the adrenal cortex.

Gonadotropins (gon″ah-do-trōp′inz) Gonad-stimulating hormones produced by the anterior pituitary.

Graded muscle responses Variations in the degree of muscle contraction by changing either the frequency or strength of the stimulus.

Graded potential A local change in membrane potential that varies directly with the strength of the stimulus, declines with distance.

Graves' disease Disorder resulting from hyperactive thyroid gland.

Gray matter Gray area of the central nervous system; contains neuronal cell bodies and their dendrites.

Growth hormone (GH) Hormone that stimulates growth in general; produced in the anterior pituitary; also called somatotropin.

Guanine (G) (gwan′ēn) One of two major purines occurring in all nucleic acids.

Gustation (gus-ta′shun) Taste.

Gyrus (ji′rus) An outward fold of the surface of the cerebral cortex.

Hair follicle Structure with outer and inner root sheaths extending from the epidermal surface into the dermis and from which new hair develops.

Hapten (hap′ten) An incomplete antigen; has reactivity but not immunogenicity.

Haversian system (hah-ver′zhen) *See* Osteon.

Heart attack (coronary) *See* Myocardial infarction.

Heart block Impaired transmission of impulses from atrium to ventricle resulting in abnormally slow heart rhythms.

Heart murmur Abnormal heart sound (usually resulting from valve problems).

Heimlich maneuver Procedure in which the air in a person's own lungs is used to expel an obstructing piece of food.

Helper T cell (T$_H$ cell) Type of T lymphocyte that orchestrates cellular immunity by direct contact with other immune cells and by releasing chemicals called cytokines; also helps to mediate the humoral response by interacting with B cells.

Hematocrit (he-mat′o-krit) The percentage of total blood volume occupied by erythrocytes.

Hematoma (he″mah-to′mah) Mass of clotted blood that forms at an injured site.

Hematopoiesis (hem″ah-to-poi-e′sis) Blood cell formation; hemopoiesis.

Hematopoietic stem cell (hem″ah-to-poi-et′ik) Bone marrow cell that gives rise to all the formed elements of blood; hemocytoblast.

Heme (hēm) Iron-containing pigment that is essential to oxygen transport by hemoglobin.

Hemoglobin (he′muh-glo-bin) Oxygen-transporting protein of erythrocytes.

Hemolysis (he-mah′lĕ-sis) Rupture of erythrocytes.

Hemophilia (he″mo-fil′e-ah) A term loosely applied to several different hereditary bleeding disorders that exhibit similar signs and symptoms.

Hemopoiesis (he″mo-poi-e′sis) *See* Hematopoiesis.

Hemorrhage (hem′or-ij) Loss of blood from the vessels by flow through ruptured walls; bleeding.

Hemostasis (he″mo-sta′sis) Stoppage of bleeding.

Heparin Natural anticoagulant secreted into blood plasma.

Hepatic portal system (hĕ-pat′ik) Circulation in which the hepatic portal vein carries dissolved nutrients to the liver tissues for processing.

Hepatitis (hep″ah-ti′tis) Inflammation of the liver.

Hernia (her′ne-ah) Abnormal protrusion of an organ or a body part through the containing wall of its cavity.

Heterozygous (het″er-o-zi′gus) Having different allelic genes at a given locus or (by extension) many loci.

Hilton's law Any nerve serving a muscle that produces movement at a joint also innervates the joint and the skin over the joint.

Hilum (hi′lum) The indented region of an organ from which blood and/or lymphatic vessels and nerves enter and exit.

Hippocampus Limbic system structure that plays a role in converting new information into long-term memories.

Histamine (his′tuh-mēn) A chemical messenger (neurotransmitter or paracrine); causes vasodilation and increased capillary permeability; in stomach causes acid secretion.

Histology (his-tol′o-je) Branch of anatomy dealing with the microscopic structure of tissues.

HIV (human immunodeficiency virus) Virus that destroys helper T cells, thus depressing adaptive immunity; symptomatic AIDS gradually appears when lymph nodes can no longer contain the virus.

Holocrine glands (hol′o-krin) Glands that accumulate their secretions within their cells; secretions are discharged only upon rupture and death of the cell.

Homeostasis (ho″me-o-sta′sis) A state of body equilibrium or stable internal environment of the body.

Homologous (ho-mol′ŏ-gus) Parts or organs corresponding in structure but not necessarily in function.

Homozygous (ho-mo-zi′gus) Having identical genes at one or more loci.

Hormones Steroidal or amino acid–based molecules released to the blood that act as chemical messengers to regulate specific body functions.

Humoral immunity (hu′mer-ul) Immunity conferred by antibodies present in blood plasma and other body fluids.

Huntington's disease Hereditary disorder leading to degeneration of the basal nuclei and the cerebral cortex.

Hyaline cartilage (hi′ah-lin) The most abundant cartilage type in the body; provides firm support with some pliability.

Hydrochloric acid (HCl) (hi″dro-klor′ik) Acid that aids protein digestion in the stomach; produced by parietal cells.

Hydrogen bond Weak bond in which a hydrogen atom forms a bridge between two electron-hungry atoms. An important intramolecular bond.

Hydrogen ion (H⁺) A hydrogen atom minus its electron and therefore carrying a positive charge (i.e., a proton).

Hydrolysis (hi′drah′lă-sis) Process in which water is used to split a substance into smaller particles.

Hydrophilic (hi″dro-fil′ik) Refers to molecules, or portions of molecules, that interact with water and charged particles.

Hydrophobic (hi″dro-fo′bik) Refers to molecules, or portions of molecules, that interact only with nonpolar molecules.

Hydrostatic pressure (hi″dro-stă′tic) Pressure of fluid in a system.

Hydroxyl ion (OH⁻) (hi-drok′sil) An ion liberated when a hydroxide (a common inorganic base) is dissolved in water.

Hyperalgesia Pain amplification.

Hypercapnia (hi″per-kap′ne-ah) High carbon dioxide levels in the blood.

Hyperemia An increase in blood flow into a tissue or organ; congested with blood.

Hyperglycemic (hi″per-gli-se′mik) Term used to describe hormones such as glucagon that elevate blood glucose level.

Hyperopia (hi″per-o′pe-ah) A condition in which visual images are routinely focused behind rather than on the retina; commonly known as farsightedness.

Hyperplasia (hi″per-pla′ze-ah) Accelerated growth, e.g., in anemia, the bone marrow produces red blood cells at a faster rate.

Hyperpnea (hi″perp-ne′ah) An increase in ventilation in response to metabolic need (e.g., during exercise).

Hyperpolarization An increase in membrane potential in which the membrane becomes more negative than resting membrane potential.

Hypersensitivity Overzealous immune response to an otherwise harmless antigen.

Hypertension (hi″per-ten′shun) High blood pressure.

Hypertonic (hi″per-ton′ik) Excessive, above normal, tone or tension.

Hypertonic solution A solution that has a higher concentration of nonpenetrating solutes than the reference cell; having greater osmotic pressure than the reference solution (blood plasma or interstitial fluid).

Hypertrophy (hi-per′trah-fe) Increase in size of a tissue or organ independent of the body's general growth.

Hyperventilation An increase in the depth and rate of breathing that is in excess of the body's need for removal of carbon dioxide.

Hypocapnia Low carbon dioxide levels in the blood.

Hypodermis (superficial fascia) Subcutaneous tissue just deep to the skin; consists of adipose plus some areolar connective tissue.

Hypoglycemic (hi″po-gli-se′mik) Term used to describe hormones such as insulin that decrease blood glucose level.

Hyponatremia Abnormally low concentrations of sodium ions in extracellular fluid.

Hypoproteinemia (hi″po-pro″te-ĭ-ne′me-ah) A condition of unusually low levels of plasma proteins causing a reduction in colloid osmotic pressure; results in tissue edema.

Hypotension Low blood pressure.

Hypothalamic-hypophyseal tract (hi″po-thah-lam′ik hi″po-fiz′-e-al) Nerve bundles that run through the infundibulum and connect the posterior pituitary to the hypothalamus.

Hypothalamus (hi″po-thal′ah-mus) Region of the diencephalon forming the floor of the third ventricle of the brain.

Hypotonic (hi″po-ton′ik) Below normal tone or tension.

Hypotonic solution A solution that is more dilute (containing fewer nonpenetrating solutes) than the reference cell. Cells placed in hypotonic solutions plump up rapidly as water rushes into them.

Hypoventilation A decrease in the depth and rate of breathing; characterized by an increase in blood carbon dioxide.

Hypovolemic shock (hi″po-vo-le′mik) Most common form of shock; results from extreme blood loss.

Hypoxia (hi-pok′se-ah) Condition in which inadequate oxygen is available to tissues.

Ileocecal valve (il″e-o-se′kal) Site where the small intestine joins the large intestine.

Ileum (il′e-um) Terminal part of the small intestine; between the jejunum and the cecum of the large intestine.

Immune system A functional system whose components attack foreign substances or prevent their entry into the body.

Immunity (im″ūn′ĭ-te) Ability of the body to resist many agents (both living and nonliving) that can cause disease; resistance to disease.

Immunocompetence Ability of the body's immune cells to recognize (by binding) specific antigens; reflects the presence of plasma membrane–bound receptors.

Immunodeficiency Any congenital or acquired condition causing a deficiency in the production or function of immune cells or certain molecules (complement, antibodies, etc.) required for normal immunity.

In vitro (in ve′tro) In a test tube, glass, or artificial environment.

In vivo (in ve′vo) In the living body.

Incompetent valve Valve which does not close properly.

Incontinence Inability to control micturition or defecation voluntarily.

Infarct (in′farkt) Region of dead, deteriorating tissue resulting from a lack of blood supply.

Infectious mononucleosis Highly contagious viral disease; marked by excessive agranulocytes.

Inferior (caudal) Pertaining to a position toward the lower or tail end of the long axis of the body.

Inferior vena cava Vein that returns blood from body areas below the diaphragm.

Inflammation (in″flah-ma′shun) An innate (nonspecific) defensive response of the body to tissue injury; includes dilation of blood vessels and an increase in vessel permeability; indicated by redness, heat, swelling, and pain.

Infundibulum (in″fun-dib′u-lum) (1) A stalk of tissue that connects the pituitary gland to the hypothalamus; (2) the distal end of the uterine (fallopian) tube.

Inguinal (ing′wĭ-nal) Pertaining to the groin region.

Inhibitory postsynaptic potential (IPSP) A graded potential in a postsynaptic neuron that inhibits action potential generation; usually hyperpolarizing.

Inner cell mass Accumulation of cells in the blastocyst from which the embryo develops.

Innervation (in″er-va′shun) Supply of nerves to a body part.

Inorganic compound Chemical substances that do not contain carbon, including water, salts, and many acids and bases.

Insertion Movable attachment of a muscle.

Insula Lobe of the cerebral cortex that is buried in the lateral sulcus beneath portions of the parietal, frontal, and temporal lobes.

Insulin A hormone that enhances the carrier-mediated diffusion of glucose into tissue cells, thus lowering blood glucose levels.

Insulin resistance State in which a greater than normal amount of insulin is required to maintain normal glucose blood levels.

Integration The process by which the nervous system processes and interprets sensory input and makes decisions about what should be done at each moment.

Integumentary system (in-teg″u-men′tar-e) Skin and its derivatives; provides the external protective covering of the body.

Intercalated discs (in-ter′kah-la″ted) Specialized connections between myocardial cells containing gap junctions and desmosomes.

Interferons (IFNs) (in-ter-fēr′ons) Proteins released from virus-infected (and other) cells that protect uninfected cells from viral takeover. Also inhibit some cancers.

Internal capsule Band of projection fibers that runs between the basal nuclei and the thalamus.

Internal respiration Exchange of gases between blood and tissue fluid and between tissue fluid and cells.

Interneuron (association neuron) Nerve cell located between motor and sensory neurons that shuttles signals through CNS pathways where integration occurs.

Interoceptor (in″ter-o-sep′tor) Sensory receptor in the viscera that is sensitive to changes and stimuli within the body's internal environment; also called visceroceptor.

Interphase One of two major periods in the cell life cycle; includes the period from cell formation to cell division.

Interstitial endocrine cells Cells located in the loose connective tissue surrounding the seminiferous tubules; they produce androgens (most importantly testosterone), which are secreted into the surrounding interstitial fluid.

Interstitial fluid (IF) (in″ter-stish′al) Fluid between the cells.

Interstitial lamellae Incomplete lamellae that lie between intact osteons, filling the gaps between forming osteons, or representing the remnants of an osteon that has been cut through by bone remodeling.

Intervertebral discs (in″ter-ver′teh-brul) Discs of fibrocartilage between vertebrae.

Intracapsular ligament Ligament located within and separate from the articular capsule of a synovial joint.

Intracellular fluid (ICF) (in″trah-sel′u-ler) Fluid within a cell.

Intrinsic factor Substance produced by the stomach that is required for vitamin B_{12} absorption.

Intron Noncoding segment or portion of DNA that ranges from 60 to 100,000 nucleotides long.

Involuntary muscle Muscle that cannot ordinarily be controlled voluntarily (e.g., smooth and cardiac muscle).

Involuntary nervous system The autonomic nervous system.

Ion (ī′on) Atom or molecule with a positive or negative electric charge.

Ionic bond (ī-ah′nik) Chemical bond formed by electron transfer between atoms.

Ipsilateral (ip″sih-lă′ter-ul) Situated on the same side.

Ischemia (is-ke′me-ah) Local decrease in blood supply.

Isograft Tissue graft donated by an identical twin.

Isomer (i′so-mer) One of two or more substances that has the same molecular formula but with its atoms arranged differently.

Isometric contraction (i″so-mĕ′trik) Contraction in which the muscle does not shorten (the load is too heavy) but its internal tension increases.

Isotonic contraction (i″so-tah′nik) Contraction in which muscle tension remains constant at a given load, and the muscle shortens.

Isotonic solution A solution with a concentration of nonpenetrating solutes equal to that found in the reference cell.

Isotopes (i′so-tōps) Different atomic forms of the same element, which vary only in the number of neutrons they contain; the heavier species tend to be radioactive.

Jejunum (jĕ-joo′num) The part of the small intestine between the duodenum and the ileum.

Joint (articulation) The junction of two or more bones.

Joint kinesthetic receptor (kin″es-thet′ik) Receptor that provides information on joint position and motion.

Juxtaglomerular complex (JGC) (juks″tah-glo-mer′u-lar) Cells of the distal part of the ascending limb of the nephron loop and afferent arteriole located close to the glomerulus; involved in blood pressure regulation (via release of the hormone renin) and autoregulation of GFR.

Karyotype (kar′e-o-tīp) The diploid chromosomal complement, typically shown as homologous chromosome pairs arranged from longest to shortest (X and Y are arranged by size rather than paired).

Keratin (ker′ah-tin) Fibrous protein found in the epidermis, hair, and nails that makes those structures hard and water resistant; precursor is keratohyaline.

Ketones (ketone bodies) (ke′tōnz) Fatty acid metabolites; strong organic acids.

Ketosis (kē-tō′sis) Excess levels of ketone bodies in blood. Called keto-acidosis if blood pH is low.

Killer T cell *See* Cytotoxic T cell.

Kilocalories (kcal) *See* Calorie.

Kinetic energy (ki-net′ik) The energy of motion or movement, e.g., the constant movement of atoms, or the push given to a swinging door that sets it into motion.

Krebs cycle Aerobic metabolic pathway occurring within mitochondria, in which food metabolites are oxidized and CO_2 is liberated, and coenzymes are reduced. Also called the citric acid cycle.

Labia (la′be-ah) Lips; singular: labium.

Labor Collective term for the series of events that expel the fetus from the uterus.

Labyrinth (lab′ĭ-rinth″) Bony cavities and membranes of the inner ear.

Lacrimal (lak′ri-mal) Pertaining to tears.

Lactation (lak-ta′shun) Production and secretion of milk.

Lacteal (lak′te-al) Special lymphatic capillaries of the small intestine that take up lipids.

Lactic acid (lak′tik) Product of anaerobic metabolism, especially in muscle.

Lacuna (lah-ku′nah) A small space, cavity, or depression; lacunae in bone or cartilage are occupied by cells.

Lamella (lah-mel′ah) A layer, such as of bone matrix in an osteon of compact bone.

Lamina (lam′ĭ-nah) (1) A thin layer or flat plate; (2) the portion of a vertebra between the transverse process and the spinous process.

Large intestine Portion of the digestive tract extending from the ileocecal valve to the anus; includes the cecum, appendix, colon, rectum, and anal canal.

Larynx (lar′ingks) Cartilaginous organ located between the trachea and the pharynx; voice box.

Latent period Period of time between stimulation and the onset of muscle contraction.

Lateral Away from the midline of the body.

Leptin Hormone released by fat cells that signals satiety.

Leukemia Refers to a group of cancerous conditions of white blood cells.

Leukocytes (loo′ko-sīts) White blood cells; formed elements involved in body protection that take part in inflammatory and immune responses.

Leukocytosis An increase in the number of leukocytes (white blood cells); usually the result of a microbiological attack on the body.

Leukopenia (loo″ko-pe′ne-ah) Abnormally low white blood cell count.

Leukopoiesis The production of white blood cells.

Lever system Consists of a lever (bone), effort (muscle action), resistance (weight of object to be moved), and fulcrum (joint).

Ligament (lig′ah-ment) Band of regular fibrous tissue that connects bones.

Ligands Signaling chemicals that bind specifically to membrane receptors.

Limbic system (lim′bik) Functional brain system involved in emotional response and memory formation.

Lipid (lih′pid) Organic compound formed of carbon, hydrogen, and oxygen; examples are fats and cholesterol.

Lipolysis (lĭ-pol′ĭ-sis) The breakdown of stored fats into glycerol and fatty acids.

Liver Lobed accessory organ that overlies the stomach; produces bile to help digest fat, and serves other metabolic and regulatory functions.

Lumbar (lum′bar) Portion of the back between the thorax and the pelvis.

Lumbar vertebrae The five vertebrae of the lumbar region of the vertebral column, commonly called the small of the back.

Lumen (loo′min) Cavity inside a tube, blood vessel, or hollow organ.

Luteinizing hormone (LH) (lu′te-in-īz″ing) Anterior pituitary hormone that aids maturation of cells in the ovary and triggers ovulation in females. In males, causes the interstitial endocrine cells of the testis to produce testosterone.

Lymph (limf) Protein-containing fluid transported by lymphatic vessels.

Lymph node Small lymphoid organ that filters lymph; contains macrophages and lymphocytes.

Lymphatic system (lim-fat′ik) System consisting of lymphatic vessels, lymph nodes, and lymph; drains excess tissue fluid from the extracellular space. The nodes provide sites for immune surveillance.

Lymphatics General term used to designate the lymphatic vessels that collect and transport lymph.

Lymphocyte Agranular white blood cell that arises from bone marrow and becomes functionally mature in the lymphoid organs of the body.

Lysosomes (li′so-sōmz) Organelles that originate from the Golgi apparatus and contain strong digestive enzymes.

Lysozyme (li′so-zīm) Enzyme in sweat, saliva, and tears that is capable of destroying certain kinds of bacteria.

Macromolecules Large, complex molecules containing from 100 to over 10,000 subunits.

Macrophage (mak′ro-fāj″) Protective cell type common in connective tissue, lymphoid tissue, and many body organs; phagocytizes tissue cells, bacteria, and other foreign debris; presents antigens to T cells in the immune response.

Macula (mak′u-lah) (1) Receptor for linear acceleration, deceleration, and gravity, located within the vestibule of the inner ear; (2) a colored area or spot.

Malignant (muh-lig′nent) Life threatening; pertains to neoplasms that spread and lead to death, such as cancer.

Malignant melanoma (mel″ah-no′mah) Cancer of the melanocytes; can begin wherever there is pigment.

Mammary glands (mam′mer-e) Milk-producing glands of the breast.

Mandible (man′dĭ-bl) Lower jawbone; U shaped, largest bone of the face.

Mass number Sum of the number of protons and neutrons in the nucleus of an atom.

Mast cells Immune cells that function to detect foreign substances in the tissue spaces and initiate local inflammatory responses against them; typically found clustered deep to an epithelium or along blood vessels.

Mastication (mas″tĭ-ka′shun) Chewing.

Meatus (me-a′tus) External opening of a canal.

Mechanical advantage (power lever) Condition that occurs when the load is close to the fulcrum and the effort is applied far from the fulcrum; allows a small effort exerted over a relatively large distance to move a large load over a small distance.

Mechanical disadvantage (speed lever) Condition that occurs when the load is far from the fulcrum and the effort is applied near the fulcrum; the effort applied must be greater than the load to be moved.

Mechanical energy The energy directly involved in moving matter; e.g., in bicycle riding, the legs provide the mechanical energy that moves the pedals.

Mechanoreceptor (meh″kĕ-no-re-sep′tor) Receptor sensitive to mechanical pressure such as touch, sound, or exerted by muscle contraction.

Medial (me′de-ahl) Toward the midline of the body.

Median (midsagittal) plane Specific sagittal plane that lies exactly in the midline.

Mediastinum (me″de-ah-sti′num) The medial cavity of the thorax containing the heart, great vessels, and trachea.

Medulla (mĕ-dul′ah) Central portion of certain organs.

Medulla oblongata (mĕ-dul′ah ob″long-gah′tah) Inferiormost part of the brain stem.

Medullary cavity Central cavity of a long bone. Contains yellow or red (bone) marrow.

Meiosis (mi-o′sis) Nuclear division process that reduces the chromosomal number by half and results in the formation of four haploid (*n*) cells; occurs only in certain reproductive organs.

Melanin (mel′ah-nin) Dark pigment formed by cells called melanocytes; imparts color to skin and hair.

Melatonin (mel″ah-to′nin) A hormone secreted by the pineal gland; secretion peaks at night and helps set sleep-wake cycles; also a powerful antioxidant.

Membrane potential Voltage across the plasma membrane.

Membrane receptors A large, diverse group of integral proteins and glycoproteins that serve as binding sites for signaling molecules.

Memory cells Members of T cell and B cell clones that provide for immunological memory.

Menarche (mĕ-nar′ke) Establishment of menstrual function; the first menstrual period.

Meninges (mĕ-nin′jēz) Protective coverings of the central nervous system; from the most external to the most internal, the dura mater, arachnoid mater, and pia mater.

Meningitis (mĕ-nin-ji′tis) Inflammation of the meninges.

Menopause Period of life when, prompted by hormonal changes, ovulation and menstruation cease.

Menstruation (men″stroo-a′shun) The periodic, cyclic discharge of blood, secretions, tissue, and mucus from the mature female uterus in the absence of pregnancy.

Merocrine glands (mer′o-krin) Glands that produce secretions intermittently; secretions do not accumulate in the gland.

Mesencephalon (mes″en-sef′ah-lon) One of the three primary vesicles of the developing brain; becomes the midbrain.

Mesenchyme (meh′zin-kīm) Common embryonic tissue from which all connective tissues arise.

Mesenteries (mes″en-ter′ēz) Double-layered extensions of the peritoneum that support most organs in the abdominal cavity.

Mesoderm (mez′o-derm) Primary germ layer that forms the skeleton and muscles of the body.

Mesothelium (mez″o-the′le-um) The epithelium found in serous membranes lining the ventral body cavity and covering its organs.

Messenger RNA (mRNA) Long nucleotide strands that reflect the exact nucleotide sequences of the genetically active DNA and carry the DNA's message.

Metabolic rate (mĕt″ah-bol′ik) Energy expended by the body per unit time.

Metabolic water (water of oxidation) Water produced from cellular metabolism (about 10% of our body's water).

Metabolism (mĕ-tab′o-lizm) Sum total of the chemical reactions occurring in the body cells.

Metaphase Second stage of mitosis.

Metastasis (mĕ-tas′tah-sis) The spread of cancer from one body part or organ into another not directly connected to it.

Metencephalon (afterbrain) A secondary brain vesicle; anterior portion of the rhombencephalon of the developing brain; becomes the pons and the cerebellum.

MHC (major histocompatibility complex) proteins Molecules on the outer surface of the plasma membrane of all cells; help the immune system distinguish self from nonself. T cells recognize antigens only when combined with these proteins.

Microfilaments (mi″kro-fil′ah-ments) Thin strands of the contractile protein actin.

Microglial cells (mi-kro′gle-al) A type of CNS supporting cell; can transform into phagocytes in areas of neural damage or inflammation.

Microtubules (mi″kro-tu′būlz) One of three types of rods in the cytoskeleton of a cell; hollow tubes made of spherical protein that determine the cell shape as well as the distribution of cellular organelles.

Microvilli (mi″kro-vil′i) Tiny projections on the free surfaces of some epithelial cells; increase surface area for absorption.

Micturition (mik″tu-rish′un) Urination, or voiding; emptying the bladder.

Midbrain (mesencephalon) Region of the brain stem between the diencephalon and the pons.

Midsagittal (median) plane Specific sagittal plane that lies exactly in the midline.

Milliequivalents per liter (mEq/L) The units used to measure electrolyte concentrations of body fluids; a measure of the number of electrical charges in 1 liter of solution.

Mineralocorticoid (min″er-al″ō-kor′tih-koyd) Steroid hormone of the adrenal cortex that regulates Na^+ and K^+ metabolism and fluid balance.

Minerals Inorganic chemical compounds found in nature; salts.

Mitochondria (mi″to-kon′dre-ah) Cytoplasmic organelles responsible for ATP generation for cellular activities.

Mitosis Process during which the chromosomes are redistributed to two daughter nuclei; nuclear division. Consists of prophase, metaphase, anaphase, and telophase.

Mitotic (M) phase One of two major periods in the cell life cycle; involves the division of the nucleus (mitosis) and the division of the cytoplasm (cytokinesis).

Mitral (bicuspid) valve (mi′tral) The left atrioventricular valve.

Mixed nerves Nerves containing the processes of motor and sensory neurons; their impulses travel to and from the central nervous system.

Molar (mo′lar) (1) A solution concentration determined by mass of solute—1 liter of solution contains an amount of solute equal to its molecular weight in grams. (2) Broad back teeth that grind and crush.

Molarity (mo-lar′ĭ-te) A way to express the concentration of a solution; moles per liter of solution.

Mole (mōl) A mole of any element or compound is equal to its atomic weight or its molecular weight (sum of atomic weights) measured in grams.

Molecule Particle consisting of two or more atoms joined together by chemical bonds.

Monoclonal antibodies (mon″o-klo′nal) Pure preparations of identical antibodies that exhibit specificity for a single antigen.

Monocyte (mon′o-sīt) Large single-nucleus white blood cell; agranular leukocyte.

Monosaccharide (mon″o-sak′ah-rīd) Literally, one sugar; building block of carbohydrates; e.g., glucose.

Morula (mor′u-lah) The mulberry-like solid mass of blastomeres resulting from cleavage in the early conceptus.

Motor areas Functional areas in the cerebral cortex that control voluntary motor functions.

Motor (efferent) nerves Nerves that carry impulses leaving the brain and spinal cord, and destined for effectors.

Motor unit A motor neuron and all the muscle cells it stimulates.

Mucous membranes (mucosae) Membranes that form the linings of body cavities open to the exterior (digestive, respiratory, urinary, and reproductive tracts).

Mucus (myoo′kus) A sticky, thick fluid secreted by mucous glands and mucous membranes; keeps the free surface of membranes moist.

Multinucleate cell (mul″tĭ-nu′kle-āt) Cell with more than one nucleus, e.g., skeletal muscle cells, osteoclasts.

Multiple sclerosis (MS) Demyelinating disorder of the CNS; causes hardened patches (sclerosis) in the brain and spinal cord.

Multipolar neurons Neurons with three or more processes; most common neuron type in the CNS.

Muscarinic receptors (mus″kah-rin′ik) Acetylcholine-binding receptors of the autonomic nervous system's target organs; named for activation by the mushroom poison muscarine.

Muscle fiber A muscle cell.

Muscle spindle Encapsulated receptor found in skeletal muscle that is sensitive to stretch.

Muscle tension The force exerted by a contracting muscle on some object.

Muscle tone Low levels of contractile activity in relaxed muscle; keeps the muscle healthy and ready to act.

Muscle twitch The response of a muscle to a single brief threshold stimulus.

Muscular dystrophy A group of inherited muscle-destroying diseases.

Muscular system The organ system consisting of the skeletal muscles of the body and their connective tissue attachments.

Myelencephalon (spinal brain) A secondary brain vesicle; lower part of the developing hindbrain, especially the medulla oblongata.

Myelin sheath (mi′ĕ-lin) Fatty insulating sheath that surrounds all but the smallest nerve fibers.

Myoblasts Embryonic mesoderm cells from which all muscle fibers develop.

Myocardial infarction (MI) (mi″o-kar′de-al in-fark′shun) Condition characterized by dead tissue areas in the myocardium; caused by interruption of blood supply to the area. Commonly called heart attack.

Myocardium (mi″o-kar′de-um) Layer of the heart wall composed of cardiac muscle.

Myofibril (mi″o-fi′bril) Rodlike bundle of contractile filaments (myofilaments) found in muscle fibers (cells).

Myofilament (mi″o-fil′ah-ment) Filament that constitutes myofibrils. Of two types: actin and myosin.

Myoglobin (mi″o-glo′bin) Oxygen-binding pigment in muscle.

Myogram A graphic recording of mechanical contractile activity produced by an apparatus that measures muscle contraction.

Myometrium (mi″o-me′tre-um) Thick uterine musculature.

Myopia (mi-o′pe-ah) A condition in which visual images are focused in front of rather than on the retina; nearsightedness.

Myosin (mi′o-sin) One of the principal contractile proteins found in muscle.

Myxedema (mik″sĕ-de′mah) Condition resulting from underactive thyroid gland.

Nares (na′rez) Nostrils.

Natural killer (NK) cell Defensive cell (a type of lymphocyte) that can kill cancer cells and virus-infected body cells before the adaptive immune system is activated.

Necrosis (nĕ-kro′sis) Death or disintegration of a cell or tissues caused by disease or injury.

Negative feedback mechanisms The most common homeostatic control mechanism. The net effect is that the output of the system shuts off the original stimulus or reduces its intensity.

Neonatal period The four-week period immediately after birth.

Neoplasm (ne′o-plazm) An abnormal mass of proliferating cells. Benign neoplasms remain localized; malignant neoplasms are cancers, which can spread to other organs.

Nephron (nef′ron) Structural and functional unit of the kidney; consists of the renal corpuscle and renal tubule.

Nerve A bundle of axons in the peripheral nervous system.

Nerve fiber Axon of a neuron.

Nerve growth factor (NGF) Protein that promotes survival and development of neurons; secreted by their target cells and many other cell types.

Nerve impulse A self-propagating wave of depolarization; also called an action potential.

Nerve plexuses Interlacing nerve networks that occur in the cervical, brachial, lumbar, and sacral regions and primarily serve the limbs.

Nervous system Fast-acting control system that triggers muscle contraction or gland secretion.

Neural tube Fetal structure that gives rise to the brain, spinal cord, and associated neural structures; formed from ectoderm by day 23 of embryonic development.

Neuroglia (nu-rog'le-ah) Nonexcitable cells of neural tissue that support, protect, and insulate the neurons; glial cells.

Neurohypophysis (nu″ro-hi-pof'ĭ-sis) Posterior pituitary plus infundibulum; portion of the pituitary gland derived from the brain.

Neuromuscular junction Region where a motor neuron comes into close contact with a skeletal muscle cell.

Neuron (nerve cell) (nu'ron) Cell of the nervous system specialized to generate and transmit electrical signals (action potentials and graded potentials).

Neuron cell body The biosynthetic center of a neuron; also called the perikaryon, or soma.

Neuronal pools Functional groups of neurons that process and integrate information.

Neuropeptides (nu″ro-pep'tīds) A class of neurotransmitters including beta endorphins and enkephalins (which act as euphorics and reduce perception of pain) and gut-brain peptides.

Neurotransmitter Chemical messenger released by neurons that may, upon binding to receptors of neurons or effector cells, stimulate or inhibit those neurons or effector cells.

Neutral fats Consist of fatty acid chains and glycerol; also called triglycerides or triacylglycerols. Commonly known as oils when liquid.

Neutralization reaction Displacement reaction in which mixing an acid and a base forms water and a salt.

Neutron (nu'tron) Uncharged subatomic particle; found in the atomic nucleus.

Neutrophil (nu'tro-fil) Most abundant type of white blood cell.

Nicotinic receptors (nik″o-tin'ik) Acetylcholine-binding receptors of all autonomic ganglionic neurons and skeletal muscle neuromuscular junctions; named for activation by nicotine.

Nitric oxide (NO) A gaseous chemical messenger; diverse functions include participation in memory formation in the brain, and causing vasodilation throughout the body.

Nociceptor (no″se-sep'tor) Receptor sensitive to potentially damaging stimuli that result in pain.

Nondisjunction Failure of sister chromatids to separate during mitosis or failure of homologous pairs to separate during meiosis; results in abnormal numbers of chromosomes in the resulting daughter cells.

Nonmyelinated fibers (non-mi'ĕ-lĭ-nāt″ed) Axons lacking a myelin sheath and therefore conducting impulses quite slowly.

Nonpolar molecules Electrically balanced molecules.

Nonvolatile (fixed) acid Acid generated by cellular metabolism that must be eliminated by the kidneys.

Norepinephrine (NE) (nor″ep-ĭ-nef'rin) A catecholamine neurotransmitter and adrenal medullary hormone, associated with sympathetic nervous system activation.

Nuclear envelope The double membrane barrier of a cell nucleus.

Nucleic acid (nu-kle'ik) Class of organic molecules that includes DNA and RNA.

Nucleoli (nu-kle'o-li) Dense spherical bodies in the cell nucleus involved with ribosomal RNA (rRNA) synthesis and ribosomal subunit assembly.

Nucleosome (nu'kle-o-sōm) Fundamental unit of chromatin; consists of a strand of DNA wound around a cluster of eight histone proteins.

Nucleotide (nu'kle-o-tīd) Building block of nucleic acids; consists of a sugar, a nitrogen-containing base, and a phosphate group.

Nucleus (nu'kle-is) (1) Control center of a cell; contains genetic material; (2) clusters of nerve cell bodies in the CNS.

Nutrients Chemical substances taken in via the diet that are used for energy and cell building.

Oblique section A cut made diagonally between the horizontal and vertical plane of the body or an organ.

Occlusion (ah-kloo'zhun) Closure or obstruction.

Octet rule (rule of eights) (ok-tet') The tendency of atoms to interact in such a way that they have eight electrons in their valence shell.

Olfaction (ol-fak'shun) Smell.

Oligodendrocyte (ol″ĭ-go-den'dro-sīt) A type of CNS supporting cell that composes myelin sheaths.

Oocyte (o'o-sīt) Immature female gamete.

Oogenesis (o″o-jen'ĕ-sis) Process of ovum (female gamete) formation.

Ophthalmic (of-thal'mik) Pertaining to the eye.

Optic (op'tik) Pertaining to the eye or vision.

Optic chiasma (op'tik ki-az'muh) The partial crossover of fibers of the optic nerves.

Organ A part of the body formed of two or more tissues and adapted to carry out a specific function; e.g., the stomach.

Organ system A group of organs that work together to perform a vital body function; e.g., the nervous system.

Organelles (or″gah-nelz') Small cellular structures (ribosomes, mitochondria, and others) that perform specific metabolic functions for the cell as a whole.

Organic compound Any compound composed of atoms (some of which are carbon) held together by covalent (shared electron) bonds.

Organic Pertaining to carbon-containing molecules, such as proteins, fats, and carbohydrates.

Organism The living animal (or plant), which represents the sum total of all its organ systems working together to maintain life.

Origin Attachment of a muscle that remains relatively fixed during muscular contraction.

Osmolality The number of solute particles dissolved in 1 kilogram (1000 g) of water; reflects the solution's ability to cause osmosis.

Osmolarity (oz″mo-lar'ĭ-te) The number of solute particles present in 1 liter of a solution.

Osmoreceptor (oz″mo-re-sep'tor) Structure sensitive to osmotic pressure or concentration of a solution.

Osmosis (oz-mo'sis) Diffusion of a solvent through a membrane from a dilute solution into a more concentrated one.

Osmotic pressure A measure of the tendency of water to move into a more concentrated solution.

Ossicles *See* Auditory ossicles.

Ossification (os″ĭ-fi-ka'shun) *See* Osteogenesis.

Osteoblasts (os'te-o-blasts) Bone-forming cells.

Osteoclasts (os'te-o-klasts) Large cells that resorb or break down bone matrix.

Osteocyte (os'te-o-sīt) Mature bone cell.

Osteogenesis (os″te-o-jen'e-sis) The process of bone formation; also called ossification.

Osteoid (os'te-oid) Unmineralized bone matrix.

Osteomalacia (os"te-o-mah-la'she-ah) Disorder in which bones are inadequately mineralized; soft bones.

Osteon (os'te-on) System of interconnecting canals in the microscopic structure of adult compact bone; unit of bone; also called Haversian system.

Osteoporosis (os"te-o-po-ro'sis) Decreased density and strength of bone resulting from a gradual decrease in rate of bone formation.

Ovarian cycle (o-vayr'e-an) Monthly cycle of follicle development, ovulation, and corpus luteum formation in an ovary.

Ovary (o'var-e) Female reproductive organ in which ova (eggs) are produced; female gonad.

Ovulation (ov"u-la'shun) Ejection of an immature egg (oocyte) from the ovary.

Ovum (o'vum) Female gamete; egg.

Oxidases Enzymes that catalyze the transfer of oxygen in oxidation-reduction reactions.

Oxidation (oks'ĭ-da"shun) Process of substances combining with oxygen or the removal of hydrogen.

Oxidation-reduction (redox) reaction A reaction that couples the oxidation (loss of electrons) of one substance with the reduction (gain of electrons) of another substance.

Oxidative phosphorylation (ok'sĭ-da"tiv fos"for-ĭ-la'shun) Process of ATP synthesis during which an inorganic phosphate group is attached to ADP; occurs via the electron transport chain within the mitochondria.

Oxyhemoglobin (ok"sĭ-he"mo-glo'bin) Oxygen-bound form of hemoglobin.

Oxytocin (ok"sĭ-to'sin) Hormone synthesized in the hypothalamus and secreted by the posterior pituitary; stimulates contraction of the uterus during childbirth and the ejection of milk during nursing.

Paget's disease (paj'ets) Disorder characterized by excessive bone breakdown and abnormal bone formation.

Palate (pal'at) Roof of the mouth.

Pancreas (pan'kre-us) Gland located behind the stomach, between the spleen and the duodenum; produces both endocrine and exocrine secretions.

Pancreatic juice (pan"kre-at'ik) Bicarbonate-rich secretion of the pancreas containing enzymes for digestion of all food categories.

Papilla (pah-pil'ah) Small, nipple-like projection; e.g., dermal papillae are projections of dermal tissue into the epidermis.

Paracrine (par'ah-krin) A chemical messenger that acts locally within the same tissue and is rapidly destroyed. Examples are prostaglandins and nitric oxide.

Parasagittal planes All sagittal planes offset from the midline.

Parasympathetic division The division of the autonomic nervous system that oversees digestion, elimination, and glandular function; the resting and digesting subdivision.

Parasympathetic tone Normal (background) level of parasympathetic output; sustains normal gastrointestinal and urinary tract activity, lowers heart rate.

Parathyroid glands (par"ah-thi'roid) Small endocrine glands located on the posterior aspect of the thyroid gland.

Parathyroid hormone (PTH) Hormone released by the parathyroid glands that regulates blood calcium level.

Parietal (pah-ri'ĕ-tal) Pertaining to the walls of a cavity.

Parietal serosa The part of the double-layered membrane that lines the walls of the ventral body cavity.

Parkinson's disease Neurodegenerative disorder of the basal nuclei due to insufficient secretion of the neurotransmitter dopamine; symptoms include tremor and rigid movement.

Partial pressure The pressure exerted by a single component of a mixture of gases.

Parturition (par"tu-rish'un) Culmination of pregnancy; giving birth.

Passive immunity Short-lived immunity resulting from the introduction of "borrowed antibodies" obtained from an immune animal or human donor; immunological memory is not established.

Passive (transport) processes Membrane transport processes that do not require cellular energy (ATP), e.g., diffusion, which is driven by kinetic energy.

Pathogen (path'o-jen) Disease-causing organism.

Pectoral (pek'tor-al) Pertaining to the chest.

Pectoral (shoulder) girdle Bones that attach the upper limbs to the axial skeleton; includes the clavicle and scapula.

Pedigree Traces a particular genetic trait through several generations and helps predict the genotype of future offspring.

Pelvic girdle (hip girdle) Consists of the paired coxal bones and sacrum that attach the lower limbs to the axial skeleton.

Pelvis (pel'vis) (1) Basin-shaped bony structure composed of the pelvic girdle, sacrum, and coccyx; (2) funnel-shaped tube within the kidney continuous with the ureter.

Penis (pe'nis) Male organ of copulation and urination.

Pepsin Enzyme capable of digesting proteins in an acid pH.

Peptide bond (pep'tīd) Bond joining the amine group of one amino acid to the acid carboxyl group of a second amino acid with the loss of a water molecule.

Perforating canals Canals that run at right angles to the long axis of the bone, connecting the vascular and nerve supplies of the periosteum to those of the central canals and medullary cavity; also called Volkmann's canals.

Pericardium (per"ĭ-kar'de-um) Double-layered sac enclosing the heart and forming its superficial layer; has fibrous and serous layers.

Perichondrium (per"ĭ-kon'dre-um) Fibrous, connective-tissue membrane covering the external surface of cartilaginous structures.

Perimysium (per"ĭ-mis'e-um) Connective tissue that bundles muscle fibers into fascicles.

Perineum (per"ĭ-ne'um) That region of the body spanning the region between the ischial tuberosities and extending from the pubic arch to the coccyx.

Periosteum (per"e-os'te-um) Double-layered connective tissue that covers and nourishes the bone.

Peripheral congestion Condition caused by failure of the right side of the heart; results in edema in the extremities.

Peripheral nervous system (PNS) Portion of the nervous system consisting of nerves and ganglia that lie outside of the brain and spinal cord.

Peripheral resistance A measure of the amount of friction encountered by blood as it flows through the blood vessels.

Peristalsis (per"ĭ-stal'sis) Progressive, wavelike contractions that move foodstuffs through the alimentary tube organs (or that move other substances through other hollow body organs).

Peritoneum (per"ĭ-to-ne'um) Serous membrane lining the interior of the abdominal cavity and covering the surfaces of abdominal organs.

Peritonitis (per"ĭ-to-ni'tis) Inflammation of the peritoneum.

Permeability That property of membranes that permits passage of molecules and ions.

Peroxisomes (pĕ-roks'ĭ-sōmz) Membranous sacs in cytoplasm containing powerful oxidase enzymes that use molecular oxygen to detoxify harmful or toxic substances, such as free radicals.

Peyer's patches (pi'erz) Lymphoid organs located in the small intestine; also called aggregated lymphoid nodules.

pH unit (pe-āch) The measure of the relative acidity or alkalinity of a solution.

Phagocytosis (fag"o-si-to'sis) Engulfing of foreign solids by (phagocytic) cells.

Phagosome (fag'o-sōm) Vesicle formed as a result of phagocytosis.

Pharmacological dose A drug dose that is dramatically higher than normal levels of that substance (e.g., hormone) in the body.

Pharyngotympanic tube Tube that connects the middle ear and the pharynx. Also called auditory tube, eustachian tube.

Pharynx (fayr'inks) Muscular tube extending from the region posterior to the nasal cavities to the esophagus.

Phenotype (fe'no-tīp) Observable expression of the genotype.

Phospholipid (fos"fo-lip'id) Modified lipid, contains phosphorus.

Phosphorylation A chemical reaction in which a phosphate molecule is added to a molecule; for example, phosphorylation of ADP yields ATP.

Photoreceptor (fo"to-re-sep'tor) Specialized receptor cells that respond to light energy; rods and cones.

Physiological acidosis (as"ĭ-do'sis) Arterial pH lower than 7.35 resulting from any cause.

Physiological dose A drug dose that replicates normal levels of that substance (e.g., hormone) in the body. (*Compare with* Pharmacological dose.)

Physiology (fiz"e-ol'o-je) Study of the function of living organisms.

Pineal gland (body) (pin'e-al) A hormone-secreting part of the diencephalon of the brain thought to be involved in setting the biological clock and influencing reproductive function.

Pinocytosis (pe"no-si-to'sis) Engulfing of extracellular fluid by cells.

Pituitary gland (pĭ-tu'ih-tayr"e) Neuroendocrine gland located beneath the brain that serves a variety of functions including regulation of gonads, thyroid, adrenal cortex, lactation, and water balance.

Placenta (plah-sen'tah) Temporary organ formed from both fetal and maternal tissues that provides nutrients and oxygen to the developing fetus, carries away fetal metabolic wastes, and produces the hormones of pregnancy.

Plasma (plaz'mah) The nonliving fluid component of blood within which formed elements and various solutes are suspended and circulated.

Plasma cells Members of a B cell clone; effector B cells specialized to produce and release antibodies.

Plasma membrane Membrane, composed of phospholipids, cholesterol, and proteins, that encloses cell contents; outer limiting cell membrane.

Platelet (plāt'let) Cell fragment found in blood; involved in clotting.

Pleurae (ploo're) Two layers of serous membrane that line the thoracic cavity and cover the external surface of the lung.

Pleural cavity (ploo'ral) A potential space between the two layers of pleura; contains a thin film of serous fluid.

Plexus (plek'sus) A network of converging and diverging nerve fibers, blood vessels, or lymphatics.

Polar molecules Nonsymmetrical molecules that contain electrically unbalanced atoms.

Polarized State of a plasma membrane of an unstimulated neuron or muscle cell in which the inside of the cell is relatively negative in comparison to the outside; the resting state.

Polycythemia (pol"e-si-the'me-ah) An abnormally high number of erythrocytes.

Polymer A substance of high molecular weight with long, chainlike molecules consisting of many similar (repeated) units.

Polypeptide (pol"e-pep'tīd) A chain of amino acids.

Polyps Benign mucosal tumors.

Polysaccharide (pol"e-sak'ah-rīd) Literally, many sugars, a polymer of linked monosaccharides; e.g., starch, glycogen.

Pons (1) Any bridgelike structure or part; (2) the part of the brain stem connecting the medulla with the midbrain, providing linkage between upper and lower levels of the central nervous system.

Pore The surface opening of the duct of a sweat gland.

Positive feedback mechanisms Feedback that tends to cause the level of a variable to change in the same direction as an initial change.

Posterior pituitary Neural part of pituitary gland; part of the neurohypophysis.

Postganglionic neuron (post"gan"gle-ah'nik) Autonomic motor neuron that has its cell body in a peripheral ganglion and projects its axon to an effector.

Potential energy Stored or inactive energy.

Preganglionic neuron Autonomic motor neuron that has its cell body in the central nervous system and projects its axon to a peripheral ganglion.

Presbyopia (pres"be-o'pe-ah) A condition that results in the loss of near focusing ability; typical onset is around age 40.

Pressure gradient Difference in pressure (hydrostatic or osmotic) that drives movement of fluid.

Primary active transport A type of active transport in which the energy needed to drive the transport process is provided directly by hydrolysis of ATP.

Prime mover Muscle that bears the major responsibility for effecting a particular movement; an agonist.

Process (1) Prominence or projection; (2) series of actions for a specific purpose.

Progesterone (pro-jes'ter-ōn) Hormone partly responsible for preparing the uterus for the fertilized ovum.

Prolactin (PRL) (pro-lak'tin) Adenohypophyseal hormone that stimulates the breasts to produce milk.

Pronation (pro-na'shun) Inward rotation of the forearm causing the radius to cross diagonally over the ulna—palms face posteriorly.

Prophase The first stage of mitosis, consisting of coiling of the chromosomes accompanied by migration of the two daughter centrioles toward the poles of the cell, and nuclear membrane breakdown.

Proprioceptor (pro"pre-o-sep'tor) Receptor located in a joint, muscle, or tendon; concerned with locomotion, posture, and muscle tone.

Prostaglandin (pros"tah-glan'din) A lipid-based chemical messenger synthesized by most tissue cells; acts locally as a paracrine.

Prostate Accessory reproductive gland; produces one-third of semen volume, including fluids that activate sperm.

Protein (pro'tēn) Organic compound composed of carbon, oxygen, hydrogen, and nitrogen; types include enzymes, structural components; 10–30% of cell mass.

Prothrombin time Diagnostic test to determine status of hemostasis system.

Proton (pro′ton) Subatomic particle that bears a positive charge; located in the atomic nucleus.

Proton acceptor A substance that takes up hydrogen ions in detectable amounts. Commonly referred to as a base.

Proton donor A substance that releases hydrogen ions in detectable amounts; an acid.

Proximal (prok′si-mul) Toward the attached end of a limb or the origin of a structure.

Pseudounipolar neuron (soo″do-u″nĭ-po′lar) Another term for unipolar neuron.

Puberty Period of life when reproductive maturity is achieved.

Pulmonary (pul′muh-nayr-e) Pertaining to the lungs.

Pulmonary arteries Vessels that deliver blood to the lungs to be oxygenated.

Pulmonary circuit System of blood vessels that serves gas exchange in the lungs; i.e., pulmonary arteries, capillaries, and veins.

Pulmonary edema (ĕ-de′muh) Leakage of fluid into the air sacs and tissue of the lungs.

Pulmonary veins Vessels that deliver freshly oxygenated blood from the respiratory zones of the lungs to the heart.

Pulmonary ventilation Breathing; consists of inspiration and expiration.

Pulse Rhythmic expansion and recoil of arteries resulting from heart contraction; can be felt from outside the body.

Pupil Opening in the center of the iris through which light enters the eye.

Pus Fluid product of inflammation composed of white blood cells, the debris of dead cells, and a thin fluid.

Pyloric sphincter (pi-lor′ik sfink′ter) Valve of the distal end of the stomach that controls food entry into the duodenum.

Pyramidal (corticospinal) tracts Major motor pathways concerned with voluntary movement; descend from pyramidal cells in the frontal lobes of each cerebral hemisphere.

Pyruvic acid An intermediate compound in the metabolism of carbohydrates.

Radioactivity The process of spontaneous decay seen in some of the heavier isotopes, during which particles or energy is emitted from the atomic nucleus; results in the atom becoming more stable.

Radioisotope (ra″de-o-i′so-tōp) Isotope that exhibits radioactive behavior.

Ramus (ra′mus) Branch of a nerve, artery, vein, or bone.

Rapid eye movement (REM) sleep Stage of sleep in which rapid eye movements, an alert EEG pattern, and dreaming occur.

Reactant A substance taking part in a chemical reaction.

Receptor (re-sep′tor) (1) A cell or nerve ending of a sensory neuron specialized to respond to particular types of stimuli; (2) protein that binds specifically with other molecules, e.g., neurotransmitters, hormones, paracrines, antigens.

Receptor-mediated endocytosis The type of endocytosis in which engulfed particles attach to receptors before endocytosis occurs.

Receptor potential A graded potential that occurs at a sensory receptor membrane.

Recessive traits A trait due to a particular allele that does not manifest itself in the presence of other alleles that generate traits dominant to it; must be present in double dose to be expressed.

Reduction Chemical reaction in which electrons and energy are gained by a molecule (often accompanied by gain of hydrogen ions) or oxygen is lost.

Referred pain Pain felt at a site other than the area of origin.

Reflex Automatic reaction to stimuli.

Refraction The bending of a light ray when it meets a different surface at an oblique rather than right angle.

Regeneration Replacement of destroyed tissue with the same kind of tissue.

Regulatory T cells (T$_{Reg}$ cells) Population of T cells (usually expressing CD4) that suppress the immune response.

Relative refractory period Follows the absolute refractory period; interval when a threshold for action potential stimulation is markedly elevated.

Renal (re′nal) Pertaining to the kidney.

Renal autoregulation Process the kidney uses to maintain a nearly constant glomerular filtration rate despite fluctuations in systemic blood pressure.

Renal clearance The volume of plasma from which a particular substance is completely removed in a given time, usually 1 minute; provides information about renal function.

Renin (re′nin) Enzyme released by the kidneys that raises blood pressure by initiating the renin-angiotensin-aldosterone mechanism.

Rennin Stomach-secreted enzyme that acts on milk protein; not produced in adults.

Repolarization Movement of the membrane potential to the initial resting (polarized) state.

Reproductive system Organ system that functions to produce offspring.

Resistance exercise High-intensity exercise in which the muscles are pitted against high resistance or immovable forces and, as a result, muscle cells increase in size.

Respiration The processes involved in supplying the body with oxygen and disposing of carbon dioxide.

Respiratory system Organ system that carries out gas exchange; includes the nose, pharynx, larynx, trachea, bronchi, lungs.

Resting membrane potential The voltage that exists across the plasma membrane during the resting state of an excitable cell; ranges from -90 to -20 millivolts depending on cell type.

Reticular activating system (RAS) (re-tik′u-lar) Diffuse brain stem neural network that receives a wide variety of sensory input and maintains wakefulness of the cerebral cortex.

Reticular connective tissue Connective tissue with a fine network of reticular fibers that form the internal supporting framework of lymphoid organs.

Reticular formation Functional system that spans the brain stem; involved in regulating sensory input to the cerebral cortex, cortical arousal, and control of motor behavior.

Reticular lamina A layer of extracellular material containing a fine network of collagen protein fibers; together with the basal lamina it is a major component of the basement membrane.

Reticulocyte (rĕ-tik′u-lo-sīt) Immature erythrocyte.

Retina (ret′ĭ-nah) Inner layer of the eyeball; contains photoreceptors (rods, cones).

Rhombencephalon (hindbrain) (romb″en-sef′ah-lon) Caudal portion of the developing brain; constricts to form the metencephalon and myelencephalon; includes the pons, cerebellum, and medulla oblongata.

Ribosomal RNA (rRNA) A constituent of ribosome; exists within the ribosomes of cytoplasm and assists in protein synthesis.

Ribosomes (ri′bo-sōmz) Cytoplasmic organelles at which proteins are synthesized.

RNA (ribonucleic acid) (ri'bo-nu-kle'ik) Nucleic acid that contains ribose and the bases A, G, C, and U. Carries out DNA's instructions for protein synthesis.

Rods One of the two types of photosensitive cells in the retina.

Rotation The turning of a bone around its own long axis.

Rugae (ru'ge) Elevations or ridges, as in stomach mucosa.

Rule of nines Method of computing the extent of burns by dividing the body into a number of areas, each accounting for 9% (or a multiple thereof) of the total body area.

S (synthetic) phase The part of the interphase period of the cell cycle in which DNA replicates itself, ensuring that the two future cells will receive identical copies of genetic material.

Sagittal plane (saj'ĭ-tal) A longitudinal (vertical) plane that divides the body or any of its parts into right and left portions.

Saliva Secretion of the salivary glands; cleanses and moistens the mouth and begins chemical digestion of starchy foods.

Saltatory conduction Transmission of an action potential along a my-elinated fiber in which the nerve impulse appears to leap from gap to gap.

Sarcolemma The plasma membrane of a muscle fiber.

Sarcomere (sar'ko-mēr) The smallest contractile unit of muscle; extends from one Z disc to the next.

Sarcoplasm The nonfibrillar cytoplasm of a muscle fiber.

Sarcoplasmic reticulum (SR) (sar"ko-plaz'mik rĕ-tik'u-lum) Specialized endoplasmic reticulum of muscle cells.

Schwann cell A type of supporting cell in the PNS; forms myelin sheaths and is vital to peripheral nerve fiber regeneration.

Sclera (skle'rah) White opaque portion of the fibrous layer of the eyeball.

Scrotum (skro'tum) External sac enclosing the testes.

Sebaceous glands (oil glands) (se-ba'shus) Epidermal glands that produce an oily secretion called sebum.

Sebum (se'bum) Oily secretion of sebaceous glands.

Second-degree burn A burn in which the epidermis and the upper region of the dermis are damaged.

Second messenger Intracellular molecule generated by the binding of a chemical (hormone or neurotransmitter) to a receptor protein; mediates intracellular responses to the chemical messenger.

Secondary sex characteristics Anatomical features, not directly involved in the reproductive process, that develop under the influence of sex hormones, e.g., male or female pattern of muscle development, bone growth, body hair distribution.

Secretion (se-kre'shun) (1) The passage of material formed by a cell to its exterior; (2) cell product that is transported to the exterior of a cell.

Secretory vesicles (granules) Vesicles that migrate to the plasma membrane of a cell and discharge their contents from the cell by exocytosis.

Section A cut through the body (or an organ) that is made along a particular plane; a thin slice of tissue prepared for microscopic study.

Segregation During meiosis, the distribution of the members of the allele pair to different gametes.

Selectively permeable membrane A membrane that allows certain substances to pass while restricting the movement of others; also called differentially permeable membrane.

Semen (se'men) Fluid mixture containing sperm and secretions of the male accessory reproductive glands.

Semilunar valves (sĕ"me-loo'ner) Valves that prevent blood return to the ventricles after contraction; aortic and pulmonary valves.

Seminiferous tubules (sem"ĭ-nif'er-us) Highly convoluted tubes within the testes; form sperm.

Sense organs Localized collections of many types of cells working together to accomplish a specific receptive process.

Sensory (afferent) nerves Nerves that contain processes of sensory neurons and carry impulses to the central nervous system.

Sensory areas Functional areas of the cerebral cortex that provide for conscious awareness of sensation.

Sensory receptor A cell or part of a cell (e.g., receptive endings of sensory neurons) specialized to respond to a stimulus.

Serosa (serous membrane) (se-ro'sah) The moist membrane found in closed ventral body cavities.

Serous fluid (sēr'us) Clear, watery fluid secreted by cells of a serous membrane.

Serum (sēr'um) Amber-colored fluid that exudes from clotted blood as the clot shrinks; plasma without clotting factors.

Sesamoid bones (ses'ah-moid) Short bones embedded in tendons, variable in size and number, many of which influence the action of muscles; largest is the patella (kneecap).

Severe combined immunodeficiency syndromes (SCIDs) Congenital conditions resulting in little or no protection against disease-causing organisms of any type.

Sex chromosomes The chromosomes, X and Y, that determine genetic sex (XX = female; XY = male); the 23rd pair of chromosomes.

Sex-linked inheritance Inherited traits determined by genes on the sex chromosomes, e.g., X-linked genes are passed from mother to son, Y-linked genes are passed from father to son.

Sexually transmitted infection (STI) Any infectious disease spread through sexual contact.

Signal sequence A short peptide segment present in a protein being synthesized that causes the associated ribosome to attach to the membrane of rough ER.

Simple diffusion The unassisted transport across a plasma membrane of a lipid-soluble or very small particle.

Sinoatrial (SA) node (si"no-a'tre-al) Specialized myocardial cells in the wall of the right atrium; pacemaker of the heart.

Sinus (si'nus) (1) Mucous-membrane-lined, air-filled cavity in certain cranial bones; (2) dilated channel for the passage of blood or lymph.

Skeletal muscle Muscle composed of cylindrical multinucleate cells with obvious striations; the muscle(s) attached to the body's skeleton; voluntary muscle.

Skeletal system System of protection and support composed primarily of bone and cartilage.

Skull Bony protective encasement of the brain and the organs of hearing and equilibrium; includes cranial and facial bones.

Small intestine Convoluted tube extending from the pyloric sphincter to the ileocecal valve where it joins the large intestine; the site where digestion is completed and virtually all absorption occurs.

Smooth muscle Spindle-shaped cells with one centrally located nucleus and no externally visible striations (bands). Found mainly in the walls of hollow organs.

Sodium-potassium (Na$^+$-K$^+$) pump A primary active transport system that simultaneously drives Na$^+$ out of the cell against a steep gradient and pumps K$^+$ back in. Also called Na$^+$-K$^+$ ATPase.

Sol-gel transformation Reversible change of a colloid from a fluid (sol) to a more solid (gel) state.

Solute (sol′yoot) The substance that is dissolved in a solution.

Solute pump Enzyme-like protein carrier that mediates active transport of solutes such as amino acids and ions uphill against their concentration gradients.

Somatic nervous system (so-mă′tik) Division of the peripheral nervous system that provides the motor innervation of skeletal muscles; also called the voluntary nervous system.

Somatic reflexes Reflexes that activate skeletal muscle.

Somatosensory system That part of the sensory system dealing with reception in the body wall and limbs; receives inputs from exteroceptors, proprioceptors, and interoceptors.

Somite (so′mīt) A mesodermal segment of the body of an embryo that contributes to the formation of skeletal muscles, vertebrae, and dermis of skin.

Spatial discrimination The ability of neurons to identify the site or pattern of stimulation.

Special senses The senses of taste, smell, vision, hearing, and equilibrium.

Specific gravity Term used to compare the weight of a substance to the weight of an equal volume of distilled water.

Sperm (spermatozoon) Male gamete.

Spermatogenesis (sper″mah-to-jen′ĕ-sis) The process of sperm (male gamete) formation; involves meiosis.

Sphincter (sfink′ter) A circular muscle surrounding an opening; acts as a valve.

Spinal cord The bundle of nervous tissue that runs from the brain to the first to third lumbar vertebrae and provides a conduction pathway to and from the brain.

Spinal nerves The 31 nerve pairs that arise from the spinal cord.

Splanchnic circulation (splangk′nik) The blood vessels serving the digestive system.

Spleen Largest lymphoid organ; provides for lymphocyte proliferation, immune surveillance and response, and blood-cleansing functions.

Spongy bone Internal layer of skeletal bone. Also called cancellous bone.

Sprain Ligaments reinforcing a joint are stretched or torn.

Static equilibrium Sense of head position in space with respect to gravity.

Stenosis (stĕ-no′sis) Abnormal constriction or narrowing.

Steroids (stĕ′roidz) Group of chemical substances including certain hormones and cholesterol; they are fat soluble and contain little oxygen.

Stimulus (stim′u-lus) An excitant or irritant; a change in the environment that evokes a response.

Stomach Temporary reservoir in the gastrointestinal tract where chemical breakdown of proteins begins and food is converted into chyme.

Stressor Any stimulus that directly or indirectly causes the hypothalamus to initiate stress-reducing responses, such as the fight-or-flight response.

Stroke See Cerebrovascular accident.

Stroke volume (SV) Amount of blood pumped out of a ventricle during one contraction.

Stroma (stro′mah) The basic internal structural framework of an organ.

Structural (fibrous) proteins Consist of extended, strandlike polypeptide chains forming a strong, ropelike structure that is linear, insoluble in water, and very stable; e.g., collagen.

Subcutaneous (sub″kyu-ta′ne-us) Beneath the skin.

Subendocardial conducting network Modified ventricular muscle fibers of the conduction system of the heart. Also called Purkinje fibers.

Substrate A reactant on which an enzyme acts to cause a chemical action to proceed.

Sudoriferous gland (su″do-rif′er-us) Epidermal gland that produces sweat.

Sulcus (sul′kus) A furrow on the brain, less deep than a fissure.

Summation Accumulation of effects, especially those of muscular, sensory, or mental stimuli.

Superficial Located close to or on the body surface.

Superior Toward the head or upper body regions.

Superior vena cava Vein that returns blood from body regions superior to the diaphragm.

Supination (soo″pĭ-na′shun) The outward rotation of the forearm causing palms to face anteriorly.

Surfactant (ser-fak′tant) Secretion produced by certain cells of the alveoli that reduces the surface tension of water molecules, thus preventing the collapse of the alveoli after each expiration.

Suspension Heterogeneous mixtures with large, often visible solutes that tend to settle out.

Suture (soo′cher) An immovable fibrous joint; with one exception, all bones of the skull are united by sutures.

Sweat gland See Sudoriferous gland.

Sympathetic division The division of the autonomic nervous system that prepares the body for activity or to cope with some stressor (danger, excitement, etc.); the fight, fright, and flight subdivision.

Sympathetic (vasomotor) tone State of partial vasoconstriction of the blood vessels maintained by sympathetic fibers.

Symphysis (sim′fih-sis) A joint in which the bones are connected by fibrocartilage.

Synapse (sin′aps) Functional junction or point of close contact between two neurons or between a neuron and an effector cell.

Synapsis (sĭ-nap′sis) Pairing of homologous chromosomes during the first meiotic division.

Synaptic cleft (sĭ-nap′tik) Fluid-filled space at a synapse.

Synaptic delay Time required for a signal to cross a synapse between two neurons.

Synaptic vesicles Small membranous sacs containing neurotransmitter.

Synarthrosis (sin″ar-thro′sis) Immovable joint.

Synchondrosis (sin″kon-dro′sis) A joint in which the bones are united by hyaline cartilage.

Syndesmosis (sin″des-mo′sis) A joint in which the bones are united by a ligament or a sheet of fibrous tissue.

Synergist (sin′er-jist) (1) Muscle that aids the action of a prime mover by effecting the same movement or by stabilizing joints across which the prime mover acts, preventing undesirable movements. (2) Hormone that amplifies the effect of another hormone at a target cell.

Synostosis (sin″os-to′sis) A completely ossified joint; a fused joint.

Synovial fluid Fluid secreted by the synovial membrane; lubricates joint surfaces and nourishes articular cartilages.

Synovial joint Freely movable joint exhibiting a joint cavity; also called a diarthrosis.

Synthesis (combination) reaction A chemical reaction in which larger, more complex atoms or molecules are formed from simpler ones.

Systemic (sis-tem′ik) Pertaining to the whole body.

Systemic circuit System of blood vessels that serves gas exchange in the body tissues.

Systole (sis′to-le) Period when either the ventricles or the atria are contracting.

Systolic pressure (sis-tah′lik) Pressure exerted by blood on the blood vessel walls during ventricular contractions.

T cells Lymphocytes that mediate cellular immunity; include helper, cytotoxic, regulatory, and memory cells. Also called T lymphocytes.

T tubule (transverse tubule) Extension of the muscle cell plasma membrane (sarcolemma) that protrudes deeply into the muscle cell.

Tachycardia (tak″e-kar′de-ah) A heart rate over 100 beats per minute.

Taste buds Sensory receptor organs that house gustatory cells, which respond to dissolved food chemicals.

Telencephalon (endbrain) (tel″en-seh′fuh-lon) Anterior subdivision of the primary forebrain that develops into olfactory lobes, cerebral cortex, and basal nuclei.

Telophase The final phase of mitosis; begins when migration of chromosomes to the poles of the cell has been completed and ends with the formation of two daughter nuclei.

Tendon (ten′dun) Cord of dense fibrous tissue attaching muscle to bone.

Tendon organ Proprioceptor located in tendon; monitors muscle tension to prevent tearing and help smooth onset and termination of muscle contraction.

Tendonitis Inflammation of tendon sheaths, typically caused by overuse.

Terminal branches Branching ends of an axon that allow it to form many axon terminals; terminal arborization.

Testis (tes′tis) Male primary reproductive organ that produces sperm; male gonad.

Testosterone (tes-tos′tĕ-rōn) Male sex hormone produced by the testes; during puberty promotes virilization, and is necessary for normal sperm production.

Tetanus (tet′ah-nus) (1) A smooth, sustained muscle contraction resulting from high-frequency stimulation; (2) an infectious disease caused by an anaerobic bacterium.

Thalamus (thal′ah-mus) A mass of gray matter in the diencephalon of the brain.

Thermogenesis (ther″mo-jen′ĕ-sis) Heat production.

Thermoreceptor (ther″mo-re-sep′ter) Receptor sensitive to temperature changes.

Third-degree burn A burn that involves the entire thickness of the skin; also called a full-thickness burn. Usually requires skin grafting.

Thoracic cage (bony thorax) Bones and costal cartilages that form the framework of the thorax; includes sternum, ribs, and thoracic vertebrae.

Thoracic duct Large duct that receives lymph drained from the entire lower body, the left upper extremity, and the left side of the head and thorax.

Thoracic vertebrae The 12 vertebrae that are in the middle part of the vertebral column and articulate with the ribs.

Thorax (tho′raks) That portion of the body trunk above the diaphragm and below the neck.

Threshold stimulus Weakest stimulus capable of producing a response in an excitable tissue.

Thrombin (throm′bin) Enzyme that induces clotting by converting fibrinogen to fibrin.

Thrombocyte (throm′bo-sīt) Platelet; cell fragment that participates in blood coagulation.

Thrombocytopenia (throm″bo-si″to-pe′ne-ah) A reduction in the number of platelets circulating in the blood.

Thrombus (throm′bus) A clot that develops and persists in an unbroken blood vessel.

Thymine (T) (thi′mēn) Single-ring base (a pyrimidine) in DNA.

Thymus (thi′mus) Lymphoid organ and endocrine gland active in immune response; site of maturation of T lymphocytes.

Thyroid gland (thi′roid) One of the largest of the body's endocrine glands; straddles the anterior trachea.

Thyroid hormone (TH) The major hormone secreted by thyroid follicles; stimulates enzymes concerned with glucose oxidation.

Thyroid-stimulating hormone (TSH) Anterior pituitary hormone that regulates secretion of thyroid hormones.

Thyroxine (T_4) (thi-rok′sin) Iodine-containing hormone secreted by the thyroid gland; accelerates cellular metabolic rate in most body tissues.

Tight junction Area where plasma membranes of adjacent cells are tightly bound together, forming an impermeable barrier.

Tissue A group of similar cells and their intercellular substance specialized to perform a specific function; primary tissue types of the body are epithelial, connective, muscle, and nervous tissue.

Tissue perfusion Blood flow through body tissues or organs.

Tonicity (to-nis′ĭ-te) A measure of the ability of a solution to cause a change in cell shape or tone by promoting osmotic flows of water.

Tonsils A ring of lymphoid tissue around the entrance to the pharynx. *See also* Adenoids.

Trabecula (trah-bek′u-lah) (1) Any of the fibrous bands extending from the capsule into the interior of an organ; (2) strut or thin plate of bone in spongy bone.

Trachea (tra′ke-ah) Windpipe; cartilage-reinforced tube extending from larynx to bronchi.

Tract A collection of axons in the central nervous system having the same origin, termination, and function.

Transcription One of the two major steps in the transfer of genetic code information from a DNA base sequence to the complementary base sequence of an mRNA molecule.

Transduction (trans-duk′shun) The conversion of the energy of a stimulus into an electrical event.

Transepithelial transport (trans-ep″ĭ-the′le-al) Movement of substances through, rather than between, adjacent epithelial cells connected by tight junctions, such as absorption of nutrients in the small intestine.

Transfer RNA (tRNA) Short-chain RNA molecules that transfer amino acids to the ribosome.

Transfusion reaction Agglutination and destruction of red blood cells following transfusion of incompatible blood.

Translation One of the two major steps in the transfer of genetic code information, in which the information carried by mRNA is decoded and used to assemble polypeptides.

Transverse (horizontal) plane A plane running from right to left, dividing the body or an organ into superior and inferior parts.

Tricuspid valve (tri-kus′pid) The right atrioventricular valve.

Triglycerides (tri-glis′er-īdz) Fats and oils composed of fatty acids and glycerol; are the body's most concentrated source of energy fuel; also known as neutral fats.

Triiodothyronine (T_3) (tri″i-o″do-thi′ro-nēn) Thyroid hormone; secretion and function similar to those of thyroxine (T_4).

Trophoblast (tro′fo-blast) Outer sphere of cells of the blastocyst.

Tropic hormone (tropin) (trōp′ik) A hormone that regulates the secretory action of another endocrine organ.

Trypsin Proteolytic enzyme secreted by the pancreas.

Tubular reabsorption The movement of filtrate components from the renal tubules into the blood.

Tubular secretion The movement of substances (such as drugs, urea, excess ions) from blood into filtrate.

Tumor An abnormal growth of cells; a swelling; may be cancerous.

Tunica (too′nĭ-kah) A covering or tissue coat; membrane layer.

Tympanic membrane (tim-pan′ik) Eardrum.

Ulcer (ul′ser) Lesion or erosion of the mucous membrane, such as gastric ulcer of stomach.

Umbilical cord (um-bĭ′lĭ-kul) Structure bearing arteries and veins connecting the placenta and the fetus.

Umbilicus (um-bĭ′lĭ-kus) Navel; marks site where umbilical cord was attached in fetal stage.

Unipolar neuron Neuron in which embryological fusion of the two processes leaves only one process extending from the cell body.

Uracil (U) (u′rah-sil) A smaller, single-ring base (a pyrimidine) found in RNA.

Urea (u-re′ah) Main nitrogen-containing waste excreted in urine.

Ureter (u-re′ter) Tube that carries urine from kidney to bladder.

Urethra (u-re′thrah) Canal through which urine passes from the bladder to outside the body.

Uric acid The nitrogenous waste product of nucleic acid metabolism; component of urine.

Urinary bladder A smooth, collapsible, muscular sac that stores urine temporarily.

Urinary system System primarily responsible for water, electrolyte, and acid-base balance and removal of nitrogenous wastes.

Uterine tube (u′ter-in) Tube through which the ovum is transported to the uterus. Also called fallopian tube.

Uterus (u′ter-us) Hollow, thick-walled organ that receives, retains, and nourishes fertilized egg; site where embryo/fetus develops.

Uvula (u′vu-lah) Tissue tag hanging from soft palate.

Vaccine Preparation that provides artificially acquired active immunity.

Vagina Thin-walled tube extending from the cervix to the body exterior; often called the birth canal.

Valence shell (va′lens) Outermost electron shell (energy level) of an atom that contains electrons.

Varicosities Knoblike swellings of certain autonomic axons containing mitochondria and synaptic vesicles.

Vas (vaz′) A duct; vessel.

Vasa recta (va′sah rek′tah) Capillary branches that supply nephron loops in the medulla region of the kidney.

Vascular Pertaining to blood vessels or richly supplied with blood vessels.

Vascular spasm Immediate response to blood vessel injury; results in constriction.

Vasoconstriction (vas″o-kon-strik′shun) Narrowing of blood vessels.

Vasodilation (vas″o-di-la′shun) Relaxation of the smooth muscles of the blood vessels, producing dilation.

Vasomotion (vas″o-mo′shun) Intermittent contraction or relaxation of the precapillary sphincters, resulting in a staggered blood flow when tissue needs are not extreme.

Vasomotor center (vas″o-mo′ter) Brain area concerned with regulation of blood vessel resistance.

Vasomotor fibers Sympathetic nerve fibers that cause the contraction of smooth muscle in the walls of blood vessels, thereby regulating blood vessel diameter.

Veins (vānz″) Blood vessels that return blood toward the heart from the circulation.

Ventral Pertaining to the front; anterior.

Ventricles (1) Paired, inferiorly located heart chambers that function as the major blood pumps; (2) cavities in the brain.

Venule (ven′ūl) A small vein.

Vertebral column (spine) (ver′tĕ-brul) Formed of a number of individual bones called vertebrae and two composite bones (sacrum and coccyx).

Vesicle (vĕ′sĭ-kul) A small liquid-filled sac or bladder.

Vesicular transport Transport of large particles and macromolecules into or out of a cell or between its compartments in membrane-bound sacs.

Vesicular follicle Mature ovarian follicle.

Vestibule An enlarged area at the beginning of a canal, i.e., inner ear, nose, larynx.

Villus (vil′us) One of the fingerlike projections of the small intestinal mucosa that tremendously increase its surface area for absorption.

Visceral (vis′er-al) Pertaining to an internal organ of the body or the inner part of a structure.

Visceral muscle Type of smooth muscle; its cells contract as a unit and rhythmically, are electrically coupled by gap junctions, and often exhibit spontaneous action potentials. Also called unitary smooth muscle.

Visceral organs (viscera) A group of internal organs housed in the ventral body cavity.

Visceral serosa (se-ro′sah) The part of the double-layered membrane that lines the outer surfaces of organs within the ventral body cavity.

Viscosity (vis′kos′ĭ-te) A measurement of thickness (stickiness) of a fluid.

Visual field The field of view seen when the head is still.

Vital capacity (VC) The volume of air that can be expelled from the lungs by forcible expiration after the deepest inspiration; total exchangeable air.

Vital signs Includes pulse, blood pressure, respiratory rate, and body temperature measurements.

Vitamins Organic compounds required by the body in minute amounts.

Vocal folds Mucosal folds that function in voice production (speech); also called the true vocal cords.

Volatile acid An acid that can be eliminated by the lungs; carbonic acid is converted to CO_2, which diffuses into the alveoli.

Volkmann's canals *See* Perforating canals.

Voluntary muscle Muscle under strict nervous control; skeletal muscle.

Voluntary nervous system The somatic nervous system.

Vulva (vul′vuh) Female external genitalia.

Wallerian degeneration (wal-er′ē-an) A process of disintegration of an axon that occurs when it is crushed or severed and cannot receive nutrients from the cell body.

White matter White substance of the central nervous system; myelinated nerve fibers.

Xenograft Tissue graft taken from another animal species.

Yolk sac (yōk) One of the extraembryonic membranes; involved in early blood cell formation.

Zygote (zi′gōt) Fertilized egg.

Photo and Illustration Credits

Photo Credits

Chapter 1
Chapter Opener: Blend Images/Alamy. 1.1: GoGo Images/Jupiter Images. 1.3: Pearson Science. 1.8.1: Jenny Thomas, Pearson Science. 1.8.2: Scott Camazine/Photo Researchers. 1.8.3: James Cavallini/Photo Researchers. 1.8.4: CNRI/Science Photo Library/Photo Researchers. 1.12a: Custom Medical Stock Photo, Inc. A Closer Look: a: Clinique Ste Catherine/CNRI/Science Photo Library/Photo Researchers. b: Zephyr/Photo Researchers. c: Willaim Klunk, Chet Mathis, University of Pittsburgh, PET Amyloid Imaging Group.

Chapter 2
Chapter Opener: Prisma, SuperStock. 2.4.1: Stockbyte/Getty Images. 2.4.2: Algecireño/Shutterstock. 2.4.3: Henry Hong – CSB, Imagineering © Pearson. 2.10b: Herman Eisenbeiss/Photo Researchers. 2.22c: Computer Graphics Laboratory, University of California, San Francisco.

Chapter 3
Chapter Opener: John Middlebrook/Cal Sport Media/Newscom. 3.9a-c: David M. Philips/Photo Researchers. 3.14b: Dr. Birgit H. Satir. 3.17b: Professors P. Motta & T. Naguro/SPL/Photo Researchers. 3.18b: CNR/Photo Researchers. 3.19b: P. Motta & T. Naguro/SPL/Photo Researchers. 3.21: Dr. Gopal Murti/Photo Researchers. 3.23a: Mary Osborn, Max Planck Institute. 3.23b: Frank Solomon and J. Dinsmore, Massachusetts Institute of Technology. 3.23c: Mark S. Ladinsky and J. Richard McIntosh, University of Colorado. 3.25b: Don W. Fawcett/Photo Researchers. 3.26.1: OMIKRON/Science Source/Photo Researchers. 3.26.2 and 3: W. L. Dentler/Biological Photo Service. 3.28: Don W. Fawcett/Photo Researchers. 3.29b.1: From L. Orci and A. Perrelet, *Freeze-Etch Histology*. (Heidelberg: Springer-Verlag, 1975) © 1975 Springer-Verlag. 3.29b.2: From A. C. Faberge, *Cell Tiss. Res.* 151 (1974):403. © 1974 Springer-Verlag. 3.29b.3: U. Aebi et al. *Nature* 323 (1996):560–564, Figure 1a. Used by permission. 3.30.1: Dr. Victoria E. Foe. 3.30.2: GF Bahr, Armed Forces Institute of Pathology. 3.33.1–6: Conly Rieder. 3.38b: Barbara Hamkalo.

Chapter 4
Chapter Opener: Fuse/Jupiter Images. 4.3a: William Karkow, Pearson Science. 4.3b, f: Allen Bell, University of New England; Pearson Science. 4.3c, d: Ed Reschke/Photolibrary. 4.3e: Nina Zanetti, Pearson Science. 4.4a: SPL/Photo Researchers, Inc. 4.8a, g:

PAL 3.0, Pearson Science. 4.8b, f, h: Nina Zanetti, Pearson Science. 4.8c: Allen Bell, University of New England; Pearson Science. 4.8d, e, k: Lisa Lee, Pearson Science. 4.8i, j: Allen Bell, University of New England; Pearson Science. 4.9a: PAL 3.0, Pearson Science. 4.9b: Ed Reschke/Photolibrary. 4.9c, 4.10: Biophoto Associates/Photo Researchers. A Closer Look: David Musher/Photo Researchers.

Chapter 5
Chapter Opener: Jupiter Images. 5.2a: Ed Reschke/Photolibrary. 5.3: Ed Reschke/Photolibrary. 5.4a: Clouds Hill Imaging/Photo Researchers. 5.4c: John Wilson White, Pearson Science. 5.5b: Manfred Kage/Photo Researchers. 5.5d: Manfred Kage/Photolibrary. 5.7: Lisa Lee, Pearson Science. 5.8a: Biophoto Associates/Photo Researchers. 5.8b: P. Marazzi/SPL/Photo Researchers. 5.8c: Zeva Oelbaum/Photolibrary. 5.10a: Scott Camazine/Photo Researchers. 5.10b: Dr. M.A. Ansary/Photo Researchers.

Chapter 6
Chapter Opener: Belinda Images/SuperStock. 6.3.1: Donald Gregory Clever. 6.3.2: Steve Gschmeissner/Photo Researchers. 6.7c.1: Andrew Syred/Photo Researchers. 6.7c.2: Ed Reschke/Photolibrary. 6.10: Lisa Lee, Pearson Science. 6.14a: PCN Photography/Alamy. 6.16: P. Motta, Department of Anatomy, University "La Sapienza," Rome/Science Photo Library/Photo Researchers. 6.17: Scott Camazine/Photo Researchers. Table 6.2.1: Lester Bergman/Corbis. Table 6.2.2: ISM/Centers for Disease Control and Prevention (CDC). Table 6.2.3: SIU/Photolibrary. Table 6.2.4: Frank Gaillard - Radiopaedia.org, Imagineering © Pearson. Table 6.2.5: William T. C. Yuh. Table 6.2.6: Charles Stewart.

Chapter 7
Chapter Opener: Exactostock/SuperStock. 7.5b, d: PAL 3.0, Pearson Science. 7.6b: PAL 3.0, Pearson Science. 7.7b: Michael Wiley - Univ. of Toronto, Imagineering © Pearson. 7.8: PAL 3.0, Pearson Science. 7.9a, b: PAL 3.0, Pearson Science. 7.10: Michael Wiley - Univ. of Toronto, Imagineering © Pearson. 7.11c: PAL 3.0, Pearson Science. 7.12a: PAL 3.0, Pearson Science. 7.17a: NMSB/Custom Medical Stock Photo. 7.17b: Nordic Photos/SuperStock. 7.17c: Steve Gorton/Dorling Kindersley. 7.18d: Neil Borden/Photo Researchers. 7.23b: Dissection by Shawn Miller, photography by Mark Nielsen and Alexa Doig. 7.24c: Pearson Science. 7.31c, d: Ralph T. Hutchings. 7.33c: PAL 3.0, Pearson Science. 7.33d: Michael Wiley - Univ. of Toronto, Imagineering © Pearson. 7.33e: Biophoto Associates/Science

Source/Photo Researchers. 7.35b: Elaine N. Marieb. 7.37: Center For Cranialfacial Anomalies, University of California, San Francisco. 7.38: Reik/age fotostock. Table 7.4.2-5: From *A Stereoscopic Atlas of Human Anatomy* by David L. Bassett.

Chapter 8
Chapter Opener: Imagesource/Photolibrary. 8.5a–f: John Wilson White, Pearson Science. 8.6a–f: John Wilson White, Pearson Science. 8.8f: PAL 3.0, Pearson Science. 8.10b: Mark Neilsen, University of Utah; Pearson Science. 8.10e: VideoSurgery/Photo Researchers. 8.11c: From *A Stereoscopic Atlas of Human Anatomy* by David L. Bassett. 8.12b: From *A Stereoscopic Atlas of Human Anatomy* by David L. Bassett. 8.14: Elaine Marieb. 8.15: SIU/Photolibrary. A Closer Look: 1: Lawrence Livermore National Laboratory/Photo Researchers. 2: Elaine N. Marieb.

Chapter 9
Chapter Opener: altrendo images/Jupiter Images. 9.1b: Lisa Lee, Pearson Science. 9.2a: Marian Rice. 9.4: John Heuser. 9.6.1: Don W. Fawcett/Photo Researchers. 9.6.2: Biophoto Associates/Photo Researchers. 9.13b: Eric Graves/Photo Researchers. A Closer Look: Corbis/SuperStock. Table 9.3.4: Eric Graves/Photo Researchers. Table 9.3.5: Marian Rice. Table 9.3.6: SPL/Photo Researchers.

Chapter 10
Chapter Opener: Aaron Packard/Jupiter Images. 10.7a: David Bassett. 10.9b: Creative Digital Visions, Pearson Science. 10.10c: Dissection by Shawn Miller, photography by Mark Nielsen and Alexa Doig. 10.11c: From *A Stereoscopic Atlas of Human Anatomy* by David L. Bassett. 10.14b: Dissection by Dr. Olga Malakhova and photography by Winston Charles Poulton of University of Florida College of Medicine, Gainesville/Pearson Science. 10.14d, e: Dissection by Shawn Miller, photography by Mark Nielsen and Alexa Doig. 10.15d: Dissection by Shawn Miller, photography by Mark Nielsen and Alexa Doig. 10.21b: David Bassett.

Chapter 11
Chapter Opener: Imagesource/Photlibrary. 11.4b: Manfred Kage/Photolibrary. 11.5b: Don W. Fawcett/ Photo Researchers. 11.16b: Oliver Meckes/Ottawa/Photo Researchers. 11.25: Tibor Harkany, Science Magazzine. A Closer Look: Brookhaven National Laboratory/Jupiter Images.

Chapter 12
Chapter Opener: Exactostock/SuperStock. 12.4a: From *A Stereoscopic Atlas of Human Anatomy*

by David L. Bassett. 12.4b: A. Glauberman/Photo Researchers. 12.5: Volker Steger/Photolibrary. 12.8a: Ralph T. Hutchings. 12.8b: From *A Stereoscopic Atlas of Human Anatomy* by David L. Bassett. 12.9b: PAL 3.0, Pearson Science. 12.10b: David Bassett. 12.12: PAL 3.0, Pearson Science. 12.15a: Ralph T. Hutchings. 12.15c: David L. Bassett. 12.18a: Hank Morgan/Photo Researchers. 12.23b: From *A Stereoscopic Atlas of Human Anatomy* by David L. Bassett. 12.25: Ansary/Custom Medical Stock Photo/Newscom. 12.26b, c, d: PAL 3.0, Pearson Science. 12.35: Biophoto Associates/Science Source/Photo Researchers.

Chapter 13
Chapter Opener: Dominique Douieb/Jupiter Images. 13.4: Thomas Deerinck, NCMIR/Photo Researchers. 13.10d: Dissection by Dr. Olga Malakhova and photography by Winston Charles Poulton of University of Florida College of Medicine, Gainesville/Pearson Science. 13.12c: Dissection by Dr. Olga Malakhova and photography by Winston Charles Poulton of University of Florida College of Medicine, Gainesville/Pearson Science. Table 13.2.8: William Thompson, Pearson Science.

Chapter 14
Chapter Opener: Paul Kennedy/SuperStock.

Chapter 15
Chapter Opener: agefotostock/SuperStock. 15.1a: Richard Tauber, Pearson Science. 15.4b: From *A Stereoscopic Atlas of Human Anatomy* by David L Bassett. 15.6c: Lisa Lee, Pearson Science. 15.7: Dr. Charles Klettke, Pearson Science. 15.9: SPL/Photo Researchers. 15.11: Keith Leighton/Alamy. 15.19b: Stephen Spector/Pearson Science. 15.22c: PAL 3.0, Pearson Science. 15.27d: P. Motta/Department of Anatomy/University "La Sapienza," Rome/Science Photo Library/Photo Researchers. 15.31: Science

Vol. 279 March 1998, p. 1870, Karen P. Steele. 15.35b: I. M. Hunter-Duvar, Department of Otolaryngology, The Hospital for Sick Children, Toronto.

Illustration Credits
All illustrations by Imagineering STA Media Services unless otherwise noted.

Chapter 1
1.3: Vincent Perez/Wendy Hiller Gee. 1.7: Imagineering STA Media Services/Precision Graphics.

Chapter 3
3.2, 3.3, 3.20, 3.27: Imagineering STA Media Services/Precision Graphics. 3.24: Campbell, Neil A., *Biology,* 4th Edition, © 1996, p. 128. Reprinted by permission of Pearson Education, Inc., Upper Saddle River, NJ. 3.37: Electronic Publishing Services, Inc./Imagineering STA Media Services.

Chapter 4
4.6: Matthews, Christopher K.; VanHolde, Kensal E.; Ahern, Kevin G., *Biochemistry,* 3rd Edition, © 2000. Adapted by permission of Pearson Education, Inc. Upper Saddle River, NJ.

Chapter 5
5.1, 5.2, 5.7: Electronic Publishing Services, Inc. System Connections: Vincent Perez/Wendy Hiller Gee.

Chapter 6
6.8: Imagineering STA Media Services/Precision Graphics. System Connections: Vincent Perez/Wendy Hiller Gee.

Chapter 8
8.7: Electronic Publishing Services, Inc./Imagineering STA Media Services.

Chapter 9
9.1, 9.2: Imagineering STA Media Services/Precision Graphics. 9.9, 9.25–9.27, 9.29: Electronic Publishing Services, Inc. System Connections: Vincent Perez/Wendy Hiller Gee.

Chapter 10
10.1: Electronic Publishing Services, Inc./Imagineering STA Media Services.

Chapter 11
11.2, 11.24: Electronic Publishing Services, Inc. 11.3, 11.5: Imagineering STA Media Services/Precision Graphics.

Chapter 12
12.1–12.3, 12.6, 12.7, 12.11, 12.13–12.17, 12.21, 12.22, 12.24, 12.28b, 12.29–12.33: Electronic Publishing Services, Inc.

Chapter 13
13.1, 13.4–13.6, 13.14, 13.15, 13.19, 13.20: Electronic Publishing Services, Inc. 13.16, 13.T02.6: Imagineering STA Media Services/Precision Graphics.

Chapter 14
14.1–14.4, 14.6–14.8: Electronic Publishing Services, Inc. System Connections: Vincent Perez/Wendy Hiller Gee.

Chapter 15
15.1–15.6, 15.8, 15.15, 15.16, 15.18, 15.20, 15.22, 15.23, 15.25–15.27, 15.30, 15.32–15.35: Electronic Publishing Services, Inc. 15.24: Electronic Publishing Services, Inc./Precision Graphics.

Index

NOTE: Page numbers in **boldface** indicate a definition. A *t* following a page number indicates tabular material, an *f* indicates an illustration, and a *b* indicates boxed material.

Word Roots, Prefixes, Suffixes, and Combining Forms

Prefixes and Combining Forms

a-, an- *absence, lack* acardia, lack of a heart; anaerobic, in the absence of oxygen

ab- *departing from, away from* abnormal, departing from normal

acou- *hearing* acoustics, the science of sound

ac-, acro- *extreme or extremity, peak* acrodermatitis, inflammation of the skin of the extremities

ad- *to, toward* adorbital, toward the orbit

aden-, adeno- *gland* adeniform, resembling a gland in shape

adren- *toward the kidney* adrenal gland, adjacent to the kidney

aero- *air* aerobic respiration, oxygen-requiring metabolism

af- *toward* afferent neurons, which carry impulses to the central nervous system

agon- *contest* agonistic and antagonistic muscles, which oppose each other

alb- *white* corpus albicans of the ovary, a white scar tissue

aliment- *nourish* alimentary canal, or digestive tract

allel- *of one another* alleles, alternative expressions of a gene

amphi- *on both sides, of both kinds* amphibian, an organism capable of living in water and on land

ana- *apart, up, again* anaphase of mitosis, when the chromosomes separate

anastomos- *come together* arteriovenous anastomosis, a connection between an artery and a vein

aneurysm *a widening* aortic aneurysm, a weak spot that causes enlargement of the blood vessel

angi- *vessel* angiitis, inflammation of a lymph vessel or blood vessel

angin- *choked* angina pectoris, a choked feeling in the chest due to dysfunction of the heart

ant-, anti- *opposed to, preventing, inhibiting* anticoagulant, a substance that prevents blood coagulation

ante- *preceding, before* antecubital, in front of the elbow

aort- *great artery* aorta

ap-, api- *tip, extremity* apex of the heart

append- *hang to* appendicular skeleton

aqua-, aque- *water* aqueous solutions

arbor *tree* arbor vitae of the cerebellum, the treelike pattern of white matter

areola- *open space* areolar connective tissue, a loose connective tissue

arrect- *upright* arrector pili muscles of the skin, which make the hairs stand erect

arthr-, arthro- *joint* arthropathy, any joint disease

artic- *joint* articular surfaces of bones, the points of connection

atri- *vestibule* atria, upper chambers of the heart

auscult- *listen* auscultatory method for measuring blood pressure

aut-, auto- *self* autogenous, self-generated

ax-, axi-, axo- *axis, axle* axial skeleton, axis of vertebral column

azyg- *unpaired* azygous vein, an unpaired vessel

baro- *pressure* baroreceptors for monitoring blood pressure

basal *base* basal lamina of epithelial basement membrane

bi- *two* bicuspid, having two cusps

bili- *bile* bilirubin, a bile pigment

bio- *life* biology, the study of life and living organisms

blast- *bud, germ* blastocyte, undifferentiated embryonic cell

brachi- *arm* brachial plexus of peripheral nervous system supplies the arm

brady- *slow* bradycardia, abnormally slow heart rate

brev- *short* fibularis brevis, a short leg muscle

broncho- *bronchus* bronchospasm, spasmodic contraction of bronchial muscle

bucco- *cheek* buccolabial, pertaining to the cheek and lip

calor- *heat* calories, a measure of energy

capill- *hair* blood and lymph capillaries

caput- *head* decapitate, remove the head

carcin- *cancer* carcinogen, a cancer-causing agent

cardi-, cardio- *heart* cardiotoxic, harmful to the heart

carneo- *flesh* trabeculae carneae, ridges of muscle in the ventricles of the heart

carot- *(1) carrot, (2) stupor* (1) carotene, an orange pigment, (2) carotid arteries in the neck, blockage of which causes fainting

cata- *down* catabolism, chemical breakdown

caud- *tail* caudal (directional term)

cec- *blind* cecum of large intestine, a blind-ended pouch

cele- *abdominal* celiac artery, in the abdomen

cephal- *head* cephalometer, an instrument for measuring the head

cerebro- *brain, especially the cerebrum* cerebrospinal, pertaining to the brain and spinal cord

cervic-, cervix *neck* cervix of the uterus

chiasm- *crossing* optic chiasma, where optic nerves cross

chole- *bile* cholesterol, cholecystokinin, a bile-secreting hormone

chondr- *cartilage* chondrogenic, giving rise to cartilage

chrom- *colored* chromosome, so named because they stain darkly

cili- *small hair* ciliated epithelium

circum- *around* circumnuclear, surrounding the nucleus

clavic- *key* clavicle, a "skeleton key"

co-, con- *together* concentric, common center, together in the center

coccy- *cuckoo* coccyx, which is beak-shaped

cochlea *snail shell* the cochlea of the inner ear, which is coiled like a snail shell

coel- *hollow* coelom, the ventral body cavity

commis- *united* gray commissure of the spinal cord connects the two columns of gray matter

concha *shell* nasal conchae, coiled shelves of bone in the nasal cavity

contra- *against, opposite* contraceptive, agent preventing conception

corn-, cornu- *horn* stratum corneum, outer layer of the skin composed of (horny) cells

corona *crown* coronal suture of the skull

corp- *body* corpse; corpus luteum, hormone-secreting body in the ovary

cort- *bark* cortex, the outer layer of the brain, kidney, adrenal glands, and lymph nodes

cost- *rib* intercostal, between the ribs

crani- *skull* craniotomy, a skull operation

crypt- *hidden* cryptomenorrhea, a condition in which menstrual symptoms are experienced but no external loss of blood occurs

cusp- *pointed* bicuspid, tricuspid valves of the heart

cutic- *skin* cuticle of the nail

cyan- *blue* cyanosis, blue color of the skin due to lack of oxygen

cyst- *sac, bladder* cystitis, inflammation of the urinary bladder

cyt- *cell* cytology, the study of cells

de- *undoing, reversal, loss, removal* deactivation, becoming inactive

decid- *falling off* deciduous (milk) teeth

delta *triangular* deltoid muscle, roughly triangular in shape

den-, dent- *tooth* dentin of the tooth

dendr- *tree, branch* dendrites, branches of a neuron

derm- *skin* dermis, deep layer of the skin

desm- *bond* desmosome, which binds adjacent epithelial cells

di- *twice, double* dimorphism, having two forms

dia- *through, between* diaphragm, the wall through or between two areas

dialys- *separate, break apart* kidney dialysis, in which waste products are removed from the blood

diastol- *stand apart* cardiac diastole, between successive contractions of the heart

diure- *urinate* diuretic, a drug that increases urine output

dors- *the back* dorsal, dorsum, dorsiflexion

duc-, duct *lead, draw* ductus deferens, tube which carries sperm from the epididymis into the urethra during ejaculation

dura *hard* dura mater, tough outer meninx

dys- *difficult, faulty, painful* dyspepsia, disturbed digestion

ec-, ex-, ecto- *out, outside, away from* excrete, to remove materials from the body

ectop- *displaced* ectopic pregnancy; ectopic focus for initiation of heart contraction

edem- *swelling* edema, accumulation of water in body tissues

ef- *away* efferent nerve fibers, which carry impulses away from the central nervous system

ejac- *to shoot forth* ejaculation of semen

embol- *wedge* embolus, an obstructive object traveling in the bloodstream

en-, em- *in, inside* encysted, enclosed in a cyst or capsule

enceph- *brain* encephalitis, inflammation of the brain

endo- *within, inner* endocytosis, taking particles into a cell

entero- *intestine* enterologist, one who specializes in the study of intestinal disorders

epi- *over, above* epidermis, outer layer of skin

erythr- *red* erythema, redness of the skin; erythrocyte, red blood cell

eso- *within* esophagus

eu- *well* euesthesia, a normal state of the senses

excret- *separate* excretory system

exo- *outside, outer layer* exophthalmos, an abnormal protrusion of the eye from the orbit

extra- *outside, beyond* extracellular, outside the body cells of an organism

extrins- *from the outside* extrinsic regulation of the heart

fasci-, fascia- *bundle, band* superficial and deep fascia

fenestr- *window* fenestrated capillaries

ferr- *iron* transferrin, ferritin, both iron-storage proteins

flagell- *whip* flagellum, the tail of a sperm cell

flat- *blow, blown* flatulence

folli- *bag, bellows* hair follicle

fontan- *fountain* fontanelles of the fetal skull

foram- *opening* foramen magnum of the skull

foss- *ditch* fossa ovalis of the heart; mandibular fossa of the skull

gam-, gamet- *married, spouse* gametes, the sex cells

gangli- *swelling, or knot* dorsal root ganglia of the spinal nerves

gastr- *stomach* gastrin, a hormone that influences gastric acid secretion

gene *beginning, origin* genetics

germin- *grow* germinal epithelium of the gonads

gero-, geront- *old man* gerontology, the study of aging

gest- *carried* gestation, the period from conception to birth

glauc- *gray* glaucoma, which causes gradual blindness

glom- *ball* glomeruli, clusters of capillaries in the kidneys

glosso- *tongue* glossopathy, any disease of the tongue

gluco-, glyco- gluconeogenesis, the production of glucose from noncarbohydrate molecules

glute- *buttock* gluteus maximus, largest muscle of the buttock

gnost- *knowing* the gnostic sense, a sense of awareness of self

gompho- *nail* gomphosis, the term applied to the joint between tooth and jaw

gon-, gono- *seed, offspring* gonads, the sex organs

gust- *taste* gustatory sense, the sense of taste

hapt- *fasten, grasp* hapten, a partial antigen

hema-, hemato-, hemo- *blood* hematocyst, a cyst containing blood

hemi- *half* hemiglossal, pertaining to one-half of the tongue

hepat- *liver* hepatitis, inflammation of the liver

hetero- *different or other* heterosexuality, sexual desire for a person of the opposite sex

hiat- *gap* the hiatus of the diaphragm, the opening through which the esophagus passes

hippo- *horse* hippocampus of the brain, shaped like a seahorse

hirsut- *hairy* hirsutism, excessive body hair

hist- *tissue* histology, the study of tissues

holo- *whole* holocrine glands, whose secretions are whole cells

hom-, homo- *same* homeoplasia, formation of tissue similar to normal tissue; homocentric, having the same center

hormon- *to excite* hormones

humor- *a fluid* humoral immunity, which involves antibodies circulating in the blood

hyal- *glass, clear* hyaline cartilage, which has no visible fibers

hydr-, hydro- *water* dehydration, loss of body water

hyper- *excess* hypertension, excessive tension

hypno- *sleep* hypnosis, a sleeplike state

hypo- *below, deficient* hypodermic, beneath the skin; hypokalemia, deficiency of potassium

hyster-, hystero- *uterus, womb* hysterectomy, removal of the uterus; hysterodynia, pain in the womb

ile- *intestine* ileum, the last portion of the small intestine

im- *not* impermeable, not permitting passage, not permeable

inter- *between* intercellular, between the cells

intercal- *insert* intercalated discs, the end membranes between adjacent cardiac muscle cells

intra- *within, inside* intracellular, inside the cell

iso- *equal, same* isothermal, equal, or same, temperature

jugul- *throat* jugular veins, prominent vessels in the neck

juxta- *near, close to* juxtaglomerular complex, a cell cluster next to a glomerulus in the kidneys

karyo- *kernel, nucleus* karyotype, the assemblage of the nuclear chromosomes

kera- *horn* keratin, the water-repellent protein of the skin

kilo- *thousand* kilocalories, equal to 1000 calories

kin-, kines- *move* kinetic energy, the energy of motion

labi-, labri- *lip* labial frenulum, the membrane which joins the lip to the gum

lact- *milk* lactose, milk sugar

lacun- *space, cavity, lake* lacunae, the spaces occupied by cells of cartilage and bone tissue

lamell- *small plate* concentric lamellae, rings of bone matrix in compact bone

lamina *layer, sheet* basal lamina, part of the epithelial basement membrane

lat- *wide* latissimus dorsi, a broad muscle of the back

laten- *hidden* latent period of a muscle twitch

later- *side* lateral (directional term)

leuko- *white* leukocyte, white blood cell

leva- *raise, elevate* levator labii superioris, muscle that elevates upper lip

lingua- *tongue* lingual tonsil, adjacent to the tongue

lip-, lipo- *fat, lipid* lipophage, a cell that has taken up fat in its cytoplasm

lith- *stone* cholelithiasis, gallstones

luci- *clear* stratum lucidum, clear layer of the epidermis

lumen *light* lumen, center of a hollow structure

lut- *yellow* corpus luteum, a yellow, hormone-secreting structure in the ovary

lymph *water* lymphatic circulation, return of clear fluid to the bloodstream

macro- *large* macromolecule, large molecule

macula *spot* macula lutea, yellow spot on the retina

magn- *large* foramen magnum, largest opening of the skull

mal- *bad, abnormal* malfunction, abnormal functioning of an organ

mamm- *breast* mammary gland, breast

mast- *breast* mastectomy, removal of a mammary gland

mater *mother* dura mater, pia mater, membranes that envelop the brain

meat- *passage* external acoustic meatus, the ear canal

medi- *middle* medial (directional term)

medull- *marrow* medulla, the middle portion of the kidney, adrenal gland, and lymph node

mega- *large* megakaryocyte, large precursor cell of platelets

meio- *less* meiosis, nuclear division that halves the chromosome number

melan- *black* melanocytes, which secrete the black pigment melanin

men-, menstru- *month* menses, the cyclic menstrual flow

meningo- *membrane* meningitis, inflammation of the membranes of the brain

mer-, mero-, *a part* merocrine glands, the secretions of which do not include the cell

meso- *middle* mesoderm, middle germ layer

meta- *beyond, between, transition* metatarsus, the part of the foot between the tarsus and the phalanges

metro- *uterus* endometrium, the lining of the uterus

micro- *small* microscope, an instrument used to make small objects appear larger

mictur- *urinate* micturition, the act of voiding the bladder

mito- *thread, filament* mitochondria, small, filament-like structures located in cells

mnem- *memory* amnesia

mono- *single* monospasm, spasm of a single limb

morpho- *form* morphology, the study of form and structure or organisms

multi- *many* multinuclear, having several nuclei

mur- *wall* intramural ganglion, a nerve junction within an organ

muta- *change* mutation, change in the base sequence of DNA

myelo- *spinal cord, marrow* myeloblasts, cells of the bone marrow

myo- *muscle* myocardium, heart muscle

nano- *dwarf* nanometer, one-billionth of a meter

narco- *numbness* narcotic, a drug producing stupor or numbed sensations

natri- *sodium* atrial natriuretic peptide, a sodium-regulating hormone

necro- *death* necrosis, tissue death

neo- *new* neoplasm, an abnormal growth

nephro- *kidney* nephritis, inflammation of the kidney

neuro- *nerve* neurophysiology, the physiology of the nervous system

noci- *harmful* nociceptors, receptors for pain

nom- *name* innominate artery; innominate bone

noto- *back* notochord, the embryonic structure that precedes the vertebral column

nucle- *pit, kernel, little nut* nucleus

nutri- *feed, nourish* nutrition

ob- *before, against* obstruction, impeding or blocking up

oculo- *eye* monocular, pertaining to one eye

odonto- *teeth* orthodontist, one who specializes in proper positioning of the teeth in relation to each other

olfact- *smell* olfactory nerves

oligo- *few* oligodendrocytes, neuroglial cells with few branches

onco- *a mass* oncology, study of cancer

oo- *egg* oocyte, precursor of female gamete

ophthalmo- *eye* ophthalmology, the study of the eyes and related disease

orb- *circular* orbicularis oculi, muscle that encircles the eye

orchi- *testis* cryptorchidism, failure of the testes to descend into the scrotum

org- *living* organism

ortho- *straight, direct* orthopedic, correction of deformities of the musculoskeletal system

osm- *smell* anosmia, loss of sense of smell

osmo- *pushing* osmosis

osteo- *bone* osteodermia, bony formations in the skin

oto- *ear* otoscope, a device for examining the ear

ov-, ovi- *egg* ovum; oviduct

oxy- *oxygen* oxygenation, the saturation of a substance with oxygen

pan- *all, universal* panacea, a cure-all

papill- *nipple* dermal papillae, projections of the dermis into the epidermal area

para- *beside, near* paranuclear, beside the nucleus

pect-, pectus *breast* pectoralis major, a large chest muscle

pelv- *a basin* pelvic girdle, which cradles the pelvic organs

peni- *a tail* penis; penile arteriole

penna- *feather* unipennate, bipennate muscles, whose fascicles have a feathered appearance

pent- *five* pentose, a 5-carbon sugar

pep-, peps-, pept- *digest* pepsin, a digestive enzyme of the stomach; peptic ulcer

per-, permea- *through* permeate; permeable

peri- *around* perianal, situated around the anus

phago- *eat* phagocyte, a cell that engulfs and digests particles or cells

pheno- *show, appear* phenotype, the physical appearance of an individual

phleb- *vein* phlebitis, inflammation of the veins

pia *tender* pia mater, delicate inner membrane around the brain and spinal cord

pili *hair* arrector pili muscles of the skin, which make the hairs stand erect

pin-, pino- *drink* pinocytosis, the engulfing of small particles by a cell

platy- *flat, broad* platysma, broad, flat muscle of the neck

pleur- *side, rib* pleural serosa, the membrane that lines the thoracic cavity and covers the lungs

plex-, plexus *net, network* brachial plexus, the network of nerves that supplies the arm

pneumo- *air, wind* pneumothorax, air in the thoracic cavity

pod- *foot* podiatry, the treatment of foot disorders

poly- *multiple* polymorphism, multiple forms

post- *after, behind* posterior, places behind (a specific) part

pre-, pro- *before, ahead of* prenatal, before birth

procto- *rectum, anus* proctoscope, an instrument for examining the rectum

pron- *bent forward* prone, pronate

propri- *one's own* proprioception, awareness of body parts and movement

pseudo- *false* pseudotumor, a false tumor

psycho- *mind, psyche* psychogram, a chart of personality traits

ptos- *fall* renal ptosis, a condition in which the kidneys drift below their normal position

pub- *of the pubis* puberty

pulmo- *lung* pulmonary artery, which brings blood to the lungs

pyo- *pus* pyocyst, a cyst that contains pus

pyro- *fire* pyrogen, a substance that induces fever

quad-, quadr- *four-sided* quadratus lumborum, a muscle with a square shape

re- *back, again* reinfect

rect- *straight* rectus abdominis, rectum

ren- *kidney* renal; renin, an enzyme secreted by the kidney

retin-, retic- *net, network* endoplasmic reticulum, a network of membranous sacs within a cell

retro- *backward, behind* retrogression, to move backward in development

rheum- *watery flow, change, flux* rheumatoid arthritis; rheumatic fever

rhin-, rhino- *nose* rhinitis, inflammation of the nose

ruga- *fold, wrinkle* rugae, the folds of the stomach, gallbladder, and urinary bladder

sagitt- *arrow* sagittal (directional term)

salta- *leap* saltatory conduction, the rapid conduction of impulses along myelinated neurons

sanguin- *blood* consanguineous, indicative of a genetic relationship between individuals

sarco- *flesh* sarcomere, unit of contraction in skeletal muscle

saphen- *visible, clear* great saphenous vein, superficial vein of the thigh and leg

sclero- *hard* sclerodermatitis, inflammatory thickening and hardening of the skin

seb- *grease* sebum, the oil of the skin

semen *seed, sperm* semen, the discharge of the male reproductive system

semi- *half* semicircular, having the form of half a circle

sens- *feeling* sensation, sensory

septi- *rotten* sepsis, infection; antiseptic

septum *fence* nasal septum

sero- *serum* serological tests, which assess blood conditions

serrat- *saw* serratus anterior, a muscle of the chest wall that has a jagged edge

sin-, sino- *a hollow* sinuses of the skull

soma- *body* somatic nervous system

somn- *sleep* insomnia, inability to sleep

sphin- *squeeze* sphincter

splanchn- *organ* splanchnic nerve, autonomic supply to abdominal viscera

spondyl- *vertebra* ankylosing spondylitis, rheumatoid arthritis affecting the spine

squam- *scale, flat* squamous epithelium, squamous suture of the skull

steno- *narrow* stenocoriasis, narrowing of the pupil

strat- *layer* strata of the epidermis; stratified epithelium

stria- *furrow, streak* striations of skeletal and cardiac muscle tissue

stroma *spread out* stroma, the connective tissue framework of some organs

sub- *beneath, under* sublingual, beneath the tongue

sucr- *sweet* sucrose, table sugar

sudor- *sweat* sudoriferous glands, the sweat glands

super- *above, upon* superior, quality or state of being above other parts

supra- *above, upon* supracondylar, above a condyle

sym-, syn- *together, with* synapse, the region of communication between two neurons

synerg- *work together* synergism

systol- *contraction* systole, contraction of the heart

tachy- *rapid* tachycardia, abnormally rapid heartbeat

tact- *touch* tactile sense

telo- *the end* telophase, the end of mitosis

templ-, tempo- *time* temporal summation of nerve impulses

tens- *stretched* muscle tension

terti- *third* fibularis tertius, one of three fibularis muscles

tetan- *rigid, tense* tetanus of muscles

therm- *heat* thermometer, an instrument used to measure heat

thromb- *clot* thrombocyte, thrombus

thyro- *a shield* thyroid gland

tissu- *woven* tissue

tono- *tension* tonicity, hypertonic

tox- *poison* toxicology, study of poisons

trab- *beam, timber* trabeculae, spicules of bone in spongy bone tissue

trans- *across, through* transpleural, through the pleura

trapez- *table* trapezius, the four-sided muscle of the upper back

tri- *three* trifurcation, division into three branches

trop- *turn, change* tropic hormones, whose targets are endocrine glands

troph- *nourish* trophoblast, from which develops the fetal portion of the placenta

tuber- *swelling* tuberosity, a bump on a bone

tunic- *covering* tunica albuginea, the covering of the testis

tympan- *drum* tympanic membrane, the eardrum

ultra- *beyond* ultraviolet radiation, beyond the band of visible light

vacc- *cow* vaccine

vagin- *a sheath* vagina

vagus *wanderer* the vagus nerve, which starts at the brain and travels into the abdominopelvic cavity

valen- *strength* valence shells of atoms

venter, ventr- *abdomen, belly* ventral (directional term), ventricle

vent- *the wind* pulmonary ventilation

vert- *turn* vertebral column

vestibul- *a porch* vestibule, the anterior entryway to the mouth and nose

vibr- *shake, quiver* vibrissae, hairs of the nasal vestibule

villus *shaggy hair* microvilli, which have the appearance of hair in light microscopy

viscero- *organ, viscera* visceroinhibitory, inhibiting the movements of the viscera

viscos- *sticky* viscosity, resistance to flow

vita- *life* vitamin

vitre- *glass* vitreous humor, the clear jelly of the eye

viv- *live* in vivo

vulv- *a covering* vulva, the female external genitalia

zyg- *a yoke, twin* zygote

Suffixes

-able *able to, capable of* viable, ability to live or exist

-ac *referring to* cardiac, referring to the heart

-algia *pain in a certain part* neuralgia, pain along the course of a nerve

-apsi *juncture* synapse, where two neurons communicate

-ary *associated with, relating to* coronary, associated with the heart

-asthen *weakness* myasthenia gravis, a disease involving paralysis

-bryo *swollen* embryo

-cide *destroy or kill* germicide, an agent that kills germs

-cipit *head* occipital

-clast *break* osteoclast, a cell that dissolves bone matrix

-crine *separate* endocrine organs, which secrete hormones into the blood

-dips *thirst, dry* polydipsia, excessive thirst associated with diabetes

-ectomy *cutting out, surgical removal* appendectomy, cutting out of the appendix

-ell, -elle *small* organelle

-emia *condition of the blood* anemia, deficiency of red blood cells

-esthesi *sensation* anesthesia, lack of sensation